STRUCTURE OF MATTER SERIES

MARIA GOEPPERT MAYER

Advisory Editor

MOLECULAR THEORY

of

GASES *and* LIQUIDS

MOLECULAR THEORY *of* GASES *and* LIQUIDS

Joseph O. Hirschfelder
DEPARTMENT OF CHEMISTRY AND
THEORETICAL CHEMISTRY INSTITUTE
UNIVERSITY OF WISCONSIN

Charles F. Curtiss
DEPARTMENT OF CHEMISTRY AND
THEORETICAL CHEMISTRY INSTITUTE
UNIVERSITY OF WISCONSIN

R. Byron Bird
DEPARTMENT OF CHEMICAL ENGINEERING
UNIVERSITY OF WISCONSIN

Corrected Printing with Notes Added

With the assistance of the staff of the former University of Wisconsin Naval Research Laboratory

JOHN WILEY & SONS, INC., NEW YORK
LONDON

SECOND PRINTING, CORRECTED, WITH NOTES ADDED, MARCH, 1964

Library of Congress Catalog Card Number: 54–7621

PRINTED IN THE UNITED STATES OF AMERICA

PREFACE

This book describes the properties of gases and liquids from a "molecular" viewpoint. These properties are divided into two groups—the equilibrium properties (such as the equation of state, Joule-Thomson coefficient, and surface tension) and the non-equilibrium properties (such as viscosity, diffusion, and thermal conductivity). Expressions for all these bulk properties in terms of molecular properties and intermolecular forces can be obtained from statistical mechanics. These expressions, along with information about intermolecular interactions, may be used to predict the values of many physical properties for which no experimental data are available. A particularly useful result of the statistical mechanical approach is the fact that equilibrium and non-equilibrium properties can be interrelated through the common link of the intermolecular force laws. In principle, these force laws can be obtained exactly from molecular quantum mechanics. Up to the present time, however, mathematical difficulties have restricted the success of this approach; nevertheless, a reasonably good qualitative picture of molecular interactions has been obtained. Hence it is customary to describe the interaction between two molecules in terms of simple empirical functions, the form of which is suggested from quantum mechanics. These functions contain several adjustable constants, which can be determined for various substances by analyzing experimental measurements of bulk properties by means of the corresponding statistical mechanical formulae. Therefore, the molecular approach gives a complete description of the bulk behavior in terms of a small number of constants characteristic of the substance under consideration.

During the last decade many theoretical, computational, and experimental developments have been made in the study of the properties of gases and liquids. Therefore it seemed desirable to survey the entire field from a unified viewpoint and to present it in consistent notation. We hope that this book will be of use to several groups of people. Students in chemical physics should find it helpful in gaining a better knowledge of the structure of matter and in understanding the interrelationships between the various branches of statistical mechanics. Problems are suggested at the end of the chapters as an aid to students and teachers. Experimental physical chemists and industrial engineers should find the chapters on calculations of the properties of gases and liquids of value in design work. Extensive tables have been included, and numerical examples are given to illustrate their use. Statistical mechanicians and theoretical chemists should find this book useful as a reference. They will notice, however, that some sections of the book are incomplete because of the unexplored regions of the theory and the gaps in the computational work. It is hoped that this lack of completeness will serve as a challenge toward further research.

The subject material in the book divides itself quite naturally into three parts: equilibrium properties, non-equilibrium properties, and intermolecular forces. The basic problems associated with each of these fields are discussed in Chapter 1. In the last part of that chapter there are presented for ready reference some results of classical and quantum mechanics which are used throughout the book. Part I (Chapters 2–6) begins with a survey of equilibrium statistical mechanics, which serves as the basis for the theoretical development of the equation of state. Two main applications of the theory are then discussed—the prediction of the *p-V-T* properties of gases and liquids, and the analysis of experimental equation of state data to obtain information about intermolecular forces. Part II (Chapters 7–11) is a discussion of non-equilibrium statistical mechanics (kinetic theory) and the theory of transport phenomena. Whenever possible this treatment parallels the discussion given in Part I. That is, the prediction of the bulk properties and the methods of obtaining information about intermolecular forces are considered. The second part of the book is concluded with a chapter on hydrodynamic applications, which contains a unified discussion of the propagation of sound waves, flames, and detonations. Part III (Chapters 12–14) deals with the electromagnetic and quantum mechanical theory of the forces between molecules, atoms, ions, and free radicals. Here the *a priori* quantum mechanical calculations of intermolecular forces are compared with the information obtained in the first two parts by the analysis of the experimental data on bulk properties.

This book has grown out of studies undertaken in the Bumblebee program sponsored by the Bureau of Ordnance, and is a synthesis of greater or lesser contributions by a large number of people. The Navy Bureau of Ordnance generously supported the preparation of preliminary drafts of the various chapters, each of which was issued as a University of Wisconsin Naval Research Laboratory report. We wish especially to thank Drs. R. E. Gibson, W. H. Avery, and F. T. McClure of the Johns Hopkins University Applied Physics Laboratory for making this arrangement possible. The treatise is a partial answer to the request of the Research and Development Board for a report on the present status of research in the fields of the equation of state and transport phenomena. It is an outgrowth of a National Defense Research Committee Report (A-116, 1942) entitled "The Thermodynamic Properties of Propellant Gases," written by J. O. Hirschfelder, F. T. McClure, C. F. Curtiss, and D. W. Osborne.

During the early stages of the writing of the manuscript, we were fortunate to have the gracious and enthusiastic cooperation of Dr. Ellen L. Spotz. She participated in the writing of Chapters 3 and 8 and generously assisted us with the preparation, proof-reading, and editing of other portions of the book. We regret that Dr. Spotz was not able to continue working on this project until its culmination.

We wish also to thank Professor J. de Boer, director of the *Instituut voor Theoretische Physica* at the Municipal University of Amsterdam, for making available to them some of his unpublished research, for assisting in the preparation of the chapters on the quantum effects (Chapters 6 and 10), and for his very helpful criticisms and advice with respect to the preparation of other portions of the book. In this connection, one of the authors (RBB) would like to acknowledge the opportunity accorded him by the Fulbright exchange program to spend a year at Professor de Boer's institute in Amsterdam.

Warm thanks are due Dr. Charles A. Boyd, formerly of the University of Wisconsin Naval Research Laboratory, for preparing the first draft of Chapter 5. We also appreciate the assistance of Dr. John S. Rowlinson in the preparation of Section 3.10 and the assistance of Dr. Howard B. Palmer for his help with Section 5.2d.

We wish to acknowledge the help of Elizabeth S. Hirschfelder, who read the text and made many helpful suggestions, and the assistance of Lois P. Curtiss in preparing the author index. In addition, we are indebted to the following people for their assistance:

For Reviewing and Criticizing the Text:

C. A. Coulson	J. F. Hornig	S. Ono
H. G. Drickamer	T. Kihara	H. B. Palmer
G. Gioumousis	R. J. Lunbeck	W. E. Rice
E. F. Haugh	E. A. Mason	H. C. Thacher

For Typing and Preparing the Manuscript:

Gertrude Heyer Joyce Johnston Anita Olson Muriel Taubert

For Computations and Figures:

Lois Brittenham, Catherine Denton, Elaine Petersen, Dorothy Campbell, Marjorie Mason

In the preparation of this book we have drawn heavily upon the scientific literature and feel a debt of gratitude to the authors of the articles to which we refer. Generous thanks are due to the authors, editors, and publishers who have given us permission to reproduce various figures and tables from original publications. Several sources are referred to frequently throughout the entire book: *The Mathematical Theory of Non-uniform Gases,* by S. Chapman and T. G. Cowling (Cambridge University Press, First Edition, 1939, Second Edition, 1952), and "Molecular Distribution and Equation of State of Gases," by J. de Boer in *Reports on Progress in Physics,* Volume 12, page 305 (1949). These works have been of such assistance to us in organizing certain sections of this book that we wish to give them special mention here.

J. O. H.
C. F. C.
R. B. B.

University of Wisconsin
February, 1954

PREFACE TO THE SECOND PRINTING

In this new printing we have taken the opportunity to correct a number of small errors in the pages of the original text. In addition, without any attempt at completeness a few corrections and additions have been assembled at the end of the book. The symbol Ⓝ has been placed next to the page number on those pages for which such Notes have been prepared.

The authors wish to thank their colleagues who have contributed suggestions for the Notes and corrections to the pages of this second printing. We hope that readers will continue to supply us with information regarding improvements in the text. We are especially grateful to I. Amdur, S. G. Brush, J. de Boer, J. S. Dahler, T. Kihara, J. M. Sengers-Levelt, P. E. Liley, E. A. Mason, K. S. Pitzer, J. M. Prausnitz, and John Ross for their suggestions. Thanks are also due the publishers for making these changes and additions possible.

J. O. H.
C. F. C.
R. B. B.

University of Wisconsin
April, 1963

CONTENTS

* This section was written with the assistance of Professor J. de Boer, University of Amsterdam, The Netherlands.

* This section was prepared with the assistance of Professor J. S. Rowlinson, Dept. of Chemical Eng., Imperial College, University of London.

* This chapter was prepared with the assistance of Dr. C. A. Boyd, Aero Projects, Inc., West Chester, Pa.

PART II. NON-EQUILIBRIUM PROPERTIES

* This discussion was prepared with the assistance of Professor H. B. Palmer, Dept. of Fuel Technology, Pennsylvania State University.

PART III. INTERMOLECULAR FORCES

NOTE ON NOTATION

An extensive table of the notation used in this book may be found at the end of the text, where the most important symbols are listed. The following general remarks about the notation should be helpful to the reader:

Style of Type

Light-face italic type is used for scalar quantities

Bold-face italic type is used for vector quantities

Sans serif type is used for tensor quantities

Script symbols are used to represent quantum mechanical operators and also quantities associated with electromagnetic fields

Marks above Symbols

— = statistical mechanical average; partial molal quantity
~ = quantity per mole
^ = quantity per gram
· = differentiation with respect to time

Superscripts

* = complex conjugate of a quantity (on wave functions, expansion coefficients, etc., in quantum mechanical discussions); quantity reduced by means of the simplest combinations of molecular parameters σ and ϵ

★ = quantity reduced by means of combinations of σ and ϵ which utilize rigid sphere values

‡ = quantity associated with the activated state

^{0} = quantity associated with the ideal gas state

′ = quantities associated with molecules after a binary collision; atoms in excited states

Subscripts

r = quantity reduced by means of combinations of critical constants
c = quantity at the critical point

Reduced Quantities

Volume	$V^* = \tilde{V}/\tilde{N}\sigma^3$	$V^\star = V/b_0 = \tilde{V}/\frac{2}{3}\pi\tilde{N}\sigma^3$
Specific volume	$v^* = V^* = v/\sigma^3$	—
Temperature	$T^* = kT/\epsilon$	—
Pressure	$p^* = p\sigma^3/\epsilon$	$p^\star = pb_0/\tilde{N}\epsilon$
Second virial coefficient	$B^* = B/\tilde{N}\sigma^3$	$B^\star = B/b_0 = B/B_{\text{rig. sph.}}$
Third virial coefficient	$C^* = C/(\tilde{N}\sigma^3)^2$	$C^\star = C/b_0^2$
Coefficient of viscosity	$\eta^* = \eta\sigma^2/\sqrt{m\epsilon}$	$\eta^\star = \eta/\eta_{\text{rig. sph.}}$
Coefficient of thermal conductivity	$\lambda^* = \lambda\sigma^2 k^{-1}\sqrt{m/\epsilon}$	$\lambda^\star = \lambda/\lambda_{\text{rig. sph.}}$
Coefficient of diffusion	$\mathscr{D}^* = \mathscr{D}\sigma^{-1}\sqrt{m/\epsilon}$	$\mathscr{D}^\star = \mathscr{D}/\mathscr{D}_{\text{rig. sph.}}$
Thermal diffusion ratio	—	$k_T^\star = k_T/k_{T_{\text{rig. sph.}}}$
Ω-integrals	—	$\Omega^{(l,s)\star} = \Omega^{(l,s)}/\Omega^{(l,s)}_{\text{rig. sph.}}$
Distance	$r^* = r/\sigma$	
Impact parameter	$b^* = b/\sigma$	
Relative kinetic energy of a colliding pair of molecules of reduced mass μ	$g^{*2} = \frac{1}{2}\mu g^2/\epsilon$	
Potential energy	$\varphi^* = \varphi/\epsilon$	
Dipole moment	$\mu^* = \mu/\sqrt{\epsilon\sigma^3}$	
Polarizability	$\alpha^* = \alpha/\sigma^3$	
Surface tension	$\gamma^* = \gamma\sigma^2/\epsilon$	
Quantum mechanical parameter	$\Lambda^* = h/\sigma\sqrt{m\epsilon}$	

VECTOR AND TENSOR NOTATION

Vectors

$\boldsymbol{i}, \boldsymbol{j}, \boldsymbol{k}$ = unit vectors in the x, y, z directions

$\boldsymbol{A} \equiv \boldsymbol{i}A_x + \boldsymbol{j}A_y + \boldsymbol{k}A_z$ = vector with components A_x, A_y, A_z

$A = \sqrt{A_x^2 + A_y^2 + A_z^2}$ = magnitude of vector $\boldsymbol{A}$

$(\boldsymbol{A} \cdot \boldsymbol{B}) \equiv A_xB_x + A_yB_y + A_zB_z$ = scalar product of $\boldsymbol{A}$ and $\boldsymbol{B}$

$$[\boldsymbol{A} \times \boldsymbol{B}] \equiv \begin{vmatrix} \boldsymbol{i} & \boldsymbol{j} & \boldsymbol{k} \\ A_x & A_y & A_z \\ B_x & B_y & B_z \end{vmatrix}$$ = vector product of $\boldsymbol{A}$ and $\boldsymbol{B}$

$$[\boldsymbol{A} \times [\boldsymbol{B} \times \boldsymbol{C}]] = (\boldsymbol{A}\cdot\boldsymbol{C})\boldsymbol{B} - (\boldsymbol{A}\cdot\boldsymbol{B})\boldsymbol{C}$$

$\boldsymbol{r}$ = position vector with components x, y, z

$\boldsymbol{r}_i$ = position vector of ith particle

$\boldsymbol{r}_{ij} \equiv \boldsymbol{r}_i - \boldsymbol{r}_j$ = vector to the ith particle from the jth particle

$\boldsymbol{r}^N \equiv (\boldsymbol{r}_1, \boldsymbol{r}_2, \cdots \boldsymbol{r}_N)$ = vector in $3N$-dimensional space describing the location of N particles

$\boldsymbol{r}^h \equiv (\boldsymbol{r}_1, \boldsymbol{r}_2, \cdots \boldsymbol{r}_h)$

$\boldsymbol{r}^{N-h} \equiv (\boldsymbol{r}_{h+1}, \boldsymbol{r}_{h+2}, \cdots \boldsymbol{r}_N)$

$$(\boldsymbol{r}^N \cdot \boldsymbol{p}^N) = \sum_{i=1}^{N} (\boldsymbol{r}_i \cdot \boldsymbol{p}_i)$$

Tensors

T = tensor with 9 components represented by the array

$$\begin{pmatrix} T_{xx} & T_{xy} & T_{xz} \\ T_{yx} & T_{yy} & T_{yz} \\ T_{zx} & T_{zy} & T_{zz} \end{pmatrix}$$

Tensors (*continued*)

$\mathsf{T}^\dagger$ = transpose of the tensor T formed by exchanging rows and columns

$$(\mathsf{T}\cdot A)_x \equiv T_{xx}A_x + T_{xy}A_y + T_{xz}A_z = \sum_\alpha T_{x\alpha}A_\alpha$$

$$(A\cdot\mathsf{T})_x \equiv A_xT_{xx} + A_yT_{yx} + A_zT_{zx} = \sum_\alpha A_\alpha T_{\alpha x}$$

$$(\mathsf{T}\cdot A) = (A\cdot\mathsf{T}^\dagger)$$

$$(\mathsf{T}\cdot\mathsf{T}')_{xy} \equiv T_{xx}T_{xy}' + T_{xy}T_{yy}' + T_{xz}T_{zy}' = \sum_\alpha T_{x\alpha}T_{\alpha y}'$$

$$(\mathsf{T}:\mathsf{T}') \equiv \sum_\alpha\sum_\beta T_{\alpha\beta}T_{\beta\alpha}' = (\mathsf{T}':\mathsf{T})$$

$$\mathsf{U} \equiv \begin{pmatrix}1 & 0 & 0\\ 0 & 1 & 0\\ 0 & 0 & 1\end{pmatrix} = \text{unit tensor}$$

$$(\mathsf{U}\cdot A) = (A\cdot\mathsf{U}) = A$$

$$(\mathsf{U}:\mathsf{T}) = T_{xx} + T_{yy} + T_{zz}$$

$$(\mathsf{U}:\mathsf{U}) = 3$$

Dyadics

AB = dyadic[1] with 9 components represented by the array

$$\begin{pmatrix}A_xB_x & A_xB_y & A_xB_z\\ A_yB_x & A_yB_y & A_yB_z\\ A_zB_x & A_zB_y & A_zB_z\end{pmatrix}$$

$$(AB\cdot C) \equiv A(B\cdot C)$$

$$(C\cdot AB) \equiv (C\cdot A)B$$

$$(\mathsf{T}:AB) \equiv ((\mathsf{T}\cdot A)\cdot B)$$

$$(AB:\mathsf{T}) \equiv (A\cdot(B\cdot\mathsf{T}))$$

$$(AB:CD) = (AC:BD) = (A\cdot(B\cdot CD)) = (A\cdot(B\cdot C)D) = (A\cdot D)(B\cdot C)$$

[1] The dyadic AB should not be confused with the scalar product $(A\cdot B)$

Differentiation Processes[2]

$$\frac{\partial}{\partial \boldsymbol{r}} \equiv \boldsymbol{i}\frac{\partial}{\partial x} + \boldsymbol{j}\frac{\partial}{\partial y} + \boldsymbol{k}\frac{\partial}{\partial z}$$

$$\frac{\partial}{\partial \boldsymbol{v}} \equiv \boldsymbol{i}\frac{\partial}{\partial v_x} + \boldsymbol{j}\frac{\partial}{\partial v_y} + \boldsymbol{k}\frac{\partial}{\partial v_z}$$

$$\frac{\partial}{\partial \boldsymbol{r}^N} \equiv \sum_{i=1}^{N} \frac{\partial}{\partial \boldsymbol{r}_i}$$

$$\frac{\partial F(\boldsymbol{r})}{\partial \boldsymbol{r}} \equiv \boldsymbol{i}\frac{\partial F}{\partial x} + \boldsymbol{j}\frac{\partial F}{\partial y} + \boldsymbol{k}\frac{\partial F}{\partial z} \equiv \text{grad}\, F$$

$$\frac{\partial G(\boldsymbol{v})}{\partial \boldsymbol{v}} \equiv \boldsymbol{i}\frac{\partial G}{\partial v_x} + \boldsymbol{j}\frac{\partial G}{\partial v_y} + \boldsymbol{k}\frac{\partial G}{\partial v_z}$$

$$\left(\frac{\partial}{\partial \boldsymbol{r}} \cdot \boldsymbol{A}\right) \equiv \frac{\partial A_x}{\partial x} + \frac{\partial A_y}{\partial y} + \frac{\partial A_z}{\partial z} \equiv \text{div}\, \boldsymbol{A}$$

$$\left[\frac{\partial}{\partial \boldsymbol{r}} \times \boldsymbol{A}\right] \equiv \begin{vmatrix} \boldsymbol{i} & \boldsymbol{j} & \boldsymbol{k} \\ \dfrac{\partial}{\partial x} & \dfrac{\partial}{\partial y} & \dfrac{\partial}{\partial z} \\ A_x & A_y & A_z \end{vmatrix} \equiv \text{curl}\, \boldsymbol{A}$$

$$\left(\frac{\partial}{\partial \boldsymbol{r}} \cdot \mathsf{T}\right)_x = \frac{\partial T_{xx}}{\partial x} + \frac{\partial T_{yx}}{\partial y} + \frac{\partial T_{zx}}{\partial z}$$

$$\left(\frac{\partial}{\partial \boldsymbol{r}} \cdot \boldsymbol{AB}\right) = \left(\boldsymbol{A} \cdot \frac{\partial}{\partial \boldsymbol{r}}\right) \boldsymbol{B} + \boldsymbol{B}\left(\frac{\partial}{\partial \boldsymbol{r}} \cdot \boldsymbol{A}\right)$$

$$\left(\boldsymbol{A} \cdot \frac{\partial}{\partial \boldsymbol{r}} \boldsymbol{B}\right) = \left(\boldsymbol{A} \cdot \frac{\partial}{\partial \boldsymbol{r}}\right) \boldsymbol{B}$$

[2] The symbol $\frac{\partial}{\partial \boldsymbol{r}}$ is frequently called the "del" or "nabla" operator and given the symbol ∇. One then usually distinguishes between $\frac{\partial}{\partial \boldsymbol{r}}$ and $\frac{\partial}{\partial \boldsymbol{v}}$ by writing $\nabla_{\boldsymbol{r}}$ and $\nabla_{\boldsymbol{v}}$.

Differentiation Processes (*continued*)

$$\left(\boldsymbol{AB}:\frac{\partial}{\partial \boldsymbol{r}}\boldsymbol{C}\right) = \left(\boldsymbol{A}\cdot\left(\boldsymbol{B}\cdot\frac{\partial}{\partial \boldsymbol{r}}\right)\boldsymbol{C}\right)$$

Integration Processes

$$\int d\boldsymbol{r} \equiv \iiint dx\,dy\,dz \qquad \int d\boldsymbol{r}^N \equiv \int\int\cdots\int d\boldsymbol{r}_1\,d\boldsymbol{r}_2\cdots d\boldsymbol{r}_N$$

$$\int d\boldsymbol{v} \equiv \iiint dv_x\,dv_y\,dv_z \qquad \int d\boldsymbol{r}^{N-h} \equiv \int\int\cdots\int d\boldsymbol{r}_{h+1}\,d\boldsymbol{r}_{h+2}\cdots d\boldsymbol{r}_N$$

$$\int F(V)\boldsymbol{VV}\,d\boldsymbol{V} = \tfrac{1}{3}\mathsf{U}\int F(V)V^2\,d\boldsymbol{V}$$

$$\int F(V)(\boldsymbol{A}\cdot\boldsymbol{V})\boldsymbol{V}\,d\boldsymbol{V} = \tfrac{1}{3}\boldsymbol{A}\int F(V)V^2\,d\boldsymbol{V}$$

$$\int_{\text{surface}} (\boldsymbol{A}\cdot d\boldsymbol{S}) = \int_{\text{surface}} (\boldsymbol{A}\cdot\boldsymbol{n})\,dS$$

$\boldsymbol{n}$ = normal unit vector outward from the surface

$$\int_{\text{curve}} (\boldsymbol{A}\cdot d\boldsymbol{s}) = \int_{\text{curve}} (\boldsymbol{A}\cdot\boldsymbol{t})\,ds$$

$\boldsymbol{t}$ = tangent unit vector along curve in direction of integration

$$\int_{\text{closed surface}} (\boldsymbol{A}\cdot d\boldsymbol{S}) = \int_{\substack{\text{volume contained}\\ \text{within closed surface}}} \left(\frac{\partial}{\partial \boldsymbol{r}}\cdot\boldsymbol{A}\right) d\boldsymbol{r}$$

Green's theorem

$$\int_{\text{closed curve}} (\boldsymbol{A}\cdot d\boldsymbol{s}) = \int_{\substack{\text{any surface bounded}\\ \text{by closed curve}}} \left(\left[\frac{\partial}{\partial \boldsymbol{r}}\times\boldsymbol{A}\right]\cdot d\boldsymbol{S}\right)$$

Stokes' theorem

· 1 ·

Introduction and Background Information

The equation of state and the transport properties of gases and liquids are intimately related to the forces between the molecules. The statistical mechanical theories which relate the bulk properties to the intermolecular forces are highly developed for dilute gases and developed to a lesser extent for dense gases and liquids. From measurements of any of these macroscopic properties it is in principle possible to determine the law of force between the molecules. Furthermore, once the law of force has been determined, it is possible to calculate the equation of state or the transport properties. In this manner one reduces the description of a great number of equilibrium and non-equilibrium phenomena to a common basis and understands their interrelation from a molecular viewpoint.

The important concepts and definitions which enter into the molecular theory of gases and liquids are introduced in this chapter. The first three sections are devoted to a simplified treatment of the main subject material of the book—the equation of state, the transport phenomena, and intermolecular forces. Following this is a discussion of some important results of classical dynamics and their application to the study of two-body collisions. Finally, a brief summary of some important quantum mechanical concepts is presented, and the quantum theory of molecular collisions is discussed. In these last four sections are given a number of important results of theoretical physics which find applications at numerous points in the text.

1. The Equation of State—The Virial Coefficients

If a gas is considered to be made up of particles which have no volume and between which there are no forces, then it may be shown by simple kinetic arguments (or by rigorous theory) that the equation of state is $p\tilde{V} = RT$. As is well known, this relation is quite valid when a gas is highly dilute, but even at atmospheric pressure deviations from this ideal gas law are appreciable. Van der Waals attempted to explain the deviations by modifying the ideal gas law to get an equation which gives a moderately good description of the p-V-T behavior in the gas phase and a qualitative description in the liquid phase:

$$\left(p + \frac{a}{\tilde{V}^2}\right)(\tilde{V} - b) = RT \qquad (1.1\text{–}1)$$

The a in the van der Waals equation accounts for the attractive forces between molecules in the gas (it can be seen that at constant T and $\tilde{V}$ an increase in a causes p to decrease); the constant b accounts for the fact that the molecules have volume—or, to be more correct, that there are strong short-range repulsive forces between molecules (an increase of b cause an increase in pressure at constant T and $\tilde{V}$). Clearly, the van der Waals equation is only a rough approximation, since the molar volume $\tilde{V}$ in the liquid phase is found experimentally to be considerably less than the value of b determined from the p-V-T data of the gas.

The van der Waals equation may be used to fit the p-V-T data of many gases over small temperature ranges. In order to fit the data over larger ranges of the variables, numerous empirical equations of varying degrees of complexity have been proposed, several of which are discussed in § 4.2. These empirical relationships have two or more adjustable constants, and hence they are quite useful for curve-fitting and interpolating existing data. It is not possible, however, to relate these adjustable parameters to the intermolecular forces, and hence little progress can be made in correlating the bulk behavior of gases with the fundamental molecular interaction.

In this section we present ultra-simplified theories of the equation of state of dilute gases and of dense gases (or liquids) made up of rigid sphere molecules. The behavior of dilute gases is described by considering the deviations from ideal gas behavior, which result from molecular interactions. The behavior of dense gases and liquids is described by considering the effects of allowing the molecules in an ideal crystal to leave their lattice positions and roam about. Although the arguments used are rather crude, the results of the simple theories have certain elements in common with the results of the rigorous theories. At the end of this section an introduction is given to the rigorous statistical mechanical approach to the theory of the equation of state.

a. An ultra-simplified theory of the equation of state of dilute gases

The experimental pV- isotherms may be fitted over a very large range of temperature and pressure, with a power series relation

$$p\tilde{V}/RT = 1 + B(T)/\tilde{V} + C(T)/\tilde{V}^2 + D(T)/\tilde{V}^3 + \cdots \qquad (1.1\text{–}2)$$

which is called the *virial equation of state*. The temperature dependent functions $B(T)$, $C(T)$, . . . are referred to as the second, third, . . . *virial coefficients*.[1]

We now derive by elementary arguments expressions for the virial coefficients for a gas made up of $\tilde{N}$ molecules, each of which may be represented as a rigid sphere of diameter σ. Let us suppose that we put these "billiard-ball" molecules one at a time into a box of volume $\tilde{V}$. The center of the first molecule which is put into the box can move about in a volume $(\tilde{V}^{1/3}-\sigma)^3$, inasmuch as it can come no closer than $\frac{1}{2}\sigma$ to the wall of the box. The center of the second molecule which is added is restricted to move in a volume $(\tilde{V}^{1/3} - \sigma)^3 - \frac{4}{3}\pi\sigma^3$ since it may not approach closer than a distance σ to the center of the first molecule which was added.

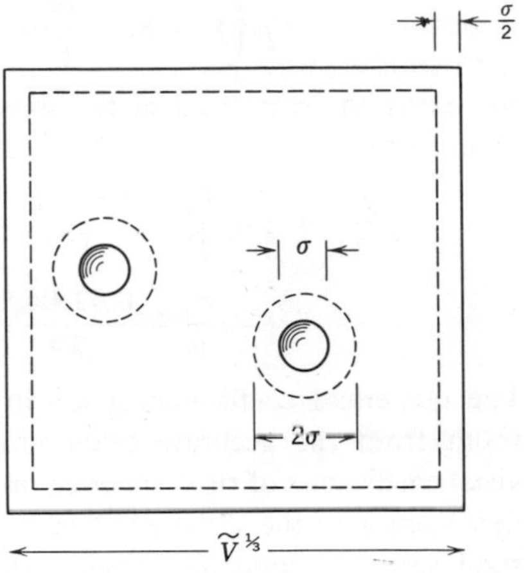

Fig. 1.1–1

In Fig. 1.1–1 we see the region to which the third molecule is restricted. This process may be continued until all $\tilde{N}$ molecules have been put in the box. We can now compute the average volume available to the center of a molecule, and this is clearly

$$(\tilde{V}^{1/3} - \sigma)^3 - (\tilde{N}/2)\left(\tfrac{4}{3}\pi\sigma^3\right) \simeq \tilde{V} - \tfrac{2}{3}\pi\tilde{N}\sigma^3$$

when the dimensions of the container are large compared with σ. The quantity $b_0 = \frac{2}{3}\pi\tilde{N}\sigma^3$ is referred to as the "co-volume" of the molecules and is equal to four times the volume of the rigid spherical molecules.

The above arguments are not completely correct since we have neglected the fact that in Fig. 1.1–1 the two spheres indicated by dotted lines may overlap, with the result that the volume excluded to the third molecule would be somewhat less than shown. The overlapping of the dotted spheres with the dotted lines a distance $\frac{1}{2}\sigma$ from the walls should also be taken into account. This, however, is a surface effect and is treated separately in theory of surface tension.[2] When we take into account the

[1] The word "virial" is derived from the Latin *vis* (pl. *vires*), which means "force." The *virial* is a quantity defined by Eq. 1.4–27 in terms of the forces acting on the molecules. The virial coefficients give the deviations from ideality in terms of the forces between molecules.

[2] Surface tension is discussed in § 5.1.

overlapping of two or more spheres, we find that the average volume available to the center of a molecule is

$$\tilde{V} - b_0 + (b_1/\tilde{V}) + (b_2/\tilde{V}^2) + \cdots \tag{1.1–3}$$

The quantities $b_1, b_2, \ldots$ are constants which depend on the solid geometry of the overlapping spheres. The equation of state for rigid spherical molecules then becomes

$$p\left(\tilde{V} - b_0 + \frac{b_1}{\tilde{V}} + \frac{b_2}{\tilde{V}^2} + \cdots\right) = \tilde{N}kT \tag{1.1–4}$$

By taking the reciprocal of the series we may write this equation in the virial form:

$$\begin{aligned} \frac{p\tilde{V}}{RT} &= 1 + \frac{b_0}{\tilde{V}} + \frac{b_0^2 - b_1}{\tilde{V}^2} + \frac{b_0^3 - 2b_0b_1 - b_2}{\tilde{V}^3} + \cdots \\ &= 1 + \frac{b_0}{\tilde{V}} + \frac{0.6250b_0^2}{\tilde{V}^2} + \frac{0.2869b_0^3}{\tilde{V}^3} + \cdots \end{aligned} \tag{1.1–5}$$

The numerical coefficients given in the second form of this expression result from the accurate calculation of the second, third, and fourth virial coefficients of rigid spherical molecules.[3, 4] There is no temperature dependence of the virial coefficients for rigid molecules.[5] Values of the rigid sphere second and third virial coefficients for several substances are given in Table 1.1–1, along with the corresponding experimental values. For low temperatures the experimental second and third virial coefficients are negative, and at high temperatures they are positive. The magnitude of the deviations from ideality at various temperatures and pressures can be seen from the experimental compressibility factors. The deviations are very large at low temperatures and high pressures.

We thus see that the equation of state of a gas which is dilute may be written in terms of the deviations from the ideal gas law, $pV = \tilde{N}kT$. It is also clear that the gas behaves ideally when the covolume of the molecules is small compared with the volume of the containing vessel.

b. An ultra-simplified theory of the equation of state of dense gases and liquids[6]

Let us again consider a dense gas or liquid composed of $\tilde{N}$ rigid, impenetrable spheres of diameter σ in a volume $\tilde{V}$. Let us imagine that

[3] H. Happel, *Ann. Physik*, (4) **21**, 342 (1906).

[4] R. Majumdar, *Bull. Calcutta Math. Soc.*, **21**, 107 (1929).

[5] The equation of state for rigid spheres according to statistical mechanics is given in § 3.5a. The virial coefficients for rigid non-spherical molecules are given in § 3.8a.

[6] See § 4.5; also H. Eyring and J. O. Hirschfelder, *J. Phys. Chem.*, **41**, 249 (1937); J. O. Hirschfelder, *J. Chem. Ed.*, **16**, 540 (1939).

TABLE 1.1–1

SOME EQUATION OF STATE QUANTITIES FROM EXPERIMENTAL MEASUREMENTS AND FROM RIGID-SPHERE CALCULATIONS

Substance	T, °K	$p\tilde{V}/RT$			$B(T)$ (cc/mole)		$C(T)$ (cc/mole)^2	
		1 atm	50 atm	1000 atm	Experimental	Rigid Sphere[a]	Experimental	Rigid Sphere[a]
He	100	1.0023	1.113	—	9.6	21.9	(60)	300
	300	1.0005	1.024	1.439	11.7		72	
	500	1.0003	1.013	1.242	10.8		(110)	
A	100	0.9783	0.174[b]	3.30[b]	−178	60.9	(−1500)	2314
	300	0.9999	0.971	1.675	−15.2		990	
	500	1.0001	1.009	1.353	(8.4)		710	
N_2	100	0.990	0.243[b]	3.84[b]	−149	66.5	(2080)	2766
	300	0.9998	0.9960	1.99	−4.4		1310	
	500	1.0004	1.0210	1.82	168		640	

Note. Values in parentheses are obtained by extrapolation of the experimental data.

[a] The rigid sphere quantities are calculated on the basis of the rigid-sphere diameters obtained from the kinetic theory of gases and given in Table 1.2–1. $B_{\text{rig sph}} = b_0 = \frac{2}{3}\pi\tilde{N}\sigma^3$ and $C_{\text{rig sph}} = \frac{5}{8}b_0^2$.

[b] These values are for the liquid.

these molecules occupy the lattice points of a cubic lattice, with the distances between their centers equal to $(\tilde{V}/\tilde{N})^{1/3}$. Now we select one of these molecules to be free to move from its fixed position in the lattice. In Fig. 1.1–2 it may be seen that the center of this "wanderer" is free to move approximately in a cube of side length $2(\tilde{V}/\tilde{N})^{1/3} - 2\sigma$. For molecules which are mass points ($\sigma = 0$), the wanderer is free to move in a cube of side length $2(V/\tilde{N})^{1/3}$.

The pressure exerted by the wanderer on the remaining molecules is equal to the rate of transfer of momentum per unit area. This rate is directly proportional to the frequency with which the molecule traverses the box, and inversely proportional to the side length of the box. Hence, the pressure exerted by the wandering rigid sphere is greater than the pressure of the wandering mass point by the inverse ratio of the side lengths of their restraining boxes:

$$\frac{p\tilde{V}}{RT} = \frac{2(\tilde{V}/\tilde{N})^{1/3}}{2(\tilde{V}/\tilde{N})^{1/3} - 2\sigma} \tag{1.1–6}$$

This may be rearranged to give

$$p[\tilde{V} - 0.7816 b_0^{1/3} \tilde{V}^{2/3}] = RT \qquad (1.1\text{–}7)$$

which is a rough equation of state for rigid spherical molecules at high densities. The numerical constant depends upon the type of assumed crystal packing. For example, for a face-centered cubic lattice the constant should be 0.6962, and for body-centered cubic packing, 0.7163.

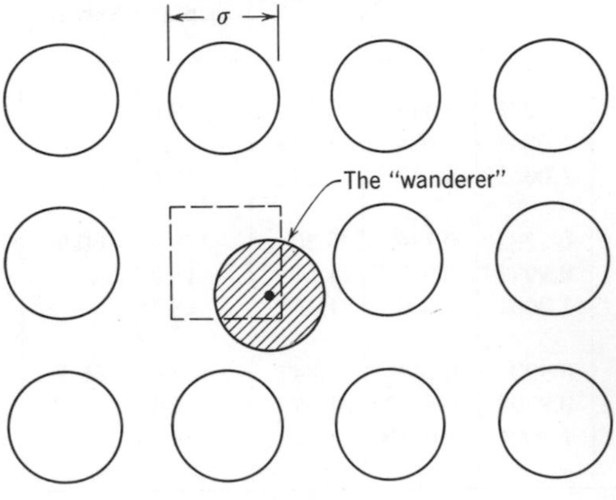

Fig. 1.1–2

c. Introduction to the rigorous statistical mechanical theory of the equation of state

In order to develop a rigorous equation of state for a gas or liquid containing a large number of particles, it is useful to apply the principles of equilibrium statistical mechanics. In Chapter 2 the basic concepts of statistical mechanics are discussed, important definitions are given, and some properties of ideal gases are discussed.

In § 3.1 it is shown how the statistical mechanical theory can be used to express the equation of state in two forms: (i) in terms of the *partition function* Z_N, and (ii) in terms of the *radial distribution function* $g(r)$:[7]

$$p = kT(\partial \ln Z_N/\partial V)_T \qquad (1.1\text{–}8)$$

$$p = \frac{NkT}{V} - \frac{2\pi N^2}{3V}\int g(r)\frac{d\varphi}{dr} r^3\, dr \qquad (1.1\text{–}9)$$

The partition function Z_N is the sum over *all* energy states (of the system of N molecules) of $\exp(-E_i/kT)$, where E_i is the energy of the ith state

[7] Equation 1.1–8 may be applied when the forces between the molecules are angle dependent, but Eq. 1.1–9 is valid for spherically symmetric interaction potentials only.

of the system. The radial distribution function $g(r)$ is defined by the statement that the number of pairs of molecules which are separated by a distance r is $(N^2/2V)g(r)4\pi r^2\,dr$.

In Chapter 3 a rigorous development of the classical equation of state at low densities is given. It is shown that both the partition function and the radial distribution function may be expanded in such a way that the equation of state is given in the virial form shown in Eq. 1.1–2. That is, statistical mechanics provides a means for expressing the virial coefficients $B(T)$, $C(T)$, $D(T)$, . . . in terms of the forces between molecules in the gas. For example, if the potential φ between two molecules in the gas is a function only of the intermolecular separation r, the second virial coefficient is shown to be

$$B(T) = -2\pi\tilde{N}\int_0^\infty [e^{-\varphi(r)/kT} - 1]r^2\,dr \tag{1.1–10}$$

Hence for those gases for which the intermolecular forces are known as a function of the separation between the molecules, a single integration leads to a value of the second virial coefficient as a function of the temperature—that is, the first correction to account for the non-ideality of the gas. From very accurate measurements of $B(T)$ one may obtain a certain amount of information about intermolecular forces. This is done by assuming for the interaction potential a functional form which is qualitatively consistent with theoretical considerations and contains several adjustable parameters. These parameters are then adjusted so as to give the best fit of the experimental values of $B(T)$. It is also possible to derive theoretical expressions for the second virial coefficient for molecules which interact according to angle-dependent potentials, for example, polar molecules and long molecules. These formulae may be used to analyze the experimental data and obtain information about intermolecular forces which depend upon the orientations of the molecules. The calculations of the virial coefficients for quite a few types of potential functions are described in detail in Chapter 3. Inasmuch as it is possible at the present time to evaluate only the first few virial coefficients, the virial equation is useful only at low and intermediate densities.

In Chapter 4 the development of the equation of state of dense gases and liquids is described. Once again the development can be discussed from the standpoint of the partition function or of the radial distribution function. It is not possible to carry through the development by either approach without the introduction of some simplifying assumptions. Hence the two approaches give different results. By far the most work has been done by means of the partition function method. The first attempts along this line are closely related to the ultra-simplified theory given in § 1.1b—that is, one simply works with the partition function of a single molecule confined to the cell formed by its nearest neighbors. Refinements of the theory have considered the correlation of the motion of molecules in adjacent cells and the presence of "holes" in the lattice structure. Extensive calculations have been made for various lattice models. Recently considerable attention has been devoted to the radial distribution function approach. Some calculations have been carried out, and the method shows promise.

In Chapter 5 the results of the two preceding chapters are used in the study of the properties of two-phase systems, in which a vapor is in equilibrium with the liquid phase. The chapter includes discussions of surface tension, the parachor, critical phenomena, and retrograde condensation.

In Chapter 6 the equation of state for monatomic and diatomic gases is discussed from a quantum mechanical viewpoint. Quantum statistical mechanics provides a means for describing the equilibrium properties of substances under those conditions where the deviations from classical behavior are important. Quantum effects are experimentally observable for the isotopes of hydrogen and helium at room temperature and become quite pronounced at low temperatures.

2. Kinetic Theory of Gases—The Transport Coefficients

The phenomena of diffusion, viscosity, and thermal conductivity are all physically similar in that they involve the transport of some physical property through the gas or liquid. *Ordinary diffusion* is the transfer of mass from one region to another because of a gradient in the concentration;[1] *viscosity* is the transport of momentum through the gas because of a gradient in the velocity; and *thermal conductivity* is the transport of thermal energy resulting from the existence of thermal gradients in the gas. These properties are appropriately termed "transport phenomena." We present here a description of these phenomena in terms of an ultra-simplified kinetic theory. Although very crude arguments are used throughout, it is nevertheless possible to obtain expressions which describe the primary dependence of the transport coefficients upon the temperature and pressure and also upon the mass and size of the molecules in the gas. Thereafter, we outline briefly a rigorous theory, and show to what extent its application has been successful.

[1] Diffusion may also result from a temperature gradient (*thermal diffusion* or the *Soret effect*), and the transfer of energy may also result from a concentration gradient (*diffusion thermo* or *Dufour effect*). These are small effects discussed in Chapter 7.

a. An ultra-simplified kinetic theory of dilute gases

In any real gas the molecules move in all directions, and their velocities are distributed over a very wide range. When two molecules come close to one another they undergo very complex interactions, since real molecules attract one another at large distances and repel one another when the intermolecular separation is quite small. In spite of the complicated behavior of the molecules, surprisingly good descriptions of the transport properties may be obtained if we consider the following very unrealistic model for a gas containing n molecules per unit volume:

(i) The molecules are rigid, non-attracting spheres with diameter σ.

(ii) All the molecules travel with the same speed; a reasonable choice for the molecular speed seems to be the arithmetic mean speed, $\Omega = (8kT/m\pi)^{1/2}$, which may be calculated from the velocity distribution function (see Problem 4, Chapter 2).

(iii) All the molecules travel in a direction parallel to one of the coordinate axes, that is, one-sixth of them are traveling in the $(+x)$-direction, one-sixth in the $(-x)$-direction, one-sixth in the $(+y)$-direction, and so forth.

i. *Rate of Molecular Collisions in a Gas*

Let us begin by examining the dependence of the rate of collisions, Γ, upon the size, number density, and average speed of the molecules. Consider a single molecule which is moving in the $(+z)$-direction and let us inquire as to the frequency with which it collides with the other molecules in the gas. Certainly it will undergo no collisions with the other molecules moving in the $(+z)$-direction, since they are all moving with the same speed, Ω. With respect to those molecules moving in the $(-z)$-direction, however, it has a relative velocity of 2Ω. This means that during a time interval Δt the molecules whose centers lie within a cylinder of cross-section $\pi\sigma^2$ and length $2\Omega\,\Delta t$ will undergo collisions with the molecule on which our attention has been focused (assuming that the latter is not deflected by the collisions). Since there are n molecules per unit volume and since one-sixth of them are moving in the $(-z)$-direction, there will be $\frac{1}{3}\pi n\sigma^2\Omega$ collisions per unit time with these molecules. Similarly, the molecule moving in the $(+z)$-direction has a velocity of $\sqrt{2}\Omega$ relative to those molecules moving in the $(+x)$-direction; hence there are $\frac{1}{6}\sqrt{2}\pi n\sigma^2\Omega$ collisions per unit time with these molecules. The same result is obtained for molecules moving in the $(-x)$-, $(+y)$-, and $(-y)$-directions, so that altogether there are

$$\Gamma = \xi' n\pi\sigma^2\Omega = \xi' p\sigma^2\sqrt{8\pi/mkT} \tag{1.2–1}$$

collisions suffered by one molecule per unit time, where $\xi' = \frac{1}{3} + \frac{2}{3}\sqrt{2}$.

The second expression given in Eq. 1.2–1 for Γ was obtained by using $p = nkT$ (ideal gas law) and $\Omega = \sqrt{8kT/m\pi}$. (If one were to assume that the molecular motion takes place in all directions and that the velocity distribution is Maxwellian, the same result is obtained, except that $\xi' = \sqrt{2}$, that is, $\xi' = 1.414$ as compared with the approximate 1.276.)

ii. *The Mean Free Path*

Since the gas we are considering is composed of impenetrable elastic spheres, a collision between two molecules is well-defined. This makes it possible to introduce a quantity known as the *mean free path*, which is the average distance traversed by a molecule between collisions. Thus a molecule moving with speed Ω, during a long time interval Δt (that is, a time interval long compared with the average time interval between collisions), will travel a distance $\Omega\,\Delta t$; if the molecule suffers Γ collisions per unit time, during the long time interval Δt the molecule will collide $\Gamma\,\Delta t$ times. Hence the average distance traversed by the molecule between collisions, that is, the mean free path, is

$$l = \frac{\Omega\,\Delta t}{\Gamma\,\Delta t} = \frac{\Omega}{\Gamma} \tag{1.2–2}$$

Substitution of Eq. 1.2–1 into Eq. 1.2–2 gives

$$l = \frac{1}{\xi' n\pi\sigma^2} = \frac{kT}{\xi' p\pi\sigma^2} \tag{1.2–3}$$

the second form arising from the application of the ideal gas law. It should be noted that at constant density the mean free path is temperature-independent; and at constant pressure it is directly proportional to the temperature.

The quantity $\pi\sigma^2$ which appears in the denominator of the expression for the mean free path is the *collision cross-section* for the rigid spherical molecule. This quantity, which appears in all the expressions for the transport coefficients, is the cross-section of the imaginary sphere surrounding a molecule into which the center of another molecule cannot penetrate.

In this simple kinetic theory the transport coefficients can be expressed in terms of the quantity l. Consequently viscosity, diffusion, and thermal conductivity are sometimes referred to as *mean free path phenomena*. However, in the more rigorous approach for real gases it is found that the mean free path does not appear naturally in the derivation of the transport properties.

iii. *Flux of Molecular Properties*

The coefficient of ordinary diffusion is the flux of mass of species i due to a unit gradient in the mass density of i; the coefficient of viscosity is the flux of the y-component of the momentum resulting from a unit gradient in the y-component of the velocity; and the coefficient of thermal conductivity is the energy flux due to a unit temperature gradient. In all three cases the fluxes are in the same direction as the gradients, and this direction defines the coordinate z. The flux of mass of species i is denoted by j_{iz}. The flux in the z-direction of the y-component of the momentum is $p_{yz} = p_{zy}$, where p is the pressure tensor. The flux of energy is denoted by q_z. Because of their physical similarity these three phenomena may be described by a common mathematical formalism. We therefore use the symbol Ψ_P to represent the z-component of any one of the three fluxes: the flux of mass of species i, the flux of the momentum in the y-direction, and the flux of energy. The symbol P represents correspondingly the mass density of species i, the momentum density, or the energy density. These definitions are illustrated in Table 1.2–1.

TABLE 1.2–1

	P	Ψ_P
Diffusion	$n_i m_i$	j_{iz}
Viscosity	nmv_y	p_{yz}
Thermal conductivity	nc_vT	q_z

Let us consider the net flux in the ($+z$)-direction of the property associated with P (that is, the mass density of molecules of species i, the momentum density in the y-direction, or the energy density) through the plane O. (See Fig. 1.2–1.) Molecules approaching O from below have suffered their last collision at a distance l below plane O. That is, they have come from plane A and have the values of the properties P_A, characteristic of that location. Similarly, molecules arriving at plane O from above have come from plane B, and possess the values of properties P_B, characteristic of that plane. If the property P has the value P_O, on plane O, then we may write:

$$P_A = P_O - l(dP/dz); \qquad P_B = P_O + l(dP/dz) \qquad (1.2\text{–}4)$$

to the approximation that the gradient in the property P is constant over distances of the order of magnitude of a mean free path.

In the case of diffusion, $P = n_i m_i$ the concentration of species i. The value of $n_i m_i$ is different at each of the planes A, O, B, and a transfer of mass results. To consider viscosity, we imagine that the molecules at the plane A are moving in the $(-y)$-direction, that those at plane O are stationary, and that those at plane B are moving in the $(+y)$-direction. Hence there is established a gradient in the y-component of the momentum, $P = nmv_y$. In the discussion of thermal conductivity, the planes A, O, and B are taken to be at different temperatures, and the property P is taken to be the energy density nc_vT (where c_v is the specific heat per molecule).

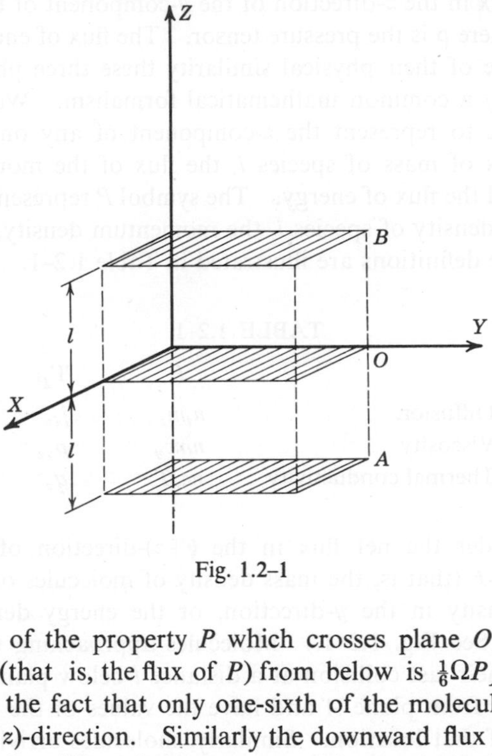

Fig. 1.2–1

The amount of the property P which crosses plane O per unit area per unit time (that is, the flux of P) from below is $\frac{1}{6}\Omega P_A$, the factor $\frac{1}{6}$ accounting for the fact that only one-sixth of the molecules on plane A move in the $(+z)$-direction. Similarly the downward flux of P is $\frac{1}{6}\Omega P_B$. Hence the net flux, Ψ_P, of the property P in the $(+z)$-direction across plane O is

$$\Psi_P = \tfrac{1}{6}\Omega(P_A - P_B) = -\tfrac{1}{3}\Omega l\left(\frac{dP}{dz}\right) = -\,\xi\,\frac{\sqrt{\pi mkT}}{nm\pi\sigma^2}\left(\frac{dP}{dz}\right) \tag{1.2–5}$$

in which the factor ξ is $(2/3\pi)$ when ξ' is taken to be $\sqrt{2}$. Specifically,

$$\Psi_{n_im_i} = j_{iz} = -\tfrac{1}{3}\Omega l\frac{dn_im_i}{dz} \tag{1.2–6}$$

$$\Psi_{nmv_y} = p_{yz} = -\tfrac{1}{3}\Omega lnm\,\frac{dv_y}{dz} \tag{1.2–7}$$

$$\Psi_{nc_vT} = q_z = -\tfrac{1}{3}\Omega lnc_v\,\frac{dT}{dz} \tag{1.2–8}$$

are the fluxes of mass of species i, momentum, and energy, respectively.

iv. *Transport Coefficients*

For the situation described in Fig. 1.2–1, the transport coefficients are defined in terms of the fluxes as follows:

$$\Psi_{n_im_i} = j_{iz} = -\mathscr{D}\,\frac{dn_im_i}{dz} \tag{1.2–9}$$

$$\Psi_{nmv_y} = p_{yz} = -\eta\,\frac{dv_y}{dz} \tag{1.2–10}$$

$$\Psi_{nc_vT} = q_z = -\lambda\,\frac{dT}{dz} \tag{1.2–11}$$

$\mathscr{D}$ being the coefficient of diffusion, η the coefficient of viscosity, and λ the coefficient of thermal conductivity. When these three equations are compared with the three preceding equations, we find that:

$$\mathscr{D} = \frac{1}{3}\Omega l = \xi\,\frac{\sqrt{\pi mkT}}{\pi\sigma^2}\,\frac{1}{\rho} = \frac{\lambda m}{\rho c_v} \tag{1.2–12}$$ [2]

$$\eta = \frac{1}{3}nm\Omega l = \xi\,\frac{\sqrt{\pi mkT}}{\pi\sigma^2} = \rho\mathscr{D} \tag{1.2–13}$$

$$\lambda = \frac{1}{3}nc_v\Omega l = \xi\,\frac{\sqrt{\pi mkT}}{\pi\sigma^2}\,\frac{c_v}{m} = \frac{c_v\eta}{m} \tag{1.2–14}$$

in which $\rho = nm = pm/kT$ is the density of the gas. The application of the rigorous kinetic theory of Chapter 7 to the rigid-sphere model gives exactly the above form for the transport coefficients. The *rigorous*

[2] This expression for $\mathscr{D}$ is really for self-diffusion, that is, the interdiffusion of particles of the same mass and size. Examples where such a formula may be applied are interdiffusion of ortho and para forms and the interdiffusion of heavy isotopes. (See § 8.2d–ii.)

theory for *rigid-sphere molecules,* however, predicts that the values of ξ are different for the various fluxes. In § 8.2 it is shown that

$$\xi_{\mathscr{D}} = \frac{3}{8} \qquad \frac{\eta}{\rho\mathscr{D}} = \frac{5}{6}$$
$$\xi_{\eta} = \frac{5}{16} \qquad \frac{\eta c_v}{\lambda m} = \frac{2}{5} \tag{1.2–15}$$
$$\xi_{\lambda} = \frac{25}{32} \qquad \frac{\rho\mathscr{D} c_v}{\lambda m} = \frac{12}{25}$$

Inserting these values into Eqs. 1.2–12, 13, 14 we may rewrite the expressions for the transport coefficients in practical units:

$$\mathscr{D} = 2.6280 \times 10^{-3} \frac{\sqrt{T^3/M}}{p\sigma^2}, \text{ cm}^2/\text{sec} \qquad (1.2\text{–}16)^3$$

$$\eta = 2.6693 \times 10^{-5} \frac{\sqrt{MT}}{\sigma^2}, \text{ g/cm sec} \tag{1.2–17}$$

$$\lambda = 1.9891 \times 10^{-4} \frac{\sqrt{T/M}}{\sigma^2} = \frac{15}{4}\frac{R}{M}\eta, \text{ cal/cm deg sec} \qquad (1.2\text{–}18)^4$$

where M = molecular weight,

T = temperature in °K,

p = pressure in atmospheres,

σ = molecular diameter in Å.

In Table 1.2–2 are shown some values of kinetic theory properties for rigid spheres, in order to give a rough idea of the orders of magnitude of the quantities with which we are dealing. The table also includes some

[3] For a mixture of two chemical species the coefficient of diffusion for the rigid-sphere model is

$$\mathscr{D}_{12} = 2.6280 \times 10^{-3} \frac{\sqrt{T^3(M_1 + M_2)/2M_1M_2}}{p\sigma_{12}^2}, \text{ cm}^2/\text{sec}$$

in which $\sigma_{12} = \frac{1}{2}(\sigma_1 + \sigma_2)$.

[4] This formula for the coefficient of thermal conductivity is applicable to monatomic gases only. For polyatomic gases use may be made of the Eucken correction (see §§ 7.6b and 8.2c–i), and then Eq. 1.2–18 is replaced by

$$\lambda = \frac{15}{4}\frac{R}{M}\eta\left(\frac{4}{15}\frac{\tilde{C}_v}{R} + \frac{3}{5}\right)$$

TABLE 1.2–2

SOME KINETIC THEORY PROPERTIES CALCULATED FROM THE SIMPLE THEORY[a] AT 1 ATM. PRESSURE[b]

Gas	Molecular Weight M	Collision Diameter σ (Å)	Temp. T (°K)	Mean Free Path l (Å)	Collisions Suffered by One Molecule in One Second Γ (10^9 sec^{-1})	Arithmetic Mean Speed Ω (10^4cm sec^{-1})	Coefficient of Self-Diffusion $\mathscr{D}$ (cm^2 sec^{-1})		Coefficient of Viscosity η (10^{-7} g cm^{-1} sec^{-1})		Coefficient of Thermal Conductivity λ (10^{-7} cal cm^{-1} sec^{-1} deg^{-1})	
							Calcd	Exptl[c]	Calcd	Exptl	Calcd	Exptl[c]
He	4.00	2.18	100	645	11.28	7.28	0.276	(0.270)	1123	951	2093	1744
			300	1936	6.51	12.60	1.437	(1.669)	1946	1981	3625	3583
			500	3226	5.04	16.27	3.091	(3.890)	2512	2790	4679	4844
A	39.9	3.64	100	231	9.95	2.30	0.031	0.023	1273	815	238	154
			300	694	5.75	3.99	0.163	0.186	2204	2271	412	422
			500	1157	4.45	5.15	0.351	(0.456)	2846	3351	531	631
N_2	28.02	3.75	100	218	12.61	2.75	0.035	0.027	1005	698	339	(232)
			300	654	7.28	4.75	0.183	0.205	1740	1663	587	(602)
			500	1090	5.64	6.15	0.395	(0.495)	2247	2657	766	(876)

[a] σ values taken from E. H. Kennard, *Kinetic Theory of Gases*, McGraw-Hill (1938), p. 149.

[b] $\Omega = \sqrt{8kT/m\pi}$; Γ and l are given by Eqs. 1.2–1 and 1.2–3, with $\xi' = \sqrt{2}$; $\mathscr{D}$, η, and λ are given by Eqs. 1.2–16, 17, 18.

[c] The values in parentheses are estimated values.

experimental values to give an indication of the inadequacy of the rigid-sphere model.

From the above relations it is seen that the coefficient of diffusion varies as the three-halves power of the temperature and is inversely proportional to the pressure. The coefficients of viscosity and thermal conductivity are both independent of the pressure and increase with the square root of the temperature. All three transport coefficients are inversely proportional to the square of the diameter of the molecules. The above equations would correctly describe these properties if the molecules actually were rigid spheres. As we shall see in Chapter 8, these results give only the approximate pressure and temperature dependence for real gases, since the true temperature dependence must include the effect of the interactions which take place between real molecules. It will be shown that the rigorous kinetic theory calculations enable us to predict the variation of these properties with considerably greater accuracy. It is, nevertheless, remarkable that the very artificial gas model which we have used here gives such good results.

TABLE 1.2–3

EXPERIMENTAL VALUES OF THE SCHMIDT AND PRANDTL NUMBERS AT 0°C

Gas	*Schmidt Number,* $\eta/\rho\mathscr{D}$	*Prandtl Number,* $\eta\hat{C}_p/\lambda$
Ne	0.73	0.66
A	0.75	0.67
N_2	0.74	0.71
CH_4	0.70	0.74
O_2	0.74	0.72
CO_2	0.71	0.75
H_2	0.73	0.71
Simple kinetic theory	0.83	0.67

The simple kinetic theory suggests ratios of molecular constants which do not vary markedly from substance to substance and which do not change appreciably with temperature. For example, the combination $\eta\hat{C}_p/\lambda$ is known as the *Prandtl number.* Since the specific heat ratio, $\gamma = \hat{C}_p/\hat{C}_v$, is equal to $\frac{5}{3}$ for monatomic molecules, the simple kinetic theory predicts that the Prandtl number should have the value $\frac{2}{3}$. Similarly the ratio, $\eta/\rho\mathscr{D}$, is known as the *Schmidt number.* According to simple kinetic theory it should have the value $\frac{5}{6}$. Table 1.2–3 gives the values for the Schmidt and Prandtl numbers for a few substances at 0°C calculated from the best available experimental values given in Chapter 8.

b. Introduction to the rigorous kinetic theory of gases

A detailed classical treatment of the rigorous kinetic theory of dilute monatomic gases and mixtures (the Chapman-Enskog theory) is presented in Chapter 7 (§7.1–4). Inasmuch as this account is necessarily rather long and involved, it seems advisable, for the benefit of those readers who are interested primarily in making practical use of the formulae and tables of Chapter 8, to outline briefly the problem and method of attack, and to summarize the assumptions which are made in the rigorous derivation of the transport coefficients. The validity of the results, as applied to specific kinds of molecules and to specific conditions of temperature and pressure, is also considered.

i. *Brief Outline of the Problem and the Method of Attack*

The rigorous development of the kinetic theory of gases is based upon the knowledge of the distribution function $f_i(\boldsymbol{r}, \boldsymbol{v}_i, t)$. This function represents the number of molecules of ith species which at time t lie in a unit volume element about the point $\boldsymbol{r}$ and which have velocities within a unit range about $\boldsymbol{v}_i$. If there are no gradients in the composition, velocity, and temperature in the gas, then $f_i(\boldsymbol{r}, \boldsymbol{v}_i, t)$ reduces to the Maxwellian distribution $f_i^{[0]} = n_i(m_i/2\pi kT)^{3/2} \exp(-m_i v_i^2/2kT)$. When the system is not at equilibrium, the distribution function satisfies the Boltzmann integro-differential equation. This equation and the methods of solution are discussed in Chapter 7.

Usually we are interested in the properties of gases which are under conditions only slightly different from equilibrium. In fact it is only under these conditions that the flux vectors are linear in the derivatives and the usual definitions of the transport coefficients apply. In this limit the distribution function is nearly Maxwellian, and the Boltzmann equation can be solved by a perturbation method developed by Chapman and Enskog. The resulting solutions are then used to obtain expressions for the fluxes and for the transport coefficients.

These expressions show that mass transfer results not only from a concentration gradient, but also from a temperature gradient (thermal diffusion[5, 6]); similarly, we find that energy transfer results not only from a temperature gradient, but also from a concentration gradient (the Dufour effect[7]). These and other second-order effects, which cannot

[5] Thermal diffusion in the liquid phase is usually called the *Soret Effect*.

[6] This effect was discovered independently by Chapman and Enskog as a result of their exact formulation of the kinetic theory of monatomic gases; it was not until several years later that Dootson gave an experimental demonstration of this phenomenon [S. Chapman and F. W. Dootson, *Phil. Mag.*, **33**, 248 (1917)].

[7] Thermal diffusion and the Dufour effect are closely related according to the reciprocal relations of Onsager (see § 11.2a).

be described in terms of simple kinetic theory, emerge quite naturally from the more rigorous approach.

The final result is that we can express all the transport coefficients in terms of a set of integrals $\Omega^{(l,s)}$. These integrals involve explicitly the dynamics of a molecular encounter and hence the intermolecular force law. The present incomplete knowledge of the nature of intermolecular forces immediately limits to some extent the applicability of the results to practical problems. On the other hand, the knowledge of a relation between the transport coefficients and intermolecular forces enables us to obtain indirectly some important information about the nature of these forces. This subject is considered in detail in Chapter 8, where practical low-density transport coefficient calculations are discussed.

ii. *Limitations of the Chapman-Enskog Theory*

The Chapman-Enskog kinetic theory of gases just described is based upon several assumptions which, to some extent, limit the applicability of the final results. Let us consider each of the limitations separately and discuss the conditions under which each is important.

Since only *binary collisions* are considered in the Chapman-Enskog theory, the results are not applicable at densities sufficiently high that three-body collisions become important. At the present time, the approximate theory of Enskog is the most usable for describing the non-equilibrium properties of dense gases. The properties of liquids, on the other hand, are best described by the Eyring theory of absolute reaction rates. A rigorous theory, based on the radial distribution function, is in a state of development. This theory will probably some day supplant the theories of Enskog and Eyring. To illustrate the order of magnitude of the effect of pressure on the transport coefficients let us consider the coefficient of viscosity. According to the theory of dilute gases the viscosity is pressure-independent at constant temperature. This fact is corroborated experimentally. Experimental measurements indicate that the viscosity of nitrogen at about 325°K increases by a factor of two and one-half as the pressure is increased from one to a thousand atmospheres, whereas an increase of only 4 per cent is observed as the pressure goes from one to sixty atmospheres. These results are in surprisingly good agreement with the theory of Enskog. The transport properties of dense gases are discussed in Chapter 9.

The use of *classical mechanics* excludes the discussion of low temperature phenomena in which quantum effects are significant. According to quantum theory there is associated with each molecule a wavelength—the "de Broglie wavelength," h/mv—which is inversely proportional to the molecular weight and molecular velocity. The de Broglie wavelength corresponding to the arithmetic mean molecular velocity is $27.4/\sqrt{MT}$ Å, where M is the molecular weight. At low temperatures the average molecular velocity is small, and the associated de Broglie wavelength is large. When the de Broglie wavelength is of the order of magnitude of molecular dimensions quantum mechanical "diffraction effects," similar to the diffraction phenomena in optics, are observed. At still lower temperatures or at high densities when the de Broglie wavelength becomes of the order of magnitude of the average distance between the molecules, "statistics effects" related to the Pauli exclusion principle, become important. Above 200°K quantum effects are less than one per cent even for the isotopes of helium and hydrogen. Below this temperature diffraction effects become quite important for the lighter gases. Statistics effects are of importance only at temperatures below about 2°K and manifest themselves in the peculiar behavior of liquid helium. These quantum effects are considered in Chapter 10.

The Chapman-Enskog method for the solution of the Boltzmann equation provides a series approximation to the distribution function. The first approximation, which is the only one discussed here, is valid for situations in which *the gradients of the physical quantities are small.* The higher approximations provide corrections for larger gradients. In the first approximation the fluxes are proportional to the first derivative of the density, velocity, and temperature, and the resulting equations, which describe the change with time of density, velocity, and temperature (the *equations of change*) are called the *Navier-Stokes equations.* The higher approximations contribute terms proportional to higher derivatives and powers of lower derivatives of the physical properties. The equations of change corresponding to the second approximation are referred to as the *Burnett equations.* Quantitatively the first approximation is valid whenever the relative changes in the density, velocity, and temperature in the distance of a mean free path are small compared with unity (that is, $l(\partial \ln n/\partial x) \ll 1$, etc.). According to Table 1.2–2 the mean free path in a gas at 1 atm pressure is of the order of 10^{-5} cm. Hence at 1 atm pressure or higher it is only under conditions of extreme gradients, such as those which occur in shock waves, that deviations of this nature occur. The subject of shock waves is considered in Chapter 11. Since the mean free path varies inversely with the pressure, deviations from the Navier-Stokes equations are encountered at low pressures under conditions of less extreme gradients. As discussed in § 7.5, there is considerable doubt as to the convergence of the Enskog series and the validity of the method. More powerful methods have been recently developed which confirm the validity of the Navier-Stokes equations, but lead to results different from the Burnett equations and the higher approximations.

In the development of the Chapman-Enskog theory it is assumed that *the dimensions of the containing vessel* and any obstacles therein *are large compared to the mean free path* so that the surface layer occupies a negligible fraction of the total volume. At very low densities the molecules collide more frequently with the walls of the containing vessel than with each other; hence there is little mechanism for the establishment of local equilibrium within the gas itself. In such a gas the concept of local density, velocity, and temperature loses meaning, and the gas no longer behaves even approximately as a continuous fluid but rather exhibits the properties of a discontinuous medium. A gas under extremely rarefied conditions is referred to as a *Knudsen gas*, and the behavior of such a gas is reasonably well understood. The theory has not yet been completely developed for a gas in the density region between a Knudsen gas and a gas at moderate density, where the Navier-Stokes equations apply.

Strictly speaking, the Chapman-Enskog kinetic theory of gases applies only to *monatomic gases* (molecules with no internal degrees of freedom for which the interaction potential is spherically symmetric). Inelastic collisions occur between molecules with internal degrees of freedom. In these collisions kinetic energy is no longer conserved, although clearly mass and momentum are conserved. Consequently the viscosity and diffusion are not appreciably affected by the presence of the internal degrees of freedom, and the theory for monatomic gases may be applied to polyatomic molecules with considerable success, provided that the molecules are not too non-spherical.

However, the coefficient of thermal conductivity is affected significantly by the presence of the internal degrees of freedom, inasmuch as the flux of energy includes a contribution due to the internal energy as well as one due to the translational energy. From the Chapman-Enskog development we obtain the relationship

$$\lambda = \eta \frac{R}{M}\left[\frac{15}{4}\right] \tag{1.2–19}$$

relating the thermal conductivity to the viscosity (see Eq. 1.2–15). Experimentally this relation is confirmed in monatomic gases, but significant deviations are observed in polyatomic gases. To account for the effect of the internal degrees of freedom, Eucken proposed the formula

$$\lambda = \eta \frac{R}{M}\left[\frac{\tilde{C}_v}{R} + \frac{9}{4}\right] \tag{1.2–20}$$

which is in good agreement with most experimental results. A derivation of this formula is given in § 7.6b and its application is discussed in § 8.2c.

When molecules in different internal states undergo a collision the probability of a transition to new internal states and the angular dependence of the scattering are described by the "angular transition probabilities." A kinetic theory of polyatomic molecules, formally quite similar to that for monatomic molecules, has been developed by Wang Chang and Uhlenbeck[8] and by de Boer[9] (see § 7.6c). Results are expressed in terms of the angular transition probabilities, rather than directly in terms of the potential function. By thus taking into account explicitly the internal transitions, the Eucken relation is obtained in the limit that the transitions take place easily. At the present time, these transitions cannot be computed theoretically except in the simplest cases. However, some information about the transition probabilities has been obtained by the interpretation of data on the dispersion of high-frequency sound waves and other phenomena which depend upon relaxation time.[10] The relaxation time is a characteristic time for the establishment of equilibrium between a particular internal degree of freedom and the translational motion. The relaxation time is given for convenience by stating the number of collisions required to establish equilibrium. To get the relaxation time, we multiply this quantity by the mean time between collisions. In hydrogen gas, for example, about 50 collisions are required to establish equilibrium between the rotational degrees of freedom and the translational motion. However, recent work on pressure-broadening of microwaves seems to indicate that this number is considerably less in the case of molecules with larger moments of inertia. The transfer of vibrational energy, however, is considerably more difficult. It has been found that for triatomic molecules, such as CO_2, N_2O, COS, and CS_2, about 2500 to 50,000 collisions are needed for the establishment of vibrational equilibrium.

c. The equations of change and their applications

In the development of the kinetic theory of dilute gases and dense gases we obtain the equations of change. These equations are differential equations which indicate the behavior of the concentration, the flow-velocity, and the temperature as functions of the distance and time. These equations together with the thermal equation of state, $p = p(V, T)$, and the caloric equation of state, $U = U(V, T)$, form the basis for the study of fluid dynamics. The applications of these equations are discussed in

[8] C. S. Wang Chang and G. E. Uhlenbeck, "Transport Properties in Polyatomic Gases," CM-681, Project NOrd 7924, University of Michigan (1951).

[9] J. de Boer (private communication).

[10] A. G. Gaydon, *Spectroscopy and Combustion Theory*, Chapman and Hall, Second Revised Edition (1948), Ch. XII.

Chapter 11. The discussion includes a number of topics of current interest in physics and chemistry: sound propagation, propagation of finite waves, flame propagation, shock waves, detonations, and the flow of propellent gases in rockets.

3. Intermolecular Forces and Intermolecular Potential Energy Functions

In the preceding discussions of the equation of state and the transport phenomena the molecules are idealized as rigid spheres. It is well-known, however, that two molecules attract each other when they are far apart and repel each other when they come close together. The force of interaction F between two spherical non-polar molecules is a function of the intermolecular separation r. For most purposes it is more convenient to use the potential energy of interaction $\varphi(r)$ rather than the force of interaction $F(r)$. These two functions are simply related:[1]

$$F(r) = -\frac{d\varphi}{dr}; \quad \varphi(r) = \int_r^\infty F(r)\,dr \tag{1.3–1}$$

Throughout this book we describe the forces between molecules in terms of such potential functions.

For *non-polar molecules* a commonly used intermolecular potential energy function is the Lennard-Jones (6-12) potential:

$$\varphi(r) = 4\epsilon[(\sigma/r)^{12} - (\sigma/r)^6] \tag{1.3–2}$$

The parameters σ and ϵ (which have dimensions of length and energy, respectively) are constants characteristic of the chemical species of the colliding molecules. At large separations ($r \gg \sigma$) the inverse sixth-power attractive component is dominant, and the molecules are attracted to one another with a force proportional to the inverse seventh power of the separation. This type of force describes accurately the induced-dipole–induced-dipole interaction between two non-polar molecules. At small separations ($r \ll \sigma$) the inverse twelfth-power repulsive component is dominant, and the molecules are repelled from one another with a force proportional to the inverse thirteenth power of the separation. This type of force describes reasonably well the repulsive forces between many kinds of molecules. At $r = \sigma$ the potential energy is zero, and therefore

[1] These relations are valid only for force laws and potential functions which are functions of the intermolecular separation alone. For an angular dependent potential the force on molecule a is $\boldsymbol{F}_a = -\frac{\partial}{\partial \boldsymbol{r}_a}\varphi_{ab}$, and in addition there is a torque tending to rotate the molecule. The dynamics of such collisions is described by Lagrange's equations (see § 1.4a).

σ is the distance of closest approach of two molecules which collide with zero initial relative kinetic energy. The parameter ϵ is the maximum energy of attraction of the two molecules, which occurs at a separation of $r = 2^{1/6}\sigma$.

For *polar molecules* the most widely used intermolecular potential energy is the Stockmayer potential. This potential energy function is the sum of the Lennard-Jones (6-12) function and an additional angle-dependent term to account for the electrostatic interaction of the two dipoles, Eq. 1.3–33.

Throughout this book we emphasize the use of the Lennard-Jones (6-12) potential for non-polar molecules and the Stockmayer potential for polar molecules. Many of the properties of gases and liquids have been calculated in terms of these two potential functions. It is therefore possible to describe a large number of equilibrium and non-equilibrium phenomena on a common basis and to understand the relationship between the various phenomena. It should be borne in mind, however, that these two potential functions are idealizations of the true energy of interaction.

The Lennard-Jones (6-12) potential and the Stockmayer potential are reasonably adequate for a number of simple molecules. The interactions of long molecules, molecules in excited states, free radicals, and ions can *not* be described by these two potential functions. In Chapters 13 and 14 the exact nature of these interactions is discussed in detail.

In this section we first indicate the various sources on which our present knowledge of intermolecular forces is based. We then proceed to summarize briefly the various common types of interactions which occur between atoms and molecules in their ground states. The analytical forms of these various types of interactions provide a basis for evaluating and interpreting the empirical potential functions which are listed at the end of this section. These empirical functions are used in various numerical calculations throughout the book.

a. Sources of information about intermolecular forces

A knowledge of intermolecular forces is obtained from both experimental observations and theoretical considerations. The theory suggests the functional form of the potential of interaction, and experimental data are used to determine empirically the adjustable parameters in the potential function. The empirical approach to the subject of intermolecular forces is discussed at various points throughout the book in connection with the properties of dilute gases (second virial coefficients in Chapter 3, and transport coefficients in Chapter 8). The theoretical approach to intermolecular forces is considered in the last three chapters of the book.

In Chapter 12 we give a discussion of those parts of electromagnetic theory which are of value in understanding intermolecular forces. Classical electrostatics provides a means for understanding interactions between ions, dipoles, and higher multipoles. It also forms the basis for the discussion of the polarizability of molecules, the latter being important in the discussion of dispersion forces between molecules.

In Chapter 13 the general theory of intermolecular forces is discussed. The greater part of the chapter is devoted to the present status of our knowledge of long-range forces, inasmuch as it is possible to give rather accurate treatments of systems of two molecules at large separations. It is shown how the long-range forces can be expressed in terms of dipole moments, quadrupole moments, polarizabilities, characteristic frequencies, and optical transition probabilities.

In Chapter 14 the quantum mechanical calculations of interatomic and intermolecular forces are given for a number of simple interactions: H-H, H-H_2, H_2-H_2, H-He, He-He, Ne-Ne, A-A, and several others. In addition to providing more information about long-range forces, these specific calculations supply us with our only theoretical knowledge of the short-range forces.

To determine intermolecular forces empirically from a macroscopic property, it is necessary that it be experimentally measurable with sufficient accuracy and that there exist a refined theoretical description of the property. Because of this latter restriction, most of our information has been obtained from properties of dilute gases and properties of crystals. The dependence of the latter on intermolecular forces is rather straightforward. The separation of spherical non-polar molecules in a crystal at absolute zero (except for small quantum corrections) is exactly equal to the separation for which the potential energy $\varphi(r)$ is a minimum; furthermore, the energy of sublimation of these crystals at absolute zero is simply related (except for a small correction for the zero-point energy of the crystal) to the minimum value of $\varphi(r)$.

In this book emphasis is placed on the determination of the adjustable parameters in various empirical potential functions by analysis of the properties of dilute gases. In subsequent chapters formulae are given for the second virial coefficient and the viscosity in terms of an intermolecular potential function $\varphi(r)$. When these properties are calculated theoretically for any empirical potential function, the experimental temperature dependence of the properties may be used to compute the adjustable parameters. In general, the parameters determined from the equilibrium properties (second virial coefficient and Joule-Thomson coefficient) are slightly different from those determined from non-equilibrium properties (viscosity, self-diffusion). This would not be the case if an exactly correct functional form were used. However, as may be seen from the various expressions, the different properties emphasize various regions of the potential differently. Generally the transport properties emphasize the repulsive portion of the potential function whereas the equilibrium properties lay greater stress on the attractive contribution.

b. Contributions to the intermolecular forces[2]

Let us now summarize briefly the various types of interaction which arise between ions, atoms, and molecules. This information provides the basis for the various molecular models (empirical potential functions) which are tabulated in § 1.3c. The discussion is limited to the interactions of molecules in their ground states.[3]

It is convenient, though somewhat arbitrary, to divide intermolecular forces into two types—*short-range forces* and *long-range forces*.[4] The short-range forces are frequently called *valence forces* or *chemical forces* and arise when the molecules come close enough together for their electron clouds to overlap. These forces are repulsive in nature and often highly directional. There are some experimental indications of the nature of short-range intermolecular forces from crystal structure, properties of surfaces, etc., but much less is known about inter- than about intramolecular forces. Much of our information about these forces comes from the specific quantum mechanical calculations which have been made for specific molecular interactions. These calculations usually are not highly accurate, inasmuch as many of the integrals encountered are so complicated that they are either approximated or simply neglected. The long-range forces, on the other hand, may be treated in a fairly rigorous manner. Furthermore, it is easy to give formulae for various types of interaction which are applicable to a variety of types of molecules. We first discuss the short-range forces briefly, and then proceed to a more detailed discussion of the long-range forces.

The contribution to the intermolecular potential associated with the *short-range* or *valence* forces, $\varphi^{(\mathrm{val})}$, varies exponentially with the separation. The true form of the function $\varphi^{(\mathrm{val})}$ is complicated and depends

[2] The material given in this section is a summary of the results obtained in § 12.1 (electrostatic forces), § 13.3 (dispersion forces), and § 13.5 (induction forces).

[3] The interactions between molecules in excited states are given detailed consideration in § 13.6. It is there shown that for such interactions there is an important contribution to the interaction potential due to "resonance," $\varphi^{(\mathrm{res})}$.

[4] There are some forces, known as *second-order exchange forces*, which are important at intermediate distances. These forces are discussed in § 14.2 in connection with the interatomic potential for helium.

on the specific type of interaction being considered. It is customary in a number of applications to approximate the short-range contribution by the oversimplified form:

$$\varphi^{(\mathrm{val})} = be^{-a(r/a_0)} \tag{1.3–3}$$

in which a and b are constants. The constant a may be approximated by[5]

$$a = \sqrt{\frac{2a_0}{e^2}}\left(\sqrt{E_I(1)} + \sqrt{E_I(2)}\right) \tag{1.3–4}$$

in which $E_I(1)$ and $E_I(2)$ are the ionization potentials of the two molecules, $a_0 = 0.5292$ is the radius of the first Bohr orbit, and e is the charge on the electron.

The various contributions to the *long-range forces* vary inversely as powers of the intermolecular separation. It is convenient to divide the long-range contributions to the interaction potential of molecules into three parts: (i) the *electrostatic* contributions $\varphi^{(\mathrm{es})}$, (ii) the *induction* contribution $\varphi^{(\mathrm{ind})}$, and (iii) the *dispersion* contribution $\varphi^{(\mathrm{dis})}$. We now summarize the general nature of these contributions and indicate where in this book more complete discussions of these forces are given. The first two types of interaction may be explained by straightforward electrostatic considerations, and the third type—dispersion forces—may be explained by means of quantum mechanics.

i. *Electrostatic Contributions*

The electrostatic contributions to the intermolecular potential energy result from the interactions of the various *multipole moments* in the molecules: charges (C), dipole moments[6] (μ), quadrupole moments[7] (Q), etc. For the purpose of indicating the analytical form of the various types of electrostatic interactions, we use the variables defined in Fig. 1.3–1. A direct application of the Coulombic law of electrostatic

[5] C. Zener, *Phys. Rev.*, **37**, 556 (1931).

[6] We consider here only "ideal dipoles," that is, dipoles for which the distance between the charges is taken to approach zero while the charges are increased in such a way as to keep the value of the dipole moment constant. A similar restriction is placed on quadrupoles. Another way of picturing the situation is to say that the dimensions of the multipoles are infinitesimally small in comparison with the intermolecular distances. The interaction of two real dipoles is considered in § 12.1f.

[7] The quadrupole moment of a molecule is really a second-order tensor with nine components. If the molecule has cylindrical symmetry, this tensor may be specified by a single scalar quantity Q, defined by Eq. 12.1–17, q.v. The formulae given in this section are written in terms of this quantity Q and hence apply only to molecules whose charge distributions are cylindrically symmetric.

interaction gives the following formulae for the various types of interaction between molecules a and b:

$$\varphi_{ab}^{(C,\,C)} = +\,\frac{C_a C_b}{r} \tag{1.3–5}$$

$$\varphi_{ab}^{(C,\,\mu)} = -\,\frac{C_a \mu_b}{r^2}\cos\theta_b \tag{1.3–6}$$

$$\varphi_{ab}^{(C,\,Q)} = +\,\frac{C_a Q_b}{4r^3}(3\cos^2\theta_b - 1) \tag{1.3–7}$$

$$\varphi_{ab}^{(\mu,\,\mu)} = -\,\frac{\mu_a \mu_b}{r^3}(2\cos\theta_a\cos\theta_b - \sin\theta_a\sin\theta_b\cos(\phi_a - \phi_b)) \tag{1.3–8}$$

$$\varphi_{ab}^{(\mu,\,Q)} = +\,\frac{3\mu_a Q_b}{4r^4}\begin{bmatrix}\cos\theta_a\,(3\cos^2\theta_b - 1) \\ -\,2\sin\theta_a\sin\theta_b\cos\theta_b\cos(\phi_a - \phi_b)\end{bmatrix} \tag{1.3–9}$$

$$\varphi_{ab}^{(Q,\,Q)} = +\,\frac{3Q_a Q_b}{16r^5}\begin{bmatrix}1 - 5\cos^2\theta_a - 5\cos^2\theta_b - 15\cos^2\theta_a\cos^2\theta_b \\ +\,2[\sin\theta_a\sin\theta_b\cos(\phi_a - \phi_b) - 4\cos\theta_a\cos\theta_b]^2\end{bmatrix} \tag{1.3–10}$$

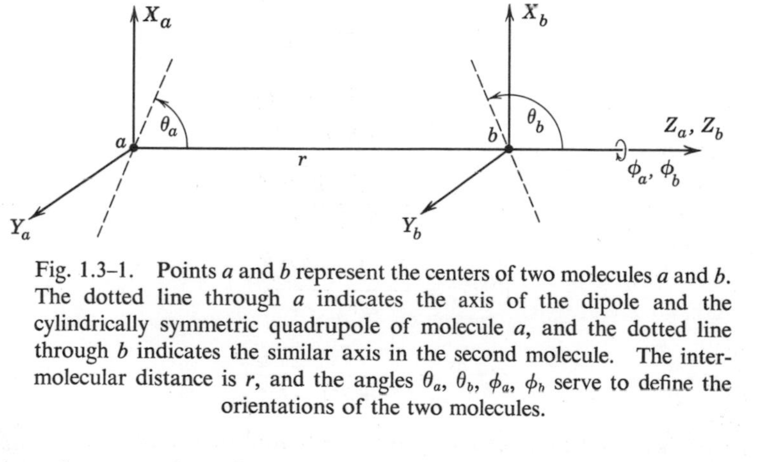

Fig. 1.3–1. Points a and b represent the centers of two molecules a and b. The dotted line through a indicates the axis of the dipole and the cylindrically symmetric quadrupole of molecule a, and the dotted line through b indicates the similar axis in the second molecule. The intermolecular distance is r, and the angles θ_a, θ_b, ϕ_a, ϕ_b serve to define the orientations of the two molecules.

A rather complete discussion of the interactions of complex charge distributions is given in § 12.1. The above formulae are derived from the general results given in that section and are used in many places throughout this book.

The angular dependence of the above expressions is somewhat complicated. For a given value of the intermolecular separation, there are relative orientations of the molecules for which the potential energy is a maximum, $(\varphi_{ab})_{max}$, or a minimum, $(\varphi_{ab})_{min}$. It is sometimes useful to use effective spherically symmetrical potential functions[8] defined by

$$\bar{\varphi}_{ab} = \frac{\iint \varphi_{ab} \exp(-\varphi_{ab}/kT)\, d\omega_a\, d\omega_b}{\iint \exp(-\varphi_{ab}/kT)\, d\omega_a\, d\omega_b} \tag{1.3-11}$$

where $d\omega = \sin\theta\, d\theta\, d\phi$. That is, we hold r_{ab} fixed and average φ_{ab} over all angles. In this averaging process the Boltzmann weighting factor $\exp(-\varphi_{ab}/kT)$ is included in order to take into account the fact that statistically the molecules spend more time in those orientations for which the energy is small. Physically the use of this effective potential corresponds to the assumption that r_{ab} does not change appreciably as the molecule undergoes a rotation. For small separations or low temperatures, where $(\varphi_{ab})_{max} - (\varphi_{ab})_{min} \gg kT$, the molecules oscillate about the orientation of minimum energy so that φ_{ab} becomes nearly equal to $(\varphi_{ab})_{min}$. For large separations, where $(\varphi_{ab})_{max} - (\varphi_{ab})_{min} \ll kT$, the Boltzmann weighting factor may be expanded in powers of $1/kT$, and we obtain (see § 13.5)

$$\bar{\varphi}_{ab}^{(C,C)} = +\frac{C_a C_b}{r} \tag{1.3-12}$$

$$\bar{\varphi}_{ab}^{(C,\mu)} = -\frac{1}{3kT}\frac{C_a^2 \mu_b^2}{r^4} \tag{1.3-13}$$

$$\bar{\varphi}_{ab}^{(C,Q)} = -\frac{1}{20kT}\frac{C_a^2 Q_b^2}{r^6} \tag{1.3-14}$$

$$\bar{\varphi}_{ab}^{(\mu,\mu)} = -\frac{2}{3kT}\frac{\mu_a^2 \mu_b^2}{r^6} \tag{1.3-15}$$

$$\bar{\varphi}_{ab}^{(\mu,Q)} = -\frac{1}{kT}\frac{\mu_a^2 Q_b^2}{r^8} \tag{1.3-16}$$

$$\bar{\varphi}_{ab}^{(Q,Q)} = -\frac{7}{40kT}\frac{Q_a^2 Q_b^2}{r^{10}} \tag{1.3-17}$$

It should be noted that these averaged potential functions (except $\bar{\varphi}_{ab}^{(C,C)}$) are dependent on the temperature.

[8] The concept of the statistical average, φ_{ab}, is due to W. H. Keesom [*Physik. Z.*, **22**, 129 (1921)], and this average interaction between two dipoles or multipoles is known as the *Keesom alignment energy*. This alignment energy between two quadrupoles was suggested by Keesom as a possible explanation of the long-range attractive forces between non-polar molecules. This effect, however, is negligible in comparison with the London dispersion forces.

ii. *Induction Contributions*

When a charged particle (for example, an ion) interacts with a neutral molecule, the charged particle a induces in the neutral molecule b a dipole moment as shown in Fig. 1.3–2. If the polarizability of molecule b is

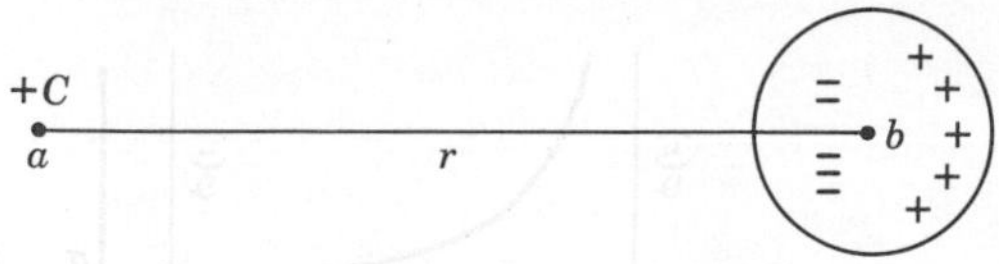

Fig. 1.3–2. Interaction of a charge a with the induced dipole of a neutral molecule b.

α_b, the dipole moment induced in molecule b is $C_a\alpha_b/r^2$, and the energy of interaction between the charge and this induced moment is (see § 13.5)

$$\varphi_{ab}^{(C,\ \mathrm{ind}\ \mu)} = -\frac{C_a^{\,2}\alpha_b}{2r^4} \tag{1.3–18}$$

Similarly it may be shown that the potential energy of the interaction between a point dipole and an induced dipole produced in a neutral molecule is

$$\varphi_{ab}^{(\mu,\ \mathrm{ind}\ \mu)} = -\frac{\mu_a^{\,2}\alpha_b(3\cos^2\theta_a + 1)}{2r^6} \tag{1.3–19}$$

This is an important contribution to the potential of interaction between a polar and non-polar molecule. This latter expression may be averaged over the angles as described previously, and the result is

$$\bar{\varphi}_{ab}^{(\mu,\ \mathrm{ind}\ \mu)} = -\frac{\mu_a^{\,2}\alpha_b}{r^6} \tag{1.3–20}$$

The subject of induction forces is discussed in detail in § 13.5.

iii. *Dispersion Contributions*[9]

When two non-polar molecules interact[10] there are long-range forces of attraction between them. The quantum mechanical theory of these

[9] These forces are referred to as dispersion forces since they may be expressed in terms of quantities called *oscillator strengths* which appear in the theory of the dispersion of light. (See §§ 12.5, 12.6, 13.3.)

[10] P. Debye [*Physik. Z.*, **21**, 178 (1920)] suggested that the attraction of two non-polar molecules might be accounted for by considering the fact that the quadrupole moment of one molecule induces a dipole in the other molecule. This quadrupole-induced-dipole interaction corresponds to a potential energy which varies as the inverse eighth power of the intermolecular separation. However, it has been found that this interaction energy accounts for only a negligibly small fraction of the observed energy. H. Falkenhagen [*Physik. Z.*, **23**, 87 (1922)] applied the induction effect to dipole gases where it is appreciable.

forces is discussed in § 13.3. At any instant the electrons in molecule *a* are in some configuration which results in an instantaneous dipole moment. This instantaneous dipole moment induces a dipole in molecule *b*. The induced dipole in *b* then interacts with the instantaneous dipole in *a* to produce an energy of attraction between the two molecules regard-

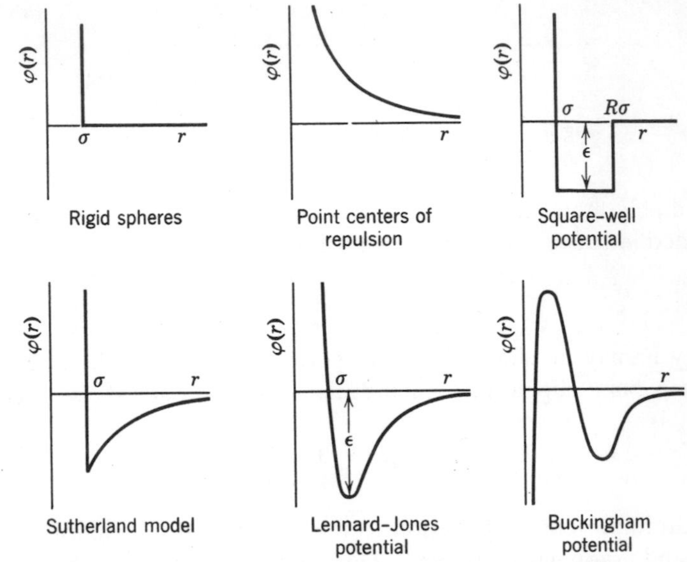

Fig. 1.3–3. Pictorial representation of some spherically symmetrical empirical potential functions. These are the most important spherically symmetrical potential functions used in this book. The analytical expressions for potentials are given in Eqs. 1.3–22 to 1.3–28.

less of the orientation of the instantaneous dipole. London developed this notion on a quantum mechanical basis and found this interaction (often called induced-dipole–induced-dipole interaction) is given approximately by[11]

$$\varphi_{ab}^{(\text{dis},\,6)} = -\frac{3}{2}\left(\frac{h\nu_a h\nu_b}{h\nu_a + h\nu_b}\right)\frac{\alpha_a\alpha_b}{r^6} \qquad (1.3\text{–}21)$$

in which $h\nu_a$ and $h\nu_b$ are characteristic energies of the two molecules approximately equal to their ionization potentials. It may be shown that there are further terms in the dispersion energy $\varphi^{(\text{dis},\,8)}$, $\varphi^{(\text{dis},\,10)}$, etc., which vary as r^{-8} (induced-dipole–induced-quadrupole), r^{-10} (induced-quadrupole–induced-quadrupole), etc.

[11] This result is applicable only to spherical molecules. The dispersion forces between long molecules are considerably different from this; such forces are discussed in § 13.4.

c. Empirical intermolecular potential functions

In selecting the form for an intermolecular potential to use in calculations of the various properties, we must consider two factors: the degree of realism desired and the numerical difficulties associated with the manipulation of the function. We here tabulate the potential functions which are used in this text, indicating what properties have been calculated using them. Virial and Joule-Thomson coefficient calculations are described in Chapter 3 (classical calculations) and in Chapter 6 (quantum calculations). Transport property calculations are given in Chapter 8 (classical theory) and in Chapter 10 (quantum theory). Pictorial illustrations of various potential functions are given in Fig. 1.3–3.

ANGLE–INDEPENDENT POTENTIALS

i. *Rigid Impenetrable Spheres*

$$\begin{aligned} \varphi(r) &= \infty \qquad r < \sigma \\ \varphi(r) &= 0 \qquad r > \sigma \end{aligned} \tag{1.3–22}$$

This potential function represents rigid impenetrable spheres of diameter σ. This model, which is frequently used for exploratory calculations because of its simplicity, gives a crude representation of the strong, short-range repulsive forces (that is, that the molecules have volume). For this potential the first five virial coefficients and the transport coefficients have been calculated classically (and some of these quantum mechanically).

ii. *Point Centers of Repulsion*

$$\varphi(r) = dr^{-\delta} \tag{1.3–23}$$

δ is called the index of repulsion, and for most molecules it has a value between 9 and 15. (When $\delta = 4$, the molecules are known as Maxwellian molecules.) This function is useful in exploratory calculations in which a differentiable potential function is needed. It also has the advantage that the angle of deflection is expressible in terms of a single variable. The second virial coefficient and the transport coefficients for this potential have been calculated in classical and quantum theory.

iii. *The Square Well*

$$\begin{aligned} \varphi(r) &= \infty \qquad r < \sigma \\ \varphi(r) &= -\epsilon \qquad \sigma < r < R\sigma \\ \varphi(r) &= 0 \qquad r > R\sigma \end{aligned} \tag{1.3–24}$$

This model represents rigid spheres of diameter σ surrounded by an attractive core of strength ϵ which extends to separations $R\sigma$. Thus, the ideas of attractive and repulsive forces are taken into account in a crude fashion. This model is useful for exploratory calculations and sometimes gives good agreement for complex molecules since there are three adjustable parameters. The second and third virial coefficients and the transport properties have been calculated for the square-well potential.

iv. *The Sutherland Model*

$$\begin{aligned} \varphi(r) &= \infty & r &< \sigma \\ \varphi(r) &= -cr^{-\gamma} & r &> \sigma \end{aligned} \tag{1.3–25}$$

This potential represents rigid spheres of diameter σ which attract one another according to an inverse power law. This is a fairly realistic model and reasonably easy to handle. The second virial coefficient and the transport properties have been calculated for this function.

v. *Lennard-Jones Potential*

$$\varphi(r) = \frac{d}{r^\delta} - \frac{c}{r^\gamma} \tag{1.3–26}$$

The term d/r^δ represents the repulsive energy, and the term $-c/r^\gamma$ the attractive energy. In this book, we use the following special form of this potential:

$$\varphi(r) = 4\epsilon[(\sigma/r)^{12} - (\sigma/r)^6] \tag{1.3–27}$$

which is frequently referred to as the Lennard-Jones (6-12) potential. σ is that value of r for which $\varphi(r) = 0$. ϵ is the maximum energy of attraction (or depth of the potential well) which occurs at $r = 2^{1/6}\sigma$. The inverse sixth-power attraction represents faithfully the induced-dipole–induced-dipole interaction. The repulsive contribution to the potential function is approximated by an inverse power term. The choice of 12 as the index of repulsion is primarily one of mathematical convenience, and is by no means unique; for some substances, other indices seem to be more desirable. This function gives a fairly simple and realistic representation for spherical non-polar molecules. Many calculations have been made for this potential function—the second and third virial coefficients and the transport properties in classical theory and extensive calculation of quantum effects.

vi. *Buckingham Potential*

$$\varphi(r) = b \exp(-ar) - cr^{-6} - c'r^{-8} \tag{1.3–28}$$

This four-parameter function includes the induced-dipole–induced-dipole interaction, the induced-dipole–induced-quadrupole interaction, and approximates the repulsive contribution to the potential by an exponential term. Thus, it is somewhat more realistic than the Lennard-Jones model, but more difficult to handle numerically. Some equation of state calculations have been made for this potential, but it has not been used for making transport property calculations. This potential is unrealistic in that it goes to $-\infty$ at the origin. For some properties this region of the potential is unimportant.

vii. *Buckingham-Corner Potential*

$$\varphi(r) = b \exp\left[-\alpha(r/r_m)\right] - (cr^{-6} + c'r^{-8}) \exp\left[-4\left(\frac{r_m}{r} - 1\right)^3\right] \qquad r \leqslant r_m$$

$$\varphi(r) = b \exp\left[-\alpha(r/r_m)\right] - (cr^{-6} + c'r^{-8}) \qquad r \geqslant r_m \qquad (1.3\text{–}29)$$

where $b = [-\epsilon + (1 + \beta)cr_m^{-6}] \exp \alpha$

$$c = \epsilon\alpha r_m^{6}/[\alpha(1 + \beta) - 6 - 8\beta]$$

$$c' = \beta r_m^{2} c$$

This is a four-parameter potential function in which ϵ is the depth of the potential at the minimum; r_m is the value of r for the energy-minimum; α is the steepness of the exponential repulsion and is usually about 13.5; $\beta = c'r_m^{-8}/cr_m^{-6}$ is the ratio of the inverse eighth-power to the inverse sixth-power contributions at the potential minimum.

This potential function includes the induced-dipole–induced-dipole and the induced-dipole–induced-quadrupole interaction and has an exponential-type repulsion. (The added complexity has been introduced mainly to eliminate the unrealistic behavior of the simple Buckingham potential in the region of the origin.) With four adjustable constants, it should be possible to get good comparisons with experiment; the functional form of the potential is rather complicated for numerical work, however. The second virial coefficient and its first quantum correction have been computed for this model.

viii. *Modified Buckingham (6-Exp) Potential*

$$\varphi(r) = \frac{\epsilon}{1 - \dfrac{6}{\alpha}}\left[\frac{6}{\alpha}\exp\left(\alpha\left[1 - \frac{r}{r_m}\right]\right) - \left(\frac{r_m}{r}\right)^6\right] \qquad r \geqslant r_{max} \qquad (1.3\text{–}30)$$

$$\varphi(r) = \infty \qquad r \leqslant r_{max}$$

where r_{max} is the value of r for which $\varphi(r)$, as given by the upper relation, has a (spurious) maximum. The ratio r_{max}/r_m is given by the smallest root of the transcendental equation,

$$\left(\frac{r_{max}}{r_m}\right)^7 \exp\left(\alpha\left[1 - \frac{r_{max}}{r_m}\right]\right) = 1 \qquad (1.3\text{–}31)$$

This is a three constant potential with the parameters ϵ, r_m, and α having the same significance as in the Buckingham-Corner potential. Tables are given for both the second virial coefficient and the collision integrals using this potential.

The modified Buckingham (6-exp) potential is somewhat more flexible than the Lennard-Jones (6–12) potential since it permits the variation of the low velocity collision diameter, σ, as compared to the separation at the minimum, r_m. (For the Lennard-Jones (6-12), $\sigma/r_m = 0.8909$.) The energy at the spurious maximum, $\varphi(r_{max})$, is ordinarily sufficiently large that it leads to no difficulties. These considerations are apparent from a study of Table 1.3–1. The induced-dipole induced-quadrupole term is not included in the 6-exp potential since its effect can be very nearly duplicated by making a small change in the value of the parameter α.

TABLE 1.3–1

α	σ/r_m	r_{max}/r_m	$\varphi(r_{max})/\epsilon$
12.0	0.87610	0.30247	1705
12.5	0.87983	0.27304	3518
13.0	0.88320	0.24697	7110
13.5	0.88627	0.22382	14115
14.0	0.88910	0.20319	27585
14.5	0.89173	0.18476	53170
15.0	0.89417	0.16825	101222

Angle–Dependent Potentials

ix. *Rigid Ellipsoids of Revolution*

This model represents rigid impenetrable ellipsoids of revolution. It may be used for studying the effect of non-spherical potential fields on physical properties. Prolate ellipsoids represent elongated molecules, and oblate ellipsoids represent flat (pancake-like) molecules. The second virial coefficient has been calculated for this model, and some work has been done on the kinetic theory of ellipsoidal molecules.

x. *Spherocylindrical Molecules* (Kihara)

In this model long molecules are represented by cylinders, capped on each end by hemispheres. The second virial coefficient has been calculated for such molecules.

xi. *Rigid Spheres Containing a Point Dipole* (Keesom)

$$\varphi(r, \theta_a, \theta_b, \phi_b - \phi_a) = \infty \qquad r < \sigma$$

$$\varphi(r, \theta_a, \theta_b, \phi_b - \phi_a) = -\frac{\mu_a\mu_b}{r^3} g(\theta_a, \theta_b, \phi_b - \phi_a) \qquad r > \sigma \tag{1.3–32}$$

where

$$g(\theta_a, \theta_b, \phi_b - \phi_a) = 2\cos\theta_a \cos\theta_b - \sin\theta_a \sin\theta_b \cos(\phi_b - \phi_a)$$

This model represents rigid impenetrable spheres of diameter σ which contain an embedded point dipole of strength μ. This potential function includes the short range repulsive forces and the dipole-dipole interaction. It is useful for exploratory calculations. Second virial coefficients have been calculated for this model.

xii. *Stockmayer Potential*

$$\varphi(r, \theta_a, \theta_b, \phi_b - \phi_a) = 4\epsilon\left[\left(\frac{\sigma}{r}\right)^{12} - \left(\frac{\sigma}{r}\right)^{6}\right] - \frac{\mu_a\mu_b}{r^3} g(\theta_a, \theta_b, \phi_b - \phi_a) \tag{1.3–33}$$

in which $g(\theta_a, \theta_b, \phi_b - \phi_a)$ is the angular dependence of the dipole-dipole interaction of Eq. 1.3–32. This potential function is a superposition of a Lennard-Jones (6–12) potential and the interaction of two point dipoles. It describes well the interaction between those polar molecules for which dipole-quadrupole and higher multipole interactions are not important. The second and third virial coefficients have been computed for this model. No transport property calculations are available for this potential function.

4. Classical Mechanics[1, 2, 3]

Both statistical mechanics and the kinetic theory of gases are direct applications of the laws of dynamics. Hence many of the discussions throughout this book are based upon the formal results given in this

[1] G. Joos, *Theoretical Physics*, Hafner (1932), Chapters 5 and 6.

[2] H. C. Corben and P. Stehle, *Classical Mechanics*, Wiley (1950).

[3] R. C. Tolman, *Principles of Statistical Mechanics*, Oxford University Press (1938), Chapters 2 and 3.

section. Classical mechanics is usually adequate to describe the motion of molecules except at very low temperatures, where quantum effects become important. Relativistic effects need not be considered for the phenomena which are discussed in this book. We begin the section with a description of the classical equations of motion. Finally, we discuss two theorems which are useful in statistical mechanics and kinetic theory—the Liouville theorem and the virial theorem.

a. Equations of motion in classical mechanics

The basis of classical mechanics is the celebrated set of Newton's laws. We shall here concern ourselves with the second of these laws, which states that[4]

$$\boldsymbol{F}_i = m_i \frac{d^2\boldsymbol{r}_i}{dt^2} \tag{1.4–1}$$

in which $\boldsymbol{F}_i$ is the force acting on the ith particle in the system, m_i and $\boldsymbol{r}_i$ are the mass and radius vector (in Cartesian coordinates) of the ith particle. In classical mechanics the complete dynamical behavior of a set of particles is determined by Newton's laws if the position $\boldsymbol{r}_i$ and velocity $\dot{\boldsymbol{r}}_i = d\boldsymbol{r}_i/dt$ of each particle are known at some initial time, t_0. In the treatment of certain dynamical systems and for the solution of certain formal problems it is convenient to use Newton's laws in one of the following forms.

i. *Lagrange's Equations*

Many problems are more conveniently formulated by using, as variables, angles or complicated functions of all the coordinates of the various particles in place of the Cartesian coordinates of the individual particles. These new coordinates are called *generalized coordinates*, $q_k(x_1, y_1, z_1, \ldots x_n, y_n, z_n)$, and they are usually defined as explicit functions of the original Cartesian coordinates.[5] The Lagrangian equations of motion are the Newtonian equations transformed to the generalized coordinate system.

[4] It is not necessary to write Newton's law in the form:

$$\boldsymbol{F}_i = \frac{d}{dt}\left(m_i \frac{d\boldsymbol{r}_i}{dt}\right)$$

since the masses of the individual particles remain invariant except for relativistic corrections.

[5] A simple example of a set of generalized coordinates is the set of spherical coordinates, r, θ, φ, which are frequently used in place of the Cartesian coordinates x, y, z, in problems involving spherical symmetry.

The *Lagrangian function*, $L(q_1, q_2, \ldots q_{3N}; \dot{q}_1, \dot{q}_2, \ldots \dot{q}_{3N})$, is defined by

$$L = K - \Phi \tag{1.4–2}$$

where Φ is the potential energy function[6] for the entire system, and K is the kinetic energy of the system. K is defined as

$$K = \tfrac{1}{2}\Sigma_i m_i \dot{\boldsymbol{r}}_i^{\,2} \tag{1.4–3}$$

the sum of the kinetic energies of the individual particles. In terms of the Lagrangian function, Newton's second law for conservative[7] systems may be written as

$$\frac{d}{dt}\left(\frac{\partial L}{\partial \dot{q}_k}\right) - \left(\frac{\partial L}{\partial q_k}\right) = 0 \tag{1.4–4}$$

These are *Lagrange's equations of motion*. The function $\partial L/\partial \dot{q}_k$ is known as the *generalized momentum*, p_k,

$$p_k = \frac{\partial L}{\partial \dot{q}_k} \tag{1.4–5}$$

It is easy to see that if the generalized coordinates are taken to be Cartesian coordinates, the generalized momenta reduce to ordinary linear momenta, and Lagrange's equations of motion reduce to Newton's equation of motion. If the new coordinates are cylindrical (ρ, z, ϕ), then p_ϕ is the usual angular momentum about the z-axis.[8] If the new coordinates are, say, Eulerian angles of a rigid body, the p_k are not easy to interpret.[9]

[6] In problems involving many molecules it is often assumed that $\Phi(\boldsymbol{r}^N) = \frac{1}{2}\sum_{i=1}^{N}\sum_{j=1}^{N}\varphi(r_{ij})$. This *assumption of additivity* or *assumption of two-body forces* is discussed in § 3.4a.

[7] A conservative system is one in which the forces depend only on the configuration of the system and are such that the following condition holds: When all of the particles except one are held fixed, the integral of the tangential component of the force on a single particle about any closed path of the single particle is zero. For this type of system the forces can be expressed in terms of a single potential function of the entire system, $\Phi(\boldsymbol{r}^N)$:

$$\boldsymbol{F}_i = -\frac{\partial}{\partial \boldsymbol{r}_i}\Phi$$

N being the number of particles in the system under consideration. For non-conservative systems, it is often possible to find a Lagrangian function such that Lagrange's equations of motion still apply. For example, this is the case for a charged particle moving in a magnetic field.

[8] A treatment of a particle in spherical coordinates is given by L. Pauling and E. B. Wilson, Jr., *Introduction to Quantum Mechanics*, McGraw-Hill (1935), p. 9.

[9] H. Margenau and G. M. Murphy, *Mathematics of Physics and Chemistry*, Van Nostrand (Second Edition, 1956), p. 282.

Lagrange's equations, like Newton's equations, are second-order differential equations; a solution of these equations is specified by a complete set of coordinates and velocities, at a particular time.

ii. *Hamilton's Equations*

The *Hamiltonian function* of a system, $H(q_1, \cdots q_{3N}; p_1, \cdots p_{3N})$, is defined by the relation:

$$H(q_1 \cdots q_{3N}; p_1 \cdots p_{3N}) = \Sigma_i p_i \dot{q}_i - L \tag{1.4-6}$$

It is important to keep in mind that the Lagrangian is a function of the coordinates and their time derivatives whereas the Hamiltonian is a function of the coordinates and their conjugate momenta. In the above expression for the Hamiltonian the $\dot{q}_k$ appear both explicitly and implicitly (in the Lagrangian), but Eq. 1.4–5 may be solved to give $\dot{q}_k = \dot{q}_k(q_i, p_i)$. Keeping these facts in mind, one may differentiate Eq. 1.4–6 with respect to p_i and q_i to get

$$\frac{\partial H}{\partial p_i} = \dot{q}_i + \Sigma_j p_j \frac{\partial \dot{q}_j}{\partial p_i} - \Sigma_j \frac{\partial \dot{q}_j}{\partial p_i} \frac{\partial L}{\partial \dot{q}_j} \tag{1.4-7}$$

$$\frac{\partial H}{\partial q_i} = \Sigma_j p_j \frac{\partial \dot{q}_j}{\partial q_i} - \frac{\partial L}{\partial q_i} - \Sigma_j \frac{\partial L}{\partial \dot{q}_j} \frac{\partial \dot{q}_j}{\partial q_i} \tag{1.4-8}$$

These relations may be simplified, using Lagrange's equations (Eq. 1.4–4) and the definition of conjugate momenta (Eq. 1.4–5), to give

$$\frac{\partial H}{\partial p_i} = \dot{q}_i \tag{1.4-9}$$

$$\frac{\partial H}{\partial q_i} = -\dot{p}_i \tag{1.4-10}$$

These are *Hamilton's (canonical) equations of motion.* The $3N$ second-order differential equations of Newton or Lagrange have thus been transformed into $6N$ first-order differential equations.

It may easily be shown that the Hamiltonian of a system is numerically equal to the total energy. From the definition of the Hamiltonian in Eq. 1.4–6 and that of the conjugate momenta in Eq. 1.4–5:

$$H = \Sigma_i \dot{q}_i \frac{\partial L}{\partial \dot{q}_i} - L = \Sigma_i \dot{q}_i \frac{\partial K}{\partial \dot{q}_i} - L \tag{1.4-11}$$

the second form being possible since the potential energy is not a function of the velocities. Since K is a homogeneous function of order two in the velocities, it follows from Euler's theorem[10] that

$$\sum_i \dot{q}_i \frac{\partial K}{\partial \dot{q}_i} = 2K \tag{1.4–12}$$

Thus:

$$H = 2K - L = 2K - (K - \Phi) = K + \Phi \tag{1.4–13}$$

and along a dynamical path the Hamiltonian function is equal to a constant, E, the energy. It should be kept in mind that this is true only for conservative systems.

iii. *The Hamilton-Jacobi Equation*

It is possible to define a function, $S(q_1, q_2, \cdots q_{3N})$:

$$S(q_1, q_2, \cdots q_{3N}) = 2\int K\, dt \tag{1.4–14}$$

Integral over the dynamical path

which is that part of the *action*[11] which does not contain time explicitly. This function bears the following relation to the generalized coordinates and momenta:

$$p_i = \frac{\partial S}{\partial q_i} \tag{1.4–15}$$

Substituting this expression for p_i in the Hamiltonian, we obtain the *Hamilton-Jacobi equation,*

$$H\left(q_1, q_2, \cdots q_{3N};\ \frac{\partial S}{\partial q_1}, \frac{\partial S}{\partial q_2}, \cdots \frac{\partial S}{\partial q_{3N}}\right) = E \tag{1.4–16}$$

This equation is of interest because of its strong resemblance to the Schrödinger equation of quantum mechanics.

[10] Euler's theorem states: If $u(x_1, x_2, \ldots x_n)$ is homogeneous of degree m and has continuous first partial derivatives, then:

$$\Sigma_i x_i(\partial u/\partial x_i) = mu$$

See, for example, I. S. and E. S. Sokolnikoff, *Higher Mathematics for Engineers and Physicists*, McGraw-Hill (1941).

[11] "Action" is defined as

$$W(t) = \int_0^t L\, dt = \int_0^t 2K\, dt - Et.$$

The natural motion of a system is characterized by the fact that the "action" has a minimum value. This is known as "Hamilton's principle of least action."

b. The Liouville equation

Let us think of all the N particles as forming a single mechanical system. The concept of *phase space* can be employed to picture the changing state of the system. Phase space is the Cartesian space of $6N$ dimensions, the coordinates of which are the $3N$ generalized configurational coordinates, q_i, and the $3N$ conjugate momenta, p_i. The dynamical state of a system is completely described by a point in phase space. Since the past and future history of a system is determined by its present state, a point in this space uniquely determines a trajectory. In time, the representative point of a system traces out the trajectory in phase space. This motion is referred to as the natural motion of the phase point and is described by Hamilton's canonical equations.

Consider now a property of the system, $F = F(q_i, p_i, t)$, which depends upon the dynamical state of the system and in general explicitly on time. Such properties may be constants of motion such as the total energy, total linear momentum, or total angular momentum of the system; or they may be properties which change with time, such as the energy, momentum, or position of a single particle in the system. The change of F with time following a point along a natural trajectory is then:

$$\frac{DF}{Dt} = \frac{\partial F}{\partial t} + \sum_i \left(\frac{\partial F}{\partial q_i} \dot{q}_i + \frac{\partial F}{\partial p_i} \dot{p}_i\right) \tag{1.4–17}$$

$$= \frac{\partial F}{\partial t} + \sum_i \left(\frac{\partial F}{\partial q_i}\frac{\partial H}{\partial p_i} - \frac{\partial F}{\partial p_i}\frac{\partial H}{\partial q_i}\right) \tag{1.4–18}$$

$$= \frac{\partial F}{\partial t} + [F, H] \tag{1.4–19}$$

In the second of these equations, Hamilton's canonical equations have been used, and the notation for the *Poisson bracket* has been introduced in the last equation. A constant of motion of the system is a function of the coordinates and momenta which is constant along each natural trajectory in phase space. Thus a constant of motion, α, has the property that

$$[\alpha, H] = 0 \tag{1.4–20}$$

These concepts are of importance in the postulational development of quantum mechanics and are used in the formal development of statistical mechanics.

If we consider a large collection of non-interacting systems which differ from each other only in their initial conditions, the state of the entire collection of systems is described by a set of points. For a sufficiently large number of systems, the set of representative points can be represented by a continuous *distribution function*,[12] $\rho\,(q_i, p_i, t)$, which is usually termed the *density in phase space*. The choice of the density function is arbitrary at the initial time, but is fixed at any subsequent time by the equations of motion. Since there are no "sources" or "sinks" of phase points, the distribution function satisfies a generalization of the ordinary equation of continuity:

$$\frac{\partial \rho}{\partial t} + \sum_i \left(\frac{\partial}{\partial q_i} (\dot{q}_i \rho) + \frac{\partial}{\partial p_i} (\dot{p}_i \rho) \right) = 0 \tag{1.4–21}$$

Then using Hamilton's canonical equations and the definition of the Poisson bracket, we obtain the *Liouville equation*:

$$\frac{D\rho}{Dt} = \frac{\partial \rho}{\partial t} + [\rho, H] = 0 \tag{1.4–22}$$

This result plays an important role in the development of statistical mechanics; more is said about its application in Chapter 2.

c. The virial theorem

The virial theorem of Clausius establishes a ratio of the average kinetic to the average potential energy of a mechanical system. The theorem is valid in quantum as well as in classical mechanics. It is a powerful tool in the determination of intermolecular forces, and it is used directly in the development of the equation of state.

In classical mechanics,[13, 14] a particle of mass, m_i, acted upon by a force, $\boldsymbol{F}_i$, moves in the x-direction in accordance with Newton's equation:

$$(F_i)_x = m_i \frac{d^2 x_i}{dt^2} \tag{1.4–23}$$

Multiplying both sides of this equation by $x_i/2$ and rearranging, we obtain

$$\begin{aligned} \tfrac{1}{2} x_i (F_i)_x &= \tfrac{1}{2} m_i x_i \frac{d^2 x_i}{dt^2} \\ &= -\tfrac{1}{2} m_i \left(\frac{dx_i}{dt} \right)^2 + \frac{1}{2} \frac{d}{dt} \left(m_i x_i \frac{dx_i}{dt} \right) \end{aligned} \tag{1.4–24}$$

[12] For a more rigorous development of Liouville's equation, the reader is referred to A. I. Khinchin, *Statistical Mechanics*, Dover (1949).

[13] E. H. Kennard, *Kinetic Theory of Gases*, McGraw-Hill (1938), p. 235.

[14] R. C. Tolman, *Statistical Mechanics*, Chemical Catalog Co. (1927), p. 63.

The last term averaged over a sufficiently long time interval, τ, vanishes:

$$\overline{\frac{1}{2}\frac{d}{dt}\left(m_i x_i \frac{dx_i}{dt}\right)} = \frac{1}{\tau}\int_0^\tau \frac{d}{dt}\left(\tfrac{1}{2}m_i x_i \frac{dx_i}{dt}\right) dt$$

$$= \frac{m_i}{2\tau}\left[\left(x_i \frac{dx_i}{dt}\right)_{t=\tau} - \left(x_i \frac{dx_i}{dt}\right)_{t=0}\right]$$

$$= 0 \text{ as } \tau \to \infty \tag{1.4–25}$$

since $x_i(dx_i/dt)$ remains bounded (provided the particle is confined to a region of space) whereas τ becomes arbitrarily large. Hence, the time average of Eq. 1.4–24 becomes

$$-\tfrac{1}{2}\overline{x_i(F_i)_x} = \tfrac{1}{2}m_i \overline{\left(\frac{dx_i}{dt}\right)^2} \tag{1.4–26}$$

Similar equations can be obtained for the motion in the y- and z-directions. Adding together the three equations of the form of Eq. 1.4–26, we get

$$\Xi_i \equiv -\tfrac{1}{2}\overline{(\boldsymbol{r}_i \cdot \boldsymbol{F}_i)} = \bar{K}_i \tag{1.4–27}$$

in which $\bar{K}_i$ is the mean value of the kinetic energy of the particle. The quantity on the left side of the equation, $\Xi_i = -\tfrac{1}{2}\overline{(\boldsymbol{r}_i \cdot \boldsymbol{F}_i)}$, was called by Clausius the *virial of the force*. Since this equation holds for any particle, it clearly applies also to any system of particles:

$$\Xi \equiv -\tfrac{1}{2}\Sigma_i\overline{(\boldsymbol{r}_i \cdot \boldsymbol{F}_i)} = \bar{K} \tag{1.4–28}$$

in which $\bar{K} = \Sigma_i \bar{K}_i$ is the total average kinetic energy, and $\Xi = \Sigma_i \Xi_i$ is the total virial of the system.

When conservative systems are under consideration, the virial theorem may be written in terms of the potential energies. If, in particular, the potential is a homogeneous function of the coordinates of degree n, the virial of the forces becomes

$$-\tfrac{1}{2}\Sigma_i\overline{(\boldsymbol{r}_i \cdot \boldsymbol{F}_i)} = +\tfrac{1}{2}\Sigma_i \overline{\left(\boldsymbol{r}_i \cdot \frac{\partial}{\partial \boldsymbol{r}_i}\Phi(\boldsymbol{r}^N)\right)} = \tfrac{1}{2}n\bar{\Phi} \tag{1.4–29}$$

where use has been made of Euler's theorem.[15] The virial theorem then becomes

$$\tfrac{1}{2}n\bar{\Phi} = \bar{K} \tag{1.4–30}$$

[15] See footnote to Eq. 1.4–12 for statement of Euler's theorem.

There are two especially important examples of potentials of this type:

(1) *Simple Harmonic Oscillator*: $\varphi = \frac{1}{2}kx^2$, $n = 2$, and $\overline{\Phi} = \overline{K}$. This is the only case in which energy is equally partitioned between kinetic and potential.

(2) *Coulombic Interaction*:[16] $\varphi = e^2/r$, $n = -1$, and $\overline{\Phi} = -2\overline{K}$.

For molecules obeying the Lennard-Jones interaction potential, $\Phi = -\Phi_a + \Phi_r$, where $\Phi_a = 4\epsilon \sum_{i>j} (\sigma_{ij}/r_{ij})^6$ and $\Phi_r = 4\epsilon \sum_{i>j} (\sigma_{ij}/r_{ij})^{12}$ and the virial theorem states that $3\overline{\Phi}_a - 6\overline{\Phi}_r = \overline{K}$.

In the last section of this chapter, the virial theorem is derived in quantum mechanics. In Chapter 3, the classical virial theorem is used in the derivation of the virial equation of state.

5. Molecular Collisions in Classical Mechanics (Monatomic Molecules)

It has been mentioned that the rigorous development of kinetic theory depends on the exact nature of the collision process which occurs when two monatomic molecules interact with one another. In this section we present an analysis of adiabatic collisions between two particles whose interaction potential is a function solely of the distance between them.[1] We first discuss those properties of an encounter which involve the motion of the system of two particles as a whole; this discussion does not require any detailed description of the motion of the individual particles. Then the trajectories of the individual molecules are discussed, and an expression for the angle of deflection is derived. The angle of deflection is the only property of the collision which enters into the computation of the transport phenomena.

a. Summational invariants of an encounter

Let us consider the colliding system to be composed of two molecules, one of the species i with mass m_i, and the other of species j with mass m_j. The two particles exert a force upon one another which depends solely on the distance between them. Let the velocity of the molecules before a collision takes place (that is, before the interaction between the colliding

[16] This special case has been considered in detail by W. Schottky, *Physik. Z.*, **21**, 232 (1920).

[1] For each electronic state, k, of the system of two colliding molecules there is a separate potential energy function, $\varphi_k(r)$. An adiabatic collision is one in which the electronic state does not change during the course of the collision. A non-adiabatic collision is one in which the system starts in the state k with the potential $\varphi_k(r)$ and ends up in another electronic state with another potential function. Such non-adiabatic collisions occur between molecules in excited states or in very fast collisions. This problem is discussed in § 13.1.

molecules becomes appreciable) be $\mathbf{v}_i$ and $\mathbf{v}_j$, respectively. We denote the corresponding velocities after the collision by $\mathbf{v}_i'$ and $\mathbf{v}_j'$. The laws of conservation of mass, linear momentum, and energy of the system as a whole define quantities known as *summational invariants*, which are of use in the derivations in Chapter 7.

If no chemical reaction takes place when molecules i and j collide, then certainly at any time during the collision the masses of the individual particles remain unaltered. Specifically this is true before and after the collision, so that we may write:

$$m_i = m_i' \qquad m_j = m_j' \tag{1.5–1}$$

Thus:

$$m_i + m_j = m_i' + m_j' \tag{1.5–2}$$

These are statements of the law of *conservation of mass* for the individual particles and for the system as a whole.

If the colliding system as a whole is under the action of no external force, Newton's second law may be integrated once with respect to time to show that the linear momentum of the system is a constant. This means that at any time during the collision the sum of the momenta of the individual particles is constant. Specifically, since this is true both before and after a collision takes place, we may write

$$m_i\mathbf{v}_i + m_j\mathbf{v}_j = m_i\mathbf{v}_i' + m_j\mathbf{v}_j' \tag{1.5–3}$$

This is a statement of the *conservation of linear momentum* of the system as a whole.

If the colliding system is not acted upon by external forces, the total energy remains constant. Hence, at any time during the collision, the sum of the kinetic energies of the colliding particles plus the energy due to the interaction is a constant value. Before and after the collision takes place, the energy of the system is simply equal to the sum of the kinetic energies of the individual particles. Hence, we may write

$$\tfrac{1}{2}m_iv_i^2 + \tfrac{1}{2}m_jv_j^2 = \tfrac{1}{2}m_iv_i'^2 + \tfrac{1}{2}m_jv_j'^2 \tag{1.5–4}$$

as a statement of the law of *conservation of kinetic energy* of the system.

Each of the above relations which state the application of the conservation laws to the colliding system is of the form

$$\psi_i + \psi_j = \psi_i' + \psi_j' \tag{1.5–5}$$

where ψ_i is successively m_i, the components of $m_i\mathbf{v}_i$, and $\tfrac{1}{2}m_iv_i^2$. Furthermore, it can be shown that any function of velocities which satisfies Eq. 1.5–5 is a linear combination of these quantities. The quantities ψ_i are the *summational invariants*.

b. The trajectories of the individual particles during a collision

Let us now consider the dynamical problem of a collision between two particles in three dimensions. This is accomplished by first reducing the problem to a two-body problem in a plane, then to a one-body problem in a plane, and finally to a problem of the one-dimensional motion of a hypothetical single particle. With each successive reduction the description of the motion is correspondingly less precise. However, it is extremely convenient to sacrifice completeness of description for the sake of obtaining a simpler means of visualizing the problem. To construct in our imagination or on the printed page the trajectories of two colliding particles with an arbitrary interaction potential is somewhat difficult. The aim of this discussion is then to provide a better understanding of the collision processes in classical dynamics and to develop a formula for the "angle of deflection" which enters into the transport coefficient formulae of Chapters 7 and 8.

To begin the description of the dynamics of a collision, we write Newton's laws of motion for both the particles:

$$\boldsymbol{F}_i = m_i \frac{d^2\boldsymbol{r}_i}{dt^2} \tag{1.5–6}$$

$$-\boldsymbol{F}_i = \boldsymbol{F}_j = m_j \frac{d^2\boldsymbol{r}_j}{dt^2} \tag{1.5–7}$$

In these equations, $\boldsymbol{F}_i$ and $\boldsymbol{F}_j$ are the forces acting on molecules i and j, and $\boldsymbol{r}_i$ and $\boldsymbol{r}_j$ are the position vectors of the two molecules. Putting $\boldsymbol{F}_j = -\boldsymbol{F}_i$ in the second equation indicates that the only force acting on molecule i is that due to the presence of molecule j, and vice versa. If the first of these equations is multiplied by m_j and the second by m_i, and if the resulting equations are then subtracted, we obtain

$$\frac{d^2}{dt^2}(\boldsymbol{r}_i - \boldsymbol{r}_j) = \frac{\boldsymbol{F}_i}{\mu} \tag{1.5–8}$$

in which μ is the reduced mass of the pair of colliding molecules, defined by[2]

$$\frac{1}{\mu} = \frac{1}{m_i} + \frac{1}{m_j} \tag{1.5–9}$$

If a cross-product is formed with the vector $(\boldsymbol{r}_i - \boldsymbol{r}_j)$ on both sides of Eq. 1.5–8, the right-hand side vanishes (because the intermolecular force

[2] It should be noted that for colliding particles of the same mass, m, the reduced mass is $(m/2)$.

is assumed to be along the lines of centers[3] and the cross-product of collinear vectors is zero. Hence:

$$\left[(\boldsymbol{r}_i - \boldsymbol{r}_j) \times \frac{d^2}{dt^2}(\boldsymbol{r}_i - \boldsymbol{r}_j)\right] = 0 \tag{1.5–10}$$

This can also be written as

$$\frac{d}{dt}\left[(\boldsymbol{r}_i - \boldsymbol{r}_j) \times \frac{d}{dt}(\boldsymbol{r}_i - \boldsymbol{r}_j)\right] - \left[\frac{d}{dt}(\boldsymbol{r}_i - \boldsymbol{r}_j) \times \frac{d}{dt}(\boldsymbol{r}_i - \boldsymbol{r}_j)\right] = 0 \tag{1.5–11}$$

The second term is zero, since it is a cross-product of collinear vectors. The remaining term may be integrated with respect to time to give

$$\left[(\boldsymbol{r}_i - \boldsymbol{r}_j) \times \frac{d}{dt}(\boldsymbol{r}_i - \boldsymbol{r}_j)\right] = [(\boldsymbol{r}_i - \boldsymbol{r}_j) \times (\boldsymbol{v}_i - \boldsymbol{v}_j)] = \boldsymbol{K} \tag{1.5–12}$$

where $\boldsymbol{K}$ is a constant vector (independent of time) in a direction perpendicular to the plane formed by the vectors $(\boldsymbol{r}_i - \boldsymbol{r}_j)$ and $(\boldsymbol{v}_i - \boldsymbol{v}_j)$. At all times the two particles and the center of mass of the system lie in a plane normal to $\boldsymbol{K}$. A pictorial description of a two particle collision is presented in Fig. 1.5–1. This figure illustrates how the colliding particles are always located in a plane of unvarying orientation, moving with the constant velocity of the center of mass.

The fact that the collision takes place in this plane moving with the center of gravity of the system makes it possible to reduce the problem to a two-dimensional one. Pictorially, this is accomplished by collapsing the collection of planes in Fig. 1.5–1 onto a single plane. The result of this manipulation is shown in Fig. 1.5–2, where the entire encounter is shown. Analytically, essentially the same thing is done—we simply select a coordinate system moving with the center of gravity and with the z-axis pointing in the $\boldsymbol{K}$ direction. In addition, for convenience, the origin of coordinates may be taken at the center of mass of the system.

In the coordinate system which has just been described, the kinetic energy of the system of two particles, relative to the center of mass, can be written

$$K = \tfrac{1}{2}m_i(\dot{x}_i^2 + \dot{y}_i^2) + \tfrac{1}{2}m_j(\dot{x}_j^2 + \dot{y}_j^2) \tag{1.5–13}$$

[3] The force would not be along the line of centers for molecules with dipoles, for cigar-shaped molecules, or for molecules in excited states. The present analysis applies only to spherical nonpolar molecules whose interaction potential depends only on the separation.

This expression may be rewritten in terms of two variables, r and θ, where r is the intermolecular separation and θ is its angle of inclination to the positive x-axis (θ goes from 0 to 2π and r goes from 0 to ∞). Since

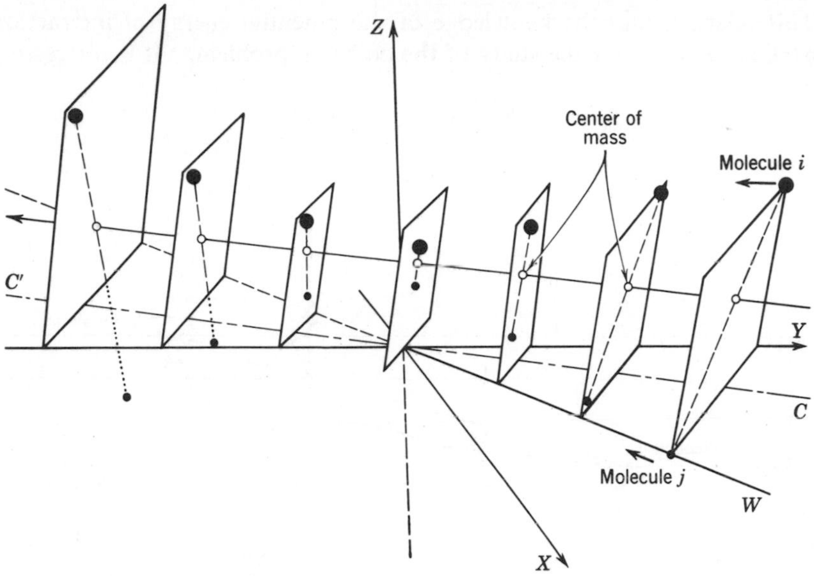

Fig. 1.5–1. Three-dimensional pictorial representation of a binary collision. Here one can see that the colliding particles are always located in a plane of unvarying orientation, moving with the constant velocity of the center of mass. The planes shown in the figure represent snapshots of the particles taken at equal intervals of time. Molecule i is moving initially with a velocity v_i in the negative y-direction. Molecule j is moving initially with a velocity v_j along line W in the XY-plane. The projection of the trajectory of the center of mass on the XY-plane is the line CC'. If we collapse all these planes onto one plane, the picture in Fig. 1.5–2 results.

the origin is the center of mass the coordinates x_i, y_i, x_j, y_j in terms of r and θ are

$$x_i = \frac{m_j}{m_i + m_j} r \cos \theta \tag{1.5–14}$$

$$y_i = \frac{m_j}{m_i + m_j} r \sin \theta \tag{1.5–15}$$

$$x_j = -\frac{m_i}{m_i + m_j} r \cos \theta \tag{1.5–16}$$

$$y_j = -\frac{m_i}{m_i + m_j} r \sin \theta \tag{1.5–17}$$

The substitution of these four relations into Eq. 1.5–13 gives, for the kinetic energy,

$$K = \tfrac{1}{2}\mu[\dot{r}^2 + r^2\dot{\theta}^2] \tag{1.5–18}$$

This relation, plus the knowledge of the potential energy of interaction $\varphi(r)$, is sufficient for the study of the collision problem. It is interesting

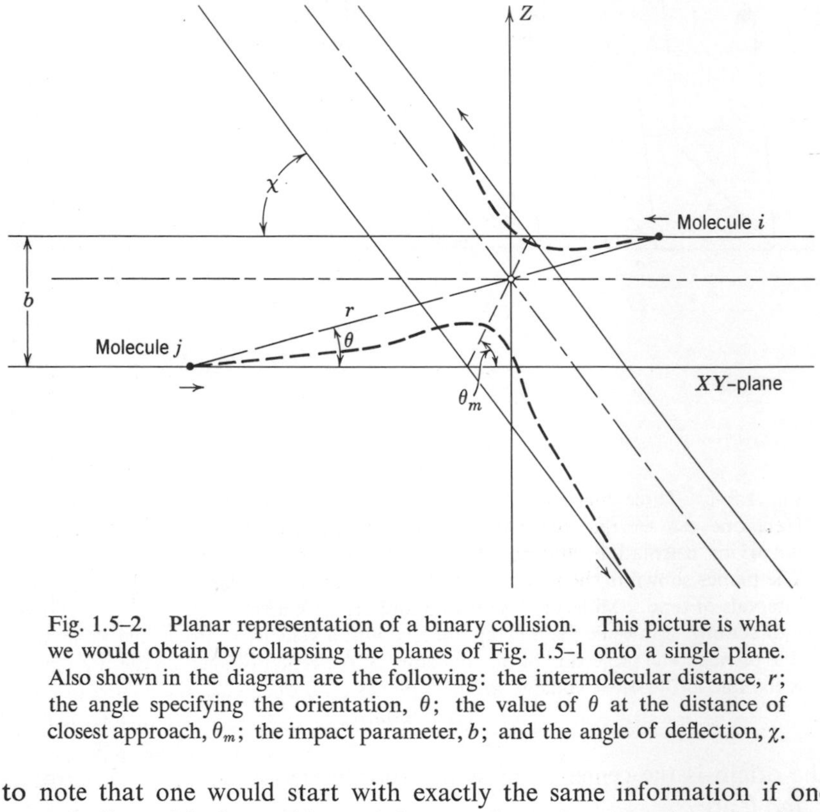

Fig. 1.5–2. Planar representation of a binary collision. This picture is what we would obtain by collapsing the planes of Fig. 1.5–1 onto a single plane. Also shown in the diagram are the following: the intermolecular distance, r; the angle specifying the orientation, θ; the value of θ at the distance of closest approach, θ_m; the impact parameter, b; and the angle of deflection, χ.

to note that one would start with exactly the same information if one were dealing with the problem of the two-dimensional motion of a single particle of mass, μ moving in the spherically symmetric potential field, $\varphi(r)$. For this reason, collision problems are frequently discussed in terms of the equivalent one-body problem. This two-dimensional one-body problem is pictured in Fig. 1.5–3.

To get the equations of motion for the equivalent one-body problem (and hence also for the two-body collision problem), one simply writes down the equations for the conservation of energy and angular momentum. This is accomplished by equating the angular momentum for r large with respect to the effective range of the potential to the angular momentum at any arbitrary point on the trajectory; a similar relation can be obtained in the same way for the energy. These two relations are

$$\mu b g = \mu r^2 \dot{\theta} \tag{1.5–19}$$

$$\tfrac{1}{2}\mu g^2 = \tfrac{1}{2}\mu(\dot{r}^2 + r^2\dot{\theta}^2) + \varphi(r) \tag{1.5–20}$$

In these equations, b, the *impact parameter*, is the distance of closest approach in the absence of the potential $\varphi(r)$; g is the *initial relative speed* of the colliding molecules. Equations 1.5–19 and 1.5–20 are the equations

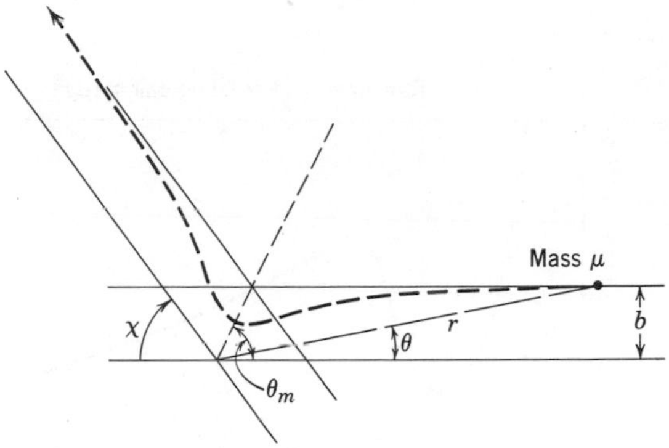

Fig. 1.5–3. Pictorial representation of equivalent one-body problem. In Fig. 1.5–2 was shown the planar representation of a collision between two particles. In this figure is shown the two-dimensional one-body problem which in all respects is dynamically equivalent to the collision problem. The quantities r, θ, θ_m, b, and χ are shown so that they can be compared with their significance in the two-body problem.

of motion for the system and give a complete dynamical description of the motion in terms of the interaction potential and the two parameters, b and g, which characterize the collision.

The graphical picture of the collision can be simplified onc step further. If the value of $\dot{\theta}$ from Eq. 1.5–19 is substituted into Eq. 1.5–20, we get the following relation for r as a function of time:

$$\tfrac{1}{2}\mu g^2 = \tfrac{1}{2}\mu\dot{r}^2 + \tfrac{1}{2}\mu g^2(b^2/r^2) + \varphi(r) \tag{1.5–21}$$

Since Eq. 1.5–21 contains no terms in θ, it can be regarded as describing a one-dimensional motion of a particle of mass μ with total energy $\tfrac{1}{2}\mu g^2$ moving in an *effective potential* field:

$$\varphi_{\text{eff}}(r) = \varphi(r) + \tfrac{1}{2}\mu g^2(b^2/r^2) \tag{1.5–22}$$

in which the term, $\frac{1}{2}\mu g^2(b^2/r^2)$ is called the *centrifugal potential.* A typical effective potential curve for a pair of interacting molecules is sketched in Fig. 1.5–4. At any point along the curve the effective potential energy and the kinetic energy of the system add up to the total energy, $\frac{1}{2}\mu g^2$. Of course, there is a whole family of $\varphi_{\text{eff}}(r)$-curves depending on the value of the product $\frac{1}{2}\mu g^2 b^2$.

c. The angle of deflection in a collision

The only feature of a collision which enters into the formulae for the transport coefficients is the *angle of deflection*—the angle, χ, between the

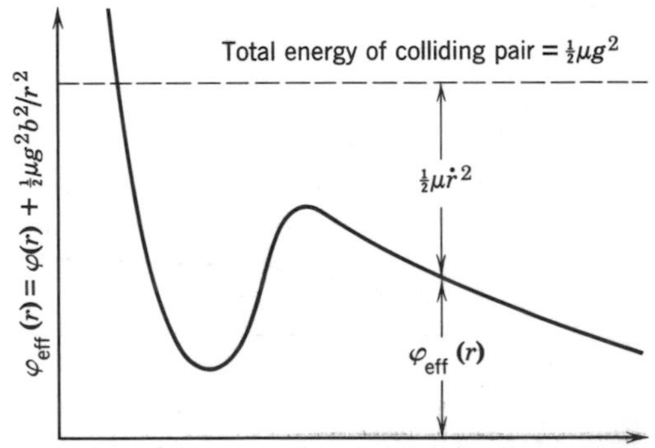

Fig. 1.5–4. Equivalent one-dimensional one-body problem. For purposes of analyzing the dynamics of collisions it is frequently convenient to study the effective potential curves of the equivalent one-body problem in one dimension. In Chapter 8 curves of this type are discussed in connection with the collisions of molecules which obey the Lennard-Jones potential.

relative velocity vectors of the two colliding particles before and after the collision. This angle is measured in the center-of-mass system of coordinates and is shown in Figs. 1.5–2 and 1.5–3. The angle χ is related simply to the angle θ_m by the relation

$$\chi = \pi - 2\theta_m \tag{1.5–23}$$

θ_m is defined as the value of the variable, θ, for which r (the intermolecular separation) has a minimum value. This minimum value is r_m, and is the *distance of closest approach.* In principle one could eliminate time from the equations of motion and get r as a function of θ—that is, the analytical description of the trajectory. Then setting $(dr/d\theta)$ equal to zero would give r_m and θ_m.

However, θ_m may be readily obtained in the following way: The derivative $(dr/d\theta)$ can be found, since r and θ as functions of time are known from Eqs. 1.5–21 and 1.5–19, respectively. Hence:

$$\frac{dr}{d\theta} = \frac{dr/dt}{d\theta/dt} = -\left(\frac{r^2}{b}\right)\sqrt{1 - \frac{\varphi(r)}{\frac{1}{2}\mu g^2} - \frac{b^2}{r^2}} \tag{1.5–24}$$

The minus sign arises from selecting the negative square root, in accordance with the fact that r decreases with increasing θ along the incoming trajectory. Then we may get θ_m by integrating Eq. 1.5–24:

$$\theta_m = \int_0^{\theta_m} d\theta = -\int_{\infty}^{r_m} \frac{(b/r^2)\,dr}{\sqrt{1-(\varphi(r)/\frac{1}{2}\mu g^2)-(b^2/r^2)}} \tag{1.5–25}$$

Combining this equation with Eq. 1.5–23, we obtain the final formula for the angle of deflection:

$$\chi(b, g) = \pi - 2b\int_{r_m}^{\infty} \frac{dr/r^2}{\sqrt{1-(\varphi(r)/\frac{1}{2}\mu g^2)-(b^2/r^2)}} \tag{1.5–26}$$

This is valid for any spherically symmetric interaction potential, $\varphi(r)$. The value of r_m is found by equating the expression for $(dr/d\theta)$ in Eq. 1.5–24 to zero.

A number of properties of dilute gases (wherein only two-body collisions are of importance) may be expressed in terms of this angle of deflection. For example, the viscosity, $\eta(T)$, and the second virial coefficient, $B(T)$, are given by

$$\frac{RT}{\eta(T)} = \tfrac{4}{5}N\sqrt{\pi}\int_0^{\infty} e^{-\gamma^2}\gamma^7\left[\int_0^{\infty}\sin^2\chi\,db^2\right]d\gamma \tag{1.5–27}$$

$$B(T) = \tfrac{4}{3}N\sqrt{\pi}\int_0^{\infty} e^{-\gamma^2}\gamma^4\left[\int_0^{\infty}\chi\,db^3\right]d\gamma \tag{1.5–28}$$ [4]

in which $\gamma^2 = \frac{1}{2}\mu g^2/kT$. The expressions for all the transport coefficients in terms of the angle of deflection are derived in Chapter 7, and in Chapter 8 the angle of deflection and the transport properties are calculated for a number of different potential functions.

[4] In § 1.1 simple formula for $B(T)$ in terms of $\varphi(r)$ was given. Equation 1.5–28 is given simply to illustrate that $B(T)$ may also be expressed in terms of χ. This formula is valid only for monotone decreasing potential functions.

6. Quantum Mechanics[1]

The theory of intermolecular forces, which is the subject of Chapters 13 and 14, and the behavior of light gases at low temperatures, which is considered in Chapters 6 and 10, require an analysis based on quantum mechanics, for classical mechanics cannot be used to describe the behavior of particles with small mass and small energy. In this section we discuss first the direct experimental evidence that has led to the formulation of quantum mechanics. Then some of the fundamental principles of quantum mechanics are presented. The Schrödinger equation is the fundamental equation which in a sense corresponds to Newton's second law of classical mechanics. This second-order partial differential equation may be solved in several cases, but for many problems discussed in this book approximation methods must be employed. The section is concluded with a derivation of the quantum mechanical virial theorem.

a. Experimental manifestations of non-classical behavior

The development of the theory of quantum mechanics has been aided considerably by a number of ingenious and important experiments, which have left no doubt of the invalidity of classical mechanics for describing atomic phenomena. The quantized nature of radiation, the existence of systems in stationary energy states, wave-particle duality of radiation and matter, and the existence of electron and nuclear spins have been confirmed by the following experiments.

i. *Quantized Nature of Radiation*

(1) Planck[2] found it necessary to assume the existence of photons each with energy $h\nu$ in order to explain the observed distribution of black body radiation.

(2) Einstein[3] predicted, and Lawrence and Beams[4] observed that, when light impinges on a metal plate, the maximum velocity of the electrons emitted never exceeds $h\nu$. Furthermore, the number of electrons emitted in unit time is proportional to the light intensity.

(3) Compton[5] showed that when a photon hits an electron it undergoes a billiard ball collision with the energy of the photon being degraded from $h\nu$ to $h\nu'$ in such a manner as to conserve both energy and momentum.

[1] For those readers who are not familiar with quantum mechanics the small book by W. Heitler, *Elementary Wave Mechanics*, Oxford (1946), is recommended. A more complete elementary text is L. Pauling and E. B. Wilson, Jr., *Introduction to Quantum Mechanics*, McGraw-Hill (1935).

[2] M. Planck, *Ann. Physik*, **4**, 553 (1901).

[3] A. Einstein, *Ann. Physik*, **17**, 132 (1905).

[4] E. O. Lawrence and J. W. Beams, *Phys. Rev.*, **32**, 478 (1928).

[5] A. H. Compton, *Phys. Rev.*, **21**, 207, 483, 715 (1923).

ii. *Stationary Energy States*

(1) The Ritz[6] combination principle showed that the frequency of light emitted or absorbed by atoms or molecules can be represented as the difference between two "term values," which Einstein interpreted as being characteristic energy levels divided by Planck's constant, h.

(2) Franck and Hertz[7] showed that when electrons are passed through a gas, there is a tendency for the molecules to absorb certain energies which correspond to the term values found in spectroscopy.

(3) The critical ionization potential for an atom measured directly by electron impact corresponds to the difference between the spectroscopic term value for the lowest state and that for the limit of the highest states.

iii. *Wave Nature of Matter*

(1) Davisson and Germer, Rupp, Kikuchi,[8] and others showed that a beam of electrons gives diffraction patterns similar to those given by x-rays with wavelengths of approximately $\lambda = \sqrt{150/E}$ Å (where E is the energy of the electrons in volts). These electron beams behave like waves and can be controlled with great precision. This has led to electron optics and the electron microscope.

(2) Dempster[9] showed that α particles produce diffraction patterns when scattered from a suitable object.

(3) Johnson, Ellett, Olson, Zahl,[10] and others have shown that a beam of atoms will produce diffraction patterns.

iv. *Electron and Nuclear Spins*

Stern and Gerlach[11] showed that electrons and nuclei possess spins which line up in particular directions with respect to an external non-homogeneous magnetic field. The ratio of the magnetic moments to the apparent angular momentum contributions of these spins is anomalous.

b. Wave-mechanical description of systems

Quantum theory was developed almost simultaneously along two lines: the wave-mechanical formulation of Schrödinger[12] and the matrix-

[6] W. Ritz, *Physik. Z.*, **4**, 406 (1903); *Ann. Physik*, **12**, 264 (1903).

[7] J. Franck and G. Hertz, *Verhandl. deut. physik. Ges.*, **16**, 457, 512, (1914).

[8] C. J. Davisson and L. H. Germer, *Phys. Rev.*, **30**, 705 (1927). E. Rupp, *Z. Physik*, **95**, 801 (1935); *Ann. Physik*, **9**, 458 (1931). S. Kikuchi, *Proc. Imp. Acad. Tokyo*, **4**, 271, 275, 354, 471 (1928); *Physik. Z.*, **31**, 777 (1930).

[9] A. J. Dempster, *Phil. Mag.*, **3**, 115 (1927).

[10] T. H. Johnson, *Phys. Rev.*, **37**, 847 (1931). A. Ellett, H. F. Olson, and H. A. Zahl, *Phys. Rev.*, **34**, 493 (1929).

[11] O. Stern, *Z. Physik*, **7**, 249 (1921). W. Gerlach and O. Stern, *Z. Physik*, **8**, 110; **9**, 349 (1922).

[12] E. Schrödinger, *Ann. Physik*, **79**, 361 (1926); *Collected Papers on Wave Mechanics*, London (1928).

mechanics of Heisenberg[13] and Born and Jordan.[14] It was demonstrated independently by Schrödinger[15] and Eckart[16] that the two formulations of quantum mechanics are equivalent. For some formal problems the matrix-mechanics is more convenient, but the Schrödinger wave-mechanical formulation is the more usable for the study of collisional processes and intermolecular forces where numerical results are required. Hence we need to consider only the Schrödinger theory here.

i. *The Schrödinger Equation*

In quantum mechanics the *state* of a system of N particles is described by the wave function $\Psi(\boldsymbol{r}^N, t)$; this function has the significance that $|\Psi(\boldsymbol{r}^N, t)|^2\, d\boldsymbol{r}^N$ is the probability that at the time t the coordinates of the system are located within a range $d\boldsymbol{r}^N$ about $\boldsymbol{r}^N$. In order for $\Psi(\boldsymbol{r}^N, t)$ to be interpretable in this fashion, it is necessary for $\Psi(\boldsymbol{r}^N, t)$ to be square integrable. That is, in a system in which there are N identical particles

$$\int_{\text{all space}} \Psi^*(\boldsymbol{r}^N, t)\Psi(\boldsymbol{r}^N, t)\, d\boldsymbol{r}^N = 1 \tag{1.6–1}$$

In problems in which there is a beam containing N identical particles per unit volume, it is conventional to normalize the wave function in such a manner that

$$\int_{\text{unit volume}} \Psi^*(\boldsymbol{r}^N, t)\Psi(\boldsymbol{r}^N, t)\, d\boldsymbol{r}^N = N \tag{1.6–2}$$

The *dynamics* of the system is completely specified by the quantum mechanical Hamiltonian,

$$\mathscr{H} = \mathscr{K} + \Phi = -\sum_{i=1}^{N} \frac{\hbar^2}{2m_i}\left(\frac{\partial}{\partial \boldsymbol{r}_i} \cdot \frac{\partial}{\partial \boldsymbol{r}_i}\right) + \Phi(\boldsymbol{r}^N) \tag{1.6–3}$$

which, like its classical counterpart, is the sum of a kinetic energy operator and a potential energy operator. (Some of the other wave-mechanical operators are discussed in § 1.6c.) The *change with time* of the state of the system is then given by

$$\mathscr{H}\,\Psi(\boldsymbol{r}^N, t) = -\frac{\hbar}{i}\frac{\partial}{\partial t}\Psi(\boldsymbol{r}^N, t) \tag{1.6–4}$$

which is the *Schrödinger time-dependent wave equation.*

[13] W. Heisenberg, *Z. Physik*, **33**, 879 (1925).
[14] M. Born and P. Jordan, *Z. Physik*, **34**, 858 (1925).
[15] E. Schrödinger, *Ann. Physik*, **79**, 734 (1926).
[16] C. Eckart, *Phys. Rev.*, **28**, 711 (1926).

There exists a set of functions, $\Psi_j(\boldsymbol{r}^N, t)$, characteristic of "stationary states" of the system. If the system is in one of these stationary states, the physical properties of the system do not change with time. In this case it is possible to define the total energy of the system, E_j, by the relation

$$\mathscr{H}\Psi_j = E_j\Psi_j = -\frac{\hbar}{i}\frac{\partial\Psi_j}{\partial t} \tag{1.6–5}$$

For these stationary states, the time-dependent part of the wave-function can be separated from the space-dependent part, $\psi_j(\boldsymbol{r}^N)$:

$$\Psi_j(\boldsymbol{r}^N, t) = \psi_j(\boldsymbol{r}^N)\exp(-iE_jt/\hbar) \tag{1.6–6}$$

and the space-dependent wave function satisfies the relation:

$$\mathscr{H}\psi_j = E_j\psi_j \tag{1.6–7}$$

which is known as the *Schrödinger time-independent wave equation.* Under conditions where classical behavior is approached, this equation may be shown to approach the Hamilton-Jacobi equation of classical mechanics. This is discussed in § 1.6d in connection with the WKB approximation method of solving the Schrödinger equation.

ii. *Normalization and Orthogonality Conditions*

The stationary states of a system are described by wave functions which are solutions of the Schrödinger time-independent equation (Eq. 1.6–7) and are in addition well-behaved in that they are continuous, have continuous first derivatives, and are everywhere finite. For bound systems it is possible, and usually convenient, to normalize the wave functions so that they satisfy either Eq. 1.6–1 or 1.6–2. Often the wave equation possesses well-behaved solutions for only a discrete set of stationary energy levels $E = E_1, E_2, \ldots$.

The wave function describing any state of the system, $\Psi(\boldsymbol{r}^N, t)$, may be written as a linear combination of the set of stationary-state wave functions, $\psi_j(\boldsymbol{r}^N)$, thus:

$$\Psi(\boldsymbol{r}^N, t) = \Sigma_j c_j(t)\psi(\boldsymbol{r}^N) \tag{1.6–8}$$

In this sense, any state of the system is a "mixture" of stationary states. This principle of superposition of wave amplitudes leads to the diffraction phenomena which are characteristic of quantum mechanics.

The eigenfunctions have another property which is used frequently in quantum mechanical derivations. If ψ_i and ψ_j are eigenfunctions corresponding to different eigenvalues, then

$$\int \psi_j{}^* \psi_i \, d\boldsymbol{r}^N = 0 \tag{1.6–9}$$

This is known as the *orthogonality condition.* If ψ_i and ψ_j have the same eigenvalues, linear combinations of ψ_i and ψ_j can be found which satisfy Eq. 1.6–9.

iii. *The Probability Current Density*

We may define a *probability current density*, $\boldsymbol{I}$, which may be regarded as the product of the probability density, $\rho = \Psi^*\Psi$, and an overall average velocity of the particles. It may be shown that:

$$\boldsymbol{I} = \frac{\hbar}{2im}\left[\Psi^* \frac{\partial}{\partial \boldsymbol{r}}\Psi - \Psi \frac{\partial}{\partial \boldsymbol{r}}\Psi^*\right] \tag{1.6–10}$$

If Ψ is real, $\boldsymbol{I}$ is zero, and there is no possibility of a net flow of particles across any area. The probability current density satisfies the continuity equation

$$\frac{\partial \rho}{\partial t} + \left(\frac{\partial}{\partial \boldsymbol{r}} \cdot \boldsymbol{I}\right) = 0 \tag{1.6–11}$$

The current density is a useful concept not only in connection with quantum mechanical flow, but also in problems involving resonance.

c. Operators in wave mechanics

Thus far we have seen that the dynamical state of a system is given by specifying the wave function, and that the future behavior of the system is governed by the Schrödinger wave equation. We now give a brief discussion of dynamical observables, which in quantum mechanics are represented by operators. First we shall give some specific examples of operators in wave mechanics and then proceed to discuss some of the operator manipulations.

i. *Some Wave-Mechanical Operators*

To every dynamical observable in classical mechanics, there corresponds a quantum mechanical operator. To the x-coordinate in classical theory there corresponds, for example,[17] a quantum mechanical operator x. Operation with this operator on a wave function $\psi(x)$ is equivalent to multiplying $\psi(x)$ by x. The same is true for any function of the position coordinates; thus the potential energy operator in Eq. 1.6–3 operating on the wave function $\psi(\boldsymbol{r}^N)$ is tantamount to the product $\Phi(\boldsymbol{r}^N)\psi(\boldsymbol{r}^N)$.

[17] Here we restrict the discussion to the *Schrödinger method.* It is quite possible to use an entirely different set of operators, as indeed is done in the *momentum method.* For a brief summary of the latter, see V. Rojansky, *Introductory Quantum Mechanics*, Prentice-Hall (1938), Chapter 8.

The operator corresponding to the classical linear momentum, p_x, in Cartesian coordinates is a differential operator:

$$p_x = \frac{\hbar}{i}\frac{\partial}{\partial x} \tag{1.6–12}$$

Hence the kinetic energy operator for a system of particles is

$$\mathscr{K} = \Sigma_i \frac{p_i^2}{2m_i} = -\Sigma_i \frac{\hbar^2}{2m_i}\left(\frac{\partial}{\partial \mathbf{r}_i}\cdot\frac{\partial}{\partial \mathbf{r}_i}\right) \tag{1.6–13}$$

as was given in Eq. 1.6–3. These last two relations are valid in Cartesian coordinates only; they are not generally valid in other coordinate systems.[18, 19]

The quantum mechanical angular momentum operators may be expressed in terms of the linear momentum operators just as may be done in classical theory:

$$\mathscr{M}_x = \Sigma_i(y_i p_{z_i} - z_i p_{y_i}) = \frac{\hbar}{i}\Sigma_i\left(y_i\frac{\partial}{\partial z_i} - z_i\frac{\partial}{\partial y_i}\right) \tag{1.6–14}$$

$$\mathscr{M}_y = \Sigma_i(z_i p_{x_i} - x_i p_{z_i}) = \frac{\hbar}{i}\Sigma_i\left(z_i\frac{\partial}{\partial x_i} - x_i\frac{\partial}{\partial z_i}\right) \tag{1.6–15}$$

$$\mathscr{M}_z = \Sigma_i(x_i p_{y_i} - y_i p_{x_i}) = \frac{\hbar}{i}\Sigma_i\left(x_i\frac{\partial}{\partial y_i} - y_i\frac{\partial}{\partial x_i}\right) \tag{1.6–16}$$

In addition to these angular momentum operators there are also the spin angular momentum operators which have no classical analog. The necessity of introducing electron spin was suggested by Uhlenbeck and Goudsmit,[20] and Pauli[21] worked out the formal methods of treating the spin quantum mechanically. Later, while examining the theory of the electron in relativistic quantum mechanics, Dirac showed that the results of the relativistic theory automatically endow the electron with the properties that account for the phenomena previously ascribed to a hypothetical spinning motion of the electron.[22, 23] The magnetic moment

[18] E. C. Kemble, *Fundamental Principles of Quantum Mechanics*, McGraw-Hill (1937), p. 237.

[19] W. Pauli, "Die Allgemeinen Prinzipien der Wellenmechanik," *Handbuch der Physik*, 2te Aufl., Band 24, 1 Teil.

[20] G. E. Uhlenbeck and S. Goudsmit, *Naturwissenschaften*, **13**, 953 (1925).

[21] W. Pauli, *Z. Physik*, **43**, 601 (1925).

[22] P. A. M. Dirac, *Proc. Roy. Soc.* (*London*), **A117**, 610 (1928); *The Principles of Quantum Mechanics*, 3rd Ed., Oxford University Press (1947), Chapter 11.

[23] V. Rojansky, *Introductory Quantum Mechanics*, Prentice-Hall (1938), Chapters 13 and 14.

associated with the electron spin is twice what would be expected if the spin were similar to other forms of angular momentum. The spins of practically all the nuclei are known.

ii. *Eigenfunctions and Eigenvalues of Operators*

For every operator, $\mathscr{A}$, there may be found functions, ϕ_j, such that operation on these functions causes the original functions to be regenerated aside from a multiplicative constant:

$$\mathscr{A}\phi_j = A_j\phi_j \tag{1.6–17}$$

If the functions ϕ_j also satisfy certain boundary conditions and other requirements, they are called *eigenfunctions* or *characteristic functions* of the operator $\mathscr{A}$, and the A_j are called the corresponding *eigenvalues*. Equation 1.6–17 may be an integral or a differential equation, and there may be only certain discrete values of A_j for which solutions, ϕ_j, may be found which are physically permissible.[24, 25] The eigenfunctions of the momentum operator, $\mathscr{p}_x$, are $\phi(x) = A \exp(-ip_x x/\hbar)$; and the eigenfunctions of $\mathscr{M}^2 = \mathscr{M}_x^2 + \mathscr{M}_y^2 + \mathscr{M}_z^2$ are the spherical harmonics.

We shall be concerned with *Hermitian operators* only. These operators are operators such that if $f(\mathbf{r}^N)$ and $g(\mathbf{r}^N)$ are arbitrary functions, then:

$$\int f^* \mathscr{A} g \, d\mathbf{r}^N = \int g(\mathscr{A} f)^* \, d\mathbf{r}^N \tag{1.6–18}$$

An important property of Hermitian operators is that they have real eigenvalues only. When the system is in a state characterized by an eigenfunction of an operator corresponding to a dynamical variable, the variable has precisely the value given by the eigenvalue; it is for this reason that we deal only with operators which are Hermitian.

If the system is not in an eigenstate, ϕ_j, but in a state characterized by some function, $\Psi(\mathbf{r}^N, t)$ (which can be expanded in terms of the eigenfunctions as in Eq. 1.6–8), the *expectation value* of the property corresponding to the operator, $\mathscr{A}$, is given by

$$\begin{aligned} \bar{A} &= \int \Psi^* \mathscr{A} \Psi \, d\mathbf{r}^N \\ &= \Sigma_{ij} c_i^* c_j \int \phi_i^* \mathscr{A} \phi_j \, d\mathbf{r}^N = \Sigma_i |c_i|^2 A_i \end{aligned} \tag{1.6–19}$$

Here use is made of the normalization and orthogonality properties of the eigenfunctions, ϕ_j.

[24] H. Margenau and G. M. Murphy, *The Mathematics of Physics and Chemistry*, Van Nostrand (1943), Chapters 8 and 14.

[25] F. D. Murnaghan, *Introduction to Applied Mathematics*, Wiley (1948), Chapters 7 and 8.

iii. *Commutability of Operators*

Some quantum mechanical operators *commute*, that is, $\mathscr{A}\,\mathscr{B}$ applied to a wave function is the same as $\mathscr{B}\,\mathscr{A}$. In general, however,

$$(\mathscr{A}\mathscr{B} - \mathscr{B}\mathscr{A}) = i\hbar[\mathscr{A}, \mathscr{B}] \tag{1.6-20}$$

in which $(\mathscr{A}\mathscr{B} - \mathscr{B}\mathscr{A})$ is the *commutator* of $\mathscr{A}$ and $\mathscr{B}$, and $[\mathscr{A}, \mathscr{B}]$ is the operator associated with the classically computed Poisson bracket of $\mathscr{A}$ and $\mathscr{B}$. From this relationship we may get the following information about some of the operators which we have discussed:

$$x\,p_x - p_x x = i\hbar \tag{1.6-21}$$

$$\mathscr{M}_x\mathscr{M}_y - \mathscr{M}_y\mathscr{M}_x = i\hbar\mathscr{M}_z \tag{1.6-22}$$

$$\mathscr{M}^2\mathscr{M}_z - \mathscr{M}_z\mathscr{M}^2 = 0 \tag{1.6-23}$$

$$\mathscr{M}^2\mathscr{H} - \mathscr{H}\mathscr{M}^2 = 0 \tag{1.6-24}$$

A particular function can be simultaneously an eigenfunction of two operators only if the two operators commute. Thus from Eq. 1.6-21 it can be shown that it is impossible to know simultaneously the position and conjugate momentum of a system.

If $\mathscr{A}$ is any operator which does not contain time explicitly, then

$$\frac{d}{dt}\int \Psi_j^*\,\mathscr{A}\,\Psi_k\,d\mathbf{r}^N = \int \Psi_j^*[\mathscr{A}, \mathscr{H}]\Psi_k\,d\mathbf{r}^N \tag{1.6-25}$$

From this it may be seen that if an operator $\mathscr{A}$ commutes with the Hamiltonian, then the dynamical variable associated with the operator $\mathscr{A}$ is a *constant of motion.*

d. Indistinguishability of identical particles

In classical theory the motion of a group of identical particles is well-defined by Newton's second law, and it is possible at any time to distinguish between the various particles. In quantum theory it is assumed that particles which are identical cannot be distinguished one from another. This gives rise to interesting effects, some of which we shall have occasion to discuss in this book.

Let us consider a system of N indistinguishable particles in which there is negligible interaction between the individual particles. Under such conditions the Hamiltonian operator for the whole system may be written as the sum of the Hamiltonian operators for the individual particles:

$$\mathscr{H} = \mathscr{H}_1 + \mathscr{H}_2 + \cdots \mathscr{H}_N \tag{1.6-26}$$

in which $\mathscr{H}_i$ depends only on the coordinates of the ith particle. The entire system of particles satisfies the Schrödinger wave equation:

$$\mathscr{H}\,\psi_k = \epsilon_k \psi_k \tag{1.6–27}$$

By virtue of Eq. 1.6–26 the Schrödinger equation separates into N equations:

$$\begin{aligned} \mathscr{H}_1 \phi_a(\boldsymbol{r}_1) &= \alpha_a \phi_a(\boldsymbol{r}_1) \\ \mathscr{H}_2 \phi_b(\boldsymbol{r}_2) &= \alpha_b \phi_b(\boldsymbol{r}_2) \\ &\cdot \\ &\cdot \\ &\cdot \\ \mathscr{H}_m \phi_j(\boldsymbol{r}_m) &= \alpha_j \phi_j(\boldsymbol{r}_m) \end{aligned} \tag{1.6–28}$$

and

$$\alpha_a + \alpha_b + \cdots + \alpha_n = \epsilon_k \tag{1.6–29}$$

$\phi_j(\boldsymbol{r}_m)$ is interpreted as describing the mth particle in the jth quantum state with an energy α_j. Mathematically, the eigenfunction for the system is the product of the eigenfunctions of all the individual particles, or any linear combinations of such products. However, physical systems behave in such a way that only certain linear combinations of wave functions are permissible in the formation of a total wave function; only those combinations which are symmetrical or antisymmetrical with respect to an interchange of two particles are allowed.

i. *Antisymmetrical Wave Functions: Fermi-Dirac Statistics*

When we require that the total wave function be antisymmetrical we may write the desired combination of wave functions for the individual particles in determinantal form:

$$\psi = \begin{vmatrix} \phi_a(\boldsymbol{r}_1) & \phi_a(\boldsymbol{r}_2) & \cdots \\ \phi_b(\boldsymbol{r}_1) & \phi_b(\boldsymbol{r}_2) & \cdots \\ \cdot & \cdot & \cdots \\ \cdot & \cdot & \cdots \\ \cdot & \cdot & \cdots \end{vmatrix} \tag{1.6–30}$$

which may also be written symbolically in the form:

$$\psi = \Sigma(-1)^p P\{\phi_a(\boldsymbol{r}_1)\phi_b(\boldsymbol{r}_2)\cdots\} \tag{1.6–31}$$

The sum is taken over all permutations, P, of the alphabetical indices. The symbol p is the parity of the permutation, an even or odd number depending on whether an even or odd number of interchanges of pairs of letters $a, b, c, \ldots$ are needed to restore a particular product, e.g., $\phi_c(\boldsymbol{r}_1)\,\phi_a(\boldsymbol{r}_2)\ldots$, into the normal order $\phi_a(\boldsymbol{r}_1)\,\phi_b(\boldsymbol{r}_2)\ldots$. It is easy to see that the wave function (Eq. 1.6–30) possesses the required symmetry properties, for an interchange of two columns of the determinant, representing an interchange of two particles, changes the sign of the total wave function. Furthermore, it should be noted that if two particles are both placed in the same energy level (that is, letting all the subscripts b be replaced by a), two rows of the determinant becomes equal, and the total wave function vanishes. Hence, from this we infer that no two particles can be situated simultaneously in the same quantum state (the Pauli exclusion principle). Particles whose wave functions have these symmetry properties are spoken of as obeying the *Fermi-Dirac statistics.* This type of statistics is required for the description of all elementary particles and for all atoms and molecules containing an odd number of elementary particles. The consequences of these symmetry restrictions will be dealt with in Chapters, 2, 6, and 10.

ii. *Symmetrical Wave Functions: Bose-Einstein Statistics*

If the particles are indistinguishable and if the total wave function is required to be symmetrical with respect to the interchange of any two particles, the total wave function may be made up thus:

$$\psi = \Sigma P\{\phi_a(\boldsymbol{r}_1)\phi_b(\boldsymbol{r}_2)\ \cdots\} \tag{1.6–32}$$

the sum being over all permutations of the alphabetical indices. The statistics obeyed by systems having this type of wave function are called *Bose-Einstein statistics.* For such systems there is no restriction as to the number of particles which can be assigned to the various possible quantum states, $a, b, \ldots n$. These symmetry properties are possessed by systems of molecules and atoms containing an even number of elementary particles.

e. Approximation methods for solving the Schrödinger equation[26]

Inasmuch as the Schrödinger equation admits a solution in closed form for only the very simplest of systems, approximate methods of solution are of considerable importance. Let us discuss briefly three methods. In the *variational method* we construct an approximate eigenfunction having the proper form and containing several variable parameters;

[26] For a discussion of approximate methods and simple applications, see P. Gombás, *Mehrteilchenproblem der Wellenmechanik*, Birkhäuser (Basel), 1950, or H. Eyring, J. Walter, and G. E. Kimball, *Quantum Chemistry*, Wiley (1944).

these parameters are adjusted so as to give the best value of the energy. In the *perturbation method* we must first know the solutions to a wave equation which differs from the true one only in the omission of certain terms whose effect on the system is small; then we correct the solutions in order to account for the additional small perturbing term in the potential. In the *WKB method*, we take the classical solution as a first approximation and compute the quantum deviations from this behavior. All these methods, important in problems of molecular interaction, are used later in the book.

i. *The Variational Method*

Let the set of functions ψ_i be the complete set of eigenfunctions of the Hamiltonian of the system, $\mathscr{H}$. The corresponding set of eigenvalues is E_i. Let ξ be an arbitrary trial solution. Then, since the ψ_i form a complete orthonormal set, one may expand the arbitrary function in a series of the ψ_i:

$$\xi = \Sigma_i a_i \psi_i \tag{1.6–33}$$

Hence:

$$\mathscr{H}\,\xi = \Sigma_i E_i a_i \psi_i \tag{1.6–34}$$

Both of these equations may be multiplied by ξ^* and integrated over all space to give:

$$\int \xi^* \xi \, d\mathbf{r}^N = \Sigma_i \,|\, a_i \,|^2 \tag{1.6–35}$$

$$\int \xi^* \mathscr{H}\, \xi \, d\mathbf{r}^N = \Sigma_i \,|\, a_i \,|^2 E_i \tag{1.6–36}$$

where use has been made of the orthonormal properties of the eigenfunctions ψ_i. Thus:

$$\frac{\int \xi^* \mathscr{H}\, \xi \, d\mathbf{r}^N}{\int \xi^* \xi \, d\mathbf{r}^N} = E_0 + \frac{\Sigma_i \,|\, a_i \,|^2 (E_i - E_0)}{\Sigma_i \,|\, a_i \,|^2} \tag{1.6–37}$$

where E_0 is the lowest eigenvalue of the Hamiltonian. Since $E_i - E_0 \geqslant 0$, it follows that

$$\int \xi^* \mathscr{H}\, \xi \, d\mathbf{r}^N / \int \xi^* \xi \, d\mathbf{r}^N \geqslant E_0 \tag{1.6–38}$$

and that the equality holds only if ξ is the exact eigenfunction, corresponding to the lowest state. This result is the basis of an approximate method of solution. An arbitrary trial function, ξ, is set up with as many parameters as is convenient. The ratio of the integrals is then computed, and the result is minimized with respect to all the parameters. The resulting ratio of the integrals is the best approximation to the energy (of the lowest state) which may be obtained with a function of this form.

It can easily be seen that if the trial function is orthogonal to the eigenfunction corresponding to the lowest eigenvalue, the ratio of integrals is greater or equal to the E_1. Similarly if the function is orthogonal to the lowest two eigenfunctions, the ratio is greater than or equal to E_2, etc. These results are of value whenever the trial function can be made orthogonal to the ground state on the basis of the symmetry.

As an example of this procedure, let us consider a trial function ξ which is a linear combination of a set of functions f_i. The set may be finite or infinite and need not be orthonormal. Thus:

$$\xi = \Sigma_i b_i f_i \tag{1.6–39}$$

For convenience, let us use the abbreviated notation:

$$\mathscr{H}_{ij} = \int f_i^* \mathscr{H} f_j \, d\mathbf{r}^N = \mathscr{H}_{ji}^* \tag{1.6–40}$$

$$\Delta_{ij} = \int f_i^* f_j \, d\mathbf{r}^N = \Delta_{ji}^* \qquad \text{(1.6–41)[27]}$$

Then, according to Eq. 1.6–38, the approximate energy is

$$E = \frac{\Sigma_{ij} b_i b_j^* \mathscr{H}_{ji}}{\Sigma_{ij} b_i b_j^* \Delta_{ji}} \tag{1.6–42}$$

The best value of E is obtained by minimizing this expression with respect to all the parameters. The resulting equations are

$$\Sigma_j b_j (\mathscr{H}_{ij} - E\Delta_{ij}) = 0 \tag{1.6–43}$$

This set of equations has a non-trivial solution only if the determinantal equation

$$| \mathscr{H}_{ij} - E\Delta_{ij} | = 0 \tag{1.6–44}$$

is satisfied. The lowest root of this secular equation is clearly an approximation to the lowest eigenvalue of $\mathscr{H}$. The higher roots are approximations to the higher eigenvalues.

ii. *Perturbation Method*

It often happens that the Hamiltonian of a system can be written as the sum of two terms,

$$\mathscr{H} = \mathscr{H}^{(0)} + \lambda \mathscr{H}^{(1)} \tag{1.6–45}$$

where $\mathscr{H}^{(0)}$ is the important term and $\lambda \mathscr{H}^{(1)}$ is a small perturbation. The quantity λ is interpreted as a small quantity which may be varied. As an example, the perturbation term may represent the effect of an external magnetic or electric field. An approximate solution may be

[27] If the f_i are orthonormal, $\Delta_{ij} = \delta_{ij}$.

obtained by using as a variational trial function a linear combination of the eigenfunctions, $\psi_i^{(0)}$, of the unperturbed Hamiltonian, $\mathscr{H}^{(0)}$. Then, if $E_i^{(0)}$ is the unperturbed energy, Eqs. 1.6–40, 41 become:

$$\mathscr{H}_{ij} = \int \psi_i^{(0)*} \mathscr{H} \psi_j^{(0)} \, d\mathbf{r}^N = E_i^{(0)} \delta_{ij} + \lambda \mathscr{H}_{ij}^{(1)} \tag{1.6–46}$$

where

$$\mathscr{H}_{ij}^{(1)} = \int \psi_i^{(0)*} \mathscr{H}^{(1)} \psi_j^{(0)} \, d\mathbf{r}^N \tag{1.6–47}$$

and

$$\Delta_{ij} = \delta_{ij} \tag{1.6–48}$$

The set of energy levels of the perturbed system may be obtained by solving the secular equation (Eq. 1.6–44), which becomes

$$\left| (E_i^{(0)} - E)\delta_{ij} + \lambda \mathscr{H}_{ij}^{(1)} \right| = 0 \tag{1.6–49}$$

If this equation were solved exactly, the set of solutions would be the exact set of energy levels of $\mathscr{H}$. Ordinarily this is not accomplished. The accuracy of perturbation solutions depends on the nature of the perturbation and the order to which the equations are solved. Because of convergence difficulties it is difficult to estimate the error which is made.

The solution of the secular equation is assumed to be close to one of the $E_i^{(0)}$ and may hence be expanded in powers of λ:

$$E_k = E_k^{(0)} + \lambda E_k^{(1)} + \lambda^2 E_k^{(2)} + \cdots \tag{1.6–50}$$

Thus correct to first powers

$$\left| (E_i^{(0)} - E_k^{(0)})\delta_{ij} + \lambda(\mathscr{H}_{ij}^{(1)} - E_k^{(1)}\delta_{ij}) \right| = 0 \tag{1.6–51}$$

Multiplying out the determinant and keeping only terms of first order in λ, one finds that, if the original set of eigenvalues is non-degenerate (so that $E_i^{(0)} \neq E_k^{(0)}$ unless $i = k$), then:

$$E_i^{(1)} = \mathscr{H}_{ii}^{(1)} \tag{1.6–52}$$

so that

$$E = E_i^{(0)} + \lambda \mathscr{H}_{ii}^{(1)} \tag{1.6–53}$$

If the original set of energy levels is degenerate, a result of comparable accuracy may be obtained by ignoring the matrix elements $\mathscr{H}_{ij}^{(1)}$ between states belonging to different degenerate groups. In this case the determinant becomes a product of determinants. The set of perturbed levels arising from one degenerate group may then be obtained by solving the equation

$$\left| (\mathscr{H}_{ij}^{(1)} - E_k^{(1)}\delta_{ij}) \right| = 0 \tag{1.6–54}$$

Here the rows and columns of the determinant refer to the original set of degenerate states.

By retaining higher powers of λ one can obtain results to a higher degree of accuracy. For non-degenerate levels we get

$$E = E_i^{(0)} + \lambda \mathscr{H}_{ii}^{(1)} - \lambda^2 \sum_{j \neq i} \frac{|\mathscr{H}_{ij}^{(1)}|^2}{E_j^{(0)} - E_i^{(0)}} \tag{1.6–55}$$

for the energy in second-order perturbation theory. Numerous applications of perturbation theory to simple problems may be found in any standard elementary textbook on quantum mechanics.

iii. *Wentzel-Kramers-Brillouin (WKB) Method*[28]

The Wentzel-Kramers-Brillouin method is very convenient for approximating the solution to one-dimensional quantum mechanical problems. This method gives the corrections to classical behavior in terms of a power series in Planck's constant. Let us consider a one-dimensional problem with a potential energy function $\Phi(x)$ and a total energy of the system E, as shown in Fig. 1.6–1. At the *classical limiting point* x_0, $\Phi(x_0) = E$ so that classically the kinetic energy at this point is zero. It is clear from the figure that for values of x larger than x_0 the kinetic energy, $E - \Phi(x)$, is positive, and this region of space is classically attainable. However, for x less than x_0, $E - \Phi(x)$ is negative, and this region cannot be reached by a classical system. This distinction manifests itself in two different forms of the solution for $x \leq x_0$ and $x \geq x_0$.

The Schrödinger equation for this one-dimensional problem is[29]

$$-\frac{\hbar^2}{2m}\frac{d^2\psi}{dx^2} + \Phi(x)\,\psi = E\psi \tag{1.6–56}$$

Let us define a new function, $S(x)$, such that

$$\psi(x) = Ae^{iS(x)/\hbar} \tag{1.6–57}$$

Then $S(x)$ satisfies the differential equation:

$$-i\hbar\frac{d^2S}{dx^2} + \left(\frac{dS}{dx}\right)^2 - 2m[E - \Phi(x)] = 0 \tag{1.6–58}$$

[28] Good short discussions of this method are given in V. Rojansky, *Introductory Quantum Mechanics*, Prentice-Hall (1938), and in L. I. Schiff, *Quantum Mechanics*, McGraw-Hill (1949). For a detailed discussion see E. C. Kemble, *Fundamental Principles of Quantum Mechanics*, McGraw-Hill (1937). Also J. L. Dunham, *Phys. Rev.*, **41**, 713, 721 (1932).

[29] When considering solutions of the radial wave equation, replace x by r and $\Phi(x)$ by $\Phi(r) + \hbar^2 l(l+1)/2mr^2$; ψ equals r times the radial wave function.

Except for the term $i\hbar \dfrac{d^2S}{dx^2}$, this equation is exactly the Hamilton-Jacobi equation (Eq. 1.4–16) of classical mechanics. If $S(x)$ is expanded in powers of $\hbar$,

$$S(x) = S_0(x) + \hbar S_1(x) + \hbar^2 S_2(x) + \cdots \tag{1.6–59}$$

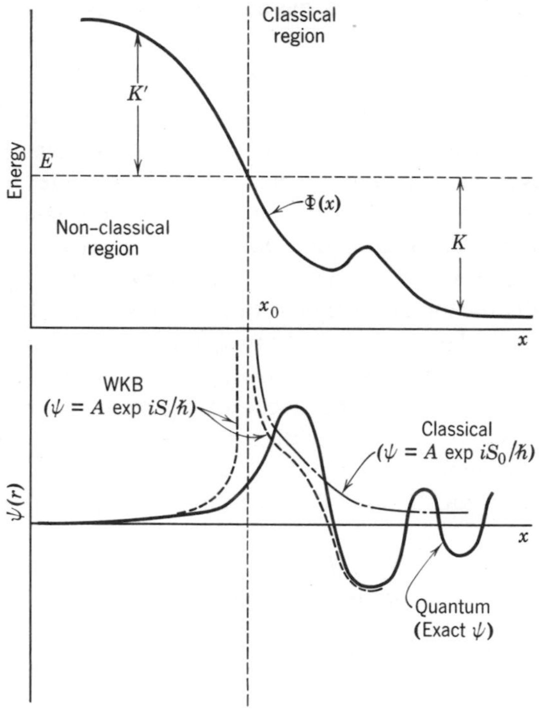

Fig. 1.6–1. A schematic illustration of the probability amplitudes computed classically, quantum mechanically, and by the WKB approximation.

and the series is substituted into Eq. 1.6–58, we get, on equating like powers of $\hbar$, a series of equations, the first two of which are

$$\left(\frac{dS_0}{dx}\right)^2 - 2m[E - \Phi(x)] = 0 \tag{1.6–60}$$

$$i\frac{d^2S_0}{dx^2} - 2\frac{dS_0}{dx}\frac{dS_1}{dx} = 0 \tag{1.6–61}$$

The Eq. 1.6–60 for the zeroth approximation, $S_0(x)$, is exactly the Hamilton-Jacobi equation. This demonstrates the *correspondence between quantum and classical mechanics.* Integration of Eq. 1.6–60 gives

$$S_0 = \pm \int_{x_0}^{x} \sqrt{2m(E - \Phi(x))}\, dx \tag{1.6–62}$$

and substitution of this into Eq. 1.6–61 yields

$$\frac{dS_1}{dx} = \frac{i}{2}\frac{d}{dx}\left(\ln\left(\frac{dS_0}{dx}\right)\right) = \frac{i}{4}\frac{d}{dx}\ln\,[2m(E - \Phi(x)] \tag{1.6–63}$$

Hence

$$S_1 = \frac{i}{4}\ln\left[\frac{2m}{\hbar^2}(E - \Phi(x))\right] \tag{1.6–64}$$

and to the first approximation the wave function $\psi(x)$ is

$$\psi(x) = \left[\frac{\hbar^2}{2m(E - \Phi(x))}\right]^{1/4} \begin{bmatrix} A_1 e^{+\frac{i}{\hbar}\int_{x_0}^{x}[2m(E - \Phi(x))]^{1/2}\,dx} \\ + A_2 e^{-\frac{i}{\hbar}\int_{x_0}^{x}[2m(E - \Phi(x))]^{1/2}\,dx} \end{bmatrix} \tag{1.6–65}$$

In the *non-classical region*, where $E - \Phi(x)$ is negative, it is more convenient to write the wave function in the equivalent form,

$$\psi(x) = \left[\frac{\hbar^2}{2m(\Phi(x) - E)}\right]^{1/4} \begin{bmatrix} B_1 e^{+\frac{1}{\hbar}\int_{x}^{x_0}[2m(\Phi(x) - E)]^{1/2}\,dx} \\ + B_2 e^{-\frac{1}{\hbar}\int_{x}^{x_0}[2m(\Phi(x) - E)]^{1/2}\,dx} \end{bmatrix} \tag{1.6–66}$$

In the general case where there is more than one classical limiting point, it is difficult to write explicitly the connection between the A_1, A_2 and B_1, B_2. However, in the case under consideration, where $\Phi(x) > E$ for all values of $x < x_0$, it is clear that B_1 is zero. It can be shown that the wave solution in the *classical region* is

$$\psi(x) = 2B_2\left(\frac{\hbar^2}{2m(E - \Phi(x))}\right)^{1/4} \cos\left[-\frac{\pi}{4} + \frac{1}{\hbar}\int_{x_0}^{x}[2m(E - \Phi(x))]^{1/2}\,dx\right] \tag{1.6–67}$$

This result may be used to derive expressions for the quantum correction to the second virial coefficient and the transport properties at high temperatures (see Chapters 6 and 10).

f. The quantum mechanical virial theorem

It has been shown[30, 31] that the virial theorem and its applications are valid in quantum as well as in classical mechanics, except that the time averages are replaced by spatial averages. The proof of the quantum mechanical virial theorem is presented here, and its applications to the equation of state are discussed in § 6.2b and to the theory of molecular structure and interaction in § 13.1c.

For a system of N particles the Schrödinger time-independent wave equations for ψ and for its complex conjugate are

$$\sum_{i=1}^{3N}\left(-\frac{\hbar^2}{2m_i}\right)\frac{\partial^2\psi}{\partial x_i^2}+(\Phi-E)\psi=0 \tag{1.6–68}$$

$$\sum_{i=1}^{3N}\left(-\frac{\hbar^2}{2m_i}\right)\frac{\partial^2\psi^*}{\partial x_i^2}+(\Phi-E)\psi^*=0 \tag{1.6–69}$$

Differentiation of the first of these with respect to x_j and multiplication by $x_j\psi^*$ gives

$$\sum_i\left(-\frac{\hbar^2}{2m_i}\right)x_j\psi^*\frac{\partial^3\psi}{\partial x_i^2\,\partial x_j}+x_j\psi^*\frac{\partial\Phi}{\partial x_j}\psi+x_j\psi^*(\Phi-E)\frac{\partial\psi}{\partial x_j}=0 \tag{1.6–70}$$

Substitution of $(\Phi-E)\psi^*$ from Eq. 1.6–69 into Eq. 1.6–70 and summation over j then yields

$$\sum_i\left(-\frac{\hbar^2}{2m_i}\right)\sum_j x_j\left(\psi^*\frac{\partial^3\psi}{\partial x_i^2\,\partial x_j}-\frac{\partial\psi}{\partial x_j}\frac{\partial^2\psi^*}{\partial x_i^2}\right)+\psi^*\left(\sum_j x_j\frac{\partial\Phi}{\partial x_j}\right)\psi=0 \tag{1.6–71}$$

The first term may be transformed, using the relation

$$\sum_j x_j\left(\psi^*\frac{\partial^3\psi}{\partial x_i^2\,\partial x_j}-\frac{\partial^2\psi^*}{\partial x_i^2}\frac{\partial\psi}{\partial x_j}\right)=-2\,\psi^*\frac{\partial^2\psi}{\partial x_i^2}+\frac{\partial}{\partial x_i}\left[\psi^{*2}\frac{\partial}{\partial x_i}\left\{\psi^{*-1}\sum_j x_j\frac{\partial\psi}{\partial x_j}\right\}\right] \tag{1.6–72}$$

Then integrating both sides of Eq. 1.6–71 with respect to x_i gives

$$\int_{-\infty}^{+\infty}\sum_j x_j\left(\psi^*\frac{\partial^3\psi}{\partial x_i^2\,\partial x_j}-\frac{\partial^2\psi^*}{\partial x_i^2}\frac{\partial\psi}{\partial x_j}\right)dx_i$$
$$=-2\int_{-\infty}^{+\infty}\psi^*\frac{\partial^2\psi}{\partial x_i^2}\,dx_i+\left[(\psi^*)^2\frac{\partial}{\partial x_i}\left\{\psi^{*-1}\sum_j x_j\frac{\partial\psi}{\partial x_j}\right\}\right]_{-\infty}^{+\infty} \tag{1.6–73}$$

[30] J. C. Slater, *J. Chem. Phys.*, **1**, 687 (1933).
[31] M. Born, W. Heisenberg, and P. Jordan, *Z. Physik*, **35**, 557 (1925, 1926).

If the system is closed, the term in the brackets vanishes at the two limits. Thus this integration gives finally

$$\int \psi^* \left(\sum_j - \frac{\hbar^2}{2m_j} \frac{\partial^2}{\partial x_j^2}\right) \psi \, d\mathbf{r}^N = -\tfrac{1}{2} \int \psi^* \left(-\sum_j x_j \frac{\partial \Phi}{\partial x_j}\right) \psi \, d\mathbf{r}^N \quad (1.6\text{–}74)$$

This is the quantum mechanical virial theorem. The term on the left is the expectation value of the kinetic energy; the term on the right is the quantum mechanical analog of the "virial."

If Φ is electrostatic in origin, $\sum_j x_j \dfrac{\partial \Phi}{\partial x_j} = -\Phi$ so that Eq. 1.6–74 becomes

$$\int \psi^* \mathscr{H} \psi \, d\mathbf{r}^N = -\tfrac{1}{2} \int \psi^* \Phi \psi \, d\mathbf{r}^N \quad (1.6\text{–}75)$$

in agreement with the result of classical theory that $\bar{K} = -\frac{1}{2}\bar{\Phi}$.

7. Molecular Collisions in Quantum Mechanics[1]

The development of the quantum theory of the equation of state and the transport properties demands a knowledge of the quantum theory of collisions. We consider only collisions between two particles for which the interaction potential is angle-independent.

We have mentioned that, in the classical theory, expressions are obtained for the properties of dilute gases (second virial coefficient and transport phenomena) in terms of the angle of deflection, $\chi(b, g)$, of the relative velocity of the two colliding particles. In quantum theory, however, the precise position and velocity of a molecule do not admit of a simultaneous determination (Heisenberg uncertainty principle). Hence it is impossible to determine exactly the angle of deflection. The best one can do is to inquire as to the probability that the angle of deflection is χ. Such a probability is expressible in terms of the phase shifts, $\eta_l(\kappa)$, of the radial wave function. In fact, the phase shifts are the only features of a collision which enter into the final quantum mechanical expressions for the second virial coefficient and low density transport coefficients. The phase shift is simply related to the angle of deflection in the correspondence limit.

a. Interaction of two particles: the phase shifts, $\eta_l(\kappa)$

In the discussion of classical collisions in § 1.5 it was pointed out that the two-body problem (involving 6 degrees of freedom) might easily be reduced to an equivalent one-body problem (involving 3 degrees of freedom), by simply separating off the overall translatory motion of the

[1] N. F. Mott and H. S. Massey, *The Theory of Atomic Collisions*, Oxford University Press (1949).

two-particle system. Similarly in quantum mechanics, the Schrödinger equation for two particles with a potential function $\varphi(r)$ is

$$-\frac{\hbar^2}{2\mu}\left(\frac{\partial}{\partial \mathbf{r}}\cdot\frac{\partial}{\partial \mathbf{r}}\right)\psi + \varphi(r)\psi = E\psi \tag{1.7–1}$$

in which E is the total energy in the center-of-mass coordinate system. If the potential energy function $\varphi(r)$ has a minimum, there are two types of eigenfunctions of this equation (see Fig. 1.7–1). If the two particles

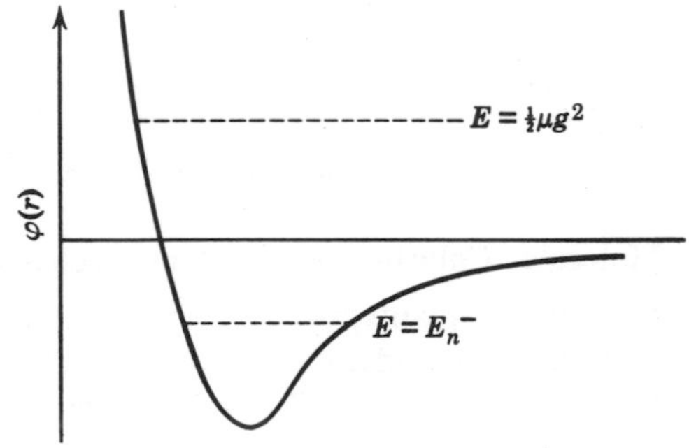

Fig. 1.7–1. A typical potential energy curve for a two-particle system, illustrating an energy level in the continuum and a discrete energy level.

are bound, the system can exist in one or more of the discrete negative energy states,[2] and $E = E_n^-$; if the particles undergo a collision, the energy is in the range of the continuum and

$$E = \tfrac{1}{2}\mu g^2$$

g being the relative speed of the colliding pair before the collision takes place. It is the latter possibility on which we wish to focus our attention. If we define κ by $\hbar\kappa = \mu g$, the Schrödinger equation assumes the form

$$\left(\frac{\partial}{\partial \mathbf{r}}\cdot\frac{\partial}{\partial \mathbf{r}}\psi\right) + \left(\kappa^2 - \frac{\varphi(r)}{\hbar^2/2\mu}\right)\psi = 0 \tag{1.7–2}$$

This equation may be solved by the method of separation of variables by putting $\psi = \psi_{\kappa l}(r)\,Y_l^m(\theta, \phi)$, where $Y_l^m(\theta, \phi)$ are the spherical harmonics,[3] and the $\psi_{\kappa l}(r)$ satisfy the radial differential equation

$$\frac{d^2}{dr^2}(r\psi_{\kappa l}) + (\kappa^2 - f_l(r))\,(r\psi_{\kappa l}) = 0 \tag{1.7–3}$$

in which $f_l(r) = [l(l+1)/r^2] + [2\mu\varphi(r)/\hbar^2]$.

[2] The zero of energy and potential is taken to be that of the separated particles.
[3] The spherical harmonics $Y_l^m(\theta, \phi)$ are defined in Appendix 12.B.

For two "ideal" particles, for which $\varphi(r) = 0$, this equation is

$$\frac{d^2}{dr^2}(r\psi_{\kappa l}{}^0) + \left(\kappa^2 - \frac{l(l+1)}{r^2}\right)(r\psi_{\kappa l}{}^0) = 0 \tag{1.7–4}$$

The superscript "0" indicates quantities which correspond to "ideal" particles. In the calculation of the second virial coefficient in quantum mechanics one needs to know the discrete energy levels for the system of two interacting particles and also the continuum of energy levels—or, more precisely, the density of energy states in the continuum.

In order to evaluate the density of states in the positive energy spectra given by Eqs. 1.7–3, 4 it is of advantage to first make the energy spectrum discrete.[4] This is accomplished by introducing the artificial boundary condition that the wavefunction of relative motion must be zero for intermolecular separation r greater than some value $r = L$. Subsequently L is allowed to become infinite.

The general solution of Eq. 1.7–4 may be written as $\sqrt{\kappa r}$ times the sum of two Bessel functions, $J_{l+1/2}(\kappa r)$ and $J_{-l-1/2}(\kappa r)$,[5] but, since the latter are infinite for $r = 0$, they must be excluded. Hence for the solution of Eq. 1.7–4 we write

$$r\psi_{\kappa l}{}^0 = A[\pi\kappa r/2]^{1/2}J_{l+1/2}(\kappa r) \tag{1.7–5}$$

which for large r becomes asymptotic to the sine function

$$r\psi_{\kappa l}{}^0 = A\sin[\kappa r - \tfrac{1}{2}l\pi] \qquad \textit{Large } r \tag{1.7–6}$$

Application of the artificial boundary condition allows κ to be determined as follows:

$$\kappa L - \tfrac{1}{2}l\pi = n\pi \qquad n = 0, 1, 2, \ldots \tag{1.7–7}$$

Equation 1.7–3 may now be treated in the same manner. For values of r beyond which the potential $\varphi(r)$ is essentially zero, the wave function may be written in the form

$$r\psi_{\kappa l} = A_l(\kappa)[\pi\kappa r/2]^{1/2}J_{l+1/2}(\kappa r) + B_l(\kappa)[\pi\kappa r/2]^{1/2}J_{-l-1/2}(\kappa r) \tag{1.7–8}$$

For large r this becomes, asymptotically,

$$r\psi_{\kappa l} = [A_l^2(\kappa) + B_l^2(\kappa)]^{1/2}\sin[\kappa r - \tfrac{1}{2}l\pi + \eta_l(\kappa)] \qquad \textit{Large } r \tag{1.7–9}$$

where

$$\eta_l(\kappa) = \arctan(-1)^l[B_l(\kappa)/A_l(\kappa)] \tag{1.7–10}$$

The artificial boundary condition then gives

$$\kappa L - \tfrac{1}{2}l\pi + \eta_l(\kappa) = n\pi \qquad n = 0, 1, 2, \cdots \tag{1.7–11}$$

[4] B. Kahn, Dissertation, Utrecht (1938).

[5] E. Jahnke and F. Emde, *Funktionentafeln*, Dover (1945), § 8.

Thus we see that the asymptotic solutions for real (interacting) and ideal (non-interacting) pairs of molecules are sinusoidal and differ only in the phase of the sine functions, the difference being the phase shifts, $\eta_l(\kappa)$. The phase shift depends upon the angular momentum quantum number l (or angular momentum $\hbar\sqrt{l(l+1)}$) and the wave number of relative motion, κ (or relative momentum $\hbar\kappa$). This is reminiscent of the classical theory where we calculate χ as a function of the impact parameter b (or angular momentum μbg) and the relative velocity g (or relative momentum μg).

The density of states $\rho^0(\kappa) = (\Delta n/\Delta\kappa)^0$ and $\rho(\kappa) = \Delta n/\Delta\kappa$ can now be determined from Eqs. 1.7–7 and 1.7–11, respectively. Differentiation of these equations gives

$$(\Delta n)^0 = (L/\pi)\,(\Delta\kappa)^0 \tag{1.7–12}$$

$$\Delta n = (L/\pi)\,\Delta\kappa + (1/\pi)\,(\Delta\eta_l/\Delta\kappa)\,\Delta\kappa \tag{1.7–13}$$

We then see that, in the limit $\Delta\kappa \to 0$, the difference in energy densities on the κ scale is

$$[\rho(\kappa) - \rho^0(\kappa)] = (1/\pi)\,(d\eta_l/d\kappa) \tag{1.7–14}$$

This result is used in the derivation of the formula for the second virial coefficient at low temperatures.

The phase shifts for almost classical collisions may be calculated by the WKB method described in §1.6e. In the first WKB approximation it is found that for a monotone decreasing potential the phase shifts are simply related to the angle of deflection: $\eta_{l+2}(\kappa) - \eta_l(\kappa) \to \chi(g, b)$, where $g = \hbar\kappa/\mu$ and $b = \sqrt{l(l+1)}/\kappa$. Higher WKB approximations then give the deviations from the classical behavior. In Chapter 10 the actual WKB expansion of the phase shifts is described. These results may then be used to calculate the quantum corrections to the second virial coefficient and to the transport properties.

b. Probability of an angle of deflection χ

Let us continue to discuss the equivalent one-body problem described by Eq. 1.7–2 and to examine the scattering of the system of reduced mass μ as it approaches in the negative direction along the $(+z)$-axis a scattering center located at the origin of coordinates. The most general solution of Eq. 1.7–2 consistent with the cylindrical symmetry of the problem and the physical requirement that the wave function be finite at $r = 0$ is

$$\psi = \sum_{l=0}^{\infty} C_l \psi_{\kappa l}(r) P_l\,(\cos\chi) \tag{1.7–15}$$

the C_l being constants. For the purpose of studying the angle dependence of the scattering we separate ψ into two parts: ψ^I, representing the incident wave, and ψ^S, representing the scattered component.

For the incident wave (the system approaching along the z-axis) we have

$$\psi^I = \exp(-i\kappa z) = \exp(i\kappa r \cos\chi) \qquad (1.7\text{–}16)^6$$

This expression may be expanded in Legendre polynomials, the coefficients of expansion involving Bessel functions:[7]

$$\psi^I = \sum_{l=0}^{\infty} (2l+1)i^l (\pi/2\kappa r)^{1/2} J_{l+1/2}(\kappa r) P_l(\cos\chi) \qquad (1.7\text{–}17)$$

which for large r may be written as

$$\psi^I = \frac{1}{\kappa r}\sum_{l=0}^{\infty} (2l+1)i^l \sin\left(\kappa r - \frac{\pi}{2}l\right) P_l(\cos\chi) \qquad (1.7\text{–}18)$$

This represents the asymptotic behavior of the incoming wave. Let us now consider the scattered wave. This wave is of the form given by Eq. 1.7–15 and hence has the asymptotic form

$$\psi^S = \frac{1}{r} e^{i\kappa r} f(\chi) \qquad (1.7\text{–}19)$$

where $f(\chi)$ is an arbitrary function of the angle χ. The complete wave function, which is the sum of this function and ψ^I (as given by Eq. 1.7–18), is a solution of the complete wave equation, including the interaction potential. In order that this be true, the function $f(\chi)$ is chosen so that the complete wave function is continuous and has continuous derivatives. This is accomplished by choosing the function $f(\chi)$ in such a manner that $\psi^I + \psi^S$ is asymptotically identical to the expression given by the Eq. 1.7–15 for some choice of the constants C_l.

The introduction of D_l as the expansion coefficients of $f(\chi)$ in terms of Legendre polynomials allows Eq. 1.7–19 to be rewritten as

$$\psi^S = \frac{1}{r} e^{i\kappa r} \Sigma_l D_l P_l(\cos\chi) \qquad (1.7\text{–}20)$$

Since the asymptotic forms of the functions ψ^I and ψ^S must add up to the asymptotic solution of the wave equation (1.7–2) as given by the total wave function, ψ, given in Eq. 1.7–15,

$$\Sigma_l \left\{\frac{i^l}{\kappa r}(2l+1)\sin\left(\kappa r - \frac{\pi}{2}l\right) + D_l \frac{1}{r} e^{i\kappa r}\right\} P_l(\cos\chi)$$

$$= \Sigma_l \left\{\frac{1}{r} C_l [A_l^2(\kappa) + B_l^2(\kappa)]^{1/2} \sin\left(\kappa r - \frac{\pi}{2}l - \eta_l(\kappa)\right)\right\} P_l(\cos\chi) \qquad (1.7\text{–}21)$$

[6] This must be modified in the case of the collision between two similar (indistinguishable) particles; the necessary symmetrization will be discussed shortly.

[7] G. N. Watson, *Bessel Functions*, Cambridge University Press (1922), pp. 56, 128, and 368.

Equating the coefficients of $P_l(\cos\chi)$ gives

$$\frac{1}{\kappa}(2l+1)i^l \sin\left(\kappa r - \frac{\pi}{2}l\right) + D_l e^{i\kappa r}$$
$$= C_l[A_l^2(\kappa) + B_l^2(\kappa)]^{1/2} \sin\left(\kappa r - \frac{\pi}{2}l + \eta_l\right) \quad (1.7\text{–}22)$$

which is an identity in r. Hence, equating coefficients of $e^{i\kappa r}$ and $e^{-i\kappa r}$, one obtains equations for C_l and D_l. In this way one finds

$$D_l = \frac{1}{2i\kappa}[2l+1][e^{2i\eta_l} - 1] \quad (1.7\text{–}23)$$

and, finally,

$$\psi^S = \frac{e^{i\kappa r}}{2i\kappa r}\Sigma_l(2l+1)(e^{2i\eta_l} - 1)P_l(\cos\chi) \quad (1.7\text{–}24)$$

The fraction of particles scattered in a given direction is the limiting value of $|\psi^S|^2/|\psi^I|^2$ for large distances. After the molecules have separated sufficiently so that they no longer "feel" the potential $\varphi(r)$, they are flying apart with a mutual velocity g. Hence, the number per unit length of time which crosses a sphere of radius r with velocities whose directions lie in a solid angle $d\omega$ about ω is

$$\alpha(g, \chi)\, d\omega = |\Psi^S|^2 g r^2\, d\omega \quad (1.7\text{–}25)$$

whence

$$\alpha(g, \chi) = \frac{g}{4\kappa^2}|\Sigma_l(2l+1)(e^{2i\eta_l} - 1)P_l(\cos\chi)|^2 \quad (1.7\text{–}26)$$

This gives the distribution of scattered particles, provided the molecules are distinguishable; that is, this formula is valid in Boltzmann statistics.

If the particles are indistinguishable, the wave functions have to be symmetrized, and hence $\psi^I = e^{i\kappa z}$ must be replaced by

$$\psi^I = (2)^{-1/2}[e^{i\kappa z} \pm e^{-i\kappa z}],$$

according as the molecules obey Bose-Einstein [(+)-sign] or Fermi-Dirac [(—)-sign] statistics. For scattering of like particles we get, for Bose-Einstein statistics,

$$[\alpha(g, \chi)]_{\text{B.E.}} = \frac{g}{2\kappa^2}\left|\sum_{l=\text{even}}(2l+1)(e^{2i\eta_l} - 1)P_l(\cos\chi)\right|^2 \quad (1.7\text{–}27)$$

and, for the particles which obey Fermi-Dirac statistics,

$$[\alpha(g, \chi)]_{\text{F.D.}} = \frac{g}{2\kappa^2}\left|\sum_{l=\text{odd}}(2l+1)(e^{2i\eta_l} - 1)P_l(\cos\chi)\right|^2 \quad (1.7\text{–}28)$$

Equations 1.7–27 and 28 are valid only for particles of zero spin. For B.E. and F.D. gases with particles of spin s:

$$[\alpha^{(s)}(g, \chi)]_{\text{B.E.}} = \left[\frac{s+1}{2s+1}\right] \alpha^{(0)}_{\text{B.E.}} + \left[\frac{s}{2s+1}\right] \alpha^{(0)}_{\text{F.D.}} \qquad (1.7\text{–}29)$$

$$[\alpha^{(s)}(g, \chi)]_{\text{F.D.}} = \left[\frac{s+1}{2s+1}\right] \alpha^{(0)}_{\text{F.D.}} + \left[\frac{s}{2s+1}\right] \alpha^{(0)}_{\text{B.E.}} \qquad (1.7\text{–}30)$$

The superscript 0 refers to those α's calculated from Eqs. 1.7–27 and 28 for zero spin. This analysis applies to collisions between atoms, each of which has a nuclear spin s. In collisions between molecules the potential is not spherically symmetric, and a more detailed treatment is necessary.

PROBLEMS

1. Using Eq. 1.1–10, calculate the second virial coefficient for (a) the rigid sphere model, (b) the square-well potential

2. For a diatomic gas with $\tilde{C}_v = \frac{5}{2} R$ compute the magnitude of the Eucken correction to the thermal conductivity.

3. What is the maximum energy of attraction for the Buckingham potential?

4. Calculate the time-average kinetic energy and potential energy for a one-dimensional harmonic oscillator, and compare the results with the prediction of the virial theorem.

5. Calculate the angle of deflection for (a) the rigid sphere model, (b) the Coulomb potential.

6. Calculate the wave function and energy levels of a particle confined to a one-dimensional box.

7. Calculate the phase shifts for the rigid sphere model.

8. Calculate for the rigid sphere model the second virial coefficient and the coefficient of viscosity from Eqs. 1.5–27 and 28, using the results of Problem 5a.

9. Expand the van der Waals equation in powers of $1/V$, and get the second virial coefficient in terms of a and b.

10. Consider two molecules which interact according to the Lennard-Jones (6–12) potential energy function. What is the force of interaction when the molecules are at a separation of $r = 2\sigma$? at a separation of $r = 0.9\sigma$?

PART I

EQUILIBRIUM PROPERTIES

· 2 ·

Statistical Mechanics

The methods of classical and quantum mechanics have been highly successful in the analysis of the behavior of simple systems involving only a few degrees of freedom. However, it is clearly impractical to apply these principles to the examination of the behavior of a very complex system, such as a gas containing 6.023×10^{23} molecules. Furthermore, a knowledge of the microscopic behavior thus provided is not particularly of interest. The macroscopic state of the system and its change with time may be predicted from statistical mechanics, when the knowledge of the initial state of the system is limited to the results of measurements of the bulk properties.

Statistical mechanics may be thought of as being made up of two important branches: equilibrium and non-equilibrium statistical mechanics. The former is well understood from the standpoint of the fundamental principles and the formal development of the theory. The basic principles and important results of the theory are presented in this chapter. In the next four chapters the application of these fundamentals to some important problems are discussed: equation of state of dilute gases, properties of dense gases and liquids, critical phenomena, quantum deviations, and low-temperature phenomena. Although progress in this direction has thus far been seriously handicapped by the numerical difficulties encountered, much has been learned about the properties of matter and their dependence on the forces between the molecules.

The non-equilibrium statistical mechanics is of more recent development and is one of the frontier fields of research today. The special case of dilute gases was investigated about a century ago by Maxwell, Boltzmann, and others, using somewhat special methods. With these latter techniques is customarily associated the name "kinetic theory." A general discussion of the formal treatment of non-equilibrium statistical mechanics is presented in Chapter 7, and the applications to hydrodynamic and transport phenomena are discussed in succeeding chapters.

1. Description of Statistical Ensembles in Classical Mechanics

In classical statistical mechanics the microscopic state of the system is described by specifying the position and momenta of all the particles in the system. In this chapter we study complex systems—such as a gas or liquid composed of N molecules, each with f degrees of freedom.[1] This section begins with a discussion of the various ways of specifying the microscopic dynamical state of the system. This is done by introducing the notions of various types of hyperspaces which afford a convenient method for summarizing information about the state of the system.

For the purpose of examining a system statistically, we consider not one such system, but a large collection (ensemble) of these systems, Γ in number. It should be kept in mind that these systems are identical in that they consist of the same number and type of molecules in the same sort of enclosure. They differ, however, in that they represent the system in various dynamical states, resulting from different initial conditions. The notions of ensembles and distribution functions are discussed in detail. This section is limited to describing the classical state of the system; the analogous quantum treatment is given in § 2.

a. Configuration, momentum, and phase spaces

There are several kinds of hyperspaces which are used for visualizing the geometry and the dynamics of a complex system. We summarize here the nomenclature necessary for describing a system (gas, liquid, or solid) consisting of N subsystems (monatomic molecules), each with three degrees of freedom. The concepts discussed here may easily be generalized to polyatomic molecules. Throughout the discussion Cartesian coordinates are employed, but generalized coordinates and momenta may equally well be used.

To specify the location of a single monatomic molecule three coordinates, x, y, z, may be given. That is, we picture the molecule as a point in a three-dimensional *molecule configuration space*. In this space the system of N molecules is then pictured as N points. Thus the specification of the position vectors $\boldsymbol{r}_1, \boldsymbol{r}_2, \ldots, \boldsymbol{r}_N$ in molecule configuration space gives the configuration of the whole system. That is just the usual way of picturing a gas in three-dimensional space. However, it is sometimes more convenient to consider a hyperspace of $3N$ dimensions (that is, with $3N$ mutually orthogonal axes). In this *gas configuration space* one point serves to define the configuration of the complete system. That

[1] The number of degrees of freedom of a molecule is that number of coordinates necessary to define its geometrical location and orientation. It is *usually* customary to consider the constituent atoms as point particles (ignoring thus nuclear and electronic motion). A monatomic molecule then has 3 degrees of freedom, a rigid diatomic molecule (one which is capable of rotation but not vibration) 5, a non-rigid diatomic molecule 6, a non-rigid n-atomic molecule $3n$.

is, the geometry of the system may be regarded as being given by[2] a vector $\boldsymbol{r}^N \equiv \boldsymbol{r}_1, \boldsymbol{r}_2, \cdots, \boldsymbol{r}_N$, with $3N$ components.

Analogously the momentum of a single monatomic molecule may be described by a point in a three-dimensional *molecule momentum space.* In this space the momenta of N molecules are then given by N points. Alternatively, one may consider a $3N$-dimensional *gas momentum space,* in which the components of a vector $\boldsymbol{p}^N \equiv \boldsymbol{p}_1, \boldsymbol{p}_2, \cdots, \boldsymbol{p}_N$ specify the three components of linear momentum for all the N molecules.

It was mentioned in Chapter 1 that a knowledge of all the momenta and coordinates of a system is tantamount to complete dynamical knowledge of the system. Therefore the concept of *phase space* is frequently used. *Molecule phase space,* or *μ-space* as it is generally called (μ for *molecule*), is a combination of molecule configuration space and molecule momentum space—that is, a six-dimensional space for a monatomic molecule. A single point in this space gives the configuration and momentum of the molecule. The dynamical state of the system of N *molecule* is accordingly given by N points in μ-space. These points move with time according to the classical laws of motion.

Gas phase space, which is usually referred to as *γ-space* (γ for *gas*), results from a combination of gas configuration space and gas momentum space and is thus a space of $6N$-dimensions. The complete dynamical state of the system is thus given by one point in γ-space. The motion of this point is described by Newton's laws of motion or the equivalent relations of Hamilton.

It is important that the connection between μ-space and γ-space be clearly understood. The dynamical state of the system of N molecules may be described either by one point in γ-space or by a cloud of points in μ-space. If all the molecules are identical, the cloud of points in μ-space presents the same appearance when any of the molecules are interchanged. There are thus $N!$ different arrangements of the molecules which correspond to the same cloud of points in μ-space (that is, the same arrangement with the points renumbered). Each of these arrangements is represented by a different point in γ-space. Hence there are $N!$ different points in γ-space which correspond to a cloud of N points in μ-space.

For molecules with f degrees of freedom the molecule configuration and momentum spaces each consist of f dimensions. μ-space is then a $2f$ dimensional space, and γ-space has $2Nf$ dimensions. One might wonder why momenta, rather than velocities, are selected for the construction of these phase spaces. The particular appropriateness of the

[2] See the note on vector notation at the front of the book.

former selection will become apparent in connection with the theorem of Liouville.

b. Ensembles and distribution functions[3]

Information concerning the macroscopic properties of a system may be acquired by a statistical examination of a large number of systems, or an *ensemble* of systems which are all dynamically similar. For example, if we want to predict the behavior of a mole of gas in a cubical container, we imagine that we set up a large number of replicas of this system, with the same *number and type* of molecules and the same sort of container. Each of these replicas is completely independent of the others, and they differ from one another only in that the phases of the motion in the various containers are all different.

The instantaneous dynamical state of each system of the ensemble can be described by its corresponding point in γ-space. If there are many systems in the ensemble, the system points in γ-space give the appearance of a cloud. In this case it is possible to introduce a function $\rho = \rho(\mathbf{r}^N, \mathbf{p}^N)$, the density of points in γ-space, such that $\rho\, d\mathbf{r}^N\, d\mathbf{p}^N$ is the number of system points in the volume element $d\mathbf{r}^N\, d\mathbf{p}^N$. There is no loss of generality in doing this since the discreteness of the points could be preserved by letting ρ be a collection of Dirac δ-functions.

It is sometimes convenient to use the normalized function:

$$P^{(N)}(\mathbf{r}^N, \mathbf{p}^N) = \frac{\rho(\mathbf{r}^N, \mathbf{p}^N)}{\iint \rho(\mathbf{r}^N, \mathbf{p}^N)\, d\mathbf{r}^N\, d\mathbf{p}^N} = \frac{\rho(\mathbf{r}^N, \mathbf{p}^N)}{\Gamma} \tag{2.1–1}$$

where Γ is the number of systems in the ensemble. $P^{(N)}(\mathbf{r}^N, \mathbf{p}^N)$ is then a *probability density* function. The probability of finding one system of the ensemble, chosen at random, in a state $d\mathbf{r}^N\, d\mathbf{p}^N$ about $\mathbf{r}^N\, \mathbf{p}^N$ is $P^{(N)}(\mathbf{r}^N, \mathbf{p}^N)\, d\mathbf{r}^N\, d\mathbf{p}^N$.

It is convenient to define probability densitites of lower order, for use in the development of the equation of state in the next chapter. Let us select a group of h molecules, $\iota, \kappa, \ldots \lambda$, and designate this collection by $\{\eta\}$. Then let it be desired to find the probability[4] $P^{(h)}(\mathbf{r}^\eta, \mathbf{p}^\eta)$ that the group of molecules $\{\eta\}$ is in the state $d\mathbf{r}^\eta\, d\mathbf{p}^\eta$ about $\mathbf{r}^\eta, \mathbf{p}^\eta$. $\mathbf{r}^\eta$ and $\mathbf{p}^\eta$ are vectors in the $3h$-dimensional configuration and momentum subspaces of the set of molecules $\{\eta\}$, and $d\mathbf{r}^\eta\, d\mathbf{p}^\eta \equiv d\mathbf{r}_\iota\, d\mathbf{r}_\kappa \cdots d\mathbf{r}_\lambda\, d\mathbf{p}_\iota\, d\mathbf{p}_\kappa \cdots d\mathbf{p}_\lambda$. Clearly,

$$P^{(h)}(\mathbf{r}^\eta, \mathbf{p}^\eta) = \iint P^{(N)}(\mathbf{r}^N, \mathbf{p}^N)\, d\mathbf{r}^{N-\eta}\, d\mathbf{p}^{N-\eta} \tag{2.1–2}$$

[3] The notation for the various kinds of distribution functions in this chapter follows closely that used by J. de Boer, *Reports on Progress in Physics*, **XII**, 305 (1949).

[4] If the group $\{\eta\}$ consists of molecules 1, 2, 3, . . . h, we use the notation $P^{(h)}(\mathbf{r}^h, \mathbf{p}^h)$.

where $d\boldsymbol{r}^{N-\eta}\, d\boldsymbol{p}^{N-\eta}$ is the volume element in the $3(N - h)$-dimensional subspace of γ-space appropriate for all molecules not belonging to the group $\{\eta\}$. Note that in the notation $P^{(h)}(\boldsymbol{r}^\eta, \boldsymbol{p}^\eta)$ the superscript on P indicates how many molecules are being considered and that the superscripts on the $\boldsymbol{r}$ and $\boldsymbol{p}$ indicate which molecules are under consideration.

Integration of $P^{(N)}(\boldsymbol{r}^N, \boldsymbol{p}^N)$ or $P^{(h)}(\boldsymbol{r}^\eta, \boldsymbol{p}^\eta)$ over the momenta gives

$$P^{(N)}(\boldsymbol{r}^N) = \int P^{(N)}(\boldsymbol{r}^N, \boldsymbol{p}^N)\, d\boldsymbol{p}^N \tag{2.1-3}$$

and

$$P^{(h)}(\boldsymbol{r}^\eta) = \int P^{(h)}(\boldsymbol{r}^\eta, \boldsymbol{p}^\eta)\, d\boldsymbol{p}^\eta = \int P^{(N)}(\boldsymbol{r}^N)\, d\boldsymbol{r}^{N-\eta} \tag{2.1-4}$$

which are, respectively, the probabilities that one system of the ensemble, chosen at random, is in the configuration $\boldsymbol{r}^N$ or $\boldsymbol{r}^\eta$.

The quantity $P^{(N)}(\boldsymbol{r}^N, \boldsymbol{p}^N)\, d\boldsymbol{r}^N\, d\boldsymbol{p}^N$ was defined as the probability of finding one system of the ensemble (chosen at random) in the volume element $d\boldsymbol{r}^N d\boldsymbol{p}^N$ around $\boldsymbol{r}^N$, $\boldsymbol{p}^N$ in γ-space. Now the probability of finding the points associated with the molecules of the system in any arbitrary order in the volume elements $d\boldsymbol{r}_1\, d\boldsymbol{p}_1, \ldots, d\boldsymbol{r}_N\, d\boldsymbol{p}_N$ around $\boldsymbol{r}_1\boldsymbol{p}_1, \ldots, \boldsymbol{r}_N\boldsymbol{p}_N$ in μ-space is just $N!$ times as large:

$$f^{(N)}(\boldsymbol{r}^N, \boldsymbol{p}^N)\, d\boldsymbol{r}_1\, d\boldsymbol{p}_1 \cdots d\boldsymbol{r}_N\, d\boldsymbol{p}_N = N!P^{(N)}(\boldsymbol{r}^N, \boldsymbol{p}^N)\, d\boldsymbol{r}^N d\boldsymbol{p}^N \tag{2.1-5}$$

Similarly, since h objects may be chosen from N objects in $[N!/(N - h)!]$ ways:

$$\begin{aligned} f^{(h)}(\boldsymbol{r}^\eta, \boldsymbol{p}^\eta) &= [N!/(N-h)!]\, P^{(h)}(\boldsymbol{r}^\eta, \boldsymbol{p}^\eta) \\ &= [(N-h)!]^{-1} \iint f^{(N)}(\boldsymbol{r}^N, \boldsymbol{p}^N)\, d\boldsymbol{r}^{N-\eta}\, d\boldsymbol{p}^{N-\eta} \end{aligned} \tag{2.1-6}$$

are the density functions of lower order in μ-space. The lowest order function of this type is $f^{(1)}(\boldsymbol{r}_1, \boldsymbol{p}_1) = NP^{(1)}(\boldsymbol{r}_1, \boldsymbol{p}_1)$. It is this function which appears in the Boltzmann equation (§ 7.1), from which the formulae for the transport coefficients are developed. Integration of $f^{(1)}(\boldsymbol{r}_1, \boldsymbol{p}_1)$ over $\boldsymbol{p}_1$ gives the number density $n(\boldsymbol{r}_1)$ of the gas. Kinetic theory workers have usually used this function not as a function of momentum, but rather of velocity. In accordance with this usage we use $f(\boldsymbol{r}_1, \boldsymbol{v}_1)$ in kinetic theory developments. (Note that this function is distinguished from $f^{(1)}(\boldsymbol{r}_1, \boldsymbol{p}_1)$ by the absence of the superscript (1).)

The probabilities of a particular configuration, analogous to the expressions given in Eqs. 2.1-3, 4, are

$$n^{(N)}(\boldsymbol{r}^N) = N!P^{(N)}(\boldsymbol{r}^N) \tag{2.1-7}$$

$$\begin{aligned} n^{(h)}(\boldsymbol{r}^\eta) &= [N!/(N-h)!]P^{(h)}(\boldsymbol{r}^\eta) \\ &= [(N-h)!]^{-1} \int n^{(N)}(\boldsymbol{r}^N)\, d\boldsymbol{r}^{N-\eta} \\ &= \int f^{(h)}(\boldsymbol{r}^\eta, \boldsymbol{p}^\eta)\, d\boldsymbol{p}^\eta \end{aligned} \tag{2.1-8}$$

The lowest order function of this type, $n^{(1)}(\boldsymbol{r}_1)$, is just the number density, $n(\boldsymbol{r}_1)$. The function $n^{(2)}(\boldsymbol{r}_i, \boldsymbol{r}_j)$ is a very important function—the probability density for pairs—which is used in the theory of gases and liquids. The quantity $n^{(2)}(\boldsymbol{r}_i, \boldsymbol{r}_j)\, d\boldsymbol{r}_i\, d\boldsymbol{r}_j$ is the probability that there is a molecule in the volume element $d\boldsymbol{r}_i$ about $\boldsymbol{r}_i$ and another in the volume element $d\boldsymbol{r}_j$ about $\boldsymbol{r}_j$. If N is large compared to unity, it is sometimes convenient to introduce the *radial distribution function* $g(\boldsymbol{r}_i, \boldsymbol{r}_{ji})$ by the relation

$$n^{(2)}(\boldsymbol{r}_i, \boldsymbol{r}_j) = n(\boldsymbol{r}_i)n(\boldsymbol{r}_j)g(\boldsymbol{r}_i, \boldsymbol{r}_{ji}) \tag{2.1–9}$$

The function $g(\boldsymbol{r}_i, \boldsymbol{r}_{ji})$ approaches unity as $r_{ji} = |\boldsymbol{r}_j - \boldsymbol{r}_i|$ approaches infinity, and deviations from unity are a measure of the correlations in the positions of pairs of molecules. Under uniform conditions in an isotropic medium $g(\boldsymbol{r}_i, \boldsymbol{r}_{ji})$ is a function of r_{ji} only, and $2\pi n^2 V g(r_{ji}) r_{ji}^2\, dr_{ji}$ is the number of pairs of molecules for which the separation r_{ji} lies between r_{ji} and $r_{ji} + dr_{ji}$.

The functions $P^{(h)}(\boldsymbol{r}^\eta, \boldsymbol{p}^\eta)$ and $P^{(h)}(\boldsymbol{r}^\eta)$ are called *specific distribution functions*, and $f^{(h)}(\boldsymbol{r}^\eta, \boldsymbol{p}^\eta)$ and $n^{(h)}(\boldsymbol{r}^\eta)$ are called *generic distribution functions*. The latter have the advantage that the factors $N!$ and $(N - h)!$ do not appear in the formulae where these relations are applied. All these distribution functions are in general functions of the time, although the time-dependence has not been explicitly indicated in the above equations.

c. The change with time of the probability density

In § 1.4 it is shown that the manner in which a function such as the probability density, $P^{(N)}(\boldsymbol{r}^N, \boldsymbol{p}^N, t)$, changes with time is given by the Liouville equation:

$$\frac{\partial}{\partial t} P^{(N)}(\boldsymbol{r}^N, \boldsymbol{p}^N, t) = [H, P] = \left(\frac{\partial H}{\partial \boldsymbol{r}^N} \cdot \frac{\partial P^{(N)}}{\partial \boldsymbol{p}^N}\right) - \left(\frac{\partial H}{\partial \boldsymbol{p}^N} \cdot \frac{\partial P^{(N)}}{\partial \boldsymbol{r}^N}\right) \tag{2.1–10}$$

As discussed in § 1.4 the Liouville equation is an equation of continuity for the flow of representative points through phase space. Since there are no sources or sinks, the equation may be written in the form:

$$\frac{DP^{(N)}}{Dt} = 0 \tag{2.1–11}$$

in which D/Dt indicates a *substantial derivative* or a *derivative following the motion.*

The vanishing of the substantial derivative indicates that, as any point moves through γ-space, there is no change with time of the density of points in the immediate neighborhood of the point. This corollary to the Liouville theorem is known as the *conservation of density in phase.* A second corollary, the *conservation of extension in phase*, may be also discussed. This corollary states that, following the motion, there is no change with time in the volume occupied by a given set of points, although the shape is continually changing. Let us consider a small region in phase space, $\Delta\tau$, which is sufficiently small that the density of the system points is essentially constant within this region. The number of system points in the region is, accordingly,

$$\Delta n = P^{(N)} \Delta\tau \tag{2.1–12}$$

If the surface of the volume element $\Delta\tau$ is always determined by the system points originally lying upon it, we can follow the behavior of the volume element as time proceeds. Because of the uniqueness of mechanical motions, none of the points within the bounding surface can leave the volume; also there are no sources or sinks of system points. Consequently,

$$\frac{D(\Delta n)}{Dt} = \frac{DP^{(N)}}{Dt} \Delta\tau + P^{(N)} \frac{D(\Delta\tau)}{Dt} = 0 \tag{2.1–13}$$

The term involving $DP^{(N)}/Dt$ vanishes according to Eq. 2.1–11, so that

$$\frac{D}{Dt}(\Delta\tau) = 0 \tag{2.1–14}$$

That the latter equation is also true for a volume extension of any size may be established by summing the results for a number of small elements of volume.

d. Ensembles which represent closed systems in equilibrium

In order for an ensemble to describe a system in equilibrium, the density of points in phase space must remain constant in time. This means, then, from Eq. 2.1–10 that we must require that

$$\frac{\partial}{\partial t} P^{(N)}(\boldsymbol{r}^N, \boldsymbol{p}^N, t) = [H, P^{(N)}] = 0 \tag{2.1–15}$$

This relation is satisfied if $P^{(N)}$ is a constant with respect to the coordinates $\boldsymbol{r}^N$, $\boldsymbol{p}^N$, or if $P^{(N)} = P^{(N)}(\alpha)$, where $\alpha = \alpha(\boldsymbol{r}^N, \boldsymbol{p}^N)$ is a constant of the motion. Constants of motion are properties of a system which do not change with time (if the system is isolated); familiar examples are energy, linear momentum, and angular momentum. Only the first of these constants of motion will concern us here, inasmuch as the second and third correspond to translation and rotation of the system and are usually unimportant thermodynamically. For constants of motion:

$$[H, \alpha] = 0 \tag{2.1–16}$$

Hence, if $P^{(N)}$ is some function of a constant of motion, then

$$[H, P^{(N)}] = (dP^{(N)}/d\alpha)\,[H, \alpha] = 0 \qquad (2.1\text{–}17)$$

So that, according to Eq. 2.1–10,

$$(\partial P^{(N)}/\partial t) = 0 \qquad (2.1\text{–}18)$$

Therefore, if $P^{(N)} = P^{(N)}(\alpha)$, the ensemble represents a steady state or equilibrium distribution.

There are two steady state distribution functions which are of sufficient importance to receive names. At this point we shall simply define the terms; later we show how these concepts are useful and why they are employed.

i. *The Microcanonical Ensemble*

The microcanonical, or energy shell, ensemble is a one-parameter set of distributions used in the study of isolated systems when the volume and energy of the system are known. The distribution function is defined by distributing system points evenly in the region between two neighboring energy surfaces in phase space, no points being distributed outside this region. Mathematically the ensemble is described by

$$\begin{aligned} P^{(N)} &= P_0 \text{ (a constant)} && \text{For energy } H(\boldsymbol{r}^N, \boldsymbol{p}^N) \text{ between } E \text{ and } E + \Delta E \\ P^{(N)} &= 0 && \text{Elsewhere} \end{aligned} \qquad (2.1\text{–}19)$$

By letting $\Delta E \to 0$ one gets a *surface ensemble* in which all systems have exactly the energy, E.

ii. *The Canonical Ensemble*

The canonical ensemble,

$$P^{(N)}(\boldsymbol{r}^N, \boldsymbol{p}^N) = [Z_N N! h^{3N}]^{-1} \exp\,[-H(\boldsymbol{r}^N, \boldsymbol{p}^N)/kT] \qquad (2.1\text{–}20)$$

is also a one-parameter distribution function for various values of T. Here k is the Boltzmann constant, and T is later identified with temperature. Z_N is called the *partition function* (or the *sum-over-states*, or the *Zustandssumme*), and Z_N^{-1} is a normalizing factor. The inclusion of the factors $N!$ and h^{3N} is discussed in § 2.4.

The canonical ensemble is used in the study of systems for which the volume and temperature are specified.[5] For a system with a very large number of degrees of freedom, it approximates closely a microcanonical distribution about an energy corresponding to the most probable value.

[5] This is demonstrated in § 2.3.

That is, the energy distribution represented by a canonical ensemble has a very sharp maximum. The density of points in other energy ranges is negligible. This can be demonstrated easily. The number of system points in a specified volume is

$$P^{(N)}\,d\mathbf{r}^N\,d\mathbf{p}^N = [Z_N N!h^{3N}]^{-1}\,e^{-H(\mathbf{r}^N,\mathbf{p}^N)/kT}\,d\mathbf{r}^N\,d\mathbf{p}^N$$

$$= [Z_N N!h^{3N}]^{-1}\,e^{-H/kT}\left(\frac{d\tau}{dH}\right)dH \qquad (2.1\text{–}21)$$

Clearly the distribution has a sharp maximum, since $(d\tau/dH)$ increases rapidly (as the $(3N-2)/2$ power of H) while the exponential falls off rapidly. (See problem 2 at the end of the chapter.)

The average values which we obtain from the canonical ensemble are exactly the same as those which one calculates from the microcanonical ensemble. In the study of fluctuations, however, we must be quite careful to select the proper ensemble.

e. Ensembles which represent open systems in equilibrium[6]

Thus far only those systems with a fixed number of molecules have been considered. These are called closed systems. Systems in which the number of molecules of each species is not specified are called *open* systems. In such cases an ensemble must be imagined in which the various systems have different numbers, ν, of subsystems (molecules). It may be shown that the ensemble which represents open systems at constant temperature T in a given volume V is the *grand canonical ensemble*:

$$P^{(\nu)}(\mathbf{r}^\nu, \mathbf{p}^\nu) = [Z^{\text{Gr}}\nu!h^{3\nu}]^{-1}\exp\left(\frac{\nu\mu}{kT}\right)\exp\left(-\frac{H(\mathbf{r}^\nu,\mathbf{p}^\nu)}{kT}\right) \qquad (2.1\text{–}22)$$

in which the normalizing constant, Z^{Gr}, is the grand partition function for the system, and μ is the chemical potential. $P^{(\nu)}(\mathbf{r}^\nu, \mathbf{p}^\nu)\,d\mathbf{r}^\nu\,d\mathbf{p}^\nu$ is the probability of finding a system, selected at random from the ensemble, with ν molecules and with coordinates and momenta in the range $d\mathbf{r}^\nu\,d\mathbf{p}^\nu$ about $\mathbf{r}^\nu, \mathbf{p}^\nu$. Similar ensembles may be constructed for open systems under other conditions—for example, a system at constant pressure and temperature.[6]

[6] For a rather detailed discussion of the grand canonical ensemble and its application, see R. H. Fowler and E. A. Guggenheim, *Statistical Thermodynamics*, Cambridge University Press (1949), Second Impression, Chapter VI.

2. Description of Statistical Ensembles in Quantum Mechanics[1, 2]

Thus far it has been assumed that the systems with which we are dealing can be described adequately by classical mechanics. It is necessary, however, to employ quantum mechanics in the treatment of systems composed of atoms and molecules. Here a different point of view must be adopted, since an essential feature of quantum mechanics is that the values of all the momenta and coordinates cannot be completely specified. Prior to the applications of quantum mechanics to ensembles of systems, some of the principal ideas and elements of notation concerned with the quantum mechanics of single systems are summarized.

a. Quantum mechanical treatment of single systems

Let the *state* of a single quantum mechanical system be given by the normalized wave function $\Psi(\boldsymbol{r}^N, t)$. This function has the significance that $|\Psi(\boldsymbol{r}^N, t)|^2 \, d\boldsymbol{r}^N$ is the probability that at time t the coordinates of the system is located within a range $d\boldsymbol{r}^N$ about $\boldsymbol{r}^N$. The *dynamics* of the system is completely specified by the quantum mechanical Hamiltonian, $\mathscr{H}$, and the *change with time* of the state of the system is then given by the Schrödinger time dependent equation (Eq. 1.6–4).

The system wave function, $\Psi(\boldsymbol{r}^N, t)$, may be "analyzed" in terms of any complete orthonormal set of wave functions, $\phi_\rho(\boldsymbol{r}^N)$, with the set of quantum numbers $\{\rho\} = \rho_1, \rho_2, \cdots \rho_{3N}$:

$$\Psi(\boldsymbol{r}^N, t) = \Sigma_\rho c_\rho(t)\phi_\rho(\boldsymbol{r}^N) \tag{2.2–1}$$

(One can, for example, make the expansion in terms of energy eigenfunctions, $\psi_\sigma(\boldsymbol{r}^N)$, with the set of quantum numbers $\{\sigma\} = \sigma_1, \sigma_2, \cdots \sigma_{3N}$). The $c_\rho(t)$ are known as "probability amplitudes", and $|c_\rho(t)|^2$ represents the probability that the system is in the state $\{\rho\}$. The fact that $\Sigma_\rho |c_\rho(t)|^2 = 1$ can be seen at once from the orthonormal properties of the functions $\phi_\rho(\boldsymbol{r}^N)$. The time-dependence of the $c_\rho(t)$ is given by the "generalized" (or "transformed") Schrödinger equation.

$$-\frac{\hbar}{i}\frac{dc_\rho}{dt} = \Sigma_{\rho'} \mathscr{H}_{\rho\rho'} c_{\rho'}(t) \tag{2.2–2}$$

where

$$\mathscr{H}_{\rho\rho'} = \int \phi_\rho^*(\boldsymbol{r}^N) \mathscr{H} \phi_{\rho'}(\boldsymbol{r}^N) \, d\boldsymbol{r}^N \tag{2.2–3}$$

[1] This section was written in collaboration with Professor J. de Boer, University of Amsterdam, The Netherlands.

[2] A more extensive treatment of the material discussed here is found in R. C. Tolman, *The Principles of Statistical Mechanics*, Oxford University Press (1938), Chapters VII, VIII, IX.

The knowledge of the state of the system can thus be given equally well by $\Psi(\boldsymbol{r}^N, t)$, or by a set of probability amplitudes $c_\rho(t)$, and the manner in which the state of the system changes with time can be given equally well by Eq. 1.6–4 or Eq. 2.2–2.

A description of the system in terms of the $c_\rho(t)$ offers a general representation freed from the special role played by the coordinates. The actual values of the probability coefficients depend, of course, upon the particular set of orthonormal functions which is used in the expansion in Eq. 2.2–1. Suppose, for example, that $\Psi(\boldsymbol{r}^N, t)$ is also expanded in a set of functions $\chi_\tau(\boldsymbol{r}^N)$:

$$\Psi(\boldsymbol{r}^N, t) = \Sigma_\tau\, d_\tau(t)\, \chi_\tau(\boldsymbol{r}^N) \tag{2.2–4}$$

If the $\chi_\tau(\boldsymbol{r}^N)$ and the $\phi_\rho(\boldsymbol{r}^N)$ are related by the unitary[3] transformation matrix, $\alpha_{\rho\tau}$:

$$\chi_\tau(\boldsymbol{r}^N) = \Sigma_\rho \alpha_{\rho\tau} \phi_\rho(\boldsymbol{r}^N) \text{ or } \phi_\rho(\boldsymbol{r}^N) = \Sigma_\tau \alpha_{\tau\rho}^{-1} \chi_\tau(\boldsymbol{r}^N) \tag{2.2–5}$$

then

$$c_\rho = \Sigma_\tau \alpha_{\rho\tau}\, d_\tau \text{ or } d_\tau = \Sigma_\rho \alpha_{\tau\rho}^{-1} c_\rho \tag{2.2–6}$$

gives the relation between the probability amplitudes $c_\rho(t)$ and $d_\tau(t)$. The matrix elements $\mathscr{H}_{\rho\rho'}$ transform in the following manner:

$$\mathscr{H}_{\tau\tau'} = \Sigma_\rho \Sigma_{\rho'} \alpha_{\tau\rho}^{-1} \mathscr{H}_{\rho\rho'}\, \alpha_{\rho'\tau'}$$

or

$$\mathscr{H}_{\rho\rho'} = \Sigma_\tau \Sigma_{\tau'} \alpha_{\rho\tau} \mathscr{H}_{\tau\tau'} \alpha_{\tau'\rho'}^{-1} \tag{2.2–7}$$

These various methods of describing quantum mechanical systems are used throughout the remainder of this section and also in the development of the quantum mechanical equation of state in Chapter 6.

b. Definition of the probability density matrix

The discussion has thus far been limited to a single quantum mechanical system. Let us now consider an ensemble of Γ identical systems, the state of the kth system being given by $\Psi^{(k)}(\boldsymbol{r}^N, t)$, or by a set of probability amplitudes, $c_\rho^{(k)}(t)$, defined by:

$$\Psi^{(k)}(\boldsymbol{r}^N, t) = \Sigma_\rho c_\rho^{(k)}(t) \phi_\rho(\boldsymbol{r}^N) \tag{2.2–8}$$

by analogy with Eq. 2.2–1.

[3] A unitary matrix is one for which the conjugate transpose of the matrix is equal to the inverse of the matrix: $\alpha_{mn}{}^* = \alpha_{nm}{}^{-1}$.

We now define a quantum mechanical probability density matrix[4] in either of the two forms:

$$\mathscr{P}^{(N)}(\boldsymbol{r}^N; \boldsymbol{r}'^N) = \Gamma^{-1} \sum_{k=1}^{\Gamma} \Psi^{(k)*}(\boldsymbol{r}'^N, t)\Psi^{(k)}(\boldsymbol{r}^N, t) \qquad (2.2\text{–}9)^5$$

$$\mathscr{P}^{(N)}_{\rho\rho'} = \Gamma^{-1} \sum_{k=1}^{\Gamma} c_{\rho'}^{(k)*}(t) c_{\rho}^{(k)}(t) \qquad (2.2\text{–}10)$$

The second form, $\mathscr{P}^{(N)}_{\rho\rho'}$, depends upon the particular set of wave functions, $\phi_\rho(\boldsymbol{r}^N)$, which is chosen as a basis for the description of the system. A transition to a new system of eigenfunctions, $\chi_\tau(\boldsymbol{r}^N)$, as given in Eq. 2.2–5, gives rise to a probability density matrix, $\mathscr{P}^{(N)}_{\tau\tau'}$, which bears the following relation to $\mathscr{P}^{(N)}_{\rho\rho'}$:

$$\mathscr{P}^{(N)}_{\tau\tau'} = \Sigma_\rho \Sigma_{\rho'} \alpha^{-1}_{\tau\rho} \mathscr{P}^{(N)}_{\rho\rho'} \alpha_{\rho'\tau'}$$

or (2.2–11)

$$\mathscr{P}^{(N)}_{\rho\rho'} = \Sigma_\tau \Sigma_{\tau'} \alpha_{\rho\tau} \mathscr{P}^{(N)}_{\tau\tau'} \alpha^{-1}_{\tau'\rho'}$$

making use of Eq. 2.2–7.

It should be pointed out that $\mathscr{P}^{(N)}(\boldsymbol{r}^N, \boldsymbol{r}'^N)$ can actually be regarded as a special form of the generalized matrix $\mathscr{P}^{(N)}_{\rho\rho'}$. In this case "coordinate eigenfunctions" (that is, Dirac δ-functions[6]) are chosen as the basis for the representation of the system:

$$\Psi^{(k)}(\boldsymbol{r}^N, t) = \int \Psi^{(k)}(\boldsymbol{r}''^N, t)\, \delta(\boldsymbol{r}''^N - \boldsymbol{r}^N)\, d\boldsymbol{r}''^N \qquad (2.2\text{–}12)$$

The transformation matrix (corresponding to $\alpha_{\rho\tau}$ in Eq. 2.2–5 connecting the expansion functions $\phi_\rho(\boldsymbol{r}^N)$ and $\delta(\boldsymbol{r}''^N - \boldsymbol{r}^N)$ is $\phi_\rho{}^*(\boldsymbol{r}''^N)$, so that we may write equations analogous to Eqs. 2.2–5, 6, and 7:

$$\delta(\boldsymbol{r}''^N - \boldsymbol{r}^N) = \Sigma_\rho \phi_\rho{}^*(\boldsymbol{r}''^N)\phi_\rho(\boldsymbol{r}^N)$$

or (2.2–13)

$$\phi_\rho(\boldsymbol{r}^N) = \int \phi_\rho(\boldsymbol{r}''^N)\delta(\boldsymbol{r}''^N - \boldsymbol{r}^N)\, d\boldsymbol{r}''^N$$

[4] It has been shown by J. von Neumann [*Gott. Nachr.*, p. 245 (1927); *Math. Grundlagen der Quantenmechanik* (Berlin)] and by P. A. M. Dirac [*Proc. Cambridge Phil. Soc.*, **25**, 62 (1929); *ibid.*, **26**, **27**, 240, 376 (1930); *The Principles of Quantum Mechanics*, Oxford University Press (1935)] that it is the quantity defined in Eq. 2.2–9, which is the quantum mechanical analogue of the classical probability in γ-space.

[5] Note that $\boldsymbol{r}^N$ and $\boldsymbol{r}'^N$ are two different vectors in $3N$-dimensional space, just as ρ and ρ' are two different sets of quantum numbers.

[6] The Dirac δ-functions $\delta(\boldsymbol{r}''^N - \boldsymbol{r}^N)$ have the property that they are zero everywhere except when $|\boldsymbol{r}''^N - \boldsymbol{r}^N| = 0$, and at this point they are so large that the integral of a Dirac δ-function over all configuration space is unity. For other properties of the Dirac δ-function, see L. I. Schiff, *Quantum Mechanics*, McGraw-Hill (1949), p. 50.

$$\left\{\begin{array}{l} c_\rho^{(k)}(t) = \int \phi_\rho^*(\boldsymbol{r}''^N)\Psi^{(k)}(\boldsymbol{r}''^N, t)\, d\boldsymbol{r}''^N \\ \text{or} \\ \Psi^{(k)}(\boldsymbol{r}''^N, t) = \Sigma_\rho \phi_\rho(\boldsymbol{r}''^N) c_\rho^{(k)}(t) \end{array}\right. \tag{2.2–14}$$

$$\left\{\begin{array}{l} \mathscr{H}(\boldsymbol{r}^N; \boldsymbol{r}'^N) = \Sigma_\rho \Sigma_{\rho'} \phi_\rho(\boldsymbol{r}^N)\, \mathscr{H}_{\rho\rho'} \phi_{\rho'}^*(\boldsymbol{r}''^N) \\ \text{or} \\ \mathscr{H}_{\rho\rho'} = \iint \phi_\rho^*(\boldsymbol{r}''^N) \mathscr{H}(\boldsymbol{r}''^N; \boldsymbol{r}'^N) \phi_{\rho'}(\boldsymbol{r}'^N)\, d\boldsymbol{r}'^N\, d\boldsymbol{r}''^N \end{array}\right. \tag{2.2–15}$$

Accordingly,

$$\left\{\begin{array}{l} \mathscr{P}^{(N)}(\boldsymbol{r}^N; \boldsymbol{r}'^N) = \Sigma_\rho \Sigma_{\rho'} \phi_\rho(\boldsymbol{r}^N)\, \mathscr{P}^{(N)}_{\rho\rho'} \phi_{\rho'}^*(\boldsymbol{r}'^N) \\ \text{or} \\ \mathscr{P}^{(N)}_{\rho\rho'} = \iint \phi_\rho^*(\boldsymbol{r}''^N) \mathscr{P}^{(N)}(\boldsymbol{r}''^N; \boldsymbol{r}'^N) \phi_{\rho'}(\boldsymbol{r}'^N)\, d\boldsymbol{r}'^N\, d\boldsymbol{r}''^N \end{array}\right. \tag{2.2–16}$$

gives the interrelation between $\mathscr{P}^{(N)}(\boldsymbol{r}^N; \boldsymbol{r}'^N)$ and $\mathscr{P}^{(N)}_{\rho\rho'}$. (2.2–17)

It is formally convenient to introduce a *probability operator* $\mathscr{P}^{(N)}$, defined by:

$$\mathscr{P}^{(N)} \phi_\rho(\boldsymbol{r}^N) = \Sigma_{\rho'} \mathscr{P}^{(N)}_{\rho\rho'} \phi_{\rho'}(\boldsymbol{r}^N) = \int \mathscr{P}^{(N)}(\boldsymbol{r}^N; \boldsymbol{r}'^N) \phi_\rho(\boldsymbol{r}'^N)\, d\boldsymbol{r}'^N \tag{2.2–18}$$

which allows Eqs. 2.2–16 and 2.2–17 to be written as:

$$\mathscr{P}^{(N)}(\boldsymbol{r}^N; \boldsymbol{r}'^N) = \Sigma_\rho \phi_\rho^*(\boldsymbol{r}'^N) \mathscr{P}^{(N)} \phi_\rho(\boldsymbol{r}^N) \tag{2.2–19}$$

$$\mathscr{P}^{(N)}_{\rho\rho'} = \int \phi_\rho^*(\boldsymbol{r}^N)\, \mathscr{P}^{(N)} \phi_{\rho'}(\boldsymbol{r}^N)\, d\boldsymbol{r}^N \tag{2.2–20}$$

The choice of this probability operator $\mathscr{P}^{(N)}$ (and hence of the matrices $\mathscr{P}^{(N)}(\boldsymbol{r}^N; \boldsymbol{r}'^N)$ and $\mathscr{P}^{(N)}_{\rho\rho'}$) depends upon the system which is to be represented by the ensemble. It will be shown presently that, for an equilibrium ensemble, the operator must be a function of an operator associated with some constant of motion of the system.

c. The physical significance of the density matrix

In classical statistical mechanics the probability density, $P^{(N)}(\boldsymbol{r}^N, \boldsymbol{p}^N)$, is a function of N position vectors, $\boldsymbol{r}^N$, and of N momentum vectors, $\boldsymbol{p}^N$. We have said that the quantum analogue of this function is $\mathscr{P}^{(N)}(\boldsymbol{r}^N; \boldsymbol{r}'^N)$, which is a function of the two sets of N vectors, $\boldsymbol{r}^N$ and $\boldsymbol{r}'^N$ (or, in general, $\mathscr{P}^{(N)}_{\rho\rho'}$, which is a function of both sets of $3N$ quantum numbers, $\{\rho\}$ and $\{\rho'\}$). It is virtually impossible to give a clear-cut physical picture of the matrices, $\mathscr{P}^{(N)}(\boldsymbol{r}^N, \boldsymbol{r}'^N)$ and $\mathscr{P}^{(N)}_{\rho\rho'}$, but, as is frequently the case in quantum mechanics, it is usually convenient to ascribe physical meaning to the diagonal elements. In the classical theory the probability of finding a system of the ensemble selected at random in a configuration $\mathbf{r}^N$ is given by

$$P^{(N)}(\mathbf{r}^N) = \int P^{(N)}(\mathbf{r}^N, \mathbf{p}^N)\, d\mathbf{p}^N \tag{2.2–21}$$

In quantum mechanics this is accomplished by taking the diagonal element, $\mathscr{P}^{(N)}(\mathbf{r}^N, \mathbf{r}^N)$. With this quantity, then, is associated the probability that any randomly selected system in the ensemble will be in the configuration $\mathbf{r}^N$. Similarly, with $\mathscr{P}^{(N)}_{\rho\rho}$ is associated the probability that the system be found in the state with a set of quantum numbers $\{\rho\}$. Of particular importance is the case where the expansion of the system wave function (Eq. 2.2–1) has been made in terms of energy eigenfunctions, $\psi_\sigma(\mathbf{r}^N)$, so that $\mathscr{P}^{(N)}_{\sigma\sigma}$ represents the probability that the system is in energy state $\{\sigma\}$.

In analogy with the normalization of the classical probability function we define the quantum mechanical probability density matrix so that

$$\int \mathscr{P}^{(N)}(\mathbf{r}^N; \mathbf{r}^N)\, d\mathbf{r}^N = \Sigma_\rho \mathscr{P}^{(N)}_{\rho\rho} = 1 \tag{2.2–22}$$

The classical operation of integrating the probability function over all of γ-space corresponds in quantum mechanics to taking the trace of the probability density matrix.

d. Other probability densities

Several other probability densities simply derivable from $\mathscr{P}^{(N)}(\mathbf{r}^N; \mathbf{r}'^N)$ may now be introduced; the use of these functions simplifies many of the formulae which we encounter in the discussion of the quantum mechanical equation of state.

First, we define the *specific probability density matrix* $\mathscr{P}^{(h)}(\mathbf{r}^\eta; \mathbf{r}'^\eta)$, thus:

$$\mathscr{P}^{(h)}(\mathbf{r}^\eta; \mathbf{r}'^\eta) = \int \mathscr{P}^{(N)}(\mathbf{r}^\eta \mathbf{r}^{N-\eta}; \mathbf{r}'^\eta \mathbf{r}^{N-\eta})\, d\mathbf{r}^{N-\eta} \tag{2.2–23}$$

This matrix is obtained by taking the diagonal elements of those molecules not belonging to the group of h molecules $\iota, \kappa, \cdots \lambda \equiv \{\eta\}$ and then integrating over the position vectors of the $(N - h)$ molecules. The diagonal element, $\mathscr{P}^{(h)}(\mathbf{r}^\eta; \mathbf{r}^\eta)$, then represents the probability that in any randomly selected system the group of molecules $\{\eta\}$ will be in the configuration $\mathbf{r}^\eta$.

In addition we define the *generic probability density matrix* as:

$$\mathscr{N}^{(h)}(\mathbf{r}^\eta; \mathbf{r}'^\eta) = \frac{N!}{(N-h)!}\, \mathscr{P}^{(h)}(\mathbf{r}^\eta; \mathbf{r}'^\eta) \tag{2.2–24}$$

the factor $[N!/(N - h)!]$ being the number of possible ways in which h objects may be selected from N objects. The diagonal elements of this matrix are the quantum mechanical analogs of the generic configurational probability density given in Eq. 2.1–8.

e. Time-dependence of the density matrix; equilibrium ensembles for closed systems

By combining Eqs. 2.2–9 and 1.6–4 or by combining Eqs. 2.2–10 and 2.2–2, we can obtain immediately the relations

$$\frac{\partial}{\partial t}\mathscr{P}^{(N)}(\boldsymbol{r}^N; \boldsymbol{r}'^N) = -\frac{i}{\hbar}(\mathscr{H}\mathscr{P}^{(N)} - \mathscr{P}^{(N)}\mathscr{H})(\boldsymbol{r}^N; \boldsymbol{r}'^N) \tag{2.2–25}$$[7]

$$\frac{\partial}{\partial t}\mathscr{P}^{(N)}_{\rho\rho'} = -\frac{i}{\hbar}(\mathscr{H}\mathscr{P}^{(N)} - \mathscr{P}^{(N)}\mathscr{H})_{\rho\rho'} \tag{2.2–26}$$

These equations are analogous to the Liouville equation in classical statistical mechanics.

A steady-state distribution (one for which $\partial\mathscr{P}^{(N)}/\partial t = 0$) is one such that $(\mathscr{H}\mathscr{P}^{(N)} - \mathscr{P}^{(N)}\mathscr{H}) = 0$. The vanishing of this commutator can occur only if the probability density matrix is a function of some matrix which represents a constant of motion. In the case of the two types of equilibrium ensembles used for the representation of closed systems discussed in the previous section, the matrices can be written explicitly:

(i) *Microcanonical Ensemble*

$$\begin{aligned} &\mathscr{P}^{(N)}_{\sigma\sigma'} = C\delta_{\sigma\sigma'} \quad \text{within a small energy range, } E_0 \leq E_\sigma \leq E_0 + \delta E \\ &\mathscr{P}^{(N)}_{\sigma\sigma'} = 0 \quad \text{outside this energy range} \end{aligned} \tag{2.2–27}$$

(ii) *Canonical Ensemble*

$$\mathscr{P}^{(N)}_{\rho\rho'} = Z_{N_q}^{-1} \exp(-\mathscr{H}_{\rho\rho'}/kT) \tag{2.2–28}$$

Here the normalizing constant Z_{N_q} is the quantum mechanical partition function, or "sum-over-states". The microcanonical ensemble clearly is useful for representing isolated, closed systems. It is shown later in this chapter that closed systems at constant temperature are represented by a canonical ensemble. Both ensembles give identical results for the calculation of average values (see § 2.3), and hence for this purpose the ensembles may be used interchangeably. Because the microcanonical ensemble is a discontinuous function of the energy and the canonical

[7] $(\mathscr{H}\mathscr{P}^{(N)} - \mathscr{P}^{(N)}\mathscr{H})(\boldsymbol{r}^N; \boldsymbol{r}'^N)$ means the $\boldsymbol{r}^N; \boldsymbol{r}'^N$ element of the matrix $(\mathscr{H}\mathscr{P}^{(N)} - \mathscr{P}^{(N)}\mathscr{H})$.

ensemble is continuous, the latter is considerably more convenient from a mathematical standpoint.

f. Equilibrium ensembles for open systems (grand canonical ensemble)

For considering open systems in a given volume V and at a constant temperature T, the probability operator may be represented by

$$\mathscr{P}^{(\nu)} = (Z_q^{\mathrm{Gr}})^{-1} \exp\left(\frac{\nu\mu}{kT}\right) \exp\left(-\frac{\mathscr{H}^{(\nu)}}{kT}\right) \tag{2.2–29}$$

in which Z_q^{Gr} is the normalizing constant (the quantum mechanical grand partition function), μ is the chemical potential, and $\mathscr{H}^{(\nu)}$ is the quantum mechanical Hamiltonian for a system of ν molecules. The number of particles of a representative ensemble, ν, is here represented by an ordinary number. Actually, to be strictly correct, ν should be replaced by an operator, in much the same way as the energy is represented by an operator.[8]

Equations 2.2–19 and 20 may be used to arrive at the following relations:

$$\mathscr{P}^{(\nu)}(\boldsymbol{r}^\nu; \boldsymbol{r}^\nu) = (Z_q^{\mathrm{Gr}})^{-1} e^{\mu\nu/kT} \Sigma_\rho \phi_\rho^*(\boldsymbol{r}^\nu)\, e^{-\mathscr{H}^{(\nu)}/kT} \phi_\rho(\boldsymbol{r}^\nu) \tag{2.2–30}$$

$$\mathscr{P}^{(\nu)}_{\sigma\sigma} = (Z_q^{\mathrm{Gr}})^{-1} e^{\mu\nu/kT}\, e^{-E_\sigma^{(\nu)}/kT} \tag{2.2–31}$$

which represent, respectively, the probability of finding, in a system selected from the ensemble at random, a system with ν molecules and configuration $\boldsymbol{r}^\nu$ and a system with ν molecules and an energy $E_\sigma^{(\nu)}$.

3. The Basis of Statistical Mechanics

We have discussed the classical and quantum mechanics of complex systems and introduced the terminology necessary for the statistical treatment of such systems. At the present time, it is very difficult to make further progress in describing the properties of such systems without utilizing statistical concepts. Such a process might be accomplished using high-speed computing devices. However, the resulting knowledge of the detailed microscopic behavior would have little value unless it were interpreted in terms of the macroscopic properties. From an empirical or thermodynamic point of view it is known that the macroscopic state of the system is specified by a small number of "state variables," such as the pressure and temperature. From the macroscopic standpoint an entire set of state variables specifies the complete past and future of the system.

[8] This has been discussed by K. Husimi, *Proc. Phys. Math. Soc. Japan*, Series 3, **22**, 264 (1940); see particularly Part II, §§ 6, 11, and 12.

a. Justification of the microcanonical ensemble

The macroscopic properties of a system in equilibrium do not change in time. On the other hand, the microscopic dynamical state of the system changes in time, and from the point of view of classical mechanics, the representative point traces out a trajectory in phase space. The observed properties of the system are time average values over a trajectory. An important theorem due to G. D. Birkhoff[1] shows that for almost all trajectories (that is, all except a set of measure zero) such a time average exists in the sense that there is a limiting value for large time intervals.

A second portion of Birkhoff's theorem states that the time average of an arbitrary function of the coordinates and momenta of a system along a trajectory is equal to the average over a subspace of the phase space. This subspace is that region of phase space for which the entire set of constants of motion have a particular specified set of values. An "ergodic" system is one such that the only constants of motion are the energy and the components of the linear and angular momenta. It is probable that most physical systems of interest are ergodic. Hence, assuming that we are dealing with an ergodic system, we may represent the system by an ensemble in which the representative points are uniformly distributed in a region of phase space in which the energy and linear and angular momenta have specified values. Statistical mechanics is usually applied to non-rotating systems at rest with respect to the chosen coordinate system.[2] Hence the members of the ensemble have zero linear and angular momenta and a specified energy. This is just the microcanonical ensemble defined in § 2.1. This ensemble represents a system of specified energy, that is, an isolated system. Quite often we are not interested in the properties of an isolated system, but rather a system in a thermostat of known temperature. As we shall see presently, the canonical ensemble represents such a system.

b. Use of the microcanonical ensemble to obtain an expression for the distribution of energies among macroscopic subsystems

Let us consider an isolated system made up of a large number, N, of identical subsystems. The subsystems are assumed to be macroscopic in size (so that they may be numbered) and separated from each other in

[1] A. L. Khinchin, *The Mathematical Foundations of Statistical Mechanics*, Dover Publications, Inc. (New York). Also see lecture notes of Harold Grad, *Kinetic Theory and Statistical Mechanics* [Institute of Mathematics and Mechanics, New York University (1950)].

[2] Rotating systems may be considered by the present method by introducing fictitious external forces or by considering a new ensemble. Tolman has considered the latter method [R. C. Tolman, *Statistical Mechanics*, Oxford University Press (1938)].

such a manner that energy but not mass may be transferred from one subsystem to another. Thus each subsystem is effectively bathed in a thermostat made up of a finite number of identical members. The terminology of classical mechanics is used to describe the situation. Later the results of the quantum treatment will be given. Let us refer to the phase space of the entire system as γ-space and that of a single subsystem as μ-space so that the microscopic dynamical state of a single system may be represented by means of a single point in γ-space or by a cloud of numbered points in μ-space. For counting purposes it is convenient to divide γ-space into a large number of small cells, each of volume $\Delta\tau_\gamma$. These cells are then numbered so that the state of a system may be specified either by giving the coordinates of the system point or by giving the number of the cell in which the point is located. Of course the second method of describing the dynamical state of the system is somewhat less precise. However, by making the cell sufficiently small, the state of the system can be specified to any degree of precision.

Now each cell of γ-space corresponds to a collection of N cells in μ-space, one associated with each of the N identical subsystems. If we are told which cell in γ-space the system point is in, then we can tell in what cells of μ-space the subsystem points lie. Because of the identity of the subsystems, the only thing that is important as far as bulk properties are concerned is how many (and not which) subsystem points are located in each cell of μ-space. Thus we define a *condition* of the system by the set of numbers specifying how many subsystem points lie in each cell of μ-space. In general, *several states* of the system correspond to *one condition*. Let n_i be the number of subsystem points in the ith cell of μ-space. The n_i, which define the condition of the system, are referred to as the *occupation numbers*. The number of cells in γ-space (that is, the number of states of the system) which correspond to a given condition is given by

$$\frac{N!}{n_1!\,n_2!\,n_2!\cdots} \tag{2.3–1}$$

As discussed above, the observable properties of the system are time average values over a natural trajectory in γ-space. This time average, however, is the same as "phase average" over an "ergodic surface." For most (if not all physical systems) this ergodic surface is a constant energy "surface" in the γ-space.[3] Hence for computing the probable behavior of a single system we represent the system by a microcanonical ensemble, that is, we say that all states of the system, of a particular

[3] For a more exact treatment see A. I. Khinchin, *The Mathematical Foundation of Statistical Mechanics*, Dover Publications (New York).

energy, are equally likely.[4] Hence the probability, W, of finding the system in a particular condition specified by the set of occupation numbers $n_1, n_2, n_3, \ldots$ is

$$W = \frac{1}{C} \frac{N!}{\Pi_j n_j!} \tag{2.3–2}$$

where C is the normalization factor.

Clearly, the most probable condition of the system is described by that set of occupation numbers which leads to a maximum value of W. However, it is not possible to vary all the occupation numbers independently, for they must satisfy the following two constraints:

$$\Sigma_j n_j = N \tag{2.3–3}$$

$$\Sigma_j n_j E_j = E \tag{2.3–4}$$

where E is the total energy of the system and E_j is the energy of a subsystem whose representative point lies in cell j.

Thus to determine the most probable condition of the system, we maximize W with respect to all variations in the n_i subject to the constraints described by Eqs. 2.3–3 and 4. We assume that the n_i are sufficiently large that Stirling's approximation is justified and also that they may be considered as continuous variables. These approximations, however, introduce no appreciable error. Let δn_j, $\delta \ln W$, δN, and δE be small variations in n_j, $\ln W$, N, and E. Then, for the stationary value of W:

$$\delta \ln W = -\Sigma_j(\ln n_j + 1)\, \delta n_j = 0 \tag{2.3–5}$$

along with the constraints:

$$\delta N = \Sigma_j\, \delta n_j = 0 \tag{2.3–6}$$

$$\delta E = \Sigma_j E_j\, \delta n_j = 0 \tag{2.3–7}$$

Using the method of Lagrangian multipliers,[5] we form the expression

$$\delta \ln W - (\alpha - 1)\, \delta N - \beta\, \delta E = 0 \tag{2.3–8}$$

where α and β are arbitrary constants to be determined later in terms of N and E. Making use of Eqs. 2.3–5, 6, and 7, we may rewrite Eq. 2.3–8 as

$$\Sigma_j(\ln n_j + \alpha + \beta E_j)\, \delta n_j = 0 \tag{2.3–9}$$

[4] It is necessary here to use the concept of the volume of the phase cell, since the distribution of representative points on the constant energy surface is not uniform but rather depends upon the rate of change of $H(\boldsymbol{r}^N, \boldsymbol{p}^N)$, with distance normal to the surface. This fact arises through the concepts of "measure theory" which enter into the proof of Birkhoff's theorem.

[5] See, for example, I. S. and E. S. Sokolnikoff, *Higher Mathematics for Engineers and Physicists*, McGraw-Hill (1941), pp. 163 et seq.

in which α and β are the undetermined constants. Since the δn_j may now be considered arbitrary variations the coefficients of each δn_j must be individually zero. Thus

$$\ln \bar{n}_j + \alpha + \beta E_j = 0$$

or (2.3–10)

$$\bar{n}_j = \exp\,[-\alpha - \beta E_j]$$

where the bar indicates the most probable value and the $\bar{n}_j$ are the values of the occupation numbers which maximize W. This result indicates the most probable condition of the system or the most probable arrangement of the subsystems among the cells in the μ-space.

c. Ensemble averages and fluctuations

In general there is a finite probability $W(n_1, n_2, \ldots)$ of finding the system in a particular condition other than the most probable condition. However, if the system contains a large number of subsystems, the $W(n_1, n_2, \ldots)$ other than the maximum value $\overline{W} = W(\bar{n}_1, \bar{n}_2, \cdots)$ approach zero as N becomes large. This result is exact in the limit as $N \to \infty$. For finite N there are small fluctuations about the most probable distribution.

Let us consider a dynamical variable, $X(\boldsymbol{r}^N, \boldsymbol{p}^N)$, of a system. The value of the dynamical variable for the system in the state k (that is, if the system point is in the kth cell of γ-space) is $X^{(k)}$. The ensemble average of X is

$$\bar{X} = \Sigma_k P_k X^{(k)} \tag{2.3–11}$$

where P_k is the normalized probability of finding the system in the state, k. That is, the set of P_k defines the ensemble. In this case, since the ensemble is the microcanonical, the P_k are zero unless the cell is one of energy, E, in which case the value is a constant determined by the normalization.

Because of the identity of the subsystems, $X^{(k)}$ has the same value for all states corresponding to one condition. Hence the sum in Eq. 2.3–11 may be rewritten as a sum over conditions rather than over states:

$$\bar{X} = \Sigma_i W_i X^{(i)} \tag{2.3–12}$$

where W_i is the probability of finding the system in the condition i specified by the set of occupation numbers n_i. The values of the W_i are given by Eq. 2.3–2. The maximum value of W_i denoted by $\overline{W}$ is that corresponding to the most probable occupation numbers shown in Eq. 2.3–10.

Let us consider the probability $\overline{W} + \delta W$ of a condition which is only slightly different from the most probable. It will be shown that the ratio of $\overline{W} + \delta W$ to the probability $\overline{W}$ of the most probable condition becomes small as the total number of subsystems, N, becomes large. Let the $\bar{n}_j$ be the occupation numbers specifying the most probable condition, and $\bar{n}_j + \delta n_j$ be those of a slightly different condition. Then, from Eq. 2.3–2,

$$\frac{\overline{W} + \delta W}{\overline{W}} = \frac{\Pi_i \bar{n}_i!}{\Pi_i (\bar{n}_i + \delta n_i)!} \qquad (2.3\text{–}13)$$

Now, making use of Stirling's approximation and the fact that both the $\bar{n}_j$ and the perturbed values $\bar{n}_j + \delta n_j$ satisfy the constraints given in Eqs. 2.3–3 and 2.3–4, we can rearrange Eq. 2.3–13 to obtain an expression for the ln $[(\overline{W} + \delta W)/\overline{W}]$ correct to terms of the second order in the variation:

$$\ln\left(\frac{\overline{W} + \delta W}{\overline{W}}\right) = -\Sigma_i\, \delta n_i \ln \bar{n}_i - \frac{1}{2} \Sigma_i \frac{(\delta n_i)^2}{\bar{n}_i} + \cdots \qquad (2.3\text{–}14)$$

Since the $\bar{n}_i$ are the occupation numbers which make W_i a maximum, the first variation is zero, and we obtain for the "curvature"

$$\ln\left(\frac{\overline{W} + \delta W}{\overline{W}}\right) = -\frac{N}{2} \Sigma_i \frac{(\delta a_i)^2}{\bar{a}_i} \qquad (2.3\text{–}15)$$

where $\bar{a}_i = \bar{n}_i/N$ and $\delta a_i = \delta n_i/N$ represent the most probable relative occupation numbers and the corresponding variation. As N becomes large, the most probable relative occupation numbers remain constant. Hence we can make the ratio of the probability of any particular condition to that of the most probable condition as small as desired by making N, the total number of subsystems, sufficiently large.

To show that in the limit of large N only the most probable condition contributes to the average value of X, let us consider the sum of Eq. 2.3–12. For large values of N, the summation may be replaced by an integration,

$$\bar{X} = \frac{\int \cdots \int XW\, dn_1\, dn_2 \cdots}{\int \cdots \int W\, dn_1\, dn_2 \cdots} \qquad (2.3\text{–}16)$$

Although the denominator is unity due to the normalization, it is convenient to write the expression in this form. The integrations are over the hypersurfaces consistent with the constraints of Eqs. 2.3–3 and 4. Now dividing numerator and denominator by the same powers of N and using the Eq. 2.3–15 for W, we find:

$$\bar{X} = \frac{\int \cdots \int X \exp\{-\frac{N}{2} \Sigma_i(a_i - \bar{a}_i)^2/\bar{a}_i\}\, da_1\, da_2 \cdots}{\int \cdots \int \exp\{-\frac{N}{2} \Sigma_i(a_i - \bar{a}_i)^2/\bar{a}_i\}\, da_1\, da_2 \cdots} \tag{2.3–17}$$

where $(a_i - \bar{a}_i)$ has been written in place of the variation $\delta\bar{a}_i$. The value of X depends only on the relative occupation numbers, and X may be expanded in a Taylor's series about the values corresponding to the most probable condition. The result is

$$\begin{aligned} X = X_0 &+ \Sigma_i(a_i - \bar{a}_i)\left(\frac{\partial X}{\partial a_i}\right)_0 \\ &+ \tfrac{1}{2}\,\Sigma_i\Sigma_j(a_i - \bar{a}_i)(a_j - \bar{a}_j)\left(\frac{\partial^2 X}{\partial a_i \partial a_j}\right)_0 + \cdots \end{aligned} \tag{2.3–18}$$

where the subscript zeros denote values corresponding to the $\bar{a}_i$. For purposes of the integration, the X_0, $(\partial X/\partial a_i)_0$, $(\partial^2 X/\partial a_i\, \partial a_j)_0, \ldots$ are constants. The first term in Eq. 2.3–17 leads to the contribution of X_0 to $\bar{X}$. The other terms lead to contributions which can be made as small as desired by making N sufficiently large. By a simple change of variables it is clear that the term in $\bar{X}$ which involves the sth derivative of X becomes zero for large values of N as $N^{-s/2}$. Thus, for large values of N,

$$\bar{X} = X_0 \tag{2.3–19}$$

This indicates that, for systems containing a large number of subsystems, the most probable condition is the only one which contributes to the average values. Furthermore in the limit of infinitely large N, fluctuations in the state of the system become zero.

d. The distribution of energy among molecules in a gas

Let us apply the formalism of the previous discussion to the case of the classical ideal gas, in which there are no forces between the molecules. In this case the system under consideration is the volume of gas, and the subsystems are the molecules in the gas. The total energy, E, of the system is the sum of the energies, E_j, of the individual molecules. The energy, E_j, is in turn the sum of the kinetic energy and the energy in the internal degrees of freedom of a molecule. The value of E_j depends upon the coordinates[6] of the jth cell $(\boldsymbol{q}, \boldsymbol{p})$ and is given by the Hamiltonian

[6] Here $\boldsymbol{q}$ represents the set of generalized coordinates describing the location and configuration of a single molecule and $\boldsymbol{p}$ the corresponding set of conjugate momenta. That is, $\boldsymbol{q}$ and $\boldsymbol{p}$ are vectors in the f-dimensional molecule configuration and momentum spaces, respectively.

function for the individual molecule, $H(\boldsymbol{q}, \boldsymbol{p})$. Since $P^{(1)}(\boldsymbol{q}, \boldsymbol{p})$ is defined to be the normalized distribution of representative points in μ-space, the occupation numbers, $\bar{n}_j$, can be expressed in the form

$$\bar{n}_j = N \int_{j\text{th cell}} P^{(1)}(\boldsymbol{q}, \boldsymbol{p})\, d\boldsymbol{q}\, d\boldsymbol{p} \tag{2.3–20}$$

Hence if the cells are chosen to be sufficiently small, the most probable distribution function is

$$P^{(1)}(\boldsymbol{q},\boldsymbol{p}) = \frac{1}{zh^f}\, e^{-\beta H(\boldsymbol{q},\boldsymbol{p})} \tag{2.3–21}$$

in which zh^f is the appropriate normalization constant. It is shown in § 2.4 that the Lagrangian multiplier β has the physical significance of $1/kT$. Since the gas is made up of a finite number of molecules, there is a finite, although small, probability of finding the gas in a different condition—that is, described by a different distribution function.

For a monatomic gas (with no intermolecular or external forces) the Hamiltonian of a single molecule is

$$H(\boldsymbol{r}, \boldsymbol{p}) = p^2/2m \tag{2.3–22}$$

Thus Eq. 2.3–21 becomes

$$P^{(1)}(\boldsymbol{r}, \boldsymbol{p}) = \frac{1}{V}(2\pi mkT)^{-3/2}\, e^{-p^2/2mkT} \tag{2.3–23}$$

This function is so normalized that integration over all μ-space gives unity. For some purposes (and in particular in discussions of kinetic theory it is more convenient to introduce the distribution function $f^{(1)}(\boldsymbol{r}, \boldsymbol{p})$, which is normalized so that integration over the molecule momentum space gives n, the number density. This function is

$$f^{(1)}(\boldsymbol{r}, \boldsymbol{p}) = n(2\pi mkT)^{-3/2}\, e^{-p^2/2mkT} \tag{2.3–24}$$

or, in terms of molecular velocity, $\boldsymbol{v}$:

$$f(\boldsymbol{r}, \boldsymbol{v}) = n(m/2\pi kT)^{3/2}\, e^{-mv^2/2kT} \tag{2.3–25}$$

which is called the "Maxwell-Boltzmann distribution of velocities." This result is also obtained as the equilibrium solution of the Boltzmann equation of kinetic theory. It may be shown that the Maxwell-Boltzmann function (Eq. 2.3–25) also describes the distribution of velocities of the molecules in a non-ideal gas (one with intermolecular forces) and also gases made up of polyatomic molecules. Examples of applications of Eqs. 2.3–21 and 25 are given in problems at the end of the chapter.

e. Justification for the use of the canonical ensemble

The methods described in the preceding section are not applicable to the treatment of the imperfect gases, liquids, or solids. For such systems, the total energy is the sum of the energies of the individual molecules and the energy associated with the intermolecular interactions. Hence it is necessary to use a more powerful method of statistical mechanics, which can be obtained by a different interpretation of the general formalism discussed in § 1.3b.

In the treatment of the perfect gas the individual molecules were regarded as subsystems, and the vessel of gas was taken to be the system. For studying real substances, in which there are forces between the molecules, we choose as the subsystem the vessel containing an imperfect gas (liquid or solid) of N molecules. The system is taken to be a very large collection, Γ, of these vessels of gas, each with rigid walls, arranged in such a way that there is thermal contact between them. That is, energy, but not mass, may be transferred between these vessels. Any one vessel of gas may be pictured as being imbedded in a large thermostat, made up of a huge collection of similar vessels of gas. Equation 2.3–10 may then be interpreted as giving the probability of finding the point representing the vessel of gas in the jth cell of phase space with energy E_j. The energy, E_j, depends upon the coordinates of the jth cell $(\boldsymbol{r}^N, \boldsymbol{p}^N)$ and is the sum of the kinetic energy of all the molecules in the vessel and the energy associated with the internal degrees of freedom and the intermolecular forces. Thus E_j is given by the Hamiltonian function $H(\boldsymbol{r}^N, \boldsymbol{p}^N)$. Since $P^{(N)}(\boldsymbol{r}^N, \boldsymbol{p}^N)$ is defined to be the normalized distribution function in the phase space corresponding to the N molecules of the gas, the occupation numbers, n_j, are given in terms of an integral over the jth cell in this phase space,

$$\bar{n}_j = \Gamma \int_{j\text{th cell}} P^{(N)}(\boldsymbol{r}^N, \boldsymbol{p}^N)\, d\boldsymbol{r}^N\, d\boldsymbol{p}^N \qquad (2.3\text{–}26)$$

Therefore, if the cells are taken to be sufficiently small, the function representing the most probable distribution of phase points (corresponding to the vessels of gas) may be written as

$$P^{(N)}(\boldsymbol{r}^N, \boldsymbol{p}^N) = \frac{1}{N!h^{3N}Z_N}\, e^{-\beta H(\boldsymbol{r}^N, \boldsymbol{p}^N)} \qquad (2.3\text{–}27)$$

where $Z_N N! h^{3N}$ is the normalization factor and β will be shown to be $1/kT$. As is shown in § 2.3c, if we assume that the system is composed of a large number, Γ, of vessels of gas, then, in the limit that Γ approaches infinity, the probability of finding this collection of vessels in a condition different from that described in Eq. 2.3–27 is zero.

The collection of a large number of similar vessels of gas surrounding and having thermal contact with the vessel under consideration forms an ideal thermostat. However, the properties of a gas at equilibrium do not depend upon the materials or constructional details of the thermostat. This fact can be shown statistically by applying arguments similar to those discussed above to a vessel in which molecules of type A are on one side of a rigid thermally conducting partition and molecules of type B are on the other side. It is found that the distribution functions of the two types of gases are characterized by the same value of β. Now, going to successively more complicated systems in which a vessel of A is surrounded by more and more vessels of B in thermal contact, we find that the value of β remains unchanged and the distribution is still given by Eq. 2.3–27.

The ensemble represented by the distribution function given by Eq. 2.3–27 is known as the canonical ensemble and represents a system of known temperature or a system imbedded in a thermostat. As discussed in § 2.1, if N is large, this distribution function leads to a distribution in energy which has a very sharp maximum. For this reason, the canonical ensemble may be considered as a convenient mathematical approximation to the microcanonical ensemble, with the energy corresponding to the most probable energy of the canonical ensemble. Indeed, insofar as all the average properties of the system are concerned, the two ensembles give identical results. However, for the study of fluctuation phenomena it is important that the system under consideration be represented by the appropriate ensemble.

The distribution function $P^{(N)}(\boldsymbol{r}^N, \boldsymbol{p}^N)$ provides a more complete description of the state of the system than that given by the simple Maxwell-Boltzmann function, $P^{(1)}(\boldsymbol{q}, \boldsymbol{p})$, derived in the previous paragraph. The function $P^{(N)}(\boldsymbol{r}^N, \boldsymbol{p}^N)$ provides information as to the probability of the relative positions of the molecules, that is, the probability of occurrence of pairs and clusters. The distribution function $P^{(1)}(\boldsymbol{q}, \boldsymbol{p})$ may be obtained from $P^{(N)}(\boldsymbol{r}^N, \boldsymbol{p}^N)$ by integration over all the momentum and configurational coordinates except those for one molecule. The function $P^{(1)}(\boldsymbol{q}, \boldsymbol{p},)$ obtained in this manner justifies the application of the Maxwell-Boltzmann distribution to the case of non-ideal gases, liquids, or solids. (It should be recalled that $P^{(1)}(\boldsymbol{q}, \boldsymbol{p})$ was obtained in § 2.3d for ideal gases only.)

f. Calculation of ensemble averages

It was shown at the beginning of this section that the observable properties of a system can be calculated as average values over an ensemble of systems. Specifically, for a property $X(\boldsymbol{r}^N, \boldsymbol{p}^N)$, the average (observed) value is

$$\bar{X} = \iint X(\boldsymbol{r}^N, \boldsymbol{p}^N) P^{(N)}(\boldsymbol{r}^N, \boldsymbol{p}^N)\, d\boldsymbol{r}^N\, d\boldsymbol{p}^N \qquad (2.3\text{–}28)$$

The distribution function for the microcanonical ensemble is given in Eq. 2.1–19. For the canonical ensemble the distribution function is given by Eq. 2.3–27 and

$$\bar{X} = \frac{1}{Z_N N! h^{3N}} \iint X(\mathbf{r}^N, \mathbf{p}^N) \exp\,[-\beta H(\mathbf{r}^N, \mathbf{p}^N)]\, d\mathbf{r}^N\, d\mathbf{p}^N \quad (2.3\text{–}29)$$

is the expression for the average value of a dynamical variable, X.

The treatment given here applies strictly only to classical systems. Similar results may be obtained using quantum mechanical methods. The quantum mechanical average value of a dynamical variable $X(\mathbf{r}^N, \mathbf{p}^N)$ (represented by the operator $\mathscr{X}$) for the kth system in the ensemble, which is in a state specified by the wave function $\Psi^{(k)}$, is

$$X^{(k)} = \int \Psi^{(k)*}(\mathbf{r}^N) \mathscr{X} \Psi^{(k)}(\mathbf{r}^N)\, d\mathbf{r}^N \quad (2.3\text{–}30)$$

The average value of the dynamical variable over the ensemble is simply the arithmetic average:

$$\begin{aligned} \bar{X} &= \Gamma^{-1}\Sigma_k X^{(k)} \\ &= \Gamma^{-1}\Sigma_k \int \Psi^{(k)*}(\mathbf{r}^N, t) \mathscr{X} \Psi^{(k)}(\mathbf{r}^N, t)\, d\mathbf{r}^N \quad (2.3\text{–}31)^7 \\ &= \Gamma^{-1}\Sigma_k \Sigma_\rho \Sigma_{\rho'} c_{\rho'}^{(k)*}(t) c_\rho^{(k)}(t) \mathscr{X}_{\rho'\rho} \end{aligned}$$

where Γ is the number of systems in the ensemble. The last expression is in terms of the expansion coefficients $c^{(k)}(t)$ (see Eq. 2.2–1). This expression may also be written in terms of the probability operator, $\mathscr{P}$:

$$\begin{aligned} \bar{X} &= \int (\mathscr{P}\mathscr{X})(\mathbf{r}^N; \mathbf{r}^N)\, d\mathbf{r}^N \\ &= \Sigma_\rho (\mathscr{P}\mathscr{X})_{\rho\rho} \end{aligned} \quad (2.3\text{–}32)$$

The probability operator for the microcanonical ensemble is given by Eq. 2.2–27 and for the canonical ensemble by Eq. 2.2–28. For the latter ensemble we have

$$\begin{aligned} \bar{X} &= \frac{1}{Z_{Nq}} \int [\Sigma_\rho \phi_\rho^*(\mathbf{r}^N) \mathscr{X} e^{-\beta\mathscr{H}} \phi_\rho(\mathbf{r}^N)]\, d\mathbf{r}^N \\ &= \frac{1}{Z_{Nq}} \Sigma_\sigma \mathscr{X}_{\sigma\sigma} e^{-\beta E_\sigma} \end{aligned} \quad (2.3\text{–}33)$$

for the average value of the dynamical property associated with the quantum mechanical operator, $\mathscr{X}$.

[7] $\mathscr{X}_{\rho\rho'}$ is an abbreviation for the integral:

$$\mathscr{X}_{\rho\rho'} = \int \phi_\rho^*(\mathbf{r}^N) \mathscr{X} \phi_{\rho'}(\mathbf{r}^N)\, d\mathbf{r}^N$$

4. The Fundamentals of Statistical Thermodynamics

In order for the statistical mechanical results of the previous sections to be useful, it is necessary that they be interpreted in terms of macroscopically measurable quantities. In this section we show how statistical mechanics may be used to define the thermodynamic quantities called internal energy, entropy, and temperature. Furthermore, the three fundamental laws of thermodynamics may be derived from statistical principles. The relationship between statistical mechanics and thermodynamics is usually discussed in terms of the *partition function.* Hence we preface the treatment of statistical thermodynamics by a brief discussion of the partition function in quantum and classical statistics.

a. The partition function

The quantum mechanical partition function[1] for a system of N molecules, Z_{Nq}, has already been defined as the normalizing constant for the quantum mechanical canonical distribution function. The partition function (which is sometimes referred to as the *sum-over-states* or *Zustandssumme*) is defined by either of the two equivalent relations:

$$Z_{Nq} = \underbrace{\Sigma_j e^{-\beta E_j}}_{\text{Sum over all energy \textit{states}}} = \underbrace{\Sigma_j g_j\, e^{-\beta E_j}}_{\text{Sum over all energy \textit{levels}}} \tag{2.4-1}$$

In the first expression E_j represents the energy of the system in a quantum state with quantum numbers $\{j\} = j_1, j_2, \cdots$. On the other hand, in the second expression, E_j is the energy associated with the jth energy level, and the degeneracy of the level is indicated by g_j (that is, the jth level is composed of g_j states). Both forms for the partition function are in common use in the literature, and in this book we use whichever form is more convenient. The partition function is a function of β (which is shown later in this section to be $1/kT$) and also of any mechanical properties of the system which influence the energy levels. Usually the only mechanical parameter of the system which enters is the volume. In § 2.5 the explicit nature of the volume dependence of the E_j will be discussed in connection with practical thermodynamical calculations.

The quantum mechanical partition function may also be written as an integral over configuration space:

$$Z_{Nq} = \int \Sigma_p \phi_p^*(\boldsymbol{r}^N) e^{-\beta \mathscr{H}} \phi_p(\boldsymbol{r}^N)\, d\boldsymbol{r}^N \tag{2.4-2}$$

analogous to the form given in Eq. 2.2–19 for $\mathscr{P}^{(N)}(\boldsymbol{r}^N, \boldsymbol{r}^N)$. When the partition function is written in this fashion, the volume dependence

[1] Both the classical and the quantum mechanical partition functions are designated by Z_N. When it is desired to distinguish between the two quantities, a subscript q serves to indicate the quantum mechanical partition function.

manifests itself in the limits of the integration over configuration space and also in the boundary conditions which the expansion function ϕ_p must satisfy.

In the correspondence limit where classical behavior is approached, it may be shown[2] that the partition function given in Eq. 2.4–2 becomes an integral over the classical phase space:

$$Z_N = [N!h^{3N}]^{-1} \iint e^{-\beta H(\mathbf{r}^N, \mathbf{p}^N)} \, d\mathbf{r}^N \, d\mathbf{p}^N \qquad (2.4\text{–}3)$$

This expression for the classical partition function[3] is valid only for a system of N identical, structureless particles. The factor $N!$ which appears in the denominator is due to the Pauli exclusion principle. Because the particles are identical, certain regions of phase space are equivalent in that they correspond to a simple renumbering of the particles. Since there are $N!$ permutations of the set of N particles, the factor $(1/N!)$ "corrects" for this equivalence. Such corrections must always be made in classical formulae. The factor h^{3N} in the expression for the classical partition function may be interpreted as the volume of a cell in γ-space. In the remainder of this section the quantum mechanical form of the partition function is used.

b. The internal energy and the first law of thermodynamics

Using the formula for the quantum mechanical partition function just given and the expression for ensemble averages given in Eq. 2.3–33, we may write at once the following expression for the internal energy, U, of a system bathed in a thermostat:[4]

$$U = \frac{\sum_j E_j e^{-\beta E_j}}{\sum_j e^{-\beta E_j}} \qquad (2.4\text{–}4)$$

The internal energy may also be expressed directly as a derivative of the logarithm of the partition function:

$$U = -\left(\frac{\partial \ln Z_N}{\partial \beta}\right)_V \qquad (2.4\text{–}5)$$

[2] In Chapter 6 the quantum-classical correspondence of the probability density is derived in detail. The proof that Z_{Nq} of Eq. 2.4–2 approaches Z_N of Eq. 2.4–3 in the correspondence limit may be proved in exactly the same way, and is therefore not presented here.

[3] The classical partition function is sometimes called the *phase integral*. This terminology should not be confused with the Sommerfeld-Wilson phase integrals of old quantum theory, $\oint p\, dq$.

[4] According to the notation of Eq. 2.3–33, we should call this quantity $\bar{E}$. We prefer, however, to use the thermodynamic symbol U instead.

where the subscript V indicates that the external mechanical parameters (such as the volume) of the system are held fixed.

In its differential form the first law of thermodynamics may be written as:

$$dU = \delta q - \delta w \tag{2.4–6}$$

δq is the small quantity of heat absorbed by the system, and δw is the work done by the system while undergoing a small change in state. dU is an exact differential whereas δq and δw are both inexact differentials. It is also possible to write an expression for dU in terms of the energy levels of the system. Letting $\bar{a}_j = Z_N^{-1} \exp(-\beta E_j)$, we may write Eq. 2.4–4 as[5]

$$U = \Sigma_j \bar{a}_j E_j \tag{2.4–7}$$

whence

$$dU = \Sigma_j E_j \, d\bar{a}_j + \Sigma_j \bar{a}_j \, dE_j \tag{2.4–8}$$

The first term on the right-hand side represents the change in energy due to a redistribution of the total energy over the various quantum states of the system. The second term gives the change in energy which results from the shift in the energy states of the system caused by the alteration of the volume (or other external parameters). This latter term may clearly be associated with δw, and the former with δq, thus:

$$\delta q = \Sigma_j E_j \, d\bar{a}_j \tag{2.4–9}$$

$$\delta w = -\Sigma \bar{a}_j \, dE_j \tag{2.4–10}$$

Equation 2.4–8 may then be regarded as giving a microscopic interpretation of the first law of thermodynamics.

c. Temperature and entropy and the second law of thermodynamics

It is now necessary to introduce the concepts of temperature and entropy. In the axiomatic thermodynamics[6] the reciprocal of the temperature is defined as an integrating factor of the heat change, and entropy is defined in terms of the perfect differential so obtained. The statistical definition of entropy is based on an analogy with this approach. We have obtained expressions which are intuitively related to the concepts of infinitesimal heat and work terms. The reciprocal of the temperature is defined as the integrating factor for this infinitesimal heat change, and the entropy is defined by the perfect differential which results.

[5] The $\bar{a}_j = \bar{n}_j/N$ are the *relative occupation numbers* introduced in § 2.3c, which are equivalent to the $\mathscr{P}_{jj}$ of § 2.2. Because of the double index,the latter notation is not convenient in the above discussion.

[6] S. Chandrasekhar, *An Introduction to the Study of Stellar Structure*, University of Chicago Press (1939), Chapter 1.

Let us define a function S, the *entropy*, by the relation

$$S = k(\ln Z_N + \beta U) + S_0 = S(E_1, E_2, \cdots \beta) \tag{2.4–11}$$

in which k is Boltzmann's constant and S_0 is a constant. It is now possible to define a perfect differential dS as

$$\begin{aligned} dS &= \left(\frac{\partial S}{\partial \beta}\right)_{E_1 E_2 \cdots} d\beta + \Sigma_j \left(\frac{\partial S}{\partial E_j}\right)_\beta dE_j \\ &= kd(\ln Z_N + \beta U) \end{aligned} \tag{2.4–12}$$

Using the definition of the partition function and the relations in Eqs. 2.4–9 and 2.4–10 for δq and δw, we get

$$\begin{aligned} dS &= -\frac{k}{Z_N}\Sigma_j(\beta\, dE_j + E_j\, d\beta)e^{-\beta E_j} + k\beta\, dU + kU\, d\beta \\ &= k\beta[dU - \Sigma_j \bar{a}_j\, dE_j] \\ &= k\beta\, \delta q \equiv \frac{1}{T}\delta q \end{aligned} \tag{2.4–13}$$

This demonstrates that $k\beta$, or $(1/T)$, is an integrating factor for the heat change. That is, multiplication of the inexact differential δq by $(1/T)$ yields an exact differential dS the differential of the entropy.

This in itself does not define the temperature T uniquely. However, if in addition it is required that the entropy be an extensive property, then it can be shown that the choice is unique except for a multiplicative constant (the scale factor). An empirical temperature is often defined by the perfect gas thermometer. This temperature is related to the equation of state by the equation $pV = NkT$. The thermodynamic temperature just defined is identical with this temperature since, as shown in § 3.1, the present treatment leads to the same equation of state.

We may hence rewrite the expression for the entropy as

$$S = k\left[\ln Z_N + \frac{U}{kT}\right] + S_0 \tag{2.4–14}$$

In this manner we have succeeded in introducing temperature and entropy by a method analogous to thermodynamics. Clearly S and T are both state functions.

To complete the statistical proof of the second law of thermodynamics it would be necessary to show that the entropy of an isolated system never decreases. This is the content of the famous H-theorem. The proof of this theorem, in general, is considerably too lengthy to be included here and may be found in other textbooks.[7] A proof applying to the special case of a perfect gas, however, is discussed in § 7.3.

d. Entropy at absolute zero and the third law of thermodynamics

The constant S_0, which occurs in the definition of entropy just given, is independent of the temperature and the mechanical parameters of the system. In the limit as the temperature goes to absolute zero:

$$\lim_{T\to 0} S = \lim_{T\to 0} k\left[\ln \Sigma_j g_j e^{-E_j/kT} + \frac{\partial \ln \Sigma_j g_j e^{-E_j/kT}}{\partial \ln T}\right] + S_0$$

$$= k \ln g_0 + S_0 \tag{2.4-15}$$

in which g_0 is the degeneracy of the ground state of the system.

Let us now consider two states of the same system: one state consists of the chemical AB in a vessel at the absolute zero; the other state consists of two vessels—one of A and one of B—both at the absolute zero. It is possible to conceive of a reversible process by which the system may be transformed from one state to the other. Hence the two states AB and $A + B$ are really two states of the same system, differing only in the mechanical parameters describing the state. Since S_0 is the same for both states, the entropy difference in the states of the system is

$$S_{AB} - S_{A+B} = k \ln (g_{AB}/g_A g_B) \tag{2.4-16}$$

If all three materials, A, B, and AB, are such that their ground states are non-degenerate, $g_A = g_B = g_{AB} = 1$, and

$$\Delta S = S_{AB} - (S_A + S_B) = 0 \tag{2.4-17}$$

For many systems the lowest state is normally considered to be multiply degenerate. However, there is usually a small separation of the energy levels due to small perturbations which are ordinarily neglected. As kT approaches zero, these very small separations become effectively large compared with kT. Hence it is probable that, strictly speaking, the ground state is always non-degenerate, and Eq. 2.4-17 is valid.

Inasmuch as S_0 always cancels out, it is convenient to let it be exactly zero and define the entropy as

$$S = k \ln Z_N + (U/T) \tag{2.4-18}$$

[7] See, for example, R. H. Tolman, *Principles of Statistical Mechanics*, Oxford University Press (1938), for a summary of the proofs of this theorem in classical and quantum statistics.

With this definition, the third law of thermodynamics assumes the form

$$\lim_{T\to 0} S = k \ln g_0 \tag{2.4–19}$$

and if the ground state of the system is non-degenerate

$$\lim_{T\to 0} S = 0 \tag{2.4–20}$$

The quantity g_0 is the true degeneracy of the lowest quantum state of the system. However, if the statistically computed entropies are compared with calorimetrically measured entropies, it may be necessary to modify somewhat the meaning of this quantity. For if the separation of the lowest levels of the system is small compared with kT_0, where T_0 is the lowest measurable temperature, there would be a small hump in the specific heat curve at a lower temperature. The contribution of this hump to the entropy would be ignored in the integration of experimental C_p/T data. For this purpose it is necessary to consider as degenerate the group of levels separated by energies small compared to kT_0.

e. The thermodynamic properties in terms of the partition function

We have now seen how the fundamental thermodynamic functions, energy and entropy, can be expressed in terms of the partition function—which in turn depends upon the energy levels of the system. Therefore, if the detailed information about the energy levels of a system is available, it is possible to calculate all the thermodynamic properties from the partition function. The relations needed for this may be summarized as follows:

$$U = kT^2 \left(\frac{\partial \ln Z_N}{\partial T}\right) \tag{2.4–21}$$

$$C_v = \frac{\partial}{\partial T}\left(kT^2 \frac{\partial \ln Z_N}{\partial T}\right) \tag{2.4–22}$$

$$S = k \ln Z_N + (U/T) \tag{2.4–23}$$

$$A = U - TS = -kT \ln Z_N \tag{2.4–24}$$

For systems in which the only external mechanical parameter is the volume V, we have the additional relations

$$p = -\left(\frac{\partial A}{\partial V}\right)_T = kT\left(\frac{\partial \ln Z_N}{\partial V}\right)_T \tag{2.4–25}$$

$$H = U + pV = kT^2\left(\frac{\partial \ln Z_N}{\partial T}\right)_V + kTV\left(\frac{\partial \ln Z_N}{\partial V}\right)_T \tag{2.4–26}$$

$$G = H - TS = -kT \ln Z_N + kTV \left(\frac{\partial \ln Z_N}{\partial V}\right)_T \tag{2.4–27}$$

The first of these last three relations is used in the derivation of the equation of state from statistical mechanics.

5. The Evaluation of the Thermodynamic Properties of Ideal Gases

In this section we discuss in detail an important application of the principles of statistical thermodynamics, namely, the calculation of the thermodynamic properties of gases at sufficiently low densities that their behavior can be considered to be ideal. It is first shown that the symmetry restrictions imposed on the wave functions for systems made up of identical particles lead to two types of distributions of energy among the molecules in the gas: one for the *Fermi-Dirac* gases and another for the *Bose-Einstein* gases. At high temperatures the two distribution functions approach one another, and the thermodynamic properties of the two kinds of gases become the same. This limiting form for the two types of statistics is referred to as *Boltzmann Statistics*. In the last half of this section the thermodynamic properties of the Boltzmann gas are calculated, and the contributions due to the internal degrees of freedom are described.

a. The partition function for the ideal gas

If the density of a gaseous system of N molecules is sufficiently low and if the intermolecular forces are short range (compared to Coulombic), the amount of time any molecule spends in collisions is negligible compared with the time between collisions. Under such conditions we may say that the intermolecular potential energy is negligible with respect to the total energy of the system and hence that the total energy is just the sum of the energies of the individual molecules. Each of the molecules may be in any one of the quantum states of the free molecule. However, since the molecules are identical, the state of the gas is specified by the number of molecules in each state. That is, it is meaningless to specify which molecules are in which states. It is hence convenient to specify the state of the gas by means of the set of occupation numbers n_j^k which give the number of molecules in the jth molecular quantum state, when the gas is in state k with total energy E_k.

Let the energy of a molecule in the jth state be ϵ_j. Then, since the energy of the gas is the sum of that of the individual molecules, the energy of the gas in the kth state is

$$E_k = \Sigma_j n_j^k \epsilon_j \tag{2.5–1}$$

where the n_j^k satisfy the relation

$$N = \Sigma_j n_j^k \tag{2.5–2}$$

There are, in addition, restrictions on the n_j^k due to statistics. As was pointed out in § 1.6, the occupation numbers are restricted to 0 and 1 for Fermi-Dirac statistics. However, for Bose-Einstein particles the symmetry requirements on the wave function of the gas do not limit the number of molecules in any state.

The partition function for the entire gas may be written as

$$\begin{aligned} Z_N &= \Sigma_k e^{-E_k/kT} \\ &= \Sigma_k e^{-[\Sigma_j n_j^k \epsilon_j]/kT} \\ &= \Sigma_k w_1^{n_1^k} w_2^{n_2^k} w_2^{n_3^k} \cdots \end{aligned} \tag{2.5–3}$$

in which

$$w_j = e^{-\epsilon_j/kT} \tag{2.5–4}$$

It is understood that the sum over k is taken only over those sets of n_j^k which are consistent with the statistics of the individual molecules and with the constraint in Eq. 2.5–2.

Let us now define a generating function $f(\zeta)$ by

$$f(\zeta) = \Pi_j(1 \pm \zeta w_j)^{\pm 1} \tag{2.5–5}$$

In this expression and those which follow, the upper sign corresponds to Fermi-Dirac statistics and lower sign to Bose-Einstein statistics. The partition function, Z_N, is then just the coefficient of ζ^N in the expansion of $f(\zeta)$. If ζ is now taken to be a complex variable, we can divide $f(\zeta)$ by $\zeta^{(N+1)}$ and use the method of residues (or Cauchy's theorem) to obtain Z_N:

$$Z_N = \frac{1}{2\pi i} \oint_C \zeta^{-N-1} f(\zeta)\, d\zeta \tag{2.5–6}$$

The closed contour C selected for the integration in the complex domain must be chosen in such a way as to enclose $\zeta = 0$. This integral can be evaluated by the "method of steepest descents,"[1] and the result is

$$\ln Z_N = -N \ln \zeta_0 \pm \Sigma_j \ln (1 \pm \zeta_0 e^{-\epsilon_j/kT}) \tag{2.5–7}$$

The auxiliary relation

$$N = \Sigma_j[\zeta_0^{-1}\, e^{+\epsilon_j/kT} \pm 1]^{-1} \tag{2.5–8}$$

serves to define the parameter ζ_0, which is a positive real number.

b. Distribution of energy among the molecules of an ideal gas

In § 2.3 the distribution of energies among the molecules in a classical (Boltzmann) gas was obtained. We now wish to find the energy distribution among the molecules for a Fermi-Dirac and Bose-Einstein gas.

[1] R. H. Fowler and E. A. Guggenheim, *Statistical Thermodynamics*, Cambridge University Press (1939), Chapter 2.

It has already been shown that the canonical ensemble represents a system for which the volume and temperature have been specified. Accordingly, Eq. 2.3–33 gives the average value of any dynamical quantity. Making use of this formula, we find that the expectation values of the n_j are given by[2]

$$\bar{n}_j = \frac{\Sigma_k n_j^k e^{-E_k/kT}}{\Sigma_k e^{-E_k/kT}} \tag{2.5–9}$$

or, expressing the E_k by means of Eq. 2.5–1, we have

$$\bar{n}_j = \frac{\Sigma_k n_j^k e^{-[\Sigma_i n_i^k \epsilon_i]/kT}}{Z_N} \tag{2.5–10}$$

and, finally,

$$\bar{n}_j = -\frac{kT}{Z_N}\left(\frac{\partial Z_N}{\partial \epsilon_j}\right) \tag{2.5–11}$$

Care must be exercised in obtaining $(\partial Z_N/\partial \epsilon_j)$ from Eq. 2.5–7 for ζ_0 is a function of the ϵ_j. The result of the differentiation is[3]

$$\bar{n}_j = [\zeta_0^{-1}\, e^{\epsilon_j/kT} \pm 1]^{-1} \tag{2.5–12}$$

This describes the manner in which the energy in a Fermi-Dirac or Bose-Einstein gas is distributed among the individual molecules. The parameter ζ_0 may be shown to be related to the Gibbs free energy by $G = NkT \ln \zeta_0$.

For most actual systems $\zeta_0^{-1} \gg 1$, the main exceptions being electrons in metals and gases at extremely low temperatures or very high densities. If this condition applies

$$\zeta_0^{-1} = (V/N)(2\pi mkT/h^2)^{3/2} = 3.122 \times 10^{-4}\tilde{V}(MT)^{3/2}$$

where $\tilde{V}$ is the volume in cubic centimeters per mole, and M is the molecular weight. For a perfect gas at standard conditions

$$\zeta_0^{-1} = 31{,}590M^{3/2}$$

Systems which have a value of ζ_0^{-1} small enough so that the ± 1 cannot be

[2] Here we use the bar to denote the average value of the occupation number, whereas in Eq. 2.3–10 the bar denotes the most probable value. For systems containing a large number of molecules these quantities are essentially identical and differ only because of the negligible fluctuations.

[3] The distribution functions for Fermi-Dirac and Bose-Einstein gases may also be obtained by combinatorial analysis, as was done in § 2.3. See, for example, R. C. Tolman, *Principles of Statistical Mechanics*, Oxford University Press (1936), Chapter X.

neglected are sometimes referred to as *degenerate* systems, or are said to be *in a state of degeneracy*. For most applications we can use the distribution

$$\bar{n}_j \doteq \zeta_0 e^{-\epsilon_j/kT} \tag{2.5–13}$$

We see thus that the Fermi-Dirac and Bose-Einstein distributions approach as a limit the Maxwell-Boltzmann distribution obtained in § 2.3. Furthermore, in this limit, the partition function for the gas as given by Eq. 2.5–7 becomes

$$Z_N = \frac{z^N}{N!} \tag{2.5–14}$$

where z is the partition function for one molecule in the vessel:

$$z = \Sigma_j e^{-\epsilon_j/kT} \tag{2.5–15}$$

The $N!$ which appears here is of course due fundamentally to the indistinguishability of the molecules. Systems whose partition functions are given by Eq. 2.5–14 are said to obey Boltzmann statistics. It is this kind of statistics which is used in the remainder of this chapter. The problem of calculating the thermodynamic properties for the Boltzmann gas has thus been reduced to that of determining the partition function for one molecule in the vessel. The computation of the partition function for a single molecule will be considered in the remaining part of this section.

c. Contributions to the thermodynamic properties due to the translational and internal motions of the molecules

In order to calculate accurately the partition function for complex molecules it is necessary to know all the energy levels of the system. Because of the large number of degrees of freedom, this is very difficult, and a great deal of information is required which is ordinarily not available. However, for most practical purposes it suffices to idealize the situation and to neglect the weak couplings between various degrees of freedom. Since the statistical thermodynamics of perfect gases has been discussed in many textbooks, only a brief discussion is presented here.

For a complex molecule, let the quantum mechanical Hamiltonian be $\mathscr{H}$, and let the wave function and energy corresponding to the jth quantum state be ψ_j and ϵ_j, respectively, so that

$$\mathscr{H}\,\psi_j = \epsilon_j \psi_j \tag{2.5–16}$$

For present purposes, the set of energy levels ϵ_j is taken relative to the ground state as zero. In considering mixtures of different chemical species it is necessary to refer the energy of the ground states of chemical species to a consistent set of standard states chosen for the elements.

This is discussed later in this section. The motions executed by the polyatomic molecule are very complex. In general, however, it is possible to consider the motion as being made up of six types of motion: the overall translation of the molecule (tr); the various stretching and bending vibrations (vib); the rotational motion of the entire molecule (rot); the various rotations or restricted rotations of groups within the molecule (int rot); the electronic motion (elec); and the nuclear spin (nucl). These several motions are to various extents independent of one another. For example, the rotational motion is nearly independent of the electronic motion but frequently rather strongly linked to the vibrational motion. Nevertheless, as a first approximation we may assume that all these motions are independent so that

$$\mathscr{H} = \mathscr{H}^{(\mathrm{tr})} + \mathscr{H}^{(\mathrm{rot})} + \Sigma\mathscr{H}^{(\mathrm{vib})} + \Sigma\mathscr{H}^{(\mathrm{int\ rot})} + \mathscr{H}^{(\mathrm{elec})} + \mathscr{H}^{(\mathrm{nucl})} \tag{2.5–17}$$

$$= \mathscr{H}^{(\mathrm{tr})} + \Sigma\mathscr{H}^{(\mathrm{i})} \tag{2.5–18}$$

Here we designate the various internal (non-translational) motions by superscript (i). This assumption then enables us to separate the Schrödinger equation (2.5–16) into component parts:

$$\mathscr{H}^{(\mathrm{tr})}\,\phi_j^{(\mathrm{tr})} = \epsilon_j^{(\mathrm{tr})}\,\phi_j^{(\mathrm{tr})} \tag{2.5–19}$$

$$\mathscr{H}^{(\mathrm{i})}\,\phi_j^{(\mathrm{i})} = \epsilon_j^{(\mathrm{i})}\,\phi_j^{(\mathrm{i})} \tag{2.5–20}$$

The solution of these individual Schrödinger equations gives the energy levels necessary to obtain partition functions for the various types of motions:

$$z^{(\mathrm{tr})} = \Sigma_j e^{-\epsilon_j^{(\mathrm{tr})}/kT} \tag{2.5–21}$$

$$z^{(\mathrm{i})} = \Sigma_j e^{-\epsilon_j^{(\mathrm{i})}/kT} \tag{2.5–22}$$

As a consequence of the definition of the molecular partition function and the partition functions for the various types of motion, and inasmuch as the energy of the molecule in any state is assumed to be simply the sum of the energies associated with the several types of motion,

$$z = z^{(\mathrm{tr})}\Pi_{\mathrm{i}} z^{(\mathrm{i})} \tag{2.5–23}$$

Now, according to Eq. 2.5–14, the partition function for the entire gas of N molecules may be written as

$$Z_N = \frac{z^N}{N!} = \frac{[z^{(\mathrm{tr})}]^N}{N!}\,[\Pi_{\mathrm{i}} z^{(\mathrm{i})}]^N \tag{2.5–24}$$

Inasmuch as it is always $\ln Z_N$ which appears in the expressions for the thermodynamic functions, these may be written as a sum of the contributions from the translational and various internal motions:

$$X = X^{(\mathrm{tr})} + \Sigma_i X^{(\mathrm{i})} \tag{2.5–25}$$

in which X can be the internal energy, specific heats, free energy, etc. It is usually customary to include the $N!$ in the translational contribution as indicated; the latter is the predominant contribution in most cases. Accordingly, the various contributions are given by[4]

$$\begin{aligned}
U^{(\mathrm{tr})} &= NkT^2\left(\frac{\partial \ln z^{(\mathrm{tr})}}{\partial T}\right) & U^{(\mathrm{i})} &= NkT^2\left(\frac{\partial \ln z^{(\mathrm{i})}}{\partial T}\right)\\
S^{(\mathrm{tr})} &= \frac{U^{(\mathrm{tr})}}{T} + Nk\left[\ln\left(\frac{z^{(\mathrm{tr})}}{N}\right) + 1\right] & S^{(\mathrm{i})} &= \frac{U^{(\mathrm{i})}}{T} + Nk \ln z^{(\mathrm{i})}\\
A^{(\mathrm{tr})} &= -NkT\ln\left(\frac{z^{(\mathrm{tr})}}{N}\right) - NkT & A^{(\mathrm{i})} &= -NkT\ln z^{(\mathrm{i})}\\
H^{(\mathrm{tr})} &= U^{(\mathrm{tr})} + NkT & H^{(\mathrm{i})} &= U^{(\mathrm{i})}\\
G^{(\mathrm{tr})} &= A^{(\mathrm{tr})} + NkT & G^{(\mathrm{i})} &= A^{(\mathrm{i})}\\
C_v^{(\mathrm{tr})} &= (\partial U^{(\mathrm{tr})}/\partial T)_V & C_v^{(\mathrm{i})} &= (\partial U^{(\mathrm{i})}/\partial T)_V\\
C_p^{(\mathrm{tr})} &= C_v^{(\mathrm{tr})} + Nk & C_p^{(\mathrm{i})} &= C_v^{(\mathrm{i})}
\end{aligned} \tag{2.5–26}$$

Thus, to calculate the thermodynamic functions of an ideal gas, we simply add together the contributions for the various types of motion which are active within the molecules. A complete description of the methods for calculating these various contributions for complex molecules would require a discussion of great length and the inclusion of many tabulated functions. Inasmuch as such complete treatments of the subject are readily available in several standard references,[5] the discussion here is confined to several simple calculations for monatomic and diatomic molecules.

i. *Translational Contributions*

Unless the gas is at a temperature very near the absolute zero, the translational contributions to the thermodynamic properties may be computed from the classical partition function. The molecule is considered to be confined to a volume V and its classical Hamiltonian

[4] In the translational contributions, Stirling's formula for $\ln N!$ has been used: $\ln N! \doteq N \ln N - N$.

[5] For instance, J. E. Mayer and M. G. Mayer, *Statistical Mechanics*, Wiley (1940).

is simply: $(p_x^2 + p_y^2 + p_z^2)/2m$. Then the phase integral for the translational motion is

$$z^{(\mathrm{tr})} = \frac{V}{h^3} \int_{-\infty}^{+\infty} \int_{-\infty}^{+\infty} \int_{-\infty}^{+\infty} e^{-\frac{p_x^2+p_y^2+p_z^2}{2mkT}} \, dp_x \, dp_y \, dp_z \qquad (2.5\text{–}27)$$

in which the factor V results from the trivial integration over the spatial coordinates, x, y, z. The integration over the momenta is a standard integral, and we get immediately

$$z^{(\mathrm{tr})} = \frac{V}{h^3} (2\pi mkT)^{3/2} = V\lambda^{-3} \qquad (2.5\text{–}28)$$

where $\lambda = h/\sqrt{2\pi mkT}$ is $2/\pi$ times the de Broglie wavelength for the arithmetic mean molecular velocity discussed in § 1.2. This shows explicitly how the partition function can depend on certain mechanical parameters of the system—in this case, the volume. From formulae relating the thermodynamic functions to the partition function, the familiar relations for the quantities per mole,

$$\tilde{U}^{(\mathrm{tr})} = \tfrac{3}{2} RT; \quad \tilde{C}_v^{(\mathrm{tr})} = \tfrac{3}{2} R; \quad \tilde{C}_p^{(\mathrm{tr})} = \tfrac{5}{2} R \qquad (2.5\text{–}29)$$

can be easily verified. It may also be shown that the entropy per mole is

$$\begin{aligned} \tilde{S}^{(\mathrm{tr})} &= R(\tfrac{3}{2} \ln M + \tfrac{3}{2} \ln T + \ln \tilde{V}) + 2.6546 \\ &= R(\tfrac{3}{2} \ln M + \tfrac{5}{2} \ln T - \ln p) - 2.3141 \end{aligned} \qquad (2.5\text{–}30)$$

in which the constants are just combinations of various universal constants.[6] This expression for the entropy is the Sackur-Tetrode equation. For a monatomic gas, the translational contributions are the sole contributions to the thermodynamic properties. For gases composed of polyatomic molecules these are generally the primary contributions.

ii. *Rotational Contributions in Diatomic Molecules*

If a diatomic molecule is pictured as a rigid dumbbell with moment of inertia I, rotating in three dimensions, the solution of the Schrödinger equation for the system gives the energy and degeneracy of the Jth level, where J is the rotational quantum number:

$$\epsilon_J^{(\mathrm{rot})} = J(J + 1)(\hbar^2/2I) \qquad (2.5\text{–}31)$$

$$g_J^{(\mathrm{rot})} = 2J + 1 \qquad (2.5\text{–}32)$$

[6] The values for the constants are correct if R is in cal/mole degree, T is degrees Kelvin, V in liters, and p in atmospheres. Throughout the book we use the defined calorie, 4.1833 international joules or 4.18401 absolute joules, as recommended by the National Bureau of Standards. Here we take $R = 1.98718$ cal/mole degree.

Thus the partition function is

$$z^{(\text{rot})} = \sum_{J=0}^{\infty} (2J+1)e^{-\frac{\hbar^2 J(J+1)}{2IkT}} \tag{2.5–33}$$

The moment of inertia can be obtained from spectroscopic data. The Euler-Maclaurin summation formula is very useful for the evaluation of such expressions:

$$\sum_{J=J_0}^{J=J_1} f(J) = \int_{J_0}^{J_1} f(J)\,dJ + \tfrac{1}{2}[f(J_0) + f(J_1)]$$
$$+ \sum_{k=1}^{\infty} (-1)^k \frac{B_k}{(2k)!}\left[\left(\frac{d^{2k-1}f}{dJ^{2k-1}}\right)_{J_0} - \left(\frac{d^{2k-1}f}{dJ^{2k-1}}\right)_{J_1}\right] \tag{2.5–34}$$

Here the B_k are the Bernoulli numbers.[7] Substituting $(2J+1)$ exp $[-\hbar^2 J(J+1)/2IkT]$ for $f(J)$ and letting $J_0 = 0$ and $J_1 = \infty$, we obtain

$$z^{(\text{rot})} = \frac{2IkT}{\hbar^2} + \frac{1}{3} + \frac{1}{15}\left(\frac{\hbar^2}{2IkT}\right) + \cdots \tag{2.5–35}$$

For diatomic molecules at normal temperatures $(2IkT/\hbar^2)$ is much greater than unity, and only the first term is important.

It is usual to include in the denominator of the rotational partition function a symmetry number, σ, which is unity for heteronuclear and 2 for homonuclear diatomic molecules. This factor arises from the restrictions which the Pauli exclusion principle makes on the number of allowed quantum states. From Eq. 2.5–35, with the symmetry number included, and neglecting the higher terms, we obtain the following expressions for the thermodynamic properties per mole:

$$\tilde{U}^{(\text{rot})} = \tilde{H}^{(\text{rot})} = RT \tag{2.5–36}$$

$$\tilde{C}_p^{(\text{rot})} = \tilde{C}_v^{(\text{rot})} = R \tag{2.5–37}$$

$$\tilde{S}^{(\text{rot})} = R\left[1 + \ln\frac{2IkT}{\sigma\hbar^2}\right] \tag{2.5–38}$$

iii. *Vibrational Contributions in Diatomic Molecules*

If in a diatomic molecule the stretching of the bond is assumed to obey Hooke's law (the force tending to restore the molecule to its equilibrium

[7] The first few Bernoulli numbers are: $B_1 = \frac{1}{6}$, $B_2 = \frac{1}{30}$, $B_3 = \frac{1}{42}$, $B_4 = \frac{1}{30}$, $B_5 = \frac{5}{66}$, etc. The Euler-Maclaurin expansion is derived and discussed in many mathematical books. See for example R. S. Burington and C. C. Torrance, *Higher Mathematics*, McGraw-Hill (1939), p. 319.

position is directly proportional to the distortion of the bond), the problem reduces itself to the solution of the Schrödinger equation for the one-dimensional simple harmonic oscillator. The energy of the nth vibrational state is

$$\epsilon_n^{(\text{vib})} = h\nu(n + \tfrac{1}{2}) \tag{2.5-39}$$

These vibrational states are all non-degenerate. The vibrational partition function is usually defined in terms of energy above the zero-point energy, so that

$$z^{(\text{vib})} = \sum_{n=0}^{\infty} e^{-nh\nu/kT} = \frac{1}{1 - e^{-h\nu/kT}} \tag{2.5-40}$$

The last step is achieved by using the formula for the sum of a geometric series. The associated thermodynamic contributions per mole are then

$$\tilde{U}^{(\text{vib})} = \tilde{H}^{(\text{vib})} = \tilde{N}h\nu\,[e^{h\nu/kT} - 1]^{-1} \tag{2.5-41}$$

$$\tilde{S}^{(\text{vib})} = \frac{\tilde{U}^{(\text{vib})}}{T} - R\ln\,[1 - e^{-h\nu/kT}] \tag{2.5-42}$$

The frequency ν is the natural vibration frequency of the molecule and is obtained from vibrational spectra. At high temperatures corrections for the increasing anharmonicity of the oscillations must be applied.

iv. *Electronic Contributions*

In most molecules rather high temperatures are required for the activation of the higher electronic levels. Consequently, in most cases $z^{(\text{elec})}$ is simply the degeneracy of the electronic ground state. The electronic degeneracy for monatomic, diatomic, and polyatomic gases may be obtained from the spectroscopists's "term values" in the following manner.

(*a*) *Monatomic molecules.* In the term symbols for the electronic state of an atom (for example, $^3P_3$, $^1S_2$, $^4F_0$), the right subscript indicates the total (orbital + spin) angular momentum of all the electrons in the atom, J. The electronic degeneracy is given by

$$g^{(\text{elec})} = 2J + 1 \tag{2.5-43}$$

(*b*) *Diatomic molecules.* In the term symbols for the electronic states of a diatomic molecule (for example, $^3\Sigma_g$, $^2\Pi_u$, $^1\Delta_g$), the upper left superscript indicates the "spin-multiplicity," $2s + 1$. The electronic degeneracy is then

$(2s + 1)$ for Σ-states

$2(2s + 1)$ for Π-, Δ-, etc., states

(*c*) *Polyatomic molecules.* In polyatomic valence-saturated molecules, $g^{(\text{elec})} = 1$ or 2, according as there are an even or an odd number of electrons (since for an even number of electrons there is no resultant spin angular momentum but for an odd number of electrons there is a resultant spin of one-half).

v. *Nuclear Spin Contributions*

The nuclear spin partition function is simply the product of the nuclear spin multiplicities for all the atoms in the molecule:

$$z^{(\text{nucl})} = g^{(\text{nucl})} = \Pi_j(2s_j^{(\text{nucl})} + 1) \tag{2.5–44}$$

where $s_j^{(\text{nucl})}$ is the nuclear spin of the *j*th atom. However, since this contribution affects only the additive constant on the entropy and always cancels out (except in processes involving transmutation of the elements), it is usually ignored. The result is "virtual" entropy rather than "absolute" entropy.

d. Ideal gas mixtures

It can be shown that for an ideal gas mixture containing N_A molecules of substance *A* and N_B molecules of *B* the partition function is

$$Z_N = \frac{z_A^{N_A} z_B^{N_B}}{N_A!N_B!} e^{-\frac{N_A(\epsilon_0)_A + N_B(\epsilon_0)_B}{kT}} \tag{2.5–45}$$

Here the z_A and z_B are the molecular partition functions discussed above in which all the energies are referred to the ground states of the respective molecules. The factors $N_A!$ and $N_B!$ arise because of the indistinguishability of molecules of the same species in the same way that the $N!$ arises in the corresponding expression for the partition function of a pure substance. The $(\epsilon_0)_A$ and $(\epsilon_0)_B$ are the energies of the ground states of molecules *A* and *B* referred to a consistent set of standard states for the elements. Thus $(\epsilon_0)_A$ is the energy of formation of a molecule of *A* in the ground state from the elements of which it is composed, each in its own standard state. The standard states of the elements are usually taken to be the elements in the form in which they naturally occur at zero degrees centigrade and one atmosphere pressure.

From the above expression, Eq. 2.5–45, for the partition function it is possible to calculate the various thermodynamic properties for mixtures of ideal gases. It is thus found that

$$\tilde{U}_{\text{mix}} = \Sigma_j x_j \tilde{U}_j \tag{2.5–46}$$

$$\tilde{H}_{\text{mix}} = \Sigma_j x_j \tilde{H}_j \tag{2.5–47}$$

$$\tilde{C}_{p_{\text{mix}}} = \Sigma_j x_j \tilde{C}_{p_j} \tag{2.5–48}$$

In these expressions $\tilde{U}_j$ and $\tilde{H}_j$ are not simply the values calculated by the methods just described, but are these values with $\tilde{N}(\epsilon_0)_j$ added to take care of the change in the zero of energy. The last expression is valid only for non-reacting mixtures. The entropy for a mixture of gases is not simply the sum of contributions from the individual components. Substitution of the partition function for a mixture into Eq. 2.4–24 for the entropy shows that the entropy of a mixture is given by:

$$\tilde{S}_{\text{mix}} = \Sigma_j x_j \tilde{S}_j - R\,\Sigma_j x_j \ln x_j \tag{2.5–49}$$

The quantity $-R\,\Sigma_j x_j \ln x_j$ is referred to as the *entropy of mixing*. Similar contributions due to mixing arise in the expressions for the Gibbs free energy, $\tilde{G}$, and the Helmholtz free energy, $\tilde{A}$.

In treating the temperature dependence of the thermodynamical properties of a mixture, careful consideration must be given to whether chemical reactions can be ignored or whether chemical equilibrium is maintained between specified molecular species. In the first case the numbers N_A and N_B remain constant whereas in the second case they vary in accordance with the equilibrium constants.

6. The Theory of Fluctuations

Thus far the discussions have been restricted to the description of the equilibrium properties which can be calculated as the most probable properties or as the averages over an ensemble. It is these equilibrium properties of the matter in bulk which obey the laws of thermodynamics. Because of the molecular nature of matter, however, there is a finite possibility of deviations from this average behavior. The methods of statistical mechanics lead not only to a description of the average behavior, but also to a method of evaluating the probability of a fluctuation from the average value of any quantity. Because of the large number of mechanical degrees of freedom in a system such as a gas or liquid, macroscopic fluctuations are usually exceedingly small and occur but seldom. It is possible to discuss the fluctuations in any of the macroscopic or thermodynamic properties of matter by means of a general formalism.[1, 2, 3, 4] We do not present this general formal treatment here, but give a rather detailed discussion of the fluctuations in the internal energy and density, inasmuch as these properties are important in the study of the critical region (Chapter 5). Fluctuations in the density give rise to the scattering of light (§ 12.7). Fluctuations in the internal energy account for the

[1] M. J. Klein and L. Tisza, *Phys. Rev.*, **76**, 1861 (1949).
[2] R. H. Fowler, *Statistical Mechanics*, Cambridge University Press (1929), Chapter 20.
[3] A. Einstein, *Ann. Physik*, **33**, 1275 (1910).
[4] M. Smoluchowski, *Ann. Physik*, **25**, 225 (1908).

anomalously large specific heat at constant volume near the critical point. We do not discuss the fluctuations in the chemical composition of a multicomponent system since this subject would require a detailed analysis, and there are no direct applications in this book.[5]

A very simple example of fluctuations in a thermodynamic quantity is provided by the internal energy, U. Equation 2.4–4 gives the average value of the internal energy, $\overline{U}$, of a system which has attained equilibrium with a thermostat at temperature T in terms of the energy states E_j. The mean square deviation of the internal energy can be written in terms of the average value of U and the average value of U^2:

$$\overline{(U - \overline{U})^2} = \overline{U^2} - 2(\overline{U\overline{U}}) + (\overline{U})^2 = \overline{(U)^2} - (\overline{U})^2 \qquad (2.6\text{–}1)$$

According to Eq. 2.3–33 we may write

$$\overline{U^2} = \frac{\Sigma_j E_j{}^2 e^{-E_j/kT}}{\Sigma_j e^{-E_j/kT}} = kT^2 \frac{\partial}{\partial T}\left(kT^2 \frac{\partial \ln Z_N}{\partial T}\right) + k^2T^4 \left(\frac{\partial \ln Z_N}{\partial T}\right)^2 \qquad (2.6\text{–}2)$$

Comparison of these two relations with Eqs. 2.4–21 and 2.4–22 indicates that

$$\overline{(U - \overline{U})^2} = kT^2 C_v \qquad (2.6\text{–}3)$$

Hence according to this relation the specific heat at constant volume is a measure of the fluctuations in the internal energy.

a. Fluctuations in the density in terms of the thermodynamic properties

Let us consider a vessel of volume V in which there are N molecules all of the same chemical species. Let us further imagine that the volume V is subdivided into many small volume elements of volume V_s by means of imaginary boundaries in the vessel. Molecules in the vessel then are free to move from one volume element to another. On the average any elementary region of volume V_s contains $\bar{\nu} = N(V_s/V)$ molecules. Because of fluctuations, however, there is a finite probability that the number of molecules in an element of volume differs from this amount.

We consider the element of volume V_s to be the "system" and the vessel of volume V to be the "ensemble" of systems. Inasmuch as both energy and matter may flow from one system to another, it is proper to represent

[5] The fluctuations in the composition of a multicomponent system with or without chemical reactions have been studied by Fowler [*Statistical Mechanics*, Cambridge (1929) Chapter 20]. These fluctuations result in the turbidity of the solutions. Recent treatments of fluctuations have been made considering higher approximations and terms which were previously neglected, but not considering chemical reactions [J. G. Kirkwood and R. J. Goldberg, *J. Chem. Phys.*, **18**, 54 (1950); W. H. Stockmayer, *J. Chem. Phys.*, **18**, 58 (1950)].

any given system in equilibrium by means of a grand canonical ensemble. According to Eq. 2.2–31 in a grand canonical ensemble the probability that the system contains ν molecules and is in quantum state i is

$$\bar{n}_i^{\,\nu} = \frac{1}{Z^{\mathrm{Gr}}}\, e^{\nu\mu(\bar{\nu})/kT}\, e^{-E_i^{(\nu)}/kT} \tag{2.6–4}$$

Here $E_i^{(\nu)}$ is the energy of the ith state of the system with ν molecules. The quantity μ is the chemical potential of the system, which may be defined either in terms of the Helmholtz free energy A or the Gibbs free energy G:

$$\mu(\nu) = \left(\frac{\partial A}{\partial \nu}\right)_{T,\,V_s} = \left(\frac{\partial G}{\partial \nu}\right)_{T,p} \tag{2.6–5}$$

The symbol Z^{Gr} stands for the grand partition function and is the normalizing factor for the $\bar{n}_i^{\,\nu}$:

$$Z^{\mathrm{Gr}} = \Sigma_{\nu,i}\, e^{\nu\mu(\bar{\nu})/kT}\, e^{-E_i^{(\nu)}/kT} \tag{2.6–6}$$

It is convenient to introduce the quantity $A(\nu)$, which is the Helmholtz free energy of a system of ν molecules and which bears the following relation to the partition function Z_ν for such a system:

$$Z_\nu = e^{-A(\nu)/kT} = \Sigma_i\, e^{-E_i^{(\nu)}/kT} \tag{2.6–7}$$

We may then write

$$\bar{n}^{\nu} = \frac{1}{Z^{\mathrm{Gr}}}\, e^{\nu\mu(\bar{\nu})/kT}\, e^{-A(\nu)/kT} \tag{2.6–8}$$

as the expression for the probability that the system contains ν molecules (and is in any state). The grand partition function may be written

$$Z^{\mathrm{Gr}} = \Sigma_\nu\, e^{\nu\mu(\bar{\nu})/kT}\, e^{-A(\nu)/kT} \tag{2.6–9}$$

The introduction of the thermodynamic quantity $A(\nu)$ eventually permits an evaluation of the fluctuations in terms of directly measurable quantities.

The mean of the square of the deviation of ν from the average value of ν is the difference between the average of the value of ν^2 and the square of the average of ν:

$$\overline{(\nu - \bar{\nu})^2} = \overline{\nu^2} - \overline{2(\nu\bar{\nu})} + (\bar{\nu})^2 = \overline{\nu^2} - (\bar{\nu})^2 \tag{2.6–10}$$

It is, however, usually more convenient to consider the relative fluctuation δ defined by

$$\delta = \overline{\left(\frac{\nu - \bar{\nu}}{\bar{\nu}}\right)^2} = \frac{\overline{\nu^2} - (\bar{\nu})^2}{(\bar{\nu})^2} \tag{2.6–11}$$

From the expression for the probability that the system contain ν molecules as given by Eq. 2.6–8 it follows that

$$\delta = \frac{\Sigma_\nu (\nu - \bar{\nu})^2 \, e^{\nu\mu(\bar{\nu})/kT} \, e^{-A(\nu)/kT}}{\Sigma_\nu (\bar{\nu})^2 \, e^{\nu\mu(\bar{\nu})/kT} \, e^{-A(\nu)/kT}} \tag{2.6–12}$$

If ν is sufficiently large the distribution in Eq. 2.6–8 is essentially Gaussian, and this expression may be evaluated easily. This can be shown by the following arguments: The Taylor expansion of $A(\nu)$ about $\bar{\nu}$ can, with the help of Eq. 2.6–5, be written in the form

$$A(\nu) = A(\bar{\nu}) + (\nu - \bar{\nu})\mu(\bar{\nu}) + \tfrac{1}{2}(\nu - \bar{\nu})^2 \left.\frac{\partial \mu(\nu)}{\partial \nu}\right|_{\bar{\nu}} + \cdots \tag{2.6–13}$$

Substitution of this into Eq. 2.6–12 gives

$$\delta = \frac{\Sigma_\nu (\nu - \bar{\nu})^2 \exp\left\{ -\dfrac{(\nu - \bar{\nu})^2}{2kT} \left.\dfrac{\partial \mu(\nu)}{\partial \nu}\right|_{\bar{\nu}} + \cdots \right\}}{\Sigma_\nu (\bar{\nu})^2 \exp\left\{ -\dfrac{(\nu - \bar{\nu})^2}{2kT} \left.\dfrac{\partial \mu(\nu)}{\partial \nu}\right|_{\bar{\nu}} + \cdots \right\}} \tag{2.6–14}$$

The exponential represents a Gaussian distribution.

Let us consider variations in the size of the region under consideration, that is, variations in the value of V_s and corresponding changes in $\bar{\nu}$. Inasmuch as the value of μ is independent of the size of the sample, the value of the exponent is proportional to V_s or $\bar{\nu}$. Thus for large values of $\bar{\nu}$ (that is, large samples) the distribution is very sharp, and the only terms in the sum which are important are those for ν near $\bar{\nu}$. Furthermore, since the higher terms in the expansion of $A(\nu)$ in Eq. 2.6–13 are of still higher order, we are justified in neglecting these terms. Then when the summation in Eq. 2.6–14 is replaced by an integration and the integration performed the result is[6]

$$\delta = \frac{kT}{(\bar{\nu})^2 \, \partial\mu(\nu)/\partial\nu|_{\bar{\nu}}} = -\frac{kT}{V_s^{\,2}\,(\partial p/\partial V_s)_T} \tag{2.6–15}$$

for the expression for relative fluctuation in the density.

[6] The second form given in Eq. 2.6–15 may be obtained as follows: Considered as a function of ν and V_s at constant T, A is a homogeneous function of order one in the variables. Hence, according to Euler's theorem: $A = V_s \dfrac{\partial A}{\partial V_s} + \nu \dfrac{\partial A}{\partial \nu}$. Differentiation of this equation with respect to V_s gives: $\dfrac{\partial^2 A}{\partial \nu \partial V_s} = -\dfrac{V_s}{\nu} \dfrac{\partial^2 A}{\partial V_s^{2}}$. Similarly, differentiation with respect to ν gives: $\dfrac{\partial^2 A}{\partial \nu \partial V_s} = -\dfrac{\nu}{V_s} \dfrac{\partial^2 A}{\partial \nu^2}$. Hence $\dfrac{\partial^2 A}{\partial \nu^2} = \dfrac{V_s^2}{\nu^2} \dfrac{\partial^2 A}{\partial V_s^{2}}$. Then, since $\mu = \dfrac{\partial A}{\partial \nu}$ and $p = -\dfrac{\partial A}{\partial V_s}$, we obtain $\left.\dfrac{\partial \mu}{\partial \nu}\right|_{\bar{\nu}} = -\dfrac{V_s^2}{\bar{\nu}^2}\left(\dfrac{\partial p}{\partial V_s}\right)_T$ which relation was used in Eq. 2.6–15.

Since the volume is an extensive quantity, this equation indicates that the fluctuation in the density is of the order of $1/\bar{\nu}$. That is,

$$\delta = \frac{1}{\bar{\nu}} \left[\frac{kT}{(\partial p/\partial n)_T} \right] \tag{2.6–16}$$

where the quantity in the bracket depends only on the state of the fluid and is independent of the volume V_s of the region under consideration. For a perfect gas, this equation gives

$$\delta = 1/\bar{\nu} \tag{2.6–17}$$

for the relative fluctuation in the density. This shows that, if the region chosen is sufficiently small, the number of molecules within the region fluctuates. This is to be expected if the region is of molecular dimensions. However, if the region is large enough so that on the average the region contains many molecules, the probability of an appreciable fluctuation from the average is small. Nevertheless, even this much instantaneous inhomogeneity in the density leads to macroscopically observable phenomena such as the scattering of light by the atmosphere and Brownian motion. The scattering of light is discussed in § 12.7.

At the critical point $(\partial p/\partial n)_T$ is zero, and Eq. 2.6–16 leads to an expression for the fluctuation which is infinite. This result, however, is not valid because of the neglect of the higher terms in the expansion of $A(\nu)$ in Eq. 2.6–14. Extending the arguments discussed in the footnote to Eq. 2.6–15, we find the following thermodynamic relations:

$$\frac{\partial^2 \mu}{\partial \nu^2} - \frac{V_s^3}{\nu^3}\left(\frac{\partial^2 p}{\partial V_s^2}\right)_T + 3\frac{V_s^2}{\nu^3}\left(\frac{\partial p}{\partial V_s}\right)_T \tag{2.6–18}$$

$$\frac{\partial^3 \mu}{\partial \nu^3} = -\frac{V_s^4}{\nu^4}\left(\frac{\partial^3 p}{\partial V_s^3}\right)_T - \frac{8V_s^3}{\nu^4}\left(\frac{\partial^2 p}{\partial V_s^2}\right)_T - 12\frac{V_s^2}{\nu^4}\left(\frac{\partial p}{\partial V_s}\right)_T \tag{2.6–19}$$

Thus at the critical point where $(\partial p/\partial V)_T$ and $(\partial^2 p/\partial V^2)_T$ are zero, the first and second derivatives of μ and the corresponding terms in the expansion of $A(\nu)$ are zero. Since $(\partial^3 p/\partial V^3)_T$ is not zero[7] at the critical point, the third derivative of μ is not zero, and in the region of the critical point terms up to this order in the expansion of $A(\nu)$ should be retained. Considerations of the fluctuation in the neighborhood of the critical point are complicated since the entire sequence of terms is necessary. However, we can quite easily evaluate the fluctuation *at* the critical point.

[7] The classical interpretation of the critical point leads to this result. However, the exact nature of the critical point is not yet well understood. See § 5.2d.

At the critical point (that is, when $\bar{\nu}$ and T are the critical values) the expansion of $A(\nu)$ is

$$A(\nu) = A(\bar{\nu}) + (\nu - \bar{\nu})\mu(\bar{\nu}) + \frac{1}{4!}(\nu - \bar{\nu})^4 \left.\frac{\partial^3 \mu(\nu)}{\delta \nu^3}\right|_{\bar{\nu}} + \cdots \tag{2.6–20}$$

Thus it follows from the distribution, Eq. 2.6–8, that the relative fluctuation is

$$\delta_c = \frac{\Sigma_\nu (\nu - \bar{\nu})^2 \exp\left\{-\dfrac{(\nu - \bar{\nu})^4}{24kT}\left.\dfrac{\partial^3 \mu(\nu)}{\partial \nu^3}\right|_{\bar{\nu}} + \cdots\right\}}{\Sigma_\nu (\bar{\nu})^2 \exp\left\{-\dfrac{(\nu - \bar{\nu})^4}{24kT}\left.\dfrac{\partial^3 \mu(\nu)}{\partial \nu^3}\right|_{\bar{\nu}} + \cdots\right\}} \tag{2.6–21}$$

Then by arguments similar to those discussed above, we replace the summation by an integration and obtain

$$\delta_c = \frac{2\sqrt{6}\,\Gamma(^3/_4)}{\Gamma(^1/_4)}\left[\frac{kT}{\bar{\nu}^4 \left.\dfrac{\partial^3 \mu(\nu)}{\partial \nu^3}\right|_{\bar{\nu}}}\right]^{1/2} \tag{2.6–22}$$

where $\Gamma(^1/_4) = 3.6256$ and $\Gamma(^3/_4) = 1.2254$ are complete gamma functions. Equation 2.6–19 may be used to express the fluctuation in terms of equation of state data, and we obtain for the fluctuation in the density

$$\delta_c = \frac{2\sqrt{6}\,\Gamma(^3/_4)}{\Gamma(^1/_4)}\left[\frac{kT}{n^2 \dfrac{\partial^3 p}{\partial n^3}}\right]^{1/2} \frac{1}{(\bar{\nu})^{1/2}} \tag{2.6–23}$$

The quantity in the brackets depends only on the nature of the equation of state in the neighborhood of the critical point. Since the fluctuation is of the order of $1/(\bar{\nu})^{1/2}$ the values are considerably larger than those given by the approximation discussed earlier. It is to be noted, however, that this result gives a finite value for the fluctuation in density at the critical point. If the fluid obeys the van der Waals equation (Eq. 4.2–1), then Eq. 2.6–23 gives

$$\delta_c = 0.90/(\bar{\nu})^{1/2} \tag{2.6–24}$$

for the relative fluctuation at the critical point. The Dieterici equation (Eq. 4.2–3) gives a numerical factor of 1.59 instead of the value of 0.90. For any equation of state it is to be expected that the numerical factor is of the order of unity.

b. Fluctuations in the density in terms of the radial distribution function[8]

An expression for the fluctuation in the density in terms of the radial distribution function may also be obtained. The expression may be derived from the results discussed above. It is, however, somewhat more convenient to derive the expression directly from fundamental considerations.

Let us consider a vessel of gas of volume V containing N molecules. The state of the gas is described by the distribution function $f^{(N)}$ in the phase space of the system. This function and its normalization are discussed in detail in § 2.1. From the definition of $f^{(N)}$ it is clear that the probability that molecule i is at $\boldsymbol{r}$ and molecule j is at $\boldsymbol{r}'$ is

$$\frac{1}{N!}\iint \delta(\boldsymbol{r}_i - \boldsymbol{r})\, \delta(\boldsymbol{r}_j - \boldsymbol{r}')\, f^{(N)}(\boldsymbol{r}^{(N)}, \boldsymbol{p}^N)\, d\boldsymbol{r}^N\, d\boldsymbol{p}^N \tag{2.6–25}$$

Now let us consider the small region of volume V_s within the vessel of gas. The probable value of the square of the number of molecules within this region may be obtained from the above expression by summing over all i and j and integrating $\boldsymbol{r}$ and $\boldsymbol{r}'$ over the volume V_s:

$$\begin{aligned}\overline{\nu^2} &= \frac{1}{N!}\sum_{i,j}\int_{V_s}\int_{V_s} d\boldsymbol{r}\, d\boldsymbol{r}' \iint \delta(\boldsymbol{r}_i - \boldsymbol{r})\delta(\boldsymbol{r}_j - \boldsymbol{r}') f^{(N)}(\boldsymbol{r}^N, \boldsymbol{p}^N)\, d\boldsymbol{r}^N\, d\boldsymbol{p}^N \\ &= \frac{1}{N!}\sum_{i}\int_{V_s} d\boldsymbol{r} \iint \delta(\boldsymbol{r}_i - \boldsymbol{r}) f^{(N)}(\boldsymbol{r}^N, \boldsymbol{p}^N)\, d\boldsymbol{r}^N\, d\boldsymbol{p}^N \qquad (2.6\text{–}26) \\ &\quad + \frac{1}{N!}\sum_{i}\sum_{j\neq i}\int_{V_s}\int_{V_s} d\boldsymbol{r}\, \delta\boldsymbol{r}' \iint \delta(\boldsymbol{r}_i - \boldsymbol{r})\delta(\boldsymbol{r}_j - \boldsymbol{r}') f^{(N)}(\boldsymbol{r}^N, \boldsymbol{p}^N)\, d\boldsymbol{r}^N\, d\boldsymbol{p}^N\end{aligned}$$

The second form of this expression is written in such a way that the term $i = j$ has been separated from the rest of the terms.

This expression can be simplified by introducing the ordinary density function $n(\boldsymbol{r})$, and the pair distribution function, $n^{(2)}(\boldsymbol{r}, \boldsymbol{r}')$, as defined in § 2.1. If all the molecules are identical, Eq. 2.6–26 becomes

$$\overline{\nu^2} = \int_{V_s} n(\boldsymbol{r})\, d\boldsymbol{r} + \int_{V_s}\int_{V_s} n^{(2)}(\boldsymbol{r}, \boldsymbol{r}')\, d\boldsymbol{r}\, d\boldsymbol{r}' \tag{2.6–27}$$

The first term in the last relation is the probable number, $\bar{\nu}$, of molecules in the region of volume V_s. The second term may be written in terms of

[8] The radial distribution function $g(r)$ is defined in Eq. 2.1–9. Its use in the description of the equation of state is discussed in §§ 3.1 and 4.9.

the pair distribution function $g(\boldsymbol{r})$. Thus Eq. 2.6–27 may be rewritten as

$$\overline{\nu^2} = \bar{\nu} + \int_{V_s}\int_{V_s} n(\boldsymbol{r})n(\boldsymbol{r}')g(\boldsymbol{r}, \boldsymbol{r}' - \boldsymbol{r})\, d\boldsymbol{r}\, d\boldsymbol{r}' \qquad (2.6\text{–}28)$$

or

$$\overline{\nu^2} - (\bar{\nu})^2 = \bar{\nu} + \int_{V_s}\int_{V_s} n(\boldsymbol{r})n(\boldsymbol{r}')[g(\boldsymbol{r}, \boldsymbol{r}' - \boldsymbol{r}) - 1]\, d\boldsymbol{r}\, d\boldsymbol{r}' \quad (2.6\text{–}29)$$

Under equilibrium conditions where the fluid is macroscopically uniform, $n(\boldsymbol{r})$ is independent of $\boldsymbol{r}$, and $g(\boldsymbol{r}, \boldsymbol{r}' - \boldsymbol{r})$ depends only on the distance $|\boldsymbol{r}' - \boldsymbol{r}|$. Furthermore, as discussed in § 4.9, $g(\boldsymbol{r})$ is unity for values of r large compared to the molecular dimensions. Thus, if V_s is large compared to molecular dimensions.

$$\overline{\nu^2} - (\bar{\nu})^2 = \bar{\nu} + 4\pi n^2 V_s \int [g(r) - 1]\, r^2\, dr \qquad (2.6\text{–}30)$$

Thus

$$\delta = \frac{1}{\bar{\nu}} [1 + 4\pi n \int [g(r) - 1]\, r^2\, dr] \qquad (2.6\text{–}31)$$

is the expression for the relative fluctuation in terms of the radial distribution function.

We have obtained two expressions for the relative fluctuation: one directly in terms of the equation of state, and a second in terms of the radial distribution function. A comparison of the two results, Eqs. 2.6–16 and 2.6–31 shows that

$$\frac{kT}{(\partial p/\partial n)_T} = 1 + 4\pi n \int [g(r) - 1] r^2\, dr \qquad (2.6\text{–}32)$$

This expression is of considerable interest and value in itself. An alternate proof of this relation has been given[9] by making use of the virial expansions of the equation of state and the radial distribution function. The virial expansion is discussed in detail in Chapter 3.

PROBLEMS

1. Discuss graphically and analytically the classical dynamics of the following systems:
   (a) Force free mass point in a one-dimensional box.
   (b) Unconstrained mass point moving with constant acceleration.
   (c) One-dimensional simple harmonic oscillator.
   (d) Two-dimensional rigid rotator.
   (e) Simple pendulum in two-dimensions.

[9] J. de Boer, *Reports on Progress in Physics*, **12**, 305 (1949).

2. Show that, for a system whose Hamiltonian contains no potential energy term, a canonical ensemble can be made to approach very closely a microcanonical ensemble of energy E. (*Hint*: The Hamiltonian for the system may be written in "polar coordinates" in the $3N$-dimensional hyperspace, by using a radial coordinate, $R = \sqrt{\Sigma_i(p_i^2/2m)}$, and $3N - 1$ angles; then $H = R^2$. The number of systems in a shell of thickness dR is then, for the microcanonical ensemble,

$$P^{(N)}\, d\tau = A \exp(-\beta H) R^{3N-1}\, dR$$

We can then find the number of systems in a shell of thickness dH, and then adjust this number so that it very nearly coincides with the microcanonical ensemble. It may be further shown that as the number of systems in the ensemble approaches infinity, the canonical distribution becomes increasingly sharp, thus approaching a microcanonical surface ensemble.)

3. Derive the following expressions for various forms of the Maxwell-Boltzmann distribution law:

(i) The number of molecules which have velocities with magnitudes in the range v to $v + dv$:

$$n(v)\, dv = 4\pi N \left(\frac{m}{2\pi kT}\right)^{3/2} e^{-mv^2/2kT}\, v^2\, dv$$

(ii) The number of molecules whose translational energy lies within the range ϵ and $\epsilon + d\epsilon$:

$$n(\epsilon)\, d\epsilon = 2\pi N \left(\frac{1}{\pi kT}\right)^{3/2} e^{-\epsilon/kT} \sqrt{\epsilon}\, d\epsilon$$

Sketch the distribution curve given in (i) and (ii). Are these results applicable to polyatomic as well as monatomic molecules?

4. There are in common use several "average" values for the speed of molecules in a gas which can be obtained from Problem 3(i). Show that:

(i) The *arithmetic mean speed*:

$$\bar{v} = \sqrt{8kT/\pi m} = 14{,}500\sqrt{T/M}\ \text{cm/sec}$$

(ii) The *root-mean-square speed*:

$$\sqrt{\overline{v^2}} = \sqrt{3kT/m} = 15{,}800\sqrt{T/M}\ \text{cm/sec}$$

(iii) The *most probable speed*:

$$\tilde{v} = \sqrt{2kT/m} = 12{,}900\sqrt{T/M}\ \text{cm/sec}$$

The last speed, $\tilde{v}$, is the maximum of the $n(v)$ curve. Calculate the root-mean-square speed for H_2 and SF_6 at 0° and 400°K. What percentage of the molecules in a gas have velocities greater than some given velocity, v? What fraction of hydrogen molecules have velocities greater than 10^4 cm sec^{-1}?

5. In many cases it is found that the total energy of the system may be regarded as equally distributed among the various degrees of freedom for the system (*The Principle of Equipartition of Energy*). It is important to note that the equipartition of energy is *not* a general consequence of statistical mechanics, but rather is a result of the specific form of the dependence of the energy upon the momentum and position variables. Several examples should make this clear:

(i) For a dilute monatomic gas, consisting of N molecules, show that the mean energy associated with the motion of the jth molecule in the x-direction, $\bar{\epsilon}_{jx}$, is $\frac{1}{2}kT$.

Then show that the mean energy of the entire gas $\bar{E}$ may be obtained by adding together the contributions from all the degrees of freedom:

$$\bar{E} = \sum_{j=1}^{N} (\bar{\epsilon}_{jx} + \bar{\epsilon}_{jy} + \bar{\epsilon}_{jz}) = \tfrac{3}{2}NkT$$

(ii) For a dilute diatomic gas (assume the molecules to be rigid rotators) show that the mean energy associated with each degree of freedom is $\frac{1}{2}kT$. Verify the fact that the law of equipartition of energy holds in this case, and that the mean energy for the entire gas is

$$\bar{E} = \tfrac{5}{2}NkT$$

(iii) The classical Hamiltonian for a crystal, expressed in terms of the normal coordinates (q_i, p_i) of the system has the form

$$H(p_i, q_i) = \Sigma_i \left(\frac{p_i^2}{2m_i} + 4\pi^2\nu_i^2 m_i q_i^2\right)$$

in which the ν_i are the frequencies of the normal vibrations. Justify the law of equipartition of energy for this case.

Note that in all these cases the Hamiltonian depends in the same general way upon the coordinates and momenta of the system:

$$H(p_i, q_i) = \Sigma_i(a^2 p_i^2 + b^2 q_i^2)$$

6. The Maxwell-Boltzmann distribution law can be applied to countless problems. Make use of this law to derive the following relationships:

(i) The variation of density with altitude in an isothermal atmosphere.

(ii) The variation of the density of colloid particles with height in a colloidal suspension.

(iii) The variation of particle density in a colloidal suspension with the distance from the axis of rotation in an ultracentrifuge.

(iv) The angular distribution of the axes of magnetic dipoles in a magnetic field. (*Hint*: The energy of a magnetic dipole of strength m in a magnetic field of strength $\mathscr{H}$ is $\epsilon(\theta) = -m\mathscr{H} \cos\theta$, where θ is the angle between the dipole and the field.)

7. Show how the rotational contribution to the molecular partition function can be obtained, aside from the symmetry number, from the classical phase integral.

8. Calculate the thermodynamic functions $\tilde{U}$, $\tilde{A}$, $\tilde{G}$, $\tilde{H}$, $\tilde{S}$, $\tilde{C}_v$, and $\tilde{C}_p$ for argon and nitrogen at 300°K and 1000°K. Disregard nuclear spin and electronic contributions. For nitrogen, use $h\nu/k = 3336.6$°K and $\hbar^2/2Ik = 2.847$°K for calculating the vibrational and rotational contributions, respectively.

9. Using data from the literature, calculate the thermodynamic functions listed in problem 8 for hydrogen atoms and bromine atoms at 300°K and 1000°K.

10. Derive the perfect gas law from the partition function for a perfect gas.

11. The energy of the system may be written in classical statistical mechanics as the average over the canonical ensemble of the Hamiltonian, $H(\mathbf{r}^N, \mathbf{p}^N)$. Verify the fact that the entropy may be written as the average of $-k \ln [N!h^{3N}P^{(N)}(\mathbf{r}^N, \mathbf{p}^N)]$; that is, show that the relations

$$TS = -kT\int\int P^{(N)}(\mathbf{r}^N, \mathbf{p}^N) \ln P^{(N)}(\mathbf{r}^N, \mathbf{p}^N)\, d\mathbf{r}^N\, d\mathbf{p}^N - kT \ln (N!h^{3N})$$

$$= -kT\int P^{(N)}(\mathbf{r}^N) \ln P^{(N)}(\mathbf{r}^N)\, d\mathbf{r}^N + \tfrac{3}{2}NkT - kT \ln (N!h^{3N})$$

are valid in classical statistical mechanics. What is the analogous expression in quantum statistical mechanics?

· 3 ·

The Equation of State of Gases at Low and Moderate Densities

(This chapter was prepared in collaboration with Dr. Ellen L. Spotz, formerly of the University of Wisconsin.)

The experimentally observed deviations from the ideal gas law were interpreted qualitatively by van der Waals[1] by assuming that the molecules are attracted to one another at large distances and repelled at very small distances. This interpretation led van der Waals to the formulation of his famous two-constant equation of state. In the years which followed the emphasis was placed on finding empirical equations of state which would give good agreement with the experimental data. Some of the more important of these empirical relations—those of Dieterici, Berthelot, and Beattie and Bridgeman—are discussed in the next chapter.

In this chapter we concern ourselves with the *virial equation of state*, which is generally written in the form[2]

$$p\tilde{V}/RT = 1 + B(T)/\tilde{V} + C(T)/\tilde{V}^2 + D(T)/\tilde{V}^3 + \cdots \quad (3.0\text{–}1)$$

The coefficients $B(T)$, $C(T)$, $D(T)$ . . . are called the second, third, fourth . . . *virial coefficients*. By means of statistical mechanics these virial coefficients may be expressed in terms of the intermolecular potential functions. Consequently it is possible to obtain a quantitative interpretation of the deviations from the ideal gas law in terms of the forces between molecules. Indeed much valuable information has been obtained about intermolecular interactions by analysis of p-V-T data.

[1] J. D. van der Waals, Sr., Doctoral Dissertation (Leiden 1873).

[2] The virial expansion of the compressibility was originally used as a means of fitting experimental data by H. Kamerlingh Onnes [*Comm. Phys. Lab. Leiden*, No. 71 (1901)]. Some workers prefer to express their data by expanding the compressibility factor in a power series in the pressure:

$$p\tilde{V}/RT = 1 + B'(T)p + C'(T)p^2 + \cdots$$

The coefficients of this expansion bear simple relationships with the coefficients in Eq. 3.0–1:

$$B' = B/RT \qquad C' = (C - B^2)/(RT)^2$$

In this text we usually use the virial expansions as defined in Eq. 3.0–1. Virial coefficients for the pressure series are distinguished by primes from coefficients in Eq. 3.0–1.

From the statistical mechanical expressions for the virial coefficients it becomes evident that the second, third, fourth, . . . virial coefficients represent the deviations from ideal behavior when collisions involving two, three, four, . . . molecules become important in the gas. Consequently at low densities deviations from ideality are adequately described by the second virial coefficient, whereas at higher densities more virial coefficients must be used. As an example, for nitrogen at 0°C the numerical contributions of the virial coefficients to the compressibility factor are given approximately by the successive terms in the following:

$$1 \text{ atm} \quad p\tilde{V}/RT = 1 - 0.0005 + 0.000003 + \cdots$$

$$10 \text{ atm} \quad p\tilde{V}/RT = 1 - 0.005 + 0.0003 + \cdots$$

$$100 \text{ atm} \quad p\tilde{V}/RT = 1 - 0.05 + 0.03 + \cdots$$

The range of validity of the virial expansion is limited by the convergence of the series. The series diverges at about the density of the liquid. Hence the primary application of the virial equation of state is in the study of gases at low and moderate densities.

In the first half of this chapter the derivation of the virial equation of state from statistical mechanics is given. Explicit expressions are obtained for the virial coefficients in terms of the forces between molecules. The last half of the chapter deals with the numerical evaluation of the virial coefficients for various types of potential fields. All the functions needed for the calculation of gas imperfections for the types of potential fields for which the virial coefficients have been evaluated to date are given in tabular form convenient for computations. The results of this chapter are not strictly valid for the isotopes of hydrogen and helium below room temperature nor for gases at very low temperatures, inasmuch as quantum effects are important in these cases. The quantum theory of the equation of state and the equilibrium phenomena at low temperatures are discussed in Chapter 6.

1. Formal Development of the Equation of State from Statistical Mechanics

Two forms of the equation of state have been useful in the study of the properties of gases and liquids. In this section it is first shown how the equation of state[1] may be developed from the statistical thermodynamical

[1] Some authors choose to refer to $p = p(V, T)$ as the *thermal equation of state.* They use this terminology to distinguish it from the *caloric equation of state* which is the internal energy, $U = U(V, T)$. The derivations for the latter parallel closely those for the thermal equation of state and hence are not given here. See Problem 1 at the end of this chapter.

relation between the pressure and the partition function. Then another development is discussed, wherein the equation of state is obtained from the classical mechanical virial theorem by taking an average of pV over a canonical ensemble. This method leads to an equation of state expressed in terms of the radial distribution function. This equation of state has a form considerably different from that obtained from the partition function, but the equivalence of the two forms may easily be demonstrated.

a. The method of the partition function

In the discussion of statistical thermodynamics in § 2.4 it was shown that the pressure of a system bears the following relationship to the partition function for the system:[2]

$$p = kT\left(\frac{\partial \ln Z_N}{\partial V}\right)_T \tag{3.1–1}$$

In classical statistics the partition function for a system of N identical molecules is given by

$$Z_N = \frac{1}{N!h^{3N}}\iint e^{-H(\mathbf{r}^N,\,\mathbf{p}^N)/kT}\,d\mathbf{r}^N\,d\mathbf{p}^N \tag{3.1–2}$$

in which the Hamiltonian, $H(\mathbf{r}^N, \mathbf{p}^N)$, is given by

$$H(\mathbf{r}^N, \mathbf{p}^N) = \sum_{i=1}^{N}\frac{p_i^2}{2m} + \Phi(\mathbf{r}^N) \tag{3.1–3}$$

For the *ideal gas* the Hamiltonian contains only a kinetic energy term, and the classical partition function may be integrated in closed form to give

$$Z_N{}^0 = V^N/\lambda^{3N}N! \tag{3.1–4}$$

where $\lambda^2 = h^2/2\pi mkT$. Substitution of this partition function into the expression for the pressure gives the ideal gas law, $pV = NkT$.

For the *non-ideal gas* the integration over momenta in the partition function may again be performed so that Z_N may be written in the form

$$Z_N = \frac{1}{N!\lambda^{3N}}\int W_N(\mathbf{r}^N)\,d\mathbf{r}^N \equiv Q_N/\lambda^{3N} \tag{3.1–5}$$

[2] It may also be shown that the pressure may be expressed in terms of the grand partition function (see § 2.1e):

$$pV = kT \ln Z^{\mathrm{Gr.}}$$

See H. Kramers, *Proc. Roy. Acad. Amsterdam*, **41**, 10 (1938) and R. H. Fowler, *Proc. Cambridge Phil. Soc.*, **34**, 382 (1938).

in which $W_N(\boldsymbol{r}^N)$ is the *Boltzmann factor*:

$$W_N(\boldsymbol{r}^N) = e^{-\Phi(\boldsymbol{r}^N)/kT} \tag{3.1–6}$$

and Q_N is the *configurational integral*[3]

$$Q_N = \frac{1}{N!} \int W_N(\boldsymbol{r}^N)\, d\boldsymbol{r}^N \tag{3.1–7}$$

§ 3.2 is concerned with the evaluation of this integral. The development presented there makes no assumptions as to the nature of $\Phi(\boldsymbol{r}^N)$, that is, the assumption of two-body forces is not introduced.

b. The method based on the virial theorem of mechanics

The classical mechanical virial theorem for a system of particles has been given in Eq. 1.4–28. In this discussion we consider the N molecules (of mass m) of a gas or liquid to be the "particles" of the system, ignoring for the moment the internal degrees of freedom of the molecules.[4] The virial theorem states that the average total kinetic energy of the molecules, $\bar{K} = \frac{1}{2}\Sigma_i m v_i^2$, is equal to the virial, $\Xi = -\frac{1}{2}\Sigma_i \overline{(\boldsymbol{r}_i \cdot \boldsymbol{F}_i)}$. Each molecule in the gas feels the forces exerted by all the other molecules and also the restraining force of the container. Corresponding to these two contributions to $\boldsymbol{F}_i$ there is the virial of the intermolecular forces, Ξ_i, and the virial of the external forces, Ξ_e.

The *virial of the intermolecular forces* is given by:

$$\Xi_i(\boldsymbol{r}^N) = \frac{1}{2} \sum_{i=1}^{N} \overline{\left(\boldsymbol{r}_i \cdot \frac{\partial}{\partial \boldsymbol{r}_i} \Phi(\boldsymbol{r}^N)\right)} \tag{3.1–8}$$

To get the *virial of the external forces* we consider the force of the molecules on the walls, which is equal but opposite in sign to the force of the walls on the molecules. Let us consider an element of area, $\boldsymbol{n}\, dS$, of the container wall where $\boldsymbol{n}$ is a unit vector in the direction of the outward normal. The time average force exerted by the molecules striking this area is $p\boldsymbol{n}\, dS$, and the force exerted by the element of area on the molecules is $-p\boldsymbol{n}\, dS$. If $\boldsymbol{r}$ is the position vector of the element of surface, the contribution of this element to the virial is $\frac{1}{2}p(\boldsymbol{r} \cdot \boldsymbol{n})\, dS$. Integration over the surface of the container gives the virial of the external forces:

$$\Xi_e = \frac{1}{2} p \int_{\substack{\text{Surface of}\\ \text{container}}} (\boldsymbol{r} \cdot \boldsymbol{n})\, dS = \frac{1}{2} p \int_{\substack{\text{Volume of}\\ \text{container}}} \left(\frac{\partial}{\partial \boldsymbol{r}} \cdot \boldsymbol{r}\right) d\boldsymbol{r} = \frac{3}{2} pV \tag{3.1–9}$$

[3] Also sometimes called the *configurational partition function*.

[4] In § 4.3c a different viewpoint is taken. There the system (gas or liquid) is considered to be made up of a collection of nuclei and electrons. Such a viewpoint enables us to get information about the kinetic energy of the electrons at high densities.

The transformation of the surface integral into a volume integral is accomplished by means of Green's theorem.[5]

The virial theorem then assumes the form

$$\bar{K} \equiv \sum_{i=1}^{N} \overline{(p_i^2/2m)} = \Xi_i + \Xi_e$$

$$= \frac{1}{2} \sum_{i=1}^{N} \overline{\left(\boldsymbol{r}_i \cdot \frac{\partial}{\partial \boldsymbol{r}_i} \Phi(\boldsymbol{r}^N) \right)} + \frac{3}{2} pV \quad (3.1\text{–}10)$$

from which we get pV in terms of the total kinetic and intermolecular potential energy of the molecules:

$$pV = \frac{2}{3} \sum_{i=1}^{N} \overline{\frac{p_i^2}{2m}} - \frac{1}{3} \sum_{i=1}^{N} \overline{\left(\boldsymbol{r}_i \cdot \frac{\partial}{\partial \boldsymbol{r}_i} \Phi(\boldsymbol{r}^N) \right)} \quad (3.1\text{–}11)$$

The bars over the quantities in this equation indicate time averages. According to statistical mechanics these time averages may be replaced by averages over an ensemble. Using the classical probability density corresponding to the canonical ensemble, we obtain for the equation of state

$$pV = \frac{1}{N! h^{3N} Z_N} \iint e^{-H(\boldsymbol{r}^N, \boldsymbol{p}^N)/kT}$$

$$\times \left[\frac{2}{3} \sum_{i=1}^{N} \frac{p_i^2}{2m} - \frac{1}{3} \sum_{i=1}^{N} \left(\boldsymbol{r}_i \cdot \frac{\partial}{\partial \boldsymbol{r}_i} \Phi(\boldsymbol{r}^N) \right) \right] d\boldsymbol{r}^N \, d\boldsymbol{p}^N$$

$$= NkT - \frac{1}{3(N-1)! \lambda^{3N} Z_N} \int W_N(\boldsymbol{r}^N) \left(\boldsymbol{r}_1 \cdot \frac{\partial \Phi(\boldsymbol{r}^N)}{\partial \boldsymbol{r}_1} \right) d\boldsymbol{r}^N \quad (3.1\text{–}12)$$

In the second form of this equation, integrations have been carried out over the momenta. This result shows explicitly the role of the intermolecular forces. If there are no forces between the molecules, the integral over configuration space vanishes, and the result is the ideal gas law, $pV = NkT$.

For a non-ideal gas the expression just given may be simplified, if it is assumed that the total potential energy of the system is the sum of the

[5] See note on vector and tensor notation at the front of the book.

potential energies of pairs of molecules, $\Phi(\boldsymbol{r}^N) = \frac{1}{2}\Sigma_i\Sigma_j\varphi(r_{ij})$. Then the equation of state becomes

$$pV = NkT - \frac{1}{6}\iint n^{(2)}(\boldsymbol{r}_1, \boldsymbol{r}_2)r_{12}\left(\frac{d\varphi_{12}}{dr_{12}}\right) d\boldsymbol{r}_1\, d\boldsymbol{r}_2$$

$$= NkT - \frac{2\pi N(N-1)}{3V}\int g(r)\left(\frac{d\varphi}{dr}\right) r^3\, dr \qquad (3.1\text{–}13)$$

in which $n^{(2)}(\boldsymbol{r}_1, \boldsymbol{r}_2)$ and $g(r)$ are pair distribution functions defined by

$$n^{(2)}(\boldsymbol{r}_1, \boldsymbol{r}_2) = \frac{1}{(N-2)!Q_N}\int W_N(\boldsymbol{r}^N)\, d\boldsymbol{r}^{N-2} = \frac{N(N-1)}{V^2}\, g(r_{12}) \qquad (3.1\text{–}14)$$

The occurrence of the pair distribution function and no functions of higher order is a direct consequence of the assumption just made that the potential energy of the system is additive. The equation of state may be transformed to the virial form by developing the pair distribution function as a power series in the density. This derivation is given in § 3.3.

c. The equivalence of the equation of state from the partition function and the equation of state from the virial theorem

The identity of the expressions for the equation of state given in Eqs. 3.1–1 and 3.1–12 has been proved by Born and Green.[6, 7] In the first of these expressions it is necessary to differentiate the partition function with respect to the volume. The volume dependence of the classical partition function occurs only in the limits of the integration over configuration space, which are taken to be the dimensions of the vessel.

The partition function may be transformed into an integral in which the dimensions of the vessel no longer occur in the limits of the integration. This is done by introducing a characteristic macroscopic length, L. This length is of the order of magnitude of the dimensions of the vessel, and the volume of the container is hence proportional to L^3 When the reduced variables $\bar{\boldsymbol{r}}_j = \boldsymbol{r}_j/L$ are introduced into the integral for the classical partition function, the latter becomes

$$Z_N = \frac{1}{N!h^{3N}}\, L^{3N}\iint e^{-H(L\bar{\boldsymbol{r}}^N,\, \boldsymbol{p}^N)/kT}\, d\boldsymbol{r}^N\, d\boldsymbol{p}^N \qquad (3.1\text{–}15)$$

Then the equation of state becomes

$$pV = kTV(\partial \ln Z_N/\partial V)_T = (kT/3)\,(L/Z_N)\,(\partial Z_N/\partial L)$$

$$= \frac{kTL^{3N}}{N!h^{3N}Z_N}\iint e^{-H(L\bar{\boldsymbol{r}}^N,\, \boldsymbol{p}^N)/kT}\left[N - \frac{L}{3kT}\frac{\partial H}{\partial L}\right] d\bar{\boldsymbol{r}}^N\, d\boldsymbol{p}^N \qquad (3.1\text{–}16)$$

[6] M. Born and H. S. Green, *Proc. Roy. Soc. (London)*, **A191**, 168 (1947).

[7] J. de Boer, *Reports on Progress in Physics*, **12**, 305 (1949).

The differentiation of the Hamiltonian may be performed, with the result that

$$L\frac{\partial H}{\partial L} = L\frac{\partial}{\partial L}\Phi(L\bar{r}^N)$$
$$= \sum_{i=1}^{N}\left(\boldsymbol{r}_i \cdot \frac{\partial}{\partial \boldsymbol{r}_i}\Phi(\boldsymbol{r}^N)\right) \tag{3.1–17}$$

Substitution of this result into Eq. 3.1–16 and transformation back to the original space variables gives

$$pV = NkT - \frac{1}{N!h^{3N}Z_N}\iint e^{-H(\boldsymbol{r}^N,\boldsymbol{p}^N)/kT}\left[\sum_{i=1}^{N}\left(\boldsymbol{r}_i \cdot \frac{\partial}{\partial \boldsymbol{r}_i}\Phi(\boldsymbol{r}^N)\right)\right] d\boldsymbol{r}^N\, d\boldsymbol{p}^N \tag{3.1–18}$$

which is equivalent to Eq. 3.1–12.

2. The Virial Equation of State from the Partition Function[1]

In this section we continue the development of the equation of state by the partition function method just described. Use is made of a technique introduced by Ursell,[2] whereby the integrand of the configurational integral is expanded in terms of "*U*-functions," with the result that the partition function for the gas can be written as a sum of products of integrals b_l. These integrals are called "cluster integrals," because they involve successively clusters of 1, 2, 3, . . . N molecules. The virial coefficients are directly expressible in terms of these cluster integrals, the jth virial coefficient being given as a combination of the cluster integrals $b_1, b_2, \ldots b_j$. The final expressions for the virial coefficients may be somewhat simplified by the assumption of two-body forces. The introduction of this assumption is postponed until § 3.4a.

a. The "U-functions"

Ursell[2] has shown that the Boltzmann factor, $W_N(\boldsymbol{r}^N)$, which appears in the integrand of the configurational integral, may be expressed as a sum of products of functions $U_l(\boldsymbol{r}^\lambda)$. These *U-functions*[3] are defined in

[1] The development and notation of this and the following section follow that given by J. de Boer, *Reports on Progress in Physics*, **12**, 305 (1949).

[2] H. D. Ursell, *Proc. Cambridge Phil. Soc.*, **23**, 685 (1927).

[3] As described in § 2.1 the subscript l tells how many molecules and the superscript λ tells which ones.

terms of various combinations of Boltzmann factors involving fewer molecules, thus:

$$\begin{aligned} U_1(\boldsymbol{r}_i) &= W_1(\boldsymbol{r}_i) \\ U_2(\boldsymbol{r}_i, \boldsymbol{r}_j) &= W_2(\boldsymbol{r}_i, \boldsymbol{r}_j) - W_1(\boldsymbol{r}_i)W_1(\boldsymbol{r}_j) \\ U_3(\boldsymbol{r}_i, \boldsymbol{r}_j, \boldsymbol{r}_k) &= W_3(\boldsymbol{r}_i, \boldsymbol{r}_j, \boldsymbol{r}_k) - W_2(\boldsymbol{r}_i, \boldsymbol{r}_j)W_1(\boldsymbol{r}_k) \\ &\quad - W_2(\boldsymbol{r}_j, \boldsymbol{r}_k)W_1(\boldsymbol{r}_i) - W_2(\boldsymbol{r}_k, \boldsymbol{r}_i)W_1(\boldsymbol{r}_j) \\ &\quad + 2W_1(\boldsymbol{r}_i)W_1(\boldsymbol{r}_j)W_1(\boldsymbol{r}_k) \end{aligned} \tag{3.2–1}$$

The scheme is to perform all possible divisions of the molecules into groups and to make a sum of products of W-functions corresponding to these divisions. It should be noted that no permutations of molecules within the group are made in this process. The coefficients before the various terms are $(-1)^{n-1}(n-1)!$, where n is the number of groups in the term. The thus-defined U-functions have the following very important property: The function $U_l(\boldsymbol{r}^\lambda)$ approaches zero for a "separate" configuration in which the molecules in the set $\{\lambda\}$ are divided into two or more groups separated from one another by a distance sufficiently great that there is negligible interaction between the groups. This property may easily be verified for the first several U-functions.

The Boltzmann factors for one, two, three, . . . particles alone in the volume V may then be written in terms of U-functions thus:

$$\begin{aligned} W_1(\boldsymbol{r}_i) &= U_1(\boldsymbol{r}_i) = 1 \\ W_2(\boldsymbol{r}_i, \boldsymbol{r}_j) &= U_2(\boldsymbol{r}_i, \boldsymbol{r}_j) + U_1(\boldsymbol{r}_i)U_1(\boldsymbol{r}_j) \\ W_3(\boldsymbol{r}_i, \boldsymbol{r}_j, \boldsymbol{r}_k) &= U_3(\boldsymbol{r}_i, \boldsymbol{r}_j, \boldsymbol{r}_k) + U_2(\boldsymbol{r}_i, \boldsymbol{r}_j)U_1(\boldsymbol{r}_k) \\ &\quad + U_2(\boldsymbol{r}_j, \boldsymbol{r}_k)U_1(\boldsymbol{r}_i) + U_2(\boldsymbol{r}_k, \boldsymbol{r}_i)U_1(\boldsymbol{r}_j) \\ &\quad + U_1(\boldsymbol{r}_i)U_1(\boldsymbol{r}_j)U_1(\boldsymbol{r}_k) \end{aligned} \tag{3.2–2}$$

Thus the expressions for the U-functions in terms of the Boltzmann factors are the same as those for the Boltzmann factors in terms of the U-functions, except for the fact that in the latter set of relations the coefficients before all terms are $+1$. The Boltzmann factor for the system of N molecules, $W_N(\boldsymbol{r}^N)$, may then be written symbolically as

$$W_N(\boldsymbol{r}^N) = \sum_{(\Sigma l m_l = N)} \prod U_l(\boldsymbol{r}^\lambda) \tag{3.2–3}$$

Here the sum of products must be carried out over all possible divisions of the N molecules into m_1 groups of 1, m_2 groups of 2, . . . m_l groups of l molecules, with the restriction that $\Sigma l m_l = N$.

The reason for employing these U-functions may be indicated by citing an example. For a dilute gas, where two-body collisions are frequent but collisions involving three molecules are rare, the functions $U_3(\boldsymbol{r}_i, \boldsymbol{r}_j, \boldsymbol{r}_k)$ vanish as do all U-functions of higher order. The expression for $W_N(\boldsymbol{r}^N)$ consists then of sums of products of the U-functions for single molecules and pairs. If we were interested only in the second virial coefficient, which results from binary collisions, the U-functions for groups of three and more molecules could be discarded at this point.

b. The cluster integrals, b_l

Having expressed the Boltzmann factor for the system of N molecules by the sum of products of U-functions according to Eq. 3.2–3, we may now formally integrate the configurational integral. The result is[4]

$$Q_N = \frac{1}{N!}\int W_N(\boldsymbol{r}^N)\, d\boldsymbol{r}^N = \Sigma \prod_{l=1}^{N} (Vb_l)^{m_l}/m_l! \qquad (3.2\text{–}4)$$

and the summation is over all sets of m_l which satisfy the condition $\Sigma l m_l = N$. The quantities of b_l are the *cluster integrals* defined by

$$b_l = (Vl!)^{-1} \int U_l(\boldsymbol{r}_1, \boldsymbol{r}_2, \cdots \boldsymbol{r}_l)\, d\boldsymbol{r}_1\, d\boldsymbol{r}_2 \cdots d\boldsymbol{r}_l \qquad (3.2\text{–}5)$$

in which the limits of integration correspond to the physical dimensions of the containing vessel of volume V.

The cluster integrals for small l are very nearly independent of the volume. This may be shown by performing (approximately) the integration over the coordinates of one molecule of the group to obtain a factor V, which cancels the V included in the definition of the b_l. The approximation may be illustrated by considering the cluster integral b_2 written for the special case of two particles in a one-dimensional box of length L, for which

$$b_2 = \frac{1}{2L}\int_0^L \int_0^L U_2(x_1, x_2)\, dx_1\, dx_2 \qquad (3.2\text{–}6)$$

[4] This result is obtained as follows. To a definite set of m_l correspond many terms in the development of Eq. 3.2–3, because of the different ways of distributing the N particles over the groups. All these terms give the same result after integration, namely,

$$\prod_{l=1}^{N} (Vl!b_l)^{m_l} \qquad (a)$$

The number of these terms is

$$N! \prod_{l=1}^{N} \frac{1}{(l!)^{m_l} m_l!} \qquad (b)$$

since the permutation of particles within a group and the permutation of groups of equal size give rise to no new terms. Multiplication of (*a*) and (b) and summing over all sets of m_l then gives Eq. 3.2–4.

Since U_2 is a function only of the relative configuration of the two particles, a change of variables may be made:

$$b_2 = \frac{1}{2L} \int_0^L \int_{-x_1}^{L-x_1} U_2(x_2 - x_1) d(x_2 - x_1)\, dx_1 \tag{3.2–7}$$

The function $U_2(x_2 - x_1) = \{\exp[-\varphi(x_2 - x_1)/kT] - 1\}$ is non-zero only over a very short range of the variable $(x_2 - x_1)$, since the intermolecular interaction can be considered negligible for distances greater than a few angstroms. If the length L is of macroscopic dimensions, the value of b_2 is almost unaffected if the limits of the integration over $(x_2 - x_1)$ are taken to be infinite:

$$b_2 = \frac{1}{2L} \int_0^L \int_{-\infty}^{+\infty} U_2(x_2 - x_1) d(x_2 - x_1)\, dx_1 \tag{3.2–8}$$

This allows us to integrate over x_1, so that

$$b_2 = \tfrac{1}{2} \int_{-\infty}^{+\infty} U_2(x_{21})\, dx_{21} \tag{3.2–9}$$

in which x_{21} is the location of molecule "2" with respect to molecule "1."

The actual three dimensional b_l may be approximated in a manner similar to that just described for the one-dimensional b_2. Since the U_l approach zero for a "separate" configuration, integration over the coordinates of one molecule may always be carried out. Thus the cluster integrals of Eq. 3.2–5 may be written as

$$b_l = \frac{1}{l!} \int \cdots \int U_l(\boldsymbol{r}_{21}, \cdots \boldsymbol{r}_{l1}) d\boldsymbol{r}_{21} \cdots d\boldsymbol{r}_{l1} \tag{3.2–10}$$

in which infinite limits on the integration are implied and the $\boldsymbol{r}_{j1}$ are coordinates relative to the position of molecule "1." This approximation of the volume-independence of the cluster integrals is excellent in the case of the lower order integrals. Hence the use of Eq. 3.2–10 offers no limitations to the theory of gases. For large values of l the approximation becomes less valid, since large clusters occupy an appreciable fraction of the volume of the vessel. Consequently Eq. 3.2–10 may not be used for liquids where large clusters predominate.

According to Eqs. 3.2–5 and 3.2–10 the first three cluster integrals are

$$b_1 = \frac{1}{V}\int d\boldsymbol{r}_1 = 1$$

$$b_2 = \frac{1}{2V}\iint [W_2(\boldsymbol{r}_1, \boldsymbol{r}_2) - W_1(\boldsymbol{r}_1)W_1(\boldsymbol{r}_2)]\, d\boldsymbol{r}_1\, d\boldsymbol{r}_2$$

$$= \frac{1}{2V}\lambda^6[2!Z_2 - Z_1^2]$$

$$= \frac{1}{2}\int_0^\infty [e^{-\varphi(r)/kT} - 1]4\pi r^2\, dr$$

$$b_3 = \frac{1}{6V}\iiint [W_3(\boldsymbol{r}_1, \boldsymbol{r}_2, \boldsymbol{r}_3) - W_2(\boldsymbol{r}_1, \boldsymbol{r}_2)W_1(\boldsymbol{r}_3) - W_2(\boldsymbol{r}_2, \boldsymbol{r}_3)W_1(\boldsymbol{r}_1) - W_2(\boldsymbol{r}_3, \boldsymbol{r}_1)W_1(\boldsymbol{r}_2) + 2W_1(\boldsymbol{r}_1)W_1(\boldsymbol{r}_2)W_1(\boldsymbol{r}_3)]\, d\boldsymbol{r}_1\, d\boldsymbol{r}_2\, d\boldsymbol{r}_3$$

$$= \frac{1}{3V}\lambda^9[3Z_3 - 3Z_2Z_1 + Z_1^3]$$

$$= \frac{1}{6}\iint [e^{-\Phi(r_{21}, r_{31})/kT} - e^{-[\varphi(r_{21})+\varphi(r_{31})+\varphi(r_{23})]/kT}]\, d\boldsymbol{r}_{21}\, d\boldsymbol{r}_{31}$$

$$+ \frac{1}{6}\iint [e^{-\varphi(r_{21})/kT} - 1][e^{-\varphi(r_{31})/kT} - 1][e^{-\varphi(r_{23})/kT} - 1]\, d\boldsymbol{r}_{21}\, d\boldsymbol{r}_{31}$$

$$+ \frac{1}{2}\left[\int_0^\infty [e^{-\varphi(r)/kT} - 1]4\pi r^2\, dr\right]^2 \qquad (3.2\text{–}11)$$

In this last formula $\Phi(\boldsymbol{r}_{21}, \boldsymbol{r}_{31})$ is the potential energy of a system of three molecules, and $\boldsymbol{r}_{21}$ and $\boldsymbol{r}_{31}$ are the coordinates of molecules "2" and "3" relative to molecule "1." If we assume that the potential energy of a system of three molecules is $\varphi(r_{12}) + \varphi(r_{23}) + \varphi(r_{13})$ the first integral is zero.

c. Evaluation of the partition function

Several methods have been proposed for the evaluation of the awkward expression for the configurational integral given in Eq. 3.2–4. We present here the method of "steepest descents" introduced into statistical mechanics by Darwin and Fowler[5] and applied to this problem by Born and Fuchs.[6]

For the application of this method we introduce the generating function:

$$g(\zeta) = \exp\left(\sum_{l=1}^{\infty} Vb_l\zeta^l\right) \tag{3.2–12}$$

in which ζ is taken to be a complex variable. When this function is expanded in a power series in ζ, the coefficient of ζ^N is equal to Q_N. After the generating function is multiplied by ζ^{-N-1}, Cauchy's residue theorem[7] may be used to obtain the following integral expression for the configurational integral:

$$Q_N = \frac{1}{2\pi i}\oint_C \zeta^{-N-1}e^{\Sigma Vb_l\zeta^l}\,d\zeta \tag{3.2–13}$$

The contour C is taken to be a circle around the origin in the ζ-plane. Introducing $\zeta = r\exp(i\phi)$ and $d\zeta = i\zeta\,d\phi$ into this last expression, we obtain

$$Q_N = \frac{1}{2\pi}\int_{-\pi}^{+\pi} e^{[\Sigma Vb_l(re^{i\phi})^l - Ni\phi - N\ln r]}\,d\phi \tag{3.2–14}$$

The integrand has a minimum on the positive real axis, $\phi = 0$, for a value of $r = z$ given by:

$$\frac{d}{dr}[r^{-N}e^{\Sigma Vb_lr^l}] = 0 \quad \text{or} \quad N = \Sigma Vlb_lz^l \tag{3.2–15}$$

As a result of the high powers of r which occur in the integral and balance each other just at $r = z$, this minimum is extremely sharp. On the other hand, the modulus of the integrand has a sharp maximum in a direction perpendicular to the positive real axis. This point, $\zeta = z$, may thus be called a "saddle point."

The exponent of the integrand in Eq. 3.2–14 may now be expanded in a power series in ϕ on the contour $|\zeta| = z$:

$$\Sigma_l Vb_l(ze^{i\phi})^l - N\ln(ze^{i\phi}) = \Sigma_l Vb_lz^l - N\ln z - \tfrac{1}{2}\phi^2\Sigma_l Vl^2b_lz^l + O(\phi^3) \tag{3.2–16}$$

[5] R. H. Fowler, *Statistical Mechanics*, 2d Ed., Cambridge University Press (1936) p. 36.

[6] M. Born and K. Fuchs, *Proc. Roy. Soc.* (*London*), **A166**, 391 (1938).

[7] The Cauchy residue theorem states: If $f(\zeta)$ is an analytic function within and on a closed contour C, except at $\zeta = 0$ where there is a pole, then integration of $f(\zeta)$ around C leads to $2\pi i$ times the coefficient of ζ^{-1} of the series expansion of $f(\zeta)$ about $\zeta = 0$.

A good approximation is obtained if the Taylor series is broken off after the term in ϕ^2. The integration in Eq. 3.2–14 can then be extended with negligible error so as to allow the variable ϕ to go from $-\infty$ to $+\infty$, giving

$$Q_N = \frac{\exp\,[\Sigma V b_l z^l]}{2\pi z^N} \int_{-\infty}^{+\infty} \exp\,[-\tfrac{1}{2}\phi^2 \Sigma V l^2 b_l z^l]\, d\phi$$

$$= \frac{\exp\left[\sum_{l=1}^{\infty} V b_l z^l\right]}{z^N \sqrt{2\pi \Sigma V l^2 b_l z^l}} \tag{3.2–17}$$

Finally, the quantity needed for the calculation of thermodynamic quantities is $\ln Z_N$, which is

$$\ln Z_N = -N \ln z\lambda^3 + \sum_{l=1}^{\infty} V b_l z^l \tag{3.2–18}$$

The terms in $\ln Z_N$ resulting from the square root in the denominator of Eq. 3.2–17 have been neglected; this may be done since both $\Sigma V b_l z^l$ and $\Sigma l^2 V b_l z^l$ are proportional to N.

Up to this point the parameter z is simply a quantity defined in Eq. 3.2–15. Its physical meaning is shown when the expression for the partition function in Eq. 3.2–18 is used to get the Gibbs' free energy, G:

$$G = NkT \ln \lambda^3 + NkT \ln z \tag{3.2–19}$$

But from thermodynamics we know that the quantity G is related to the fugacity f and activity a of the gas by the following relations:

$$G = G^0 + NkT \ln \frac{f}{f^0} = G^0 + NkT \ln a \tag{3.2–20}$$

in which the superscript 0 indicates the standard state quantities; for our purpose we choose the standard state to be the ideal gas at the same temperature and volume. Then G^0 may be calculated by the methods outlined in § 2.5. This quantity is found to be $G^0 = NkT \ln \lambda^3(N/V)$, so that Eq. 3.2–20 becomes

$$G = NkT \ln \lambda^3 + NkT \ln \frac{aN}{V} \tag{3.2–21}$$

Comparison of this equation with Eq. 3.2–19 indicates that z bears the following relation to the activity a:

$$z = \frac{aN}{V} = an \tag{3.2–22}$$

in which $n = N/V$ is the number density. The parameter z has the dimensions of a concentration and indeed is for very low densities almost equal to the number density. That this is true may be seen from Eq. 3.2–15. The parameter z may be thought of as the *active number density*.[8]

d. The equation of state in the virial form

Substitution of the expression for the partition function given in Eq. 3.2–18 into the Eq. 3.1–1 for the pressure gives the equation of state in terms of the active number density z:

$$pV = kTV\left(\frac{\partial \ln Z_N}{\partial V}\right)_T = kT\Sigma_l Vb_l z^l \tag{3.2–23}$$

To express pV as a power series in the number density, it is necessary to know z in terms of n. It has been shown[9, 10] that Eq. 3.2–15, where n is given in terms of z, may be solved for z to give

$$z = n\exp\left(-\sum_{k=1}^{\infty}\beta_k n^k\right) \tag{3.2–24}$$

in which the β_k are various combinations of the cluster integrals:

$$\begin{aligned}\beta_1 &= 2b_2\\ \beta_2 &= 3b_3 - 6b_2^2\\ \beta_3 &= 4b_4 - 24b_2b_3 + \frac{80}{3}b_2^3, \text{ etc.}\end{aligned} \tag{3.2–25}$$

Higher β_k may be obtained by expanding z from Eq. 3.2–24 in powers of n, substituting this in Eq. 3.2–15, and equating the coefficients of equal powers of n.

Substitution of the expression for z, Eq. 3.2–24, into the formula for pV, Eq. 3.2–23, gives the equation of state in the virial form of Eq. 3.0–1:

$$\frac{pV}{NkT} = 1 - \sum_{k=1}^{\infty}\frac{k\beta_k}{k+1}\left(\frac{N}{V}\right)^k \tag{3.2–26}$$

It is thus seen that the β_k are closely related to the virial coefficients:

$$\begin{aligned}B(T) &= -\tfrac{1}{2}\tilde{N}\beta_1\\ C(T) &= -\tfrac{2}{3}\tilde{N}^2\beta_2\\ D(T) &= -\tfrac{3}{4}\tilde{N}^3\beta_3\end{aligned} \tag{3.2–27}$$

Explicit formulae for the virial coefficients are given in § 3.4b.

[8] The parameter z has been referred to by Guggenheim as the *activity* and by Mayer and Mayer as the *fugacity*. The term *active number density* seems to be more appropriate.

[9] J. E. Mayer, *J. Chem. Phys.*, **5**, 67 (1937).

[10] B. Kahn, Dissertation, Utrecht (1938).

3. The Virial Equation of State from the Virial Theorem[1, 2]

In this section we show how the equation of state can be developed from the virial theorem method, continuing the discussion begun in § 3.1. The equation of state is expressed there in terms of the *pair distribution function* $n^{(2)}(\mathbf{r}_1,\mathbf{r}_2)$. This expression for the equation of state may be transformed into the virial form, by expanding the distribution function in powers of the density. This is accomplished by a modification of the method given in the preceding section, inasmuch as the distribution functions, $n^{(h)}(\mathbf{r}^h)$, are integrals of the Boltzmann factor over all but the first h molecules:

$$n^{(h)}(\mathbf{r}^h) = \frac{1}{(N-h)!Q_N} \int W_N(\mathbf{r}^N)\, d\mathbf{r}^{N-h} \tag{3.3–1}$$

First the Boltzmann factor is written as a sum of products of *modified U-functions.* Then integration over a limited number of the coordinates of the modified U-functions gives rise to the *modified cluster integrals.* It is in terms of these integrals that the distribution functions $n^{(h)}(\mathbf{r}^h)$ are expressed. From the pair distribution function as a power series in the density, the virial equation of state may then be obtained.

a. The "modified U-functions"

In this development it is convenient to consider the group of molecules $\{h\} \equiv 1, 2, \cdots h$ formally as a single molecule with position coordinate $\mathbf{r}^h \equiv \mathbf{r}_1, \mathbf{r}_2, \cdots \mathbf{r}_h$. The U-functions which do not contain the molecules $\{h\}$ are defined exactly as in Eq. 3.2–1. For groups of molecules which include the group $\{h\}$ the *modified U-functions* are defined as

$$\begin{aligned} U(\mathbf{r}^h) &= W(\mathbf{r}^h) \\ U(\mathbf{r}^h, \mathbf{r}_j) &= W(\mathbf{r}^h, \mathbf{r}_j) - W(\mathbf{r}^h)W_1(\mathbf{r}_j) \\ U(\mathbf{r}^h, \mathbf{r}_j, \mathbf{r}_k) &= W(\mathbf{r}^h, \mathbf{r}_j, \mathbf{r}_k) - W(\mathbf{r}^h, \mathbf{r}_j)W_1(\mathbf{r}_k) \\ &\quad - W(\mathbf{r}^h, \mathbf{r}_k)W_1(\mathbf{r}_j) - W(\mathbf{r}_j, \mathbf{r}_k)W_1(\mathbf{r}^h) \\ &\quad + 2W(\mathbf{r}^h)W_1(\mathbf{r}_j)W_1(\mathbf{r}_k) \end{aligned} \tag{3.3–2}$$

The Boltzmann factors are then given by the following sum of products of U-functions:

$$\begin{aligned} W(\mathbf{r}^h) &= U(\mathbf{r}^h) \\ W(\mathbf{r}^h, \mathbf{r}_j) &= U(\mathbf{r}^h, \mathbf{r}_j) + U(\mathbf{r}^h)U_1(\mathbf{r}_j) \\ W(\mathbf{r}^h, \mathbf{r}_j, \mathbf{r}_k) &= U(\mathbf{r}^h, \mathbf{r}_j, \mathbf{r}_k) + U(\mathbf{r}^h, \mathbf{r}_j)U_1(\mathbf{r}_k) \\ &\quad + U(\mathbf{r}^h, \mathbf{r}_k)U_1(\mathbf{r}_j) + U(\mathbf{r}_j, \mathbf{r}_k)U(\mathbf{r}^h) \\ &\quad + U(\mathbf{r}^h)U_1(\mathbf{r}_j)U_1(\mathbf{r}_k) \end{aligned} \tag{3.3–3}$$

[1] J. de Boer, *Reports on Progress in Physics*, **12**, 305 (1949).
[2] J. de Boer, *Physica*, **15**, 680 (1949).

These two sets of equations are the same as those given in Eqs. 3.2–1 and 2, except that $\boldsymbol{r}_i$ is replaced by $\boldsymbol{r}^h$.

b. The "modified cluster integrals"

The Boltzmann function $W_N(\boldsymbol{r}^N) \equiv W(\boldsymbol{r}^h, \boldsymbol{r}^{N-h})$ may then be written as a sum of products of U-functions, and in each product there occurs one modified U-function of the type given in Eq. 3.3–2. It is possible to show that $W_N(\boldsymbol{r}^N)$ may finally be written in the following form:

$$W_N(\boldsymbol{r}^N) = U(\boldsymbol{r}^h)W_{N-h}(\boldsymbol{r}^{N-h}) + \Sigma_j U(\boldsymbol{r}^h, \boldsymbol{r}_j)W_{N-h-1}(\boldsymbol{r}^{N-h-1}) + \Sigma_j\Sigma_k U(\boldsymbol{r}^h, \boldsymbol{r}_j, \boldsymbol{r}_k)W_{N-h-2}(\boldsymbol{r}^{N-h-2}) + \cdots \tag{3.3–4}$$

Substitution of this function into the expression for $n^{(h)}(\boldsymbol{r}^h)$ in Eq. 3.3–1 gives

$$n^{(h)}(\boldsymbol{r}^h) = \sum_{l=1}^{N-h+1} l b_l^{(h)} \left(\frac{Q_{N-h-l+1}}{Q_N}\right) \tag{3.3–5}$$

in which the $b_l^{(h)}$ are the *modified cluster integrals* defined by

$$b_l^{(h)}(\boldsymbol{r}^h) = \frac{1}{l!V}\int\cdots\int U(\boldsymbol{r}^h, \boldsymbol{r}_{h+1}, \cdots \boldsymbol{r}_{h+l})\, d\boldsymbol{r}_{h+1}\cdots d\boldsymbol{r}_{h+l}$$
$$\doteq \frac{1}{l!}\int\cdots\int U(\boldsymbol{r}^h, \boldsymbol{r}_{h+1}, \cdots \boldsymbol{r}_{h+l-1})\, d\boldsymbol{r}_{h+1}\cdots d\boldsymbol{r}_{h+l-1} \tag{3.3–6}$$

To perform the integration over the volume the coordinates are referred to the position of molecule l. After the integration the coordinate system is shifted in such a way that the $\boldsymbol{r}_j$ are positions relative to some one molecule in the group $\{h\}$. The modified cluster integrals are thus functions of the relative coordinates $\boldsymbol{r}^h$. They are dependent on the volume in much the same way as ordinary cluster integrals. In fact the cluster integrals are a special case of the $b_l^{(h)}$, with $h = 1$.

c. The pair distribution function in terms of the density

Equation 3.3–5 for the distribution functions $n^{(h)}(\boldsymbol{r}^h)$ may be written in terms of the active number density z by using Eq. 3.2–17 to evaluate the ratio of configurational integrals. The result for the pair distribution function ($h = 2$) is

$$n^{(2)}(r_{12}) = \sum_{l=1}^{N-1} l b_l^{(2)}(r_{12}) z^{l+1} \tag{3.3–7}$$

Using Eq. 3.2–24, which gives the relationship between z and n, we may write the pair distribution function as a power series in the number density:

$$n^{(2)}(r_{12}) = \sum_{k=1}^{\infty} c_k(r_{12}) n^{k+1} \tag{3.3–8}$$

The $c_k(r_{12})$ are various combinations of the modified cluster integrals:

$$c_1(r_{12}) = b_1^{(2)}(r_{12})$$

$$c_2(r_{12}) = 2b_2^{(2)}(r_{12}) - 4b_2 b_1^{(2)}(r_{12})$$

$$c_3(r_{12}) = 3b_3^{(2)}(r_{12}) - 12b_2 b_2^{(2)}(r_{12}) + (4b_2{}^2 - 6b_3)b_1^{(2)}(r_{12}), \text{ etc.} \tag{3.3–9}$$

Similar expansions for the higher-order distribution functions in terms of the number density may be made.[3] The distribution function $n^{(1)}$ is identically equal to the number density, $n = N/V$.

d. The equation of state in the virial form

If we assume that the total potential energy of the system is the sum of the potential energies of pairs of molecules, the expression for the pair distribution function given in Eq. 3.3–8 may be substituted into Eq. 3.1–13 for pV. The equation of state then becomes

$$\frac{pV}{NkT} = 1 - \frac{2\pi}{3kT} \sum_{k=1}^{\infty} \left(\frac{N}{V}\right)^k \int c_k(r_{12}) r_{12}{}^3 \frac{d\varphi_{12}}{dr_{12}} dr_{12} \tag{3.3–10}$$

The virial coefficients are thus given by

$$B(T) = -\frac{2\pi\tilde{N}}{3kT} \int c_1(r_{12}) r_{12}{}^3 \frac{d\varphi_{12}}{dr_{12}} dr_{12} \tag{3.3–11}$$

$$C(T) = -\frac{2\pi\tilde{N}^2}{3kT} \int c_2(r_{12}) r_{12}{}^3 \frac{d\varphi_{12}}{dr_{12}} dr_{12}, \text{ etc.} \tag{3.3–12}$$

Explicit formulae for the virial coefficients in terms of the intermolecular forces are given in the next section.

[3] The expressions for the functions $n^{(h)}(r^h)$ obtained by the method outlined here have also been obtained by J. E. Mayer and E. Montroll, *J. Chem. Phys.*, 9, 2 (1941). They assumed the additivity of intermolecular forces from the very beginning, whereas such an assumption has not been made in deriving Eq. 3.3–7 and the formulae for higher distribution functions. The advantage of the formalism here presented is that it may be taken over completely into quantum mechanics merely by giving a different interpretation to the $W_N(r^N)$. These *Boltzmann factors* of classical theory become the *Slater sums* of quantum statistical mechanics. See Chapter 6.

4. The Virial Coefficients

The development of the equation of state in the virial form from the partition function (§ 3.2) and the expansion of the distribution functions $n^{(h)}(\boldsymbol{r}^h)$ in powers of the number density were both accomplished without assuming the additivity of forces. In this section this assumption is made, and the resulting simplifications are summarized. Then the formulae for the virial coefficients, both from the partition function method and from the virial theorem, are given explicitly in terms of the forces between pairs of molecules. The extensions of the results to polyatomic molecules and to gaseous mixtures are given.

a. The assumption of additivity

If the force between any two molecules is independent of the configuration of all the other molecules present, the total potential energy of the system may be written as $\Phi(\boldsymbol{r}^N) = \frac{1}{2}\Sigma_i\Sigma_j\varphi_{ij}$, where φ_{ij} is the interaction potential for an isolated pair of molecules. This assumption is generally valid,[1] except for molecules which tend to associate (for example, molecules with hydroxyl or amino groups) or for molecules which are capable of hydrogen bonding.

Mayer[2] and his co-workers, in their derivations of equation of state phenomena, make use of the function

$$f_{ij}(r_{ij}) = [e^{-\varphi_{ij}/kT} - 1] \tag{3.4–1}$$

This function has the property of differing from zero only if the two molecules concerned are close enough to have an interaction energy appreciably different from zero. The approximate shape of the function f_{ij} for real molecules is shown in Fig. 3.4–1. The assumption of additivity allows the U-functions to be written in terms of the f_{ij}:

$$U_1(\boldsymbol{r}_1) = 1$$

$$U_2(\boldsymbol{r}_1, \boldsymbol{r}_2) = f_{12}$$

$$U_3(\boldsymbol{r}_1, \boldsymbol{r}_2, \boldsymbol{r}_3) = f_{12}f_{23}f_{13} + f_{12}f_{23} + f_{23}f_{13} + f_{12}f_{13} \tag{3.4–2}$$

In general the function $U_k(\boldsymbol{r}^k)$ contains all products of f_{ij}, such that all molecules in the group $\{k\}$ are at least singly "connected." The four

[1] This is almost true for the London dispersion forces but is not valid in the case of repulsive or first-order chemical forces (see Chapter 12). B. M. Axilrod and E. Teller, *J. Chem. Phys.*, **11**, 299 (1943), have calculated the error which arises in the third-order perturbation and varies as $1/r^9$. The error has little effect, however, in the usual thermal collisions.

[2] See J. E. Mayer and M. G. Mayer, *Statistical Mechanics*, Wiley (1940).

combinations of f_{ij} which make up $U_3(\mathbf{r}_1, \mathbf{r}_2, \mathbf{r}_3)$ are illustrated in Fig. 3.4–2. The basic property of the U-functions, that they approach zero for a "separate" configuration, may be easily understood in terms of the

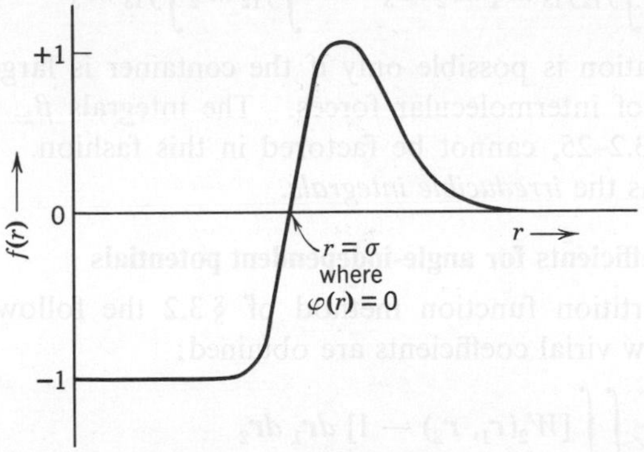

Fig. 3.4–1. Approximate shape of the function $f(r)$.

f_{ij}. For then at least one of the factors f_{ij} connecting a molecule of one group with a molecule of the other group must be zero.

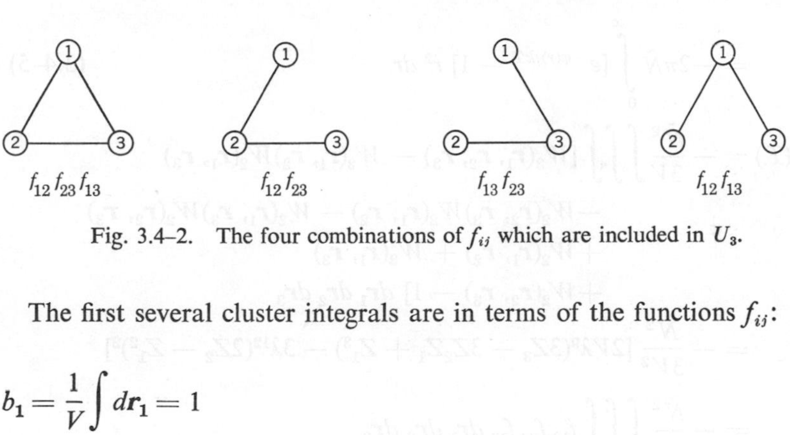

Fig. 3.4–2. The four combinations of f_{ij} which are included in U_3.

The first several cluster integrals are in terms of the functions f_{ij}:

$$b_1 = \frac{1}{V}\int d\mathbf{r}_1 = 1$$

$$b_2 = \frac{1}{2V}\iint f_{12} d\mathbf{r}_1 d\mathbf{r}_2 \tag{3.4–3}$$

$$b_3 = \frac{1}{6V}\iiint [f_{12}f_{13} + f_{12}f_{23} + f_{13}f_{23} + f_{12}f_{13}f_{23}]\, d\mathbf{r}_1\, d\mathbf{r}_2\, d\mathbf{r}_3$$

The b_l are *reducible integrals* in that some of their terms may be factored into products of integrals. For example, the first term in b_3 may be written

$$\iiint f_{12}f_{13}\, d\boldsymbol{r}_1\, d\boldsymbol{r}_2\, d\boldsymbol{r}_3 = V\int f_{12}\, d\boldsymbol{r}_2 \int f_{13}\, d\boldsymbol{r}_3 \tag{3.4-4}$$

Such a factorization is possible only if the container is large compared with the range of intermolecular forces. The integrals β_k, which were defined in Eq. 3.2–25, cannot be factored in this fashion. Hence they are referred to as the *irreducible integrals.*

b. The virial coefficients for angle-independent potentials

From the partition function method of § 3.2 the following expressions the first few virial coefficients are obtained:

$$\begin{aligned}
B(T) &= -\frac{\tilde{N}}{2V}\iint [W_2(\boldsymbol{r}_1, \boldsymbol{r}_2) - 1]\, d\boldsymbol{r}_1\, d\boldsymbol{r}_2 \\
&= -\frac{\tilde{N}}{2V}\lambda^6[2Z_2 - Z_1^2] \\
&= -\frac{\tilde{N}}{2V}\iint f_{12}\, d\boldsymbol{r}_1\, d\boldsymbol{r}_2 \\
&= -2\pi\tilde{N}\int_0^\infty [e^{-\varphi(r)/kT} - 1]\, r^2\, dr
\end{aligned} \tag{3.4-5}$$

$$\begin{aligned}
C(T) &= -\frac{\tilde{N}^2}{3V}\iiint [W_3(\boldsymbol{r}_1, \boldsymbol{r}_2, \boldsymbol{r}_3) - W_2(\boldsymbol{r}_1, \boldsymbol{r}_2)W_2(\boldsymbol{r}_1, \boldsymbol{r}_3) \\
&\qquad - W_2(\boldsymbol{r}_2, \boldsymbol{r}_3)W_2(\boldsymbol{r}_1, \boldsymbol{r}_2) - W_2(\boldsymbol{r}_1, \boldsymbol{r}_3)W_2(\boldsymbol{r}_2, \boldsymbol{r}_3) \\
&\qquad + W_2(\boldsymbol{r}_1, \boldsymbol{r}_2) + W_2(\boldsymbol{r}_1, \boldsymbol{r}_3) \\
&\qquad + W_2(\boldsymbol{r}_2, \boldsymbol{r}_3) - 1]\, d\boldsymbol{r}_1\, d\boldsymbol{r}_2\, d\boldsymbol{r}_3 \\
&= -\frac{\tilde{N}^2}{3V^2}[2V\lambda^9(3Z_3 - 3Z_2Z_1 + Z_1^3) - 3\lambda^{12}(2Z_2 - Z_1^2)^2] \\
&= -\frac{\tilde{N}^2}{3V}\iiint f_{12}f_{23}f_{13}\, d\boldsymbol{r}_1\, d\boldsymbol{r}_2\, d\boldsymbol{r}_3 \\
&= -\frac{8\pi^2\tilde{N}^2}{3}\iiint f_{12}f_{13}f_{23}r_{12}r_{13}r_{23}\, dr_{12}\, dr_{13}\, dr_{23}
\end{aligned}$$

[Integral over *all* r_{12}, r_{23}, r_{13} which form a triangle]

$$= -8\pi^2\tilde{N}^2\iiint f_{12}f_{13}f_{23}r_{12}r_{13}r_{23}\, dr_{12}\, dr_{13}\, dr_{23} \tag{3.4-6}$$

[Integral over those r_{12}, r_{13}, r_{23} which form a triangle and for which $r_{12} \geqslant r_{13}$ and $r_{12} \geqslant r_{23}$]

$$D(T) = -\frac{\tilde{N}^3}{8V}\iiiint [3f_{12}f_{23}f_{34}f_{14} + 6f_{12}f_{13}f_{14}f_{23}f_{34} + f_{12}f_{13}f_{14}f_{23}f_{24}f_{34}]\, d\boldsymbol{r}_1\, d\boldsymbol{r}_2\, d\boldsymbol{r}_3\, d\boldsymbol{r}_4 \tag{3.4-7}$$

The formulae written in terms of the f_{ij} are valid only as long as the assumption of additivity is reasonable; the formulae involving the partition functions or the Boltzmann factors do not depend on this assumption. Furthermore, these formulae are derived for monatomic molecules with spherically symmetric interaction potentials which interact according to classical mechanics. The first of these assumptions is not serious for molecules which are reasonably symmetric, for the internal degrees of freedom have little effect on the equation of state[3] and only the translational motion need be considered. If the molecules are non-spherical, the above results must be generalized for angular dependent potential fields. The fact that classical mechanics is used in the derivation means that the above formulae may not be applied at very low temperatures nor may they be used for the isotopes of hydrogen and helium even at temperatures as high as room temperatures. Formulae for the light gases and low temperatures are given in Chapter 6, where the quantum mechanical equation of state is discussed.

From the virial theorem method outlined in § 3.3. the following expressions are obtained for the second and third virial coefficients:

$$B(T) = -\frac{2\pi\tilde{N}}{3kT}\int_0^\infty r^3 \frac{d\varphi}{dr} e^{-\varphi(r)/kT}\, dr \tag{3.4-8}$$

$$C(T) = -\frac{4\pi^2\tilde{N}^2}{3kT}\iiint (1 + f_{12})f_{23}f_{13}r_{12}^{\,2}r_{23}r_{13}\frac{d\varphi_{12}}{dr_{12}}\, dr_{12}\, dr_{23}\, dr_{13} \tag{3.4-9}$$

[Integral over all r_{12}, r_{23}, r_{13} which form a triangle]

The equivalence of Eq. 3.4-8 and the last form given for the second virial coefficient in Eq. 3.4-5 may easily be verified by partial integration. The corresponding two forms for the third virial coefficient may also be shown to be equivalent.

c. The virial coefficients for angle-dependent potentials[4]

Thus far the discussion has been confined to monatomic molecules, each with three translational degrees of freedom. It has also been understood that the interaction potential is dependent only on the separation

[3] This is true to the extent that the intermolecular force is independent of the orientation and internal configuration of the molecules. In quantum mechanical language, the requirement is that the intermolecular potential be independent of the quantum states of the molecules.

[4] C. S. Wang Chang, Doctoral Dissertation, University of Michigan (1944).

of the molecules. Let us now consider molecules which can be represented as rigid rotators, with three degrees of translational and two degrees of rotational freedom. The interaction potential for such molecules may be assumed to be a function of the intermolecular distance and the three angles which describe the mutual orientation of the molecules. This model is useful in the study of diatomic and other linear molecules and is also appropriate for those molecules which have dipole moments. Formulae for the virial coefficients for a gas made up of rigid rotators may be obtained easily from the results for monatomic molecules, by reinterpreting some of the symbols used in the derivation.

The Hamiltonian for a gas composed of N rigid rotators of mass m and moment of intertia I is

$$H(\boldsymbol{q}^N, \boldsymbol{p}^N) = \sum_i \frac{1}{2m} p_i^{\,2} + \sum_i \frac{1}{2I}\left(p_{\theta_i}^{\,2} + \frac{p_{\phi_i}^{\,2}}{\sin^2 \theta_i}\right) + \Phi(\boldsymbol{q}^N) \qquad (3.4\text{–}10)$$

in which $\boldsymbol{q}$ represents the collection of five coordinates x, y, z, θ, ϕ necessary to specify the location and orientation of a single molecule. The quantities p_θ and p_ϕ are the momenta conjugate to the coordinates θ and ϕ. The partition function for the system is then

$$Z_N = \frac{1}{N!h^{5N}} \int \cdots \int e^{-H(\boldsymbol{q}^N, \boldsymbol{p}^N)/kT} \, dp_{x_1} \, dp_{y_1} \, dp_{z_1} \, dp_{\theta_1} \, dp_{\phi_1} \qquad (3.4\text{–}11)$$
$$\times \, dx_1 \, dy_1 \, dz_1 \, d\theta_1 \, d\phi_1 \cdots$$

Integration over the momenta leads to the expression

$$Z_N = \frac{1}{N!\lambda_{\text{tr}}^{3N} \lambda_{\text{rot}}^{2N}} \int \cdots \int e^{-\Phi(\boldsymbol{q}^N)/kT} \{\sin \theta_1 \sin \theta_2 \cdots\} \qquad (3.4\text{–}12)$$
$$\times \, d\theta_1 \, d\phi_1 \, dx_1 \, dy_1 \, dz_1 \cdots d\theta_N \, d\phi_N \, dx_N \, dy_N \, dz_N$$

in which $\lambda_{\text{tr}}^2 = h^2/2\pi mkT$ and $\lambda_{\text{rot}}^2 = h^2/2\pi IkT$. This expression may be written in the form

$$Z_N = \frac{(4\pi)^N}{N!\lambda_{\text{tr}}^{3N} \lambda_{\text{rot}}^{2N}} \int \cdots \int W_N(\boldsymbol{q}^N) \, d\boldsymbol{q}_1 \cdots d\boldsymbol{q}_N \qquad (3.4\text{–}13)$$

in which $W_N(\boldsymbol{q}^N)$ is the classical Boltzmann factor defined analogously to Eq. 3.1–6 and

$$d\boldsymbol{q}_i = \frac{1}{4\pi} \, dx_i \, dy_i \, dz_i \sin \theta_i \, d\theta_i \, d\varphi_i \qquad (3.4\text{–}14)$$

The derivation from this point onward may be performed according to the scheme outlined in § 3.2. The only change is the replacement of the volume element $d\mathbf{r}_i$ by the more general element $d\mathbf{q}_i$. The factor of 4π is introduced in the definition of $d\mathbf{q}_i$ for convenience. In the limit that the potential is independent of the angular coordinates, then integration of $d\mathbf{q}_i$ over the angles gives simply $d\mathbf{r}_i$. In this respect the 4π is a normalizing factor. The necessity of this normalization appears in the formal analysis in the treatment of Eq. 3.2–15. Unless the volume element $d\mathbf{q}_i$ is so chosen that b_1 is unity, Eq. 3.2–24 and the subsequent equations are not valid.

The final formulae for the second and third virial coefficients for angle dependent potentials are

$$B(T) = -\frac{\tilde{N}}{32\pi^2 V}\iint f_{12}\, d\mathbf{q}_1\, d\mathbf{q}_2$$

$$= -\frac{\tilde{N}}{4}\int_0^\infty\int_0^{2\pi}\int_0^\pi\int_0^\pi f_{12} \sin\theta_1\, d\theta_1 \sin\theta_2\, d\theta_2\, d(\phi_2 - \phi_1) r_{12}^2\, dr_{12} \tag{3.4–15}$$

$$C(T) = -\frac{\tilde{N}^2}{192\pi^3 V}\iiint f_{12} f_{13} f_{23}\, d\mathbf{q}_1\, d\mathbf{q}_2\, d\mathbf{q}_3 \tag{3.4–16}$$

In these formulae $f_{ij} = \{\exp[-(\varphi_{ij}/kT)] - 1\}$ as before, except that now the f_{ij} are functions not only of the intermolecular distance but also of the three angles needed to specify the mutual orientation of two molecules. These formulae are used in §§ 3.8 and 3.10 for the calculation of the equation of state for long molecules and for polar molecules.

d. The virial coefficients for mixtures

The virial equation of state of mixtures may be obtained by writing the partition function for a gaseous mixture and following the general procedure of § 3.2.[5] It is thus found that the equation of state for a mixture of ν components is described by Eq. 3.0–1, where the virial coefficients are given by

$$B(T)_{\text{mixture}} = \sum_{\alpha=1}^{\nu}\sum_{\beta=1}^{\nu} B_{\alpha\beta}(T)\, x_\alpha x_\beta \tag{3.4–17}$$

$$C(T)_{\text{mixture}} = \sum_{\alpha=1}^{\nu}\sum_{\beta=1}^{\nu}\sum_{\gamma=1}^{\nu} C_{\alpha\beta\gamma}(T)\, x_\alpha x_\beta x_\gamma \tag{3.4–18}$$

[5] J. E. Mayer, *J. Phys. Chem.*, **43**, 71 (1939).

Here x_α is the mole fraction of species α in the gas mixture. The function $B_{\alpha\alpha}(T)$ is the second virial coefficient for the pure substance α. $B_{\alpha\beta}(T)$ is the second virial coefficient calculated for a potential function $\varphi_{\alpha\beta}(r_{12})$, which describes the interaction between molecules of species α and species β:

$$B_{\alpha\beta}(T) = -\frac{\tilde{N}}{2V}\iint f_{12}^{\alpha\beta}\, d\mathbf{r}_1\, d\mathbf{r}_2 \tag{3.4–19}$$

The function $f_{ij}^{\alpha\beta} = \{\exp[-(\varphi_{ij}^{\alpha\beta}/kT)] - 1\}$ are defined analogously with Eq. 3.4–1. The superscripts α and β indicate the chemical species of molecules i and j. In a similar fashion the $C_{\alpha\beta\gamma}(T)$ are defined by

$$C_{\alpha\beta\gamma}(T) = -\frac{\tilde{N}^2}{3V}\iiint f_{12}^{\alpha\beta} f_{13}^{\alpha\gamma} f_{23}^{\beta\gamma}\, d\mathbf{r}_1\, d\mathbf{r}_2\, d\mathbf{r}_3 \tag{3.4–20}$$

The $C_{\alpha\beta\gamma}(T)$ are the same for any permutation of the indices, and $C_{\alpha\alpha\alpha}(T)$ is the third virial coefficient for the pure substance α.

e. The determination of virial coefficients from equation of state data

The virial coefficients may be obtained from experimental p-V-T data in several different ways. In one method the equation of state through the third virial coefficient is rearranged thus:

$$\mathscr{A} \equiv \left(\frac{p\tilde{V}}{RT} - 1\right)\tilde{V} = B + \frac{C}{\tilde{V}} + \cdots \tag{3.4–21}$$

From this it may be seen that the second virial coefficient is given by

$$B(T) = \lim_{p\to 0}\left(\frac{p\tilde{V}}{RT} - 1\right)\tilde{V} = \lim_{p\to 0}\mathscr{A} \tag{3.4–22}$$

The third virial coefficient is equal to the slope of $\mathscr{A}$ at zero pressure or

$$C(T) = \lim_{p\to 0}(\mathscr{A} - B)\tilde{V} \tag{3.4–23}$$

This method of obtaining B and C requires extremely accurate compressibility data at very low densities.

Another method is used when the experimental data are presented in the form of a *finite* polynomial in $1/\tilde{V}$ for the compressibility:

$$\frac{p\tilde{V}}{RT} = 1 + \frac{A_1(T)}{\tilde{V}} + \frac{A_2(T)}{\tilde{V}^2} + \cdots + \frac{A_n(T)}{\tilde{V}^n} \tag{3.4–24}$$

a set of constants, A_j, being given for various temperatures. These constants are determined by a least-square or other type of curve-fit of the data. The quantities $A_j(T)$ are then taken directly to be the virial coefficients. Considerable caution must be exercised, however, in such an interpretation, because the $A_j(T)$ depend both on the pressure range of the measurements and upon the degree of polynomial used in the curve-fit process. Hence, unless the data extend to sufficiently low pressures, the function $A_1(T)$ is not necessarily the second virial coefficient. Most of the careful measurements of compressibilities of gases have been made at moderate and high pressures so that it is difficult to obtain reliable values of the virial coefficients. The coefficient $A_2(T)$ and higher coefficients are extremely sensitive to the degree of the polynomial chosen; hence considerable difficulty is encountered in obtaining experimental third virial coefficients.

Frequently experimentalists express their results by giving finite polynomials of a form different from that given in Eq. 3.4–24. The Dutch workers (Michels and co-workers in Amsterdam and Kamerlingh Onnes and co-workers in Leiden) use the international atmosphere as their unit of pressure. Their unit of volume known as the "Amagat" unit of volume is the volume of the gas under consideration at one international atmosphere pressure and 0°C. This standard unit of volume, $\tilde{V}_s$, is slightly different for each gas and differs from 22,414 cm³/mole because of the slight gas imperfection even at one atmosphere. The volume of the gas at an arbitrary pressure and temperature is specified by giving the ratio of the true volume to the standard unit of volume:

$$v_a = \tilde{V}/\tilde{V}_s \tag{3.4-25}$$

and v_a is then the volume "in Amagat units." Similarly the density of the gas in Amagat units, ρ_a, is defined as:

$$\rho_a = \frac{1}{v_a} = \frac{\tilde{V}_s}{\tilde{V}} \tag{3.4-26}$$

It is common practice to write the equation of state in the form

$$pv_a = a + b\rho_a + c\rho_a^2 + d\rho_a^3 + \cdots \tag{3.4-27}$$

and to summarize the experimental data by giving values of $a, b, c, \ldots$ for various temperatures (using finite series to fit the data). Comparison of this equation with the virial equation given in Eq. 3.0–1 indicates that the coefficients $B, C, D, \ldots$ may be obtained from $a, b, c, d, \ldots$ from the following relations:

$$\begin{aligned} B &= (b/a)\tilde{V}_s \\ C &= (c/a)\tilde{V}_s^2 \\ D &= (d/a)\tilde{V}_s^3, \text{ etc.} \end{aligned} \tag{3.4-28}$$

where $V_s = RT/a$. Since these relationships are true only if Eq. 3.4–27 is an infinite series, they may be used only as approximations in obtaining the virial coefficients.

The German investigators (in particular Holborn and Otto at Berlin) use as their unit of pressure 1 meter of mercury. The unit of volume is taken to be the volume of a mole of gas at 1 meter of mercury and 0°C. The equation of state is written in the form

$$p\tilde{V} = \bar{A} + \bar{B}p + \bar{C}p^2 + \cdots \tag{3.4–29}$$

and $\bar{A}$, $\bar{B}$, $\bar{C}$, . . . are reported for various temperatures. In terms of these quantities the virial coefficients of Eq. 3.0–1 are

$$B = (0.76RT)\,(\bar{B}/\bar{A})$$

$$C = (0.76RT)^2\,(\bar{C}/\bar{A}) + B^2 \tag{3.4–30}$$

Again these expressions are strictly valid only if the series in Eq. 3.4–29 is infinite.

5. Virial Coefficients for Simple Angle-Independent Potentials

In this section the results of the virial development are used to calculate the equation of state for several simple molecular models. For each of these simple potential functions the integrations to obtain the virial coefficients may be performed analytically. These simple analytical expressions are convenient for fitting the experimental data over small ranges of temperature. For fitting the data over large temperature ranges, more realistic potential functions must be used. Furthermore, the more realistic potential functions are required to obtain "force constants" which may be used interchangeably for equation of state or transport property calculations. Virial coefficients for these better potentials are given in subsequent sections.

a. Rigid spheres

Because of its simplicity the rigid sphere model (see Eq. 1.3–22) found much use in early studies of the equation of state and in exploratory calculations of the higher virial coefficients. The second and third virial coefficients may be calculated easily from the formulae given in the preceding section. The fourth,[1] fifth,[2] and higher virial coefficients are, however, much more difficult to evaluate. The values of the second

[1] H. Happel, *Ann. Physik*, (4) **21**, 342 (1906); R. Majumdar, *Bull. Calcutta Math. Soc.*, **21**, 107 (1929).

[2] Private communication from M. N. and A. W. Rosenbluth, Los Alamos Scientific Laboratory, June 19, 1953. This value for the fifth virial coefficient was calculated by the Monte Carlo method by means of the IBM 701 Computing Machine at Los Alamos.

through the fifth virial coefficients for a gas made up of rigid spheres of collision diameter σ are:

$$\begin{aligned} B &= \tfrac{2}{3}\pi\tilde{N}\sigma^3 = b_0 \\ C &= \tfrac{5}{8}b_0^2 \\ D &= 0.2869b_0^3 \\ E &= (0.115 \pm 0.005)b_0^4 \end{aligned} \tag{3.5–1}$$

The virial coefficients for rigid spheres are temperature-independent and are probably all positive. The compressibility factor, $p\tilde{V}/RT$, is therefore always greater than unity and a function only of the density.

The rigid sphere approximation is quite good at very high temperatures, where the attractions between the molecules become unimportant. For example, this model has been used to good advantage for approximating the equation of state of hot powder gases in the study of interior ballistics. Given the energy of interaction between a pair of real molecules, it is very difficult to know exactly what value is appropriate for the rigid sphere collision diameter.[3] One reasonable definition for σ might be the distance of closest approach of two molecules colliding with an energy of kT. Often σ is evaluated by setting b_0 equal to the co-volume, b, in van der Waals equation of state, but the value of van der Waals b is not uniquely specified. Another common method of choosing σ involves the coefficient of viscosity (see Chapter 8). For high-temperature powder gas equations of state, it appears[4] that σ should equal 0.81 times the Lennard-Jones force constant σ (see § 3.6).

b. Point centers of repulsion

Substitution of the potential function $\varphi(r) = dr^{-\delta}$ (Eq. 1.3–23) into the formula for the second virial coefficient given in Eq. 3.4–8 gives[5]

$$\begin{aligned} B(T) &= -\frac{2\pi\tilde{N}}{3kT}\int_0^\infty r^3(-\delta\, dr^{-\delta-1})\exp(-dr^{-\delta}/kT)\,dr \\ &= \frac{2\pi\tilde{N}}{3}\left(\frac{d}{kT}\right)^{3/\delta}\Gamma\left(\frac{\delta-3}{\delta}\right) \qquad \delta > 3 \end{aligned} \tag{3.5–2}$$

[3] H. A. Stuart, *Molekülstruktur*, Springer (1934), p. 36, has a listing of collision diameters for rigid spheres as determined from different types of experimental data.

[4] The high-temperature region of powder gases happens to lie close to the temperature range for which the Lennard-Jones potential gives a maximum value of the second virial coefficient of approximately 0.52 b_0. See J. O. Hirschfelder, F. T. McClure, C. F. Curtiss, and D. W. Osborne, "Thermodynamic Properties of Propellant Gases," NDRC Report, A-116 (November 1942).

[5] J. Jeans, *Dynamical Theory of Gases*, Cambridge University Press (1925), p. 134.

Since the integral diverges at the upper limit unless $\delta > 3$, this result is applicable neither to an electron gas nor to an ionized gas. The second virial coefficient is always positive for a gas made up of molecules which are regarded as point centers of repulsion.

c. The Sutherland model

For this model the molecules are regarded as rigid spheres of diameter σ surrounded by an attractive field $\varphi(r) = -cr^{-\gamma}$ (see Eq. 1.3–25). Substitution of this potential function into Eq. 3.4–5 for the second virial coefficient gives[6]

$$B(T) = \frac{2\pi\tilde{N}\sigma^3}{3} - 2\pi\tilde{N}\int_{\sigma}^{\infty}[\exp(cr^{-\gamma}/kT) - 1]r^2\,dr$$

$$= -\frac{2\pi\tilde{N}\sigma^3}{3}\sum_{j=0}^{\infty}\frac{1}{j!}\left(\frac{3}{j\gamma - 3}\right)\left(\frac{c}{\sigma^{\gamma}kT}\right)^j \tag{3.5–3}$$

The integration is carried out by first expanding the exponential in a Taylor series. The Sutherland model is a special case of the Lennard-Jones potential with infinitely steep repulsion. At low temperatures this model gives a negative second virial coefficient. This is due to the importance of the attractive part of the potential in the low velocity collisions.

d. The square-well potential

For the square-well potential

$$\begin{aligned} \varphi(r) &= \infty & 0 < r < \sigma \\ \varphi(r) &= -\epsilon & \sigma < r < R\sigma \\ \varphi(r) &= 0 & r > R\sigma \end{aligned} \tag{1.3–24}$$

the expressions given in § 3.4b may be used to evaluate the second and third virial coefficients. The results are[7]

$$B(T) = b_0[1 - (R^3 - 1)\Delta] \tag{3.5–4}$$

$$\begin{aligned} C(T) = \tfrac{1}{8}b_0^2[5 &- (R^6 - 18R^4 + 32R^3 - 15)\Delta \\ &- (2R^6 - 36R^4 + 32R^3 + 18R^2 - 16)\Delta^2 \\ &- (6R^6 - 18R^4 + 18R^2 - 6)\Delta^3] \qquad R \leqslant 2 \end{aligned} \tag{3.5–5}$$

$$\begin{aligned} C(T) = \tfrac{1}{8}b_0^2[5 &- 17\Delta - (-32R^3 + 18R^2 + 48)\Delta^2 \\ &- (5R^6 - 32R^3 + 18R^2 + 26)\Delta^3] \qquad R \geqslant 2 \end{aligned}$$

[6] W. H. Keesom, *Comm. Phys. Lab. Leiden*, Suppl., **24B**, 32 (1912).

[7] T. Kihara, *Nippon-Sugaku-Buturigakukaisi*, **17**, 11 (1943) in Japanese.

in which Δ stands for $[\exp(\epsilon/kT) - 1]$, and $b_0 = \frac{2}{3}\pi\tilde{N}\sigma^3$. Values of the parameters b_0, ϵ/k and R have been obtained for a large number of molecules[8] by fitting the second virial coefficient data with Eq. 3.5–4. A complete list of these parameters is given in Table 3.5–1; the list includes many complex organic molecules such as hydrocarbons and freons.

The square-well potential is particularly useful for the description of the equation of state behavior of gases made up of complex molecules, inasmuch as the potential function has three adjustable constants. The results for the square-well potential do not apply to gases at high temperatures, since this potential does not allow for the interpenetration of the molecules in high energy collisions which predominate at elevated temperatures.

It has been found that the second virial coefficient for the square-well approximates that for the Lennard-Jones (6-12) potential (Eq. 1.3–27) if R is taken to be 1.8, the value of σ for the square-well taken to be the same as that for the Lennard-Jones (6-12) potential, and the depth of the square-well is taken to be 0.56 times the maximum energy of attraction of the Lennard-Jones potential. For this particular choice of parameters, the expressions for the second and third virial coefficients become

$$B(T)/b_0 = 1 - 4.832\Delta \tag{3.5–6}$$

$$C(T)/b_0^2 = 0.6250 - 2.085\Delta + 10.118\Delta^2 - 8.430\Delta^3 \tag{3.5–7}$$

Although the first of these relations gives good agreement with the corresponding result for the Lennard-Jones (6-12) potential, the above value for the third virial coefficient differs by about a factor of two from the third virial coefficient calculated from the Lennard-Jones potential. This is an indication of the fact that the second virial coefficient is relatively insensitive to the shape of the intermolecular potential function, whereas the higher virial coefficients are considerably more sensitive.

The square-well may be used to calculate[7] the second and third virial coefficients of mixtures. The potential of interaction between two molecules i and j of species α and β is given by

$$\begin{aligned} \varphi^{\alpha\beta}(r_{ij}) &= \infty & \sigma_{\alpha\beta} &> r_{ij} \\ \varphi^{\alpha\beta}(r_{ij}) &= -\epsilon_{\alpha\beta} & \sigma_{\alpha\beta} &< r_{ij} < R_{\alpha\beta}\sigma_{\alpha\beta} \\ \varphi^{\alpha\beta}(r_{ij}) &= 0 & r_{ij} &> R_{\alpha\beta}\sigma_{\alpha\beta} \end{aligned} \tag{3.5–8}$$

[8] J. O. Hirschfelder, F. T. McClure, and I. F. Weeks, *J. Chem. Phys.*, **10**, 201 (1942).

TABLE 3.5–1
FORCE CONSTANTS FOR THE SQUARE-WELL POTENTIAL OBTAINED FROM SECOND VIRIAL COEFFICIENT DATA[a]

Gas	σ (Å)	$b_0 = \frac{2}{3}\pi\tilde{N}\sigma^3$ (cc/mole)	R	ϵ/k (°K)	Reference for $B(T)$ Data
Neon	2.382	17.05	1.87	19.5	*b*
Argon	3.162	39.87	1.85	69.4	*b*
Krypton	3.362	47.93	1.85	98.3	*c*
Nitrogen	3.299	45.29	1.87	53.7	*b*
Carbon dioxide	3.917	75.79	1.83	119	*d*
Ethane	3.535	55.72	1.652	244	*e*
Propane	4.418	108.8	1.464	347	*f*
n-Butane	4.812	140.6	1.476	387	*g*
n-Heptane	6.397	330.3	1.314	629	*h*
Ethene	3.347	47.28	1.677	222	*i*
Propene	4.316	101.4	1.460	339	*i*
Propadiene	4.511	115.8	1.373	382	*i*
1-Butene	5.592	220.6	1.249	492	*i*
2-Methylpropene	5.570	218.0	1.254	490	*i*
trans-2-Butene	5.276	185.3	1.324	465	*i*
cis-2-Butene	5.747	239.5	1.215	537	*i*
CCl_3F	4.534	117.6	1.545	399	*j*
$CHCl_2F$	2.797	27.60	2.321	306	*k*
CCl_2F_2	4.812	140.6	1.394	345	*l*
$CCl_2F\text{-}CClF_2$	3.697	63.73	2.075	335	*m*
Methyl chloride	4.294	99.90	1.337	469	*n*
Ammonia	2.902	30.83	1.268	692	*o*
Steam	2.606	22.33	1.199	1260	*p*

[a] The force constants for the complex molecules noted here were taken from J. O. Hirschfelder, F. T. McClure, and I. F. Weeks, *J. Chem. Phys.*, **10** 201 (1942).
[b] L. Holborn and J. Otto, *Z. Physik*, **33**, 1 (1925).
[c] J. A. Beattie. J. S. Brierley, and R. J. Barriault, *J. Chem. Phys.*, **20**, 1613, 1615 (1952).
[d] K. E. MacCormack and W. G. Schneider, *J. Chem. Phys.*, **18**, 1269 (1950).
[e] Beattie, Hadlock, and Poffenberger, *J. Chem. Phys.*, **3**, 93 (1935).
[f] Beattie, Kay, and Kaminsky, *J. Am. Chem. Soc.*, **59**,1589 (1937).
[g] Beattie, Simard, and Su, *J. Am. Chem. Soc.*, **61**, 26 (1939).
[h] Smith, Beattie, and Kay, *J. Am. Chem. Soc.*, **59**, 1587 (1937).
[i] E. E. Roper, *J. Phys. Chem.*, **44**, 835 (1940).
[j] *Thermodynamic Properties of Trichloromonofluoromethane*, Kinetic Chemicals, Inc. (1938).
[k] *Thermodynamic Properties of Dichloromonofluoromethane*, Kinetic Chemicals, Inc. (1939).
[l] *Thermodynamic Properties of Dichlorodifluoromethane*, Circular 12, Am. Soc. Refrig. Eng. (1931).
[m] *Thermodynamic Properties of Trichlorotrifluoroethane*, Kinetic Chemicals, Inc. (1938).
[n] *Methyl Chloride*, E. I. du Pont de Nemours & Co., the R. and H. Chemicals Department (1940), 5th Ed.
[o] C. H. Meyers and R. S. Jessup, *Refrig. Eng.*, **11**, 345 (1925).
[p] J. H. Keenan and F. G. Keyes, *Thermodynamic Properties of Steam*, Wiley (1936).

Then, letting $(b_0)_{\alpha\beta} = \frac{2}{3}\pi\tilde{N}\sigma_{\alpha\beta}^3$ and $\Delta_{\alpha\beta} = [\exp(\epsilon_{\alpha\beta}/kT) - 1]$, we may write the following relations for $B_{\alpha\beta}(T)$ and $C_{\alpha\beta}(T)$:

$$B_{\alpha\beta}(T) = (b_0)_{\alpha\beta}[1 - (R_{\alpha\beta}{}^3 - 1)\Delta_{\alpha\beta}] \tag{3.5–9}$$

$$\begin{aligned} 3C_{\alpha\beta\gamma}(T) = I(0) - [&I(1,1)\Delta_{\alpha\beta} + I(1,2)\Delta_{\alpha\gamma} + I(1,3)\Delta_{\beta\gamma}] \\ &+ I(2,1)\Delta_{\alpha\beta}\Delta_{\alpha\gamma} + I(2,2)\Delta_{\alpha\beta}\Delta_{\beta\gamma} + I(2,3)\Delta_{\alpha\gamma}\Delta_{\beta\gamma}] \\ &- [I(3)\Delta_{\alpha\beta}\Delta_{\alpha\gamma}\Delta_{\beta\gamma}] \end{aligned} \tag{3.5–10}$$

in which

$$\begin{aligned} I(0) &= J(\sigma_{\alpha\beta}, \sigma_{\alpha\gamma}, \sigma_{\beta\gamma}) \\ I(1,1) &= J(R_{\alpha\beta}\sigma_{\alpha\beta}, \sigma_{\alpha\gamma}, \sigma_{\beta\gamma}) - I(0) \\ I(1,2) &= J(\sigma_{\alpha\beta}, R_{\alpha\gamma}\sigma_{\alpha\gamma}, \sigma_{\beta\gamma}) - I(0) \\ I(1,3) &= J(\sigma_{\alpha\beta}, \sigma_{\alpha\gamma}, R_{\beta\gamma}\sigma_{\beta\gamma}) - I(0) \\ I(2,1) &= J(R_{\alpha\beta}\sigma_{\alpha\beta}, R_{\alpha\gamma}\sigma_{\alpha\gamma}, \sigma_{\beta\gamma}) - [I(0) + I(1,1) + I(1,2)] \\ I(2,2) &= J(R_{\alpha\beta}\sigma_{\alpha\beta}, \sigma_{\alpha\gamma}, R_{\beta\gamma}\sigma_{\beta\gamma}) - [I(0) + I(1,1) + I(1,3)] \\ I(2,3) &= J(\sigma_{\alpha\beta}, R_{\alpha\gamma}\sigma_{\alpha\gamma}, R_{\beta\gamma}\sigma_{\beta\gamma}) - [I(0) + I(1,2) + I(1,3)] \\ I(3) &= J(R_{\alpha\beta}\sigma_{\alpha\beta}, R_{\alpha\gamma}\sigma_{\alpha\gamma}, R_{\beta\gamma}\sigma_{\beta\gamma}) - \left[I(0) + \sum_{k=1}^{3} I(1,k) + \sum_{k=1}^{3} I(2,k)\right] \end{aligned} \tag{3.5–11}$$

The function $J(a, b, c)$, which occurs in the formulae for the I's is

$$J(a, b, c) = \frac{16\pi^2}{9}\left[\frac{a^3b^3c^3}{d^3}\right] \qquad 2d \geqslant a + b + c$$

$$\begin{aligned} J(a, b, c) &= \frac{\pi^2}{18}\begin{bmatrix} a^6 + b^6 + c^6 + 18a^2b^2c^2 \\ + 16(b^3c^3 + c^3a^3 + a^3b^3) \\ - 9\{a^4(b^2 + c^2) + b^4(c^2 + a^2) + c^4(a^2 + b^2)\} \end{bmatrix} \qquad 2d \leqslant a + b + c \end{aligned} \tag{3.5–12}$$

where d is the largest of a, b, c.

6. The Virial Coefficients for the Lennard-Jones (6-12) Potential[1]

The Lennard-Jones (6-12) potential

$$\varphi(r) = 4\epsilon \left[\left(\frac{\sigma}{r}\right)^{12} - \left(\frac{\sigma}{r}\right)^{6}\right] \tag{1.3–27}$$

has been widely used for the calculation of the properties of matter in the gaseous, liquid, and solid states. Consequently, the calculation of the virial coefficients for this important model is given here in detail. It is also shown how the parameters σ and ϵ of the potential function may be determined by analysis of the second virial coefficient data. Finally, it is shown that experimental Joule-Thomson coefficients may also be used to gain information about the forces between molecules.

In the discussion which follows many of the formulae assume simpler forms if the following reduced quantities are used:[2]

$$r^* = r/\sigma \qquad T^* = kT/\epsilon$$

$$B^\star = B/(\tfrac{2}{3}\pi\tilde{N}\sigma^3) = B/b_0 \qquad C^\star = C/b_0{}^2$$

$$B_k{}^\star = T^{*k}(d^kB^\star/dT^{*k}) \qquad C_k{}^\star = T^{*k}(d^kC^\star/dT^{*k}) \tag{3.6–1}$$

The quantities $B_k{}^\star$ and $C_k{}^\star$ are dimensionless derivatives in terms of which the thermodynamic properties may be expressed.

a. Calculation of the second virial coefficient

The second virial coefficient integral may be integrated analytically for the Lennard-Jones potential.[3] Substitution of the Lennard-Jones

[1] Some calculations of virial coefficients have been made for Lennard-Jones potentials with indices of repulsion other than twelve. Inasmuch as it has been found that the inverse twelfth power repulsion gives the best agreement with the experimental data on second virial coefficients and Joule-Thomson coefficients of many substances, we give in this chapter the results for the (6–12) potential only. However, for helium, mercury, and some other molecules the (6–9) potential might be slightly better. Rather extensive second virial coefficient calculations have been made by punched card methods for the Lennard-Jones (6-9) potential from $T^* = 0.5$ to $T^* = 100$ by L. F. Epstein and C. J. Hibbert, *J. Chem. Phys.*, **20**, 752 (1952). The third virial coefficient for the (6-9) potential has been evaluated by T. Kihara, *J. Phys. Soc. Japan*, **6**, 184 (1951).

[2] Two conventions have been adopted in the literature for the reduction of quantities such as the second virial coefficient. Some workers have used $B^* = B/\tilde{N}\sigma^3$; others have used $B^\star = B/B_{\text{rig sph}} = B/b_0$. Both systems of reduction have their advantages. We use the asterisk (*) to indicate reduction of quantities by means of the simplest combinations of the potential parameters σ and ϵ, and the star ($\star$) to indicate reduction with respect to combinations of σ and ϵ which make use of rigid sphere values. The two types of reduced quantities are of course simply related.

[3] J. E. Lennard-Jones, *Proc. Roy. Soc.* (*London*), **A106**, 463 (1924).

(6-12) potential (Eq. 1.3-27) into the formula for the second virial coefficient given in Eq. 3.4-8 gives

$$B^\star(T^*) = -\frac{4}{T^*}\int_0^\infty r^{*2}\left[-\frac{12}{r^{*12}}+\frac{6}{r^{*6}}\right]e^{-\frac{4}{T^*}\left(\frac{1}{r^{*12}}-\frac{1}{r^{*6}}\right)}dr^* \quad (3.6\text{-}2)$$

When exp $[(4/T^*)r^{*-6}]$ is expanded in an infinite series, the integration may be performed analytically. The reduced second virial coefficient may then be written as[4]

$$B(T) = b_0B^\star(T^*); \quad B^\star(T^*) = \sum_{j=0}^{\infty} b^{(j)}T^{*-(2j+1)/4} \quad (3.6\text{-}3)$$

The coefficients[5] $b^{(j)}$ are given by

$$b^{(j)} = -\frac{2^{j+\frac{1}{2}}}{4j!}\,\Gamma\left(\frac{2j-1}{4}\right) \quad (3.6\text{-}4)$$

and are Tabulated in Table I-E. (The tables numbered with roman numerals are in the general appendix at the back of the book.) The summation in Eq. 3.6-3 converges very rapidly for reduced temperatures greater than 4. For smaller values of T^* the convergence is less rapid; for $T^* = 0.30$ about thirty terms are needed in the series to obtain an accuracy of five significant figures. The function $B^\star$ has been calculated by punched card methods[6] for values of T^* from 0.3 to 400; this tabulation is given in the appendix in Table I-B. Also given in this tabulation are the functions, $B_k^\star(T^*)$, which occur in the expressions for the thermodynamic properties. A table of the various thermodynamic properties in terms of the virial coefficients is given in Appendix 3.B at the end of the chapter.

Let us examine the characteristics of the function $B^\star(T^*)$. As seen in Figure 3.6-1 for low temperatures $B^\star$ is negative, and above the *Boyle temperature*,[7] $T_B{}^* = 3.42$, it is positive with a maximum at about $T^* = 25$. This behavior may be understood from the nature of the potential function. For low temperatures the average energies of the molecules

[4] For the general Lennard-Jones potential of Eq. 1.3-26, the same development leads to the following formula for $B(T)$:

$$B(T) = -\frac{2\pi\tilde{N}}{3}\left(\frac{d}{c}\right)^{3/(\delta-\gamma)} y^{3/(\delta-\gamma)}\sum_{j=0}^{\infty} b^{(j)}(\gamma,\delta)y^j \quad (3.6\text{-}3a)$$

$$b^{(j)}(\gamma,\delta) = \frac{3}{j!\,\delta}\,\Gamma\left(\frac{j\gamma-3}{\delta}\right) \qquad y = \left(\frac{c}{kT}\right)\left(\frac{kT}{d}\right)^{\gamma/\delta} \quad (3.6\text{-}3b)$$

[5] The coefficients $b^{(j)}$ should not be confused with the cluster integrals, the b_l, of § 3.2b.

[6] R. B. Bird and E. L. Spotz, University of Wisconsin, CM 599 (Project NOrd 9938), May 10, 1950.

[7] See Problem 4 at the end of the chapter.

are of the same order of magnitude as the depth of the potential well. Consequently, colliding pairs of molecules spend a large portion of their time in the attractive region of the potential. This emphasis on the attraction between the molecules results in a decrease in the pressure, and the second virial coefficient is thus negative. For high temperatures

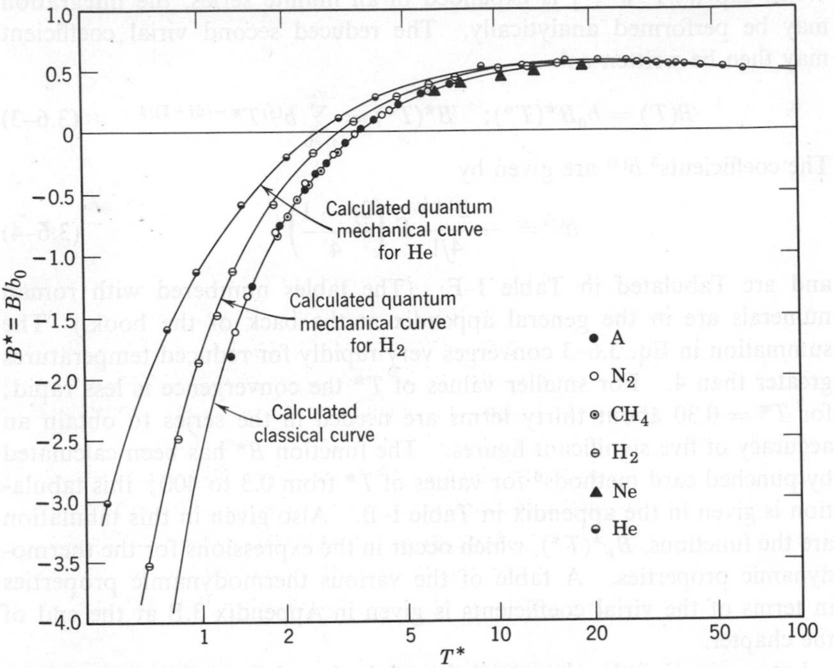

Fig. 3.6–1. The reduced second virial coefficient for the Lennard-Jones potential. The classical curve of $B^{\star}(T^{*})$ is shown here along with the experimental points for several gases. Also shown are the curves for hydrogen and helium, which have been calculated by quantum mechanics according to § 6.5b, c. We can see the extent to which quantum deviations are important for these gases. (From R. J. Lunbeck, Doctoral Dissertation, Amsterdam, 1950.)

the average energies of the molecules are large with respect to the maximum energy of attraction. The molecules do not "see," as it were, the dip in the potential curve, so that the predominant contribution to the virial coefficient is that due to the repulsive portion of the potential. The emphasis on the repulsion between the molecules results in an increase in the pressure, and thus the second virial coefficient is positive. For very high temperatures those collisions are emphasized in which the molecules collide with such force that considerable interpenetration takes place, causing the molecules to behave as if they had a smaller volume. It is for this reason that the $B^\star$ goes up to a maximum, and then begins to fall off. This maximum has been observed for helium.[8]

In order to calculate the second virial coefficient for a gas using Table I–B, the only information needed is the values of the parameters σ and ϵ in the Lennard-Jones potential. These parameters are obtained by analysis of the experimental data for second virial coefficients (this is discussed in the next subsection), transport coefficients (§ 8.4), constants characteristic of the critical, melting, or boiling points (§ 4.1c), or other properties. Values of these *force constants* are given in the Appendix in Table I–A for a large number of molecules. In Table 3.6–1 are given a few of these parameters. When force constants have been obtained

TABLE 3.6–1

FORCE CONSTANTS FOR THE LENNARD-JONES (6–12) POTENTIAL DETERMINED FROM SECOND VIRIAL COEFFICIENTS[a]

Gas	ϵ/k (°K)	σ (Å)	b_0 (*cc/mole*)	*Experimental Data*
Ne	34.9	2.78	27.10	*b*
A	119.8	3.405	49.80	*c*
Kr	171	3.60	58.86	*d*
Xe	221	4.10	86.94	*e*
N_2	95.05	3.698	63.78	*f*
O_2	118	3.46	52.26	*g*
CH_4	148.2	3.817	70.16	*h*
CO_2	189	4.486	113.9	*i*

[a] A more complete table of force constants for the Lennard-Jones (6-12) potential is given in the Appendix (Table I–A). There also are given the force constants determined from viscosity data.

[b] L. Holborn and J. Otto, *Z. Physik*, **33**, 1 (1925).

[c] A. Michels, Hub. Wijker, and Hk. Wijker, *Physica*, **15**, 627 (1949).

[d] J. A. Beattie, R. J. Barriault, J. S. Brierley, *J. Chem. Phys.*, **20**, 1613, 1615 (1952).

[e] J. A. Beattie, R. J. Barriault, J. S. Brierley, *J. Chem. Phys.*, **19**, 1222 (1951).

[f] A. Michels, H. Wouters, J. de Boer, *Physica*, **1**, 587 (1934).

[g] L. Holborn and J. Otto, *Z. Physik*, **10**, 367 (1922).

[h] A. Michels and G. W. Nederbragt, *Physica*, **3**, 569 (1936).

[i] A. Michels and C. Michels, *Proc. Roy. Soc.* (*London*), **A153**, 201 (1936).

from several types of experimental data, it is usually advisable to use those parameters obtained from second virial coefficients for the calculation of equation of state properties. For some gases several sets of force constants have been obtained by the analysis of two or more sets of equation of state data. Let us consider a numerical example to

[8] L. Holborn and J. Otto, *Z. Physik*, **33**, 1 (1925).

illustrate the use of the tabulated quantities and the formulae related to equation of state calculations.

Illustrative Example

Problem. Calculate the compressibility factor for argon at 5 atm at 15°C and at 250°C.

Solution. From Table 3.6–1 the constants $\epsilon/k = 119.8$°K and $b_0 = 49.80$ cc/mole are obtained for argon. Then $T = 15 + 273.2 = 288.2$°K and $T^* = kT/\epsilon = 288.2/119.8 = 2.406$, for which $B^\star$ is found from Table I–B to be -0.3605. The second virial coefficient is then $B = b_0 B^\star = (49.80)(-0.3605) = 17.95$ cc/mole. The second virial coefficient for the pressure series (see footnote to Eq. 3.0–1) is then $B' = B/RT = (-17.95)/(82.06)(288.2) = -0.00076$ atm^{-1}. Finally, the compressibility factor is

$$pV/NkT = 1 + B'(T)p + \cdots = 1 - (0.00076)(5) + \ldots$$
$$= 0.9962$$

Similarly for $T = 250°C$, $B^\star = 0.1702$, and the compressibility factor is 1.0010.

b. Determination of intermolecular forces from experimental second virial coefficients

Having determined experimental values of second virial coefficients according to one of the methods given in § 3.4e, we may use this information to obtain the parameters in any potential function. The two adjustable parameters of the Lennard-Jones potential may be determined from the experimental $B(T)$ values at two temperatures. The following procedure may be used. First we define a quantity k_B by

$$k_B = \left[\frac{B(T_2)}{B(T_1)}\right]_{\text{exptl}} \tag{3.6–5}$$

Then ϵ/k may be determined by trial and error solution of the equation

$$k_B = \left[\frac{B^\star(kT_2/\epsilon)}{B^\star(kT_1/\epsilon)}\right] \tag{3.6–6}$$

As a first approximation to ϵ/k, we may use the value calculated from the boiling temperature, melting temperature, or critical temperature, using the relations given in § 4.1. The collision diameter is obtained from

$$b_0 = 1.2615\sigma^3 = \left[\frac{B(T_i)}{B^\star(T_i^*)}\right] \qquad (3.6–7)^9$$

in which T_i is either T_1 or T_2. Slightly different sets of force constants may be obtained for different choices of the temperatures, T_1 and T_2.

[9] In this equation b_0 is in units of cubic centimeters per mole, and the collision diameter, σ, is expressed in angstroms.

This discrepancy, however, is small and results from the fact that the Lennard-Jones potential is an empirical function and does not give an exact description of the dependence of the intermolecular force on the distance. A numerical example is given here to illustrate the determination of force constants from second virial coefficients.

Illustrative Example

Problem. Using the experimental data[10] in Table 3.6–2, determine the force constants in the Lennard-Jones potential for xenon. The critical temperature of Xe is 289.8°K.

Solution. Since for a large number of gases $kT_c/\epsilon = 1.3$, an approximate value for ϵ/k is 223°K. We now solve Eq. 3.6–6 for three combinations of T_1 and T_2. The trial and error solutions may be tabulated as follows:

T_1	T_2	k_B	Trial ϵ/k	$B^\star(T_2^*)/B^\star(T_1^*)$
298.2	498.2	0.3003	223	0.3060
			220	0.3010
			219	0.2993
348.2	548.3	0.2963	223	0.3009
			220	0.2940
			221	0.2964
373.2	573.3	0.2894	220	0.2839
			221	0.2867
			222	0.2895

For each pair of temperatures the best value of ϵ/k is indicated by an underline. The closeness of the values obtained in the widely spaced temperature range illustrates the accuracy of the Lennard-Jones potential. For $\epsilon/k = 221$°K the collision diameter according to Eq. 3.6–7 is $\sigma = 4.10$ Å. Values of $B(T)$ calculated from Table I–B and these force constants are compared with the experimental data in Table 3.6–2.

TABLE 3.6–2

EXPERIMENTAL AND CALCULATED VALUES OF $B(T)$ FOR XENON

Temperature (°K)	$B(T)$ (*Experimental*) *cc/mole*	$B(T)$ (*Calculated*) *cc/mole*
298.2	−130.2	−128.4
348.2	−94.5	−94.5
373.2	−81.2	−81.5
498.2	−39.1	−38.9
548.3	−28.0	−28.0
573.3	−23.5	−23.4

Force constants determined for the Lennard-Jones potential in this manner for several gases are given in Table 3.6–1. A more complete tabulation may be found in the Appendix in Table I–A. Wherever data

[10] J. A. Beattie, R. J. Barriault, and J. S. Brierley, *J. Chem. Phys.*, **19**, 1222 (1951).

are available from two different groups of investigators two sets of force constants have been computed. The force constants for hydrogen, deuterium, and helium shown in the table have been obtained by the method just described, and also by an analogous method in which quantum effects are taken into account (see § 6.5c). The curve $B^\star(T^*)$ for the Lennard-Jones potential is plotted in Fig. 3.6–1. Experimental data for a large number of gases have been reduced, using the Lennard-Jones force constants, and this information is plotted on the same graph. It is seen that this potential function describes rather well the temperature-dependence of the second virial coefficient. This is a nice illustration of the applicability of the principle of corresponding states, which is discussed in detail in the next chapter.

Thus far the calculation of force constants has been restricted to the interactions between molecules of the same chemical species. In principle it is possible to determine the force law between molecules of different chemical species from the second virial coefficients for gaseous mixtures and Eq. 3.4–17. The virial coefficients for mixtures, however, depend not only upon the forces between unlike molecules but also strongly on the interaction between molecules of the same species. Consequently, to get the forces between unlike molecules it is necessary to have extremely accurate experimental data for the second virial coefficients of the pure components and the mixtures. Such information is not generally available. Another possibility is to use the volume change when two gases are mixed.[11] Here again the dependence on the forces between unlike molecules is to a certain extent masked by the dependence on the interaction between similar molecules. Measurements of the diffusion coefficient and the thermal diffusion ratio provide the best source of information about forces between unlike molecules.[12]

When other information[12] is lacking, it is necessary to use the *empirical combining laws* which relate the force constants between unlike molecules to those between like molecules:

$$\sigma_{\alpha\beta} = \tfrac{1}{2}(\sigma_\alpha + \sigma_\beta) \tag{3.6–8}$$

$$\epsilon_{\alpha\beta} = (\epsilon_\alpha \epsilon_\beta)^{1/2} \tag{3.6–9}$$

The first of these rules is clearly exact for rigid spherical molecules. The second rule follows from a simple interpretation of the dispersion

[11] A. E. Edwards and W. E. Roseveare, *J.A.C.S.*, **64**, 2816 (1942).

[12] Table 8.4–17 shows a comparison of force constants obtained from experimental diffusion and thermal diffusion data with those calculated using the empirical combining laws.

forces in terms of the polarizabilities of the individual molecules (see § 13.3). Force constants obtained from these combining laws seem to give reasonably good results in calculations involving mixtures. Table 3.6–3 compares the experimental values of $B_{12}(T)$ obtained from the volume change on mixing with those calculated by means of the empirical combining laws.

TABLE 3.6–3

EXPERIMENTAL AND CALCULATED VALUES OF $B_{12}(T)$

Gas Mixture	Temperature (°C)	$B_{12}(T)$ (cc/mole) Experimental (a)	(b)	(c)	Calculated
H_2–N_2	25	13.5	12.8	(11.1)[d]	11.5
H_2–C_2H_4	25	−41.3	—	—	0.8
H_2–CO_2	25	−39.0	−1.1	—	3.0
N_2–He	25	12.5	—	—	17.7
N_2–O_2	30	—	—	−9.7	−10.1
N_2–CO_2	25	−50.4	−42.6	—	−41.1
	30	—	—	−40.6	−49.1
N_2–C_2H_4	25	−54.8	—	—	−44.2
N_2–CH_3F	25	—	−36.	—	−40.6
CO_2–He	25	−40.2	—	—	21.3
CO_2–O_2	25	−58.3	—	—	−52.1
	30	—	—	−41.5	−49.9
CO_2–C_2H_4	25	−128.	—	—	−133.
CO_2–CH_3F	25	—	−149.	—	−105.

[a] A. E. Edwards and W. E. Roseveare, *J.A.C.S.*, **64**, 2816 (1942). These values are probably not so accurate as some of the more recent results.

[b] Experimental data of A. Michels and A. J. H. Boerboom as quoted by R. J. Lunbeck and A. J. H. Boerboom, *Physica*, **17**, 76 (1951).

[c] R. A. Gorski and J. G. Miller, *J.A.C.S.*, **75**, 550 (1953).

[d] This result was obtained by direct compressibility measurements by A. Michels and T. Wassenaar, *Appl. Sci. Res.*, **A1**, 258 (1949).

Illustrative Example

Problem. Calculate the second virial coefficient at 50°C (323.2°K) for a mixture of 25 mole per cent N_2 and 75 mole per cent CH_4.

Solution. From Table I–A the following parameters are obtained:

$$N_2: \ b_0 = 63.78 \text{ cc/mole} \qquad \epsilon/k = \ \ 95.05°\text{K}$$

$$CH_4: \ b_0 = 70.16 \text{ cc/mole} \qquad \epsilon/k = 148.2°\text{K}$$

The parameters for the interaction between a nitrogen molecule and a methane molecule are obtained from Eqs. 3.6–8 and 9:

$$b_0(N_2 - CH_4) = \tfrac{1}{8}\{[b_0(N_2)]^{1/3} + [b_0(CH_4)]^{1/3}\}^3 = 66.96 \text{ cc/mole}$$

$$\epsilon/k(N_2 - CH_4) = \{(\epsilon/k)\,(N_2) \cdot (\epsilon/k)\,(CH_4)\}^{\frac{1}{2}} = 118.7°\text{K}$$

Using these values we then get:

$$N_2: \ T^* = 3.400 \quad B^\star = -0.0043 \quad B = -0.2743 \text{ cc/mole}$$

$$CH_4: \ T^* = 2.181 \quad B^\star = -0.4942 \quad B = -34.67 \text{ cc/mole}$$

$$N_2 - CH_4: \ T^* = 2.723 \quad B^\star = -0.2143 \quad B = -14.34 \text{ cc/mole}$$

Then from Eq. 3.4–17 we get

$$B = (0.25)^2\,(-0.2743) + 2(0.25)\,(0.75)\,(-14.35)$$
$$+ (0.75)^2\,(-34.67) = -24.90 \text{ cc/mole}$$

for the virial coefficient of the mixture.

c. Evaluation of the third virial coefficient

The third virial coefficient integral may be evaluated by a method similar to that used for the evaluation of the second virial coefficient.[13] The result for the Lennard-Jones (6-12) potential is

$$C(T) = b_0^2 C^\star(T^*); \qquad C^\star(T^*) = \sum_{j=0}^{\infty} c^{(j)} T^{*-(j+1)/2} \qquad (3.6\text{–}10)$$

This expression has a form very similar to that for the second virial coefficient given in Eq. 3.6–3. Although the $b^{(j)}$ in the latter equation are just gamma functions, the expansion coefficients $c^{(j)}$ for the third virial coefficient are complicated integrals. The values of $c^{(j)}$ calculated by Kihara[14] are given in Table I–E. The method of obtaining the $c^{(j)}$ is described in Appendix 3A at the end of this chapter.

The third virial coefficient has also been evaluated by direct punched card calculation of the irreducible integral β_2.[6,15] The results of this

[13] T. Kihara, *J. Phys. Soc. Japan*, **3**, 265 (1948).

[14] T. Kihara, *J. Phys. Soc. Japan*, **6**, 184 (1951). The constants $c^{(j)}$ given in this publication are a revision of those given in Ref. 13.

[15] R. B. Bird, E. L. Spotz, J. O. Hirschfelder, *J. Chem. Phys.*, **18**, 1395 (1950).

work[16] are given in Table I–C for values of the reduced temperature, T^*, from 0.70 to 400. Also tabulated there are the functions $C_k^\star(T^*)$, which are useful for the calculation of the thermodynamic properties. Third virial coefficient calculations have also been made by two other groups of workers[17,18] over limited temperature ranges.

In Fig. 3.6–2 is plotted the function $C^\star(T^*)$, obtained from the punched card calculations[15] and a number of experimental points are also given.

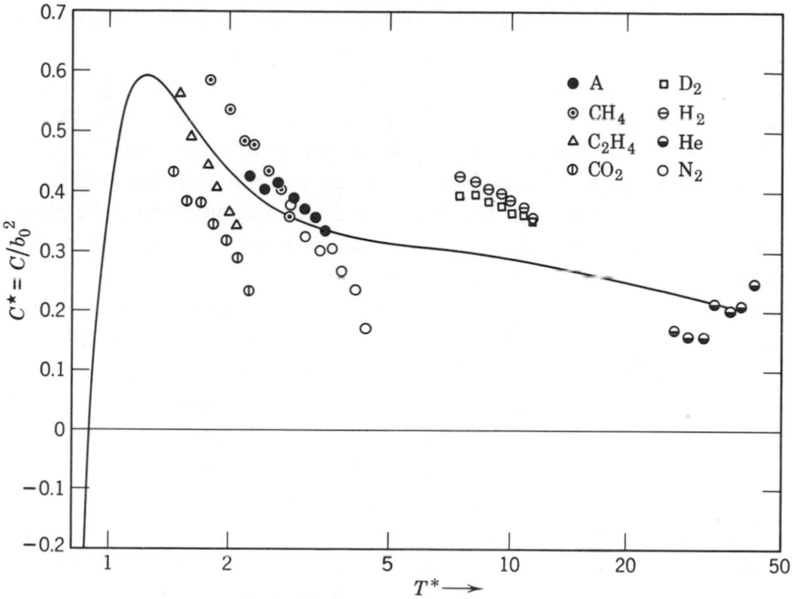

Fig. 3.6–2. The reduced third virial coefficient for the Lennard-Jones potential. This curve was obtained by a punched-card evaluation of the irreducible integral β_2. The experimental points of a number of gases are shown. The non-spherical molecules (carbon dioxide and ethylene) deviate markedly from the calculated curve. Also the light gases (hydrogen, deuterium, and helium) exhibit different behavior because of quantum effects. [From R. B. Bird, E. L. Spotz, and J. O. Hirschfelder, *J. Chem. Phys.*, **18**, 1395 (1950).]

These experimental values have been reduced, using the force constants obtained from the second virial coefficient. In general the agreement is not outstanding. For the simple gases the experimental points lie generally above the calculated curve. The disagreement is probably due

[16] The revised calculations of Kihara[14] are in good agreement with the punched card calculations.

[17] E. W. Montroll and J. E. Mayer, *J. Chem. Phys.*, **9**, 626 (1941).

[18] J. de Boer and A. Michels, *Physica*, **6**, 97 (1939).

to some extent to the methods by which third virial coefficients are determined from compressibility data (see § 3.4e). Deviations should, however, also be expected because of the empirical nature of the Lennard-Jones potential. The third virial coefficient integral emphasizes different regions of the potential curve from those emphasized by the integral for the second virial coefficient. Kihara[14] has found that somewhat better agreement is obtained with a Lennard-Jones (6–9) potential. This does not imply that the (6–9) potential is better than the (6–12) function. The choice of 12 as the repulsive index was made because it afforded the best agreement between calculated and experimental results for the second virial coefficients and the Joule-Thomson coefficients of a large number of gases. Furthermore, the (6–12) potential has been shown to give exceptionally good agreement for the transport properties (see Chapter 8). The only conclusion we can draw from these results is that a potential function more realistic than the Lennard-Jones potential must be chosen if consistent information about intermolecular forces is to be derived from the various physical properties.

Exceptionally poor agreement between experimental and calculated third virial coefficients of elongated molecules is observed. Even in the second virial coefficient, which is relatively insensitive to the form of the potential, the non-spherical nature of the molecules is evident in that the observed $B(T)$ curve has a curvature different from that suggested by the Lennard-Jones potential. It has been shown (see § 3.8) that quite good agreement with experimental $B(T)$-values is obtained when the calculations are made for potential functions which include the angle dependence of the interaction potential. Thus far no calculations of the third virial coefficients for elongated molecules have been made.

Quite large deviations from the theoretical curve are also observed in the isotopes of hydrogen and helium. These discrepancies, which are undoubtedly due to quantum effects, are discussed in Chapter 6. No calculations of the magnitude of the quantum deviations in third virial coefficients have been made, and hence no quantitative explanations may be given.

In view of the above-mentioned discrepancies the table of reduced third virial coefficients, $C^{\star}(T^*)$, has a somewhat more limited range of application than does the corresponding tabulation for the second virial coefficient. The $C^{\star}$-table should give quite good results for spherical non-polar molecules at high temperatures and at densities such that the correction to the compressibility due to the third virial coefficient is small compared with that due to the second virial coefficient. To illustrate the use of the tables for making practical calculations, a numerical example is given here.

Illustrative Example

Problem. Calculate the third virial coefficient for krypton at 250°K.

Solution. From Table 3.6–1 the force constants for krypton are $\epsilon/k = 171$°K and $b_0 = 58.86$ cc/mole. The reduced temperature T^* is $T/(\epsilon/k) = 250/171 = 1.46$. $C^\star$ for $T^* = 1.46$ may be found from Table I–C to be 0.55357. The third virial coefficient is then $C(T) = b_0^2 C^\star(T^*) = (58.86)^2\,(0.55357) = 1918$ (cc/mole)^2.

Thus far the discussion has been restricted to the third virial coefficients for pure substances. No calculations have yet been made of the $C_{\alpha\beta\gamma}(T)$ of Eq. 3.4–18 for the Lennard-Jones potential. However, these quantities may be estimated by making use of the fact that the third virial coefficient for mixtures has been evaluated analytically for the square well, and in particular for a two-constant square well (see Eq. 3.5–10). We define a function $A(T^*)$ such that its cube is the ratio of $C(T)$ for the pure component α calculated for the Lennard-Jones potential to $C(T)$ calculated for the two-constant square well potential of Eq. 3.5–7:

$$[C_{\alpha\alpha\alpha}(T)]_{\text{L.J.}} = [C_{\alpha\alpha\alpha}(T)]_{\text{S.W.}}\,[A(T_\alpha^*)]^3 \qquad (3.6\text{–}11)$$

The function A is slowly varying in T^* and is tabulated in Table I–D. It seems reasonable to write the contributions $C_{\alpha\beta\gamma}(T)$ to the third virial coefficient of a mixture of components α, β, and γ as

$$[C_{\alpha\beta\gamma}(T)]_{\text{L.J.}} \doteq [C_{\alpha\beta\gamma}(T)]_{\text{S.W.}}\,[A(T_\alpha^*)A(T_\beta^*)A(T_\gamma^*)] \qquad (3.6\text{–}12)$$

where $[C_{\alpha\beta\gamma}(T)]_{\text{S.W.}}$ is given by Eq. (3.5–10) in which $R_{\alpha\beta} = R_{\beta\gamma} = R_{\gamma\alpha} = 1.8$ and in which the depths of the three square wells are taken to be 0.56 times the depths of the corresponding Lennard-Jones (6-12) potentials. This approximation should provide a reasonable method for estimating the high-temperature compressibilities of mixtures.

d. The Joule-Thomson coefficient

The Joule-Thomson coefficient μ, which is defined as the rate of change of temperature with pressure in an isenthalpic expansion, is related to the equation of state as follows:

$$\mu = \left(\frac{\partial T}{\partial p}\right)_H = C_p^{-1}\left[T\left(\frac{\partial V}{\partial T}\right)_p - V\right] \qquad (3.6\text{–}13)$$

This expression may be expanded[19] in powers of $(1/V)$, and the Joule-Thomson coefficient may then be written in terms of the reduced second and third virial coefficients and their derivatives:

$$\mu = \frac{b_0}{\tilde{C}_p^{\,0}}[B_1^\star - B^\star] + \frac{b_0^2}{\tilde{V}\tilde{C}_p^{\,0}}[C_1^\star - 2C^\star + 2B^{\star 2} - 2B^\star B_1^\star + \mu^0 B_2^\star R/b_0] + \cdots \qquad (3.6\text{–}14)$$

[19] The expansions of the specific heat and other thermodynamic properties are given in Appendix 3.B.

in which $\tilde{C}_p{}^0$ is the zero pressure value of the molar heat capacity at the temperature under consideration.[20] The first term in the expansion is the Joule-Thomson coefficient at zero pressure, μ^0. The coefficient of the $(1/V)$ term, when divided by RT, is the zero pressure slope of the μ versus pressure curve.

In Table I–B is given the function $B_1^\star - B^\star$, which is needed to calculate the Joule-Thomson coefficient at zero pressure. This function is also given in graphical form in Fig. 3.6–3. In the same figure are shown

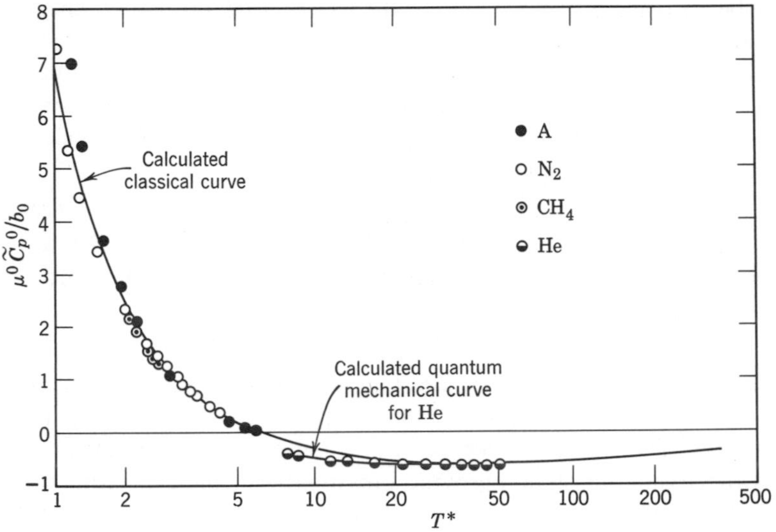

Fig. 3.6–3. The reduced Joule-Thomson coefficient for the Lennard-Jones potential. The classical curve $B_1^\star - B^\star$ is shown along with the corresponding experimental values. Also shown are the experimental points for helium, which exhibits quantum deviations. (From R. J. Lunbeck, Doctoral Dissertation, Amsterdam, 1950.)

experimental values of $\mu^0 C_p{}^0/b_0$. The force constants obtained from second virial coefficients are used for the purpose of reduction of the experimental data. The agreement between the theoretical and experimental values is extremely good. This comparison is a convincing illustration of the use of information about intermolecular forces obtained from one property to make calculations of another property, which is measured in a different manner. It should be noticed that $(B_1^\star - B^\star)$ is positive for low temperatures (cooling by expansion) and that it is negative (warming on expansion) above the *inversion temperature*, $T_I{}^* = 6.47$ (see Problem 5 at the end of this chapter).

[20] $\tilde{C}_p{}^0$ may be calculated by the methods of § 2.5.

It is of course also possible to use the tables of $(B_1^\star - B^\star)$ to evaluate the force constants in the Lennard-Jones potential. The values of σ and ϵ so obtained are comparable in accuracy with those determined from the second virial coefficient. These force constants may then be used to compute the second virial coefficients. It is thus possible to determine second virial coefficients from experimental Joule-Thomson

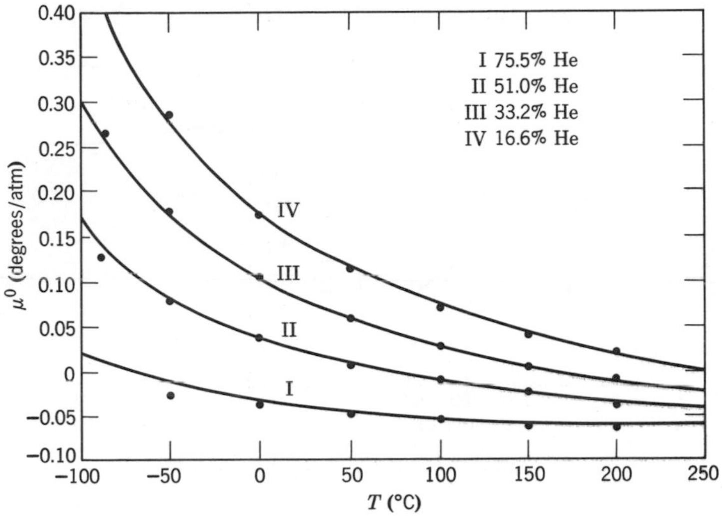

Fig. 3.6–4. The zero pressure Joule-Thomson coefficient for helium-nitrogen mixtures. [From J. O. Hirschfelder and W. E. Roseveare, *J. Phys. Chem.*, **43**, 15 (1939).]

coefficients by the use of the results of statistical mechanics. From the thermodynamics alone it is not possible to do this, inasmuch as the result contains an unknown constant of integration.

Illustrative Example

Problem. Calculate the inversion temperature for xenon and for neon.

Solution. In Table I–B it may be seen that the function $(B_1^\star - B^\star)$ changes sign at $T_I^* = 6.47$. Since (ϵ/k) is 221°K for xenon, the inversion temperature T_I is (6.47) (221) = 1430°K = 1157°C. For neon, $(\epsilon/k) = 34.9$°K so that $T_I = (6.47)\cdot(34.9) = 226$°K = −47°C is the inversion temperature.

It is also possible to use Table I–B to compute the Joule-Thomson coefficients of mixtures. The specific heat $\tilde{C}_p{}^0$ for the ideal gas mixture may be obtained from Eq. 2.5–48, and Eq. 3.4–17 gives the expression for the second virial coefficient for mixtures. These substitutions give for the zero-pressure Joule-Thomson coefficient of a binary mixture the formula:

$$\mu^0_{\text{mix}} = \frac{x_1^2(\tilde{C}_p{}^0)_1\mu_1{}^0 + x_2^2(\tilde{C}_p{}^0)_2\mu_2{}^0 + 2x_1x_2(b_0)_{12}[(B_1{}^\star)_{12} - (B^\star)_{12}]}{x_1(\tilde{C}_p{}^0)_1 + x_2(\tilde{C}_p{}^0)_2} \tag{3.6–15}$$

In Fig. 3.6–4 are shown the calculated zero-pressure Joule-Thomson coefficients for He-N_2 mixtures [21, 22] along with the experimental values.[23] The combining laws given in Eqs. 3.6–8 and 3.6–9 were used for the calculation of the quantity $(b_0)_{12}[(B_1{}^\star)_{12} - (B^\star)_{12}]$. In principle it would

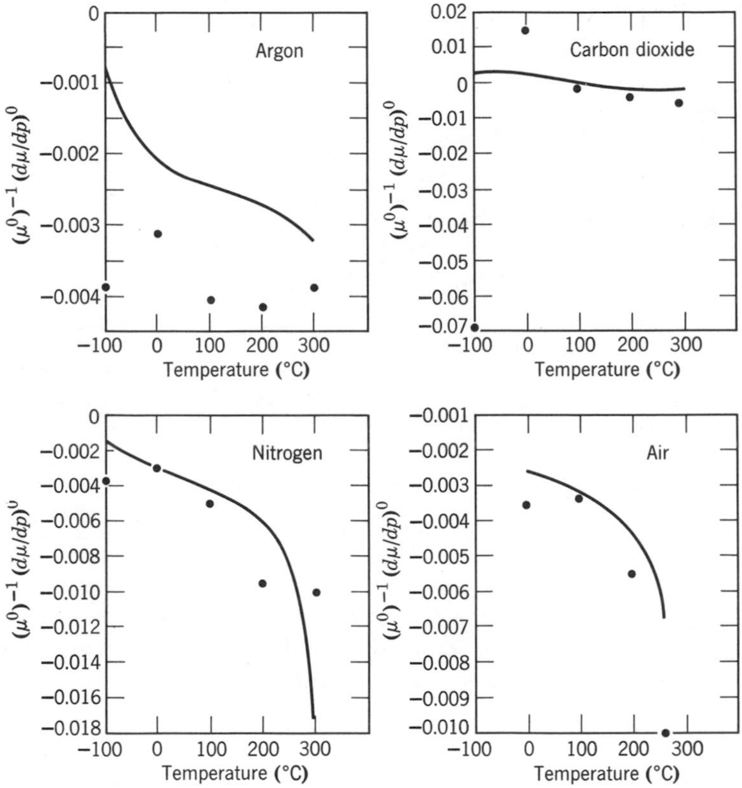

Fig. 3.6–5. Comparison of calculated and experimental values of $(\mu^\circ)^{-1}(d\mu/dp)^\circ$ for several gases. [From R. B. Bird, E. L. Spotz, and J. O. Hirschfelder, *J. Chem. Phys.*, **18**, 1395 (1950).]

[21] J. O. Hirschfelder and W. E. Roseveare, *J. Phys. Chem.*, **43**, 15 (1939).

[22] The calculated values are based on the use of "effective" force constants for He. That is, the experimental data were fit using the classical formulae. The force constants obtained in this way do not include the quantum effects.

[23] J. R. Roebuck and H. Osterberg, *J. Am. Chem. Soc.*, **60**, 341 (1938).

be possible to get forces between unlike molecules from the measurements of Joule-Thomson coefficients for mixtures. With the existing data it is, however, impossible to determine a unique set of constants in this fashion.

The zero pressure slope of the μ versus p curve obtained from Eq. 3.6–14 has been compared with the corresponding experimental values in Fig. 3.6–5, where $(\mu^0)^{-1}(\partial\mu/\partial p)^0$ is given for several gases as a function of the temperature. For argon the calculated curve is definitely higher than the experimental points. This corresponds to the fact that in this temperature region $C^\star_{\text{calcd}} < C^\star_{\text{exptl}}$ and $C^\star_{1_{\text{calcd}}} > C^\star_{1_{\text{exptl}}}$ (as may be seen in Fig. 3.6–2). The two effects are additive in producing an error in $(\mu^0)^{-1}(\partial\mu/\partial p)^0$. For carbon dioxide and nitrogen, however, $C^\star_{\text{calcd}} > C^\star_{\text{exptl}}$ and $C^\star_{1_{\text{calcd}}} > C^\star_{1_{\text{exptl}}}$, and these two effects tend to cancel one another. Indeed for these gases the experimental points do not fall below the calculated curve as they did for argon. It would thus seem that the discrepancies between calculated and experimental Joule-Thomson coefficients are reasonably consistent with the differences between calculated and observed third virial coefficients.

To conclude this section on the Lennard-Jones potential let us summarize the applicability of the results and indicate how further progress may be made in the correlation of intermolecular forces and equation of state. For the noble gases and molecules which are very nearly spherically symmetrical the Lennard-Jones potential gives excellent agreement for the second virial coefficient and the zero-pressure Joule-Thomson coefficient over a rather wide temperature range. The agreements for the third virial coefficient and the slope of the Joule-Thomson coefficient versus pressure curve at zero pressure are not quite so good. Furthermore, slightly different force constants are obtained from the transport properties and properties of crystals than are calculated from the virial coefficients. Consequently we must accept the conclusion that, although the Lennard-Jones potential has been quite valuable in studying the connection between various properties of matter, more exact information may be obtained about intermolecular forces by the adoption of more complex force laws. In the next section we summarize the progress which is being made in the problem of the refinement of the intermolecular potential functions for spherical non-polar molecules.

For all the properties discussed in this section, slightly greater deviations between experimental and calculated results are observed for molecules which are very non-spherical. For such molecules the angle-dependence of the interaction potential should be taken into account in the calculation of the virial coefficients. The virial coefficients for non-spherical non-polar molecules are discussed in § 3.8. A discussion of polar molecules is reserved for the last section of the chapter.

7. The Second Virial Coefficient for More Elaborate Spherically Symmetric Potentials

Calculations of the second virial coefficient have been performed for several intermolecular potential energy functions of the Buckingham type. These functions have an exponential repulsion term and more than two adjustable constants. In this section we indicate briefly what calculations are available for these more elaborate potential functions and how the adjustable parameters are determined.

a. The Buckingham-Corner potential

Rather extensive second virial coefficient calculations (both classical and quantum) have been made for the Buckingham-Corner potential:

$$\varphi(r) = be^{-\alpha(r/r_m)} - \left(\frac{c}{r^6} + \frac{c'}{r^8}\right) e^{-4\left(\frac{r_m}{r}-1\right)^3} \qquad r \leqslant r_m$$

$$\varphi(r) = be^{-\alpha(r/r_m)} - \left(\frac{c}{r^6} + \frac{c'}{r^8}\right) \qquad r \geqslant r_m \tag{1.3–29}$$

$$\begin{cases} b = \{-\epsilon + (1+\beta)cr_m^{-6}\}e^{\alpha} \\ c = \{\epsilon\alpha r_m^{6}/[\alpha(1+\beta) - 6 - 8\beta]\} \\ c' = \beta r_m^{2}c \end{cases}$$

This is a four-constant potential in which the parameters have the following significance:

ϵ = depth of potential well

r_m = value of r at potential minimum

α = steepness of exponential repulsion

$\beta = c'/cr_m^2$

This potential function, which is more realistic than the Lennard-Jones potential, represents the repulsion as an exponential and includes in its general form the attractive contributions to the potential proportional to both r^{-8} and r^{-6}.

Buckingham and Corner[1] performed the numerical integration of the second virial coefficient integral for the potential of Eq. 1.3–29. They expressed their results for the second virial coefficient and the zero-pressure Joule-Thomson coefficient in the form

$$B(T) = 2\pi\tilde{N}r_m^3F_0(\alpha, \beta; T^*) \tag{3.7–1}$$

$$\mu^0\tilde{C}_p^0 = 2\pi\tilde{N}r_m^3G_0(\alpha, \beta; T^*) \tag{3.7–2}$$

[1] R. A. Buckingham and J. Corner, *Proc. Roy. Soc.* (*London*), **A189**, 118 (1947).

in which $T^* = kT/\epsilon$. The functions F_0 and G_0 are given in Tables VI–A and VI–B for $\beta = 0$ and 0.2, α from 12.5 to 14.5 at intervals of 0.5, and T^* from 1.25 to 100. The maximum computational error in the tables is claimed to be less than 0.1 per cent. The functions F_0 and G_0 have, of course, the same characteristic shapes as the functions $B^\star$ and $(B_1^\star - B^\star)$ for the Lennard-Jones potential. The first quantum correction to the second virial coefficient and the Joule-Thomson coefficient has also been calculated (see § 6.5d). But no calculations of transport properties have yet been made for this potential function.

The results of these calculations have not been widely used for obtaining intermolecular forces from equation of state data. The parameters in the Buckingham-Corner potential are given in Table 3.7–1 for two of the noble gases, neon and argon. The constants were obtained by Corner,[2] who took into account the small quantum effects. The values of the second virial coefficients calculated on the basis of these constants agree within 0.5 per cent of the experimental values[3] over a 600° temperature range, and similar agreement is reported for the zero-pressure Joule-Thomson

TABLE 3.7–1

PARAMETERS FOR THE BUCKINGHAM-CORNER POTENTIAL FUNCTION

α, β, ϵ/k, r_m = parameters in potential

l_0 = distance between nearest neighbors in the crystal lattice at 0°K (in angstroms)

h_0 = heat of sublimation of crystal at 0°K. Corrected for zero point energy (in cal/mole)

Gas	β	α	ϵ/k	r_m	l_0	h_0
Neon[a]	0.00	13.6	37.1	3.16	3.20[b]	589[c]
	0.15	13.3	37.4	3.16		
	0.20	13.2	37.5	3.16		
Argon[a]	0.00	13.9	123	3.87	3.81[d]	2030[e]
	0.14	13.5	125	3.87		
	0.20	13.4	125	3.87		

[a] J. Corner, *Trans. Faraday Soc.*, **44**, 914 (1948).
[b] J. de Smelt, W. H. Keesom, and W. H. Mooij, *Leiden. Comm.* 203e (1930).
[c] W. H. Keesom and Haantjes, *Physica*, **2**, 460 (1935).
[d] F. Simon and C. von Simson, *Z. Physik*, **25**, 160 (1924).
[e] M. Born, *Ann. Phys.*, **69**, 473 (1922).

[2] J. Corner, *Trans. Faraday Soc.*, **44**, 914 (1948).
[3] L. Holborn and J. Otto, *Z. Physik*, **33**, 1 (1925).

coefficients. The fact that equally good agreement is obtained for $\beta = 0$ and $\beta = 0.2$ seems to indicate that the second virial coefficient is not sufficiently sensitive to the form of the potential to get information about the relative importance of the r^{-6} and r^{-8} contributions. According to the quantum mechanical calculations of Margenau[4] β should be about 0.15. Recent measurements of the quadrupole moment of molecules from the pressure broadening of microwaves (see § 13.7) have made it possible to determine β accurately for various molecules. The values so obtained differ considerably from Margenau's estimate and depend strongly on the exact electronic configuration.

b. The modified Buckingham (6-exp) potential

Recently Rice and Hirschfelder[5] have prepared extensive tables of the second virial coefficient for the modified Buckingham (6-exp) potential:

$$\varphi(r) = \frac{\epsilon}{1 - (6/\alpha)} \left[\frac{6}{\alpha} \exp\left(\alpha\left[1 - \frac{r}{r_m}\right]\right) - \left(\frac{r_m}{r}\right)^6\right] \qquad r \geqslant r_{\max} \qquad (1.3\text{–}30)$$

$$\varphi(r) = \infty \qquad r < r_{\max}$$

In Eq. 1.3–30 $r_{\max}$ is that value of r for which $\varphi(r)$ as given by the upper relation has a spurious maximum. The three constants ϵ, r_m, and α have the same significance as in the Buckingham-Corner potential.

For the modified Buckingham (6-exp) potential the second virial coefficient can be written

$$B(T) = b_m B^\star(\alpha; T^*) \qquad (3.7\text{–}3)$$

in which $b_m = \frac{2}{3}\pi\tilde{N}r_m{}^3$ and $T^* = kT/\epsilon$. The function $B^\star(\alpha; T^*)$ is tabulated in Table VII–A, and the values of the parameters ϵ, r_m, and α for various gases are given in Table 3.7–2. These parameters were determined by fitting viscosity coefficients, second virial coefficients, and crystal properties. The experimental data used for determining each set of parameters are indicated in the last three columns of Table 3.7–2.

The integrals needed for the calculation of the transport coefficients have also been evaluated for the modified Buckingham (6-exp) potential. These calculations are described in § 8.4.

[4] See § 14.2.

[5] W. E. Rice and J. O. Hirschfelder, *J. Chem. Phys.*, **22**, 187 (1954).

TABLE 3.7–2

PARAMETERS FOR THE MODIFIED BUCKINGHAM (6-EXP) POTENTIAL[a]

Substance	Parameters			Experimental Data Used for Determination of the Parameters		
	r_m (Å)	ϵ/k (°K)	α	Viscosity Coefficients[b]	Second Virial Coefficients	Crystal Properties[c]
H_2	3.337	37.3	14.0	*d*	*e*	—
He	3.135	9.16	12.4	*f*	*g*	—
Ne	3.147	38.0	14.5	*h*	*i*	*j*
A	3.866	123.2	14.0	*k*	*l*	*j*
Kr	4.056	158.3	12.3	—	*m*	*j*
Xe	4.450	231.2	13.0	—	*n*	*j*
CH_4	4.206	152.8	14.0	*o*	*p*	*q*
N_2	4.040	113.5	16.2	—	*r*	*q*
	4.011	101.2	17.0	*s*	—	—
CO	$<$4.099	$>$132.0	$>$17	—	*t*	*q*
	3.937	119.1	17.0	*u*	—	—

[a] E. A. Mason and W. E. Rice, *J. Chem. Phys.*, **22**, 522, 843 (1954).

[b] The relationship between the coefficient of viscosity and intermolecular forces is discussed in § 8.4.

[c] The relationship between crystal properties and intermolecular forces is discussed in § 13.9.

[d] Y. Ishida, *Phys. Rev.*, **21**, 550 (1923); P. Guenther, *Z. physik. Chem.*, **110**, 626 (1924); M. Trautz and P. B. Baumann, *Ann. Physik*, **2**, 733 (1929); M. Trautz and F. W. Stauff, *ibid.*, **2**, 737 (1929); M. Trautz and K. F. Kipphan, *ibid.*, **2**, 743 (1929); M. Trautz and W. Ludewigs, *ibid.*, **3**, 409 (1929); M. Trautz and H. E. Binkele, *ibid.*, **5**, 561 (1930); M. Trautz and A. Melster, *ibid.*, **7**, 409 (1930); M. Trautz and R. Zink, *ibid.*, **7**, 427 (1930); M. Trautz and F. Kurz, *ibid.*, **9**, 981 (1931); M. Trautz and K. G. Sorg, *ibid.*, **10**, 81 (1931); M. Trautz and R. Heberling, *ibid.*, **10**, 155 (1931); B. P. Sutherland and O. Maass, Can. J. Research, **6**, 428 (1932); M. Trautz and R. Heberling, *Ann. Physik*, **20**, 118 (1934); M. Trautz and I. Husseini, *ibid.*, **20**, 121 (1934); M. Trautz and H. Zimmermann, *ibid.*, **22**, 189 (1935); A. van Itterbeek and A. Claes, *Nature*, **142**, 793 (1938); *Physica*, **5**, 938 (1938); A. van Itterbeek and O. van Paemel, *Physica*, **7**, 265 (1940); H. L. Johnston and K. E. McCloskey, *J. Phys. Chem.*, **44**, 1038 (1940); R. Wobser and F. Mueller, *Kolloid-Beihefte*, **52**, 165 (1941); van Itterbeek, van Paemel, and van Lierde, *Physica*, **13**, 88 (1947); de Troyer, van Itterbeek, and Rietveld, *ibid.*, **17**, 938 (1951); J. W. Buddenberg and C. R. Wilke, *J. Phys. Coll. Chem.*, **55**, 1491 (1951).

[e] L. Holborn and J. Otto, *Ann. Physik.*, **63**, 674 (1920); *Z. Physik*, **23**, 77 (1924); **33**, 1 (1925); **38**, 359 (1926); G. P. Nijhoff and W. H. Keesom, *Leiden Comm.* 188d (1927); Gibby, Tanner, and Masson, *Proc. Roy. Soc.* (*London*), **A122**, 283 (1929); A. Michels and M. Goudeket, *Physica*, **8**, 347 (1941).

[f] Y. Ishida, *Phys. Rev.*, **21** 550 (1923); M. N. States, *ibid.*, **21**, 662 (1923); A. G. Nasini and C. Rossi, *Gazz. chim. ital.*, **58**, 433, 898 (1928); M. Trautz and H. E. Binkele, *Ann. Physik*, **5**, 561 (1930); M. Trautz and R. Zink, *ibid.*, **7**, 427 (1930); M. Trautz and R. Heberling, *ibid.*, **20**, 118 (1934); M. Trautz and I. Husseini, *ibid.*, **20**, 121 (1934); M. Trautz and H. Zimmermann, *ibid.*, **22**, 189 (1935); A. van Itterbeek and W. H. Keesom, *Physica*, **5**, 257 (1938); A. van Itterbeek and O. van Paemel, *ibid.*, **7**, 265 (1940); R. Wobser and F. Mueller, *Kolloid-Beihefte*, **52**, 165 (1941); H. L. Johnston and E. R. Grilly, *J. Phys. Chem.*, **46**, 948 (1942); van Itterbeek, van Paemel, and van Lierde, *Physica*, **13**, 88 (1947).

[g] J. D. A. Boks and H. Kamerlingh Onnes, *Leiden Comm.*, **170a** (1924); L. Holborn and J. Otto, *Z. Physik.*, **10**, 367 (1922); **23**, 77 (1924); **33**, 1 (1925); **38**, 359 (1926); G. P. Nijhoff and W. H. Keesom, *Leiden Comm.*, **188b** (1927); Nijhoff, Keesom and Iliin, *ibid.*, **188c** (1927); Gibby, Tanner, and Masson, *Proc. Roy. Soc.* (*London*), **A122**, 283 (1929); A. Michels and H. Wouters, *Physica*, **8**, 923 (1941); W. G. Schneider and J. A. H. Duffie, *J. Chem. Phys.*, **17**, 751 (1949); J. L. Yntema and W. G. Schneider, *ibid.*, **18**, 641 (1950).

[h] R. S. Edwards, *Proc. Roy. Soc.* (*London*), **A119**, 578 (1928); M. Trautz and H. E. Binkele, *Ann. Physik* **5**, 561 (1930); M. Trautz and R. Zink, *ibid.*, **7**, 427 (1930); M. Trautz and H. Zimmermann, *ibid.*, **22**, 189 (1935); A. van Itterbeek and O. van Paemel, *Physica*, **7**, 265 (1940); R. Wobser and F. Mueller, *Kolloid-Beihefte*, **52**, 165 (1941); H. L. Johnston and E. R. Grilly, *J. Phys. Chem.*, **46**, 948 (1942); van Itterbeek, van Paemel, and van Lierde, *Physica*, **13**, 88 (1947); J. W. Buddenberg and C. R. Wilke, *J. Phys. Coll. Chem.*, **55**, 1491 (1951).

[i] H. Kamerlingh Onnes and C. A. Crommelin, *Leiden Comm.*, **147d** (1915); Crommelin, Martinez, and Kamerlingh Onnes, *ibid.*, **154a** (1919); L. Holborn and J. Otto, *Z. Physik*, **33**, 1 (1925); **38**, 359 (1926).

[j] G. Kane, *J. Chem. Phys.*, **7**, 603 (1939).

[k] Y. Ishida, *Phys. Rev.*, **21**, 550 (1923); M. Trautz and W. Ludewigs, *Ann. Physik*, **3**, 409 (1929); M. Trautz and H. E. Binkele, *ibid.*, **5**, 561 (1930); M. Trautz and R. Zink, *ibid.*, **7**, 427 (1930); A. van Itterbeek and O. van Paemel, *Physica*, **5**, 1009 (1938); R. Wobser and F. Mueller, *Kolloid-Beihefte*, **52**, 165 (1941); H. L. Johnston and E. R. Grilly, *J. Phys. Chem.*, **46**, 948 (1942); V. Vasilesco, *Ann. phys.*, **20**, 137, 292 (1945).

[l] H. Kamerlingh Onnes and C. A. Crommelin, *Leiden Comm.*, **118b** (1910); L. Holborn and J. Otto, *Z. Physik*, **23**, 77 (1924); **30**, 320 (1924); **33**, 1 (1925); Michels, Wijker, and Wijker, *Physica*, **15**, 627 (1949).

[m] Beattie, Brierley, and Barriault, *J. Chem. Phys.*, **20**, 1615 (1952).

[n] Beattie, Barriault, and Brierley, *J. Chem. Phys.*, **19**, 1222 (1951).

[o] A. O. Rankine and C. J. Smith, *Phil. Mag.*, **42**, 615 (1921); Y. Ishida, *Phys. Rev.*, **21m**, 550 (1923); G. Jung and H. Schmick. *Z. physik Chem.*, **B7**, 130 (1930); M. Trautz and R. Zink, *Ann. Physik*, **7**, 427 (1930); M. Trautz and K. G. Sorg, *ibid.*, **10**, 81 (1931); H. L. Johnston and K. E. McCloskey, *J. Phys. Chem.*, **44**, 1038 (1940); R. Wobser and F. Mueller, *Kolloid-Beihefte*, **52**, 165 (1941).

[p] F. A. Freeth and T. T. H. Verschoyle, *Proc. Roy. Soc.* (*London*), **A130**, 453 (1931); A. Michels and G. W. Nederbragt, *Physica*, **2**, 1000 (1935).

[q] Landolt-Börnstein, *Physikalisch-Chemische Tabellen*; K. Clusius, *Z. physik. Chem.*, **B3**, 41 (1929); J. O. Clayton and W. F. Giauque, *J. Am. Chem. Soc.*, **54** 2610 (1932); **55**, 4875, 5071 (1933).

[r] H. Kamerlingh Onnes and A. T. van Urk, *Leiden Comm.*, **169d**, **e** (1924); *Z. Physik*, **10**, 367 (1922); **23**, 77 (1924); **30**, 320 (1924); **33**, 1 (1925); Michels, Wouters, and de Boer, *Physica*, **1**, 587 (1934).

[s] C. J. Smith, *Proc. Phys. Soc.* (*London*), **34**, 155 (1922); M. Trautz and P. B. Baumann, *Ann. Physik*, **2**, 733 (1929); M. Trautz and W. Ludewigs, *ibid.*, **3**, 409 (1929); M. Trautz and A. Melster, *ibid.*, **7**, 409 (1930); M. Trautz and R. Zink, *ibid.*, **7**, 427 (1930); M. Trautz and R. Heberling, *ibid.*, **10**, 155 (1931); M. Trautz and E. Gabriel, *ibid.*, **11**, 606 (1931); A. van Itterbeek and W. H. Keesom. *Physica*, **2**, 97 (1935); P. J. Rigden, *Phil. Mag.*, **25**, 961 (1938); H. L. Johnston and K. E. McCloskey, *J. Phys. Chem.*, **44**, 1038 (1940); R. Wobser and F. Mueller, *Kolloid-Beihefte*, **52**, 165 (1941); V. Vasilesco, *Ann. Phys.*, **20**, 137, 292 (1945); van Itterbeek, van Paemel, and van Lierde, *Physica*, **13**, 88 (1947).

[t] T. T. H. Verschoyle, *Proc. Roy. Soc.* (*London*), **A111**, 552 (1926); G. A. Scott, *ibid.*, **A125**, 330 (1929); D. T. A. Townend and L. A. Bhatt, *ibid.*, **A134**, 502 (1931); Michels, Lupton, Wassenaar, and de Graaf, *Physica*, **18**, 121 (1952).

[u] C. J. Smith, *Proc. Phys. Soc.* (*London*), **34**, 155 (1922); M. Trautz and P. B. Baumann, *Ann. Physik*, **2**, 733 (1929); M. Trautz and W. Ludewigs, *ibid.*, **3**, 409 (1929); M. Trautz and A. Melster, *ibid.*, **7**, 409 (1930); R. Wobser and F. Mueller, *Kolloid-Beihefte*, **52**, 165 (1941); H. L. Johnston and E. R. Grilly, *J. Phys. Chem.*, **46**, 948 (1942); van Itterbeek, van Paemel, and van Lierde, *Physica*, **13**, 88 (1947).

8. The Second Virial Coefficient for Non-spherical Molecules

Just as the simplest model for a spherical molecule is a rigid impenetrable sphere, so also can non-spherical molecules be regarded as rigid impenetrable objects of various shapes. Hence this discussion begins with a summary of the work of Isihara, who has shown how the second virial coefficient of any rigid convex molecule may be evaluated. Kihara has extended the latter work to examine elongated and flat molecules which interact according to a Lennard-Jones potential in which the separation is taken to be the shortest distance between the "cores" of the molecules. Finally the section is concluded with a discussion of the earlier work of Corner, who calculated the second virial coefficient for cylindrical molecules. He visualized cylindrical molecules as being represented by three or four centers of force distributed along an axis. The intermolecular potential is then given by the sum of the interactions between the various centers of force in the two molecules.

a. Isihara's treatment of rigid convex molecules

In § 3.5a it is shown that the second virial coefficient for rigid spheres is just equal to four times the volume of the molecules in the gas. For rigid non-spherical molecules, the second virial coefficient may be written as

$$B = 4\tilde{N}v_m f \tag{3.8–1}$$

in which v_m is the volume of a single molecule and f is a factor (always greater than unity) which indicates deviation from rigid sphere behavior.

Isihara[1,2] has shown how this factor f may be evaluated for any rigid convex molecule by the use of group theory and differential geometry. The result of his rigorous mathematical treatment is quite simple in form. For a gas containing molecules of a single kind the factor f is given by

$$f = 1 + \left[\frac{\bar{R}s_m}{4v_m} - \frac{3}{4}\right] \tag{3.8-2}$$

in which s_m is the surface area of a molecule and $\bar{R}$ is the average of the mean radius of curvature. The latter is given by

$$\bar{R} = \frac{1}{4\pi}\int \tfrac{1}{2}(R_1 + R_2)\, d\omega \tag{3.8-3}$$

TABLE 3.8-1

THE FACTOR f FOR VARIOUS NON-SPHERICAL MODELS[a,b]

Shape→	Sphere	Cube	Regular Tetra-hedron	Regular Octa-hedron	Cylinder
Size→	Radius = 1	Side = 1	Side = 1	Side = 1	Lengths = l Radius = a
v_m	$4\pi/3$	1	$\sqrt{2}/12$	$\sqrt{2}/3$	$\pi a^2 l$
s_m	4π	6	$\sqrt{3}$	$2\sqrt{3}$	$2\pi a(a + l)$
$\bar{R}$	1	3/4	$\frac{3}{2\pi}\tan^{-1}\sqrt{2}$	$\frac{3}{\pi}\cot^{-1}\sqrt{2}$	$\frac{1}{4}(l + a\pi)$
f	1	11/8	1.926	1.330	$\frac{\pi a^2 + (\pi + 3)al + l^2}{8al}$

[a] This table is taken from A. Isihara and T. Hayashida, *J. Phys. Soc. Japan*, **6**, 40 (1951), as corrected by T. Kihara, *J. Phys. Soc. Japan*, **8**, 686 (1953).

[b] The expressions for f for ellipsoidal molecules and spherocylindrical molecules are given in Eqs. 3.8-4 through 7.

[1] A. Isihara, *J. Chem. Phys.*, **18**, 1446 (1950).

[2] A. Isihara and T. Hayashida, *J. Phys. Soc. Japan*, **6**, 40 (1951).

where R_1 and R_2 are the principal radii of curvature, and $d\omega$ is the surface element on a unit sphere. These results have been generalized for molecular models which are not smooth (for example, rigid tetrahedrons) and for mixtures of molecules of different shapes. The fact that f is always greater than unity indicates that non-spherical molecules always

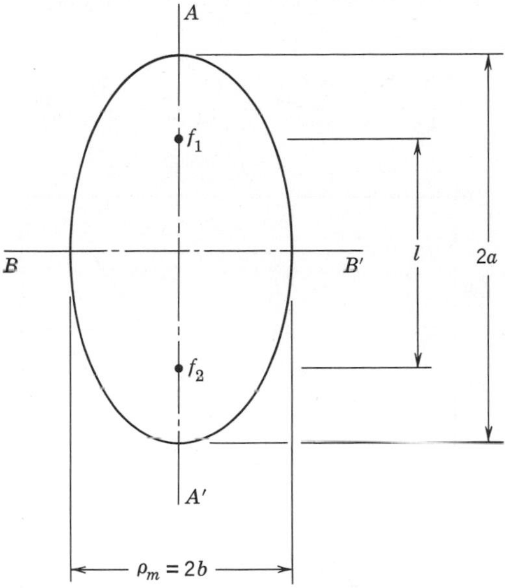

Fig. 3.8–1. Ellipsoidal molecules. Rotation about AA' generates prolate (cigar-shaped) ellipsoids, and rotation about BB' generates oblate (pancake-shaped) ellipsoids. a and b are the major and minor semi-axes, respectively. l is the distance between the foci f_1 and f_2.

have second virial coefficients which are larger than those for spherical molecules of the same volume. The second virial coefficients for all rigid molecules are temperature independent. The methods used in this treatment may well find application to other problems which are difficult geometrically.

The factor f has been computed for a number of non-spherical molecular models,[3] and the results of these calculations are given in Table 3.8–1. The calculation has also been made for ellipsoids[3] of revolution,

[3] A. Isihara and T. Hayashida, *J. Phys. Soc. Japan*, **6**, 46 (1951).

and the result is (for both prolate and oblate ellipsoids)

$$f = \frac{1}{4} + \frac{3}{16}\left(1 + \frac{1}{\sqrt{1-\epsilon_0^2}}\frac{\sin^{-1}\epsilon_0}{\epsilon_0}\right)\left(1 + \frac{1-\epsilon_0^2}{2\epsilon_0}\ln\frac{1+\epsilon_0}{1-\epsilon_0}\right) \quad (3.8\text{–}4)$$

in which ϵ_0 is the eccentricity, defined by $\epsilon_0^2 = (a^2 - b^2)/a^2$, a and b being the major and minor semi-axes of the generating ellipse. (See Fig. 3.8–1.) When the eccentricity is small compared with unity, the result may be written as a power series[4] in ϵ_0^2:

$$f = 1 + \frac{1}{15}\epsilon_0^4 + \frac{1}{15}\epsilon_0^6 + \frac{11}{175}\epsilon_0^8 + \frac{31}{525}\epsilon_0^{10} + \cdots \quad (3.8\text{–}5)$$

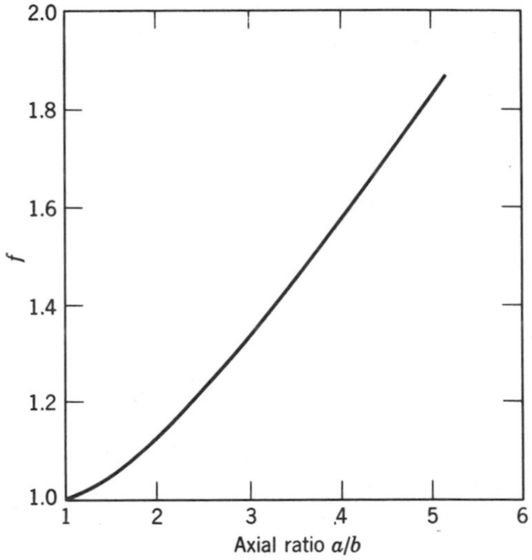

Fig. 3.8–2. Variation of f with the axial ratio for ellipsoidal molecules.

In Figure 3.8–2 is shown the variation of the function f with the axial ratio a/b. This result has been useful in the determination of molecular shapes from the osmotic pressure of high-polymer solutions.[3]

The second virial coefficients for *spherocylindrical* molecules have been calculated by Kihara.[5] *Prolate spherocylinders* are generated when

[4] Such a series solution had been obtained previously by C. S. Wang Chang, Doctoral Dissertation, Michigan (1944), and by M. Kotani (1946, unpublished). The coefficient of the ϵ_0^6 term is given incorrectly in Refs. 1 and 3 as (37/60).

[5] T. Kihara, *J. Phys. Soc. Japan*, **6**, 289 (1951); *Revs. Mod. Phys.*, **25**, 831 (1953).

the figure in Fig. 3.8–3 is rotated about axis AA', and *oblate spherocylinders* are obtained when the figure is rotated about axis BB'. For such molecules the function f is given by

$$f = 1 + [\tfrac{8}{3}\xi^2 + 4\xi]^{-1} \qquad \text{(prolate)} \quad (3.8\text{–}6)$$

$$f = 1 + \frac{\left(\dfrac{\pi^2}{4} - 2\right)\xi + \dfrac{\pi}{4}}{\frac{8}{3}\xi^3 + 2\pi\xi^2 + 4\xi} \qquad \text{(oblate)} \quad (3.8\text{–}7)$$

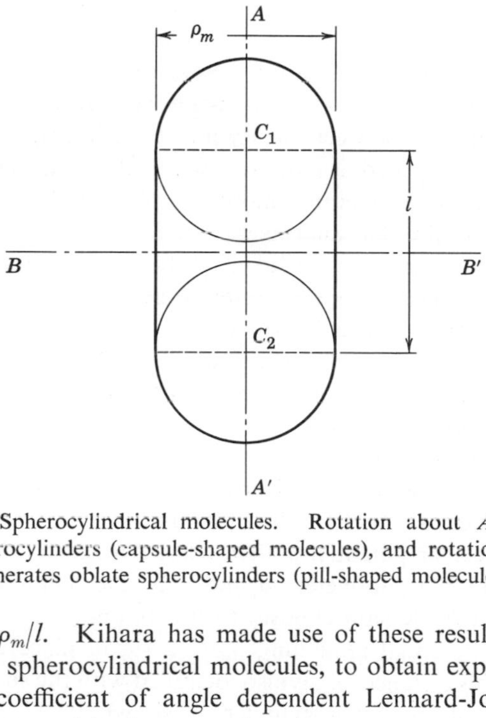

Fig. 3.8–3. Spherocylindrical molecules. Rotation about AA' generates prolate spherocylinders (capsule-shaped molecules), and rotation about BB' generates oblate spherocylinders (pill-shaped molecules).

in which $\xi = \rho_m/l$. Kihara has made use of these results for the rigid ellipsoidal and spherocylindrical molecules, to obtain expressions for the second virial coefficient of angle dependent Lennard-Jones molecules. This work is discussed in the next subsection.

b. Kihara's generalized spherocylindrical molecules

Kihara[5] has shown how the spherocylindrical model can be generalized to include attractive and repulsive forces according to a Lennard-Jones type interaction. The generalization has been performed in such a way as to preserve the integrability of the second virial coefficient. The results are applicable to both long and flat molecules.

First it is necessary to define what is meant by the *core* of the molecule. For a homopolar diatomic molecule the line segment between the nuclei is taken to be the core of the molecule. The core of other molecules of a prolonged shape may be specified in a similar way with respect to the basic molecular skeleton. For example, the O–O distance in CO_2 and the C–C distance in C_2H_2, C_2H_4, or C_2H_6 form cores. The lengths of the core, l, so defined are given in Table 3.8–2 for several molecules. The energy of interaction $\varphi(\rho)$ between two such long molecules is then taken to be of the Lennard-Jones (6-12) form (Eq. 1.3–27). However, the argument of the function, ρ, is *not* defined as the distance between the centers of the two molecules but rather as the shortest distance between their cores. The physical reality of such a potential is questionable, particularly in collisions in which both ends of both cores are within interaction distance of one another. Nevertheless, this approach introduces the principal notion of a non-spherical interaction, and good agreement is obtained between theory and experiment. The method of Corner, described in § 3.8d, is more realistic in this connection; however, Corner's method is considerably more complex for long molecules and does not apply at all to flat molecules.

The core of flat molecules is taken to be a thin circular disk. For benzene, for example, the core is chosen to be the circular disk ringed by the six carbon atoms. The intermolecular distance is then defined as the shortest distance between these cores. When it is necessary to distinguish between the cores of long molecules and those of flat molecules, the latter are referred to as *disk cores* and the former as *rod cores*. The length of the rod core and the diameter of the disk core are designated by l. This quantity is readily obtainable from information about intramolecular distances available in the literature.

The intermolecular potential is then characterized by three quantities: the length l and the parameters σ and ϵ of the Lennard-Jones (6-12) potential. Actually Kihara chooses to use as one of his parameters the position of the potential minimum, $\rho_m = 2^{1/6}\sigma$, in place of the collision diameter σ. This distance, ρ_m, is also identified with the shorter dimension ("minor axis") of the spherocylinder as shown in Fig. 3.8–3. When $l = 0$ the intermolecular potential reduces to the ordinary spherically symmetrical Lennard-Jones (6-12) potential. When $\epsilon = 0$ and the repulsive index 12 is replaced by ∞, the model reduces to the rigid spherocylindrical molecules of Fig. 3.8–3.

For spherically symmetrical molecules the second virial coefficient may be written in the form

$$B(T) = \int_{r=0}^{r=\infty} [1 - e^{-\varphi(r)/kT}]\, db_0(r) \qquad (3.8\text{–}8)$$

in which $b_0(r)$ is the second virial coefficient for rigid spheres with diameter

r: $b_0(r) = 2\pi\tilde{N}r^3/3$. Similarly for the generalized spherocylindrical model, the second virial coefficient[6] is given by

$$B(T) = \int_{\rho=0}^{\rho=\infty} [1 - e^{-\varphi(\rho)/kT}]\, db_l(\rho) + b_l(0) \qquad (3.8\text{–}9)$$

In this expression $b_l(\rho)$ is the second virial coefficient for rigid spherocylinders with core length l and minor axis ρ: $b_l(\rho) = 4\tilde{N}v_m(l, \rho)f(l, \rho)$, where f is given in Eqs. 3.8–6, 3.8–7 for prolate and oblate spherocylinders, respectively.

Insertion of the Lennard-Jones potential for $\varphi(\rho)$ and substitution of the expression for $b_l(\rho)$ into Eq. 3.8–9 gives a formula for the second virial coefficient which may be integrated analytically. The method of integration is the same as that used for the integration of the second virial coefficient for the Lennard-Jones potential in Eq. 3.6–2. The final result is

Prolate spherocylinders:

$$B(T) = \frac{2\pi\tilde{N}\rho_m^3}{3} F_3\left(\frac{\epsilon}{kT}\right) + \pi\tilde{N}\rho_m^2 l\, F_2\left(\frac{\epsilon}{kT}\right) + \frac{\pi\tilde{N}\rho_m l^2}{4} F_1\left(\frac{\epsilon}{kT}\right) \qquad (3.8\text{–}10)$$

Oblate spherocylinders:

$$B(T) = \frac{2\pi\tilde{N}\rho_m^3}{3} F_3\left(\frac{\epsilon}{kT}\right) + \frac{\pi^2\tilde{N}\rho_m^2 l}{2} F_2\left(\frac{\epsilon}{kT}\right) + \frac{\pi\tilde{N}}{2}\left(1 + \frac{\pi^2}{8}\right)\rho_m l^2 F_1\left(\frac{\epsilon}{kT}\right) + \frac{\pi^2\tilde{N}l^3}{16} \qquad (3.8\text{–}11)$$

in which

$$F_k\left(\frac{\epsilon}{kT}\right) = -\frac{k}{12}\sum_{j=0}^{\infty}\frac{2^j}{j!}\left(\frac{\epsilon}{kT}\right)^{(j/2)+(k/12)}\Gamma\left(\frac{6j-k}{12}\right) \qquad (3.8\text{–}12)$$

[6] That the second virial coefficient for this model may be written in such a form may be seen as follows: Eq. 3.4–15 for the second virial coefficient is written in terms of the distance, r, between the centers of the two molecules. The distance, ρ, between ends of cores, is then a function of r, and the three angles specifying the mutual orientation of the molecules, θ_1, θ_2, ϕ. This function may be solved to give $r = r(\rho, \theta_1, \theta_2, \phi)$. Then Eq. 3.4–15 may be written as:

$$B(T) = \frac{\tilde{N}}{4}\iiiint (1 - e^{-\varphi(\rho)/kT})[r(\rho, \theta_1, \theta_2, \phi)]^2 \frac{dr}{d\rho}\, d\rho \sin\theta_1 \sin\theta_2\, d\theta_1\, d\theta_2\, d\phi$$

Since the potential function $\varphi(\rho)$ is angle-independent for Kihara's model, integration over the angles gives

$$B(T) = \frac{\tilde{N}}{4}\int_0^{\infty} (1 - e^{-\varphi(\rho)/kT})\, Y(\rho)\, d\rho$$

in which the function $Y(\rho)$ is the same for any interaction $\varphi(\rho)$. The similarity between this result and Eq. 3.8–9 is clear.

The functions F_k are given in Table VIII. These results may easily be generalized[5] for cases where the indices of attraction and repulsion are different from 6 and 12.

In Table 3.8–2 are given values of the core lengths for four molecules and also the values of the parameters ρ_m and ϵ which have been obtained by fitting second virial data. A comparison of calculated and experimental second virial coefficients is given for these gases in Fig. 3.8–4.

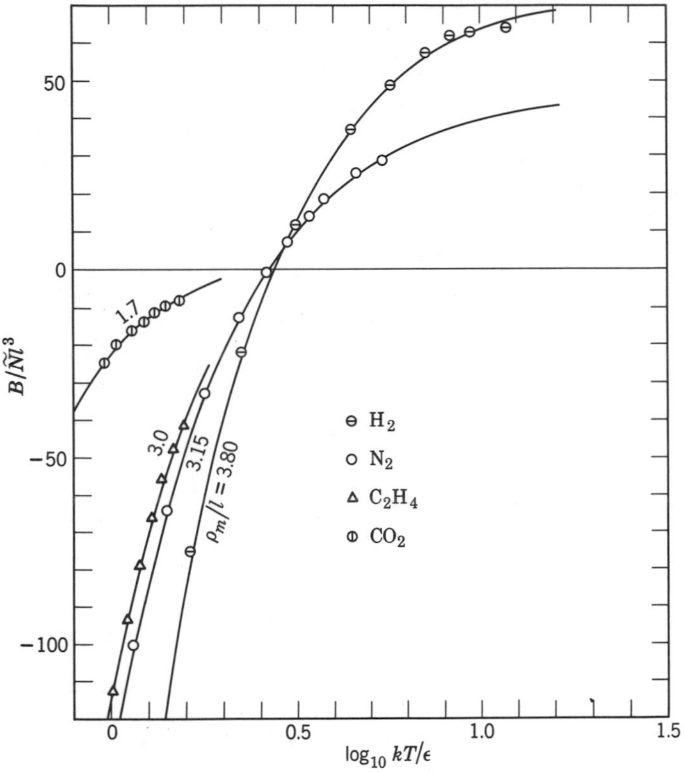

Fig. 3.8–4. Comparison of calculated and experimental results for Kihara's generalized spherocylindrical molecules. [From T. Kihara, *J. Phys. Soc., Japan*, **6**, 289 (1951).]

c. Kihara's generalized ellipsoidal molecules[5]

The rigid ellipsoidal model may be generalized to include the attractive and repulsive intermolecular forces in a manner similar to that described in the previous section for spherocylindrical molecules. The rod-core of a long molecule is taken to be the line segment between the foci of a prolate ellipsoid of revolution. The distance ρ is defined in the following way. We construct on both cores congruent ellipsoids of such a size that they just contact one another. Then the length of the minor axis of the contacting ellipsoids is taken to be the distance ρ, and the intermolecular potential $\varphi(\rho)$ is taken to be the Lennard-Jones interaction. Similarly, for flat molecules the distance ρ is taken to be the minor axis of two contacting congruent oblate spheroids which are constructed upon

TABLE 3.8–2

PARAMETERS FOR KIHARA'S GENERALIZED SPHEROCYLINDRICAL AND ELLIPSOIDAL MODELS DETERMINED FROM SECOND VIRIAL COEFFICIENTS[5]

		Spherocylindrical Model		Ellipsoidal Model	
Gas	l (Å)	ρ_m (Å)	ϵ/k (°K)	ρ_m (Å)	ϵ/k (°K)
H_2	0.74	2.81	39.4	3.24	32.4
N_2	1.10	3.47	124.0	4.09	101.0
$CH_2{=}CH_2$	1.34	4.0	266.0	4.8	216.0
CO_2	2.2	3.7	279.0	4.6	224.0

the disk cores. This model for intermolecular interaction reduces to the Lennard-Jones model when the foci are coincident and to the rigid ellipsoidal model when there is no attractive energy and the repulsive index of the Lennard-Jones potential is taken to be infinite.

Equation 3.8–9 may now be used to compute the second virial coefficient for the generalized ellipsoidal molecules. The result may be expressed as a power series in l/ρ_m:

$$B(T) = \tfrac{2}{3}\pi\tilde{N}\rho_m{}^3\left[F_3\left(\frac{\epsilon}{kT}\right) + k_1\left(\frac{l}{\rho_m}\right)^2 F_1\left(\frac{\epsilon}{kT}\right) + k_2\left(\frac{l}{\rho_m}\right)^4 F_{-1}\left(\frac{\epsilon}{kT}\right) + \cdots\right] \quad (3.8\text{–}13)$$

The k_j for the prolate ellipsoid are

$$k_1 = \frac{1}{2},\ k_2 = -\frac{7}{120},\ k_3 = \frac{7}{240},\ k_4 = -\frac{1201}{67200},\ k_5 = \frac{1643}{134400},\ \cdots$$

and, for the oblate ellipsoid,

$$k_1 = 1,\ k_2 = \frac{1}{15},\ k_3 = 0,\ k_4 = -\frac{2}{525},\ k_5 = \frac{2}{525},\ \cdots$$

The functions $F_k(\epsilon/kT)$ have been defined in Eq. 3.8–12, and they are tabulated in Table VIII. Since the expression in Eq. 3.8–13 does not converge when l is greater than or equal to ρ_m, it is sometimes convenient to express the second virial coefficient as a power series in the eccentricity[7] ϵ_0. The result is

$$B(T) = \tfrac{2}{3}\pi\tilde{N}\rho_m^{\,3}\left[K_0\left(\frac{\epsilon}{kT}\right) + \epsilon_0^{\,2}K_1\left(\frac{\epsilon}{kT}\right) + \epsilon_0^{\,4}K_2\left(\frac{\epsilon}{kT}\right) + \cdots\right] \quad (3.8\text{–}14)$$

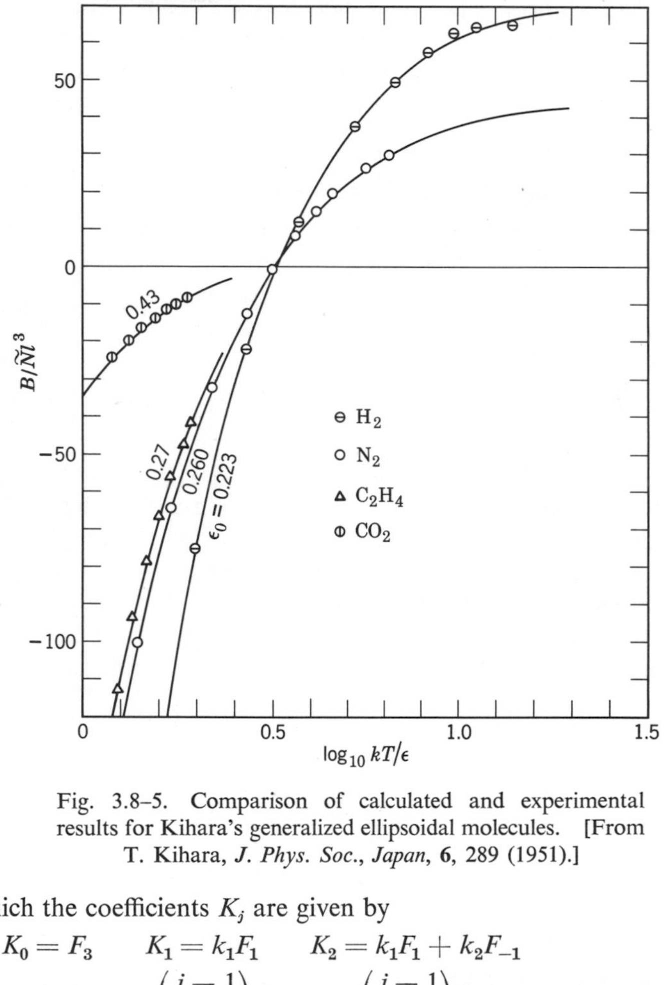

Fig. 3.8–5. Comparison of calculated and experimental results for Kihara's generalized ellipsoidal molecules. [From T. Kihara, *J. Phys. Soc., Japan*, **6**, 289 (1951).]

in which the coefficients K_j are given by

$$K_0 = F_3 \qquad K_1 = k_1F_1 \qquad K_2 = k_1F_1 + k_2F_{-1}$$

$$K_j = k_1F_1 + \binom{j-1}{1}k_2F_{-1} + \binom{j-1}{2}k_3F_{-3} + \cdots + k_jF_{3-2j}$$

[7] The eccentricity is $\epsilon_0 = l/\sqrt{l^2 + \rho_m^{\,2}}$.

The choice of the core length l (that is, the focal length) is made as before. The parameters ϵ and ρ_m are then obtained from second virial coefficient data and Eq. 3.8–13 or Eq. 3.8–14. The values of the parameters thus found are given in Table 3.8–2, and the calculated and experimental virial coefficient curves are shown in Fig. 3.8–5. The difference between the major and minor axis of the ellipsoidal molecule is much smaller than the corresponding quantity of the spherocylindrical one. From second virial data alone, it is impossible to say definitely which model is the more realistic. For hydrogen, however, the ellipsoidal model is to be less favored than the spherocylindrical model. For the latter, the lengths of the major and minor axes are only a few percent smaller than the corresponding quantities of the potential functions calculated quantum mechanically by Margenau[8] and de Boer[9] (see § 14.4).

d. Corner's four-center model for long molecules

To study the second virial coefficients of long molecules Corner[10] adopted a *four center model*, in which a molecule is represented by four centers of force distributed evenly along a line of length $2^{5/6}\,l$ (see Fig. 3.8–6). The interaction energy for a pair of these four-center molecules is then assumed to be

$$\varphi(r) = \sum_{i=1}^{4} \sum_{j=1}^{4} 4\epsilon_c \left[\left(\frac{\sigma_c}{r_{ij}} \right)^{12} - \left(\frac{\sigma_c}{r_{ij}} \right)^{6} \right] \qquad (3.8\text{–}15)$$

in which r_{ij} is the distance between point center i in the first molecule and center j in the second. The summation is over all the sixteen possible interactions between centers of force.[11] The subscript, c, on the above force-constants indicates that they apply to interactions between centers of force and not between the entire molecules.

This expression for the intermolecular potential may be written in the form:

$$\varphi(r, \omega) = 4\epsilon(\omega) \left[\left(\frac{\sigma(\omega)}{r} \right)^{12} - \left(\frac{\sigma(\omega)}{r} \right)^{6} \right] \qquad (3.8\text{–}16)$$

where now the force constants depend on the orientation, $\omega \equiv \{\theta_1, \theta_2, \phi\}$.

[8] H. Margenau, *Phys. Rev.*, **63**, 385 (1943); **64**, 131 (1943); A. A. Evett and H. Margenau, *J. Chem. Phys.*, **21**, 958 (1953).

[9] J. de Boer, *Physica*, **9**, 363 (1942).

[10] J. Corner, *Proc. Roy. Soc.* (*London*), **A192**, 275 (1948).

[11] F. London (*J. Phys. Chem.*, **46**, 305 (1942)) has criticized the use of point centers to represent the dispersion forces because it does not take into account the tensor nature of the molecular polarizability (see § 13.4). For the calculation of second virial coefficients, however, such effects can safely be neglected.

Corner obtained formulae for the angle dependence of $\sigma(\omega)$ and $\epsilon(\omega)$ by computing $\varphi(r)$ by Eq. 3.8–15 for a great many orientations and then curve-fitting his calculated results. His expressions contain l/σ_c parametrically and are good for values of l/σ_c from 0 to 0.75.

The angle-dependent potential of Eq. 3.8–16 is then substituted into the integral for the second virial coefficient given in Eq. 3.4–15. The integration over r may be carried out analytically, using the same method which was employed for the evaluation of the second virial coefficient

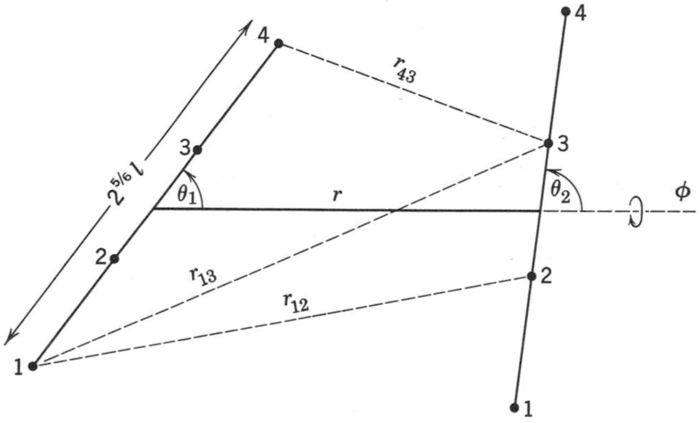

Fig. 3.8–6. Pictorial representation of two interacting "four-center" molecules.

for the Lennard-Jones potential (Eq. 3.6–2), after which the integrations over angles may be performed. The second virial coefficient then contains three parameters, σ_c, l, and $\bar{\epsilon}$, the latter[12] being a sort of average well depth for the Lennard-Jones potential. The final form for $B(T)$ is

$$B(T) = \frac{2\pi\tilde{N}\sigma_c^3}{3}\,\alpha\left[B^\star\left(\frac{kT}{\bar{\epsilon}}\right) + \beta\left\{6B_1^\star\left(\frac{kT}{\bar{\epsilon}}\right) + 4B_2^\star\left(\frac{kT}{\bar{\epsilon}}\right)\right\}\right] \quad (3.8\text{–}17)$$

in which $B^\star$, $B_1^\star$, and $B_2^\star$ are the functions defined in Eq. 3.6–3 and tabulated in Table I–B. The quantities α and β are functions of l/σ_c; α is given by

$$\alpha = 1 + \frac{29}{15}\left(\frac{l}{\sigma_c}\right) + \frac{53}{15}\left(\frac{l}{\sigma_c}\right)^3 + \cdots \quad (3.8\text{–}18)$$

and β is given in Table 3.8–3. The small values of β indicate the very

[12] Here $\bar{\epsilon}$ is the following average value of $\epsilon(\omega)$ over the orientation ω:

$$\bar{\epsilon} = \left[\frac{\iiint\sqrt{\epsilon(\omega)}\,[\sigma(\omega)]^3\sin\theta_1\sin\theta_2\,d\theta_1\,d\theta_2\,d(\phi_2-\phi_1)}{\iiint[\sigma(\omega)]^3\sin\theta_1\sin\theta_2\,d\theta_1\,d\theta_2\,d(\phi_2-\phi_1)}\right]^2$$

small variation of the temperature dependence of the second virial coefficient as a result of the deviations from spherical shape. In fact, it is evident that the second virial coefficient for non-spherical molecules is very nearly that for spherical molecules of collision diameter $\sigma_c\alpha^{1/3}$.

TABLE 3.8–3

l/σ_c	β
0.00	0.0000
0.15	0.0024
0.30	0.0084
0.45	0.0143
0.60	0.0159
0.75	0.0129

The values of the constants l, σ_c, $\bar{\epsilon}$ for some typical molecules are given in Table 3.8–4. The values of the reduced critical constants $kT_c/\bar{\epsilon}$ and $\tilde{V}_c/(\sqrt{2}\sigma_c^3\alpha \cdot 10^{24})$ are also given. If the molecules were spherical, these reduced critical constants would be constant. A rather well-defined trend in their values is noted with increasing length of the molecules. It is apparent that the reduced critical temperature is rather insensitive to the elongation of the molecules but that the critical volume becomes appreciably smaller. The possibility of packing long molecules together certainly makes such a trend seem reasonable. Graphical comparisons of experimental and calculated results are given for several gases in the next section, where the results for several potential functions are compared.

TABLE 3.8–4

PARAMETERS FOR CORNER'S FOUR-CENTER MODEL AND THE REDUCED CRITICAL CONSTANTS[10]

Gas	l/σ_c	σ_c (Å)	$\bar{\epsilon}$ (°K)	$kT_c/\bar{\epsilon}$	$\tilde{V}_c/(\sqrt{2}\sigma_c^3\alpha \cdot 10^{24})$
Nitrogen	0.15	3.37	95	1.33	1.29
Carbon monoxide	0.14	3.60	98	1.37	1.07
Carbon dioxide	0.29	3.57	198	1.54	0.90
Methane	0.00	3.79	148	1.29	1.28
Ethylene	0.21	4.1	192	1.47	0.92
Ethane	0.19	4.5	206	1.48	0.82
Propane	0.25	4.9	228	1.62	0.78
Propylene	0.26	4.9	220	1.66	0.70
Trans-2-butene	0.38	4.9	281	1.53	0.75
n-Butane	0.39	4.9	254	1.68	0.77

9. Discussion of the Results for Several Non-polar Potential Functions

The preceding four sections are devoted to a discussion of the various calculations which have been made for the virial coefficients of non-polar substances. Before going on to the study of polar molecules, we summarize the information about the virial coefficients and the intermolecular forces which has been obtained for non-polar molecules. In this section the various non-polar potential functions and the virial coefficients obtained from them are compared. We first consider some of the rare gases as examples of spherical molecules and then nitrogen and carbon dioxide as examples of non-spherical molecules.

a. Spherical molecules

The experimental and theoretical results for helium, neon, argon, and krypton are summarized in Figs. 3.9–1, 2, 3, and 4. For each of these gases the experimental $B(T)$ values are plotted and also the second virial coefficients calculated on the basis of several empirical potential functions. A comparison of the various potential functions is also shown. Let us consider each of the gases separately.

i. *Helium*

At temperatures above 400°K the classical theory may be used to describe the second virial coefficient of helium. At room temperature quantum effects are small but experimentally observable. The quantum deviations are described quite well by the theory and calculations given in § 6.5. At temperatures below 20°K quantum effects are appreciable. The low-temperature theory and calculations are given in § 6.4.

There is a great deal of experimental data which can be used to determine the energy of interaction of two helium atoms. Four potential curves have been fitted to the experimental data. Massey, Buckingham, and Hamilton[1, 2, 3, 4] have fitted a Buckingham potential to the low-temperature data; de Boer, Michels, and Lunbeck[5] have fitted a Lennard-Jones

[1] R. A. Buckingham, *Proc. Roy. Soc.* (*London*), **A168**, 264 (1938).

[2] H. S. W. Massey and R. A. Buckingham, *Proc. Roy. Soc.* (*London*), **A168**, 378 (1938).

[3] H. S. W. Massey and R. A. Buckingham, *Proc. Roy. Soc.* (*London*), **A169**, 205 (1939).

[4] R. A. Buckingham, J. Hamilton, and H. S. W. Massey, *Proc. Roy. Soc.* (*London*), **A179**, 103 (1941).

[5] Values of the force constants in the Lennard-Jones (6-12) potential were first obtained in this way by J. de Boer and A. Michels, *Physica*, **5**, 945 (1938). The values quoted here are those taken from the doctoral dissertation (Amsterdam, 1951) of R. J. Lunbeck, who revised the previous values of de Boer and Michels by using the newer values of the fundamental constants, k, N, and h given by J. W. M. du Mond and E. R. Cohen, *Revs. Mod. Phys.*, **20**, 82 (1948), **21**, 651 (1949).

(6-12) potential to both low- and high-temperature data; Yntema and Schneider[6] have fitted a Buckingham potential to their high-temperature second virial coefficient measurements; and Mason and Rice[7] have fitted a modified Buckingham (6-exp) potential to both the second virial and viscosity data. In Fig. 3.9–1 the second virial coefficient

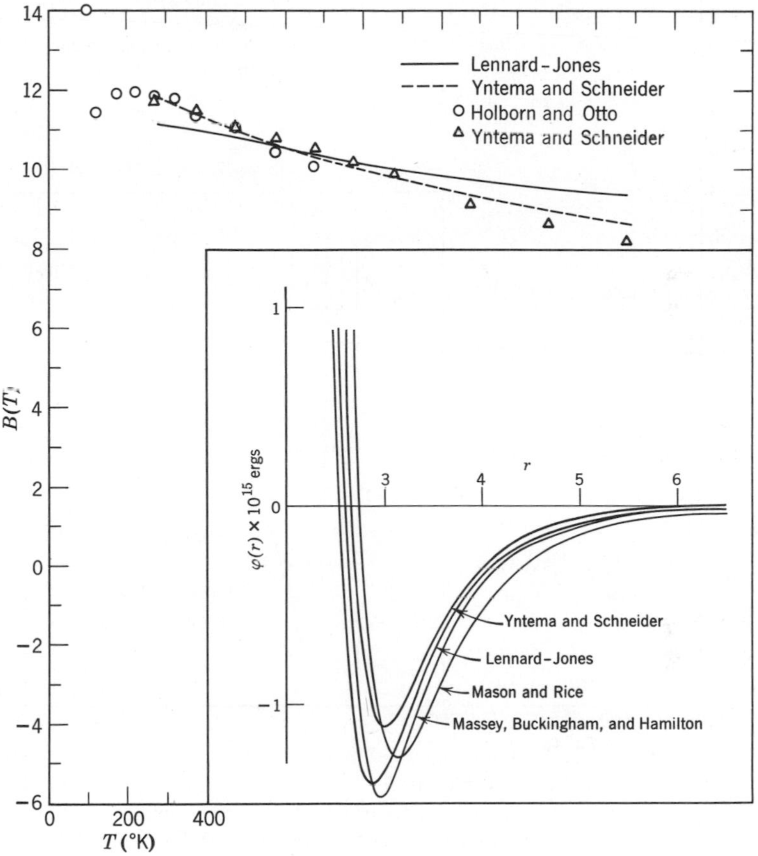

Fig. 3.9–1. Second virial coefficients for *helium* calculated for several molecular models. The potential functions obtained from the experimental $B(T)$ data are also shown. The experimental data are those of L. Holborn and J. Otto, *Z. Physik*, **33**, 1 (1925); and J. L. Yntema and W. G. Schneider, *J. Chem. Phys.*, **18**, 641 (1950).

[6] J. L. Yntema and W. G. Schneider, *J. Chem. Phys.*, **18**, 646 (1950).
[7] E. A. Mason and W. E. Rice, *J. Chem. Phys.*, **22** (1954).

calculated on the basis of the de Boer-Michels-Lunbeck, the Yntema-Schneider, and the Mason-Rice potentials are compared with the experimental values of Holborn and Otto[8] and those of Yntema, Schneider, and Duffie.[9,10] Unfortunately no calculations have yet been made on the

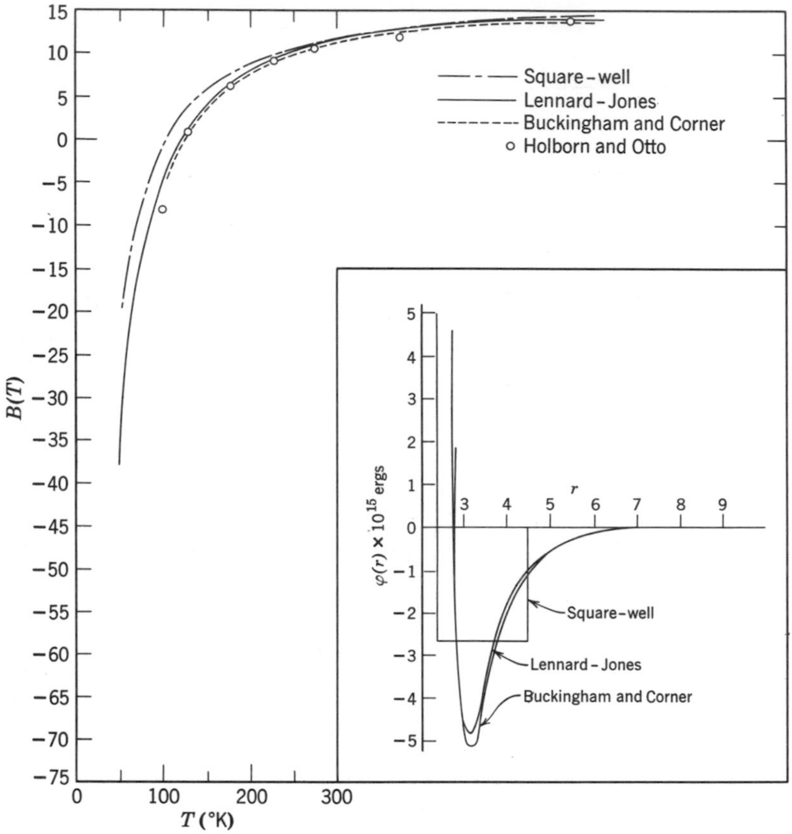

Fig. 3.9–2. Second virial coefficients for *neon* calculated for several molecular models. The potential functions obtained from the experimental $B(T)$ data are also shown. The experimental data are those of L. Holborn and J. Otto, *Z. Physik*, **33**, 1 (1925).

second virial coefficient at high temperatures on the basis of the Massey-Buckingham-Hamilton function. However, from Fig. 3.9–1 it can be seen that this function has very nearly the same contour as the

[8] L. Holborn and J. Otto, *Z. Physik*, **33**, 1 (1925).
[9] W. G. Schneider and J. A. H. Duffie, *J. Chem. Phys.*, **17**, 751 (1949).
[10] J. L. Yntema and W. G. Schneider, *J. Chem. Phys.*, **18**, 641 (1950).

de Boer-Michels-Lunbeck potential so that it would have nearly the same values for the second virial coefficient.

Massey, Buckingham and Hamilton[1,2,3,4] made a careful analysis of the low-temperature second virial coefficient data on helium, taking

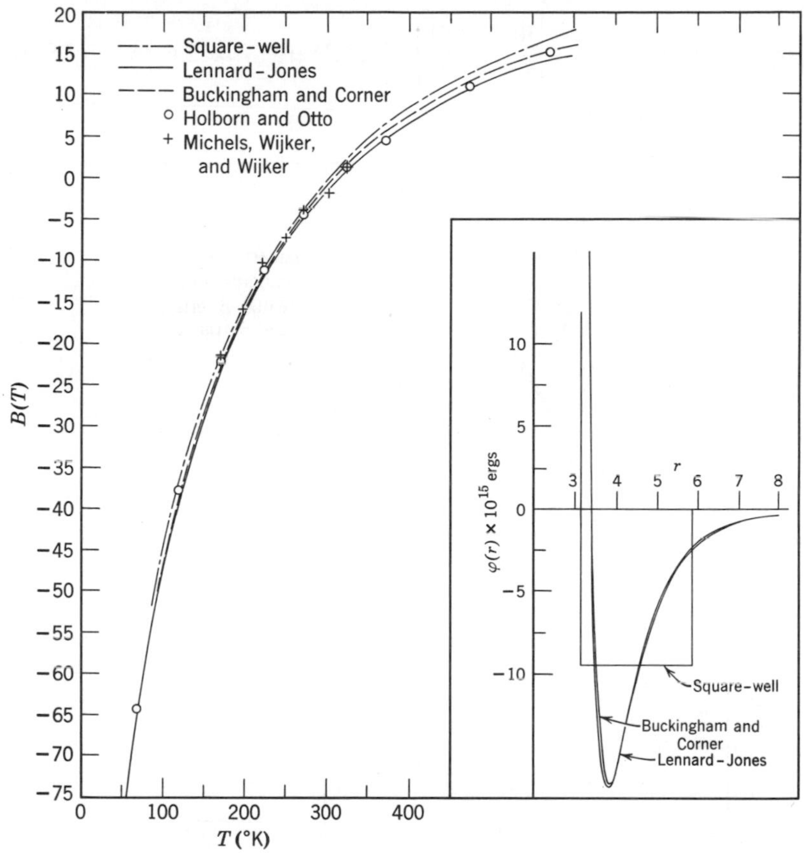

Fig. 3.9–3. Second virial coefficients for *argon* calculated for several molecular models. The potential functions obtained from the experimental $B(T)$ data are also shown. The experimental data are those of L. Holborn and J. Otto, *Z. Physik*, **33**, 1 (1925), and A. Michels, Hub. Wijker, and Hk. Wijker, *Physica*, **15**, 627 (1949).

quantum effects into consideration. They fitted the experimental data with a potential function consisting of two segments of the Buckingham form (Eq. 1.3–28). For $r \leqslant 2.61$ Å (the value at which the potential is zero) they used the theoretical expression of Slater and Kirkwood (see § 14.2). For $r \geqslant 2.61$ Å they took the constant a to be that in the

Slater-Kirkwood expression and the ratio of c to c' to be that predicted by Margenau (see § 14.2). The remaining two constants were then fitted to the experimental data. The complete potential is then

$$\varphi(r) = \left[770e^{-4.60r} - \frac{1.49}{r^6}\right] \times 10^{-12}\ \text{erg} \qquad r \leqslant 2.61\ \text{Å} \qquad (3.9\text{–}1a)$$

$$\varphi(r) = \left[977e^{-4.60r} - \frac{1.50}{r^6} - \frac{2.51}{r^8}\right] \times 10^{-12}\ \text{erg} \quad r \geqslant 2.61\ \text{Å} \qquad (3.9\text{–}1b)$$

in which r is in angstroms.

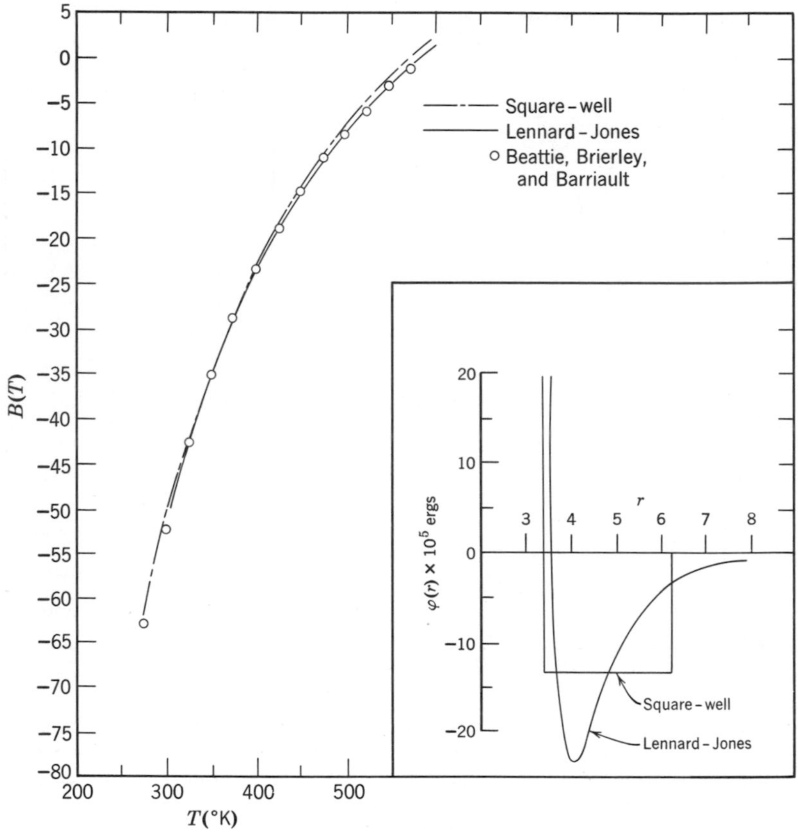

Fig. 3.9–4. Second virial coefficients for *krypton* calculated for several molecular models. The potential functions obtained from the experimental $B(T)$ data are also shown. The experimental data are those of J. A. Beattie, J. S. Brierley, and R. J. Barriault, *J. Chem. Phys.*, **20**, 1615 (1952).

De Boer, Michels, and Lunbeck[5] determined the parameters in the Lennard-Jones (6-12) potential by fitting the experimental second virial coefficients from 20°K to 400°K with the theoretical calculations described in § 6.5c. These calculations take into account the quantum deviations in this temperature range. In this way it is found that[5] $\sigma = 2.556$ Å and $\epsilon/k = 10.22$°K. These parameters enable us to describe fairly well the second virial coefficient of He^4 down to about 1°K by means of the theory outlined in § 6.4c.[11] The viscosity and thermal conductivity of gaseous He^4

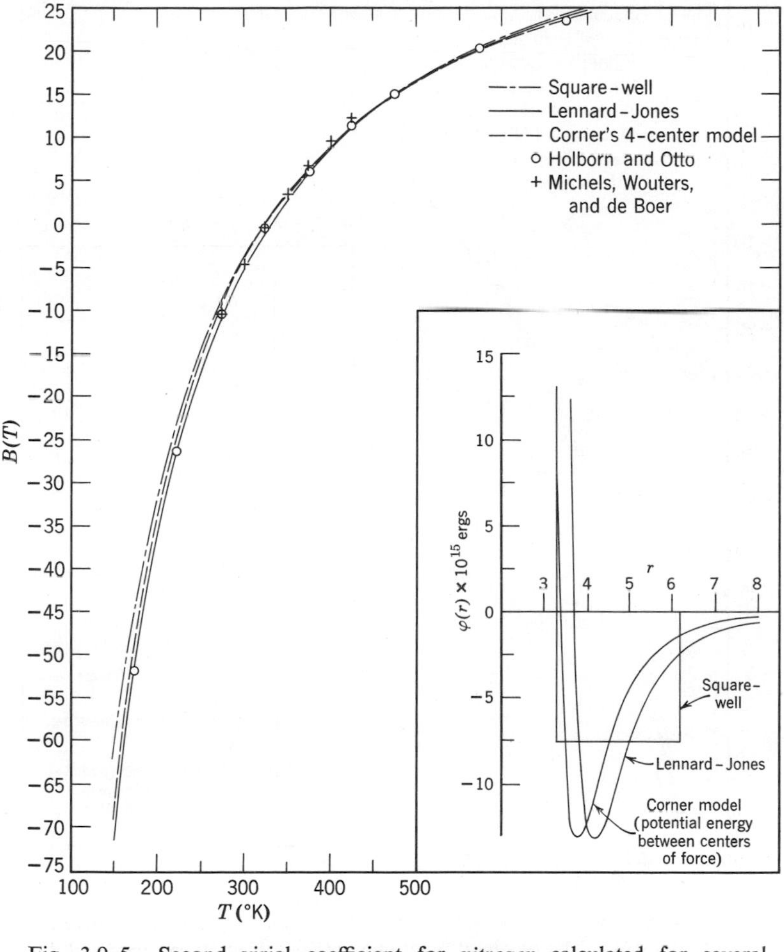

Fig. 3.9–5. Second virial coefficient for *nitrogen* calculated for several molecular models. The potential functions obtained from experimental $B(T)$ data are also shown. The experimental data are those of L. Holborn and J. Otto, *Z. Physik*, **33**, 1 (1925), and A. Michels, H. Wouters, and J. de Boer, *Physica*, **1**, 587 (1934).

[11] J. de Boer and A. Michels, *Physica*, **6**, 409 (1939).

have been calculated for the Lennard-Jones (6-12) potential with these parameters. Calculations have been made both at very low temperatures[12] (from 1° to 15°K), where the quantum mechanical calculations of § 10.2c are used, and at higher temperatures[13] (from about 100°K to 500°K), where the classical theory may be used. Quite good agreement is obtained

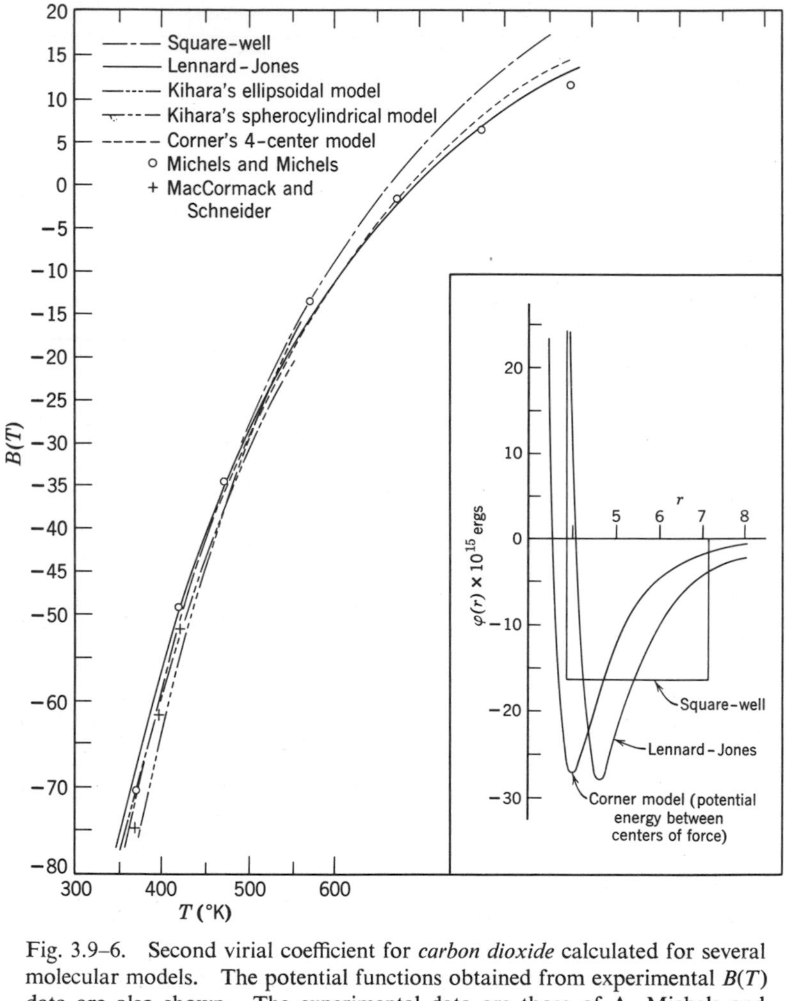

Fig. 3.9–6. Second virial coefficient for *carbon dioxide* calculated for several molecular models. The potential functions obtained from experimental $B(T)$ data are also shown. The experimental data are those of A. Michels and C. Michels, *Proc. Roy. Soc.* (*London*), **A153**, 201 (1936), and K. E. MacCormack and W. G. Schneider, *J. Chem. Phys.*, **18**, 1269 (1950).

[12] J. de Boer, *Physica*, **10**, 348 (1943).
[13] J. de Boer and J. van Kranendonk, *Physica*, **14**, 442 (1948).

over the whole temperature range. Because these parameters give satisfactory agreement for equilibrium and non-equilibrium properties, it is safe to say that they are probably the best constants for use in the Lennard-Jones (6-12) potential function.

Yntema and Schneider[6] fitted their experimental second virial coefficient data from 0° to 1200°C with a Buckingham potential. The constant c was taken to be that suggested by the simple London theoretical treatment, and the ratio of c to c' was taken to be the value suggested by idealizing the atom by a simple harmonic oscillator[14] (see § 14.2). Their best potential was then found to be

$$\varphi(r) = \left[1200 \exp(-4.72r) - \frac{1.24}{r^6} - \frac{1.89}{r^8}\right] \times 10^{-12} \text{ erg} \qquad (3.9\text{–}2)$$

in which r is in angstroms. They also fitted Lennard-Jones curves to their data, but the fit is not good.

Mason and Rice[7] were able to fit both the second virial coefficient from 0° to 1200°C and the viscosity from 200° to 1100°K with the modified Buckingham (6-exp) potential (Eq. 1.3–30). They found the constants $\alpha = 12.4$, $\epsilon/k = 9.16°$K, $r_m = 3.135$ Å. The fit is within the experimental error over the whole temperature range and is a definite improvement over the fit given by the Lennard-Jones (6-12) potential.

In Fig. 3.9–1 it is seen that the Yntema-Schneider potential has a minimum about 0.3×10^{-15} erg higher than the de Boer-Michels-Lunbeck and the Massey-Buckingham curves. The Mason-Rice potential has a minimum intermediate between the other two curves. For small separations the Yntema-Schneider and the Mason-Rice potentials cross the Lennard-Jones curve indicating a weaker repulsion. In § 14.2 it is seen that the theoretical Slater-Kirkwood potential lies intermediate between these curves. The Rosen-Margenau-Page potential (which represents the most careful theoretical treatment up to the present time) has a minimum about 0.3×10^{-15} erg higher than the Yntema and Schneider potential.

ii. *Neon*

Buckingham[1] and Corner[15] have obtained expressions for the potential of interaction between two neon atoms based on measurements of the second virial coefficient from 65° to 673°K, the distance between nearest neighbors in the crystal at 0°K, and the heat of sublimation of the crystal

[14] The best theoretical estimates of c and c' are 1.39×10^{-12} erg, Å^{11} and 3.0×10^{-12} erg Å^{14} respectively [H. Margenau, *Phys. Rev.*, **56**, 1000 (1939).] However, Yntema and Schneider were unable to curve fit their data using these constants.

[15] J. Corner, *Trans. Faraday Soc.*, **44**, 914 (1948).

at 0°K. Buckingham assumed that for r greater than about 4.4 Å the potential is given by the theoretical expression (see § 13.3).

$$\varphi(r) = -\left[\frac{6.1}{r^6} + \frac{8.8}{r^8}\right] \times 10^{-12} \text{ erg} \qquad (r \text{ in Å}) \qquad (3.9\text{–}3)$$

He then found that for r between 2.6 Å and 3.0 Å,

$$\varphi(r) = \left[2570 \exp(-4.26r) - \frac{9}{r^6}\right] \times 10^{-12} \text{ erg} \qquad (r \text{ in Å}) \quad (3.9\text{–}4)$$

Corner fitted the data by a potential of the Buckingham-Corner form, Eq. 1.3–29. The results are discussed in § 3.7 and given in Table 3.7–1. Mason and Rice[7] used the same crystal structure and second virial coefficient data together with the coefficient of viscosity (from 80° to 1100°K) to fit the modified Buckingham potential; they obtained the constants given in Table 3.7–2. These results are in substantial agreement with those of Corner.

Corner also fitted the data by a potential of the Lennard-Jones form (Eq. 1.3–27) with an attractive index, $\gamma = 6$, and a variable repulsive index, δ. He found that the best fit of the data, including the properties of the solid, was obtained with $\delta = 12$. The other constants were found to be

$$\epsilon = 5.01 \times 10^{-15} \text{ erg} \quad \text{or} \quad \epsilon/k = 36.3°\text{K}$$
$$\sigma = 2.82 \text{ Å} \qquad (3.9\text{–}5)$$

Very nearly the same constants are obtained from the temperature dependence of viscosity, as may be seen in Table I–A.

iii. *Argon*

Buckingham[1] and Corner[15] also studied the interaction potential between two argon atoms. Buckingham used the properties of the crystal and the measurements of the second virial coefficient from 173°K to 673°K. Corner used these data and in addition measurements of the zero pressure Joule-Thomson coefficient over approximately the same temperature range. Buckingham's potential is

$$\varphi(r) = -\left[\frac{60}{r^6} + \frac{180}{r^8}\right] \times 10^{-12} \text{ erg} \qquad r > 5.3 \text{ Å} \qquad (3.9\text{–}6a)$$

$$\varphi(r) = 1.69 \times 10^{-8} \exp(-3.66r) - \frac{1.02 \times 10^{-10}}{r^6} \text{ ergs} \quad 3.4 \text{ Å} < r < 3.6 \text{ Å} \qquad (3.9\text{–}6b)$$

in which r is in angstroms. Corner's constants are given in Table 3.7–1.

Mason and Rice[7] also analyzed the data for argon on the crystal, the second virial coefficient, and the viscosity (from 55° to 1900°K) to obtain the modified Buckingham potential parameters given in Table 3.7–2. Their potential is very similar to that of Corner.

The data have also been fitted with a Lennard-Jones potential by Corner. For argon he found that the best index is 12.3. However, if the index 12 is chosen, the constants are found to be[16]

$$\epsilon = 1.647 \times 10^{-14} \text{ erg} \quad \text{or} \quad \epsilon/k = 119.3\text{°K.}$$
$$\sigma = 3.45 \text{ Å} \tag{3.9–7}$$

These parameters are very nearly the same as those obtained from viscosity measurements (see Table I–A).

O. K. Rice[17] has obtained an estimate of the intermolecular potential by a more detailed analysis of the properties of the solid and use of the virial coefficient data. He assumed that at large separations the potential is that given by Buckingham, Eq. 3.9 6a. He then found two expressions for the potential in the region of the minimum,

$$\varphi(r) = [-1.923 + 5.344(r - 3.8267)^2 - 6.726(r - 3.8267)^3 + 2.043(r - 3.8267)^4] \times 10^{-14} \text{ erg} \tag{3.9–8}$$
$$\varphi(r) = [-1.945 + 5.430(r - 3.8608)^2 - 4.885(r - 3.8608)^3] \times 10^{-14} \text{ erg}$$

in which r is in angstroms. The two potentials were obtained from different assumptions about the disorder in the solid.

iv. *Krypton*

The agreement between the experimental second virial coefficient data of Beattie, Brierley, and Barriault[18] and values calculated on the basis of the Lennard-Jones (6-12) potential are shown in Fig. 3.9–4. This is typical of the agreement to be expected for spherical molecules where there are no forces acting besides the short-range valence and the long-range dispersion force.

b. Non-spherical molecules

Two examples are given of molecules which are somewhat asymmetrical, N_2 and CO_2. Because they are so nearly spherical, the dependence of

[16] R. J. Lunbeck (Doctoral Dissertation, Amsterdam, 1951) gives the constants $\sigma = 3.405$ and $\epsilon/k = 119.8$ as the best choice of constants to fit the data of A. Michels, Hub. Wijker, and Hk Wijker [*Physica*, **15**, 627 (1949)] between 0° and 150°C.

[17] O. K. Rice, *J. Am. Chem. Soc.*, **63**, 3 (1941).

[18] J. A. Beattie, J. S. Brierley, and R. J. Barriault, *J. Chem. Phys.*, **20**, 1615 (1952).

the second virial coefficient on temperature is quite well represented by the Lennard-Jones (6-12) potential. Whereas the second virial coefficient is not sensitive to the shape of the molecules, the effect of asymmetry manifests itself in the temperature dependence of the third virial coefficient. However, it would be very difficult to distinguish between those deviations in the third virial coefficient which are due to asymmetry and those which can be explained by the inaccuracy of the radial dependence of a spherical potential

i. *Nitrogen*

Excellent experimental measurements have been made of the equation of state of nitrogen both by Holborn and Otto[8] and by Michels, Wouters, and de Boer.[19] The former covers a considerably larger temperature range. Figure 3.9–5 compares the experimental values of the second virial coefficient with theoretical values based on: (a) the Lennard-Jones (6-12) potential with constants adjusted to the Holborn and Otto data, (b) the Kihara spherocylindrical and generalized ellipsoidal models (see § 3.8b and 3.8c), and (c) the four-center model of Corner (see § 3.8d). The agreement in all cases is good. From Table 3.8–2 the ratio of the length to the breadth of the nitrogen molecule is seen to be approximately 1.3 so that the molecule is only slightly asymmetrical.

ii. *Carbon Dioxide*

The second virial coefficient of carbon dioxide calculated on the basis of the potentials discussed in the previous paragraph are shown in Figure 3.9–6. These are compared with the excellent experimental measurements of Michels and Michels[20] and MacCormack and Schneider.[21] The carbon dioxide molecule is considerably more asymmetric than the nitrogen, having a length-to-breadth ratio (according to Table 3.8–2) of about 1.6. However, because of the insensitivity of the second virial coefficient to molecule shape, all these potentials give good agreement with experiment.

c. Comparison of different types of potential energy functions

In the figures comparing the second virial coefficients for the noble gases, nitrogen, and carbon dioxide are plotted the potential energy functions of different types which are fitted to give the best agreement with the experimental second virial coefficients as functions of temperature.

[19] A. Michels, H. Wouters, and J. de Boer, *Physica*, **1**, 587 (1934).
[20] A. Michels and C. Michels, *Proc. Roy. Soc.* (*London*), **A153**, 201 (1936).
[21] K. MacCormack and W. Schneider, *J. Chem. Phys.*, **18**, 1269 (1950).

These different potentials have quite different shapes and depth of their minima, yet they all fit the experimental data reasonably well over a rather large temperature range. These graphical comparisons emphasize the fact that the temperature dependence of $B(T)$ is insensitive to the form of the functions chosen to represent the intermolecular potential. The one feature which all of these curves seem to have in common is that the area contained within the potential well is approximately the same. This area, $\int_\sigma^\infty \varphi(r)\, dr$, for the Lennard-Jones (6-12) potential is $(24/55)\epsilon\sigma$; for the square-well potential the area is $(R-1)\epsilon\sigma$. The ratio of the square-well to the Lennard-Jones (6-12) areas is given in Table 3.9–1 for the five gases under consideration. It is seen that the ratio is very close to unity.

TABLE 3.9–1

Molecule	$\left[\dfrac{(R-1)\,(\epsilon\sigma)_{\text{S.W.}}}{(24/55)\,(\epsilon\sigma)_{\text{L.J.}}}\right]$
Ne	0.96
A	1.03
Kr	1.05
N_2	0.99
CO_2	1.06

Hill[22] has adjusted the parameters in the Buckingham potential,

$$\varphi = b \exp(-r/a) - c/r^6 \tag{3.9–9}$$

so as to obtain the best agreement with the experimental second virial coefficient of helium, neon, and argon. He compared these potentials with the Lennard-Jones (6-12) potentials in which the constants were also adjusted to the same second virial coefficient data, and expressed the constants in the Buckingham potential in terms of the constants in the Lennard-Jones potential. He found that

$$b = 828000\epsilon \qquad a = 0.0826\sigma \qquad c = 4.50\epsilon\sigma^6 \tag{3.9–10}$$

The minimum of the Buckingham potential occurs at a separation of 1.1310σ (as compared to 1.2616σ for the Lennard-Jones potential), and the minimum value of the potential is -1.210ϵ. The zero in the Buckingham potential occurs as a separation of 1.003σ.

[22] T. L. Hill, *J. Chem. Phys.*, **16**, 399 (1948).

The Buckingham potential (an exponential repulsion term and inverse sixth [and eighth] power attraction terms) has the defect that at a very small separation, r_{max}, the potential has a maximum, and, as r approaches zero, the potential becomes negative and approaches minus infinity. Table 3.9–2 gives the separation and energy of this maximum for a few examples. It is seen that the energy of the maximum is extremely large from the standpoint of thermal collisions. There is little need to divide the potential into two portions in the manner of the Buckingham-Corner potential. Rather, it is easier to set the potential equal to infinity for all separations smaller than r_{max} and use the Buckingham potential for all separations larger than r_{max}.

TABLE 3.9–2

SPURIOUS MAXIMUM IN BUCKINGHAM POTENTIAL

Substance	Name of Potential	r_{max}	$\varphi(r_{max})$	
		(Å)	(10^{-12} erg)	(Kcal/mole)
Helium	Yntema-Schneider, Eq. 3.9–2	0.82	11.7	168
	Slater-Kirkwood, Eq. 3.9–1a	0.65	19.0	270
Neon	Corner, Table 3.7–1	0.73	55.2	795
Argon	Corner, Table 3.7–1	0.78	520	7490

The test of a good potential function is that it describes both the equilibrium and non-equilibrium properties of the bulk substance in the solid, liquid, and gaseous phase. The square-well parameters determined for three substances from second virial data and also from viscosity measurements (see § 8.3d) are shown in Table 3.9–3. It is evident that those parameters determined from one property are not useful for calculating another bulk property. The same comparison is also shown for the Lennard-Jones potential. The agreement is considerably better than for the square-well, in accordance with the fact that the potential function is more realistic.

TABLE 3.9–3

COMPARISON OF POTENTIAL PARAMETERS FROM SECOND VIRIAL COEFFICIENTS AND FROM VISCOSITY COEFFICIENTS

Gas	Square-well Potential			Lennard-Jones Potential		
	Force Constants	From $B(T)$	From $\eta(T)$	Force Constants	From $B(T)$	From $\eta(T)$
Ne	σ ϵ/k R	2.38 19.5 1.87	2.38 101. 1.54	σ ϵ/k	2.74 35.7	2.80 35.7
A	σ ϵ/k R	3.16 69.4 1.85	2.98 167. 1.96	σ ϵ/k	3.405 119.75	3.418 124.0
N_2	σ ϵ/k R	3.30 53.7 1.87	3.36 80. 2.08	σ ϵ/k	3.698 95.05	3.681 91.46

10. Virial Coefficients for Polar Gases

(This section was prepared in collaboration with Professor J. S. Rowlinson, Imperial College, University of London.)

Virial coefficient calculations have been described for a great variety of potential functions, but thus far the discussion has been restricted to molecules which are non-polar. The interaction between two complex polar molecules is quite involved, and hence it is sometimes convenient to consider the total intermolecular potential as being the sum of several contributions: (i) The *valence* contribution associated with the short-range repulsion, $\varphi^{(\text{val})}$. (ii) The London *dispersion* contributions, which vary as r^{-6}, r^{-8}, etc., and depend only slightly on the orientations of the molecules, $\varphi^{(\text{dis})}$. (iii) The angle-dependent *electrostatic* contributions due to the interactions of the multipoles, the most important being the dipole-dipole interaction $\varphi^{(\mu,\mu)}$ proportional to r^{-3} and the dipole-quadrupole interaction $\varphi^{(\mu,Q)}$ proportional to r^{-4}. And, finally, (iv) the *induction* contributions, the most important being the dipole—induced-dipole potential $\varphi^{(\mu,\text{ind}\mu)}$ proportional to r^{-6}. These various interactions are discussed briefly in § 1.3b and are given detailed consideration in § 13.5.

In this section we first show how the virial coefficient calculations may be performed for the simplest polar-molecule model, namely, rigid spheres with imbedded point dipoles. This model embodies the two most important contributions to the potential—the short-range repulsive forces and the dipole-dipole interaction. Next a discussion is given of the calculations which have been made for the Stockmayer potential. This potential includes r^{-12} and r^{-6} contributions for the repulsion and induced-dipole-induced-dipole attraction and also includes the dipole-dipole interaction. Extensive tables have been prepared for this potential which enable us to calculate second and third virial coefficients and Joule-Thomson coefficients for polar molecules. Good agreement is generally obtained between calculated and experimental results. Better agreement would no doubt result if the important quadrupole-dipole contribution to the potential function were included. Some calculations along this line have been made; they are discussed at the end of this section.

a. Rigid spheres with imbedded point dipoles

For rigid spheres of diameter σ, at the centers of which are imbedded point dipoles of strength μ, the interaction potential is given by

$$\begin{cases} \varphi(r, \theta_1, \theta_2, \phi_2 - \phi_1) = \infty & r < \sigma \\ \varphi(r, \theta_1, \theta_2, \phi_2 - \phi_1) = -\dfrac{\mu^2}{r^3} g(\theta_1, \theta_2, \phi_2 - \phi_1) & r > \sigma \end{cases} \tag{1.3–32}$$

$$g(\theta_1, \theta_2, \phi_2 - \phi_1) = 2 \cos \theta_1 \cos \theta_2 - \sin \theta_1 \sin \theta_2 \cos (\phi_2 - \phi_1)$$

The variables r, θ_1, θ_2, ϕ_1, and ϕ_2 are described by Fig. 3.10–1. The second virial coefficient is calculated[1] by substituting this potential into Eq. 3.4–15. For $r < \sigma$ the integration gives $(2\pi\tilde{N}\sigma^3/3)$, the second virial coefficient for rigid spheres. For $r > \sigma$, the quantity $\exp(-\varphi/kT)$ may be expanded in a power series in $(1/kT)$, whereupon the integration over r is easily performed. Subsequent integration over the angles results in the disappearance of the odd powers of $(1/kT)$, and the final result is

$$B(T) = \tfrac{2}{3}\pi\tilde{N}\sigma^3 \left[1 - \sum_{k=1}^{\infty} \frac{G_k}{(2k)!\,(2k-1)} \left(\frac{\mu^2}{\sigma^3 kT}\right)^{2k}\right]$$

$$= \tfrac{2}{3}\pi\tilde{N}\sigma^3 \left[1 - \tfrac{1}{3}\left(\frac{\mu^2}{\sigma^3 kT}\right)^2 - \frac{1}{75}\left(\frac{\mu^2}{\sigma^3 kT}\right)^4 - \frac{29}{55125}\left(\frac{\mu^2}{\sigma^3 kT}\right)^6 - \cdots\right] \tag{3.10–1}$$

[1] W. H. Keesom, *Comm. Phys. Lab. Leiden*, Suppl. 24b, Section 6 (1912).

The quantities G_k result from the integrations over orientation and are defined as

$$G_k = \frac{1}{8\pi}\int_0^{2\pi}\int_0^{\pi}\int_0^{\pi} [g(\theta_1, \theta_2, \phi_2 - \phi_1)]^{2k} \sin\theta_1 \sin\theta_2 \, d\theta_1 \, d\theta_2 \, d(\phi_2 - \phi_1) \tag{3.10–2}$$

Keesom also computed the second virial coefficient for rigid spherical molecules containing quadrupole moments.[2]

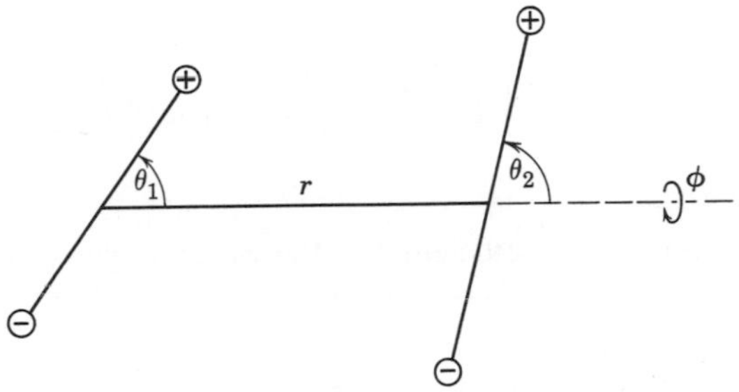

Fig. 3.10–1. The coordinates describing the mutual orientation of two polar molecules.

b. The second virial coefficient for the Stockmayer potential

Most of the calculations of virial coefficients for polar molecules are based upon the Stockmayer[3] potential:

$$\varphi(r, \theta_1, \theta_2, \phi_2 - \phi_1) = 4\epsilon\left[\left(\frac{\sigma}{r}\right)^{12} - \left(\frac{\sigma}{r}\right)^{6}\right] - \frac{\mu^2}{r^3} g(\theta_1, \theta_2, \phi_2 - \phi_1) \tag{1.3–33}$$

in which $g(\theta_1, \theta_2, \phi_2 - \phi_1)$ is the function defined in the preceding paragraph. The parameters σ and ϵ, which have a slightly different interpretation here than in the Lennard-Jones potential, may be used to define the following reduced quantities:[4]

$$\begin{aligned} B^\star &= B/b_0 = B/(\tfrac{2}{3}\pi\tilde{N}\sigma^3) & T^* &= kT/\epsilon \\ B_1^\star &= T^*(dB^\star/dT^*) & \mu^* &= \mu/\sqrt{\epsilon\sigma^3} \\ C^\star &= C/b_0^2 & t^* &= 8^{-\frac{1}{2}}\mu^{*2} \end{aligned} \tag{3.10–3}$$

[2] W. H. Keesom, *Comm. Phys. Lab. Leiden*, Suppl. 39a, (1915).

[3] W. H. Stockmayer, *J. Chem. Phys.*, **9**, 398 (1941).

[4] The quantity t^* was introduced by Rowlinson[7]; the factor of $\sqrt{8}$ was inserted for mathematical convenience in certain formulae.

When the Stockmayer potential is substituted into Eq. 3.4–15 for the second virial coefficient, the integration over r, which may be performed as in the integration of $B(T)$ for the Lennard-Jones potential, results in an infinite series of gamma functions. The integration over the angles, indicated in § 3.10a, gives rise to the coefficients G_k defined in Eq. 3.10–2. The final result is

$$B^{\star}(T^*) = \left(\frac{4}{T^*}\right)^{1/4} \left[\Gamma\left(\frac{3}{4}\right) - \frac{1}{4} \sum_{n=1}^{\infty} \sum_{k=0}^{k \leqslant n/2} \frac{2^{n-3k} G_k}{n!} \right.$$
$$\left. \times \binom{n}{2k} \Gamma\left(\frac{2n-2k-1}{4}\right) \mu^{*4k} T^{*-(n+k)/2} \right] \quad (3.10\text{–}4)$$

Hence the second virial coefficient for the Stockmayer potential may be written as

$$B(T) = b_0 B^{\star}(T^*; \mu^*) \quad (3.10\text{–}5)$$

This is analogous to the result obtained in Eq. 3.6–3 for the Lennard-Jones potential, except that the reduced second virial coefficient now depends not only on the reduced temperature but also parametrically on the reduced dipole moment μ^*. This latter dependence is illustrated in Fig. 3.10–2, where $B^{\star}$ is plotted as a function of T^* for several values of the parameter, $t^* = 8^{-1/2}\mu^{*2}$. The fact that the $B^{\star}$ curve for polar molecules lies beneath that for non-polar molecules indicates that polar gases are more compressible than non-polar gases (with the same σ and ϵ). This behavior results from the additional attractive contribution to the potential for two molecules containing electric moments.[5]

The information given in Fig. 3.10–2 is also presented in Table II–A.[6] With this table and the list of force constants given in Table 3.10–1,

[5] A recent extensive tabulation of dipole moments is given by L. G. Wesson, *Table of Electric Dipole Moments*, M.I.T., The Technology Press (1948).

[6] This table was prepared by J. S. Rowlinson from the punched-card calculations by R. B. Bird, Ph.D. Dissertation, University of Wisconsin (1950). This type of presentation is more convenient for the interpretation of experimental data than that used by previous investigators, and is of the form given previously by J. S. Rowlinson, *Trans. Faraday Soc.*, **45**, 974 (1949). Less extensive tables have also been given by J. O. Hirschfelder, F. T. McClure, and I. F. Weeks, *J. Chem. Phys.*, **10**, 201 (1942). and by R. J. Lunbeck and C. A. ten Seldam, *Physica*, **17**, 788 (1951).

second virial coefficients for polar molecules may be calculated. The determination of the force constants from experimental data is discussed in the next subsection.

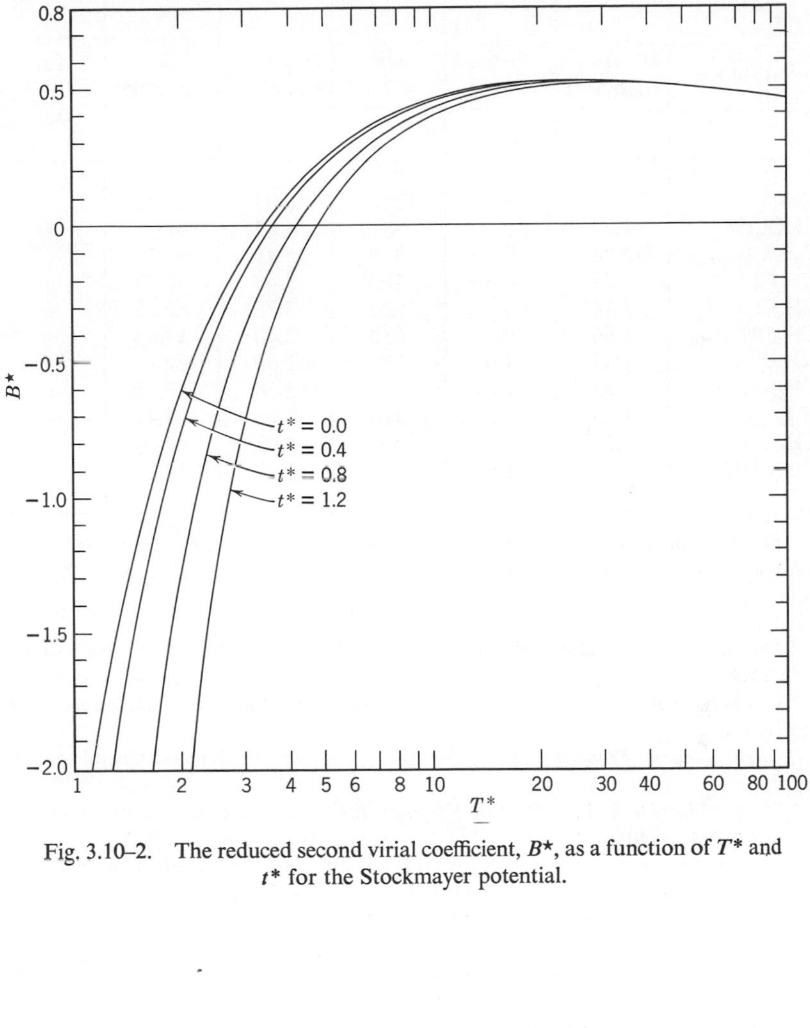

Fig. 3.10–2. The reduced second virial coefficient, B^*, as a function of T^* and t^* for the Stockmayer potential.

TABLE 3.10–1

FORCE CONSTANTS FOR THE STOCKMAYER POTENTIAL [a,b]

$$b_0(\text{cc/mole}) = 2\pi\tilde{N}\sigma^3/3 = 1.2615[\sigma(\text{Å})]^3$$

$$t^* = (8)^{-1/2}\,\mu^{*2} \qquad \mu^* = \mu/\sqrt{\epsilon\sigma^3}$$

Substance	μ (debyes[c])	t^*	ϵ/k (°K)	σ (Å)	b_0 (cc/mole)	Ref. for $B(T)$ Data
$CHCl_3$	1.05	0.1	1060	2.98	33.45	*e*
$CHCl_2F$[d]	1.29	0.1	381	4.82	141.	*f*
C_2H_5Cl	2.02	0.2	320	5.41	199.7	*e*
CH_3Cl	1.89	0.6	380	3.43	50.73	*g*
CH_3COCH_3	2.74	0.7	520	3.76	66.87	*e*
CH_3OH	1.66	0.8	630	2.40	17.48	*e*
NH_3	1.47	1.0	320	2.60	22.12	*h*
CH_3F	1.82	1.07	207	3.36	47.85	*i*
H_2O	1.83	1.2	380	2.65	23.42	*j*
CH_3CN	3.5	1.2	400	4.02	82.04	*e*
CH_3CHO	2.7	1.4	270	3.68	62.75	*k*

[a] From a table given by J. S. Rowlinson, *Trans. Faraday Soc.*, **45**, 980 (1949).

[b] The values given for CH_3F were calculated by R. J. Lunbeck and C. A. ten Seldam, *Physica*, **27**, 788 (1951).

[c] 1 debye = 1×10^{-18} esu.

[d] The force constants for $CHCl_2F$ are those calculated in the illustrative example in § 3.10c.

[e] Lambert, Roberts, Rowlinson, and Wilkinson, *Proc. Roy. Soc.* (*London*), **A196**, 113 (1949).

[f] *Thermodynamic Properties of Dichloromonofluoromethane*, Kinetic Chemicals, Inc. (1939).

[g] *Methyl Chloride*, E. I. du Pont de Nemours & Co. The R & H Chemicals Department), 5th Ed. (1940).

[h] F. G. Keyes, *J. Am. Chem. Soc.*, **60**, 1761 (1938), has correlated the experimental data of C. H. Meyers and R. S. Jessup, *Refrig. Eng.*, **11**, 345 (1925); J. A. Beattie and C. K. Lawrence, *J. Am. Chem. Soc.*, **52**, 6 (1930)

[i] A. Michels and A. Visser (in preparation).

[j] F. G. Keyes, L. B. Smith, and H. T. Gerry, *Proc. Am. Acad. Arts Sci.*, **70**, 319 (1936); S. C. Collins and F. G. Keyes, *ibid*, **72**, 283 (1938).

[k] Alexander and Lambert, *Trans. Faraday Soc.*, **37**, 421 (1941).

Illustrative Example

Problem. (a) Calculate the compressibility factor ($p\tilde{V}/RT$) for steam at 15 atm and 300°C.

(b) What is the Boyle temperature, T_B, for steam?

Solution. (a) From Table 3.10–1 we find $b_0 = 23.42$ cc/mole, $\epsilon/k = 380°$K, $t^* = 1.2$. The reduced temperature is then $T^* = kT/\epsilon = 573/380 = 1.51$. From Table II–A it can be found that $B^\star(T^* = 1.51,\ t^* = 1.2) = -4.750$. Accordingly, $B(T) = b_0 B^\star(T^*; t^*) = (23.42)(-4.750) = -111.2$ cc/mole. This is the $B(T)$ for the virial expansion as powers of $(1/V)$. The corresponding quantity in the pressure series is $B' = B/RT = (-111.2)/(82.06)(573) = -0.002365$. The compressibility factor is then $(p\tilde{V}/RT) = 1 + B'p + \cdots = 1 + (-0.002365)(15) + \cdots = 1 - 0.03548 = 0.9645$.

(b) The Boyle temperature is that temperature for which $B^\star(T^*, t^*) = 0$. From Table II–A it can be seen that

$$T_B{}^* = 4.876. \text{ Hence } T_B = T_B{}^* \cdot \epsilon/k$$
$$= (4.876)(380) = 1853°\text{K} = 1580°\text{C}.$$

c. Determination of the parameters in the Stockmayer potential from experimental second virial coefficients

If the dipole moment of the molecules in the gas is known, the second virial coefficient data can be analyzed to find the values of σ and ϵ and also the value of the parameter $t^* = 8^{-1/2}(\mu^2/\epsilon\sigma^3)$ which is consistent with these values. Since there are two parameters to determine, it is necessary to use two independent experimentally determined quantities. We choose to use the value of the second virial coefficient and the slope of the B versus T curve at some specified temperature.[7]

First, we define a quantity, y, by

$$y = \left(\frac{TB(T)}{\mu^2}\right)\left(\frac{k\sqrt{8}}{\frac{2}{3}\pi\tilde{N}}\right) = \frac{TB(T)}{3231\,\mu^2} \qquad (3.10\text{–}6)^8$$

which contains only experimentally measured quantities. Second, we introduce the "apparent temperature coefficient," s, defined by

$$B(T) = AT^s \qquad (3.10\text{–}7)$$

in which A is a constant. The quantity s, the slope of $\log |B|$ versus $\log |T|$, is determined graphically. These two quantities correspond to a knowledge of the second virial coefficient and its temperature derivative at some temperature, T. Making use of the reduced quantities defined in Eq. 3.10–3, we may write these quantities as

$$y = \frac{T^*}{t^*} B^\star(T^*, t^*) = y(T^*, t^*) \qquad (3.10\text{–}8)$$

$$y(s - 1) = \frac{T^*}{t^*}(B_1{}^\star - B^\star) = z(T^*, t^*) \qquad (3.10\text{–}9)$$

[7] The method described here is a slight modification of the procedure described by J. S. Rowlinson, *Trans. Faraday Soc.*, **45**, 974 (1949).

[8] μ is expressed in debyes; 1 debye $= 1 \times 10^{-18}$ esu.

These two simultaneous equations may be solved numerically for t^* and T^* (and hence ϵ/k) with the help of the tables of the functions $(T^*/t^*)B^\star$ and $B_1^\star - B^\star$ given in the appendix. (See Tables II–B and II–C.) The quantities b_0 (and σ) are then obtained from $b_0 = B/B^\star$. The following example serves to illustrate this method.

Illustrative Example

Problem. At a temperature of 283°K, the second virial coefficient of $CHCl_2F$ is $-616\ cm^3$/mole. The temperature index, s, of Eq. 3.10–7 is found to be (-1.72). The dipole moment is $\mu = 1.29$ debye. Find σ and ϵ for the Stockmayer potential. Check to be sure that the values of σ, ϵ, and t^* are consistent.

Solution. The quantity y of Eq. 3.10–6 must first be calculated. At 283°K this is

$$y = \frac{TB}{3231\mu^2} = \frac{(283)\,(-616)}{(3231)\,(1.29)^2} = -32.44$$

and

$$y(s - 1) = (-32.44)\,(-2.72) = +88.24$$

We now must solve the simultaneous equation:

$$y(T^*, t^*) = -32.44 \qquad \text{(a)}$$

$$z(T^*, t^*) = +\,88.24 \qquad \text{(b)}$$

to get t^* and T^*; the functions y and z are defined in Eqs. 3.10–8 and 3.10–9, respectively. The function $y(T^*, t^*)$ is given in Table II–C, and the function $(B_1^\star - B^\star) = (t^*/T^*)\,z(T^*, t^*)$ is given in Table II–B.

We begin by picking a value of t^*, say 0.3. Using Table II–C, we can solve Eq. a numerically to get $T^* = 0.399$. Using these values of T^* and t^*, we get from Table II–B for $z(T^*, t^*)$ the value 136. This value is far too high, since $z = 88.24$ according to Eq. b. Hence, we repeat the process with other values of t^*, until a t^* and T^* are found which satisfy Eq. b. The results may be tabulated as follows:

t^*	T^*	$\frac{T^*}{t^*}(B_1^\star - B^\star)$
0.3	0.399	136
0.2	0.427	115
0.1	0.742	$90 \doteq y(s - 1)$

Here we find that the values $t^* = 0.1$ and $T^* = 0.742$ satisfy both Eqs. a and b within an error consistent with the accuracy of the experimental data. Using these values, we then get

$$\epsilon/k = T/T^* = (283)/(0.472) = 381°\text{K}$$

$$b_0 = B/B^\star = (-616)/(-4.3765) = 141 \text{ cc/mole}$$

$$\sigma = (b_0/1.2615)^{1/3} = (112)^{1/3} = 4.82 \text{ Å}$$

The consistency may be checked by computing t^*:

$$t^* = \frac{\mu^2}{\sqrt{8}\,\epsilon\sigma^3} = \frac{1.664}{16.66} = 0.0999 \doteq 0.1$$

To check the applicability of the results, we now calculate $B(T)$ and compare it with the experimental data [source of the data is given in Table 3.10–1]:

T	T^*	$B^\star$	B_{calcd} (cc/mole)	B_{exptl} (cc/mole)	$\dfrac{B_{\text{calcd}} - B_{\text{exptl}}}{B_{\text{calcd}}} \times 100$
239	0.627	−5.942	−838	−766	+8.6
250	0.656	−5.455	−769	−734	+4.6
283	0.742	−4.377	−616	−616	0.0
311	0.816	−3.704	−522	−528	−1.1
339	0.890	−3.180	−448	−446	+0.4
366	0.960	−2.784	−393	−403	−2.5
394	1.034	−2.443	−345	−354	−2.6
422	1.107	−2.163	−305	−310	−1.6
450	1.181	−1.925	−271	−271	0.0

It is thus seen that the parameters $t^* = 0.1$, $b_0 = 141$ cc/mole, and $(\epsilon/k) = 381°K$ give calculated values of $B(T)$ which agree with the corresponding experimental values within an amount consistent with the accuracy of the experimental data.

Rowlinson[7] has analyzed the equation of state data for nine polar gases to obtain the parameters which are presented in Table 3.10–1. Second virial coefficients calculated from these parameters give agreement with the experimental data within 2 or 3 per cent, as may be seen in Table 3.10–2. Also given in Table 3.10–1 are the parameters for methyl fluoride determined by Lunbeck and ten Seldam.[9] The sources of the experimental data are included.

TABLE 3.10–2

AGREEMENT BETWEEN EXPERIMENTAL $B(T)$ VALUES AND THOSE COMPUTED FOR THE STOCKMAYER POTENTIAL[7] (B IS IN cc/mole)

Gas	$-B(T)$	50°C	70°C	90°C	110°C	130°C
Acetonitrile	Expt	4000	2840	2110	1690	1330
	Calc	3760	2750	2160	1740	1410
Acetone	Expt	1560	1280	1040	850	700
	Calc	1530	1230	1010	850	730
Ethyl chloride	Expt	580	510	450	390	350
	Calc	560	500	450	410	370
Chloroform	Expt	1000	840	730	630	—
	Calc	1010	850	730	630	—

d. Joule-Thomson coefficients for the Stockmayer potential

The zero-pressure Joule-Thomson coefficient for the Stockmayer potential is given by

$$\mu^0 = \frac{b_0}{\tilde{C}_p^{\,0}} [B_1^\star(T^*, t^*) - B^\star(T^*, t^*)] \qquad (3.10\text{–}10)$$

[9] R. J. Lunbeck and C. A. ten Seldam, *Physica*, **17**, 788 (1951).

which is analogous to the expression for the Lennard-Jones potential given in Eq. 3.6–14. The function $B_1^\star - B^\star$ for polar molecules is tabulated in Table II–B as a function of T^* for various values of the parameter $t^* = \mu^{*2}/\sqrt{8}$. Hence, if the parameters in the Stockmayer potential are known, it is easy to calculate the zero-pressure Joule-Thomson coefficient.

Also Joule-Thomson data may be used for the determination of the parameters σ and ϵ in the same way that equation of state data are used. This has been done for steam,[10] and the force constants obtained are compared with those calculated from second virial coefficients in Table 3.10–3. A comparison of calculated and experimental Joule-Thomson coefficients [10] is given in Table 3.10–4, and the agreement is seen to be excellent. Hence we see that the Joule-Thomson coefficient is a useful alternative source of information about the intermolecular forces of polar molecules.

TABLE 3.10–3

FORCE CONSTANTS[10] FOR H_2O

	t^*	ϵ/k	σ	b_0
From $B(T)$ Data: [a]	1.2	380	2.65	23.42
From $\mu^0\tilde{C}_p{}^0$ Data: [b,c]	1.2	373	2.68	24.30

[a] References given in Table 3.10–1.

[b] Joule-Thomson data from H. N. Davis and R. V. Kleinschmidt, quoted by F. G. Keyes, L. B. Smith, and H. T. Gerry, *Proc. Am. Acad. Arts and Sci.*, **70**, 320 (1936); S. C. Collins and F. G. Keyes, *Proc. Am. Acad. Arts and Sci.*, **72**, 283 (1938).

[c] Specific heat data from the spectroscopic data quoted by A. R. Gordon [*J. Chem. Phys.*, **2**, 65 (1934)] and modified by E. B. Wilson, Jr. [*J. Chem. Phys.*, **4**, 526 (1936)].

TABLE 3.10–4

EXPERIMENTAL AND CALCULATED JOULE-THOMSON COEFFICIENTS[10] FOR H_2O

T(°C)	39	59	80	100	125	166
$\mu^\circ\tilde{C}_p{}^\circ$ (exptl)	5170	3640	2710	2110	1590	987
$\mu^\circ\tilde{C}_p{}^\circ$ (calcd)	5150	3620	2700	2080	1570	980
T(°C)	196	225	260	300	347	
$\mu^\circ\tilde{C}_p{}^\circ$ (exptl)	780	646	507	400	322	
$\mu^\circ\tilde{C}_p{}^\circ$ (calcd)	780	640	510	400	320	

[10] J. S. Rowlinson, Doctoral Dissertation, Oxford (1950).

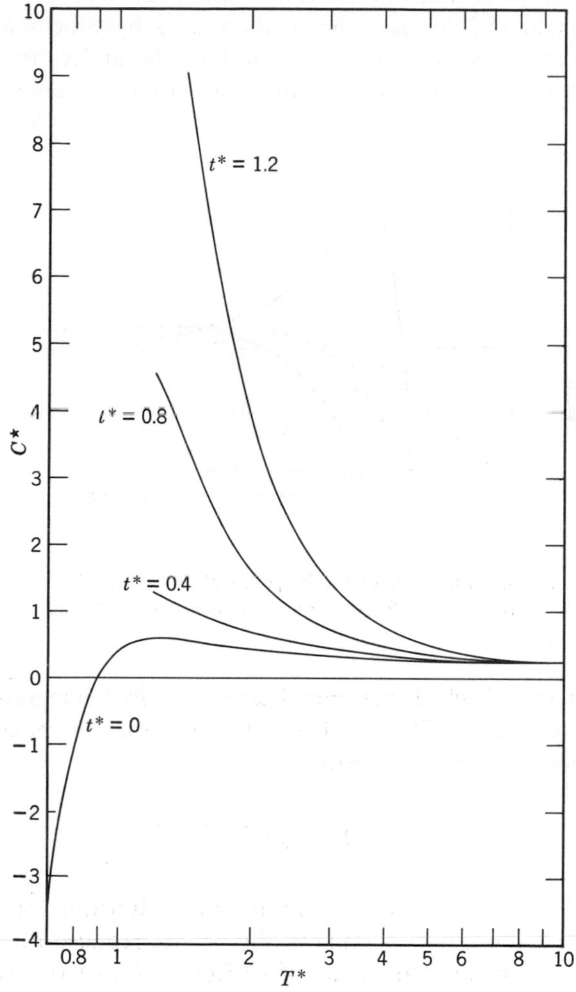

Fig. 3.10–3. The reduced third virial coefficient, $C^\star$, as a function of T^* and t^*, for the Stockmayer potential.

e. The third virial coefficient for the Stockmayer potential

Rowlinson[11] has shown how the third virial coefficient for polar molecules may be integrated numerically by making use of the change of variables used by Kihara for the third virial coefficient for the Lennard-Jones potential (§ 3.6c) and the method used by Stockmayer for the integration of the second virial coefficient for polar molecules. The result is expressed in terms of a double sum over various powers of t^* and T^*,

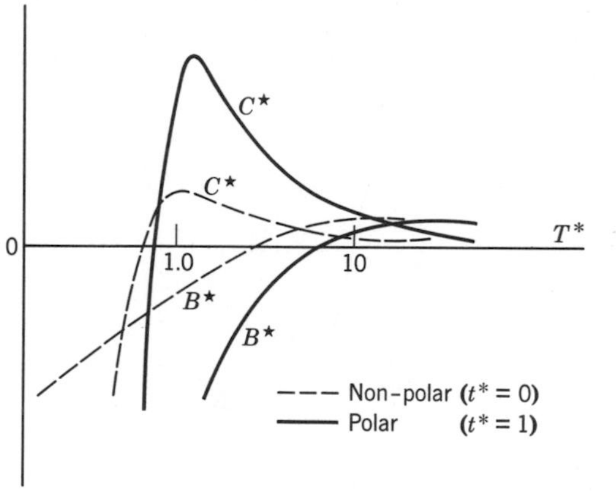

Fig. 3.10–4. Summary of the behavior of $B(T)$ and $C(T)$ for polar gases. [From J. S. Rowlinson, *J. Chem. Phys.*, **19**, 827 (1951).]

the coefficients of which are complicated eightfold integrals, which are not presented here. The third virial coefficient for polar molecules may be finally written in the form

$$C(T) = b_0^2 C^\star(T^*, t^*) \tag{3.10–11}$$

The reduced third virial coefficient is thus a function of the reduced temperature and depends parametrically on the reduced dipole moment. $C^\star(T^*, t^*)$ is tabulated for values of T^* from 0.70 to 400 for a number of values of t^* in Table II–D. The function $C^\star$ is shown in Fig. 3.10–3 as a function of T^* for several values of t^*. It should be noted that the deviations from non-polar behavior are in the opposite direction from those for the second virial coefficient. Rowlinson estimates, however, that the $C^\star$ curve for $t^* = 1$ becomes negative at about $T^* = 1$ and that

[11] J. S. Rowlinson, *J. Chem. Phys.*, **19**, 827 (1951).

the polar curve lies beneath the non-polar curve in that region. This information is summarized in Fig. 3.10-4.

Comparison of the calculated results with experimental data has been made for only three gases: H_2O, NH_3, CH_3F. This comparison is shown in Fig. 3.10-5; the parameters in Table 3.10-1 are used for the

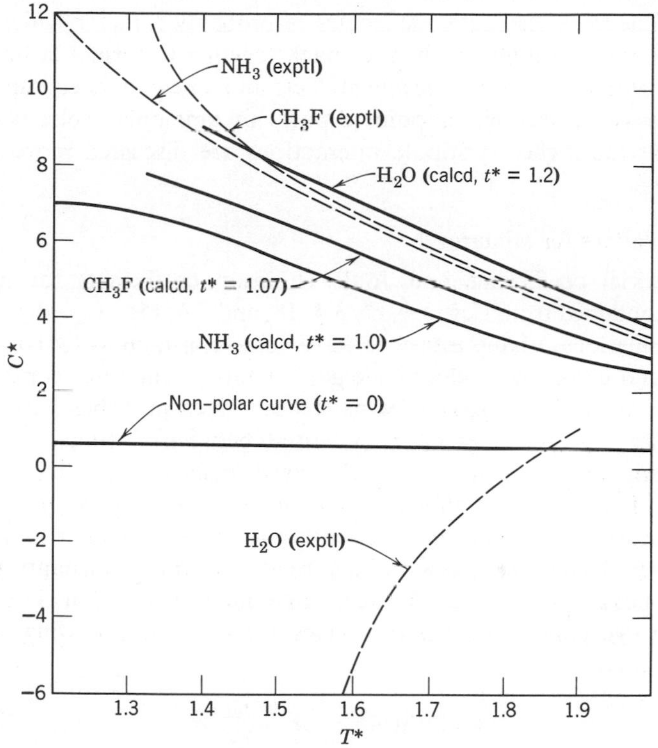

Fig. 3.10-5. A comparison of the calculated and experimental third virial coefficients for ammonia, methyl fluoride, and water vapor.

reduction of the experimental data. The agreement is reasonably good for ammonia and also for methyl fluoride. For both these gases the experimental points lie slightly above the calculated curve and have a somewhat steeper slope. These deviations are in the same direction and of about the same order of magnitude as those which were found for the third virial coefficient for the Lennard-Jones (6-12) potential (see § 3.6c). The distinct disagreement between the calculated and the experimental values for H_2O is undoubtedly due to the neglect of the interaction of higher multipoles (particularly the dipole-quadrupole interaction) in the Stockmayer potential function. Even for the second virial coefficient, the effect of these is several times larger for water than for ammonia, which is symmetrical.[12] Apparently this difference is even more striking in the third virial coefficient. The effect is to make the water molecules cluster together more than would be expected, so that $C^{\star}$ becomes negative at temperatures below $T^* = 1.8$, instead of about $T^* = 1.0$. The geometry of the water molecules is probably a factor which favors this clustering, as it allows them to pack together to form a lattice of the wurzite type where each molecule attracts all its neighbors equally. This is not possible with either point dipoles or ammonia molecules. The effects of the higher multipole interactions are discussed more fully in § 3.10g.

f. Calculations for mixtures

The virial coefficients and Joule-Thomson coefficients for mixtures may be obtained from Eqs. 3.4–17, 3.4–18, and 3.6–15. In order to make any calculations it is necessary to have force constants between all pairs of like and unlike molecules in the gas mixture. The force constants for pairs of similar polar molecules have been given in Table 3.10–1. The parameters for the interaction potential between dissimilar molecules can in principle be obtained from the virial coefficients of mixtures or the volume of mixing. The difficulties encountered in doing this have already been discussed in § 3.6b. Consequently the best we can do is to make use of empirical combining laws which relate the force constants between unlike molecules to those between like molecules. For interactions between two polar molecules of species 1 and 2 the following relations may be used:

$$\sigma_{12} = \tfrac{1}{2}(\sigma_1 + \sigma_2) \qquad (3.10\text{–}12)$$

$$\epsilon_{12} = \sqrt{\epsilon_1 \epsilon_2} \qquad (3.10\text{–}13)$$

$$t_{12}^* = \frac{\mu_1 \mu_2}{\sqrt{8}\, \epsilon_{12} \sigma_{12}^3} \doteq \sqrt{t_1^* t_2^*} \qquad (3.10\text{–}14)$$

There are no available data whereby the applicability of these relations may be checked.

[12] J. S. Rowlinson, *Trans. Faraday Soc.*, **47**, 120 (1951).

In mixtures where both polar and non-polar molecules are present, it is necessary to specify the interaction between polar and non-polar molecules. It may be shown (see § 13.5) that the effective total energy of interaction between a polar and a non-polar molecule has the same form as that between two non-polar molecules. Hence, for the calculation of the B_{ij} in mixture formulae, the tables of $B^{\star}(T^{*})$ for the Lennard-Jones potential may be used. The force constants describing the potential of interaction between a polar (subscript p) and a non-polar (subscript n) molecule may be obtained from the empirical combining laws:

$$\sigma_{np} = \tfrac{1}{2}(\sigma_n + \sigma_p)\xi^{-1/6} \tag{3.10–15}$$

$$\epsilon_{np} = \sqrt{\epsilon_n \epsilon_p}\, \xi^2 \tag{3.10–16}$$

The factor ξ is given by:

$$\xi = \left[1 + \frac{1}{4}\frac{\alpha_n \mu_p^{*2}}{\sigma_n^{\ 3}}\sqrt{\frac{\epsilon_p}{\epsilon_n}}\right] = \left[1 + 0.892\frac{\alpha_n t_p^{*}}{(b_0)_n}\sqrt{\frac{\epsilon_p}{\epsilon_n}}\right] \tag{3.10–17}$$

in which α_n is the polarizability of the non-polar molecule in cubic angstroms, σ_n is the collision diameter of the non-polar molecule in angstroms, and $(b_0)_n$ is expressed in cubic centimeters per mole. The use of the various combining formulae is illustrated in a numerical example.

Illustrative Example

Problem. Calculate the second virial coefficient at 400°K for a mixture of 50 mole per cent air, 45 mole per cent $CHCl_2F$, and 5 mole per cent water vapor. Assume that air is four-fifths nitrogen and one-fifth oxygen.

Solution. The second virial coefficient for a four-component mixture is:

$$\begin{aligned} B(T) = {} & x_1^2 B_{11} + x_2^2 B_{22} + x_3^2 B_{33} + x_4^2 B_{44} \\ & + 2x_1x_2B_{12} + 2x_1x_3B_{13} + 2x_1x_4B_{14} \\ & + 2x_2x_3B_{23} + 2x_2x_4B_{24} + 2x_3x_4B_{34} \end{aligned}$$

We must hence calculate the contributions to the second virial coefficient due to the ten different types of interaction occurring. First of all, we must calculate the force constants for the various types of interactions. Then, using these parameters, we may compute the various B_{ij} from the tables. The calculations are summarized in a tabular form in Table 3.10–5 to illustrate how the work may be organized. Footnotes give the details of the calculations.

TABLE 3.10–5

CALCULATION OF $B(T)$ FOR A FOUR-COMPONENT POLAR–NON-POLAR MIXTURE

Components:	Mole Fractions:	Polarizabilities:[a]
1 = N_2	$x_1 = 0.40$	$\alpha_1 = 1.76$ Å^3
2 = O_2	$x_2 = 0.10$	$\alpha_2 = 1.60$ Å^3
3 = $CHCl_2F$	$x_3 = 0.45$	
4 = H_2O	$x_4 = 0.05$	

i	j	σ_{ij} (Å)	$(b_0)_{ij}$ cc/mole	ϵ_{ij}/k (°K)	t_{ij}^*	T_{ij}^* h	B_{ij}^* j	B_{ij} k	Contribution to $B(T)$ Due to i–j Interaction[l]
1	1	3.698[b]	63.78[b]	95.05[b]	—	4.208	+0.1478	+9.427	+1.508
1	2	3.58[d]	57.88[e]	105.9[d]	—	3.777	+0.0759	+4.393	+0.351
1	3	4.26[f]	97.53[e]	192[f]	—	2.083	−0.5637	−54.98	−19.79
1	4	3.14[f]	39.05[e]	213[f]	—	1.878	−0.7350	−28.70	−1.148
2	2	3.46[b]	52.26[b]	118[b]	—	3.389	−0.0070	−0.366	−0.004
2	3	4.14[f]	89.51[e]	214[f]	—	1.869	−0.7435	−66.55	−5.990
2	4	3.03[f]	35.09[e]	237[f]	—	1.688	−0.9385	−32.93	−0.329
3	3	4.82[c]	141[c]	381[c]	0.1[c]	1.050	−2.3750	−334.9	−67.82
3	4	3.74[g]	66.0[e]	380[g]	0.35[g]	1.053	−2.9017	−191.5	−8.618
4	4	2.65[c]	23.42[c]	380[c]	1.2[c]	1.053	−14.2	−332.6	−0.832
								$B(T) = \Sigma_{ij} x_i x_j B_{ij} =$	−102.7 cc/mole

[a] From H. A. Stuart, *Molekulstruktur*, Springer (1934); see also Table 13.2–3.
[b] Table 3.6–1. [c] Table 3.10–1. [d] Use Eqs. 3.6–8 and 9.
[e] $(b_0)_{ij} = \frac{2}{3}\pi \tilde{N}\sigma_{ij}^3$. [f] Use Eqs. 3.10–15, 16, and 17.
[g] Use Eqs. 3.10–12, 13, and 14. [h] $T_{ij}^* = kT/\epsilon_{ij} = 400/(\epsilon_{ij}/k)$.
[j] For the nonpolar-nonpolar and polar-nonpolar interactions calculate $B^\star(T^*)$ from Table I–B. For polar-polar interactions calculate $B^\star(T^*, t^*)$ from Table II–A.
[k] $B(T) = b_0 B^\star(T^*)$.
[l] For i-i interaction the contribution is $x_i^2 B_{ii}$ and for i-j interaction the contribution is $2x_i x_j B_{ij}$. Then $[B(T)]_{\text{mix}} = \Sigma x_i x_j B_{ij}$.

g. Dipole-quadrupole interaction in complex molecules

If the molecules have a complex charge distribution it may be necessary to include in the potential function terms accounting for the interaction of higher multipoles. Such terms are probably quite important in the interaction between molecules which have a tendency to form hydrogen bonds. The most important contribution of higher-multipole interaction is the term $\varphi^{(\mu, Q)}$ proportional to r^{-4}, due to the interaction of the dipole of one charge distribution with the quadrupole of the other. The next term, proportional to r^{-5}, is the sum of the quadrupole-quadrupole and dipole-octupole interactions. This term is usually negligible even for complex molecules. The interactions between general charge distributions is given detailed attention in § 12.1.

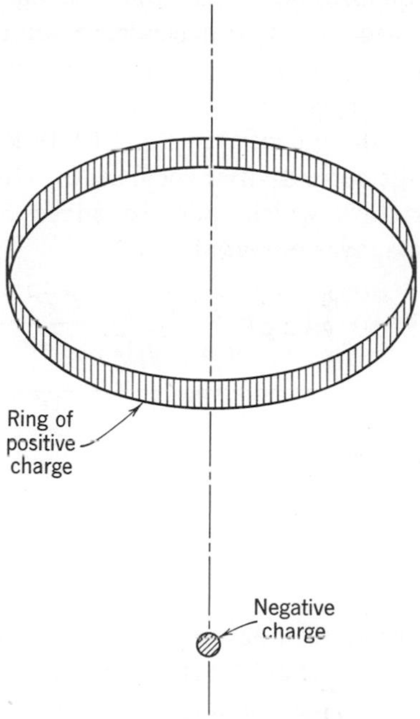

Fig. 3.10–6. Charge distribution used in § 3.10 in studying the importance of dipole-quadrupole interaction in polar molecules.

Let us study the effect of the dipole-quadrupole interaction on the second virial coefficient. The expression for this interaction is considerably more complicated than that for the dipole-dipole interaction, inasmuch as the quadrupole is a tensor and has in general more than one non-zero component. The most important case is that of quadrupoles which have cylindrical symmetry about the dipole axis. This includes distributions of three or more charges along a line or distributions such as that shown in Fig. 3.10–6, where a circular ring of positive charge is located in a plane above a negative charge. For molecules which exhibit this type of symmetry we may represent the interaction potential by a modified Stockmayer potential including a term proportional to r^{-4}, which accounts for the dipole-quadrupole energy:

$$\varphi(r, \theta_1, \theta_2, \phi_2 - \phi_1) = 4\epsilon[(\sigma/r)^{12} - (\sigma/r)^6] - (\mu^2/r^3)g(\theta_1, \theta_2, \phi_2 - \phi_1) - (\tfrac{3}{2}\,\mu Q/r^4)\,h(\theta_1, \theta_2, \phi_2 - \phi_1) \qquad (3.10\text{–}18)$$

in which μ is the dipole moment and Q the cylindrically symmetric quadrupole moment of the molecule.[13] The function g is defined in Eq. 1.3–32, and h has the form

$$h(\theta_1, \theta_2, \phi_2 - \phi_1) = \tfrac{1}{2}(\cos\theta_1 - \cos\theta_2)\,[2\sin\theta_1 \sin\theta_2 \cos(\phi_2 - \phi_1) - 3\cos\theta_1\cos\theta_2 - 1] \quad (3.10\text{–}19)$$

The function h represents the angle dependence of the interaction between the dipole of "1" and the quadrupole of "2" plus the interaction between the quadrupole of "1" and the dipole of "2." Margenau and Myers[14] assumed an angle dependence for the r^{-4} term similar to that for the dipole-dipole term in their calculations of the second virial coefficient for water vapor.

For the potential in Eq. 3.10–18 Rowlinson[12] has derived an expression for the second virial coefficient. His results may be given by stating the correction which must be added to the result in Eq. 3.10–4 for the Stockmayer potential:

$$\Delta B^\star = -\tfrac{1}{2}\left(\frac{4}{T^*}\right) \sum_{n=2}^{\infty} \sum_{k=2}^{n} \sum_{l=1}^{l\geqslant k/2} \frac{2^{n-(l/3)} H_{kl}}{n!} \binom{n}{k} \binom{k}{2l} \Gamma\left(\frac{6n - 3k + 2l - 3}{12}\right) \times T^{*-(6n+3k-2l)/12}\, t^{*k-2l}\, u^{*2l} \quad (3.10\text{–}20)$$

The coefficients H_{kl}, which result from the integrations over angles, are

$$H_{kl} = \frac{1}{8\pi} \int_0^{2\pi}\int_0^{\pi}\int_0^{\pi} g^{k-2l} h^{2l} \sin\theta_1 \sin\theta_2 \, d\theta_1\, d\theta_2\, d(\phi_2 - \phi_1) \quad (3.10\text{–}21)$$

and $u^* = (3/\sqrt{32})\,(\mu Q/\epsilon\sigma^4)$. Although this expression is true only for a cylindrical charge distribution, it may be readily generalized to describe more complex interactions. The number of terms needed in the summation over l in the expression for $\Delta B^\star$ depends on the values of T^*, t^*, and u^* under consideration. For water vapor above 100°C terms with $l > 1$ are negligible, and hence only the coefficients H_{k1} are needed. The first few of these coefficients are shown in Table 3.10–6.[12] Using

TABLE 3.10–6

VALUES OF THE EXPANSION COEFFICIENTS H_{k1}

k	2	3	4	5	6
H_{k1}	0.8889	−0.2844	1.0464	−1.088	2.283

these values, Rowlinson[12] has calculated the parameters for water vapor appropriate for the potential function in Eq. 3.10–18. These parameters,

[13] Q is defined in § 12.1c.

[14] H. Margenau and V. W. Myers, *Phys. Rev.*, **66**, 307 (1944).

along with those for the Stockmayer potential, are given in Table 3.10–7. A comparison of experimental second virial coefficients and those calculated with these two sets of force constants is given in Table 3.10–8.

TABLE 3.10–7

FORCE CONSTANTS FOR WATER VAPOR

Parameter	*Stockmayer Potential*	*Potential in Eq.* 3.10–18
σ	2.65 Å	2.725 Å
ϵ/k	380°K	356°K
t^*	1.2	1.2
u^*	—	0.654

It is seen that the agreement is not improved by including the dipole-quadrupole term, particularly at high temperatures. However, the derived parameters are certainly more reliable when the dipole-quadrupole interaction is included. In particular the value of σ determined from Eq. 3.10–18 is much closer to the intermolecular distance in ice.

TABLE 3.10–8

CALCULATED AND EXPERIMENTAL SECOND VIRIAL COEFFICIENTS FOR WATER VAPOR

	$-B(T)$		
T°C	Experimental[a]	Calculated[7] from Stockmayer Potential	Calculated[12] from Potential in Eq. 3.10–16
100	450	460	450
150	284	290	281
200	197	202	205
300	112	115	123
400	72	74	80

[a] F. G. Keyes, L. B. Smith, H. T. Gerry, *Proc. Am. Acad. Arts Sci.*, **70**, 319 (1936). S. C. Collins and F. G. Keyes, *ibid.*, **72**, 283 (1938).

Rowlinson's calculations show that the contribution to the second virial coefficient of water vapor in the temperature range 100° to 400°C of the dipole-quadrupole interaction is about 25 per cent of that due to the dipole-dipole interaction. Hence the dipole-quadrupole interaction cannot be neglected in virial coefficient calculation for complex polar molecules.

APPENDIX A. KIHARA'S EXPANSION OF THE THIRD VIRIAL COEFFICIENT

The last form given for the third virial coefficient in Eq. 3.4–6 may be easily transformed into[1]

$$C(T) = -4\pi^2\tilde{N}^2 \int_0^{3/4} \int_{1-\sqrt{1-y^2}}^{\sqrt{1-y^2}} \left[\int_0^\infty f_{12} f_{13} f_{23} r_{12}^5 \, dr_{12} \right] dx \, d(y^2) \quad (3.A\text{–}1)$$

The new variables x and y are defined in Fig. 3.A–1 and bear the following relationship to the variables r_{23} and r_{13}:

$$r_{13} = r_{12}\sqrt{x^2 + y^2}$$

$$r_{23} = r_{12}\sqrt{(1 - x^2) + y^2} \quad (3.A\text{–}2)$$

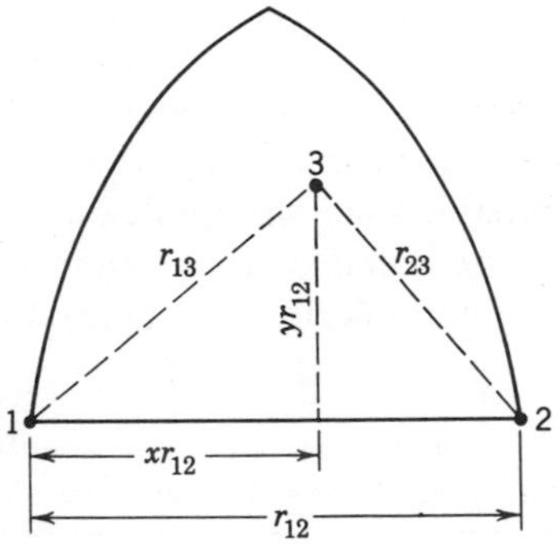

Fig. 3.A–1. Definition of the variables x and y. The spade-shaped region bounded by the solid lines is that region to which the third molecule is restricted to move for a given value of r_{12} consistent with the fact that $r_{13} \leqslant r_{12}$ and $r_{23} \leqslant r_{12}$.

The integration over r_{12} may be performed first, inasmuch as r_{12} does not appear in the limits of the other integration. The integral over r_{12} may be transformed by partial integration to give

$$-\tfrac{1}{6} \int_0^\infty \left[\frac{\partial(f_{12} f_{13} f_{23})}{\partial r_{12}} \right] r_{12}^6 \, dr_{12} \quad (3.A\text{–}3)$$

The product of the f-functions may be written as the sum:

$$f_{12} f_{13} f_{23} = f^{(0)} - \sum_{k=1}^{3} f^{(k)} + \sum_k \sum_{j>k} f_{jk} \quad (3.A\text{–}4)$$

in which

$$f^{(0)} = \exp\left[-\frac{\varphi(r_{12}) + \varphi(r_{23}) + \varphi(r_{13})}{kT} \right] - 1$$

$$f^{(1)} = \exp\left[-\frac{\varphi(r_{12}) + \varphi(r_{13})}{kT} \right] - 1$$

$$f^{(2)} = \exp\left[-\frac{\varphi(r_{12}) + \varphi(r_{23})}{kT} \right] - 1$$

$$f^{(3)} = \exp\left[-\frac{\varphi(r_{13}) + \varphi(r_{23})}{kT} \right] - 1 \quad (3.A\text{–}5)$$

[1] T. Kihara, *J. Phys. Soc. Japan*, **3**, 265 (1948).

The potential function φ is taken to be the general Lennard-Jones potential function of Eq. 1.3–19, with index of repulsion n and index of attraction m. For the moment m is assumed to be greater than 6; presently the limit $m \to 6$ is considered.

After the substitution of Eqs. 3.A–4 and 5 into Eq. 3.A–3, the integration may be performed in a manner similar to that of Eq. 3.6–2. The result is that the bracket in Eq. 3.A–1 is expanded to give

$$-\frac{1}{6}\left(\frac{\nu}{kT}\right)^{6/n}\left[A_0\Gamma\left(\frac{n-6}{n}\right)-\frac{6}{n}\sum_{j=1}^{\infty}A_j\Gamma\left(\frac{jm-6}{n}\right)\frac{t^j}{j!}\right] \quad (3.A\text{–}6)$$

in which $t = (\mu/kT)(kT/\nu)^{m/n}$. The coefficients A_j are functions of the variables x and y and are given by the following expression, in which $\xi^{-1} = \sqrt{x^2 + y^2}$ and $\eta^{-1} = \sqrt{(1-x)^2 + y^2}$:

$$\begin{aligned} A_j = {} & (1+\xi^n+\eta^n)^{6/n}\left[\frac{1+\xi^m+\eta^n}{(1+\xi^n+\eta^m)^{m/n}}\right]^j \\ & -(1+\xi^n)^{6/n}\left[\frac{1+\xi^m}{(1+\xi^n)^{m/n}}\right]^j \\ & -(1+\eta^n)^{6/n}\left[\frac{1+\eta^m}{(1+\eta^n)^{m/n}}\right]^j \\ & -(\xi^n+\eta^n)^{6/n}\left[\frac{\xi^m+\eta^n}{(\xi^n+\eta^n)^{m/n}}\right]^j \\ & +(1+\xi^6+\eta^6) \end{aligned} \quad (3.A\text{–}7)$$

Substitution of the expression in Eq. 3.A–6 into Eq. 3.A–1 and subsequent integration of the A_j over x and y gives[2]

$$C(T) = b_0^2 \sum_{j=0}^{\infty} c^{(j)}(m,n)\left(\frac{m}{n-m}\frac{\epsilon}{kT}\right)^{[j(n-m)+6]/n} \quad (3.A\text{–}8)$$

in which the coefficients $c^{(j)}(m, n)$ are given by the double integrals:

$$c^{(j)}(m,n) = -\frac{18}{n}\left(\frac{1}{j!}\right)\left(\frac{n}{m}\right)^j\Gamma\left(\frac{jm-6}{n}\right)\int_0^{3/4}\int_{1-\sqrt{1-y^2}}^{\sqrt{1-y^2}} A_j\,dx\,d(y^2) \quad (3.A\text{–}9)$$

Numerical integration must be used to compute the $c^{(j)}(m, n)$, although for the higher j values analytical integration is possible by the method of steepest descents, and simple asymptotic formulae thus result. The

[2] $b_0 = \frac{2}{3}\pi\tilde{N}\sigma^3$, and σ is the value of r for which $\varphi(r) = 0$. ϵ is the maximum energy of attraction.

coefficient $c^{(1)}(6, n)$ contains $\Gamma[(m - 6)/n]$, with $m = 6$. However, it has been shown by Kihara[1] that

$$\lim_{m\to 6} A_1\Gamma\left(\frac{m-6}{n}\right) = \ln\frac{(1+\xi^n)(1+\eta^n)}{1+\xi^n+\eta^n} + \xi^6 \ln\frac{(1+\xi^n)(\xi^n+\eta^n)}{\xi^n(1+\xi^n+\eta^n)}$$
$$+ \eta^6 \ln\frac{(1+\eta^n)(\xi^n+\eta^n)}{\eta^n(1+\xi^n+\eta^n)} \quad (3.A\text{–}10)$$

For the Lennard-Jones (6-12) potential the expression for $C(T)$ assumes the form given in Eq. 3.6–10, and the expansion coefficient $c^{(j)}(6, 12)$ are given in Table I–E. Kihara[3] has also computed the expansion coefficients $c^{(j)}(6, 9)$.

APPENDIX B. THE THERMODYNAMIC PROPERTIES IN TERMS OF THE EQUATION OF STATE AND THE VIRIAL COEFFICIENTS

The deviations of the thermodynamic functions from the ideal values may be written in terms of the equation of state or the virial coefficients. In this appendix we tabulate expressions for the various functions directly in terms of the equation of state, in terms of the virial coefficients, and in terms of the reduced virial coefficients, the reduced molar volume, $V^\star = \tilde{V}/b_0$, and the reduced temperature $T^* = kT/\epsilon$.

1. *Internal Energy*

$$\tilde{U} - \tilde{U}^0 = -\int_{\tilde{V}}^{\infty} \left\{T\left(\frac{\partial p}{\partial T}\right)_{\tilde{V}} - p\right\} d\tilde{V} \quad (3.B\text{–}1)$$

$$\tilde{U} - \tilde{U}^0 = -RT\left\{\frac{T}{\tilde{V}}\frac{dB}{dT} + \frac{T}{2\tilde{V}^2}\frac{dC}{dT} + \cdots\right\}$$

$$\frac{U - U^0}{\tilde{N}\epsilon} = -T^*\left\{\frac{B_1^\star}{V^\star} + \frac{1}{2}\frac{C_1^\star}{(V^\star)^2} + \cdots\right\}$$

2. *Enthalpy*

$$\tilde{H} - \tilde{H}^0 = p\tilde{V} - RT - \int_{\tilde{V}}^{\infty} \left\{T\left(\frac{\partial p}{\partial T}\right)_{\tilde{V}} - p\right\} d\tilde{V} \quad (3.B\text{–}2)$$

$$\tilde{H} - \tilde{H}^0 = RT\left\{\frac{1}{\tilde{V}}\left[B - T\frac{dB}{dT}\right] + \frac{1}{\tilde{V}^2}\left[C - \frac{1}{2}T\frac{dC}{dT}\right] + \cdots\right\}$$

$$\frac{\tilde{H} - \tilde{H}^0}{\tilde{N}\epsilon} = T^*\left\{\frac{B^\star - B_1^\star}{V^\star} + \frac{C^\star - \frac{1}{2}C_1^\star}{(V^\star)^2} + \cdots\right\}$$

[3] T. Kihara, *J. Phys. Soc. Japan*, **6**, 184 (1951).

3. *Entropy*[1]

$$\tilde{S} - \tilde{S}^0 = -R \ln p + R \ln \frac{p\tilde{V}}{RT} - \int_{\tilde{V}}^{\infty} \left[\left(\frac{\partial p}{\partial T} \right)_{\tilde{V}} - \frac{R}{\tilde{V}} \right] d\tilde{V} \qquad (3.B\text{–}3)$$

$$\tilde{S} - \tilde{S}^0 = -R \left\{ \ln p + \frac{T}{\tilde{V}} \frac{dB}{dT} + \frac{B^2}{2\tilde{V}^2} - \frac{C}{2\tilde{V}^2} + \frac{T}{2\tilde{V}^2} \frac{dC}{dT} + \cdots \right\}$$

$$\frac{\tilde{S} - \tilde{S}^0}{R} = -\ln p - \left\{ \frac{B_1^\star}{V^\star} + \frac{(B^\star)^2 - C^\star + C_1^\star}{2(V^\star)^2} + \cdots \right\}$$

4. *Heat Capacity at Constant Volume*

$$\tilde{C}_v - \tilde{C}_v^0 = -T \int_{\tilde{V}}^{\infty} \left(\frac{\partial^2 p}{\partial T^2} \right)_{\tilde{V}} d\tilde{V} \qquad (3.B\text{–}4)$$

$$\tilde{C}_v - \tilde{C}_v^0 = -R \left\{ \frac{2T}{\tilde{V}} \frac{dB}{dT} + \frac{T^2}{\tilde{V}} \frac{d^2B}{dT^2} + \frac{T}{\tilde{V}^2} \frac{dC}{dT} + \frac{T^2}{2\tilde{V}^2} \frac{d^2C}{dT^2} + \cdots \right\}$$

$$\frac{\tilde{C}_v - \tilde{C}_v^0}{R} = -\frac{2B_1^\star + B_2^\star}{V^\star} - \frac{2C_1^\star + C_2^\star}{2(V^\star)^2} + \cdots$$

5. *Heat Capacity at Constant Pressure*

$$\tilde{C}_p - \tilde{C}_p^0 = -R - \frac{T \left(\dfrac{\partial p}{\partial T} \right)_{\tilde{V}}^2}{\left(\dfrac{\partial p}{\partial \tilde{V}} \right)_T} - T \int_{\tilde{V}}^{\infty} \left(\frac{\partial^2 p}{\partial T^2} \right)_{\tilde{V}} d\tilde{V} \qquad (3.B\text{–}5)$$

$$\tilde{C}_p - \tilde{C}_p^0 = -R \left\{ \frac{T^2}{\tilde{V}} \frac{d^2B}{dT^2} - \frac{\left\{ B - T \dfrac{dB}{dT} \right\}^2 - C + T \dfrac{dC}{dT} - \dfrac{T^2}{2} \dfrac{d^2C}{dT^2}}{\tilde{V}^2} + \cdots \right\}$$

$$\frac{\tilde{C}_p - \tilde{C}_p^0}{R} = -\frac{B_2^\star}{V^\star} + \frac{\{B^\star - B_1^\star\}^2 - C^\star + C_1^\star - \frac{1}{2} C_2^\star}{(V^\star)^2} + \cdots$$

[1] The ideal value $\tilde{S}^0$ is defined in such a way that in the limit as $p \to 0$,
$\tilde{S} \to \tilde{S}^0 - R \ln p$.

6. *Joule-Thomson Coefficient*

$$\mu = \frac{1}{\tilde{C}_p}\left[T\left(\frac{\partial \tilde{V}}{\partial T}\right)_p - \tilde{V}\right] \tag{3.B–6}$$

$$\mu = \frac{1}{\tilde{C}_p{}^0}\left[T\frac{dB}{dT} - B + \frac{1}{\tilde{V}}\left[\begin{matrix} 2B^2 - 2TB\dfrac{dB}{dT} - 2C + T\dfrac{dC}{dT} \\ + \dfrac{RT^2}{C_p{}^0}\dfrac{d^2B}{dT^2}\left(T\dfrac{dB}{dT} - B\right)\end{matrix}\right] + \cdots\right]$$

$$\frac{\mu\tilde{C}_p{}^0}{b_0} = B_1{}^\star - B^\star + \frac{1}{V^\star}\left[\begin{matrix} 2(B^\star)^2 - 2B^\star B_1{}^\star - 2C^\star + C_1{}^\star \\ + \dfrac{R}{\tilde{C}_p{}^0} B_2{}^\star(B_1{}^\star - B^\star)\end{matrix}\right] + \cdots$$

7. *The Velocity of Sound*

$$c_0{}^2 = -\frac{\gamma V^2}{M}\left(\frac{\partial p}{\partial V}\right)_T \tag{3.B–7}$$

$$c_0{}^2 = \frac{\gamma^0 RT}{M}\left[1 + \frac{1}{\tilde{V}}\left\{2B + 2(\gamma^0 - 1)T\frac{dB}{dT} + \frac{(\gamma^0 - 1)^2}{\gamma^0}T^2\frac{d^2B}{dT^2}\right\} + \cdots\right]$$

$$c_0{}^2 = \frac{\gamma^0 RT}{M}\left[1 + \frac{1}{V^\star}\left\{2B^\star + 2(\gamma^0 - 1)B_1{}^\star + \frac{(\gamma^0 - 1)^2}{\gamma^0}B_2{}^\star\right\} + \cdots\right]$$

in which $\gamma = \tilde{C}_p/\tilde{C}_v$.

PROBLEMS

1. Derive the *caloric equation of state* (see footnote 1 of § 3.1) by two methods: (a) Use the relationship given in Chapter 2 between the internal energy and the partition function. (b) Use the fact that the internal energy of a gas or liquid at a given temperature and volume is the average over a canonical ensemble of the classical Hamiltonian for the system. Show that the results from the two derivations are in agreement.

2. Assume in § 3.2 that the U_l with $l \geqslant 3$ are all identically zero. Carry through the derivation of the equation of state and obtain an expression for the second virial coefficient.

3. Derive the expression for the change in volume when a_1 moles of A_1 are mixed with a_2 moles of A_2 and simplify the result by expanding and keeping only first order terms in the density. We see from this result that the volume change depends upon the forces between like molecules as well as upon the forces between unlike molecules.

4. At low temperatures the curve of pV versus p has a minimum, which is called the *Boyle point*. As the temperature is increased, the Boyle point shifts towards smaller and smaller values of the pressure. Finally for one temperature (the *Boyle* temperature)

the point of zero slope occurs at $p = 0$. Above this temperature the isotherms have no point of zero slope. Show that, for the Boyle temperature, $B(T) = 0$. Then use this fact to calculate ϵ/k for the Lennard-Jones (6-12) potential from the Boyle temperatures of the following four gases:

Air, 74°C	Argon, 137°C
Nitrogen, 50°C	Oxygen, 150°C

5. At low temperatures the Joule-Thomson coefficient is positive, which means that an isenthalpic expansion results in cooling. At high temperatures the Joule-Thomson coefficient is negative, which corresponds to heating by throttling. For any pressure there is a temperature at which the Joule-Thomson coefficient changes sign (*an inversion point*). The temperature at which the zero-pressure Joule-Thomson coefficient changes sign is called the *inversion temperature.* Show that for the inversion temperature $d(B/T)/dT$ is zero. Would an inversion temperature be expected for molecules which behave as point centers of repulsion?

6. Using the tables prepared for the Lennard-Jones potential, calculate: (a) The volume change when 4 liters of N_2 and 1 liter of O_2 are mixed at 10 atm pressure and 300°K. (b) The second virial coefficient at −50°C for a mixture of 10 mole per cent CH_4, 50 mole per cent CO_2, and 40 mole per cent N_2.

7. Using the tables prepared for the Stockmayer potential, calculate: (a) The compressibility factor, $p\tilde{V}/RT$, of steam at 600°C and 50 atm pressure. (b) The change in volume when 10 liters of argon are mixed with 5 liters of ammonia at 50 atm pressure and 500°C. (c) The zero-pressure Joule-Thomson coefficient at 400°K for a mixture of 25 mole per cent air and 75 mole per cent methyl fluoride.

8. Plot the potential function:

$$\varphi(r) = \infty \qquad r < \sigma$$

$$\varphi(r) = -ne\epsilon\left(\frac{\sigma}{r}\right)^n \ln\left(\frac{r}{\sigma}\right) \qquad r > \sigma$$

What is the meaning of the parameters n, ϵ, and σ? Show that the second virial coefficient for this potential is:

$$B(T) = -2\pi\tilde{N}\sigma^3 \sum_{j=0}^{\infty} \frac{u^j}{(nj-3)^{j+1}} \qquad u = \frac{n\epsilon e^{1/n}}{kT}$$

9. For non-spherical molecules, a potential of the form

$$\varphi(r, \theta_1, \theta_2, \phi_2 - \phi_1) = \varphi_1(r) + \varphi_2(r)[\cos^2\theta_1 + \cos^2\theta_2]$$

may be used. Show that for this potential the classical second virial coefficient is given by

$$B(T) = -2\pi\tilde{N}\int_0^\infty \left[\frac{kT}{\varphi_2} e^{-\varphi_1/kT}\left(\frac{\sqrt{\pi}}{2}\,\mathrm{erf}\sqrt{\frac{\varphi_2}{Tk}}\right)^2 - 1\right] r^2\, dr$$

10. Use the Yntema-Schneider potential for the interaction of two He atoms as given by Eq. 3.9–2 to calculate the second virial coefficient at 300°K by numerical integration. Compare this value with that given by the best potential of the Lennard-Jones (6-12) form.

· 4 ·

The Equation of State of Dense Gases and Liquids

In the preceding chapter it is shown that the equation of state may be developed by two methods: (i) the partition function method and (ii) the pair distribution function method. It is further shown that both methods lead to an expression for the compressibility factor as a power series in the density. This virial expansion is used quite successfully to explain quantitatively the equilibrium properties of gases at low and moderate densities. It may also be used to give a qualitative explanation of condensation and critical phenomena; this is discussed in Chapter 5.

In this chapter we discuss the extensions of the above two methods to the high-density region. The *partition function method* may be applied by making various approximations to the true partition function for N molecules. These approximations form the basis for the so-called lattice theories or free volume theories. The lattice theories, in turn, fall into two general categories: the "cell theories", in which each molecule is confined to a cell but no account is taken of the fact that some cells are really empty, and the "hole theories", which account for vacant cells. Extensive calculations have been made for these lattice theories.

The *pair distribution function method* may be applied to the high-density region by obtaining the solution of an approximate integral equation for the pair distribution function. The comparatively few numerical results obtained as yet are in reasonable agreement with experimental values, and the method appears to be of value.

Although a great deal has been learned in recent years during the development of these various theories, much work, both theoretical and numerical, will have to be done before an adequate description of the properties of dense gases and liquids is achieved. Because of the shortcomings of the present theories, we begin this chapter with a discussion of the principle of corresponding states. This principle has been useful in the correlation of the various properties of substances, and, it is the basis for the Hougen and Watson[1] generalized compressibility charts.

[1] O. A. Hougen and K. M. Watson, *Chemical Process Principles*, Wiley (1947), Part II, Ch. XII.

We also present a short discussion of some of the empirical equations of state.

1. The Principle of Corresponding States[2]

The principle of corresponding states is a useful guide for estimating the behavior of dense gases and liquids. This principle, in the form originally stated by van der Waals, is based on the reduction of the variables using the critical constants. This formulation is the basis of the generalized compressibility charts of Hougen and Watson. In another form of the principle of corresponding states, the variables are reduced by means of molecular constants. In this form it is possible to introduce additional parameters so as to extend the principle, in a theoretically sound manner, to the study of various types of molecules—long molecules, polar molecules, and light molecules for which quantum effects[3] are important.

a. The empirical principle of corresponding states

The critical point is defined as that point for which both $(\partial p/\partial V)_T$ and $(\partial^2 p/\partial V^2)_T$ are zero; the values of the pressure, volume, and temperature at this point—the critical constants—are designated by p_c, $\tilde{V}_c$, and T_c, respectively. We may use these constants to define a set of reduced variables:

$$p_r = p/p_c \qquad V_r = \tilde{V}/\tilde{V}_c \qquad T_r = T/T_c \tag{4.1–1}$$

The *empirical principle of corresponding states* may then be stated in the form: "All substances obey the same equation of state in terms of the reduced variables." In general, the state of a system may be described by any two of the three variables: pressure, volume, and temperature. Thus, according to the principle of corresponding states, any dimensionless group is a universal function of any two of the three reduced variables. In particular the compressibility factor, $p\tilde{V}/RT$, can be written as a universal function of the reduced volume and temperature,

$$p\tilde{V}/RT = F(V_r, T_r) \tag{4.1–2}$$

For actual systems, it is usually somewhat more convenient to use the reduced pressure and temperature as the parameters. In this form,

$$p\tilde{V}/RT = z(p_r, T_r) \tag{4.1–3}$$

[2] This discussion of the principle of corresponding states is confined to *p-V-T* properties. The same ideas may be applied to the transport properties (see § 9.1).

[3] The principle of corresponding states in quantum mechanics is discussed in § 6.6 (*p-V-T* properties) and § 10.4 (transport properties).

According to the principle of corresponding states both F and z are universal functions, identical for all substances.

In terms of the reduced parameters, the critical point[4] occurs at $V_r = 1$ and $T_r = 1$. Thus from Eq. 4.1–2 we note that at the critical point

$$p_c\tilde{V}_c/RT_c = F(1, 1) \tag{4.1–4}$$

Thus the value of the critical ratio—the compressibility at the critical point—should be a universal constant. The critical ratios for a number of substances are shown in Table 4.1–1. The simple molecules which are essentially spherical and non-polar have values of the critical ratio quite close to 0.292. Hence these molecules would seem likely to satisfy a single equation of state in reduced variables.

Also shown in Table 4.1–1 are the values of the critical ratio for some hydrocarbons. For these substances $p_c\tilde{V}_c/RT_c$ is approximately 0.267. Hence we would expect the hydrocarbons to satisfy a single reduced equation of state, but one which is different from that appropriate for the spherical molecules. Most of the hydrocarbons are more or less ellipsoidal in shape. Kamerlingh Onnes realized quite early that substances containing molecules of the same general shape should have similar bulk properties. He termed this the *principle of mechanical equivalence.*

A number of polar gases are also listed in Table 4.1–1. Along with the values of the critical ratio are the values of $t^* = (\mu^2/\epsilon\sigma^3\sqrt{8})$, which is a characteristic parameter for polar molecules (see § 3.10). The critical ratio may be seen to vary from 0.269 down to 0.181 as the parameter t^* increases. It is therefore apparent that a single principle of corresponding states can apply to all substances (irrespective of the shape, mass, and dipole moment) only in a very rough and approximate sense.

From the statement of the principle of corresponding states, Eq. 4.1–2, it follows that

$$p_r = \left(\frac{RT_c}{p_c\tilde{V}_c}\right)\left(\frac{T_r}{V_r}\right)F(V_r, T_r) \tag{4.1–5}$$

Since the same expression implies that the critical ratio $(p_c\tilde{V}_c/RT_c)$ is a universal number, it follows that p_r is a universal function of V_r and T_r:

$$p_r = G(V_r, T_r) \tag{4.1–6}$$

The nature of this dependence is indicated in Fig. 4.1–1.

[4] From Eq. 4.1–2 it follows that

$$p = \frac{RT_c}{\tilde{V}_c}\left[\frac{T_r}{V_r}F(V_r, T_r)\right]$$

Now, applying the definition of the critical point, we obtain from this equation two equations involving only V_r, T_r, the function, F, and its first two derivatives. These equations are then conditions on the function at the point (1, 1), which are satisfied if the function represents the experimental compressibility.

TABLE 4.1–1

THE COMPRESSIBILITY FACTOR, $p\tilde{V}/RT$, AT THE CRITICAL POINT

Simple Almost Spherical Non-polar Molecules

Substance	$p_c\tilde{V}_c/RT_c$	*Substance*	$p_c\tilde{V}_c/RT_c$
He	0.300	Xe	0.293
H_2	0.304	N_2	0.292
Ne	0.296	O_2	0.292
A	0.291	CH_4	0.290
		CO_2	0.287

Hydrocarbons

Substance	$p_c\tilde{V}_c/RT_c$	*Substance*	$p_c\tilde{V}_c/RT_c$
Ethane	0.267	Benzene	0.265
Propane	0.270	Cyclohexane	0.276
Isobutane	0.276	Diisopropyl	0.266
n-Butane	0.257	Diisobutyl	0.262
Isopentane	0.268	Ethyl ether	0.262
n-Pentane	0.266	Ethylene	0.291
n-Hexane	0.260	Propylene	0.273
n-Heptane	0.258	Acetylene	0.275
n-Octane	0.258		

Polar Molecules

Substance	$p_c\tilde{V}_c/RT_c$	$t^* = \left(\frac{\mu^2}{\epsilon\sigma^3\sqrt{8}}\right)$
CH_3CN	0.181	1.2
H_2O	0.224	1.2
NH_3	0.238	1.0
CH_3OH	0.220	0.8
CH_3Cl	0.258	0.6
C_2H_5Cl	0.269	0.2

The principle of corresponding states provides a convenient and rough means for determining the properties of a dense gas or a liquid. The only information required is the value of two of the critical constants for the substance under consideration. The critical volume is extremely difficult to measure with even moderate precision, and consequently it is usually more convenient to use the expression for the compressibility in terms of p_r and T_r (Eq. 4.1–3), rather than in terms of V_r and T_r (Eq. 4.1–2). The values of the critical constants may in turn be estimated from more readily available data such as the boiling point, melting point, parachor, and liquid density.[1] Hence very meager information is needed to estimate the equation of state behavior of a substance to within 10 or 15 per cent.

Empirically it has been found that[5]

$$T_b = \tfrac{2}{3}T_c \qquad (4.1\text{–}7)^{6,7}$$

$$T_m = \tfrac{2}{5}T_c \qquad (4.1\text{–}8)^{8}$$

$$\tilde{V}_b^{(\text{liq})} = 0.376\tilde{V}_c \qquad (4.1\text{–}9)^{9}$$

$$\tilde{V}_m^{(\text{sol})} = 0.321\tilde{V}_c \qquad (4.1\text{–}10)^{9}$$

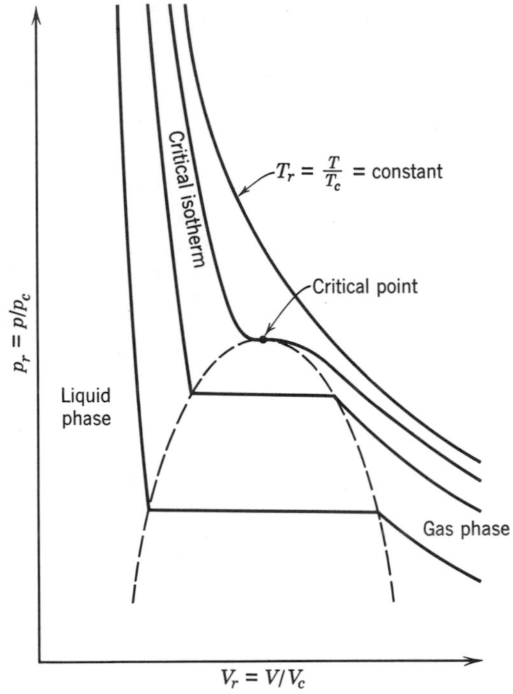

Fig. 4.1–1. Characteristic pattern of isotherms.

The first of these relations, which is known as *Guldberg's Rule* (and was proposed independently by Guye), states that at one atmosphere pressure the boiling point (on an absolute scale) is approximately two-thirds of the critical temperature. Actually the principle of corresponding states

[5] A detailed discussion of empirical relations of this type is given by J. R. Partington, *Treatise on Physical Chemistry* (Longmans, Green (1949)), Vol. I, Sec. 7.

[6] Guldberg, *Z. physik. Chem.*, **5**, 374 (1890).

[7] Guye, *Bull. soc. chim.*, **4**, 262 (1890).

[8] Clark, *Am. Chem. J.*, **18**, 618 (1896); *Z. physik. Chem.*, **21**, 183 (1896). van Laar, *Ann. physik Boltzmann Festschr.*, 316 (1904). Lorenz and Herz, *Z. anorg. Chem.*, **116**, 103 (1921).

[9] Lorenz, *Z. anorg. Chem. u. allgem. Chem.*, **94**, 240 (1916). Herz, *Z. Elektrochem.*, **25**, 215 (1919). Lorenz and Herz, *Z. anorg. Chem. u. allgem. Chem.*, **138**, 331 (1924).

suggests that the boiling point at a fixed reduced pressure (that is, at a fixed fraction of the critical pressure) is a universal fraction of the critical temperature. Thus the comparison of the boiling points at one atmosphere pressure, rather than at a particular value of the reduced pressure p/p_c, can be justified only to the extent that the critical pressures of most substances are of the same order of magnitude, and the boiling point (on an absolute scale) is relatively insensitive to the pressure. Trends in the value of the ratio T_b/T_c with molecular weight are observed for homologous series; this is to be expected because of the corresponding trend in the critical pressure. However, we would not expect that the analogous relations for the melting point would hold with any appreciable accuracy for the following reasons: Some molecules rotate in the liquid phase but not in the crystal. Sometimes the melting process is accompanied by a change in the basic lattice structure (the number of nearest neighbors and the symmetry type). Then, too, quantum effects may be important in the crystal and not in the liquid. For these reasons, the phenomena of melting may be quite different for different substances, and the principle of corresponding states would not be expected to apply. Nevertheless, the relations given above may be of value for crude estimates.

b. The Hougen and Watson generalized charts for the compressibility and thermodynamic properties of dense gases and liquids

The practical utilization of the principle of corresponding states has been enhanced by the publication of Hougen and Watson's charts of the generalized compressibility and thermodynamic properties of gases and liquids.[1, 10] These properties are plotted as functions of the reduced pressure, $p_r = p/p_c$, for different values of the reduced temperature, $T_r = T/T_c$. The charts were prepared by averaging data for the following seven gases: H_2, N_2, CO_2, NH_3, CH_4, C_3H_8, C_5H_{12}. Because this group is made up of many types of molecules, the resulting set of curves cannot be expected to reproduce accurately the properties of any one of the gases listed. However, these charts are highly useful in making approximate calculations because of the speed and ease with which the results are obtained. For a complete treatment of the use of the charts, the reader is referred to the original text.[1] Actual calculations are best made from the greatly enlarged charts which are published separately.[10] To indicate the characteristics of these charts, Figs. 4.1–2, 3, 4, and 5 are given.

[10] O. A. Hougen, K. M. Watson, and R. A. Ragatz, *Chemical Process Principles Charts*, Wiley, New York (1960)—Second Edition. Extensive corresponding states charts for light, medium, and heavy hydrocarbons, which are similar to the Hougen and Watson charts, have been given by J. B. Maxwell, *Data Book on Hydrocarbons*, Van Nostrand (1951).

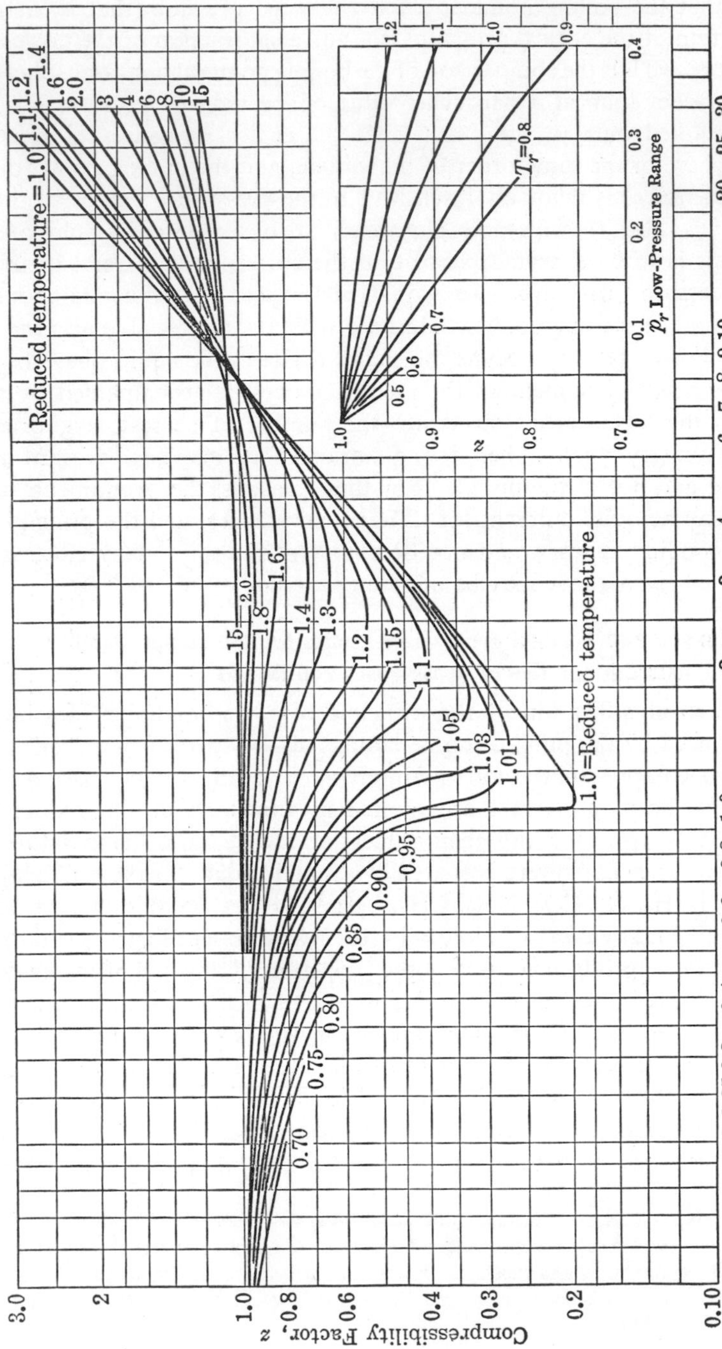

Fig. 4.1-2. The compressibility factor as a function of the reduced pressure and the reduced temperature. [From O. A. Hougen and K. M. Watson, *Chemical Process Principles*, Wiley (1947), Part II.]

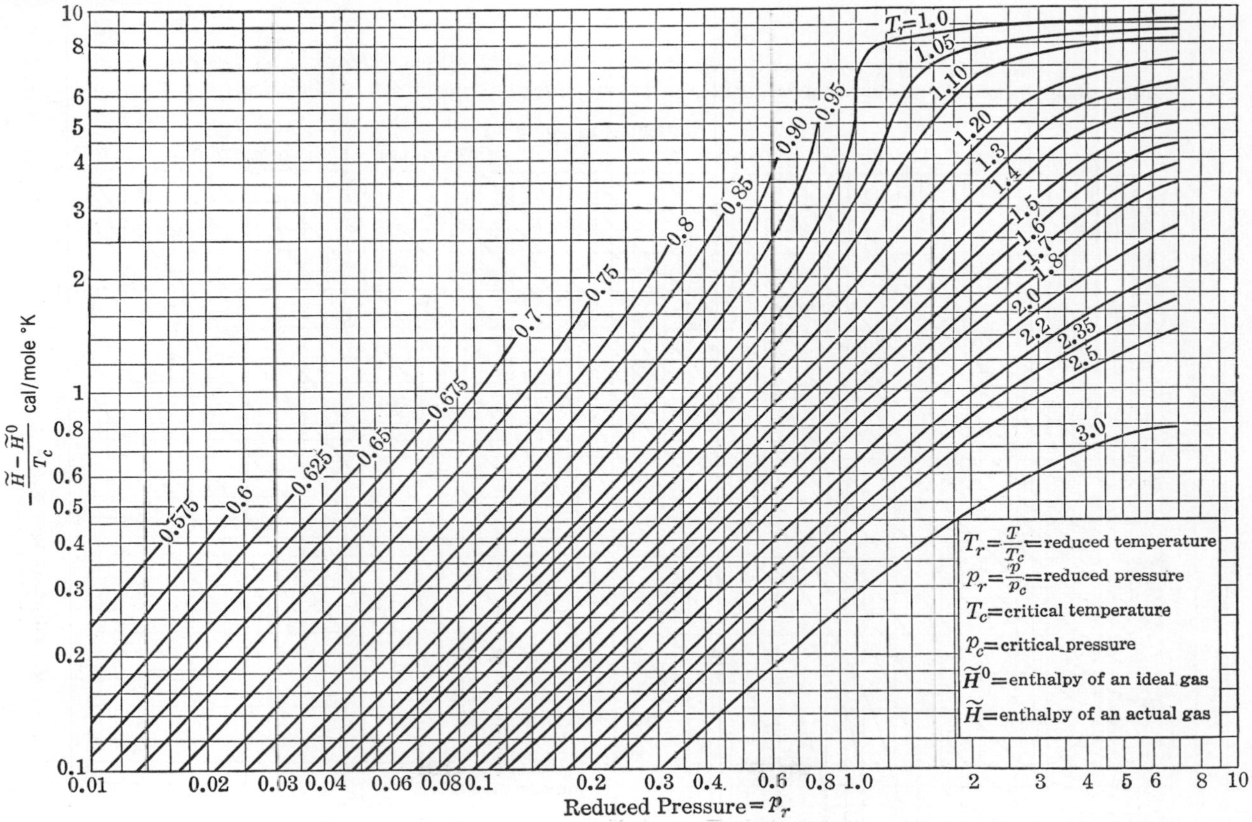

Fig. 4.1–3. The enthalpy of gas imperfection as a function of the reduced pressure and the reduced temperature. [From O. A. Hougen and K. M. Watson, *Chemical Process Principles*, Wiley (1947), Part II.]

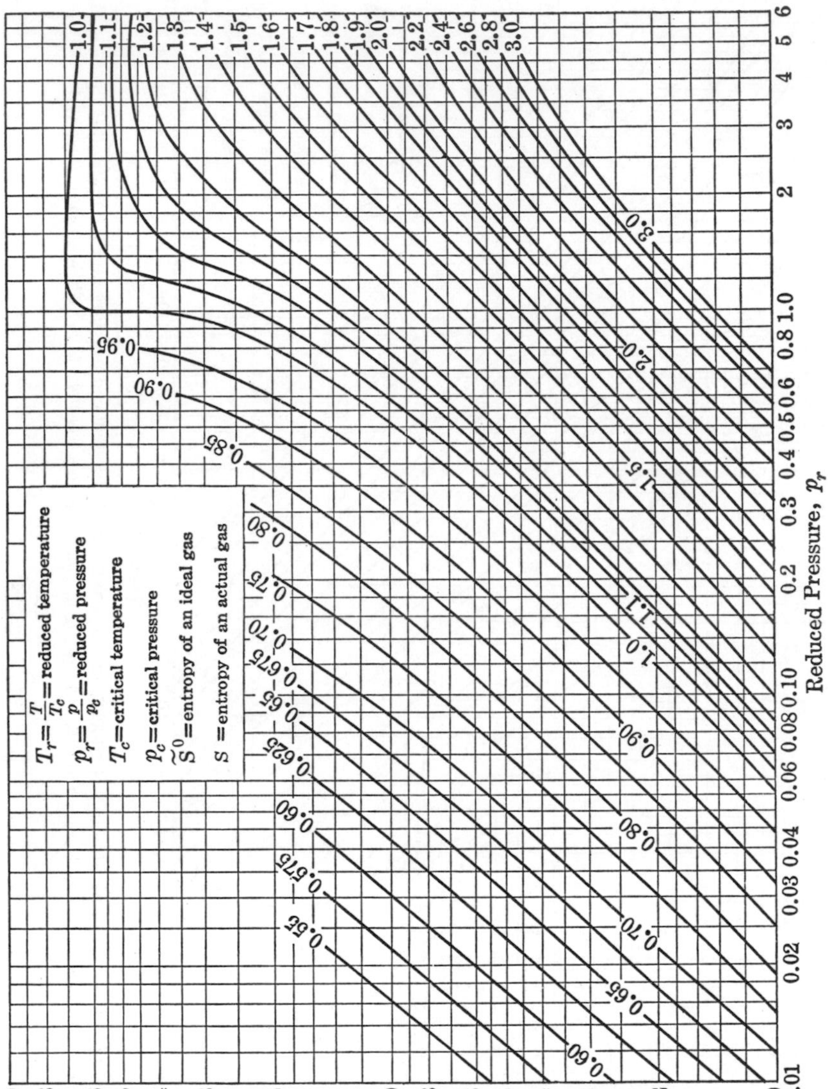

Fig. 4.1–4. The entropy of gas imperfection as a function of the reduced pressure and the reduced temperature. [From O. A. Hougen and K. M. Watson, *Chemical Process Principles*, Wiley (1947), Part II.]

They show the generalized compressibility factor and the non-ideality corrections for the enthalpy, entropy, and heat capacity of dense gases. The charts which show the pressure corrections to the various thermodynamic properties were obtained by using the generalized compressibility

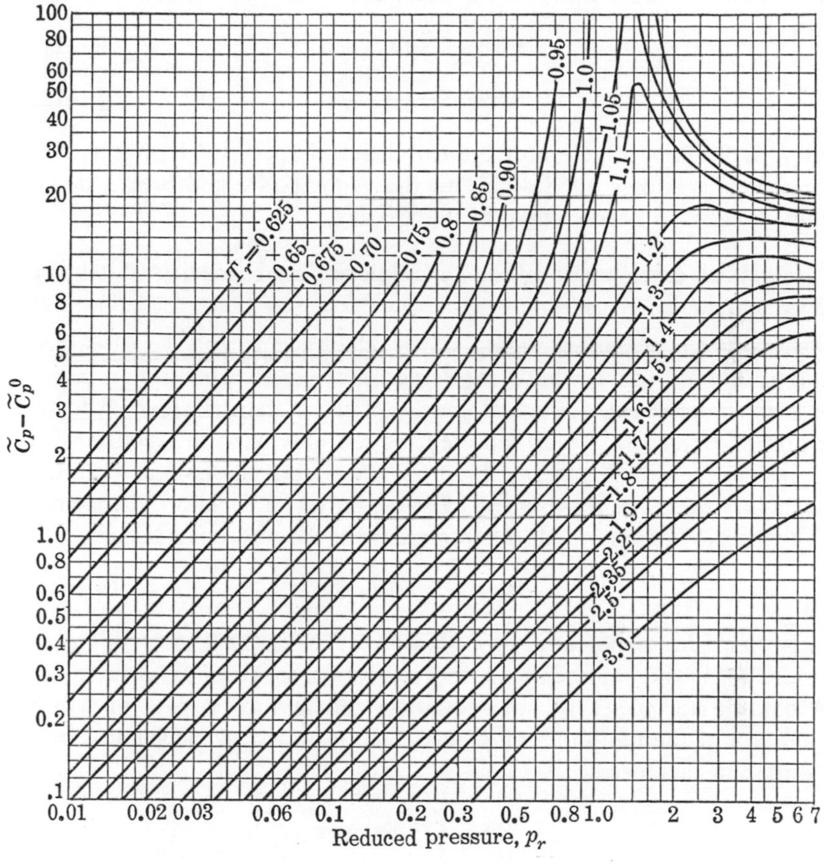

Fig. 4.1-5. The heat capacity of gas imperfection as a function of the reduced pressure and the reduced temperature. [From O. A. Hougen and K. M. Watson, *Chemical Process Principles*, Wiley (1947), Part II.]

factor together with standard thermodynamic relations (see Appendix 3.B). The symbols with superscript "0" denote properties of ideal gases (that is, values applying in the limit of low pressures) and the unmarked symbols refer to the properties of the real gas. Other Hougen and Watson charts are available for the following properties:

Gases. Fugacity, viscosity.

Liquids. Enthalpy correction, entropy correction, thermal expansion and compression, heat capacity correction, differential effect of pressure upon enthalpy.

These charts are often used in connection with mixtures. It is observed that to a good approximation a mixture behaves as a single component with critical constants equal to the molar averages:

$$T_c' = \Sigma_i x_i (T_c)_i \tag{4.1–11}$$

$$p_c' = \Sigma_i x_i (p_c)_i \tag{4.1–12}$$

Here x_i is the mole fraction of the ith chemical species. However, this treatment of mixtures applies only to the vapor phase and breaks down within or near the border curve of the mixture.

c. Theoretical development of the principle of corresponding states for spherical non-polar gases

The existence of corresponding states relationships may be explained theoretically for gases whose molecules are spherical and non-polar. For such molecules the potential energy of the system is assumed to be the sum of terms $\varphi(r_{ij})$ each representing the energy of interaction of a pair of molecules. Furthermore, it is reasonable to assume that the potentials $\varphi(r)$ can be represented by some universal function, f, together with two scale factors σ and ϵ characteristic of the molecular species:

$$\varphi(r) = \epsilon f(r/\sigma) \tag{4.1–13}$$

The Lennard-Jones potential, $\varphi(r) = 4\epsilon[(\sigma/r)^{12} - (\sigma/r)^6]$, is of this two-constant form and represents an approximation to a universal function.

According to Eq. 3.1–1, the equation of state of a gas (in which the motion of the molecules may be treated by classical mechanics) may be written in this form:

$$p = kT \frac{\partial}{\partial V} \ln \int e^{-\Phi(\mathbf{r}^N)/kT} d\mathbf{r}^N \tag{4.1–14}$$

That is, the pressure depends only on kT, the volume, the two scale factors ϵ and σ in the potential function, and the form of the universal function f. The quantities ϵ and σ may be used to define the reduced variables.[11]

$$p^* = p\sigma^3/\epsilon \qquad V^* = \tilde{V}/\tilde{N}\sigma^3 \qquad T^* = kT/\epsilon \tag{4.1–15}$$

[11] The quantities $p^\star = pb_0/\tilde{N}\epsilon$ and $V^\star = \tilde{V}/b_0$ may also be used for reduced pressure and volume.

Now from these considerations and dimensional analysis, it follows that it is possible to write the reduced pressure as a universal function of the reduced volume and temperature:

$$p^* = p^*(V^*, T^*) \tag{4.1-16}$$

The nature of the function depends only on the nature of the potential function f.

From this form of the law of corresponding states and the definition of the critical point it follows that the critical constants reduced in terms of the molecular constants, p_c^*, V_c^*, and T_c^*, are universal constants. The values given in Table 4.1-2 show that there is considerable spread in these values. For He and H_2 the deviations are due in part to the quantum effects considered in § 6.6.

TABLE 4.1-2

CRITICAL CONSTANTS FOR SOME ALMOST SPHERICAL NON-POLAR MOLECULES REDUCED BY MEANS OF LENNARD-JONES (6-12) FORCE CONSTANTS

Gas	T_c(°K)	$\tilde{V}_c$(cm³)	p_c(atm)	T_c^*	$V_c^\star$	V_c^*	$p_c^\star$	p_c^*	$p_c\tilde{V}_c/RT_c$
He	5.3	57.8	2.26	0.52	2.75	5.75	0.057	0.027	0.300
H_2	33.3	65.0	12.8	0.90	2.05	4.30	0.134	0.064	0.304
Ne	44.5	41.7	25.9	1.25	1.59	3.33	0.232	0.111	0.296
A	151	75.2	48	1.26	1.51	3.16	0.243	0.116	0.291
Xe	289.81	120.2	57.89	1.31	1.38	2.90	0.276	0.132	0.293
N_2	126.1	90.1	33.5	1.33	1.41	2.96	0.274	0.131	0.292
O_2	154.4	74.4	49.7	1.31	1.28	2.69	0.297	0.142	0.292
CH_4	190.7	99.0	45.8	1.29	1.41	2.96	0.264	0.126	0.290

The approximation that p_c^*, V_c^*, and T_c^* are universal constants leads directly to simple methods of estimating the values of the force constants. Thus we obtain the approximate relations for spherical non-polar molecules obeying the Lennard-Jones (6-12) potential:

$$\epsilon/k = 0.77T_c \tag{4.1-17}$$

$$b_0 = 0.75\tilde{V}_c = 18.4T_c/p_c \tag{4.1-18}$$

The relations between the values of T and $\tilde{V}$ at the melting, normal boiling and critical points discussed in § 4.1a then lead to other approximate relations:

$$\epsilon/k = 1.15T_b \tag{4.1-19}$$

$$\epsilon/k = 1.92T_m \tag{4.1-20}$$

$$b_0 = 2.0\tilde{V}_b^{(\text{liq})} \tag{4.1-21}$$

$$b_0 = 2.3\tilde{V}_m^{(\text{sol})} \tag{4.1-22}$$

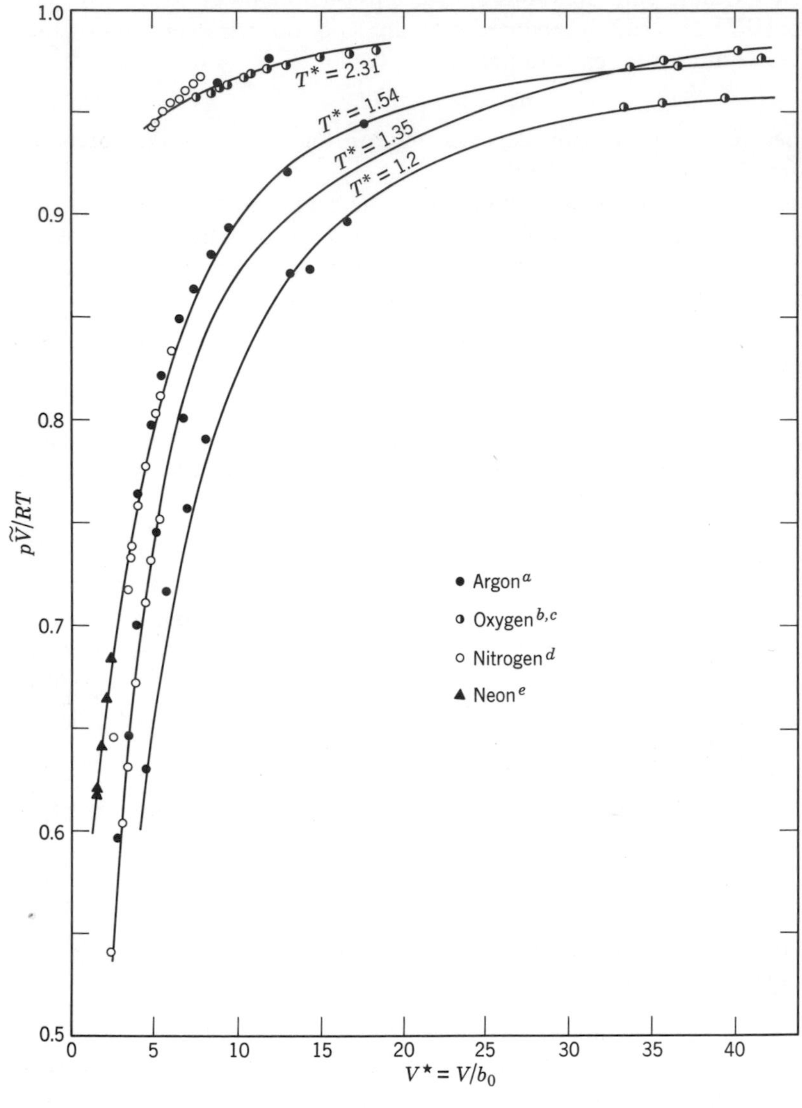

Fig. 4.1–6. The compressibilities of some spherical non-polar gases as a function of the reduced volume $V^\star$ for several values of the reduced temperature T^*. (*a*) H. Kamerlingh Onnes and C. A. Crommelin, *Commn. Phys. Lab. Leiden*, No. 118b (1910). (*b*) G. P. Nijhoff and W. H. Keeson, *ibid.*, No. 179b (1925). (*c*) A. Th. van Urk and G. P. Nijhoff, *ibid.*, No. 169c (1924). (*d*) H. Kamerlingh Onnes and A. Th. van Urk, *ibid.*, No. 169d (1924). (*e*) H. Kamerlingh Onnes and C. A. Crommelin, *ibid.*, No. 147d (1915).

Experimentally it is observed that

$$b_0 = 2.293\tilde{V}_0^{(\text{sol})} \tag{4.1–23}$$

where $\tilde{V}_0^{(\text{sol})}$ is the molar volume of the solid at 0°K. From the table of the second virial coefficient (Table I–B) it is seen that[12]

$$\epsilon/k = 0.292T_B \tag{4.1–24}$$

where T_B is the Boyle temperature. These expressions represent simple methods of estimating intermolecular potentials. To obtain information about any particular molecule somewhat more accuracy may be obtained by applying the principle of corresponding state to molecules of similar structure. The results of these procedures should, however, be considered as rough estimates to be used only when data for more accurate methods are not available.

It is clear from the principle of corresponding states as formulated by Eq. 4.1–16 that the compressibility is a universal function of V^* and T^*, that is,

$$\frac{p\tilde{V}}{RT} = \frac{p^*V^*}{T^*} = \frac{V^*}{T^*}p^*(V^*, T^*) \tag{4.1–25}$$

Experimental verifications of this result are shown in Fig. 4.1–6. Since the reduced parameters at the critical point V_c^* and T_c^* have universal values, the empirical law of corresponding states, Eq. 4.1–2, follows directly from this expression as does the alternate formulation, Eq. 4.1–3.

d. The principles of corresponding states for polyatomic molecules

Several specific examples may be given to illustrate how the principle of corresponding states may be extended to polyatomic molecules. In these examples additional parameters are introduced which describe the internal structure of the molecules. The additional parameters appear in the expression for the reduced equation of state and show clearly what is meant by the idea of mechanical equivalence of Kamerlingh Onnes.

In § 3.8d Corner's "four-center" model of cylindrical molecules was discussed. This model assumes that long molecules (cigar-shaped) may be represented by four centers of force arranged rigidly along a line. The length l specifies the distance between the centers of force in a molecule. The total intermolecular force is given by the sum of the interactions between the force centers, each interaction being of the form shown in Eq. 4.1–13, with parameters ϵ and σ. From the considerations discussed above it follows that the equation of state for such a model has the form

$$p = p(\tilde{V}, kT, \epsilon, \sigma, l) \tag{4.1–26}$$

[12] J. E. Lennard-Jones, *Physica*, **4**, 941 (1937).

Introduction of the reduced variables given in Eq. 4.1–15 and the reduced distance $l^* = l/\sigma$ leads to

$$p^* = p^*(V^*, T^*; l^*) \tag{4.1–27}$$

Hence for cylindrical molecules with the same value of the ratio l^*, the reduced pressure is a universal function of V^* and T^*.

A "round" polyatomic molecule of the type XY_n (such as NH_3, CBr_4, SF_6) may be regarded as a rigid system of n force centers which are identical and occupy equivalent positions at a distance a from the center of the molecule. Then, as in the Corner model, the interaction energy between a pair of molecules is assumed[13] to be the sum of the interactions between these force centers (the central atom being disregarded in these interactions). The potential describing the interactions between the force centers is assumed to be of the form of Eq. 4.1–13. The equation of state for this model is then of the form

$$p = p(\tilde{V}, kT, \epsilon, \sigma, a, n) \tag{4.1–28}$$

Introducing the reduced distance $a^* = a/\sigma$ and the reduced variables given in Eq. 4.1–15, we get from dimensional considerations

$$p^* = p^*(V^*, T^*; a^*, n) \tag{4.1–29}$$

This is another example of more generalized types of corresponding states relationships. Eq. 4.1–29 may also be obtained by substituting the expression for the intermolecular potential into the integral for the classical partition function.[14]

e. The principle of corresponding states for polar molecules

A simple corresponding states relation can be obtained for polar molecules, if the interaction potential is assumed to be of the form

$$\varphi(r) = \epsilon f(r/\sigma) - (\mu^2/r^3)g(\theta_1, \theta_2, \phi_2 - \phi_1) \tag{4.1–30}$$

in which $f(r/\sigma)$ is a universal function of the reduced distance, r/σ, and $g(\theta_1, \theta_2, \phi_2 - \phi_1)$ describes the angle dependence of the interaction of two point dipoles. The equation of state for a substance made up of molecules obeying this type of potential is of the form

$$p = p(\tilde{V}, kT, \epsilon, \sigma, \mu) \tag{4.1–31}$$

The scale factors ϵ and σ may be used to define reduced variables as was done in Eq. 4.1–15, and also a reduced dipole moment, $\mu^* = \mu/\sqrt{\epsilon\sigma^3}$.

[13] The objections raised to the assumption of this type of interaction have been mentioned in a footnote in § 3.8–d.

[14] N. Trappeniers, *Physica*, **17**, 501 (1951).

Then from dimensional considerations the relation between the reduced pressure, volume, and temperature is of the form

$$p^* = p^*(V^*, T^*; \mu^*) \tag{4.1–32}$$

This explains the fact that the various equilibrium properties of polar substances, in dimensionless form, exhibit systematic deviations from the properties of non-polar substances according to the value of μ^* characteristic of the substance. In Chapter 3 the dependence of the virial

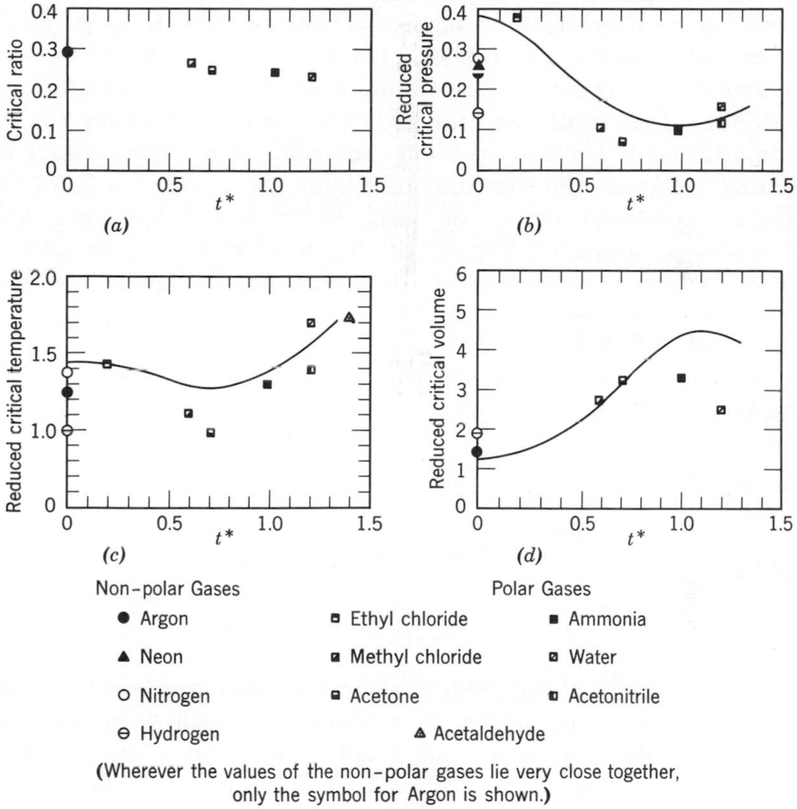

Fig. 4.1–7. The reduced critical constants for polar gases. In this figure are shown the variations of the various reduced critical properties with the parameter $t^* = \mu^{*2}/\sqrt{8}$. In (*a*) is plotted the ratio $p_c\tilde{V}_c/RT_c$ for several polar gases; in (*b*) is shown $p_c^\star = p_c b_o/\tilde{N}\epsilon$; in (*c*) is given $kT_c/\epsilon = T_c^*$; and the reduced critical volume, $V_c^\star = V_c/b_o$, is plotted in (*d*). All these properties vary but slowly with the parameter t^*. Force constants used for the reduction of the critical values are those obtained for the Stockmayer potential from experimental second virial coefficients. [From J. S. Rowlinson, *J. Chem. Phys.*, **19**, 831 (1951).]

coefficients on μ^* was shown explicitly for the Stockmayer potential. Similar behavior can be expected for the vapor pressure curves, melting lines, and critical properties. The variation in the reduced critical constants with the reduced dipole moment is shown in Fig. 4.1–7.[15]

2. Empirical Equations of State

Numerous empirical relations have been proposed for describing the p-V-T behavior of gases and liquids, each of which is designed for a particular application.[1] Some of these equations are quite accurate over a small range of temperature and density; others apply to the properties in the gaseous and liquid phases. First, a discussion is given of several two-constant equations of state—those of van der Waals, Dieterici, and Berthelot. These equations are handy because of their simple analytic form. Of more cumbersome form, but considerably more useful for accurate work, are the equations of Beattie and Bridgeman (with five arbitrary constants) and of Benedict, Webb, and Rubin (with eight adjustable parameters). The section is concluded with a summary of the semi-empirical equations which have been used for liquids.

a. Two-constant equations of state

For a semi-quantitative understanding of the principal features of the equation of state, the following equations are quite useful:

van der Waals:
$$\left(p + \frac{a}{\tilde{V}^2}\right)(\tilde{V} - b) = RT \tag{4.2–1}$$

Berthelot:
$$\left(p + \frac{a}{T\tilde{V}^2}\right)(\tilde{V} - b) = RT \tag{4.2–2}$$

Dieterici:
$$(pe^{a/\tilde{V}RT})(\tilde{V} - b) = RT \tag{4.2–3}$$

The constant a is a measure of the cohesion between the molecules, and b is proportional to the volume of the molecules. All these equations predict a Boyle temperature and a critical isotherm. None of them predicts a maximum in the second virial coefficient as a function of temperature, and the first two equations have temperature-independent third virial coefficients. The critical constants and the virial coefficients for these three simple equations of state are summarized in Table 4.2–1. The Dieterici equation gives a value of $p_c\tilde{V}_c/RT_c$, which is in excellent

[15] J. S. Rowlinson, *J. Chem. Phys.*, **19**, 831 (1951).

[1] Excellent summaries of empirical equations of state may be found in H. S. Taylor and S. Glasstone, *States of Matter*, Van Nostrand (1951), and in J. R. Partington, *Advanced Treatise of Physical Chemistry*, Longmans, Green (1949), Vol. I, Ch. 7.

agreement with the average of the values for twenty-five non-polar gases[2] —0.272. The Dieterici equation is hence remarkably accurate in the neighborhood of the critical point and is the best all-round analytical two-constant equation of state.

It is interesting to compare the second virial coefficient for the van der Waals (or Dieterici) equation with that for the Lennard-Jones potential, which has been shown to represent quite faithfully the behavior of dilute gases. According to the van der Waals equation, the second virial

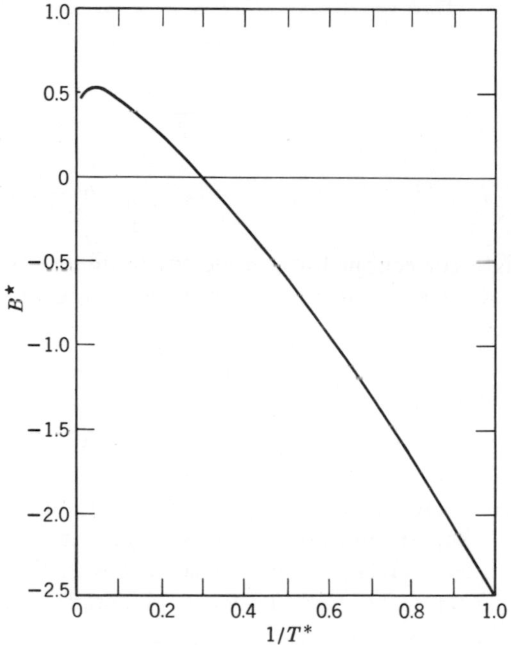

Fig. 4.2–1. $B^\star$ vs. $1/T^*$ for the Lennard-Jones potential.

coefficient is linear in $1/T$. In Fig. 4.2–1 it may be seen that $B(T)$ for the Lennard-Jones potential deviates considerably from linear behavior. This fact explains why the van der Waals constants, a and b, vary a great deal with temperature or with the manner in which they are determined. The maximum in the second virial curve for the Lennard-Jones potential should be noted. It occurs between $T^* = 10$ and $T^* = 100$, which is the important temperature range in combustion and ballistic powder gas problems. In this range the second virial coefficient is very nearly independent of temperature and can be satisfactorily represented by a simple volume equal approximately to $b_0/2$.

[2] J. A. Beattie and W. H. Stockmayer, *Reports on Progress in Physics*, 7, 195 (1940).

TABLE 4.2–1

SUMMARY OF INFORMATION ABOUT TWO-CONSTANT EQUATIONS OF STATE

	van der Waals	*Berthelot*	*Dieterici*
p_c	$\frac{a}{27b^2}$	$\sqrt{\frac{aR}{216b^3}}$	$\frac{a}{4e^2b^2} = \frac{a}{29.56b^2}$
$\tilde{V}_c$	$3b$	$3b$	$2b$
T_c	$\frac{8a}{27bR}$	$\sqrt{\frac{8a}{27bR}}$	$\frac{a}{4bR}$
$p_c\tilde{V}_c/RT_c$	0.375	0.375	0.2706
$B(T)$	$b - \frac{a}{RT}$	$b - \frac{a}{RT^2}$	$b - \frac{a}{RT}$
$C(T)$	b^2	b^2	$b^2 - \frac{ab}{RT} + \frac{a^2}{2R^2T^2}$

For making slight corrections for non-ideality in dilute gases, Berthelot proposed the following expression for the second virial coefficient:

$$B(T) = \frac{9}{128}\frac{RT_c}{p_c}\left[1 - 6\frac{T_c^2}{T^2}\right] \tag{4.2–4}$$

This expression for the second virial coefficient is widely used[3] in the determination of molecular weights from gas densities and in the determination of latent heats from vapor pressures; in both cases small corrections for gas imperfections are involved. The use of Eq. 4.2–4 is justified, inasmuch as it gives excellent agreement with the temperature dependence of $B(T)$ for the Lennard-Jones potential[4] over the range between $T^* = 0.3$ to $T^* = 2$.

The three two-constant equations given above may be applied to mixtures. The parameters a and b are taken to vary in the following manner with composition:

$$a = a_{11}x_1^2 + 2a_{12}x_1x_2 + a_{22}x_2^2 \tag{4.2–5}$$

$$b = b_{11}x_1^2 + 2b_{12}x_1x_2 + b_{22}x_2^2 \tag{4.2–6}$$

The x_i are the mole fractions of the components, and the constants a_{ii} and b_{ii} are just the constants for the pure components. The a_{12} and b_{12}

[3] J. R. Partington, *Advanced Treatise of Physical Chemistry*, Vol. I, Longmans, Green (1949).

[4] J. D. Lambert, G. A. H. Roberts, J. S. Rowlinson, and V. J. Wilkinson, *Proc. Roy. Soc.* (*London*), **A196**, 113 (1949).

are constants characteristic of collisions between unlike molecules. If no experimental data are available to indicate their values, they may be estimated roughly by the empirical combining laws:

$$\sqrt[3]{b_{12}} = \tfrac{1}{2}\,[\sqrt[3]{b_{11}} + \sqrt[3]{b_{22}}] \tag{4.2–7}$$

$$a_{12} = \sqrt{a_{11}a_{22}} \tag{4.2–8}$$

These relations correspond to those given in Eqs. 3.6–8 and 9. Equations 4.2–5 and 6 were originally proposed by van der Waals.[5] In some actual examples they have explained experimental results quite accurately.

b. The Beattie-Bridgeman equation of state[6]

The Beattie-Bridgeman equation is one of the best empirical representations of p-V-T data for gases up to pressures of the order of 250 atm. This equation is:

$$p\tilde{V}^2 = RT\left(1 - \frac{c}{\tilde{V}T^3}\right)\left(\tilde{V} + B_0 - \frac{bB_0}{\tilde{V}}\right) - A_0\left(1 - \frac{a}{\tilde{V}}\right) \tag{4.2–9}$$

The five adjustable constants, A_0, B_0, a, b, and c, have been determined for a large number of gases and are given in Table 4.2–2.

At very high pressures the Beattie-Bridgeman equation fails badly. At very low pressures the equation may be examined by expanding it into the virial form. The second virial coefficient is

$$B(T) = B_0 - (A_0/RT) - (c/T^3) \tag{4.2–10}$$

This expression agrees with the second virial coefficient for the Lennard-Jones potential over a wide range of temperatures, provided that the constant c is properly chosen. In order to have agreement over the physically important range of temperatures, we choose[7]

$$c = 0.0236(A_0^3/R^3B_0^2) \tag{4.2–11}$$

and then

$$\epsilon = 0.04127(A_0/RB_0) \times 10^{-15} \tag{4.2–12}$$

$$b_0 = 1.249B_0 \tag{4.2–13}$$

The first relation may be used as a test of the validity of the Lennard-Jones potential. Table 4.2–3 compares the values of ϵ and b_0, calculated from Eqs. 4.2–12 and 13 with the values determined directly from second virial or viscosity data. In the last two columns the value of c calculated

[5] J. D. van der Waals, *Die Kontinuität des gasförmigen u. flüssigen Zustandes*, Barth, Leipzig (1899, 1900).

[6] J. A. Beattie and O. C. Bridgeman, *J. Am. Chem. Soc.*, **49**, 1665 (1927); *Proc. Am. Acad. Arts Sci.*, **63**, 229 (1928).

[7] J. O. Hirschfelder and W. E. Roseveare, *J. Phys. Chem.*, **43**, 15 (1939).

TABLE 4.2–2

VALUES OF THE CONSTANTS OF THE BEATTIE-BRIDGEMAN EQUATION OF STATE FOR SEVERAL GASES[a]

$$p = [RT(1 - \delta)/\tilde{V}^2]\,[\tilde{V} + B] - A/\tilde{V}^2$$

$$A = A_0(1 - a/\tilde{V}) \qquad B = B_0(1 - b/\tilde{V}) \qquad \delta = c/\tilde{V}T^3$$

Units: Normal atmospheres, liters/mole, °K.

Gas	A_0	a	B_0	b	$c \times 10^{-4}$
He	0.0216	0.05984	0.01400	0.0	0.0040
Ne	0.2125	0.02196	0.02060	0.0	0.101
A	1.2907	0.02328	0.03931	0.0	5.99
Kr[b]	2.4230	0.02865	0.05261	0.0	14.89
Xe[c]	4.6715	0.03311	0.07503	0.0	30.02
H_2	0.1975	−0.00506	0.02096	−0.04359	0.504
N_2	1.3445	0.02617	0.05046	−0.00691	4.20
O_2	1.4911	0.02562	0.04624	0.004208	4.80
Air	1.3012	0.01931	0.04611	−0.01101	4.34
I_2	17.0	0.0	0.325	0.0	4000.
CO_2	5.0065	0.07132	0.10476	0.07235	66.00
NH_3	2.3930	0.17031	0.03415	0.019112	476.87
CH_4	2.2769	0.01855	0.05587	−0.15870	12.83
C_2H_4	6.1520	0.04964	0.12156	0.03597	22.68
C_2H_6	5.8800	0.05861	0.09400	0.01915	90.00
C_3H_8	11.9200	0.07321	0.18100	0.04293	120.00
1-C_4H_8	16.6979	0.11988	0.24046	0.10690	300.00
iso-C_4H_8	16.9600	0.10860	0.24200	0.08750	250.00
n-C_4H_{10}	17.7940	0.12161	0.24620	0.09423	350.00
iso-C_4H_{10}	16.6037	0.11171	0.23540	0.07697	300.00
n-C_5H_{12}	28.2600	0.15099	0.39400	0.13960	400.00
neo-C_5H_{12}	23.3300	0.15174	0.33560	0.13358	400.00
n-C_7H_{16}	54.520	0.20066	0.70816	0.19179	400.00
CH_3OH	33.309	0.09246	0.60362	0.09929	32.03
$(C_2H_5)_2O$	31.278	0.12426	0.45446	0.11954	33.33

[a] H. S. Taylor and S. Glasstone, *States of Matter*, D. Van Nostrand (1951).

[b] Constants obtained from J. A. Beattie, J. S. Brierley, and R. A. Barriault, *J. Chem. Phys.*, **20**, 1613 (1952).

[c] Constants obtained from J. A. Beattie, R. A. Barriault, and J. S. Brierley, *J. Chem. Phys.*, **19**, 1219 (1951).

by Eq. 4.2–11 is compared with the observed value. The agreement is good in those cases in which other evidence would indicate that the Lennard-Jones potential should apply. This seems to form a sensitive criterion for the validity of the Lennard-Jones potential.

The internal energy, U, is one of the most significant properties of

TABLE 4.2–3[6]
VALUES OF b_0, ϵ, AND c

Gas	b_0 (Calculated from Beattie-Bridgeman Constants) (cc/mole)	b_0 (Calculated from Lennard-Jones Potential) (cc/mole)	ϵ (Calculated from Beattie-Bridgeman Constants) (10^{-15} erg)	ϵ (Calculated from Lennard-Jones Potential) (10^{-15} erg)	$c \times 10^{-4}$ (Calculated from Eq. 4.2–11) (liters/degree mole)	$c \times 10^{-4}$ (Observed) (liters/degree mole)
He	17.49	21.17[a]	0.776	1.402	0.00022	0.0040
Ne	25.73	25.95	5.189	4.928	0.0966	0.101
A	49.10	49.80	16.02	16.529	5.942	5.99
H_2	26.18	31.41[a]	4.739	5.075	0.07488	0.0504
N_2	63.02	63.78	13.40	13.12	4.077	4.20
O_2	57.75	57.75	16.22	16.22	6.625	4.80
Air	57.59	55.11	14.19	13.69	4.425	4.34
I_2	405.9		26.30		198.2	4000
CO_2	130.85	113.9	24.03	26.09	48.84	66.00
NH_3	42.65		35.25		50.19	476.87
CH_4	69.78	70.16	20.49	20.46	16.15	12.83
C_2H_4	151.8		25.45		67.30	22.68
C_2H_6	117.4	78	31.46	33.54	98.26	90.00
C_3H_8	226.1	226	33.12	33.40	220.8	120.00
1-C_4H_8	300.3		34.92		343.9	300.00
iso-C_4H_8	302.3		35.25		355.7	250.00
n-C_4H_{10}	307.5	155	36.35	40.99	397.0	350.00
iso-C_4H_{10}	294.0		35.47		352.8	300.00
n-C_5H_{12}	492.1		36.07		620.9	400.00
neo-C_5H_{12}	419.2		34.96		481.5	400.00
n-C_7H_{16}	884.5	884	38.72	38.92	1380	400.00
CH_3OH	753.9		27.75		433200	32.03
$(C_2H_5)_2O$	567.6		34.61		632.7	33.33

[a] These force constants were obtained by fitting the experimental data with the theoretical expression which includes the quantum effects.

equations of state. It can be determined (up to an additive function of the temperature only) from the thermodynamic equation,

$$\underset{\text{Internal pressure}}{\left(\frac{\partial U}{\partial V}\right)_T} = \underset{\text{Thermal pressure}}{T\left(\frac{\partial p}{\partial T}\right)_V} \underset{\text{External pressure}}{- p} \qquad (4.2\text{–}14)$$

The internal pressure $(\partial U/\partial V)_T$ is the difference between the thermal pressure and the external pressure. Integrating $(\partial U/\partial V)_T$ with respect to volume (at constant temperature) gives the internal energy. Thus,

(1) van der Waals:

$$\tilde{U} = \tilde{U}^0(T) - \frac{a}{\tilde{V}} \tag{4.2–15}$$

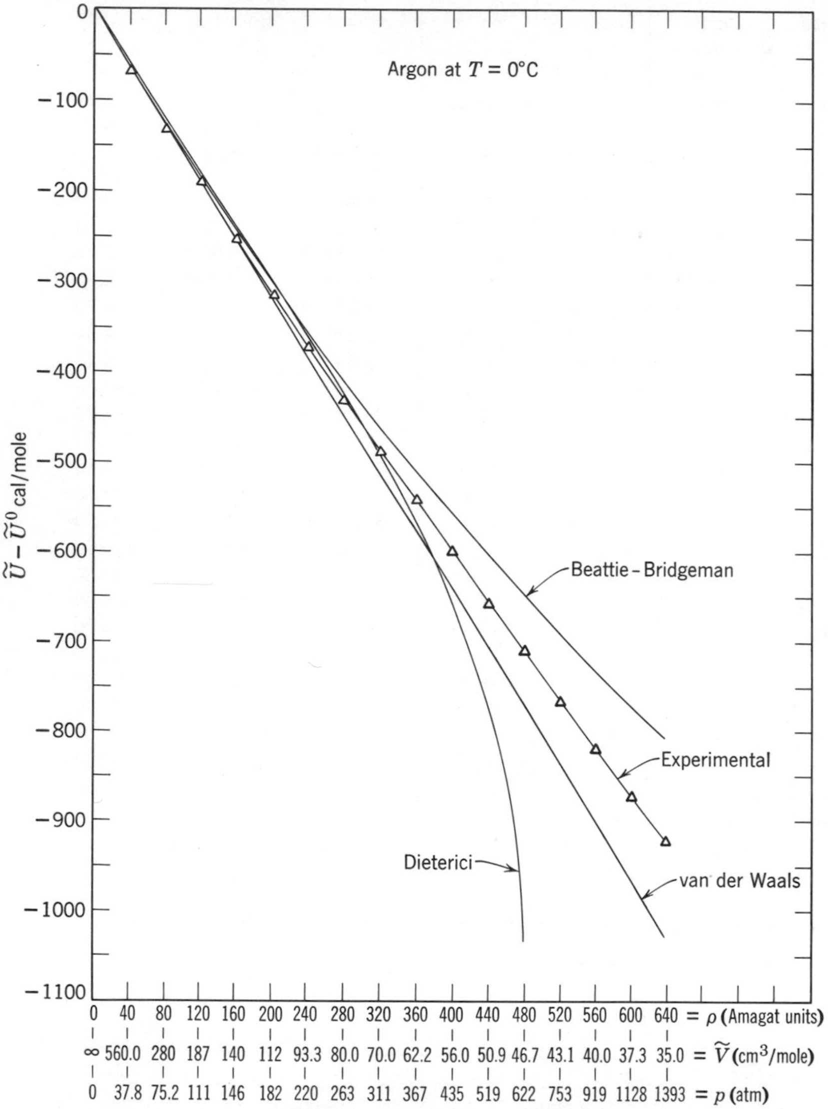

Fig. 4.2–2. A comparison of the experimental internal energy of argon at 0°C with values calculated using three empirical equations of state.

(2) Dieterici:[8]

$$\tilde{U} = \tilde{U}^0(T) - \frac{a}{b} e^{-a/bRT} \left\{ \mathrm{Ei}\left(\frac{a}{bRT}\right) - \mathrm{Ei}\left(\frac{a}{bRT}\left[1 - \frac{b}{\tilde{V}}\right]\right) \right\} \quad (4.2\text{–}16)$$

(3) Beattie-Bridgeman:

$$\tilde{U} = \tilde{U}^0(T) - \left(A_0 + \frac{3Rc}{T^2}\right)\frac{1}{\tilde{V}} - \frac{1}{2\tilde{V}^2}\left(-aA_0 + \frac{3RcB_0}{T^2}\right) + \frac{RcbB_0}{T^2\tilde{V}^3} \quad (4.2\text{–}17)$$

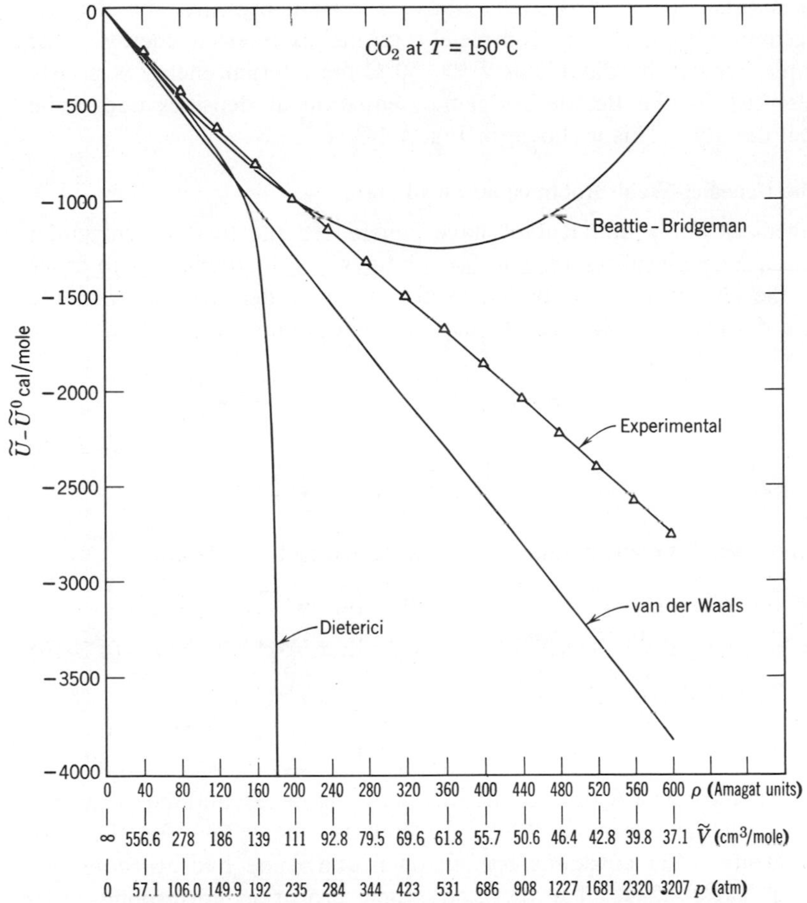

Fig. 4.2–3. A comparison of the experimental internal energy of CO_2 at 150°C with values calculated using three empirical equations of state.

[8] Ei(x) is the exponential integral function.

Figure 4.2–2 compares these calculated internal energies with the experimental measurements for argon at 0°C. The Beattie-Bridgeman constants are taken from Table 4.2–2. The constants a and b for use in the van der Waals and Dieterici expressions are obtained by setting $b - (a/RT)$ equal to the Beattie-Bridgeman second virial coefficient and a/RT^2 equal to the temperature derivative of the Beattie-Bridgeman second virial coefficient. The van der Waals form for the internal energy is surprisingly accurate. The Beattie-Bridgeman form accidentally errs in the opposite direction. The Dieterici form is quite unsuited to high densities where $\tilde{V}$ is less than or comparable to b. This is obvious from Eq. 4.2–16 since $Ei(0)$ is equal to $-\infty$. Usually above a certain pressure, the Beattie-Bridgeman equation gives completely erroneous internal energy. For example, for carbon dioxide at $T = 150$°C the internal energy is poorly represented by the Beattie-Bridgeman equation at densities above the critical density. This is shown in Fig. 4.2–3.

c. The Benedict-Webb-Rubin equation of state

Benedict, Webb, and Rubin[9] have generalized the Beattie-Bridgeman equation for pure substances and for mixtures. They found that in order to fit the observed p-V-T for hydrocarbons up to densities of twice the critical density it is necessary to use an eight-parameter equation:

$$p = \frac{RT}{\tilde{V}} + \frac{1}{\tilde{V}^2}\left[RT\left(B_0 + \frac{b}{\tilde{V}}\right) - \left(A_0 + \frac{a}{\tilde{V}} - \frac{a\alpha}{\tilde{V}^4}\right) - \frac{1}{T^2}\left\{C_0 - \frac{c}{\tilde{V}}\left(1 + \frac{\gamma}{\tilde{V}^2}\right)e^{-\gamma/\tilde{V}^2}\right\}\right] \qquad (4.2\text{–}18)$$

For mixtures the eight parameters are assumed to have the form

$$\begin{aligned} A_0 &= [\Sigma_i x_i (A_0)_i^{1/2}]^2 & a &= [\Sigma_i x_i a_i^{1/3}]^3 \\ B_0 &= \tfrac{1}{8}\,\Sigma_{ij} x_i x_j [(B_0)_i^{1/3} + (B_0)_j^{1/3}]^3 & b &= [\Sigma_i x_i b_i^{1/3}]^3 \\ C_0 &= [\Sigma_i x_i (C_0)_i^{1/2}]^2 & c &= [\Sigma_i x_i c_i^{1/3}]^3 \\ \alpha &= [\Sigma_i x_i \alpha_i^{1/3}]^3 & \gamma &= [\Sigma_i x_i \gamma_i^{1/2}]^2 \end{aligned} \qquad (4.2\text{–}19)$$

The x_i are the mole fractions of the various components, and the subscripts i and j on the constants A_0, B_0, $\cdots$ indicate the values for the pure components. The constants for nitrogen and some hydrocarbons are given in Table 4.2–4. The thermodynamic properties corresponding to the Benedict-Webb-Rubin equation of state are

[9] M. Benedict, G. B. Webb, and L. C. Rubin, *J. Chem. Phys.*, **8**, 334 (1940); **10**, 747 (1942).

(1) Fugacity:

$$RT\ln f_i = RT\ln(x_i RT/\tilde{V}) + \frac{1}{\tilde{V}}\left[\begin{array}{l}\tfrac{1}{4}RT\,\Sigma_j x_j[(B_0)_j^{1/3} + (B_0)_j^{1/3}]^3 \\ -\,2[A_0(A_0)_i]^{1/2} - (2/T^2)\,[C_0(C_0)_i]^{1/2}\end{array}\right]$$
$$+ \frac{3}{2\tilde{V}^2}[RT(b^2b_i)^{1/3} - (a^2a_i)^{1/3}]$$
$$+ \frac{3}{5\tilde{V}^5}[a(\alpha^2\alpha_i)^{1/3} + \alpha(a^2a_i)^{1/3}]$$
$$+ \frac{3(c^2c_i)^{1/3}}{\tilde{V}^2T^2}\left[\frac{1 - e^{-\gamma/\tilde{V}^2}}{\gamma/\tilde{V}^2} - \frac{e^{-\gamma/\tilde{V}^2}}{2}\right]$$
$$- \frac{2c}{\tilde{V}^2T^2}\left(\frac{\gamma_i}{\gamma}\right)^{1/2}\left[\frac{1 - e^{-\gamma/\tilde{V}^2}}{\gamma/\tilde{V}^2} - e^{-\gamma/\tilde{V}^2} - \frac{\gamma e^{-\gamma/\tilde{V}^2}}{2\tilde{V}^2}\right] \qquad (4.2\text{–}20)$$

(2) Enthalpy:

$$\tilde{H} = \Sigma_i x_i\tilde{H}_i^0 + \frac{1}{\tilde{V}}\left[B_0RT - 2A_0 - \frac{4C_0}{T^2}\right]$$
$$+ \frac{1}{2\tilde{V}^2}[2bRT - 3a] + \frac{6a\alpha}{5\tilde{V}^5}$$
$$+ \frac{c}{\tilde{V}^2T^2}\left[\frac{3\tilde{V}^2}{\gamma}(1 - e^{-\gamma/\tilde{V}^2}) - \tfrac{1}{2}e^{-\gamma/\tilde{V}^2} + \frac{\gamma}{\tilde{V}^2}e^{-\gamma/\tilde{V}^2}\right] \qquad (4.2\text{–}21)$$

(3) Entropy:

$$\tilde{S} = \Sigma_i x_i[\tilde{S}_i^0 - R\ln(x_iRT/\tilde{V})]$$
$$- \frac{1}{\tilde{V}}\left[RB_0 + \frac{2C_0}{T^3}\right] - \frac{bR}{2\tilde{V}^2}$$
$$+ \frac{2c}{\tilde{V}^2T^3}\left[\frac{\tilde{V}^2}{\gamma}(1 - e^{-\gamma/\tilde{V}^2}) - \tfrac{1}{2}e^{-\gamma/\tilde{V}^2}\right] \qquad (4.2\text{–}22)$$

These equations reproduce the full range from liquid to gas, including the critical region for a number of hydrocarbon mixtures.

TABLE 4.2–4

EMPIRICAL CONSTANTS FOR BENEDICT-WEBB-RUBIN EQUATION[a]

Units: Atmospheres, liters, moles, °K. *Gas Constants:* $R = 0.08207$; $T = 273.13 + t(°C)$

Gas	A_0	B_0	$C_0 \cdot 10^{-6}$	a	b	$c_0 \cdot 10^{-6}$	$\alpha \cdot 10^3$	$\gamma \cdot 10^2$
Nitrogen	1.19250	0.0458000	0.00588907	0.0149000	0.00198154	0.000548064	0.291545	0.750000
Methane	1.85500	0.0426000	0.0225700	0.494000	0.00338004	0.00254500	0.124359	0.60000
Ethylene	3.33958	0.0556833	0.131140	0.259000	0.0086000	0.021120	0.178000	0.923000
Ethane	4.15556	0.0627724	0.179592	0.345160	0.0111220	0.0327670	0.243389	1.18000
Propylene	6.11220	0.0850647	0.439182	0.774056	0.0187059	0.102611	0.455696	1.82900
Propane	6.87225	0.0973130	0.508256	0.947700	0.0225000	0.129000	0.607175	2.20000
i-Butane	10.23264	0.137544	0.849943	1.93763	0.0424352	0.286010	1.07408	3.40000
i-Butylene	8.95325	0.116025	0.927280	1.69270	0.0348156	0.274920	0.910889	2.95945
n-Butane	10.0847	0.124361	0.992830	1.88231	0.0399983	0.316400	1.10132	3.40000
i-Pentane	12.7959	0.160053	1.74632	3.75620	0.0668120	0.695000	1.70000	4.63000
n-Pentane	12.1794	0.156751	2.12121	4.07480	0.0668120	0.824170	1.81000	4.75000
n-Hexane	14.4373	0.177813	3.31935	7.11671	0.109131	1.51276	2.81086	6.66849
n-Heptane	17.5206	0.199005	4.74574	10.36475	0.151954	2.47000	4.35611	9.00000

[a] M. Benedict, G. B. Webb, and L. C. Rubin, *Chem. Eng. Progress*, **47**, 419 (1951). The constants for nitrogen are from a personal communication from M. Benedict.

d. Empirical relations for liquids

The Tait equation[10] and its modification by Kirkwood are the best empirical representations of the equation of state of liquids. Tait's equation, which was originally proposed to describe the compressibility of water, is

$$dV/dp = -K/(L + p) \tag{4.2–23}$$

in which K is a constant and L is a function of the temperature. In its integrated form the equation reads (with $n = V_0/K$):

$$\ln\left(\frac{p + L(T)}{p_0 + L(T)}\right) = n\left(\frac{V_0 - V}{V_0}\right) \tag{4.2–24}$$

p_0 is some standard pressure, and V_0 is the corresponding liquid volume. There is at the present time little theoretical justification for this equation. Nevertheless, studies of the properties of a large number of liquids[11] have shown that Eq. 4.2–24 gives almost perfect agreement with experimental observations. The equation proves to be applicable to many types of liquids (benzene derivatives, salt solutions, etc.) and suitable over a wide range of temperatures and pressures (up to 1000 atm).

At extremely high pressures the Tait equation requires modification since the left-hand side of Eq. 4.2–24 approaches infinity whereas the right-hand side cannot exceed n. Hence this modification has been suggested:[12]

$$\ln\left(\frac{p + A(S)}{A(S)}\right) = n \ln\left(\frac{V(0, S)}{V(p, S)}\right) \tag{4.2–25}$$

In this relation entropy, rather than temperature, has been chosen as the independent variable, and the increment in the volume has been replaced by the logarithm of the ratio of the volume at zero pressure, $V(0, S)$, to that at some pressure p. This equation has been shown to give an excellent representation of the equation of state for water up to 25,000 atm.[13]

Equation 4.2–25 may be written in a form reminiscent of perfect gas adiabats:

$$[p + A(S)]\, V^n = F(S) \tag{4.2–26}$$

[10] D. M. Newitt, *High Pressure Plant and the Properties of Fluids at High Pressures*, Oxford University Press (1940).

[11] R. E. Gibson and O. H. Loeffler, *Ann. N.Y. Acad. Sci.*, **51**, 727 (1949); *J. Am. Chem. Soc.*, **61**, 2515 (1939).

[12] J. G. Kirkwood and H. Bethe, "The Pressure Wave Produced by an Underwater Explosion," Part I, OSRD Report No. 588 (Dept. of Comm. Bibliography No. PB32182); J. G. Kirkwood and J. M. Richardson, "The Pressure Wave Produced by an Underwater Explosion," Part III, OSRD Report No. 813 (Dept. of Comm. Bibliography No. PB32184).

[13] J. M. Richardson, A. B. Arons, and R. R. Halverson, *J. Chem. Phys.*, **15**, 785 (1947).

in which $F(S) = A(S)\,[V(0, S)]^n$. The internal energy may then be obtained from $(\partial U/\partial V)_S = -p$, which after integration becomes

$$U(p, S) - U(0, S) = \left(\frac{pV}{n-1}\right) - \left(\frac{n}{n-1}\right) A(S)[V(0, S) - V] \tag{4.2–27}$$

The first term, $pV/(n-1)$, is the principal contribution. The second term expresses the correction due to the volume increment $[V(0, S) - V]$. As long as the latter is small, it is clear that Eqs. 4.2–27 and 4.2–25 are capable of fitting the experimental data. However, for large changes in the volume we would expect to find it necessary to include additional terms in the internal energy proportional to higher powers of the volume increment. It is interesting to note that n is equal to the specific heat ratio, γ, only in the case of a perfect gas, where $p\tilde{V} = RT$ and $A(S) = 0$.

A crude but convenient equation of state for liquid adiabats is

$$pV^3 = F(S) \tag{4.2–28}$$

This corresponds to setting $n = 3$ and neglecting the correction term corresponding to $A(S)$. For this equation both the velocity of sound and the Riemann characteristic (see § 11.5) are proportional to the pressure.

3. Gases at Very High Pressures

In this section we discuss some of the problems which are encountered in the study of powder gas combustion, detonations, and other processes where very high pressures are involved. First some empirical equations useful for describing the p-V-T behavior of gases at very high pressures are discussed. Then we consider the distortion of the molecules at high pressures. In this latter discussion the virial theorem is invoked to examine the increase in the kinetic energy of the electrons due to high compression.

a. An equation of state for powder gases

For gases at moderately high pressure, the following equation has been recommended:[1]

$$p\tilde{V}/RT = 1 + B(T)/\tilde{V} + 0.625b_0^2/\tilde{V}^2 + 0.2869b_0^3\tilde{V}^3 + 0.1928b_0^4/\tilde{V}^4 \tag{4.3–1}$$

$B(T)$ is the second virial coefficient and b_0 is the usual van der Waals

[1] J. O. Hirschfelder and W. E. Roseveare, *J. Chem. Phys.*, **43**, 15 (1939); J. O. Hirschfelder, D. P. Stevenson, and H. Eyring, *J. Chem. Phys.*, **5**, 896 (1937).

constant. The third and fourth virial coefficient would be correct for rigid spheres with volumes equal to $b_0/4\tilde{N}$. The fifth virial coefficient is adjusted to make the compressibility agree with the Eyring equation (Eq. 4.5–3) in the range of liquid densities.

For powder gases at temperatures around 2500°C, the second virial coefficient is almost independent of temperature. This may be seen from Fig. 4.2–1 or from the tabulation of $B(T)$ for the Lennard-Jones potential given in Table I–B. The value of $B(T)$ changes very little between $T^* = kT/\epsilon = 10$ and $T^* = 100$. There is a maximum value of $B(T) = 0.527b_0$ at about $T^* = 30$ which corresponds to the high temperatures found in powder-gas flames. Thus for such problems $B(T)$ is set equal to b, and b is taken to be $0.527b_0$. The value of b_0 for the powder gas mixture can be estimated by the combining rule (which is simple though not particularly accurate):

$$(b_0)_{\text{mix}} = \Sigma_i x_i (b_0)_i \qquad (4.3\text{–}2)$$

x_i is the mole fraction of the ith component and the $(b_0)_i$ are the Lennard-Jones b_0's for the individual components. Because of the accidental maximum in the second virial coefficient in this temperature range, studies of ballistics in which the molecules are considered to be rigid spheres with the covolume described above have been remarkably successful.

b. Equation of state behavior in detonations

In detonation problems in which the pressure may increase to 200,000 atm, the Lennard-Jones-Devonshire equation of state (see § 4.7) might seem to be the most accurate representation. However, the Halford-Kistiakowsky-Wilson[2] equation has been used to good advantage:

$$p\tilde{V}/RT = 1 + KT^{-1/4} \exp (0.3K/T^{1/4}) \qquad (4.3\text{–}3)$$

The constant K is given by

$$K = \Sigma n_i K_i \qquad (4.3\text{–}4)$$

where n_i is the number of moles in the ith component per cubic centimeter of mixture. The K_i are empirical constants characteristic of each of the chemical species and are taken to be 5.5 times the values of the Lennard-Jones b_0 for the species. For water and ammonia the K_i are 108 and 164 cm³ per mole, respectively. Much of the success of this equation is due to the fact that most detonation phenomena are not sensitive to the equation of state.

[2] This modified Becker equation was formulated by R. S. Halford and reported in Div. B. NDRC Report Serial No. 52 (OSRD 114), by G. Kistiakowsky and E. B. Wilson, Jr.; J. Kirkwood, S. Brinkley, and J. Richardson, Div. B. NDRC (OSRD 2022), p. 113; Final Report NDRC, Div. 8.

c. Use of the virial theorem to study distortion of molecules at extremely high pressures

When a substance is subjected to extremely high pressures the constituent molecules become distorted, the electronic energy levels are shifted, and the chemical bonds are weakened or destroyed. The tremendous change brought about in the properties of matter at high pressures may be illustrated by the electrical conductivity—at low pressures a gas is an insulator, as the pressure is raised it becomes a semi-conductor, and finally at extremely high pressures it becomes a metallic conductor. At the present time it would appear that this metallic state is reached at a pressure of the order of 1,000,000 atm, depending upon the substance. A great deal of experimental research is needed in this very high range of pressures. Many interesting results can be anticipated. For example, some chemical reactions which at atmospheric pressure take place at exceedingly high temperature may occur at room temperature and high pressure.

The quantum mechanical energy levels of the molecules are shifted and the kinetic energy of the system is increased as the pressure is raised. This behavior can be explained in terms of the virial theorem. The change in the internal energy and the change in the kinetic energy of the system can be expressed in terms of the experimental equation of state. Absorbtion spectroscopy would provide the most direct experimental information, but there are no experimental data available along these lines at the present time. In principle the variations in the dielectric constant or the index of refraction should indicate the compression of the molecules, but at the present time the theoretical understanding of these properties (see § 12.2) is not sufficiently well developed for this purpose.

In § 3.1 the virial theorem is used to develop a formal expression for the equation of state in terms of intermolecular forces. In that derivation the gas is assumed to be made up of molecules, and the internal structure of the molecules is completely ignored. In this section we apply the virial theorem to the equation of state, considering the gas to be made up of nuclei and electrons. According to Eq. 3.1–10 the average kinetic energy of the particles may be written as the sum of the virial due to the external forces (that is, the effect of the containing walls), $\frac{3}{2}pV$, and the virial due to the interparticle forces:

$$\bar{K} = \tfrac{3}{2}pV - \tfrac{1}{2}\,\overline{\textstyle\sum_i(\boldsymbol{r}_i \cdot (\boldsymbol{F}_i)_{\text{int}})} \qquad (4.3\text{–}5)$$

Here $(F_i)_{\text{int}}$ is the force on the ith particle (nucleus or electron) due to all the other particles. Inasmuch as the nuclei and electrons interact according to the Coulombic force law, the virial of the interparticle forces can be expressed in terms of Φ, the total potential energy of the system (see Eq. 1.4–29):

$$\tfrac{1}{2}\,\overline{\textstyle\sum_i(\boldsymbol{r}\cdot(\boldsymbol{F}_i)_{\rm int})} = \tfrac{1}{2}\,\bar{\Phi} \tag{4.3–6}$$

Hence Eq. 4.3–5 may be rewritten as

$$pV = \tfrac{2}{3}\bar{K} + \tfrac{1}{3}\,\bar{\Phi} \tag{4.3–7}$$

The sum of the average kinetic energy and the average potential energy is just the internal energy U of thermodynamics:

$$U = \bar{K} + \bar{\Phi} \tag{4.3–8}$$

The last two relations give the pV-product and the internal energy in terms of $\bar{K}$ and $\bar{\Phi}$.

These relations may be solved to get $\bar{K}$ and $\bar{\Phi}$ in terms of experimentally measurable thermodynamic quantities:

$$\bar{K} = -U + 3pV \tag{4.3–9}$$

$$-\bar{\Phi} = -2U + 3pV \tag{4.3–10}$$

Differentiation of these equations (known as *Schottky's Relations*[3]) and use of standard thermodynamic formulae[4] give[5]

$$d\bar{K} = \left[4p\left(\frac{\partial V}{\partial T}\right)_p - C_p\right]dT + \left[3V + T\left(\frac{\partial V}{\partial T}\right)_p + 4p\left(\frac{\partial V}{\partial p}\right)_T\right]dp \tag{4.3–11}$$

$$-d\bar{\Phi} = \left[5p\left(\frac{\partial V}{\partial T}\right)_p - 2C_p\right]dT + \left[3V + 2T\left(\frac{\partial V}{\partial T}\right)_p + 5p\left(\frac{\partial V}{\partial p}\right)_T\right]dp \tag{4.3–12}$$

The total kinetic energy $\bar{K}$ is the sum of the kinetic energy of the atomic nuclei, $\bar{K}_{at}$, and the kinetic energy of the electrons, $\bar{K}_e$. If the translational and vibrational motions of the atomic nuclei behaved classically, $\bar{K}_{at}$ would be a function of the temperature only and would be independent of pressure. In this case the change in $\bar{K}_e$ with pressure would be exactly equal to the change in $\bar{K}$. Although this cannot be strictly true, it is clear that the change in $\bar{K}_e$ is an appreciable fraction of the change in $\bar{K}$.

Bridgman[5] used Eq. 4.3–11 to obtain the change of $\bar{K}$ with pressure in solids. From his experimental data the increase in the kinetic energy in lithium is 18 kcal per mole, 30 kcal per mole for bismuth, 14 kcal per mole for aluminum, and 9 kcal per mole for iron at 19,000 atm pressure.

[3] W. Schottky, *Physik. Z.*, **21**, 232 (1920).

[4] Specifically one uses the relation

$$dU = \left[C_p - p\left(\frac{\partial V}{\partial T}\right)_p\right]dT - \left[T\left(\frac{\partial V}{\partial T}\right)_p + p\left(\frac{\partial V}{\partial p}\right)_T\right]dp$$

to eliminate dU.

[5] P. W. Bridgman, *Revs. Mod. Phys.*, **7**, 1 (1935); *Phys. Rev.*, **46**, 930 (1934).

For gases Michels and his coworkers[6–8] showed that the change in the kinetic energy is proportional to the pressure. Figure 4.3–1 shows that, for CO_2, the kinetic energy changes by 8 kcal per mole at a pressure of 2800 atm, and Fig. 4.3–2 shows that for nitrogen it changes 15 kcal per mole at 7800 atm. For ethylene, the kinetic energy increases 9 kcal per mole when the pressure is raised to 2500 atm;[9] for argon, 4 kcal per mole when the pressure is raised to 2000 atm.[10]

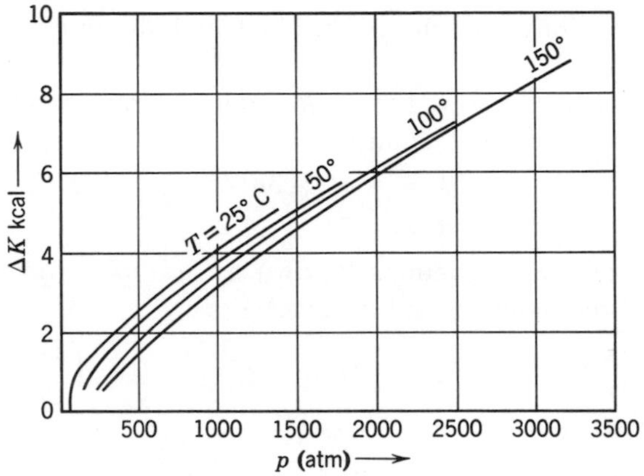

Fig. 4.3–1. Change of kinetic energy in carbon dioxide as a function of pressure. [From A. Michels and S. R. de Groot, *Nederland. Tijdschr. Natuurk.*, **12**, 77 (1946).]

Originally Michels and others had thought that there would be a large shift in the total (kinetic plus potential) energy of the electrons corresponding to the large shift in the kinetic energy with pressure. If this had been the case, chemical bonds would be weakened or non-existent at pressures as low as 50,000 atm. However, Cottrell[11–12] applied the virial theorem to show that the total electronic energy shifts only approximately one-twentieth as much as the kinetic energy. Thus pressures of the order of 1,000,000 atm would be required to destroy the chemical bonds.

[6] A. Michels, J. de Boer, and A. Bijl, *Physica*, **4**, 981 (1937).

[7] A. Michels and S. R. de Groot, *Nederland. Tijdschr. Natuurk.*, **12**, 77 (1946).

[8] A. Michels, R. J. Lunbeck, and G. J. Wolkers, *Physica*, **17**, 801 (1951).

[9] A. Michels, S. R. de Groot, and M. Geldermans, *Applied Sci. Research*, **A1**, 55 (1947); *Physica*, **12**, 105 (1946).

[10] A. Michels, R. J. Lunbeck, and G. J. Wolkers, *Physica*, **15**, 689 (1949); A. Michels, Hub. Wijker, and Hk. Wijker, *Physica*, **15**, 627 (1949).

[11] T. L. Cottrell, *Trans. Faraday Soc.*, **47**, 337 (1951).

[12] T. L. Cottrell, *J. Chem. Phys.*, **18**, 1117 (1950).

Cottrell considered a gas made up of diatomic molecules. Suppose that the potential energy functions (Morse curves for example), $\Phi_n(r)$, are known for these molecules as a function of the separation r between the

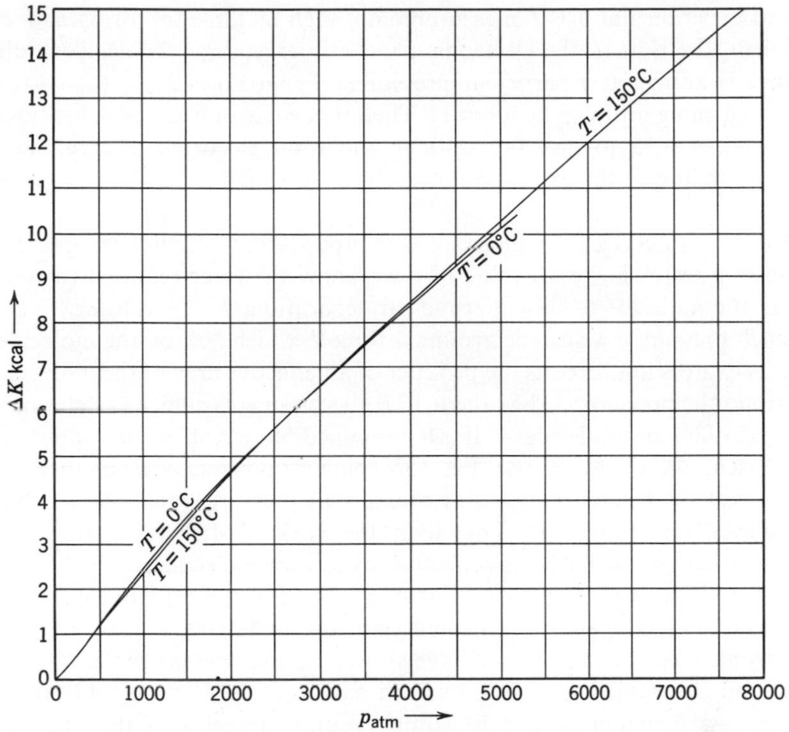

Fig. 4.3–2. Change of kinetic energy in nitrogen as a function of pressure. [From A. Michels, R. J. Lunbeck, and G. J. Wolkers, *Physica*, **17**, 801 (1951).]

two nuclei. Then, according to Slater's application of the virial theorem to molecular problems (see § 13.1c), the average electronic kinetic energy is a known function of r:

$$\bar{K}_e(r) = -\Phi_n(r) - r\frac{d\Phi_n}{dr} \qquad (4.3\text{–}13)$$

or if r_0 is the equilibrium separation, the shift in the electronic kinetic energy when the molecule is compressed from r_0 to r is given by

$$\Delta\bar{K}_e = \bar{K}_e(r) - \bar{K}_e(r_0) = \Phi_n(r_0) - \Phi_n(r) - r\frac{d\Phi_n}{dr} \qquad (4.3\text{–}14)$$

This same compression leads to a shift in the average total electronic energy

$$\Delta\overline{\Phi}_e = \overline{\Phi}_e(r) - \overline{\Phi}_e(r_0) = \Phi_n(r) - \Phi_n(r_0) \qquad (4.3\text{–}15)$$

From experimental p-V-T measurements, such as those of Bridgman or Michels, the shift in the electronic kinetic energy, $\Delta\bar{K}_e$, for a given substance is known at a particular pressure. From Eq. 4.3–14, the corresponding value for r can be found. Then this value of r can be substituted into Eq. 4.3–15 to give the shift in the total electronic energy, $\Delta\overline{\Phi}_e$, corresponding to the experimentally observed shift in the kinetic energy, $\Delta\bar{K}_e$.

In order to check the validity of this procedure, Cottrell developed the following test. For each value of r we know the force required to compress the molecule to this internuclear separation, $F = -d\Phi_n/dr$. Thus at each pressure p we can determine a force F which acts on the molecule. Let us express this force as the product of an effective area of the molecule, A, times the pressure. Then the p-V-T measurements suffice to determine A for different molecules. If A remained constant as the pressure increased, we could reverse the foregoing arguments and predict the change of the kinetic energy with pressure at pressures much higher than have ever been measured. Thus from the work of Michels, de Boer, and Bijl[6] it is found that for N_2 the effective area of the molecule is $A = 145$ Å^2, and remains constant up to 3000 atm, the limit of the experimental data. If this cross-sectional area remained constant, at 100,000 atm the average electronic kinetic energy would have shifted by 180 kcal per mole, whereas the total electronic energy $\Phi_n(r)$ would have increased by only 4 kcal per mole. As a matter of fact it would require pressures of the order of millions of atmospheres to increase $\Phi_n(r)$ by the amount of the energy of dissociation. Long before this million atmospheres was reached, the neighboring nitrogen molecules would strongly perturb each other so that the meaning of Cottrell's extrapolation to very high pressures is not clear. However, the large ratio of the shift in the kinetic energy to the shift in the electronic total energy should serve as a warning to those who expect loosening of chemical bonds and other changes in the electronic structures to take place at comparatively low pressures.

d. Quantum mechanical treatment of the distortion of molecules at high pressure

Another method of studying the effect of very high pressures on substances is the use of quantum mechanics to examine theoretically the effect of squeezing a single atom. Two problems of this type have received consideration: a hydrogen atom in a rigid spherical container,[13] and a hydrogen molecule ion (H_2^+) in a spheroidal enclosure.[11] We consider here only the treatment of the H-atom by de Groot and ten Seldam.[14]

A free hydrogen atom has an infinite number of bound (negative) energy states and a continuum of positive energy states. When the atom is enclosed in a large spherical box the continuum becomes discrete and

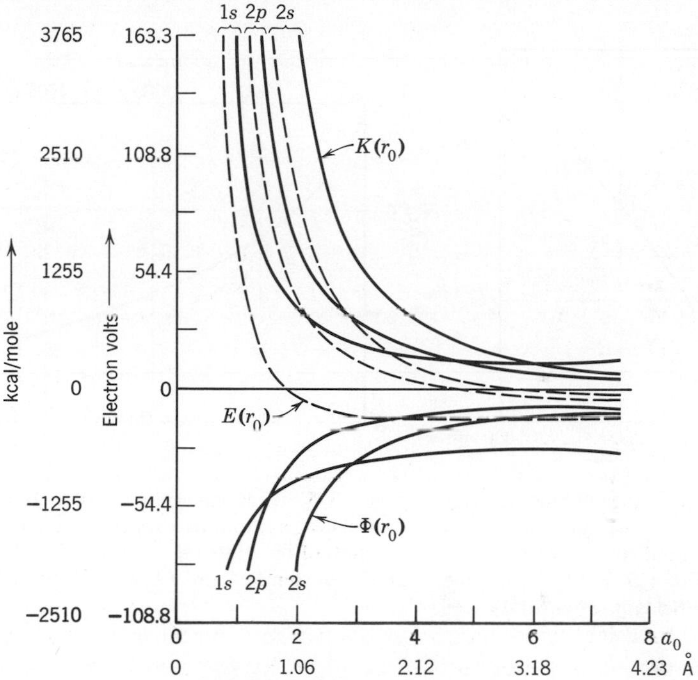

Fig. 4.3–3. Kinetic, potential, and total energy of a hydrogen atom in a rigid spherical container of radius r_0. [From S. R. de Groot and C. A. ten Seldam, *Physica*, **12**, 669 (1946).]

the number of bound states becomes finite. As the radius r_0 of the spherical box is made smaller the energy levels of the bound states gradually rise and those at the top of the potential well become positive—that is, the electron in those energy states prefers to be free. The 2*s*-state has

[13] S. R. de Groot and C. A. ten Seldam, *Physica*, **12**, 669 (1946).

[14] Recently C. A. ten Seldam has summarized the quantum mechanical treatment in his doctoral dissertation, "Energies and Polarizabilities of Compressed Atoms," University of Utrecht, Holland (1953). Also ten Seldam and de Groot have made quantum mechanical calculations of the properties of compressed helium and argon. [C. A. ten Seldam and S. R. de Groot, *Physica*, **18**, 891, 905, 910 (1952).]

an energy of zero for $r_0 = 6.153a_0$, the $2p$-state for $r_0 = 5.086a_0$, and the $1s$-state at $r_0 = 1.835a_0$. In Fig. 4.3–3 is shown the energy E, the average electron kinetic energy $\bar{K}$, and the average electron potential energy $\bar{\Phi}$ for various values of the radius r_0 of the enclosing box for the $1s$, $2s$, and $2p$ states. In Fig. 4.3–4 is shown the change in the electronic kinetic energy as a function of the pressure exerted by the atom on the walls of the circular enclosure. It is surprising that at 2700 atm the change in

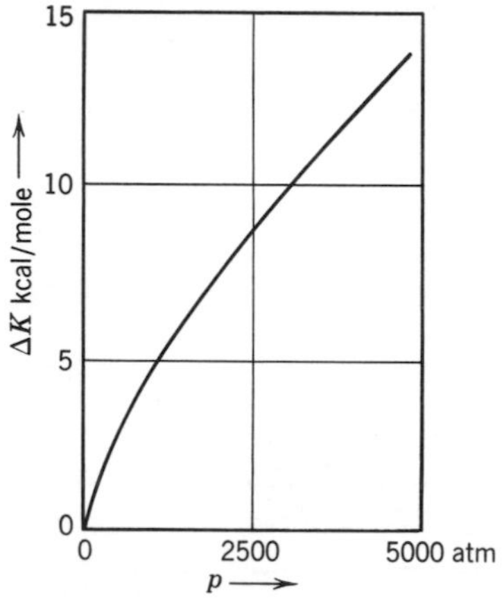

Fig. 4.3–4. Change of kinetic energy as a function of pressure of a hydrogen atom in a spherical container. [From S. R. de Groot and C. A. ten Seldam, *Physica*, **12**, 669 (1946).]

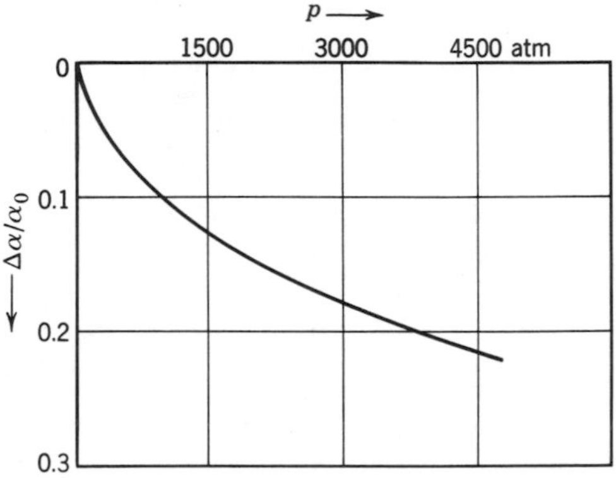

Fig. 4.3–5. Fractional change of polarizability of a hydrogen atom in a spherical container as a function of the pressure. [From S. R. de Groot and C. A. ten Seldam, *Physica*, **12**, 669 (1946).]

the electronic kinetic energy is 8 kcal per mole. This is in substantial agreement with the observed experimental values for CO_2 and N_2. Perhaps one of the most significant features of the molecular compression is the change of polarizability with pressure. This is shown in Fig. 4.3–5 for the atomic hydrogen calculations.

Another approach to the problem has been made by Wigner and Huntington,[15] who considered the possibility of a metallic modification of hydrogen. They calculated the physical properties of a body-centered cubic lattice made up of hydrogen atoms. They found that it may be possible to compress hydrogen into a metallic crystal of density 0.80 (as compared to the normal density of solid hydrogen of 0.087). Actually the metallic form may not be stable at any pressure. However, Wigner

[15] E. P. Wigner and H. Huntington, *J. Chem. Phys.*, **3**, 764 (1935).

and Huntington state: "One calculates easily, that even under the assumption of the most advantageous compressibility at high pressures, the pressure which is necessary for this transformation is 250,000 atmospheres." A similar conclusion was reached by Kronig, de Boer, and Korringa.[16]

e. Optical and electrical methods for studying the distortion of molecules at high pressure[14]

The variation of the index of refraction η or the dielectric constant ϵ' with pressure provide simple experimental methods for studying the distortion of molecules at high pressures. To a first approximation the Clausius-Mosotti function, $(1/\rho)(\epsilon' - 1)/(\epsilon' + 2)$, and the Lorentz-Lorenz function, $(1/\rho)(\eta^2 - 1)/(\eta^2 + 2)$, depend only on the polarizability of the molecules. Variations in these functions should therefore provide an experimental method for determining changes of the polarizability as the molecules become distorted. In § 12.2 we see that refinements in the theory of electric susceptibility lead to corrections in the Clausius-Mosotti and Lorentz-Lorenz functions at high densities because of the addition of the electric field of the induced dipoles to the electric field acting on the surrounding molecules. Taking these corrections into account Böttcher[17] has examined the experimental data of Michels, de Boer, and Bijl[6] for the index of refraction for carbon dioxide as a function of density, and has found that the polarizability of the CO_2 decreases by 10 per cent when a pressure of only 100 to 200 atm is applied and by 20 per cent when the pressure is of the order of 2000 atm. This is somewhat larger but still in accord with the theoretical calculation for the compressed hydrogen atom.

Considerable improvements must be made in the theoretical treatment of electric susceptibilities before the variations of the polarizability of molecules with pressure can be determined with high accuracy.

4. Some General Considerations about the Cell Methods

Thus far the discussion has been confined to empirical considerations and general results obtainable from the principle of corresponding states. We now turn to the theoretical investigation of the behavior of liquids and dense gases. A liquid or a dense gas may be regarded either as a very imperfect gas in which multiple collisions are frequent or as a distorted crystal in which the long-range order has been lost.

[16] R. Kronig, J. de Boer, and J. Korringa, *Physica*, **12**, 245 (1946).

[17] C. J. F. Böttcher, *Physica*, **9**, 937 and 945 (1942); S. R. de Groot and C. A. ten Seldam, *Physica*, **13**, 47 (1947).

The gas-like approach is exemplified by the virial development, which was described in Chapter 3. The results of the latter theory are quite satisfactory from a theoretical point of view except for possible convergence difficulties in the liquid range. The theory has been used in the study of condensation phenomena (see § 5.2e). However, the virial equation of state is at present of no value in making practical numerical calculations in the high-density region.

The crystal-like approach, on the other hand, has not led to formal solutions. Nevertheless, it has proved valuable, inasmuch as it has led to several approximate treatments which can be used to give numerical results. There are two main types of approaches which have been used: (i) the *cell theories*, in which the liquid is regarded as a distorted crystal with one molecule located at or near each lattice point, and (ii) the *hole theories*, in which it is realized that liquids differ from crystals in that some of the lattice sites are vacant. In this and the following three sections we discuss the cell theories in detail. In § 4.8 various hole theory calculations are summarized.

a. Crystal structure as the basis for cell methods

A solid composed of molecules without internal degrees of freedom is pictured as a set of particles executing small vibrations about their equilibrium positions. The partition function of such a system is the product of harmonic oscillator partition functions, each representing one of the (mathematical) oscillators. If it were possible to analyze the vibrations into the normal modes it would be possible to write down the exact partition function of the system. But to a reasonable approximation (the Einstein or Grüneisen approximation) we can picture each of the molecules as vibrating independently in that field which would be present if all the neighboring molecules were at their equilibrium positions. To this approximation all the vibration frequencies are the same, and the partition function for a system of N particles is simply the product of N identical factors.[1]

For a liquid in which the density of particles is slightly less than in a solid, the amplitude of the motion of the molecules is larger. The concept of small vibrations is not valid in liquids. However, the specific heat of a material in the liquid phase just above the melting point is almost the same as that for the solid phase. This fact makes it tempting to retain the idea of the molecule moving in the force field which would exist if all the neighboring molecules were in their mean positions. This

[1] For the statistical mechanical theory of crystals, see, for example, J. E. Mayer and M. G. Mayer, *Statistical Mechanics*, Wiley (1940), Ch. 11, or R. H. Fowler and E. A. Guggenheim, *Statistical Thermodynamics*, Cambridge University Press (1949), Ch. 4.

is the essence of the "cell methods" of obtaining the equation of state. The space is divided into a regular lattice of cells with one molecule per cell. Such a model for the liquid state has quite clearly two defects. (i) There is no correlation between the motion of molecules in neighboring cells. Because of the lack of long-range order in a liquid or dense gas, the neglect of correlations between motions of neighboring molecules is probably a better approximation than the Einstein approximation in a solid. (ii) Free interchange of molecules between cells is completely denied. This restriction introduces an error in the entropy of the system, which is usually corrected by the addition of what is termed the *communal entropy*. The communal entropy problem is discussed in the next subsection.

There have been two major developments of the cell theories: that of Eyring and his colleagues and that due to Lennard-Jones and Devonshire. Both these groups of investigators established their theories of the liquid state by means of well-founded physical intuition. The basic expressions which were the starting point for their researches have recently been justified by Kirkwood;[2] he has shown rigorously what assumptions are inherent in the theories of Eyring and of Lennard-Jones and Devonshire. Consequently, we depart from the historical order and present first a summary of Kirkwood's results.

b. The concept of communal entropy

The problem of communal entropy may be understood by considering an idealized system of N non-interacting particles. Let us calculate the difference in entropy of the two states of this system, which are represented pictorially in Fig. 4.4–1. In State I the total volume V is shared by all of the molecules. The classical partition function is then just that for an ideal gas of N molecules:

$$Z_N^{(\mathrm{I})} = \lambda^{-3N} (V^N/N!) \tag{4.4–1}$$

in which $\lambda^2 = h^2/2\pi mkT$. In State II, where each molecule is restricted to move within its own cell of volume V/N, the partition function is

$$Z_N^{(\mathrm{II})} = (z)^N = (\lambda^{-3} V/N)^N = \lambda^{-3N}(V/N)^N \tag{4.4–2}$$

In the latter expression there is no $N!$ because of the virtual distinguishability of the particles. The two partition functions $Z_N^{(\mathrm{I})}$ and $Z_N^{(\mathrm{II})}$ give exactly the same expressions for the internal energy and the pressure. Hence, as far as internal energy and pressure are concerned, the presence

[2] J. G. Kirkwood, *J. Chem. Phys.*, **18**, 380 (1950).

of the partitions is immaterial if the particles are non-interacting. However, the two partition functions do give different values for the entropy, $S = k \ln Z_N + U/T$. The entropy difference between the two states is

$$S^{(\mathrm{I})} - S^{(\mathrm{II})} = k \ln [Z_N^{(\mathrm{I})}/Z_N^{(\mathrm{II})}] = k \ln (N^N/N!) = Nk \qquad (4.4\text{–}3)$$

Here Stirling's formula for $\ln N!$ has been used.

This last result means that the cell model for a gas gives, in the low density limit, an entropy too low by Nk and a free energy too high by NkT. This defect may be corrected by inserting a factor of e^N in the

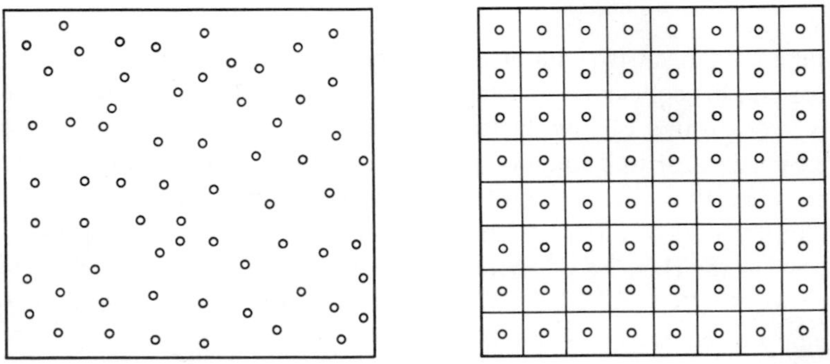

I
Perfect gas of N molecules in volume V

II
N molecules, each one confined to a cell of volume V/N

Fig. 4.4–1. Illustration of the concept of communal entropy.

expression for the partition function $Z_N^{(\mathrm{II})}$. This method is, however, not very satisfactory: a factor e^N is needed in the perfect gas limit but not for a system in the crystalline state. Somewhere between these two limits the "communal entropy" becomes effective. One suggestion is[3] that this "communal entropy" appears discontinuously at the melting point, where it contributes an extra amount of entropy, R per mole, to the liquid. This view has, however, been criticized by Rice,[4] who maintains that the factor e^N in the partition function appears more gradually. This would make it a function of volume as well as of temperature and so would cause it to contribute to the equation of state.

A more complete understanding of the communal entropy problem may be obtained by the following[2] more formal treatment, in which a system of N identical interacting particles is considered. In § 3.1a it was

[3] J. O. Hirschfelder, D. P. Stevenson, and H. Eyring, *J. Chem. Phys.*, **5**, 896 (1937).
[4] O. K. Rice, *J. Chem. Phys.*, **6**, 476 (1938).

shown how the equation of state may be written in terms of the partition function Z_N:

$$Z_N = (N!h^{3N})^{-1} \iint \exp\,[-H(\boldsymbol{r}^N, \boldsymbol{p}^N)/kT]\, d\boldsymbol{r}^N\, d\boldsymbol{p}^N$$

$$= (N!\lambda^{3N})^{-1} \int \exp\,[-\Phi(\boldsymbol{r}^N)/kT]\, d\boldsymbol{r}^N \equiv \lambda^{-3N} Q_N \qquad (4.4\text{–}4)$$

in which Q_N is called the configurational integral. Let us now divide the coordinate space into N cells, $\Delta_1, \Delta_2, \cdots \Delta_N$ in any arbitrary manner. The configurational integral can then be written as a sum of terms in which the coordinates of each molecule are confined to a particular cell. When there are N molecules and N cells, Q_N contains N^N terms, corresponding to the N^N ways of placing N molecules in N cells:

$$Q_N = (N!)^{-1} \sum_{l_1=1}^{N} \sum_{l_2=1}^{N} \cdots \sum_{l_N=1}^{N} \int_{\Delta_{l_1}} \int_{\Delta_{l_2}} \cdots \int_{\Delta_{l_N}} \exp[-\Phi(\boldsymbol{r}^N)/kT]\, d\boldsymbol{r}_1\, d\boldsymbol{r}_2 \cdots d\boldsymbol{r}_N \qquad (4.4\text{–}5)$$

Since the molecules are indistinguishable, the value of a term is unchanged by a permutation of the molecules in the cells.

Let us denote by $Q_N(m_1, m_2, \ldots, m_N)$ the various terms in Eq. 4.4–5 which correspond to m_1 molecules in cell 1, m_2 molecules in cell 2, . . . m_N molecules in cell N. Because of the possible permutations of the N molecules, there are $(N!/\Pi_i m_i!)$ ways of obtaining a particular set $\{m\} = m_1, m_2, \ldots m_N$. Consequently the total configuration integral is given by

$$Q_N = (N!)^{-1} \Sigma_{\{m\}} (N!/\Pi_i m_i!) Q_N(m_1, m_2, \cdots m_N)$$

$$= \Sigma_{\{m\}} Q_N(m_1, m_2, \cdots m_N)/(\Pi_i m_i!) \qquad (4.4\text{–}6)$$

The summations are over all sets of occupation numbers $\{m\}$ subject to the constraint that $\Sigma_i m_i = N$.

The last expression may be written formally as

$$Q_N = \bar{\sigma}^N Q_N^{(1)} \qquad (4.4\text{–}7)$$

in which

$$Q_N^{(1)} \equiv Q_N(1, 1, \cdots, 1) \qquad (4.4\text{–}8)$$

$$\bar{\sigma}^N = \Sigma_{\{m\}} (\Pi_i m_i!)^{-1} [Q_N(m_1, m_2, \cdots, m_N)/Q_N^{(1)}] \qquad (4.4\text{–}9)$$

At sufficiently high densities the repulsive forces between the molecules prevent multiple occupancy, and all $Q_N(m_1, m_2, \ldots, m_N)$ except $Q_N^{(1)}$ are equal to zero, so that:

$$\bar{\sigma} = 1 \qquad \textit{(high density limit)} \qquad (4.4\text{–}10)$$

For an extremely dilute gas there is effectively no interaction between the molecules so that all the $Q_N(m_1, m_2, \ldots m_N)$ are equal, with the result that[5]

$$\bar{\sigma} = e \qquad (low\ density\ limit) \tag{4.4-11}$$

These two results are in agreement with the results of the simple picture described earlier.

In general $\bar{\sigma}$ lies between 1 and e, and the change in the value of $\bar{\sigma}$ with density represents the appearance of the communal entropy. In the free volume treatments described in the following two sections it is assumed that $\bar{\sigma} = e$. This may well be a source of error in the resulting equations of state, inasmuch as the derivative of $\bar{\sigma}$ with respect to the specific volume gives a contribution to the pressure. An approximate evaluation of $\bar{\sigma}$ may be obtained by considering the effect of multiple occupancy of the cells (see § 4.6b and § 4.7d). The problem may be avoided by allowing holes in the lattice structure (see § 4.8).

c. The concept of free volume[2]

It may now be shown that the result given in Eq. 4.4–7 can be used to obtain the starting expressions for the cell methods described in the next section. This development makes clear the assumptions which are inherent in the cell methods.

We begin by defining the probability densities $P_1^{(N)}(\boldsymbol{r}^N, \boldsymbol{p}^N)$ and $P_1^{(N)}(\boldsymbol{r}_N)$ by

$$P_1^{(N)}(\boldsymbol{r}^N, \boldsymbol{p}^N) = [N!h^{3N}Z_N^{(1)}]^{-1} \exp\left[-H(\boldsymbol{r}^N, \boldsymbol{p}^N)/kT\right] \tag{4.4-12}$$

$$P_1^{(N)}(\boldsymbol{r}^N) = [N!\lambda^{3N}Z_N^{(1)}]^{-1} \exp\left[-\Phi(\boldsymbol{r}^N)/kT\right] \tag{4.4-13}$$

The partition function $Z_N^{(1)} = (\lambda^{3N}N!)^{-1}Q_N^{(1)}$ is for a system of N interacting molecules, which are required to remain within the confines of their particular cells (with one molecule per cell). These distribution functions differ from those in Eqs. 2.1–1 and 3 only in the fact that the molecules are not allowed to move beyond the boundaries of their own private cells, although they may still interact with the molecules in other cells. We now introduce the approximation that the probability density in configuration space may be expressed as a product of functions, each of which is a function of the coordinate of only one molecule:[6]

$$P_1^{(N)}(\boldsymbol{r}^N) = \Pi_i s(\boldsymbol{r}_i) \tag{4.4-14}$$

[5] For this case Eq. 4.4–9 simplifies to

$$\bar{\sigma}^N = \Sigma_{\{m\}} (\Pi_i m_i!)^{-1}; \qquad \Sigma_i m_i = N$$

so that $\bar{\sigma}$ is just equal to the number of terms in the original summation (Eq. 4.4–6) divided by $N!$; that is, $\bar{\sigma}^N = N^N/N! = e^N$ according to Stirling's formula.

[6] This approximation is similar to that employed by Hartree in the solution of the Schrödinger equation for the many-body problem.

The function $s(\boldsymbol{r})$ is normalized over one cell:

$$\int_{\Delta} s(\boldsymbol{r})\, d\boldsymbol{r} = 1 \tag{4.4–15}$$

The vector $\boldsymbol{r}$ is taken to be the position vector of the molecule referred to some convenient origin in the cell. The best choice of the function $s(\boldsymbol{r})$ is obtained by minimizing the Helmholtz free energy, $A = U - TS$, at constant T and Δ subject to the constraint given by the normalization condition for $s(\boldsymbol{r})$.

The Helmholtz free energy is given by

$$\begin{aligned} A &= -kT \ln Z_N = -kT \ln (\lambda^{-3N} Q_N) \\ &= -NkT \ln \bar{\sigma} - kT \ln (\lambda^{-3N} Q_N^{(1)}) \\ &= -NkT \ln \bar{\sigma} + A^{(1)} - kT \ln N! \end{aligned} \tag{4.4–16}$$

The quantity $A^{(1)} = U^{(1)} - TS^{(1)}$ is the work function for a system of N interacting particles which are confined to their cells. $U^{(1)}$ and $S^{(1)}$ are given by[7]

$$\begin{aligned} U^{(1)} &= \int_{\Delta}\int_{\Delta} P_1^{(N)}(\boldsymbol{r}^N, \boldsymbol{p}^N) H(\boldsymbol{r}^N, \boldsymbol{p}^N)\, d\boldsymbol{r}^N\, d\boldsymbol{p}^N \\ &= \int_{\Delta} P_1^{(N)}(\boldsymbol{r}^N) \Phi(\boldsymbol{r}^N)\, d\boldsymbol{r}^N + \tfrac{3}{2}NkT \end{aligned} \tag{4.4–17}$$

$$\begin{aligned} TS^{(1)} &= -kT \int_{\Delta}\int_{\Delta} P_1^{(N)}(\boldsymbol{r}^N, \boldsymbol{p}^N) \ln P_1^{(N)}(\boldsymbol{r}^N, \boldsymbol{p}^N)\, d\boldsymbol{r}^N\, d\boldsymbol{p}^N - kT \ln (N! h^{3N}) \\ &= -kT \int_{\Delta} P_1^{(N)}(\boldsymbol{r}^N) \ln P_1^{(N)}(\boldsymbol{r}^N)\, d\boldsymbol{r}^N + \tfrac{3}{2}NkT - kT \ln (N! \lambda^{3N}) \end{aligned} \tag{4.4–18}$$

The quantity $A^{(1)}$ in terms of the functions $s(\boldsymbol{r})$ is, accordingly,

$$\begin{aligned} A^{(1)}/NkT = &\int_{\Delta} s(\boldsymbol{r}) \ln s(\boldsymbol{r})\, d\boldsymbol{r} + \frac{1}{2kT}\int_{\Delta}\int_{\Delta} E(\boldsymbol{r} - \boldsymbol{r}')\, s(\boldsymbol{r}) s(\boldsymbol{r}')\, d\boldsymbol{r}\, d\boldsymbol{r}' \\ &+ (1/N) \ln (N! \lambda^{3N}) \end{aligned} \tag{4.4–19}$$

In this expression the quantity $E(\boldsymbol{r})$ is defined by

$$E(\boldsymbol{r}) = \sum_{j=2}^{N} \varphi(|\boldsymbol{R}_{1j} - \boldsymbol{r}|) \tag{4.4–20}$$

and is the contribution to the total potential energy due to the interaction of particle 1 at location $\boldsymbol{r}$ with respect to the origin of its cell with particles

[7] See Problem 11, Chapter 2.

2, 3, . . . N located at the origins of their respective cells. The vector $\boldsymbol{R}_{1j}$ is the position vector of the origin of the jth cell with respect to the origin of cell 1. Now regarding A as a function of $s(\boldsymbol{r})$, we obtain for the extremalization condition:

$$\delta A = \int_{\Delta} \{kT \ln s(\boldsymbol{r}) + \int_{\Delta} E(\boldsymbol{r} - \boldsymbol{r}')s(\boldsymbol{r}')\, d\boldsymbol{r}'\}\, \delta s\, d\boldsymbol{r} = 0 \quad (4.4\text{–}21)$$

along with the restraint

$$\int_{\Delta} \delta s\, d\boldsymbol{r} = 0 \quad (4.4\text{–}22)$$

Using Lagrangian multipliers, we may obtain from Eqs. 4.4–21 and 22 an integral equation for $s(\boldsymbol{r})$. We choose rather to write this as an integral equation for $\psi(\boldsymbol{r})$, which bears the following relation to $s(\boldsymbol{r})$:

$$s(\boldsymbol{r}) = \exp\,[(\alpha - \psi)/kT] \quad (4.4\text{–}23)$$

$$\exp\,(-\alpha/kT) = \int_{\Delta} \exp\,[-\psi(\boldsymbol{r})/kT]\, d\boldsymbol{r} \quad (4.4\text{–}24)$$

Then the integral equation for $\psi(\boldsymbol{r})$ is

$$\psi(\boldsymbol{r}) = \int_{\Delta} w(\boldsymbol{r} - \boldsymbol{r}') \exp\,[(\alpha - \psi(\boldsymbol{r}'))/kT]\, d\boldsymbol{r}' \quad (4.4\text{–}25)$$

in which

$$w(\boldsymbol{r}) = E(\boldsymbol{r}) - E_0 \quad (4.4\text{–}26)$$

$$E_0 = \int_{\Delta}\int_{\Delta} E(\boldsymbol{r} - \boldsymbol{r}')s(\boldsymbol{r})s(\boldsymbol{r}')\, d\boldsymbol{r}\, d\boldsymbol{r}' \quad (4.4\text{–}27)$$

The solution of the integral equation in Eq. 4.4–25 determines the best approximation to $P_1^{(N)}(\boldsymbol{r}^N)$ as a product of functions $s(\boldsymbol{r})$.

The preceding development allows the partition function, Z_N, to be written in terms of the partition function z for a single molecule:

$$Z_N = z^N = (\lambda^{-3}\bar{\sigma} v_f \exp\,[-E_0/2kT])^N \quad (4.4\text{–}28)$$

in which v_f is the *free volume* defined by

$$v_f = \int_{\Delta} \exp\,(-\psi(\boldsymbol{r})/kT)\, d\boldsymbol{r} \quad (4.4\text{–}29)$$

From these expressions the other thermodynamic properties and the equation of state can be obtained.

As a 0th approximation it may be assumed that the molecules are located at the centers of their cells. Accordingly, when the $s(\boldsymbol{r})$ are represented by Dirac δ-functions,[8] we get for a first approximation[9] to the molecular partition function and the free volume

$$z = \lambda^{-3}\bar{\sigma}v_f \exp\left[-E(0)/2kT\right] \tag{4.4–30}$$

$$v_f = \int_\Delta \exp\{-[E(\boldsymbol{r}) - E(0)]/kT\}d\boldsymbol{r} \tag{4.4–31}$$

in which $E(\boldsymbol{r})$ is given by Eq. 4.4–20, and $\lambda^2 = h^2/2\pi mkT$.

These equations, along with the relation

$$p = kT\left(\frac{\partial \ln Z_N}{\partial V}\right)_T = NkT\left(\frac{\partial \ln z}{\partial V}\right)_T \tag{4.4–32}$$

form the starting point for the cell theories given in the next three sections. We have thus seen what approximations enter into the foundations of the cell methods. Though the cell methods represent an important advance in the theory of liquids and dense gases, it is clear that the power of such methods is limited because of the difficulty in evaluating $\bar{\sigma}$. The hole theories, which are discussed in § 4.8, are superior to the cell theories in this respect.

5. A Simple Cell Model for Liquids and Dense Gases[1, 2]

A surprisingly good simple theory for liquids may be obtained from the final equations of the last section by making rough approximations for the free volume, v_f, and the "lattice energy," $NE(0)/2$. The results of this simple cell model are compared with the experimental and calculated values for several equilibrium properties. Trouton's rule and the Hildebrand rule for vapor pressures can be obtained from this model.

a. Approximate expressions for the free volume and the lattice energy

For the evaluation of the free volume we assume that the molecules are rigid spheres of diameter σ. We fix all the molecules but one (the "wanderer") at their equilibrium positions on a regular cubic lattice.

[8] The use of Gaussian functions in this connection has recently been considered by G. Careri, *J. Chem. Phys.*, **20**, 1001 (1952).

[9] Substitution of the zeroth approximation for $\psi(\boldsymbol{r})$ into the right-hand side of Eq. 4.4–25 gives $\psi_1(\boldsymbol{r})$, the first approximation to $\psi(\boldsymbol{r})$. ψ_1 may, in turn, be substituted into the integral to get the next approximation $\psi_2(\boldsymbol{r})$. The usefulness of this is doubtful in view of the inherent error due to the difficulty of evaluating $\bar{\sigma}$.

[1] H. Eyring and J. O. Hirschfelder, *J. Phys. Chem.*, **41**, 249 (1937).

[2] J. O. Hirschfelder, *J. Chem. Ed.*, **16**, 540 (1939).

The wanderer is free to bounce around in the cell formed by the "nearest neighbors." This "free volume" has a very complicated geometrical shape.[3] For the purpose of this simple theory, however, the free volume is calculated in the following way: Consider a row of molecules along the x-axis in the lattice as shown in Fig. 4.5–1. The center of the wanderer (the shaded molecule) moves a maximum distance of $2\,[v^{1/3} - \sigma]$ along

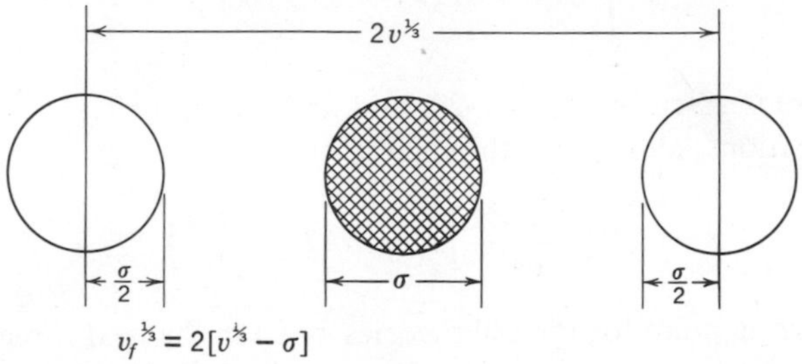

Fig. 4.5–1. The approximate free-volume for simple cubic packing of molecules.

the x-direction and has a similar range of freedom along the y- and z-directions. The free volume is then given approximately by

$$v_f = 8\,[v^{1/3} - \sigma]^3 \qquad \textit{(simplified free volume)} \qquad (4.5\text{–}1)$$

$$= 8\,[(\tilde{V}/\tilde{N})^{1/3} - 0.7816(b/\tilde{N})^{1/3}]^3$$

in which we have introduced $b = 2\pi\tilde{N}\sigma^3/3$, the van der Waals b.

Let us now consider the lattice energy per mole, $\frac{1}{2}\tilde{N}E(0)$. A fairly good approximation to the lattice energy may be obtained by saying that it is just the negative of the internal energy of vaporization per mole, $\Delta\tilde{U}_{\text{vap}}$. Hildebrand[4] has shown that $\Delta\tilde{U}_{\text{vap}}$ may be expressed by a function of the form $a(T)/\tilde{V}^n$. In Table 4.5–1 it is shown that, for a great many substances, $n = 1$ is quite satisfactory. Making this choice for n, we may write for the lattice energy

$$\tfrac{1}{2}\tilde{N}E(0) = -\Delta\tilde{U}_{\text{vap}} = -a(T)/\tilde{V} \qquad \textit{(simplified lattice energy)} \qquad (4.5\text{–}2)$$

The function $a(T)$ may be seen later in the development to be the van der Waals a.

[3] The exact shape is considered in § 4.6.

[4] J. L. Hildebrand and R. L. Scott, *Solubility of Non-Electrolytes*, 3rd ed., Reinhold (1950), p. 97.

TABLE 4.5–1

INTERNAL ENERGY OF VAPORIZATION[4]

Experimentally determined values of n in the formula

$$\Delta\tilde{U}_{\text{vap}} = a(T)/\tilde{V}^n$$

n-Heptane	1.09	Chloroform	1.02
Silicon tetrachloride	1.09	Ethyl ether	1.01
Carbon tetrachloride	1.07	Acetone	0.89
Benzene	1.05	Carbon disulfide	0.89
Silicon tetrabromide	1.04	Methanol	0.34
Stannic chloride	1.04	Mercury	0.33
Titanium tetrachloride	1.02		

Strictly speaking, the lattice energy and the free volume depend on both the attractive and the repulsive forces between the molecules. In this simplified approach, however, use is made of the fact that the free volume depends primarily on the repulsive force (the van der Waals b) and that the lattice energy depends primarily on the force of attraction (the van der Waals a).

b. The Eyring equation of state

Substitution of these simplified expressions for the free volume and the lattice energy into the formula for the molecular partition function (Eq. 4.4–30) and use of Eq. 4.4–32 give

$$\left(p + \frac{a(T)}{\tilde{V}^2}\right)(\tilde{V} - 0.7816 b^{1/3}\tilde{V}^{2/3}) = RT \qquad (4.5\text{–}3)^5$$

which is the Eyring equation of state. The constant 0.7816 is appropriate for a simple cubic lattice. For a body-centered cubic lattice the constant is 0.7163, and for face-centered cubic packing it is 0.6962. This equation is similar to the van der Waals equation except that the excluded volume now varies as the two-thirds power of the volume instead of being a constant.

Actually the Eyring equation may be considered as the limiting form of the van der Waals equation when the latter is corrected for the overlapping of the hard spheres. The necessity for doing this was recognized

[5] To show the explicit dependence on v_f, this may also be written as

$$\left(p + \frac{a(T)}{\tilde{V}^2}\right)(\tfrac{1}{2}v_f^{1/3}\, v^{2/3}) = kT \qquad (4.5\text{–}3a)$$

with v_f given by Eq. 4.5–1.

both by van der Waals and by Boltzmann. They wrote the equation of state as an infinite series of the form

$$(p + (a/\tilde{V}^2)) = (RT/\tilde{V})\,[1 + (b/\tilde{V}) + 0.625(b/\tilde{V})^2 + 0.2869(b/\tilde{V})^3 + \cdots] \tag{4.5-4}$$

Boltzmann and Jaeger computed the term $0.625(b/\tilde{V})^2$ by considering the simultaneous collisions of three molecules. Happel[6] and Majumdar[7] calculated the coefficient of the next term by considering the simultaneous collisions of four molecules. In order to make Eq. 4.5–4 agree with the Eyring equation throughout the range of liquid densities,[8] the series may be terminated with a term $0.1928(b/V)^4$. Inasmuch as this term is of the same order of magnitude as the other terms, the Eyring equation seems to be a logical extension of the van der Waals equation for the region of close packing.

Tables can be prepared showing excellent numerical agreement between the constants, a and b, determined from the liquid and from the gas. But the different methods for calculating them from the gas data give such varied values that the tabulated agreement is illusory. A rather sensitive test for the equation of state is given by a comparison of calculated and experimental coefficients of compressibility and coefficients of thermal expansion. A sample of the agreement which is obtained is shown in Table 4.5–2.

TABLE 4.5–2

THE COEFFICIENTS OF COMPRESSIBILITY AND THERMAL EXPANSION FOR LIQUIDS

Coefficient of compressibility: $\beta = V^{-1}(\partial V/\partial p)_T$
Coefficient of expansion: $\alpha = V^{-1}(\partial V/\partial T)_p$

Substance	$\beta \times 10^4$ atm^{-1}		$\alpha \times 10^3$ deg^{-1}	
	Calculated[a]	Observed	Calculated[a]	Observed
$(C_2H_5)_2O$	2.12	1.29	1.68	1.58
CCl_4	1.07	1.05	1.14	1.23
$CHCl_3$	1.03	1.00	1.31	1.27
C_6H_6	0.85	0.95	1.12	1.24

[a] Calculated from Eq. 4.5–3.

[6] H. Happel, *Ann. phys.* (4), **21**, 342 (1906).

[7] R. Majumdar, *Bull. Calcutta Math. Soc.*, **21**, 107 (1929).

[8] J. O. Hirschfelder and W. E. Roseveare, *J. Phys. Chem.*, **43**, 15 (1939). J. O. Hirschfelder, D. P. Stevenson, H. Eyring, *J. Chem. Phys.*, **5**, 896 (1937).

c. The vapor pressure: Hildebrand's rule and Trouton's rule[4]

An expression for the vapor pressure may be obtained by equating the Gibbs free energy $\tilde{G}$ of a mole of the liquid to that of a mole of the gas. We assume that the gas is ideal and further that pV for the liquid is negligible in comparison with pV for the gas. These assumptions enable us to write for the free energies per mole:

$$\tilde{G}_{\text{vap}} = -RT \ln [\lambda^{-3} kT/p] \tag{4.5–5}$$

$$\tilde{G}_{\text{liq}} = -RT \ln [\lambda^{-3} \bar{\sigma} v_f \exp(-E(0)/2kT)] \tag{4.5–6}$$

in which $\lambda^2 = h^2/2\pi mkT$. Equating the free energies in the two phases, we obtain

$$p_{\text{vap}} = (kT/\bar{\sigma} v_f) \exp [E(0)/2kT] \tag{4.5–7}$$

We see thus that $\bar{\sigma}$ appears in the expression for the vapor pressure. In this simple theory we assume that $\bar{\sigma} = 1$ in the solid phase and that it assumes the value e discontinuously at the melting point. Accordingly in this treatment of liquid-vapor equilibrium $\bar{\sigma}$ is given the value e.

If it is assumed that the lattice energy is the negative of the internal energy of vaporization, the expression for the vapor pressure may be written as

$$p_{\text{vap}} = (kT/v_f) \exp(-\Delta \tilde{H}_{\text{vap}}/RT) \tag{4.5–8}$$

in which $\Delta \tilde{H}_{\text{vap}}$ is the molar enthalpy of vaporization. Using the Eyring equation of state in the form given in Eq. 4.5–3a, we may write the free volume in the form

$$\begin{aligned} v_f &= 8\tilde{N}^2 k^3 T^3 \tilde{V}^{-2} [p + (a/\tilde{V}^2)]^{-3} \\ &\doteq 8(\tilde{V}/\tilde{N}) [(\Delta \tilde{H}_{\text{vap}}/RT) - 1]^{-3} \end{aligned} \tag{4.5–9}$$

In the second form we have assumed that the pressure p can be neglected with respect to the internal pressure, $a/\tilde{V}^2$, which may be written in terms of the molar heat of vaporization according to Eq. 4.5–2. Substitution of this expression for the free volume into that for the vapor pressure gives

$$p_{\text{vap}} = (RT/8\tilde{V}) [(\Delta \tilde{H}_{\text{vap}}/RT) - 1]^3 \exp [-\Delta \tilde{H}_{\text{vap}}/RT] \tag{4.5–10}$$

Mayer[9] has shown that $p_{\text{vap}} \tilde{V}/RT$ is a universal function of $\Delta \tilde{H}_{\text{vap}}/RT$ for a great many substances, which result is in agreement with this equation. From this result we can obtain the Hildebrand rule for vapor pressure. The concentration of the vapor, $c_{\text{vap}} = p_{\text{vap}}/RT$, is a universal function of $\Delta \tilde{H}_{\text{vap}}/RT$. According to Eq. 4.5–10 this statement is true except for a factor $\tilde{V}^{-1}$. However, the variation of this factor from compound to compound is unimportant when compared to the strong temperature dependence of the exponential factor.

[9] J. E. Mayer, *J. Chem. Phys.*, **5**, 67 (1937); J. E. Mayer and P. G. Ackermann, *J. Chem. Phys.*, **5**, 74 (1937).

Trouton's rule may be obtained by approximating $RT/8\tilde{V}$ by a universal number. For $T = 300°\text{K}$ and $\tilde{V} = 82$ cc per mole,

$$p_{\text{vap}} = 35[(\Delta\tilde{H}_{\text{vap}}/RT) - 1]^3 \exp[-\Delta\tilde{H}_{\text{vap}}/RT] \tag{4.5–11}$$

At the normal boiling point, characterized by $T = T_b$ and $p = 1$ atm, this equation may be solved for the heat of vaporization to obtain

$$[\Delta\tilde{H}_{\text{vap}}/RT_b] = 10.4 \tag{4.5–12}$$

This is Trouton's rule with the best value of the numerical constant. This constant is quite insensitive to the number which is taken for $RT/8\tilde{V}$: when the latter is changed by a factor of two the Trouton constant is altered by only a few per cent. For the noble gases, which have very low boiling points and small molal volumes, Eq. 4.5–10 gives a Trouton constant of about 12; such a value is in accord with experiment.

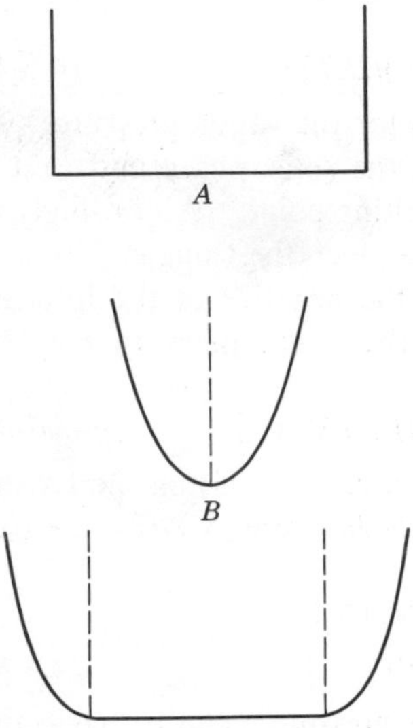

Fig. 4.5–2. Potential energy of a molecule in a cell: A is the simplest version of the liquid. B is the solid. C is the potential for a molecule in the liquid which leads to the correct heat capacity.

d. Heat capacities

The simple theory of liquids requires further corrections before we can calculate the heat capacity. Up to this point we have assumed that the potential field in which the molecules move is a box similar to that shown in drawing A of Fig. 4.5–2. The perpendicular walls correspond to rigid, elastic molecules. But we know that in a solid, where the molecules are almost always in a state of collision with their neighbors, the potential field is nearly parabolic (as shown in the drawing B) and has a curvature related to the characteristic temperature. In improving the potential field for the molecules in the liquid we assume: (1) In between collisions the molecules move in a force-free space as before. (2) During collisions the molecules are repelled by their neighbors with exactly the same forces as in the solid. Thus the walls of the potential well for the liquid have the same curvature as the potential for the solid. The improved free volume is formed by splitting the potential for the solid B along the dotted line in the middle and inserting a force-free region as shown in drawing *C*. In this manner, Kincaid and Eyring[10] were able to calculate the heat capacity and most of the other thermodynamical properties of liquid mercury to within the experimental errors. To be sure, the few constants occurring in their equations were determined from experimental data, but the agreements establish the theoretical relationships as at least good empirical interpolation formulas.

e. The entropy change on melting

It has already been stated that in this simple theory $\bar{\sigma}$ is assumed to jump discontinuously from 1 to e at the melting point. This discontinuity in $\bar{\sigma}$ corresponds to an entropy of fusion of R per mole. This "communal entropy" has been discussed in § 4.4b. According to this theory it would seem reasonable to expect that the entropy of fusion would be about 2 e.u. per mole. Experimentally it has been found that the average entropy of fusion of a large number of monatomic substances is 2.2 e.u.

The entropy of fusion of polyatomic molecules is further complicated by vibrations in the solid phase. The entropy of vibration, S_v, can be estimated if the vibration frequencies are known from Raman spectra or other data. Here, for the purpose of numerical calculations, the value 50 cm^{-1} is used in accordance with Pauling's[11] observations. The entropy of rotation $\tilde{S}_r$ in the liquid phase can be computed from the moments of inertia. The entropy of fusion $\tilde{S}_f$ is then

$$\tilde{S}_f = R + \tilde{S}_r - \tilde{S}_v \tag{4.5–13}$$

Table 4.5–3 shows the sort of agreement which is obtained. In general the entropy of fusion of polyatomic molecules should be roughly $\tilde{S}_f = 2 + 3D$ e.u., where D is the number of degrees of vibration which are converted into rotations during the melting process.

TABLE 4.5–3

Substance	$\tilde{S}_r$	$\tilde{S}_v$	$(\tilde{S}_f)_{\text{calcd}}$	$(\tilde{S}_f)_{\text{obs}}$
Cl_2	13.6	8.8	6.8	6.8
Br_2	16.1	9.9	8.2	9.5
I_2	18.3	10.7	9.6	9.5
CS_2	14.5	7.2	9.3	8.4
N_2O	13.4	7.7	7.7	8.6

Although the picture of the melting process described here is reasonably convincing and the agreement of the predictions with experiment reasonably good, the concept should not be accepted too seriously. For it was

[10] J. F. Kincaid and H. Eyring, *J. Chem. Phys.*, **5**, 587 (1937); **6**, 620 (1938); *J. Phys. Chem.*, **43**, 37 (1939).

[11] L. Pauling, *Phys. Rev.*, **36**, 430 (1930).

shown in § 4.4c that there is substantial theoretical evidence that the parameter $\bar{\sigma}$ varies smoothly from the melting point of the substance up to its boiling point.

Lennard-Jones and Devonshire[12] assume that, in the process of melting, a number of new lattice positions (called β-sites) equal in number to the original sites (α-sites) appear. The redistribution of the atoms between the old α-sites and the new β-sites involves an increase in entropy, energy, and volume, and with a suitable and reasonable choice of parameters excellent agreement with experiment has been obtained by these authors.

6. The Equation of State for Rigid Non-attracting Spheres

In the preceding section a simple cell model was described for dense gases and liquids. In this model assumptions were made as to the free volume and the lattice energy, and it is difficult to determine the extent to which the assumptions are reasonable. In this section we discuss rigid spherical molecules and introduce no assumptions other than those discussed in § 4.4. First of all, we examine the calculation of the exact free volume and the errors involved in "smearing" the free volume. We also consider the effects of choosing points in the cell other than the central point as the "origin" in the cell. We find that by an appropriate choice of the origin we can obtain an equation of state for dense gases which gives the correct second virial coefficient at low densities.

a. The exact and "smeared" free volume

In this discussion we consider rigid spheres of diameter σ, occupying a volume V and arranged in the form of a face-centered cubic lattice. Each molecule in the lattice has twelve nearest neighbors, a distance of a away. This may best be pictured, as in Fig. 4.6–1, by realizing that the nearest neighbors occupy the midpoints of the twelve edges of an imaginary cube constructed about any given molecule. The volume per molecule, $v = V/N$, is related to the distance between nearest neighbors by the relation

$$v = a^3/\sqrt{2} \tag{4.6–1}$$

As may be seen in Fig. 4.6–1 the cell corresponding to this volume is a dodecahedron. The total volume V may then be regarded as being made up of these dodecahedral cells with one molecule in each cell. These cells are the same as those used in the discussion in § 4.4.

Let us now label the central molecule in Fig. 4.6–1 the "wanderer." It is free to move about while its neighbors remain fixed in their lattice

[12] J. E. Lennard-Jones and A. F. Devonshire, *Proc. Roy. Soc.* (*London*), **A169**, 317 (1939); **A170**, 464 (1939). J. E. Lennard-Jones, *Proc. Phys. Soc.*, **52**, 38 (1940).

positions, as long as $v > \sigma^3/\sqrt{2}$ (the specific volume corresponding to the tightest possible packing). At high densities ($v < 2\sigma^3$) the wanderer cannot escape from the "cage" formed by its nearest neighbors. Under such conditions the free volume, defined according to Eq. 4.4–31, is just that volume available to the center of the wandering molecule. At moderately low densities ($v > 2\sigma^3$) the wanderer is no longer confined to

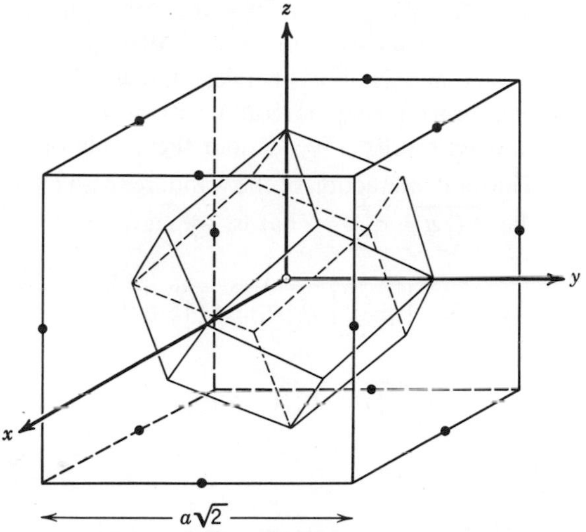

Fig. 4.6–1. The dodecahedron formed by planes bisecting the distances between a molecule located at the origin and its twelve nearest neighbors. The dodecahedron represents the volume per molecule, $v = V/N = a^3/\sqrt{2}$. [From R. J. Buehler, R. H. Wentorf, J. O. Hirschfelder, C. F. Curtiss, *J. Chem. Phys.*, **19**, 61 (1951).]

the cage formed by the nearest neighbors. The free volume is, however, still defined by Eq. 4.4–31. According to this definition the wanderer is confined to move in a region bounded partially by nearest neighbors and partially by the imaginary boundaries of the dodecahedral cell. At very low densities ($v > 4\sqrt{2}\sigma^3$) the wanderer suffers no collisions with its nearest neighbors and is free to move about the whole cell (that is, $v_f = v$). In terms of the reduced specific volume, $v^* = v/\sigma^3$, the above information may be summarized as:

$v^* = 1/\sqrt{2}$	tightest possible packing
$v^* = 2$	wanderer can just escape from cage
$v^* \geq 4\sqrt{2}$	entire cell available to wanderer

In Fig. 4.6–2 are shown several examples of the exact shapes of the free volume for the model under consideration. The geometry of the model and the analytical expression for the exact free volume are very complicated and are not given here.[1]

Because of the great complexity of the exact free volume, even for rigid spheres, it is customary in free volume calculations to employ a "smeared" or "sphericalized" free volume. This is done by replacing the angle-dependent quantity $[E(\boldsymbol{r}) - E(0)]$ in Eq. 4.4–31 by an approximately equivalent spherically symmetric function. We first take an angle average of the interaction $\varphi(|\boldsymbol{a}+\boldsymbol{r}|)$ between the wanderer (at position $\boldsymbol{r}$ in its cell) and *one* nearest neighbor (at position $\boldsymbol{a}$ with respect to the center of the wanderer's cell). We denote the result of this averaging by $\overline{\varphi(|\boldsymbol{a}+\boldsymbol{r}|)}$. The total interaction of the wanderer with all its c neighbors is then taken to be $c\overline{\varphi(|\boldsymbol{a}+\boldsymbol{r}|)}$. That is, we let

$$E(r) - E(0) \doteq c\left[\frac{1}{4\pi}\int\!\!\int \varphi(|\boldsymbol{a}+\boldsymbol{r}|)\sin\theta\, d\theta\, d\phi - \varphi(a)\right]$$

$$= c[\overline{\varphi(|\boldsymbol{a}+\boldsymbol{r}|)} - \varphi(a)] \qquad (4.6\text{–}2)$$

with the result that

$$v_f = \int \exp\left[-\frac{c}{kT}[\overline{\varphi(|\boldsymbol{a}+\boldsymbol{r}|)} - \varphi(a)]\right] 4\pi r^2\, dr \qquad (4.6\text{–}3)$$

For rigid sphere lattice under consideration the sphericalization is particularly simple. The smeared free volume is the largest sphere which can fit inside the exact free volume discussed above:

$V_f = 4/3 (a-\sigma)^3$

$$v_f^* = v_f/\sigma^3 = \tfrac{4}{3}\pi\left(\frac{a}{\sigma} - 1\right)^3 \qquad (4.6\text{–}4)$$

The equation of state is then

$$\frac{pV}{NkT} = \left[1 - \frac{\sigma}{a}\right]^{-1} \qquad (4.6\text{–}5)$$

The free volume and the equation of state for this sphericalized model are

[1] R. J. Buehler, R. H. Wentorf, J. O. Hirschfelder, C. F. Curtiss, *J. Chem. Phys.*, **19**, 61 (1951).

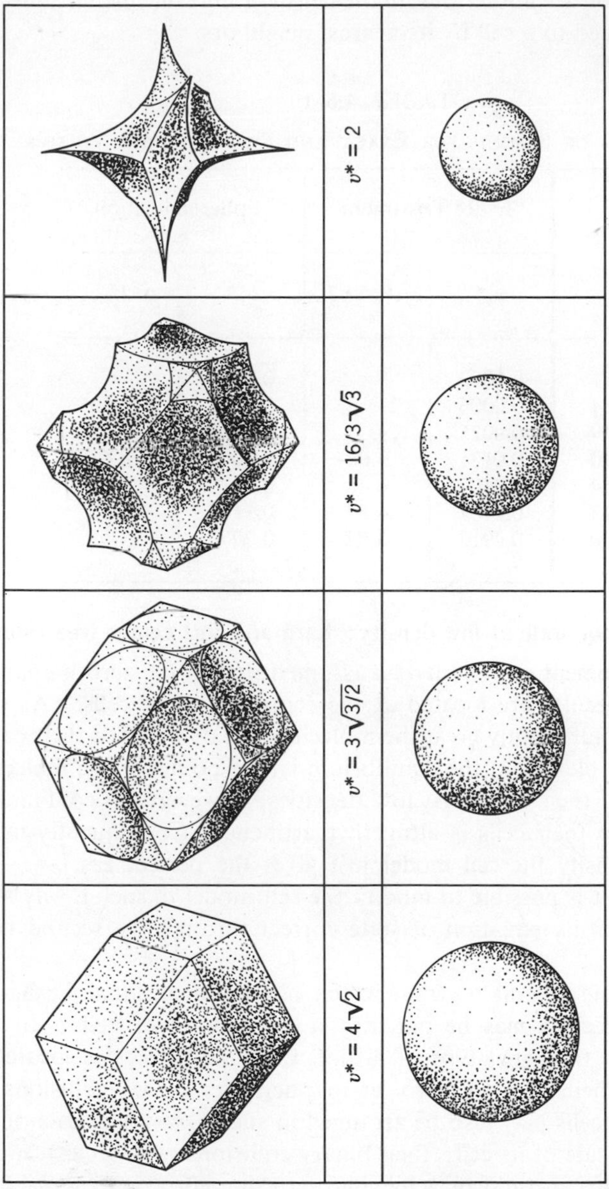

Fig. 4.6-2. The figures in the top row show the shape of the exact free volumes. The corresponding "smeared" free volumes are shown in the bottom row. [From R. J. Buehler, R. H. Wentorf, J. O. Hirschfelder, and C. F. Curtiss, *J. Chem. Phys.*, **19**, 61 (1951).]

compared in Table 4.6–1, with analogous results for the exact treatment. This comparison shows that the errors in the equation of state introduced by sphericalization are not serious, in the density range in which a molecule is actually confined to a cell by its nearest neighbors.

TABLE 4.6–1

COMPARISON OF RESULTS FOR EXACT AND SMEARED FREE VOLUME

v^*	Exact Treatment		Sphericalization	
	v_f^*	pV/NkT	v_f^*	pV/NkT
0.7071	0.0000	∞	0.0000	∞
0.8104	0.0006	23.	0.0004	22.50
0.8779	0.0025	14.	0.0018	14.37
1.0240	0.0131	9.04	0.0095	8.61
1.1854	0.0407	6.48	0.0275	6.32
1.5573	0.1767	4.53	0.1143	4.32
2.0000	0.4912	3.77	0.2977	3.41

b. The equation of state at low density: hard and soft center free volumes

In the development of § 4.4 it was assumed that in the zeroth approximation the molecules are located at the centers of their cells. As long as the density is sufficiently great the molecules are confined to their cages, and it is reasonable to put the equilibrium lattice points of the molecules at the centers of their cells. At low densities, however, the confining of the molecules to their cells is altogether artificial. Consequently in the limit of low density the cell model just gives the perfect gas law. We now show how it is possible to modify the cell model in such a way as to obtain a low-density equation of state correct through the second virial coefficient.

Let us examine several ways in which a two-dimensional hexagonal array of N molecules may be put into a latticework of cells. In Fig. 4.6–3a is shown the usual type of lattice, with the molecules located at the centers of their cells. Clearly at low densities binary collisions are excluded. The cells may also be arranged in such a way that each molecule lies on the side of its cell; then binary collisions may occur (see Fig. 4.6–3b). Another method of achieving the same effect is to replace the vertical partitions with new ones passing through the molecules (as in Fig. 4.6–3c). For the three-dimensional face-centered cubic lattice it has been found that the choice analogous to Fig. 4.6–3c is simpler to handle. Both the last two models, (*b*) and (*c*), give the correct value for the second virial coefficient. However, the overall equation of state of the two patterns is different. It therefore appears that the requirement of giving the correct second virial coefficient does not uniquely specify the cell.

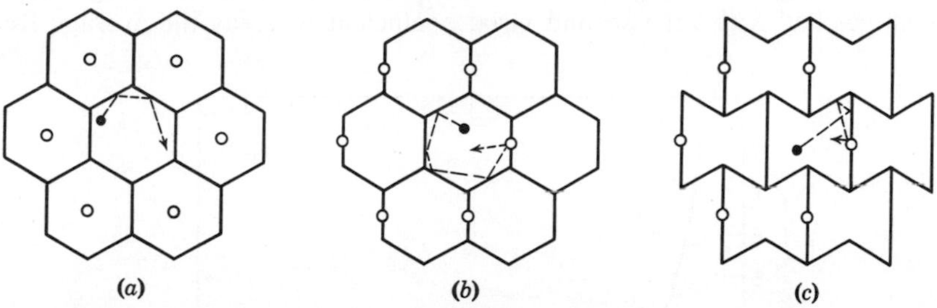

Fig. 4.6–3. Several methods of arranging a network of cells about a hexagonal lattice of molecules. The black molecule is the "wanderer." All other molecules are held fixed.

Let us consider the arrangement described in Fig. 4.6–3c. When the wanderer is in the left half of the unit cell, it behaves as if it were alone in the cell of the type in Fig. 4.6–3a, with twelve nearest neighbors. On the other hand, when the wanderer is in the right half of the cell, it behaves as if it were in a hexagonal cell with another molecule at the center and

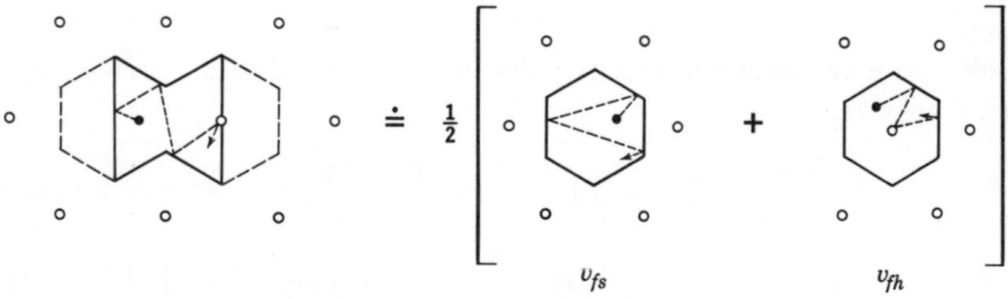

Fig. 4.6–4. Replacement of the free volume by an "average free volume," v_{fa}. The volumes labeled v_{fs} and v_{fh} are the "soft center" and "hard center" free volumes, respectively. The black molecule is the wanderer.

with eleven nearest neighbors. Hence this approach may be represented by using an arithmetic average of the two types of free volume. We refer to this *average free volume* as being a sum of a *soft center* free volume (the wanderer alone in the cell) and a *hard center* free volume (the wanderer in a cell with another molecule at the center of the cell and eleven nearest neighbors. This is illustrated in Fig. 4.6–4.

The free volume and the equation of state have been calculated for a face-centered cubic lattice of rigid spherical molecules using a "soft-center" model (which corresponds to the usual technique of centering the cells on lattice positions as described in *a* of this section) and also for the "average" free volume just described. The two methods give identical results at high density. For low density the soft-center model gives the ideal gas law with zero second virial coefficient whereas the average free

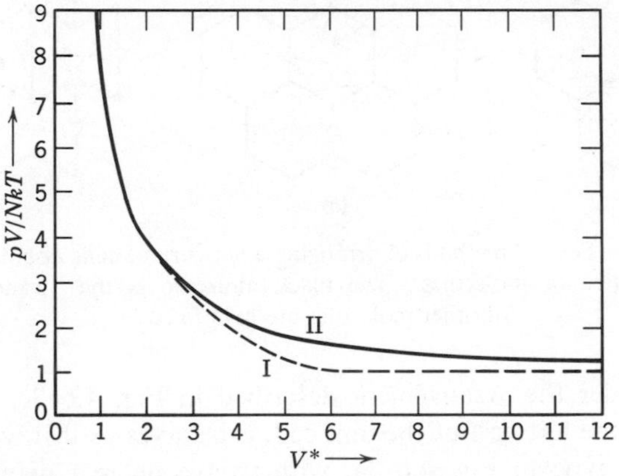

Fig. 4.6–5. A comparison of the compressibility factors obtained by the "soft center" model (curve I) and by the "averaged free volume" method (curve II). [From R. J. Buehler, R. H. Wentorf, J. O. Hirschfelder, and C. F. Curtiss, *J. Chem. Phys.*, **19**, 61 (1951).]

volume model gives the proper value for the second virial coefficient of rigid spheres:

$$\frac{p\tilde{V}}{RT} = \left(1 - \frac{b_0}{\tilde{V}}\right)^{-1} = 1 + \frac{b_0}{\tilde{V}} + \frac{b_0^2}{\tilde{V}^2} + \cdots \tag{4.6–6}$$

The third virial coefficient by this procedure is incorrect, being b_0^2 instead of $\frac{5}{8}b_0^2$. The compressibility factors for the two models are shown graphically in Fig. 4.6–5.

Pople[2] has considered in more detail some of the implications of Kirkwood's development, which was described in § 4.4. By an approximate procedure, Pople obtained an expression for $\bar{\sigma}$. The expression takes into account the effect of multiple occupancy of the cells. If we consider only the results of double occupancy, Pople's result can be

[2] J. Pople, *Phil. Mag.*, **42**, 459–467 (1951). Pople's work is summarized at the end of § 4.7.

written formally in terms of the soft-center and hard-center free volume defined above:

$$v_f = \bar{\sigma} v_{fs} = v_{fs} + \sqrt{2 v_{fs} v_{fh}} \tag{4.6–7}$$

This result leads to an equation of state which is somewhat different from those which we have thus far described. It gives a second virial coefficient which is 58.6 per cent of the correct value.

7. The Equation of State of Lennard-Jones and Devonshire[1]

As in the preceding two sections we take as our starting point[2] the last three equations of § 4.4. This time, however, we use a more realistic potential function for the calculations, namely the Lennard-Jones (6-12) potential:

$$\varphi(r) = 4\epsilon \left[\left(\frac{\sigma}{r}\right)^{12} - \left(\frac{\sigma}{r}\right)^{6} \right] \tag{1.3–27}$$

The parameters, σ and ϵ, in this function may be used to define the following reduced variables:

$T^* = kT/\epsilon$	reduced temperature
$r^* = r/\sigma$	reduced distance
$a^* = a/\sigma$	reduced nearest-neighbor distance
$v^* = v/\sigma^3$	reduced cell size $= a^{*3}/\sqrt{2}$ and reduced volume per molecule
$v_f^* = v_f/\sigma^3$	reduced free volume
$p^* = p\sigma^3/\epsilon$	reduced pressure (4.7–1)

In addition it is usual to define two other dimensionless quantities:

$$y = (r/a)^2 = (r^*/a^*)^2$$
$$g = (v_f/2\pi a^3) = (v_f^*/2\pi a^{*3}) \tag{4.7–2}$$

the use of which simplifies some of the formulae.

Since the Lennard-Jones potential function gives quite a good description of the equation of state and transport properties of dilute gases, its use in the cell method should provide a fairly good test of the validity of this method. As is to be expected from the previous discussions, good agreement is obtained in the density range of liquids, but unsatisfactory

[1] J. E. Lennard-Jones and A. F. Devonshire, *Proc. Roy. Soc. (London)*, **A163**, 53 (1937).

[2] As was mentioned in § 4.4 the order of the subject material is not historical. The development described in this section was originally obtained on a semi-intuitive basis. Kirkwood's justification of the method came considerably later.

results are found at critical densities and lower. Calculations of Pople[3] and of Janssens and Prigogine[4] indicate that the model may be somewhat improved by taking into account double occupancy.

a. Development of the equation of state

Once again we use for our model the face-centered cubic lattice. The actual potential within a unit cell is of course angle-dependent. To simplify the calculations, an equivalent sphericalized potential is used. The nature of the potential field within a cell for various cell sizes is shown in Fig. 4.7–1. The situation when the gas density is quite low is shown

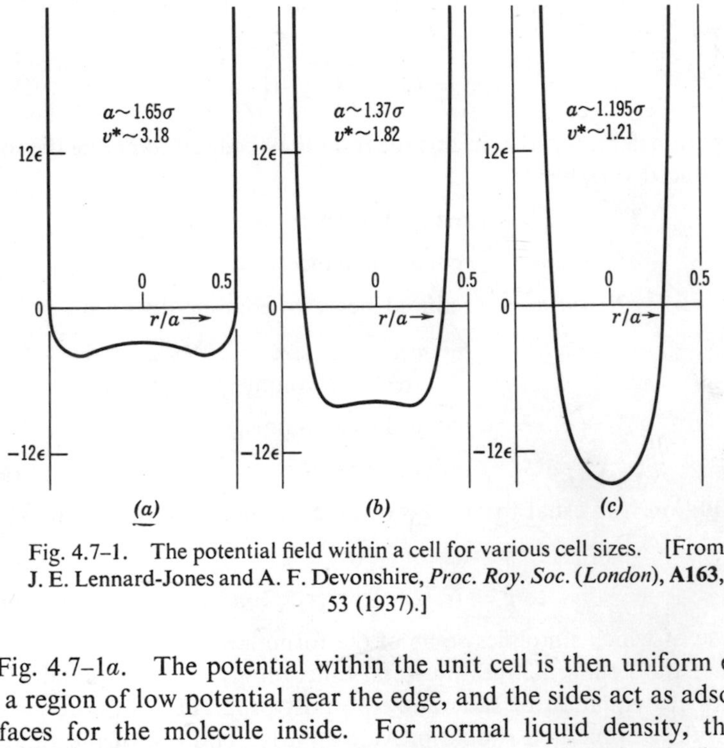

Fig. 4.7–1. The potential field within a cell for various cell sizes. [From J. E. Lennard-Jones and A. F. Devonshire, *Proc. Roy. Soc.* (*London*), **A163**, 53 (1937).]

in Fig. 4.7–1*a*. The potential within the unit cell is then uniform except for a region of low potential near the edge, and the sides act as adsorbing surfaces for the molecule inside. For normal liquid density, the low potential regions overlap, with the formation of an energy barrier between them as shown in Fig. 4.7–1*b*. As the density is increased to normal crystal density, a stage is reached at which the barrier disappears and the two minima coincide as in *c*. With further increase in the density, the overlapping repulsive fields cause the minimum to rise.

[3] J. Pople, *Phil. Mag.*, **42**, 459 (1951).

[4] P. Janssens and I. Prigogine, *Physica*, **16**, 851 (1950).

Let us assume for the moment that the wanderer interacts with no molecules farther removed than the shell of twelve nearest neighbors. Accordingly we replace the quantity $[E(r) - E(0)]$ of Eq. 4.4–31 by the smeared function described in § 4.6a. For the Lennard-Jones potential the result is

$$[E(r) - E(0)] \doteq c\left[\frac{1}{4\pi}\int\int \varphi(\sqrt{a^2 + r^2 - 2ar\cos\theta})\sin\theta\, d\theta\, d\phi - \varphi(a)\right]$$

$$= c\epsilon\left[\frac{l(y)}{v^{*4}} - 2\frac{m(y)}{v^{*2}}\right] \tag{4.7–3}$$

in which

$$l(y) = (1 + 12y + 25.2y^2 + 12y^3 + y^4)(1 - y)^{-10} - 1$$

$$m(y) = (1 + y)(1 - y)^{-4} - 1 \tag{4.7–4}$$

Substitution of this expression for $[E(r) - E(0)]$ into Eq. 4.4–31 gives the free volume. We may then calculate the equation of state from Eqs. 4.4–30 and 32, and, assuming that $\bar{\sigma}$ is volume independent, we get[5]

$$\frac{pV}{NkT} = 1 + \frac{24}{T^*}\left[\frac{1}{v^{*4}}\left(1 + \frac{2g_l}{g}\right) - \frac{1}{v^{*2}}\left(1 + \frac{2g_m}{g}\right)\right] \tag{4.7–5}$$

The quantity g is the dimensionless free volume defined in Eq. 4.7–2, and g_l and g_m are combinations[6] of the derivatives of g with respect to T^* and v^*. These quantities are given by the following integrals:[7]

$$g(v^*, T^*) = \int_0^{y_0} \sqrt{y}\exp\left\{-\frac{c}{T^*}\left[\frac{l(y)}{v^{*4}} - 2\frac{m(y)}{v^{*2}}\right]\right\} dy \tag{4.7–6}$$

$$g_l(v^*, T^*) = \int_0^{y_0} l(y)\sqrt{y}\exp\left\{-\frac{c}{T^*}\left[\frac{l(y)}{v^{*4}} - 2\frac{m(y)}{v^{*2}}\right]\right\} dy \tag{4.7–7}$$

$$g_m(v^*, T^*) = \int_0^{y_0} m(y)\sqrt{y}\exp\left\{-\frac{c}{T^*}\left[\frac{l(y)}{v^{*4}} - 2\frac{m(y)}{v^{*2}}\right]\right\} dy \tag{4.7–8}$$

[5] In their original treatment Lennard-Jones and Devonshire used $[1.2 + (2g_m/g)]$ as the coefficient of the $1/v^{*2}$ term instead of $[1.0 + (2g_m/g)]$. This accounts for the effect of the second and third shells on the lattice energy but not on the free volume.

[6] In particular,
$$v^*(\partial g/\partial v^*) = (4c/T^*)\left(\frac{g_l}{v^{*4}} - \frac{g_m}{v^{*2}}\right)$$
$$T^*(\partial g/\partial T^*) = (c/T^*)\left(\frac{g_l}{v^{*4}} - 2\frac{g_m}{v^{*2}}\right)$$

[7] The limiting values of the integrals g, g_l, and g_m at high and low temperatures have been given by J. S. Rowlinson and C. F. Curtiss, *J. Chem. Phys.*, **19**, 1519 (1951).

In these integrals the upper limit of integration is

$$y_0 = (3/4\pi\sqrt{2})^{2/3} = 0.30544 \tag{4.7–9}$$

for a face-centered cubic lattice.

Equation 4.7–5 is the Lennard-Jones–Devonshire equation of state. It gives the compressibility factor pV/NkT as a function of the reduced temperature T^* and the reduced specific volume (that is, the reduced cell size) v^*. This is consistent with the principle of corresponding states discussed in § 4.1. The compressibility factor clearly approaches unity in the limit of high temperatures and/or low densities. The equation predicts a critical isotherm and at lower temperatures the p-V curves are S-shaped like the isotherms of the van der Waals equation. That the isotherms do not have a horizontal portion connecting the gas and liquid phases is a result of approximations inherent in the theory. As described in Chapter 5, it is possible to use ordinary thermodynamic arguments to introduce the horizontal portion and discuss liquid-vapor equilibria.

The integrals g, g_l, and g_m have been evaluated by Lennard-Jones and Devonshire,[1] by Prigogine and Raulier,[8] by Prigogine and Garikian,[9] and by Hill.[10] The results of their calculations are in substantial agreement. Prigogine and Garikian made their calculations for the Lennard-Jones (6-12) potential and also the Sutherland model. They found that the thermodynamic properties, as calculated by the cell method, are relatively insensitive to the form of the potential. Consequently, it does not seem worthwhile to make calculations for the Lennard-Jones–Devonshire equation of state, using more elaborate intermolecular potential functions. Quantum corrections to the Lennard-Jones–Devonshire equation have been calculated by Lunbeck;[11] these calculations are discussed in § 6.6b.

b. The three-shell modification of the Lennard-Jones and Devonshire equation of state

The most extensive calculations which have been made for the Lennard-Jones–Devonshire equation of state are those performed by Wentorf, Buehler, Hirschfelder, and Curtiss.[12] In their calculations the interaction of the wanderer with the first three neighboring shells of molecules is

[8] I. Prigogine and S. Raulier, *Physica*, **9**, 396 (1942).
[9] I. Prigogine and G. Garikian, *J. Chim. Physique*, **45**, 273 (1948).
[10] T. L. Hill, *J. Phys. Colloid Chem.*, **51**, 1219 (1947).
[11] R. J. Lunbeck, Doctoral Dissertation, Amsterdam (1951).
[12] R. H. Wentorf, R. J. Buehler, J. O. Hirschfelder, and C. F. Curtiss, *J. Chem. Phys.*, **18**, 1484 (1950).

included. (The first shell of 12 molecules is at a distance a, the second shell of 6 molecules at a distance $a\sqrt{2}$, and the third shell of 24 at a distance $a\sqrt{3}$.) With this modification the equation of state is given by

$$\frac{pV}{NkT} = 1 + \frac{24}{T^*}\left[\frac{1}{v^{*4}}\left(1.0110 + \frac{2G_L}{G}\right) - \frac{1}{v^{*2}}\left(1.2045 + \frac{2G_M}{G}\right)\right] \quad (4.7\text{–}10)$$

The quantities G, G_L, and G_M are integrals like those for g, g_l, and g_m,

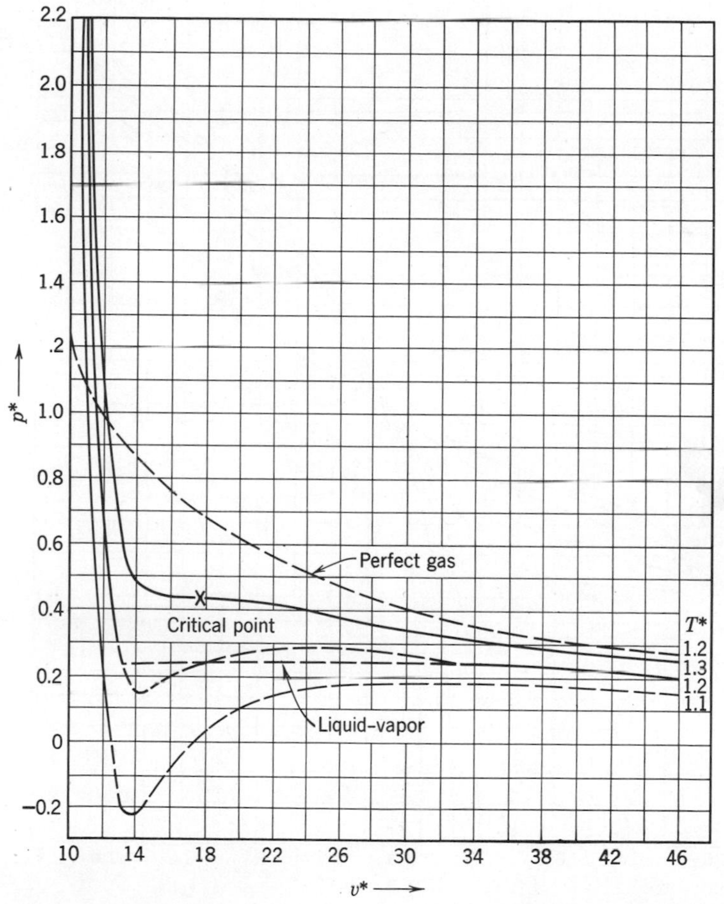

Fig. 4.7–2. Reduced pressure $p^* = p\sigma^3/\epsilon$ as a function of the reduced volume, v^*. The curves are isotherms and are labeled with the values of the reduced temperature, T^*. [From R. H. Wentorf, R. J. Buehler, J. O. Hirschfelder, and C. F. Curtiss, *J. Chem. Phys.*, **18**, 1484 (1950).]

except that the functions $l(y)$ and $m(y)$ are replaced by the functions $L(y)$ and $M(y)$, which are

$$L(y) = l(y) + \frac{1}{128} l(\tfrac{1}{2}y) + \frac{2}{729} l(\tfrac{1}{3}y)$$

$$M(y) = m(y) + \frac{1}{16} m(\tfrac{1}{2}y) + \frac{2}{27} m(\tfrac{1}{3}y) \tag{4.7–11}$$

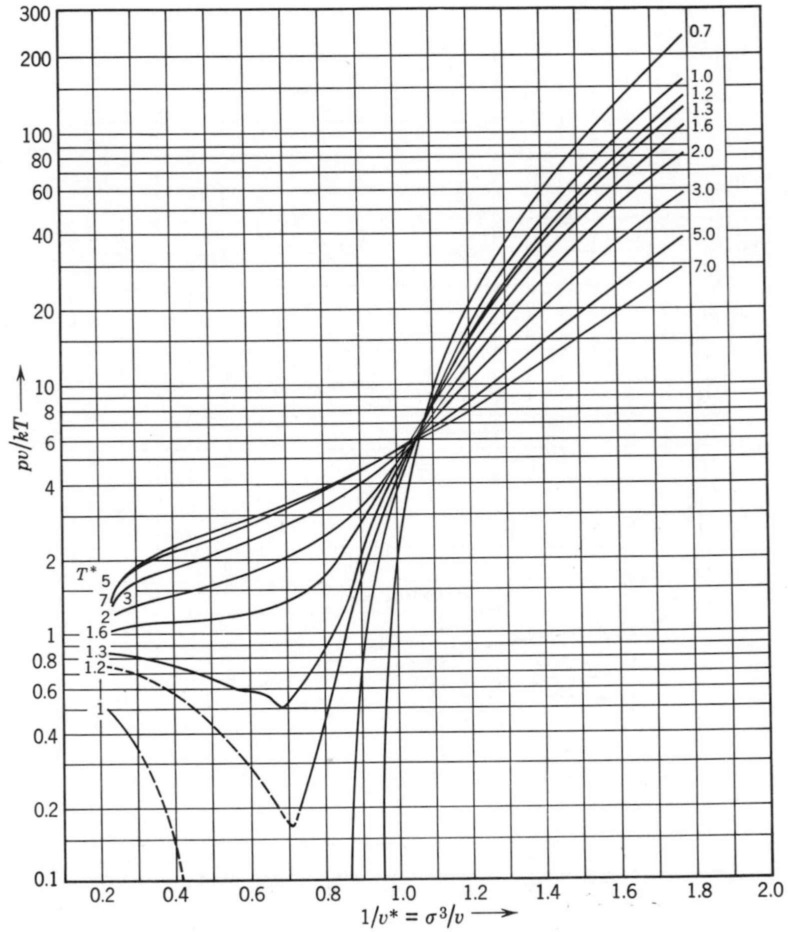

Fig. 4.7–3. The compressibility factor as a function of the reduced density. The curves are isotherms and are labeled with the values of the reduced temperature T^*. [From R. H. Wentorf, R. J. Buehler, J. O. Hirschfelder, and C. F. Curtiss, *J. Chem. Phys.*, **18**, 1484 (1950).]

In Fig. 4.7–2 p^* is shown as a function of v^* and T^*, as calculated according to Eq. 4.7–10. Also calculated from this equation is the graph of the compressibility factor, pV/NkT, which is given in Fig. 4.7–3. This same information is given in tabular form in Table I-H. The effect on the compressibility factor of including the interaction of the wanderer with next-nearest neighbors is indicated by the comparison given in Table 4.7–1.

TABLE 4.7–1

EFFECTS OF NEXT-NEAREST NEIGHBORS ON THE COMPRESSIBILITY IN THE MODEL OF LENNARD-JONES AND DEVONSHIRE

(a) Calculations include only *one* shell of neighbors. (Based on the g-functions of Prigogine and Garikian[9] and using Eq. 4.7–5.)

(b) Calculations include *one* shell of neighbors in the calculations of the free volume and *three* shells in the computation of the lattice energy. (Based on the one-shell g-functions of Prigogine and Garikian[9] and using Eq. 4.7–5, with the coefficient 1.2—see footnote 5.)

(c) Calculations include *three* shells of neighbors in both the computation of the free volume and the lattice energy. (Based on the three-shell G-functions of Wentorf, Buehler, Hirschfelder, and Curtiss[12] and using Eq. 4.7–10.)

pV/NkT

v^* \ T^*		0.7	1.0	1.7
1.195	a	3.607	3.764	2.000
	b	−1.161	0.459	0.053
	c	−3.292	−0.344	2.194
1.414	a	0.018	1.935	2.994
	b	−3.395	−0.453	1.588
	c	−3.566	−0.852	1.515
1.826	a	0.071	1.194	2.181
	b	−1.998	−0.255	1.329
	c	−2.142	−0.325	1.300
2.575	a	0.099	0.888	1.667
	b	−0.951	−0.255	1.235
	c	−0.923	−0.325	1.200

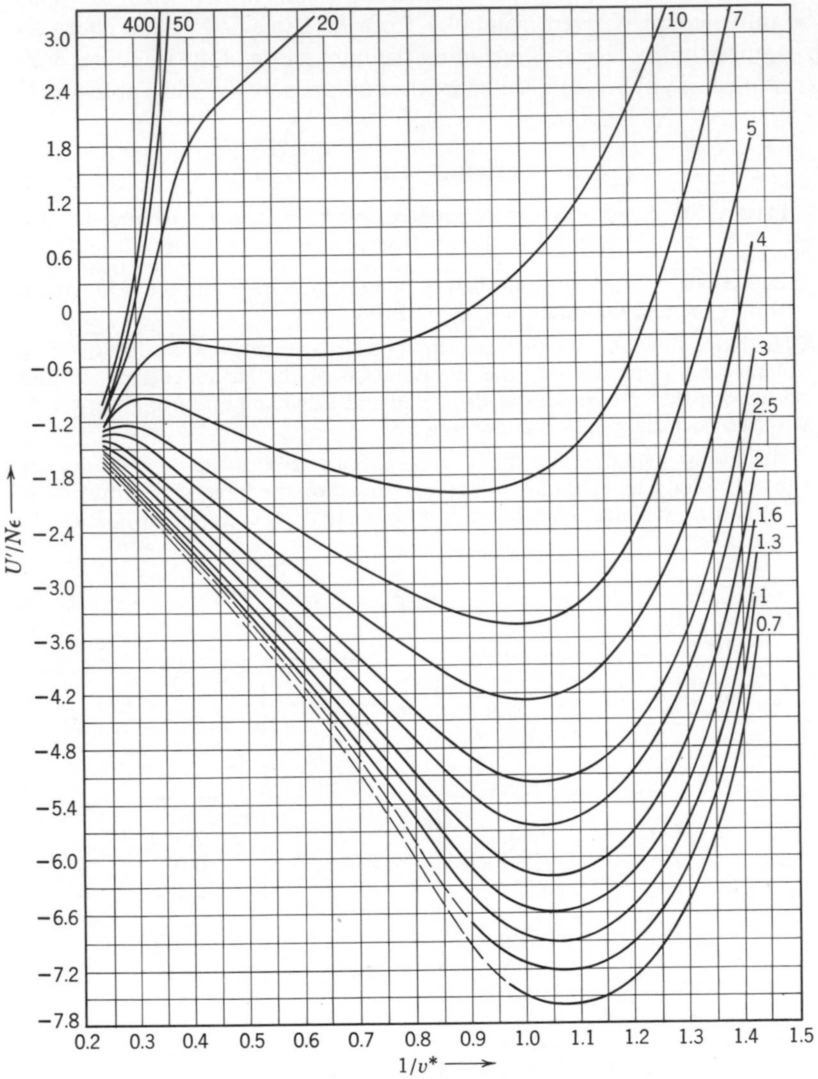

Fig. 4.7–4. Reduced internal energy of gas imperfection $U'/N\epsilon$ as a function of the reduced density. The curves are isotherms and are labeled with the values of the reduced temperature, T^*. [From R. H. Wentorf, R. J. Buehler, J. O. Hirschfelder, and C. F. Curtiss, *J. Chem. Phys.*, **18**, 1484 (1950).]

Differences between the values of the thermodynamic properties for the non-ideal substance and the corresponding values for the ideal gas at the same temperature are denoted by primes, that is,

$$\begin{aligned} U'(v, T) &= U(v, T) - U^0(T) \\ C_v'(v, T) &= C_v(v, T) - C_v^0(T) \\ S'(v, T) &= S(v, T) - S^0(T) + R \ln p(v, T) \end{aligned} \tag{4.7–12}$$

$U^0(T)$ and $C_v^0(T)$ are the values of the internal energy and specific heat at temperature T and zero pressure. $S^0(T)$ is defined as the limit of $(S + R \ln p)$ as $p \to 0$. In Fig. 4.7–4, 5 and 6 are shown the quantities

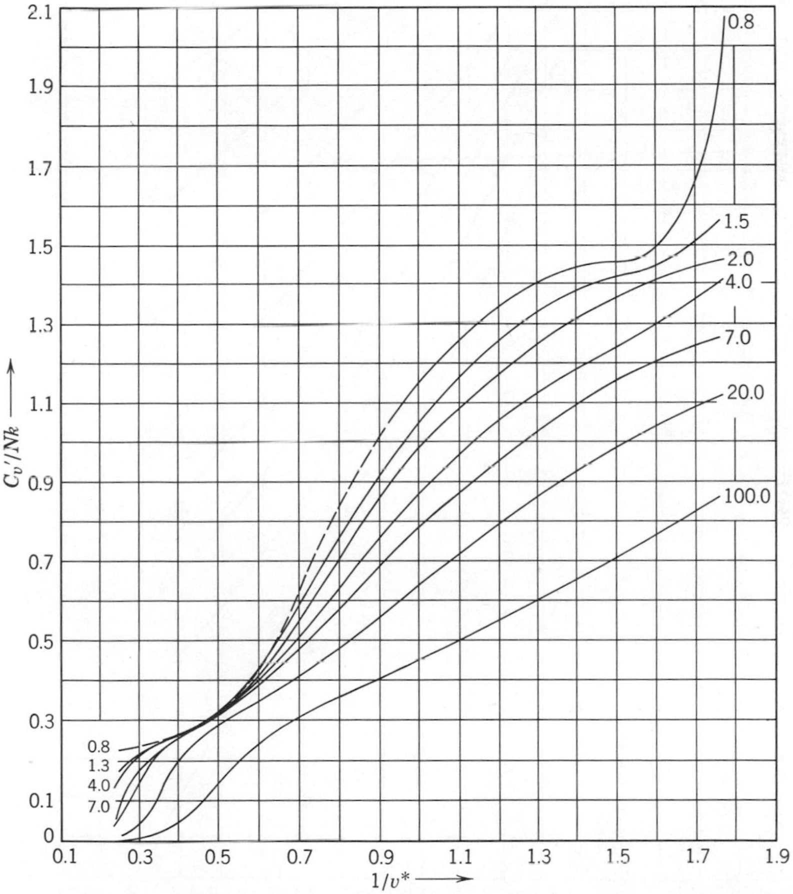

Fig. 4.7–5. Reduced heat capacity of gas imperfection, C_v'/Nk, vs. reduced density. The curves are isotherms and are labeled with the values of the reduced temperature, T^*. [From R. H. Wentorf, R. J. Buehler, J. O. Hirschfelder, and C. F. Curtiss, *J. Chem. Phys.*, **18**, 1484 (1950).]

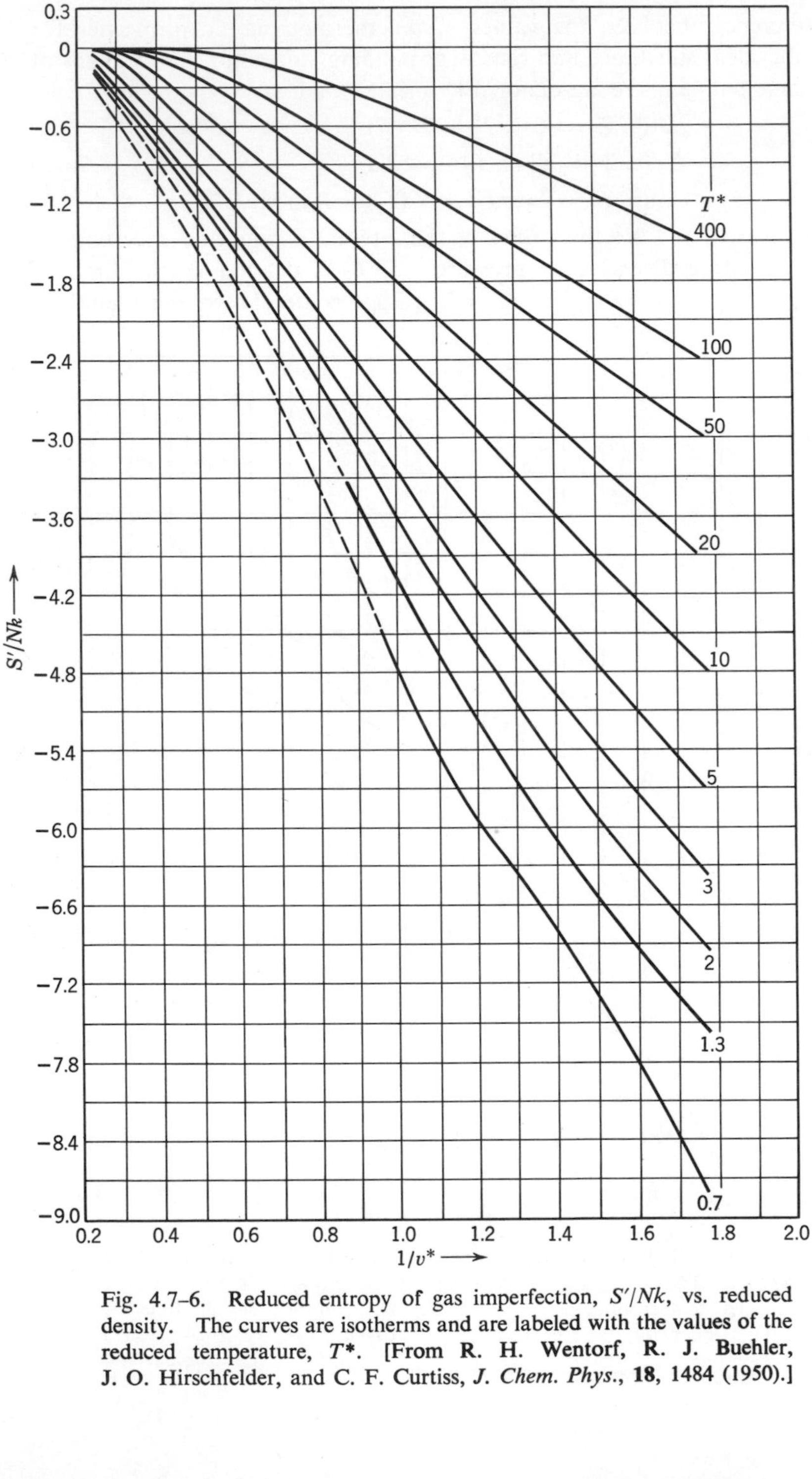

Fig. 4.7–6. Reduced entropy of gas imperfection, S'/Nk, vs. reduced density. The curves are isotherms and are labeled with the values of the reduced temperature, T^*. [From R. H. Wentorf, R. J. Buehler, J. O. Hirschfelder, and C. F. Curtiss, *J. Chem. Phys.*, **18**, 1484 (1950).]

U', C_v', and S' as functions of T^* and v^*, which were calculated from the integrals G, G_L, and G_M. The same information may be found in the appendix in tabular form (see Tables I–J, K, L).

c. Comparison with experimental results

A sensitive test of any theoretical equation of state is its description of the critical phenomena. From Table I–H it may be found that

$$\begin{aligned} T_c^* &= kT_c/\epsilon &&= 1.30 \\ v_c^* &= v_c/\sigma^3 &&= 1.77 \\ p_c^* &= p_c\sigma^3/\epsilon &&= 0.434 \\ && p_c v_c/kT_c &= 0.591 \end{aligned} \tag{4.7–13}$$

These values may be compared with the corresponding experimental values in Table 4.1–2.[13] The Lennard-Jones and Devonshire method is seen to predict T_c^* quite well, but the theoretical values for p_c^*, v_c^*, and $p_c v_c/kT_c$ are clearly in error. Prigogine and Garikian[9] showed that the value of $p_c v_c/kT_c$ is relatively insensitive to the form of the potential function, and hence it is not likely that this model can give a satisfactory quantitative treatment of the critical region. It is shown in the next section that the introduction of holes in the liquid enables us to obtain a much better value of the critical ratio.

In Table 4.7–2 theoretical and experimental values of the volume of the liquid in equilibrium with its vapor at various temperatures are compared. The agreement is fair and shows the proper trend. This comparison, however, does not offer a very sensitive test because of the rapid variation of pressure with volume in the region under consideration.

Experimental and calculated compressibility factors are compared in Table 4.7–3 for argon, nitrogen, and hydrogen. It is clear that the theory is most satisfactory at low temperatures and high densities. Under such conditions the molecules are more nearly restricted to move in cells as pictured by the theory. At low densities and high temperatures the increased molecular motion makes a cell-type picture much less attractive.

[13] He and H_2 are given in this tabulation. Their reduced critical constants deviate considerably from the values of the heavier gases because of quantum effects. This behavior receives further attention in Chapter 6.

To illustrate the accuracy which we may expect in the calculation of thermodynamic properties with the Lennard-Jones–Devonshire method, calculated and experimental values of the imperfections in the internal energy, heat capacity, and entropy are compared in Tables 4.7–4, 5, and 6. The "experimental" values are those obtained by numerical analysis of the compressibility data. It may be seen that the internal energy agrees somewhat more closely for argon than for nitrogen. This might be attributed to the fact that diatomic nitrogen molecules have a large quadrupole moment and do not interact according to a spherically symmetric potential. For specific heat, the discrepancy between calculated and experimental values increases markedly with increasing temperature. The nature of the disagreement in the entropy shows that the theory attributes more order to the system than it actually possesses at low density, that is, the model allows the molecules to roam from their cells considerably less than is actually the case.

TABLE 4.7–2

COMPARISON OF CALCULATED AND EXPERIMENTAL LIQUID VOLUMES[a]

Gas	T(°K)	T^*	*Experimental Liquid Density* (g/cc)	*Pressure* (*atm*)	v_l^* (*exptl*)	v_l^* (*calcd*)
Nitrogen	77	0.844	0.804	1	1.16	1.09
Neon	27.26	0.764	1.204	1	1.27	1.07
Argon	90	0.726	1.374	1.5	1.209	1.05
	111	0.9026	1.224	7.4	1.357	1.11
	122	0.9871	1.138	13.7	1.459	1.17
Methane	111.6	0.818	0.4245	1	1.07	1.08
	133	0.976	0.3916	4.38	1.16	1.15
	153	1.122	0.3547	11.84	1.28	1.27
	191.05	1.400	0.1615	45.8	2.82	1.77

[a] R. H. Wentorf, R. J. Buehler, J. O. Hirschfelder, and C. F. Curtiss, *J. Chem. Phys.*, **18**, 1484 (1950).

d. The double-occupancy modification of the Lennard-Jones–Devonshire equation of state

At low densities, the Lennard-Jones–Devonshire equation of state is physically unsatisfactory because it does not allow the molecules to roam from cell to cell. Because of this freedom of movement, some cells become multiply occupied while some become vacant.

The effects of multiple occupancy have recently been studied independently and along almost identical lines by Janssens and Prigogine[4] and by Pople.[3] Let us restrict the discussion here to double occupancy, that is, the cells may contain 0, 1, or 2 molecules but no more. The results of such considerations are quite similar to those of Lennard-Jones and Devonshire, except that the quantity $\bar{\sigma}$ (which is usually taken to be e in the L-J–D treatment) becomes

$$\bar{\sigma} = 1 + \frac{v_f^{(2)}}{v_f^{(1)}}\sqrt{2} \tag{4.7–14}$$

The quantities $v_f^{(1)}$ and $v_f^{(2)}$ are, respectively, free volumes for one and two particles in the unit cell formed by the nearest neighbors:

$$v_f^{(1)} = \int_\Delta e^{-\omega(\boldsymbol{r}_1)/kT}\, d\boldsymbol{r}_1 \tag{4.7–15}$$

$$v_f^{(2)} = \left[\iint_\Delta e^{-\omega(\boldsymbol{r}_1)/kT} e^{-\omega(\boldsymbol{r}_2)/kT} e^{-\varphi(r_{12})/kT} d\boldsymbol{r}_1\, d\boldsymbol{r}_2\right]^{1/2} \tag{4.7–16}$$

in which $\omega(r)$ is used as an abbreviation for the quantity $c[\varphi(\boldsymbol{a}+\boldsymbol{r}) - \varphi(a)]$. The limiting values of $\bar{\sigma}$ from Eq. 4.7–14 are 1 in the high density limit and $1+\sqrt{2}$ in the low density limit. The value at the low density limit should be e; this indicates that at low density 88 per cent of the communal entropy is due to double occupation.

The free volumes $v_f^{(1)}$ and $v_f^{(2)}$ are related to the hard- and soft-center free volumes, v_{fh} and v_{fs}, described in the preceding section by[3]

$$v_f^{(1)} = v_{fs} \tag{4.7–17}$$

$$v_f^{(2)} \doteq \sqrt{v_{fs}v_{fh}} \tag{4.7–18}$$

It is from these relations that Eq. 4.6–6 was derived. Hence the hard-and-soft-center technique is very nearly equivalent to taking into account double occupancy.

The double-occupancy modification gives results identical with the original Lennard-Jones and Devonshire treatment at high densities, but deviates from it considerably at low densities, as would be expected. Only limited calculations have been made for the model, and they indicate that the critical constants for argon can be calculated more accurately than when the model is restricted to single occupancy.[4]

TABLE 4.7–3

COMPARISON OF EXPERIMENTAL AND CALCULATED COMPRESSIBILITY FACTORS FOR SEVERAL SUBSTANCES

ARGON[a]

		$T\rightarrow$	0°C			75°C			150°C		
		$T^*\rightarrow$	2.203			2.808			3.413		
Density (amagat units)	Density (gm/cc)	v^*	p(atm) (exptl)[b]	pv/kT (exptl)[b]	pv/kT (calcd)	p(atm) (exptl)[b]	pv/kT (exptl)[b]	pv/kT (calcd)	p(atm) (exptl)[b]	pv/kT (exptl)[b]	pv/kT (calcd)
316.6	0.5642	2.944	310	0.97	1.45	450	1.14	1.64	610	1.25	1.76
419.9	0.7483	2.219	470	1.13	1.61	710	1.36	1.87	980	1.50	2.02
503.6	0.8975	1.851	900	1.38	1.77	1090	1.64	2.09	1400	1.80	2.28
626.3	1.1161	1.488	1330	2.07	2.10	1820	2.34	2.51	2250	2.32	2.74

NITROGEN[c]

		$T\rightarrow$	0°C			50°C			100°C		
		$T^*\rightarrow$	2.987			3.533			4.080		
Density (amagat units)	Density (gm/cc)	v^*	p(atm) (exptl)[d]	pv/kT (exptl)[d]	pv/kT (calcd)	p(atm) (exptl)[d]	pv/kT (exptl)[d]	pv/kT (calcd)	p(atm) (exptl)[d]	pv/kT (exptl)[d]	pv/kT (calcd)
186.6	0.2332	3.998	190	1.03	1.41	250	1.11	1.44	300	1.16	1.46
233.6	0.2795	3.337	240	1.07	1.62	310	1.16	1.70	370	1.22	1.75
315.1	0.3938	2.368	390	1.25	1.87	510	1.37	1.98	630	1.46	2.06
415.9	0.5198	1.794	680	1.63	2.21	880	1.79	2.36	1070	1.89	2.46
578.5	0.7231	1.290	1750	3.03	3.07	2170	3.17	3.28	2570	3.25	3.40

TABLE 4.7–3 (*continued*)

HYDROGEN[e]

		T	0°C			50°C			150°C		
		T^*	8.20			9.70			12.71		
Density (amagat units)	Density (gm/cc)	v^*	p(atm) (exptl)[f]	pv/kT (exptl)[f]	pv/kT (calcd)[g]	p(atm) (exptl)[f]	pv/kT (exptl)[f]	pv/kT (calcd)[g]	p(atm) (exptl)[f]	pv/kT (exptl)[f]	pv/kT (calcd)[g]
939.0	0.08441	1.516	2540	2.707	3.126	2932	2.640	3.122	—	—	3.118
758.1	0.06815	1.878	1610	2.124	2.612	1882	2.098	2.630	2406	2.049	2.619
675.5	0.06072	2.108	1290	1.910	2.415	1516	1.900	2.434	1952	1.866	2.429
583.1	0.05241	2.442	995	1.706	2.215	1175	1.704	2.234	1525	1.688	2.224
483.3	0.04345	2.946	735	1.520	1.977	872	1.525	1.976	1140	1.522	1.933
391.7	0.03516	3.640	539	1.378	1.593	641	1.386	1.542	842	1.389	1.498
348.8	0.03135	4.082	461	1.321	1.342	548	1.329	1.313	721	1.334	1.275

[a] Critical density, 0.531 g/cc; liquid density (90°K), 1.41 g/cc; solid density (40°K), 1.65 g/cc; normal volume, 22,390 cc/g mole.
[b] A. Michels, Hub. Wijker, and Hk. Wijker, *Physica*, **15**, 627 (1949).
[c] Critical density, 0.311 g/cc; liquid density (77°K), 0.804 g/cc; solid density (20°K), 1.03 g/cc; normal volume, 22,407 cc/g mole.
[d] A. Michels, H. Wouters, and J. de Boer, *Physica*, **3**, 585 (1936).
[e] Critical density, 0.03172 g/cc; liquid density (20°K), 0.070 g/cc; solid density (13°K), 0.076 g/cc; normal volume, 22,427 cc/g mole.
[f] A. Michels and M. Goudeket, *Physica*, **8**, 347 (1941).
[g] Calculations based on classical theory.

TABLE 4.7–4

COMPARISON OF EXPERIMENTAL AND CALCULATED INTERNAL ENERGY OF GAS IMPERFECTION, $\tilde{U}'$ (IN CAL/MOLE)

ARGON

		T	0°C		75°C		150°C	
		T^*	2.203		2.808		3.413	
Density (amagat units)	Density (gm/cc)	v^*	Exptl[a]	Calcd	Exptl[a]	Calcd	Exptl[a]	Calcd
280	0.4995	3.325	−429	−445.1	−401.5	−415.4	−385.6	−386.2
400	0.7136	2.3275	−600.9	−634.2	−563.8	−592.0	−539.0	−549.8
520	0.9277	1.7904	−769.3	−825.7	−717.8	−768.5	−679.5	−711.8
640	1.1418	1.4547	−923.8	−1035.3	−851.0	−956.2	−971.3	−879.4

NITROGEN

		T	0°C		50°C		150°C	
		T^*	2.987		3.533		4.627	
Density (amagat units)	Density (gm/cc)	v^*	Exptl[b]	Calcd	Exptl[b]	Calcd	Exptl[b]	Calcd
200	0.2500	3.731	−302	−267	−285	−252	−270	−226
240	0.3000	3.109	−360	−316	−340	−295	−312	−254
280	0.3500	2.665	−418	−370	−395	−346	−372	−297
320	0.4000	2.332	−475	−423	−449	−395	−422	−340
400	0.5000	1.865	−588	−531	−554	−495	−514	−424
480	0.6000	1.554	−693	−640	−650	−594	−594	−504

[a] A. Michels, R. J. Lunbeck, and G. Wolkers, *Physica*, **15**, 689 (1949).
[b] A. Michels, H. Wouters, and J. de Boer, *Physica*, **3**, 597 (1936).

TABLE 4.7–5

COMPARISON OF EXPERIMENTAL AND CALCULATED HEAT CAPACITY OF GAS IMPERFECTION, $\tilde{C}_v'$ (IN CAL/MOLE DEGREE)

ARGON

		$T\rightarrow$	0°C		75°C		150°C	
		$T^*\rightarrow$	2.203		2.808		3.413	
Density (amagat units)	Density (gm/cc)	v^*	Exptl[a]	Calcd	Exptl[a]	Calcd	Exptl[a]	Calcd
280	0.4995	3.325	0.42	0.411	0.30	0.395	0.16	0.379
400	0.7136	2.3275	0.55	0.558	0.42	0.562	0.26	0.564
520	0.9277	1.7904	0.74	0.765	0.62	0.761	0.43	0.755
640	1.1418	1.4547	1.02	1.069	0.91	1.039	0.69	1.015

NITROGEN

		$T\rightarrow$	0°C		50°C		150°C	
		$T^*\rightarrow$	2.987		3.533		4.627	
Density (amagat units)	Density (gm/cc)	v^*	Exptl[b]	Calcd	Exptl[b]	Calcd	Exptl[b]	Calcd
200	0.2500	3.731	0.40	0.31	0.27	0.29	0.06	0.24
240	0.3000	3.109	0.45	0.42	0.33	0.41	0.07	0.40
280	0.3500	2.665	0.49	0.49	0.38	0.49	0.10	0.49
320	0.4000	2.332	0.56	0.55	0.45	0.55	0.14	0.55
400	0.5000	1.865	0.71	0.72	0.60	0.72	0.22	0.71
480	0.6000	1.554	0.91	0.93	0.78	0.92	0.33	0.89

[a] A. Michels, R. J. Lunbeck, and G. Wolkers, *Physica*, **15**, 689 (1949).
[b] A. Michels, H. Wouters, and J. de Boer, *Physica*, **3**, 597 (1936).

TABLE 4.7–6

COMPARISON OF EXPERIMENTAL AND CALCULATED ENTROPY OF GAS IMPERFECTION, $\tilde{S}'$ (IN CAL/MOLE DEGREE)

ARGON

		$T\rightarrow$	0°C		75°C		150°C	
		$T^*\rightarrow$	2.203		2.808		3.413	
Density (amagat units)	Density (gm/cc)	v^*	Exptl[a]	Calcd	Exptl[a]	Calcd	Exptl[a]	Calcd
280	0.4995	3.325	−1.234	−0.6635	−1.147	−0.5365	−1.101	−0.4773
400	0.7136	2.3275	−1.861	−1.699	−1.741	−1.561	−1.671	−1.450
520	0.9277	1.7904	−2.600	−2.754	−2.433	−2.567	−2.329	−2.418
640	1.1418	1.4547	−3.480	−3.924	−3.244	−3.666	−3.085	−3.463

NITROGEN

		$T\rightarrow$	0°C		50°C		150°C	
		$T^*\rightarrow$	2.987		3.533		4.627	
Density (amagat units)	Density (gm/cc)	v^*	Exptl[b]	Calcd	Exptl[b]	Calcd	Exptl[b]	Calcd
200	0.2500	3.731	−1.05	−0.28	−1.00	−0.22	−0.95	−0.16
240	0.3000	3.109	−1.29	−0.66	−1.22	−0.59	−1.16	−0.48
280	0.3500	2.665	−1.54	−1.08	−1.46	−1.00	−1.39	−0.87
320	0.4000	2.332	−1.80	−1.49	−1.72	−1.40	−1.63	−1.25
400	0.5000	1.865	−2.38	−2.34	−2.28	−2.22	−2.16	−2.03
480	0.6000	1.554	−3.05	−3.21	−2.91	−3.05	−2.74	−2.82

[a] A. Michels, R. J. Lunbeck, and G. Wolkers, *Physica*, **15**, 689 (1949).
[b] A. Michels, H. Wouters, and J. de Boer, *Physica*, **3**, 597 (1936).

8. Hole Theories of Liquids and Dense Gases[1]

In the preceding section it is indicated that one of the difficulties of the Lennard-Jones–Devonshire theory is that it fails to allow for vacant sites in the lattice. It has long been realized that there are many holes in the lattice structure of liquids (about 0.5 per cent for normal liquids and about 50 per cent near the critical point). Various theories have been proposed to account for this behavior. In these theories the communal entropy factor $\bar{\sigma}$ does not appear. We begin the discussion by showing how the idea of vacant lattice sites may be incorporated into the theory. Thereafter four methods of calculating the free volume are discussed.

a. General theory of holes in liquids[2]

As in the development of the general cell theory in § 4.4 the starting point for the derivation is the classical partition function, Z_N, or the associated configurational integral, Q_N, for an assembly of N monatomic molecules:

$$Z_N = \lambda^{-3N} Q_N = \frac{1}{\lambda^{3N} N!} \int e^{-\Phi(\mathbf{r}^N)/kT} \, d\mathbf{r}^N \tag{4.8–1}$$

where $\lambda^2 = h^2/2\pi mkT$, and the integrations are over the entire volume, V, of the vessel. We now divide this volume into a number of cells. In order to allow for the presence of holes in the liquid structure we choose the number of cells, L, to be somewhat larger than the number of molecules, N. The cell size, q, and the volume per molecule, v, are then different:[3]

$$q = V/L \qquad v = V/N \tag{4.8–2}$$

It is always assumed that the cell is (*a*) sufficiently small that there is a negligible probability of finding two molecules in the same cell, and (*b*) sufficiently large that the intermolecular forces do not extend beyond immediately adjacent cells. Both these conditions can be satisfied only if the intermolecular forces are sufficiently short ranged. This is, however, the case for the interactions between non-polar neutral molecules. The exact choice of the cell-size will be discussed presently.

The configurational integral may now be written as a sum of integrals over the cells:

$$Q_N = \frac{1}{N!} \sum_{l_1=1}^{L} \sum_{l_2=1}^{L} \cdots \sum_{l_N=1}^{L} \int_{\Delta_{l_1}} d\mathbf{r}_1 \int_{\Delta_{l_2}} d\mathbf{r}_2 \cdots \int_{\Delta_{l_N}} d\mathbf{r}_N \, e^{-\Phi(\mathbf{r}^N)/kT} \tag{4.8–3}$$

[1] J. S. Rowlinson and C. F. Curtiss, *J. Chem. Phys.*, **19**, 1519 (1951).

[2] This development follows closely that given by S. Ono, *Memoirs of the Faculty of Engineering* (Kyushu University, Japan), **10**, 190, No. 4 (1947).

[3] In the preceding sections the cell size and the volume per molecule are the same, and both are indicated by the symbol v.

The sum contains L^N terms corresponding to the L different cells to which the coordinates of each of the N different molecules may be restricted. Since the cells are chosen so that the probability of finding two molecules in the same cell is negligible, the terms in the sum in Eq. 4.8–3, corresponding to multiple occupancy of a cell, can be discarded. The sum thus contains only $L!/(L-N)!$ non-negligible terms corresponding to the total number of ways in which the N molecules can be arranged in the L cells with no more than one molecule per cell. These terms consist of $L!/N!(L-N)!$ groups of $N!$ terms, each of which differs from the others only in that the molecules are numbered differently. Since the molecules are identical, these terms have the same numerical value. Consequently, the configurational integral may be rewritten

$$Q_N = \sum \int_{\Delta_{l_1}} d\boldsymbol{r}_1 \int_{\Delta_{l_2}} d\boldsymbol{r}_2 \cdots \int_{\Delta_{l_N}} d\boldsymbol{r}_N \, e^{-\Phi(\boldsymbol{r}^N)/kT} \tag{4.8–4}$$

where the sum is over all the arrangements of the N molecules in L cells which differ by more than a permutation (or renumbering) of the molecules and in which there is no more than one molecule per cell.

As in the cell methods just discussed, the evaluation of the integral depends upon the choice of the lattice system and the shape and orientation of the cells. Let us consider a lattice system such that for any one lattice site there are c nearest neighbors at a distance a. (For face-centered cubic packing $c = 12$, and $a^3 = q\sqrt{2}$.) For any given configuration we may define:

$$\omega_i = \text{fraction of nearest neighbor sites of the } i\text{th molecule which are vacant} \tag{4.8–5}$$

$$\Omega = \sum_{i=1}^{N} \omega_i$$

When all the molecules are at the origins of the various cells in space, the potential energy of the ith molecule is $c(1-\omega_i)\varphi(a)$. Accordingly, the total potential energy of the system is

$$\Phi(\boldsymbol{r}^N) = (c/2)(N - \Omega)\varphi(a) \quad \textit{(molecules at origins of cells)} \tag{4.8–6}$$

When the molecules are not located at the origins of the various cells, the potential energy of the system may be approximated in a manner similar to that used in the cell theories. First we consider the interaction of a wanderer with one nearest neighbor, the latter being located at the origin of its cell. When the wanderer is at position $\boldsymbol{r}$ in its cell, it has a potential energy $[\varphi(\boldsymbol{a}+\boldsymbol{r}) - \varphi(a)]$ greater than it does at the origin of its cell. The analogous potential difference when there are $(1-\omega_i)c$ nearest neighbors is obtained by a sphericalization process as described in § 4.6. That is, we assume that the potential energy of the wanderer depends, not on the location of its neighbors, but only on the number of neighbors. Consequently, the total potential energy of the system is assumed to be given very nearly by

$$\Phi(\boldsymbol{r}^N) = (c/2)(N - \Omega)\varphi(a) + \sum_{i=1}^{N} c(1 - \omega_i)\,[\overline{\varphi(\boldsymbol{a} + \boldsymbol{r}_i)} - \varphi(a)]$$

(molecules not at origins of cells) (4.8–7)

Actually, of course, the energy does not have such a simple dependence on ω_i and does depend on the arrangement of the vacant sites as well as their number.

The partition function, Z_N, may now be obtained by substituting this last result into Eq. 4.8–4:

$$Z_N = \lambda^{-3N} e^{-Nc\varphi(a)/2kT} \sum \{ j(\omega_1) j(\omega_2) \cdots j(\omega_N) \} e^{\Omega c\varphi(a)/2kT} \quad (4.8\text{–}8)$$

in which

$$j(\omega) = \int_{\Delta} \exp\left[-\frac{(1-\omega)c}{kT} (\overline{\varphi(\boldsymbol{a} + \boldsymbol{r})} - \varphi(a)) \right] 4\pi r^2\, dr \quad (4.8\text{–}9)$$

The function $j(\omega)$ is a *generalized free volume*, in that it accounts for neighboring lattice sites which are vacant. When no nearest neighbors are missing, ω is equal to zero, and $j(\omega)$ becomes exactly the same as the sphericalized free volume defined in Eq. 4.6–3. When all the nearest neighbors are missing, ω equals unity, and $j(\omega)$ is just the cell size.

From Eq. 4.8–8 the limiting forms of the partition function at high and low densities may be obtained:

$$Z_N = \lambda^{-3N} [j(0)]^N e^{-Nc\varphi(a)/2kT} \qquad \textit{(high density limit)} \quad (4.8\text{–}10)$$

$$Z_N = \lambda^{-3N} [j(1)]^N \frac{L!}{N!(L-N)!} \doteq \lambda^{-3N} e^N (V/N)^N$$

(low density limit) (4.8–11)

The first of these equations is just the Einstein approximation for the partition function of a crystal. The second equation contains the factor e^N, which is necessary in the perfect gas limit (see § 4.4b). We see thus that Eq. 4.8–3 avoids all mention of the doubtful "communal entropy" and allows for a smooth transition from the highest to the lowest densities.

b. The linear approximation for the logarithm of the free volume

In order to carry out the summation in Eq. 4.8–8 it is necessary to assume some simple functional dependence for $j(\omega)$. The exact dependence on ω is very complicated as may be seen in Eq. 4.8–9. Comparison of Eq. 4.8–9 with Eq. 4.6–3 shows that $j(\omega)$ at temperature T is the same as v_f at a temperature $T/(1 - \omega)$ for the same cell size. Hence the functional dependence of $j(\omega)$ may be obtained from the function $g(v^*, T^*)$, defined in Eqs. 4.7–2 and 4.7–6:

$$j(\omega; q^*, T^*) = 2\pi a^3 g\left(q^*, \frac{T^*}{1-\omega}\right) \tag{4.8–12}$$

where q^* is the reduced cell size q/σ^3. In Fig. 4.8–1 is shown a graph of $\ln j(\omega)$ versus ω obtained from this relation and the tables of $g(v^*, T^*)$ described in the preceding section.

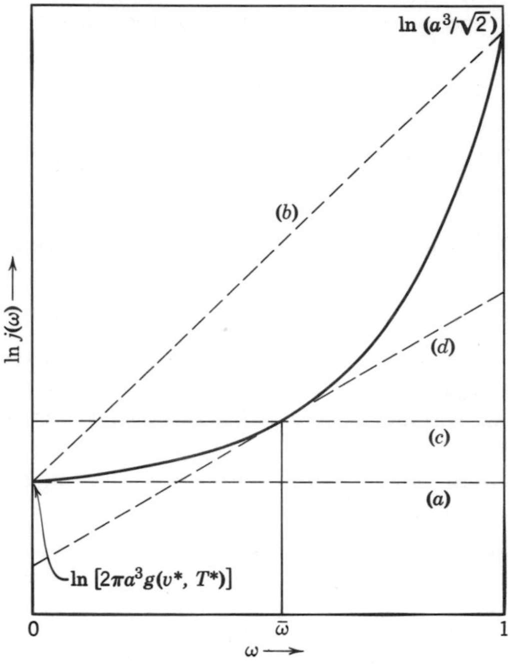

Fig. 4.8–1. The solid curve shows the true dependence of the generalized free volume, $j(\omega)$, on ω as calculated by Eq. 4.8–12. The four dotted lines are the linear approximations to $j(\omega)$ used by various investigators in hole-theory calculations: (*a*) Cernuschi and Eyring[4] (1939). (*b*) Ono[2] (1947). (*c*) Peek and Hill[5] (1950). (*d*) Rowlinson and Curtiss[1] (1951). $\bar{\omega}$ is the average value of ω at the temperature, density, and cell size for which the curve was drawn. [From J. S. Rowlinson and C. F. Curtiss, *J. Chem. Phys.*, **19**, 1519 (1951).]

Thus far the only calculations which have been made on the basis of hole theory have used the assumption that $\ln j(\omega)$ is a linear function of ω:

$$\ln j(\omega) = \ln j_0 + \omega \ln (j_1/j_0) \tag{4.8–13}$$

in which j_0 and j_1 are the intercepts of the straight line at $\omega = 0$ and $\omega = 1$.

In Fig. 4.8–1 are shown the four linear approximations to $\ln j(\omega)$ which have been made: the approximations of Cernuschi and Eyring,[4] Ono,[2] Peek and Hill,[5] and Rowlinson and Curtiss.[1] Clearly the straight lines do not describe well the dependence of $\ln j(\omega)$ on ω.

When the linear approximation of Eq. 4.8–13 is substituted into Eq. 4.8–8, the expression for the partition function becomes

$$Z_N = \lambda^{-3N} e^{-Nc\varphi(a)/2kT} \{j_0{}^N \sum_{\Omega} K(N, L, \Omega)\, e^{\Omega\zeta/kT}\} \qquad (4.8\text{–}14)$$

in which

$$\zeta = \frac{c}{2}\varphi(a) + kT \ln \frac{j_1}{j_0} \qquad (4.8\text{–}15)$$

The quantity $K(N, L, \Omega)$ is the number of configurations with a particular value of Ω when N molecules are distributed among L cells. This function cannot be evaluated explicitly but has been estimated by means of a "quasi-chemical approximation."[6] This enables us to write the partition function in the final form:

$$Z_N = \lambda^{-3N} e^{-Nc\varphi(a)/2kT} \left\{ \frac{L!\, j_0{}^N}{N!(L-N)!} K_N^{Nc/2} K_L^{Lc/2} \right\} \qquad (4.8\text{–}16)$$

in which

$$K_N = \left(\frac{x}{1-x}\right)\left(\frac{\beta+1-2x}{\beta-1+2x}\right) \qquad \beta = \sqrt{1 + 4\alpha x(x-1)}$$

$$\alpha = 1 - \exp\,[-2\zeta/ckT] \qquad (4.8\text{–}17)$$

$$K_L = (1-x)\left(\frac{\beta+1}{\beta+1-2x}\right) \qquad x = N/L = q/v$$

The quantity x is related to the average number of holes around any one molecule, $c\bar{\omega}$, thus:

$$\bar{\omega} = 2(1-x)/(\beta+1) \qquad (4.8\text{–}18)$$

At high densities the number of cells is very nearly equal to the number of molecules, x approaches unity, and $\bar{\omega}$ approaches zero, that is, on the average there are no vacant nearest-neighbor lattice sites. At low densities the number of cells is much greater than the number of molecules, x approaches zero, and $\bar{\omega}$ approaches unity; that is, on the average all the nearest-neighbor lattice sites are unoccupied. It has been shown that at the critical point approximately half the lattice sites are vacant.

[4] F. Cernuschi and H. Eyring, *J. Chem. Phys.*, **7**, 547 (1939).

[5] H. M. Peek and T. L. Hill, *J. Chem. Phys.*, **18**, 1252 (1950).

[6] This technique was worked out in different forms by Guggenheim and Bethe. See R. H. Fowler and E. A. Guggenheim, *Statistical Thermodynamics*, Cambridge University Press, London (1939), pp. 246–251, 361–364.

From the expression for the partition function in Eq. 4.8–16 may be obtained the equation of state and expressions for the various thermodynamic properties.[7] These quantities may not be evaluated explicitly until cell size and the parameters j_0 and j_1 are specified. When this has been done the various properties are given as functions of temperature and density. The parameters j_0 and j_1 may be chosen in a number of ways; we discuss later the choices which have been indicated in Fig. 4.8–1. The cell size may be put equal to some arbitrary constant independent of the density and temperature; for example, the cell size may be put equal to the volume per molecule in the crystal at absolute zero. Or it may be chosen so as to make the Helmholtz free energy, $A = U - TS$, a minimum at each density and temperature. The latter is to be preferred on theoretical grounds. The former, however, has the advantage that it sometimes allows explicit expressions to be written down for the critical constants.

c. Comparison of hole-theory calculations with experiment

It is disappointing that these four hole theories show little improvement over the treatment of Lennard-Jones and Devonshire. It is particularly significant that the approximation of Rowlinson and Curtiss (line *d* in Fig. 4.8–1) does not provide a better description of dense gases and liquids. Their approximation should be the best of the four shown in Fig. 4.8–1, inasmuch as their line is chosen so that both $j(\omega)$ and its first derivative are given correctly at $\omega = \bar{\omega}$. The fact that this choice of linear approximation seems only slightly better than the others seems to indicate that little further progress can be made without removing some of the assumptions inherent in the fundamental theory.

We conclude this section by comparing the results of the four hole-theory calculations with each other and with available experimental data.

i. *The Low Density Limit: Second Virial Coefficient*

These theories are designed primarily to give the equation of state of liquids. It is a severe test to expect them to give good values of the second virial coefficient. On the other hand, there is reason to believe that any model which does not give a reasonable value for the second virial coefficient will not give a good value for the critical ratio, $p_c\tilde{V}_c/RT_c$.

The theory of Lennard-Jones and Devonshire gives zero for the second virial coefficient inasmuch as the first term in the non-ideality correction is proportional to v^{*-2}. The second virial coefficients for the four hole theories are given in Fig. 4.8–2, along with the curve of $B^{\star}(T^*)$ for the

[7] Explicit expressions for the four hole theories have been given by J. S. Rowlinson and C. F. Curtiss (Ref. 1).

Lennard–Jones (6-12) potential calculated from Eq. 3.6–3. Approximation (*d*) gives the best curve for the second virial coefficient. It is an interesting fact that approximations *b*, *c*, and *d*, with cell size determined by minimizing $A = U - TS$, all give at high temperatures:

$$B^{\star}(T^*) = \text{const} \times T^{*-1/4} \tag{4.8–19}$$

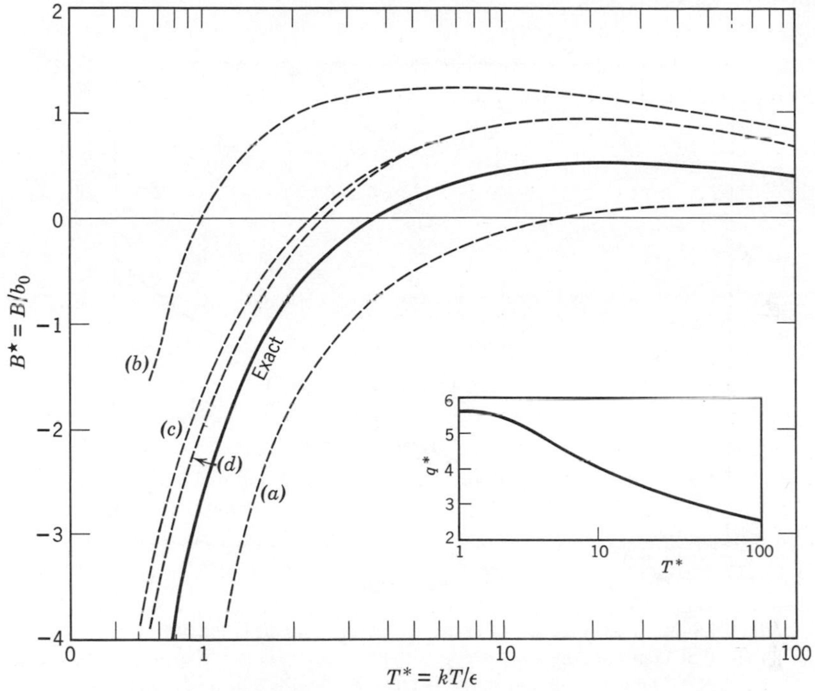

Fig. 4.8–2. The calculated second virial coefficient as a function of the reduced temperature according to the four hole theories given in this section: (*a*) Cernuschi and Eyring,[4] (*b*) Ono,[2] (*c*) Peek and Hill,[5] and (*d*) Rowlinson and Curtiss.[1] The inset shows the variation of cell size with the reduced temperature according to (*d*). [From J. S. Rowlinson and C. F. Curtiss, *J. Chem. Phys.*, **19**, 1519 (1951).]

The dependence on T^* is correct in the high temperature limit as may be seen in Eq. 3.6–3, and the proportionality constant is surprisingly good, being about 15 per cent too large.

ii. *Compressibility Factor in the Dense Gas Region*

The success with the second virial coefficient made it seem likely that the calculations of the equation of state on the basis of hole theories might give good agreement with experiment at high densities. The comparison in Fig. 4.8–3 indicates that such is not the case. There a comparison is made between the high density measurements of hydrogen and the results of the Lennard-Jones and Devonshire and Rowlinson and Curtiss calculations. It is seen that the two calculated curves approach each other as $\bar{\omega} \to 0$, but that neither is an adequate representation of the experimental results.

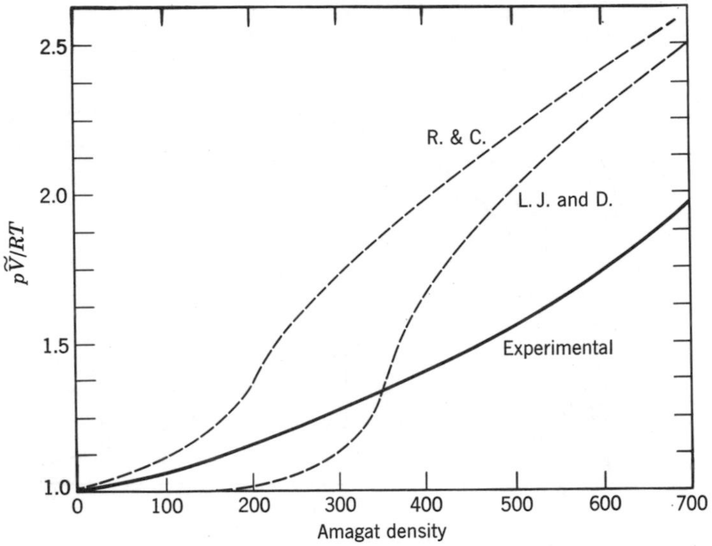

Fig. 4.8–3. The equation of state of hydrogen at 0° C according to the theory of Lennard-Jones and Devonshire and according to Rowlinson and Curtiss. The experimental curve is from A. Michels and M. Goudeket, *Physica*, **8**, 347 (1941). [From J. S. Rowlinson and C. F. Curtiss, *J. Chem. Phys.*, **20** (1952).]

iii. *The Critical Point*

A comparison of the results of the various lattice theories as regards the calculation of critical constants is shown in Table 4.8–1. None of the theories gives a good set of values for the critical constants. No values are given for the method of Rowlinson and Curtiss since the critical point appears to lie at a cell size of about 5, which is outside the region of the tabulated values of g, g_l, and g_m. This is in itself a weakness of the theory, for one of the conditions to which the cell size should conform is that it should be sufficiently small that there is a negligible chance that any cell contains more than one molecule.

TABLE 4.8–1

	$p_c\tilde{V}_c/RT_c$	T_c^*	p_c^*	v_c^*	$\overline{\omega}_c$
Mean Value for Ne, A, N_2	0.293	1.28	0.119	3.15	—
Lennard-Jones and Devonshire	0.591	1.30	0.434	1.77	0.000
Cernuschi and Eyring[a]	0.342	2.74	0.469	2.00	0.455
Ono[b]	0.342	0.75	0.128	2.00	0.455
Peek and Hill[c]	0.719	1.18	0.261	3.25	0.175

[a] F. Cernuschi and H. Eyring, *J. Chem. Phys.*, **7**, 547 (1939).
[b] S. Ono, *Memoirs of the Faculty of Engineering* (Kyushu University, Japan), **10**, 190, No. 4 (1947).
[c] H. M. Peek and T. L. Hill, *J. Chem. Phys.*, **18**, 1252 (1950).

iv. *Liquid Vapor Equilibrium*

Comparisons have been made[1] of the experimental vapor pressures and those obtained from the theory of Lennard-Jones and Devonshire and that of Ono. The calculated curves show the linear variation of $\log p_{\text{vap}}$ with $1/T$ characteristic of the experimental curves. The Lennard-Jones and Devonshire treatment gives somewhat better agreement than the theory of Ono.

v. *Boiling Point*

The boiling point of a liquid at one atmosphere is not a quantity which can be calculated from equations of the "corresponding states" kind. However, if it is assumed that most critical pressures are about 40 atm, the boiling point may be taken as that temperature at which $p_{\text{vap}}/p_c = 1/40$. The experimental value of T_b^* is about 0.87. The theory of Lennard-Jones and Devonshire gives about 0.80 and that of Ono about 0.51. However, the ratios of T_b^* to T_c^* are remarkably constant.

$$\text{(Experimental)} \qquad T_b^*/T_c^* = 0.67$$

$$\text{(L.J.D.)} \qquad T_b^*/T_c^* = 0.62$$

$$\text{(Ono)} \qquad T_b^*/T_c^* = 0.68$$

These results are in substantial agreement with the older empirical rule of Guldberg and Guye (see § 4.1a).

vi. *Entropies of Evaporation at the Boiling Point*

The experimental value of the entropy of vaporization at the boiling point is about 16.8 cal per mole for the rare gases and about 21 cal per mole for the higher boiling non-polar compounds. The theory of Lennard-Jones and Devonshire and that of Ono give 20.3 and 23.2 cal per mole, respectively.

It is fairly evident from the results of this and the previous sections that the various lattice theories contain assumptions which seriously restrict the applicability of the results. At the present time it seems as if more accurate results may be obtainable from the method of the radial distribution function, which is discussed in the following § 4.9.

9. The Equation of State in Terms of the Pair Distribution Function[1]

The various lattice theories of the equation of state discussed in the preceding section are based upon various approximations to the N-particle partition function. The approximations involved are appropriate at very high densities when the system is more or less characterized by a lattice-like configuration. For intermediate densities no satisfactory results have yet been obtained.

The most promising alternative approach to the problem is based on an expression for the equation of state in terms of the *pair distribution function*, $n^{(2)}(r_{12})$, or the *radial distribution function*,[2] $g(r_{12})$, which are defined in Eq. 3.1–14. In Section 3.1–b it was shown that the equation of state may be expressed as

$$pV = NkT - (^1/_6) \iint (d\varphi/dr_{12}) n^{(2)}(\mathbf{r}_1, \mathbf{r}_2) r_{12}\, d\mathbf{r}_1\, d\mathbf{r}_2 \qquad (3.1\text{–}13)$$

or

$$p = nkT - (n^2/6) \int (d\varphi/dr_{12}) g(r_{12}) 4\pi r_{12}^3\, dr_{12}$$

Inherent in these expressions are the assumptions that (*i*) the intermolecular forces are two-body forces (that is, the force between any pair of molecules is independent of the presence of any additional molecules), (ii) the intermolecular potential $\varphi(r)$ is angle independent, and (iii) classical mechanics applies to the description of the system. The fact that the equation of state depends only on the pair distribution function and not upon higher order distribution functions is a consequence of the assumption of two-body forces.

First we discuss the behavior of the pair distribution function and its relation to the *potential of average force*. We then derive exact integral

[1] J. de Boer, *Reports on Progress in Physics*, **12**, 354–370 (1949).

[2] In liquids $g(r)$ is usually referred to as the Debye-Menke distribution function.

equations for $n^{(2)}(r_{12})$ by several methods. The difficulty encountered here is that these equations also contain $n^{(3)}(\boldsymbol{r}_1, \boldsymbol{r}_2, \boldsymbol{r}_3)$, the distribution function for triples. Hence approximations must be made to eliminate these functions from the equations; this is generally accomplished by means of the so-called *superposition approximation.* Much numerical work remains to be done in order to assess the applicability of these methods

a. Behavior of the pair distribution function[3]

The pair distribution function, $n^{(2)}(\boldsymbol{r}_1, \boldsymbol{r}_2)$, and the radial distribution function, $g(r_{12})$, have been defined by

$$n^{(2)}(\boldsymbol{r}_1, \boldsymbol{r}_2) = n^2 g(r_{12}) = [(N-2)!Q_N]^{-1} \int e^{-\Phi(\boldsymbol{r}^N)/kT}\, d\boldsymbol{r}^{N-2} \qquad (3.1\text{–}14)$$

The function $g(r)$ approaches unity as r becomes infinite and the quantity $\frac{1}{2}Nng(r)\,4\pi r^2\,dr$ is the number of pairs of molecules for which the separation r lies between r and $r + dr$.

It is shown in § 3.3c that the radial distribution function has the following limiting form at low densities:

$$g(r_{12}) = n^{(2)}/n^2 = e^{-\varphi(r_{12})/kT} \qquad \textit{(low density limit)} \qquad (4.9\text{–}1)$$

For moderate densities the radial distribution function may be expanded in a power series in the number density as shown in Eq. 3.3–8. When the additivity of intermolecular forces is assumed, this equation becomes

$$g(r_{12}) = e^{-\varphi(r_{12})/kT}[1 + n \int (e^{-\varphi(r_{13})/kT} - 1)(e^{-\varphi(r_{23})/kT} - 1)\, d\boldsymbol{r}_3 + O(n^2)]$$
$$\textit{(moderate densities)} \qquad (4.9\text{–}2)$$

Comparison of this expression with Eqs. 3.3–8 and 3.3–10 shows that the term in the bracket proportional to n is related to the third virial coefficient.

Calculations[4] of $g(r_{12})$ have been made for the Lennard-Jones (6-12) potential. In Fig. 4.9–1 are shown the results corresponding to Eq. 4.9–1 for several values of the reduced temperature T^* in the limit of low density. The distribution function has a single maximum corresponding to the fact that there is a somewhat higher probability of finding a pair of molecules at a separation equal to the distance for which the potential energy is a minimum ($r = 2^{1/6}\sigma$) than at any other distance. The decrease in the height of the maximum with increasing T^* corresponds to the disorder which accompanies increased thermal motion.

[3] For the various kinds of distribution functions in classical statistical mechanics, see § 2.1.

[4] Evaluations of the pair distribution function have been performed by J. de Boer and A. Michels, *Physica*, **6**, 97 (1939), and also by E. Montroll and J. E. Mayer, *J. Chem. Phys.*, **9**, 626 (1941). The results of the two groups are essentially in agreement.

In Fig. 4.9–2 are shown the curves of $g(r)$ in the second approximation[4] as given by Eq. 4.9–2 for the Lennard-Jones potential. The graph (*a*) shows the change of $g(r)$ with density at constant temperature, and (*b*) indicates the change of $g(r)$ with temperature at constant density. These functions have two maxima—that is, about any given molecule there are two shells in which there is a relatively high probability of finding another

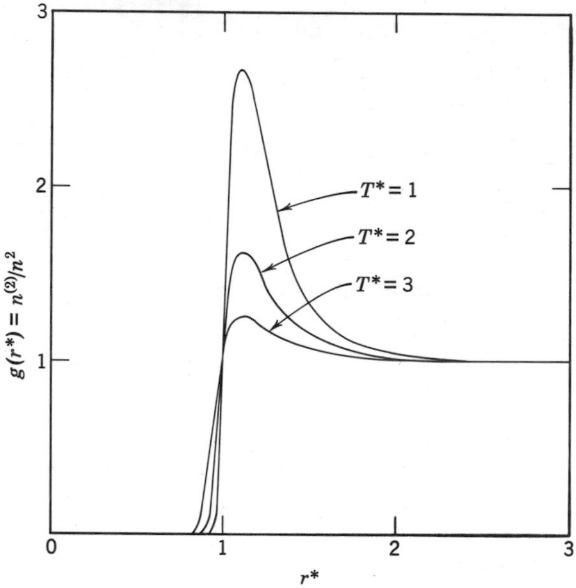

Fig. 4.9–1. Pair distribution function in the first approximation, as given in Eq. 4.9–1. These curves are drawn for the Lennard-Jones (6–12) potential. [J. de Boer, *Reports on Progress in Physics*, **12**, 355 (1949).]

molecule. The third, fourth . . . approximations to $g(r)$ lead to curves with three, four, . . . humps. This corresponds to the increase of "local order" with increasing density.

The curves of $g(r)$ may be calculated from x-ray scattering,[5–10] and the curves thus obtained exhibit the same general behavior as is predicted from the theory.[10] Indeed we might wonder why x-ray data cannot be

[5] H. Menke, *Physik. Z.*, **33**, 593 (1932).

[6] P. Debye and H. Menke, *Physik. Z.*, **31**, 797 (1930); *Ergeb der Tech. Röntgenkunde* II (1937).

[7] F. Zernike and J. A. Prins, *Z. Physik*, **41**, 184 (1927).

[8] A. Eisenstein and N. S. Gingrich, *Phys. Rev.*, **58**, 307 (1940); **62**, 261 (1942).

[9] B. E. Warren, *J. Appl. Phys.*, **8**, 645 (1937).

[10] W. E. Morrell and J. H. Hildebrand, *J. Chem. Phys.*, **4**, 224 (1936).

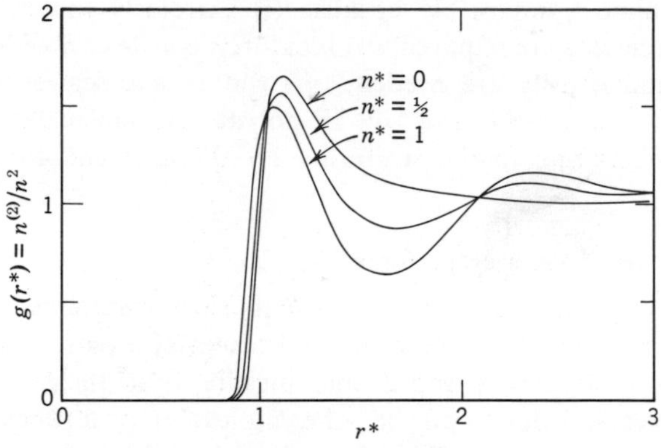

(*a*) Variation of the pair distribution function with density for $T^* = 2$

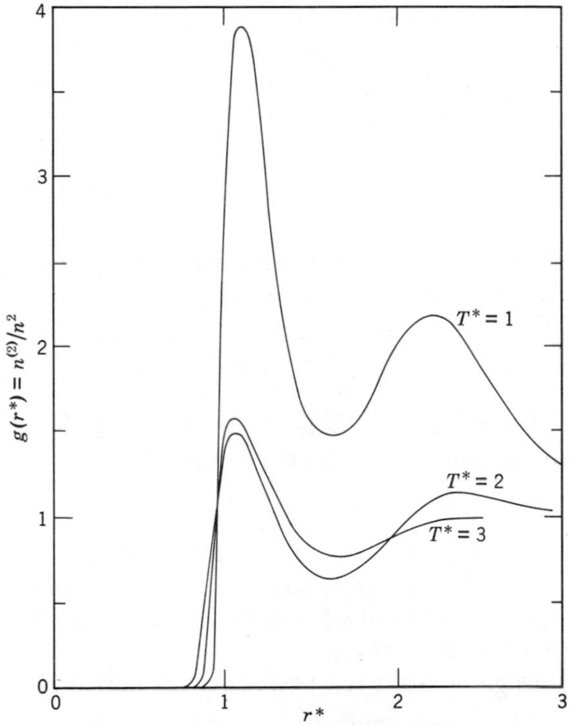

(*b*) Variation of the pair distribution function with temperature for $n^* = 1$

Fig. 4.9–2. The pair distribution function in the second approximation, as given in Eq. 4.9–2. The curves are drawn for the Lennard-Jones (6–12) potential. [J. de Boer, *Reports on Progress in Physics*, **12**, 355 (1949).]

used to calculate the equation of state. Unfortunately this is at the present time almost impossible because (i) extremely accurate experimental measurements are required, (ii) measurements over a wide range of temperature and density are needed, (iii) the atomic scattering factors must be known accurately, and (iv) in polyatomic molecules there are interference effects due to the scattering by the different atoms in the molecules.

b. The "potential of the average force"

Another way of thinking of the pair distribution function is in terms of the average force exerted on one of the molecules of a pair. Let us consider a pair of molecules, 1 and 2, and inquire as to the average force exerted on molecule 1 due to all the other molecules, as a function of the intermolecular distance r_{12}. This is obtained by taking the appropriate average of $\boldsymbol{F}_1(\boldsymbol{r}^N) = -\partial\Phi(\boldsymbol{r}^N)/\partial\boldsymbol{r}_1$ over the canonical ensemble representing the system of molecules:

$$\bar{\boldsymbol{F}}_1(\boldsymbol{r}_1, \boldsymbol{r}_2) = \frac{\displaystyle\iint \left(-\frac{\partial\Phi(\boldsymbol{r}^N)}{\partial\boldsymbol{r}_1}\right) e^{-H(\boldsymbol{r}^N,\boldsymbol{p}^N)/kT}\, d\boldsymbol{p}^N\, d\boldsymbol{r}^{N-2}}{\displaystyle\iint e^{-H(\boldsymbol{r}^N,\boldsymbol{p}^N)/kT}\, d\boldsymbol{p}^N\, d\boldsymbol{r}^{N-2}} \tag{4.9-3}$$

$$= [(N-2)!\,Q_{N-2}]^{-1} \int \left(-\frac{\partial\Phi}{\partial\boldsymbol{r}_1}\right) e^{-\Phi(\boldsymbol{r}^N)/kT}\, d\boldsymbol{r}^{N-2}$$

From the definition of $n^{(2)}(\boldsymbol{r}_1, \boldsymbol{r}_2)$ it is clear the $\boldsymbol{F}_1(\boldsymbol{r}_1, \boldsymbol{r}_2)$ bears the following relation to the pair distribution function:

$$\bar{\boldsymbol{F}}_1(\boldsymbol{r}_1, \boldsymbol{r}_2) = -\frac{\partial\Psi(\boldsymbol{r}_1, \boldsymbol{r}_2)}{\partial\boldsymbol{r}_1} = kT\frac{\partial \ln n^{(2)}(\boldsymbol{r}_1, \boldsymbol{r}_2)}{\partial\boldsymbol{r}_1} \tag{4.9-4}$$

Here we have also introduced the potential of average force, $\Psi(\boldsymbol{r}_1, \boldsymbol{r}_2)$. Accordingly, the pair distribution function is given by

$$n^{(2)}(\boldsymbol{r}_1, \boldsymbol{r}_2) = n^2\, e^{-\Psi(\boldsymbol{r}_1,\boldsymbol{r}_2)/kT} \tag{4.9-5}$$

The factor n^2, appearing in connection with the arbitrary constant of integration, is so chosen that $\Psi(\boldsymbol{r}_1\, \mathrm{r}_2) \to 0$ as $r_{12} \to \infty$. Clearly, in the low density limit, the potential of average force approaches the intermolecular potential function $\varphi(r_{12})$.

The expressions given in the last two equations may be generalized to

$$\bar{\boldsymbol{F}}_1(\boldsymbol{r}^h) = -\frac{\partial\Psi(\boldsymbol{r}^h)}{\partial\boldsymbol{r}_1} = kT\frac{\partial \ln n^{(h)}(\boldsymbol{r}^h)}{\partial\boldsymbol{r}_1} \tag{4.9-6}$$

$$n^{(h)}(\boldsymbol{r}^h) = n^h e^{-\Psi(\boldsymbol{r}^h)kT} \tag{4.9-7}$$

Here $\bar{F}_1(r^h)$ is the force exerted by the other molecules on molecule 1 as a function of the configuration of the group of molecules $\{h\} = 1, 2, 3, \cdots h$.

c. Derivation of integral equations for the pair distribution function

It has been shown that the equation of state may be expressed in terms of the pair distribution function, $n^{(2)}$. We now discuss the derivation of an integral equation for this function. The resulting equation contains not only $n^{(2)}$ but also $n^{(3)}$. Similarly, the equation for $n^{(3)}$ contains the distribution function of one higher order, and so on. Hence in order to obtain an exact solution for $n^{(2)}$ it is necessary to solve a set of N coupled integral equations.

We present here three different derivations which result in such a set of N integral equations. In the next subsection the methods of solving these equations approximately are discussed.

i. *Derivation from the Potential of Average Force*

The concept of the potential of average force may be used as the starting point for the derivation of an equation for the pair distribution function. If the intermolecular forces are two body forces, then

$$-\boldsymbol{F}_1 = \frac{\partial}{\partial \boldsymbol{r}_1}\Phi(\boldsymbol{r}^N) = \sum_{k=2}^{N} \frac{\partial}{\partial \boldsymbol{r}_1}\varphi(r_{1k}) \tag{4.9–8}$$

Using this relation and the expression for $\bar{\boldsymbol{F}}_1$ in Eq. 4.9–3 along with the definition of $n^{(3)}$, we obtain

$$\bar{\boldsymbol{F}}_1 = -\frac{\partial}{\partial \boldsymbol{r}_1}\varphi(r_{12}) - \int \frac{\partial\varphi(r_{13})}{\partial \boldsymbol{r}_1}\frac{n^{(3)}(\boldsymbol{r}_1, \boldsymbol{r}_2, \boldsymbol{r}_3)}{n^{(2)}(\boldsymbol{r}_1, \boldsymbol{r}_2)}\,d\boldsymbol{r}_3 \tag{4.9–9}$$

The first term on the right-hand side of this equality is the direct force acting on molecule 1 due to molecule 2. The second term gives the contribution of the other molecules to the average force—the quantity $n^{(3)}/n^{(2)}$ being the probability of finding a third molecule in a position $\boldsymbol{r}_3$ when molecules 1 and 2 are held fixed. Equating this last expression with that for $\bar{\boldsymbol{F}}_1$ in Eq. 4.9–4, we get

$$kT\frac{\partial \ln n^{(2)}(\boldsymbol{r}_1, \boldsymbol{r}_2)}{\partial \boldsymbol{r}_1} = -\frac{\partial\varphi(r_{12})}{\partial \boldsymbol{r}_1} - \int \frac{\partial\varphi(r_{13})}{\partial \boldsymbol{r}_1}\frac{n^{(3)}(\boldsymbol{r}_1, \boldsymbol{r}_2, \boldsymbol{r}_3)}{n^{(2)}(\boldsymbol{r}_1, \boldsymbol{r}_2)}\,d\boldsymbol{r}_3 \tag{4.9–10}$$

In a similar fashion we may obtain equations for other $n^{(h)}$ in which the higher order function $n^{(h+1)}$ occurs also.

The foregoing result may be somewhat simplified by recognizing that the functions $n^{(h)}$ are functions only of the relative coordinates:[11]

$$\begin{aligned} n^{(2)}(\boldsymbol{r}_1, \boldsymbol{r}_2) &= n^{(2)}(r_{12}) \equiv n^{(2)}_{12} \\ n^{(3)}(\boldsymbol{r}_1, \boldsymbol{r}_2, \boldsymbol{r}_3) &= n^{(3)}(r_{12}, r_{23}, r_{13}) \equiv n^{(3)}_{123} \end{aligned} \tag{4.9–11}$$

[11] These relations are valid only at equilibrium.

Multiplication of Eq. 4.9–10 by $(\boldsymbol{r}_{12}/r_{12}) = (\boldsymbol{r}_1 - \boldsymbol{r}_2)/r_{12}$ then results in

$$kT \frac{\partial \ln n_{12}^{(2)}}{\partial r_{12}} = -\frac{\partial \varphi_{12}}{\partial r_{12}} - \int \frac{\partial \varphi_{13}}{\partial r_{13}} \frac{n_{123}^{(3)}}{n_{12}^{(2)}} \left(\frac{\boldsymbol{r}_{12}}{r_{12}} \cdot \frac{\boldsymbol{r}_{13}}{r_{13}}\right) d\boldsymbol{r}_3$$

$$= -\frac{\partial \varphi_{12}}{\partial r_{12}} - 2\pi \int_0^{\infty} \int_{|r_{12}-r_{13}|}^{(r_{12}+r_{13})} \frac{\partial \varphi_{13}}{\partial r_{13}} \frac{n_{123}^{(3)}}{n_{12}^{(2)}} \left(\frac{{r_{13}}^2 + {r_{12}}^2 - {r_{23}}^2}{2{r_{12}}^2}\right) \times r_{23}\, dr_{23}\, dr_{13} \qquad (4.9\text{–}12)$$

The latter form of the equation is written in "two-center" coordinates.

ii. *Derivation from the Liouville Equation*

The distribution functions $n^{(h)}(\boldsymbol{r}^h)$ are obtainable from the distribution functions $f^{(N)}(\boldsymbol{r}^N, \boldsymbol{p}^N)$ by integration over $\boldsymbol{p}^N$ and $\boldsymbol{r}^{N-h}$, as described in §2.1. The time behavior of $f^{(N)}(\boldsymbol{r}^N, \boldsymbol{p}^N)$ is given by the Liouville equation (Eq. 2.1–10). It is thus possible to get an equation for $n^{(h)}(\boldsymbol{r}^h)$ by integrating the Liouville equation over $\boldsymbol{p}^N$ and $\boldsymbol{r}^{N-h}$, and making use of the fact that we are considering an equilibrium situation.

The Liouville equation for $f^{(N)}(\boldsymbol{r}^N, \boldsymbol{p}^N)$ may be written in the form

$$\frac{\partial f^{(N)}}{\partial t} + \sum_{k=1}^{N} \left[\left(\frac{\boldsymbol{p}_k}{m} \cdot \frac{\partial f^{(N)}}{\partial \boldsymbol{r}_k}\right) + \left(\boldsymbol{F}_k \cdot \frac{\partial f^{(N)}}{\partial \boldsymbol{p}_k}\right)\right] = 0 \qquad (4.9\text{–}13)$$

in which $\boldsymbol{F}_k$ is the force on the kth molecule due to all the other molecules. An equation for the lower-order distribution function $f^{(h)}$ (for the molecules in the set $\{h\} = 1, 2, 3, \cdots h$) may be obtained by integrating this equation over the remaining $N - h$ coordinates:

$$\frac{\partial f^{(h)}}{\partial t} + \sum_{k=1}^{h} \left[\left(\frac{\boldsymbol{p}_k}{m} \cdot \frac{\partial f^{(h)}}{\partial \boldsymbol{r}_k}\right) + \frac{1}{(N-h)!}\left(\frac{\partial}{\partial \boldsymbol{p}_k} \cdot \iint \boldsymbol{F}_k f^{(N)}\, d\boldsymbol{r}^{N-h}\, d\boldsymbol{p}^{N-h}\right)\right] = 0 \qquad (4.9\text{–}14)$$

To obtain this, Green's theorem is used, and it is assumed that $f^{(N)}$ vanishes sufficiently rapidly for $|\boldsymbol{p}_k| \to \infty$ and $|\boldsymbol{q}_k| \to \infty$. When it is assumed that the forces are two-body forces, relations like Eq. 4.9–8 may be used to rewrite Eq. 4.9–14:

$$\frac{\partial f^{(h)}}{\partial t} + \sum_{k=1}^{h} \left[\left(\frac{\boldsymbol{p}_k}{m} \cdot \frac{\partial f^{(h)}}{\partial \boldsymbol{r}_k}\right) - \left(\frac{\partial \Phi(\boldsymbol{r}^h)}{\partial \boldsymbol{r}_k} \cdot \frac{\partial f^{(h)}}{\partial \boldsymbol{p}_k}\right)\right]$$

$$= \sum_{k=1}^{h} \iint \left(\frac{\partial \varphi_{k,\,h+1}}{\partial \boldsymbol{r}_k} \cdot \frac{\partial f^{(h+1)}}{\partial \boldsymbol{p}_k}\right) d\boldsymbol{r}_{h+1}\, d\boldsymbol{p}_{h+1} \qquad (4.9\text{–}15)$$

Thus the single equation for the function $f^{(N)}$ has been transformed into a set of coupled equations for the distribution functions of various orders.

The equation for each $f^{(h)}$ involves the next higher function $f^{(h+1)}$. That there are distribution functions of two different orders appearing in these equations is a consequence of the assumption of two body forces.

Since the set of equations just obtained above is coupled and involves $6N$ variables, it is of no more practical value than the original Liouville equation unless some approximation is introduced which permits a closure. The sequence of equations can be cut off by an approximation for $f^{(h+1)}$ in terms of the lower-order distribution functions. For example, if it is assumed that the system is nearly a perfect gas so that only binary collisions are of importance, and, if "molecular chaos" is assumed, then it is possible to write $f^{(2)}$ exactly in terms of $f^{(1)}$. This approximation leads to the ordinary Boltzmann equation of kinetic theory (see § 7.1).

The properties of dense gases may be expressed in terms of $f^{(2)}(\boldsymbol{r}_1, \boldsymbol{r}_2, \boldsymbol{p}_1, \boldsymbol{p}_2)$. Actually for equilibrium properties we need only $n^{(2)}(\boldsymbol{r}_1, \boldsymbol{r}_2)$. An equation for this function may be obtained by multiplying Eq. 4.9–15 by $\boldsymbol{p}_i$ and integrating over the momenta $\boldsymbol{p}^h$. We make use of the relations

$$\int \boldsymbol{p}_i f^{(h)}\, d\boldsymbol{p}^h = 0 \qquad i = 1, 2, 3, \cdots h \qquad (4.9\text{–}16)$$

$$\frac{1}{2m}\int \boldsymbol{p}_i^2 f^{(h)}\, d\boldsymbol{p}^h = \tfrac{3}{2}kT \qquad i = 1, 2, 3, \cdots h \qquad (4.9\text{–}17)$$

The first relation is the statement that the average momentum is equal to zero, and the second is the kinetic theory definition of temperature (see § 7.2). The equation for $n^{(h)}(\boldsymbol{r}^h)$ is then readily obtained:

$$kT\frac{\partial \ln n^{(h)}}{\partial \boldsymbol{r}_i} = -\frac{\partial}{\partial \boldsymbol{r}_i}\Phi(\boldsymbol{r}^h) - \int \frac{\partial \varphi_{i,\,h+1}}{\partial \boldsymbol{r}_i}\frac{n^{(h+1)}(\boldsymbol{r}^{h+1})}{n^{(h)}(\boldsymbol{r}^h)}\, d\boldsymbol{r}_{h+1} \qquad (4.9\text{–}18)$$

When $h = 2$ this is the same result as that given in Eq. 4.9–10.

iii. *Derivation by the Coupling Parameter Method*[12]

Another way of attacking the problem is to write the total potential energy of the system, $\Phi(\boldsymbol{r}^N)$, in such a form as to include a coupling parameter, ξ:

$$\Phi(\boldsymbol{r}^N) = \xi \sum_{j=2}^{N} \varphi_{1j} + \sum_{j=2}^{N}\sum_{k=j+1}^{N} \varphi_{jk} \qquad (4.9\text{–}19)$$

The actual situation is of course represented by $\xi = 1$. When $\xi = 0$, the total potential energy does not include the interaction molecule 1 with the other molecules, that is, molecule 1 is "uncoupled." When the distribution functions are written for the potential in Eq. 4.9–19, they are accordingly functions of the parameter ξ.

[12] J. G. Kirkwood, *J. Chem. Phys.*, **3**, 300 (1935).

Substitution of the above expression for $\Phi(\boldsymbol{r}^N)$ into the formula for $n^{(2)}$ and subsequent differentiation with respect to the coupling parameter gives:

$$kT\frac{\partial \ln n_{12}^{(2)}}{\partial \xi} = -\varphi(r_{12}) - \int \varphi(r_{13})\left[\frac{n^{(3)}(\boldsymbol{r}_1, \boldsymbol{r}_2, \boldsymbol{r}_3)}{n^{(2)}(\boldsymbol{r}_1, \boldsymbol{r}_2)} - \frac{n^{(2)}(\boldsymbol{r}_1, \boldsymbol{r}_3)}{n}\right] d\boldsymbol{r}_3$$

$$= -\varphi(r_{12}) - 2\pi \int_0^\infty \int_{|r_{12}-r_{13}|}^{(r_{12}+r_{13})} \varphi_{13}\left[\frac{n_{123}^{(3)}}{n_{12}^{(2)}} - \frac{n_{13}^{(2)}}{n}\right]\frac{r_{13}\,r_{23}}{r_{12}}\,dr_{23}\,dr_{13} \tag{4.9–20}$$

By this procedure we arrive at a set of coupled integral equations which is different from, but equivalent to, that obtained by the two other methods described.

d. Solution of the integral equation for the pair distribution function: the superposition approximation

The integral equations given in Eq. 4.9–12 and Eq. 4.9–20 cannot be solved for $n^{(2)}$ until something has been done about writing $n^{(3)}$ approximately in terms of $n^{(2)}$. For this purpose the so-called superposition approximation has been suggested. The extent to which it is valid is not known.

It is customary to assume that the potential energy of a system of three molecules may be written as

$$\Phi(\boldsymbol{r}_1, \boldsymbol{r}_2, \boldsymbol{r}_3) = \varphi(r_{12}) + \varphi(r_{13}) + \varphi(r_{23}) \tag{4.9–21}$$

If the same relation is written for the potential of average force,

$$\Psi(\boldsymbol{r}_1, \boldsymbol{r}_2, \boldsymbol{r}_3) = \Psi(r_{12}) + \Psi(r_{13}) + \Psi(r_{23}) \tag{4.9–22}$$

then it follows from Eq. 4.9–7 that

$$n^{(3)}(\boldsymbol{r}_1, \boldsymbol{r}_2, \boldsymbol{r}_3) = \frac{n^{(2)}(r_{12})n^{(2)}(r_{13})n^{(2)}(r_{23})}{n^3} \tag{4.9–23}$$

This "superposition approximation" is clearly exact in the low density limit. At higher densities it is an approximation which has not yet been fully justified.[13, 14]

[13] This superposition approximation may be regarded as analogous to the Hartree approximation in quantum mechanics applied to the function $n^{(3)}$ in the configuration space of molecule triples as the product of the functions $n^{(2)}$ in the configuration space of molecule pairs. The corresponding Hartree-like approximation in the configuration space for a single molecule leads to the free-volume theory of dense gases and liquids (see § 4.4).

[14] B. R. A. Nijboer and L. van Hove [*Koninklijke Nederlandse Akademie van Wetenschappen*, **54**, 256 (1951); *Phys. Rev.*, **85**, 777 (1952)] have recently suggested another type of approximation which gives better results for rigid spheres than the superposition approximation.

The superposition approximation has been used to eliminate $n^{(3)}$ from the two integral equations for $n^{(2)}$. Because Eq. 4.9–23 is not exact its use in Eqs. 4.9–12 and 20 leads to two different approximate integral equations for the pair distribution function—that of Born and Green and Yvon and that due to Kirkwood. The solutions of these two equations are different, and the difference is a measure of the validity of the superposition approximation. Inasmuch as the superposition principle treats $n^{(3)}$ exactly in the limit of low densities, the resulting solution for $n^{(2)}$ as a power series in n is correct through the second term. Therefore the resulting equation of state has the correct third virial coefficient. The expressions for the higher virial coefficients, however, are only approximate.[15]

i. *The Born-Green-Yvon Approximate Integral Equation*[16, 17]

Let us now consider the first integral equation for $n^{(2)}$ (Eq. 4.9–12) and make use of the superposition approximation. The equation can be integrated explicitly over r_{12} from an arbitrary value $r_{12} = r$ to $r_{12} = \infty$. We make use of the limiting values: $n^{(2)} \to n^2$ and $\varphi \to 0$ as $r_{12} \to \infty$. In order to evaluate the integral over r_{12}, r_{23}, r_{13} the order of integration must be changed. However, in this particular case the convergence of the integrals is not such as to permit the simple interchange of the order of integration. Straightforward (but lengthy) manipulations result in the following equation for $g(r) = n^{(2)}/n^2$:

$$kT \ln g(r) = -\varphi(r) + 2\pi n \int_0^\infty \int_{r-r_{13}}^{r+r_{13}} \frac{\partial \varphi_{13}}{\partial r_{13}} g_{13}(g_{23} - 1) \times \left[\frac{r_{13}{}^2 - (r_{23} - r)^2}{2r}\right] r_{23}\, dr_{23}\, dr_{13} \tag{4.9–24}$$

Here φ and g with negative arguments are defined by $\varphi(-r) = \varphi(r)$ and $g(-r) = g(r)$, and $g_{ij} = g(r_{ij})$. This approximate equation was obtained independently by Born and Green[17] and by Yvon.[16] Green[18] has

[15] For rigid spheres the exact value of the fourth virial coefficient is $D = 0.2869 b_0{}^3$. According to the superposition principle and the approximate integral equation of Yvon, Born, and Green, $D = 0.2252 b_0{}^3$. (This value has recently been obtained by R. W. Hart, R. Wallis, and L. Pode, *J. Chem. Phys.*, **19**, 139 (1951), and also by G. S. Rushbrooke and H. I. Scoins, *Nature*, **167**, 366 (1951).) According to the approximation of Nijboer and van Hove (Ref. 14), $D = 0.2500 b_0{}^3$.

[16] J. Yvon, *Actualités scientifiques et industrielles*, Hermann & Cie, Paris (1935), p. 203.

[17] M. Born and H. S. Green, *Proc. Roy. Soc.* (*London*), **A188**, 10 (1946).

[18] H. S. Green, *Proc. Roy. Soc.* (*London*), **A189**, 103 (1947).

succeeded in solving this integral equation by introducing further assumptions which are somewhat difficult to analyze. From the solution approximate integrals for the virial coefficients have been obtained; these integrals are considerably easier to handle than the corresponding exact ones discussed in Chapter 3. The equation of state has been calculated for rigid spheres by means of Eq. 4.9–24.[19]

ii. *The Approximate Integral Equations of Kirkwood*[12]

Now we examine the application of the superposition principle to the second integral equation for $n^{(2)}$ (Eq. 4.9–20). Integrating this equation over ξ and using the fact that $g \to 1$ for $\xi \to 0$, we can obtain

$$kT \ln g(r, \xi) = -\xi\varphi(r) - 2\pi n \int_0^\infty \int_0^\xi \int_{|r-r_{13}|}^{(r+r_{13})} \varphi_{13} g_{13}(g_{23} - 1) \frac{r_{13}r_{23}}{r}\, dr_{23}\, d\xi\, dr_{13} \tag{4.9–25}$$

This is the approximate integral equation developed by Kirkwood.[12] It has recently been used to calculate the pair distribution function for rigid spheres.[20]

iii. *Comparison of the Two Approximate Integral Equations*

The two approximate integral equations just described may be written in a common form. We introduce the coupling parameter ξ into the Born and Green equations and define a kernel $K(t, \xi)$ for the two cases as

$$K(t, \xi) = \tfrac{1}{2}\xi \int_{|t|}^\infty \frac{d\varphi_{13}}{dr_{13}} g_{13}(r_{13}{}^2 - t^2)\, dr_{13} \qquad \text{(Born-Green-Yvon)} \tag{4.9–26}$$

$$K(t, \xi) = -\int_0^\xi \int_{|t|}^\infty \varphi_{13} g_{13} r_{13}\, dr_{13}\, d\xi \qquad \text{(Kirkwood)} \tag{4.9–27}$$

In terms of these functions both the approximate integral equations take the form:

$$kT \ln g(r, \xi) = -\xi\varphi(r) + 2\pi n \int_0^\infty [K(r - r_{23}, \xi) - K(r + r_{23}, \xi)]\, (g_{23} - 1) \frac{r_{23}}{r}\, dr_{23} \tag{4.9–28}$$

[19] J. G. Kirkwood and E. M. Boggs, *J. Chem. Phys.*, **10**, 394 (1942).

[20] J. G. Kirkwood, E. K. Maun and B. J. Alder, *J. Chem. Phys.*, **18**, 1040 (1950). The results of Kirkwood, Maun, and Alder have recently been verified and extended by A. G. McLellan, *Proc. Roy. Soc. (London)*, **A210**, 509 (1952).

iv. *The Numerical Solution of the Approximate Integral Equations*

The integral equations for the radial distribution function have been solved both for rigid-sphere molecules[20] and for molecules which interact according to a modified Lennard-Jones (6-12) potential.[21] Figure 4.9–3

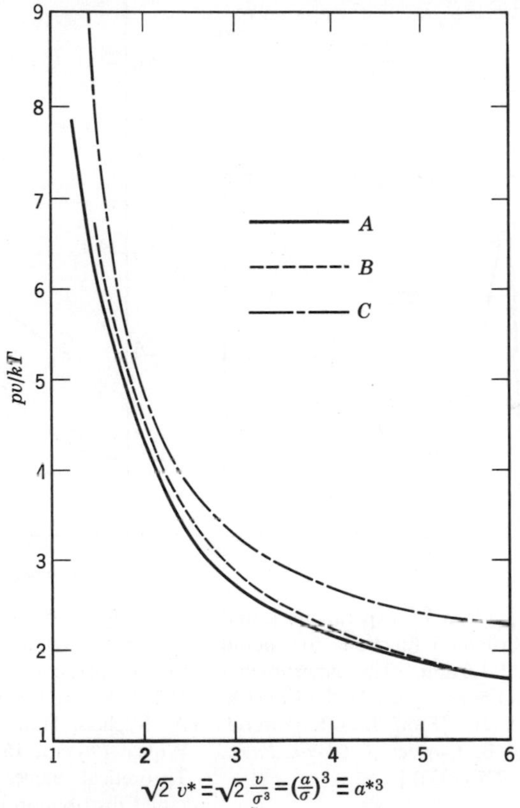

Fig. 4.9–3. Compressibility factor pv/kT as a function of the reduced volume, v^*, for rigid spherical molecules of diameter σ. (*A*) From the Kirkwood approximate integral equation, Eq. 4.9–25. (*B*) From the Born-Green-Yvon approximate integral equation, Eq. 4.9–24. (*C*) From the sphericalized free volume theory, Eq. 4.6–5. [From J. G. Kirkwood, V. A. Lewinson, and B. J. Alder, *J. Chem. Phys.*, **20**, 929 (1952).]

compares the compressibility factors calculated from the Born-Green-Yvon equation and the Kirkwood equation for rigid-sphere molecules. The corresponding curve obtained from the sphericalized free-volume theory of rigid spheres Eq. 4.6–5 is also shown. It may be seen from this

[21] J. G. Kirkwood, V. A. Lewinson, and B. J. Alder, *J. Chem. Phys.*, **20**, 929 (1952).

graphical representation that the Born-Green-Yvon equation gives a value of pV/NkT, almost the same as the Kirkwood equation in the low-density limit. For higher densities the agreement is moderately good.

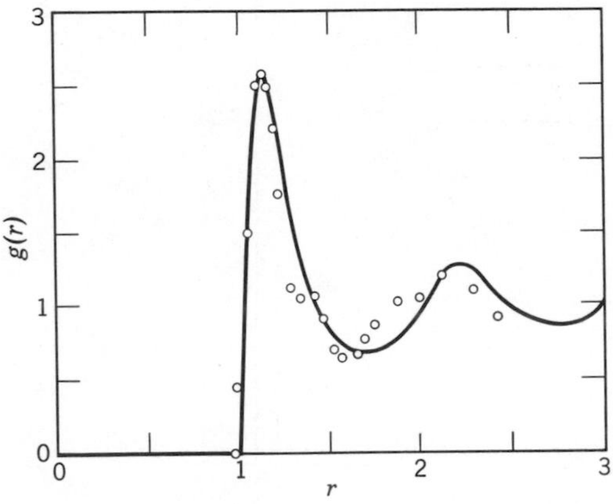

Fig. 4.9–4. A comparison of experimental and theoretical radial distribution functions for liquid argon at 91.8° K and 1.8 atm. The experimental values are those of A. Eisenstein and N. S. Gingrich, *Phys. Rev.* **62**, 261 (1942). [From J. G. Kirkwood, V. A. Lewinson, and B. J. Alder, *J. Chem. Phys.*, **20**, 929 (1952).]

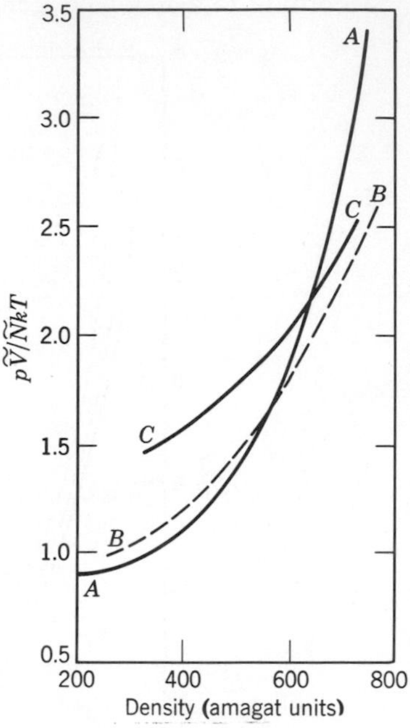

Fig. 4.9–5. A comparison of experimental and theoretical values of the compressibility factor of argon at 273° K. (*A*) experimental values, A. Michels, Hub. Wijker, and Hk. Wijker, *Physica*, **15**, 627 (1949). (*B*) Theoretical values based on the radial distribution function method. (*C*) Theoretical values based on the cell method. [From J. G. Kirkwood, V. A. Lewinson, and B. J. Alder, *J. Chem. Phys.*, **20**, 929 (1952).]

The modified Lennard-Jones (6-12) potential used in the solution of the equations for the radial distribution function is a Lennard-Jones (6-12) potential for $r > \sigma$ but is infinite for $r < \sigma$. The compressibility factor and the corrections to the internal energy and entropy at a number of values of the reduced volume and temperature as calculated from Born-Green-Yvon equations are given in Tables 4.9–1, 2, and 3. The values of the reduced critical constants are

$$p_c^* = 0.199 \qquad V_c^* = 2.585$$

$$T_c^* = 1.433 \qquad p_c\tilde{V}_c/RT_c = 0.358$$

A comparison of the theoretical and experimental radial distribution functions of liquid argon at 91.8°K and 1.8 atms is indicated in Fig. 4.9–4. The value of σ in the intermolecular potential function was chosen so that the first peaks of the two curves coincide. It is seen that the agreement between the two curves is good. In Fig. 4.9–5, experimental measurements of the compressibility factor of argon at 273°K as a function of density are compared with the theoretical values obtained from the radial distribution function and also with the theoretical values obtained by the cell method of Lennard-Jones and Devonshire (see § 4.7).

TABLE 4.9 1

THE COMPRESSIBILITY FACTOR AS OBTAINED FROM THE RADIAL DISTRIBUTION FUNCTION[21]

v^* \ T^*	0.833	1.000	1.250	1.677	2.500	5.000	∞
13.82		0.629	0.768	0.883			1.167
3.632	−0.594	−0.156	0.264	0.670	1.064	1.456	1.833
2.260	−1.445	−0.734	−0.038	0.649	1.326	1.998	2.667
1.483	−2.433	−1.268	−0.115	1.018	2.139	3.242	4.333
1.222	−2.829	−1.382	0.052	1.467	2.856	4.223	5.567

TABLE 4.9–2

$-\dfrac{\tilde{U}'}{\tilde{N}\epsilon} = -\dfrac{\tilde{U} - \tilde{U}^0}{\tilde{N}\epsilon}$, THE REDUCED "EXCESS" INTERNAL ENERGY[21]

v^* \ T^*	0.833	1.000	1.250	1.667	2.500	5.000
13.82		0.741	0.621	0.537		
3.632	2.280	2.148	2.035	1.939	1.856	1.787
2.260	3.370	3.277	3.192	3.118	3.050	2.990
1.483	5.073	5.024	4.974	4.925	4.873	4.822
1.222	6.313	6.280	6.232	6.181	6.125	6.066

TABLE 4.9–3

$\frac{\tilde{S}'}{R} = \frac{\tilde{S} - \tilde{S}^0 + R \ln p}{R}$, THE REDUCED "EXCESS" ENTROPY[21,a]

v^* \ T^*	1.000	1.250	1.667	2.500	5.000
13.82	−0.74	−0.50	−0.33		
3.632		−1.24	−1.39	−0.99	−0.73
2.260			−1.99	−1.36	−1.00
1.483			−2.55	−1.90	−1.54
1.222		−6.31	−2.97	−2.39	−2.06

[a] This table differs from that of Ref. 21 because of the difference in the definition of the "excess" entropy. (See § 4.7b.)

PROBLEMS

1. For the rigid-sphere model, with diameter σ, use Eq. 4.9–2 to calculate the radial distribution function. Let $n^* = n\sigma^3$ be the reduced number density; let $r^* = r/\sigma$ be the reduced intermolecular separation, so that the potential is

$$\varphi(r^*) = \infty \qquad r^* < 1$$

$$\varphi(r^*) = 0 \qquad r^* > 1$$

Show that[1]

$$g(r^*) = 0 \qquad r^* < 1$$

$$g(r^*) = 1 + \frac{4\pi n^*}{3}[1 - \tfrac{3}{4}r^* + \tfrac{1}{16}r^{*3}] \qquad 1 < r^* < 2$$

$$g(r^*) = 1 \qquad 2 < r^*$$

Compare this result with that shown for the Lennard-Jones potential.

2. For the rigid-sphere model calculate the potential of average force $\Psi(r_{12}^*)$ for $n^* = 1$. Plot $\Psi(r^*)$ and $\varphi(r^*)$ on the same graph. Note that for $r^* < 2$, $\Psi(r^*)$ decreases with decreasing distance, giving rise to an attractive force. This average force, which acts on molecule 1 in the direction of molecule 2, may be interpreted as follows: Molecule 2 shields molecule 1 from collisions with the remaining $N - 2$ molecules, and hence, for $r^* < 2$, there is a resultant force on 1 in the direction of 2.

3. Use the principle of the corresponding states to estimate the compressibility factor, the enthalpy, the entropy, and C_p for N_2 at 60 atm and 100°K.

4. Use the van der Waals, the Berthoiet, the Dieterici, the Beattie-Bridgeman, and the Benedict-Webb-Rubin equations to estimate the compressibility factor of N_2 at 60 atm and 100°K.

5. Use the theory of Lennard-Jones and Devonshire to calculate the compressibility factor, the enthalpy, the entropy, and the specific heat of N_2 at 60°K and 1 atm.

[1] J. de Boer, *Reports on Progress in Physics*, **12**, 305 (1949).

6. The following two constant equation of state has recently been proposed:[2]

$$p = \frac{RT}{\tilde{V} - b\tilde{V}^{-1/2}} - \frac{a}{\tilde{V}^{5/3}T^{2/3}}$$

Show that $a = 0.9099RT_c^{5/3}\tilde{V}_c^{2/3}$ and $b = 0.1567\tilde{V}_c^{3/2}$, and that this equation of state gives a value of $p_c\tilde{V}_c/RT_c$ of 0.276, which is in good agreement with experiment.

[2] S. W. Benson and R. A. Golding, *J. Chem. Phys.*, **19**, 1413 (1951).

· 5 ·

Vapor-Liquid Equilibria and Critical Phenomena

(This chapter was prepared in collaboration with Dr. C. A. Boyd, Aero Projects, West Chester, Pa.)

In the preceding two chapters the equilibrium properties of gas-phase systems and liquid-phase systems have been considered. This chapter deals with the behavior of systems in which both the gaseous and the liquid phases are present in equilibrium with one another.

We discuss first the nature of the interfacial region between the liquid and vapor phases. A thermodynamic approach to the study of interfaces relates the surface tension to the thermodynamic properties of the surface. A statistical mechanical approach, on the other hand, gives an insight into the microscopic nature of the transition region. It is found that the transition zone or surface layer between the gas and the liquid phases becomes progressively broader as the temperature of the substance is raised. When the temperature approaches the critical temperature, then, under the influence of gravity there is a density gradient throughout the entire containing vessel. At this point the distinction between liquid and vapor is meaningless. One method of determining the critical point makes use of the disappearance of the meniscus as the temperature is raised. There is some question at the present time as to whether the temperature of the disappearance of the meniscus is really the same as the critical temperature defined by the geometrical characteristics of the isotherms. Present experimental measurements indicate that the difference between the critical points as determined by the two methods cannot be more than a few hundredths of a degree.

Then we turn to a discussion of the classical theory of phase behavior and critical phenomena. This theory is based upon the artificial notion that two well-defined, completely homogeneous phases exist right up to the critical point, and a well-defined meniscus separates the two phases. This theory gives an adequate explanation for many phenomena associated with phase transitions and critical phenomena. There are, however, a number of deviations from this classical behavior such as the density gradients in a fluid and the hysteresis effect which require a considerably more detailed analysis of the problem. These "anomalies" can be explained to a greater or lesser extent by considering the effects of gravity and density fluctuations. A considerable amount of experimental and theoretical work needs yet to be done in order to understand this subject. We attempt here to summarize the present status of the research and to indicate how the results of the two preceding chapters may be used to interpret some of the phenomena associated with two-phase systems.

This chapter concludes with a discussion of some of the interesting phenomena which have been observed in connection with the phase transitions in binary systems. The phenomena of retrograde condensation, important in connection with petroleum recovery, are discussed in terms of phase diagrams. The two-phase behavior of binary systems is also considered from a thermodynamic viewpoint.

1. The Interfacial Region between a Liquid and a Vapor

A theoretical treatment of two phase systems must consider the interfacial region and the nature of surface tension. In the theoretical description of surface tension the same two approaches may be used as have been employed for the equilibrium properties of liquids,[1] the *free volume method* and the *radial distribution function method.* Calculations using the former method have been carried out by Lennard-Jones and Corner; the latter method has been used by Kirkwood and Buff.[2] We discuss the work of these two groups of investigators and then give some consideration to the surface tension of droplets and the relationship between the parachor and the intermolecular forces.

a. Definition of surface tension

A two-phase system in a tall box arranged along the z-axis is pictured in Fig. 5.1–1. A plot of the variation in number density with height is shown in an accompanying graph. In the body of the liquid phase the number density has a value $n^{(l)}$ which does not change with height; similarly, in the body of the vapor phase the number density has a constant value $n^{(v)}$. From a macroscopic standpoint the number density jumps discontinuously from one value to the other at the interface. For the

[1] In addition the hole theory of liquids (discussed in § 4.8) has been used to study the surface tension of liquids. See S. Ono, *Memoirs of the Faculty of Engineering*, Kyushu University, **10**, 195 (1947). This theory leads to density versus distance curves similar to those given in Fig. 5.1–2.

[2] A. G. MacLellan, *Proc. Roy. Soc.* (*London*), **A213**, 274 (1952), has recently compared and extended the two approaches.

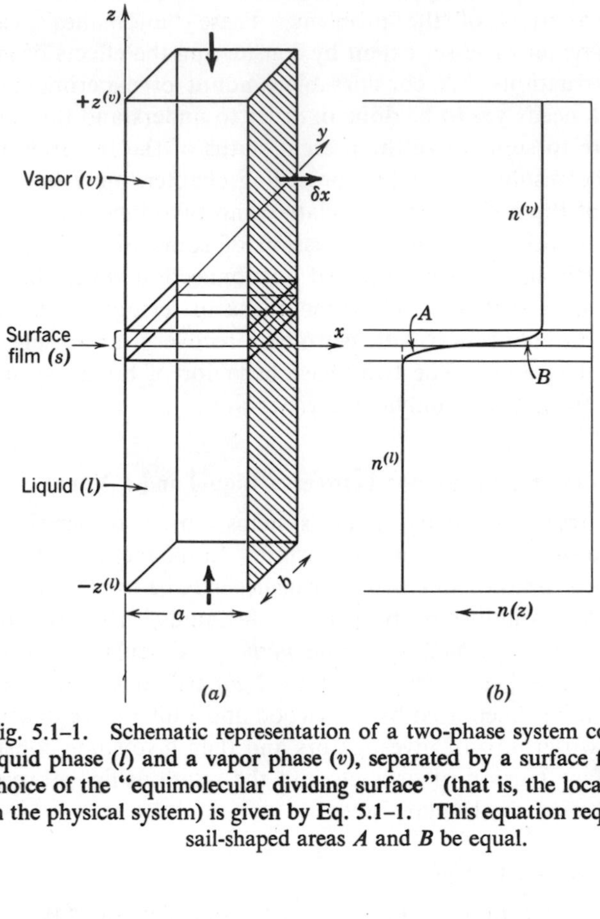

Fig. 5.1–1. Schematic representation of a two-phase system composed of a liquid phase (l) and a vapor phase (v), separated by a surface film (s). The choice of the "equimolecular dividing surface" (that is, the location of $z = 0$ in the physical system) is given by Eq. 5.1–1. This equation requires that the sail-shaped areas A and B be equal.

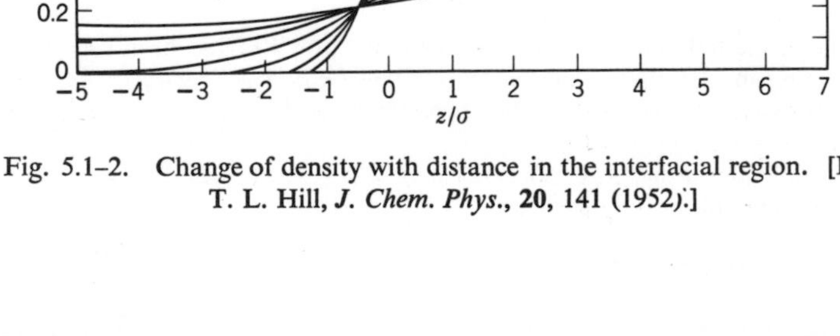

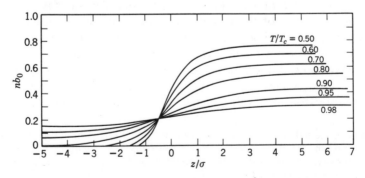

Fig. 5.1–2. Change of density with distance in the interfacial region. [From T. L. Hill, *J. Chem. Phys.*, **20**, 141 (1952).]

formulation of a microscopic theory of surface tension it must be taken into account that such a discontinuity does not really exist. The number density actually varies continuously across the interface as indicated in Fig. 5.1–2.[3] The other equilibrium properties of the substance vary in a similar manner. The pressure tensor, for example, has the value $p_0\mathsf{U}$ in the liquid and vapor phases alike (p_0 is the static pressure). In the transition region between the two phases the pressure tensor $\mathsf{p}(z)$ varies smoothly from the liquid region to the vapor region.

It was pointed out by Gibbs[4] that it is convenient from a mathematical standpoint to introduce a "dividing surface" between the liquid and vapor phases. This dividing surface is normal to the density gradient. The position of the dividing surface is arbitrary. A convenient choice is to require that $z = 0$ be defined in such a way that

$$\int_{-z^{(l)}}^{0} [n^{(l)} - n(z)]\, dz = \int_{0}^{+z^{(v)}} [n(z) - n^{(v)}]\, dz \tag{5.1-1}$$

as illustrated pictorially in Fig. 5.1–1. We call this choicc of dividing surface the *equimolecular dividing surface*. For this choice of dividing surface, a hypothetical system in which thc density changes discontinuously from that of the homogeneous liquid to that of the homogeneous vapor at the dividing surface would contain the same number of molecules as the actual system.

Let us now imagine that the shaded wall of the container is displaced reversibly and isothermally in the positive x-direction an amount δx, as

[3] Terrell L. Hill [*J. Chem. Phys.*, **19**, 261 and 1203 (1951), and **20**, 141 (1952)] has developed a very simple but rough method for calculating surface tension. He requires that the chemical potential have the same value not only in the homogenous liquid and gas phases but also at all intermediate points through the interface. The chemical potential is determined from the free volume and the energy of interaction of the molecules. The free volume as a function of the density is obtained from a modified van der Waals equation. The molecular density is "smeared" in the sense that the radial distribution function is taken to be zero up to a rigid-sphere collision diameter and unity for all larger separations. This makes it easy to calculate the energy of interaction of the molecules as a function of the variation of the density with height. The equality of the chemical potential at arbitrary heights provides an integral equation for the density distribution. Once the density distribution has been determined it is easy to find the stress as a function of height and hence the surface tension. The present calculations are for molecules which are rigid up to a collision diameter, σ, and at larger separations attract each other with an energy inversely proportional to the sixth power of the separation.

[4] J. W. Gibbs, *The Collected Works*, Vol. I, p. 219, Longmans, Green (1928).

shown in Fig. 5.1–1. The work done by the system in this process is

$$\delta w_1 = b\,\delta x \int_{-z^{(l)}}^{+z^{(v)}} p_{xx}(z)\,dz \tag{5.1–2}$$

The only component of the pressure tensor which need be considered is the xx-component, which is related to the force in the x-direction on an element of surface perpendicular to the x-direction. Let us now push in the top and bottom of the container reversibly and isothermally so as to return the system to its original volume. The work done by the system in this process is

$$\delta w_2 = -(z^{(v)} + z^{(l)})\,bp_0\,\delta x = -b\,\delta x \int_{-z^{(l)}}^{+z^{(v)}} p_0\,dz \tag{5.1–3}$$

At the conclusion of this manipulation the system finds itself at the same volume, pressure, and temperature as it was initially. The distribution of molecules above and below the dividing surface is the same before and after the entire process.[5] The only difference is that the area of the surface film has been increased. The work done *on* the system to cause a unit increase in the area of the film is called the surface tension, γ. Accordingly, we may write for an increase, $\delta\alpha = b\,\delta x$, in the area of the film:

$$\gamma\,\delta\alpha = -\delta w = \delta\alpha \int (p_0 - p_{xx}(z))\,dz \tag{5.1–4}$$

The surface tension is thus the stress acting in the x-direction on a strip of unit area in the yz-plane in addition to the uniform normal pressure, p_0, which acts on both phases.

[5] Because of the definition of the equimolecular dividing surface the number of molecules above the surface (this is referred to as the number of molecules of the vapor) is $abz^{(v)}n^{(v)}$. Thus the condition that the number of molecules of vapor be the same before and after the two-stage manipulation just described is

$$abz^{(v)}n^{(v)} = (a + \delta x)bz^{(v)\prime}n^{(v)}$$

Similarly for the liquid phase:

$$abz^{(l)}n^{(l)} = (a + \delta x)bz^{(l)\prime}n^{(l)}$$

Here $z^{(v)\prime}$ and $z^{(l)\prime}$ are the distances from the dividing surface of the ends of the container after the manipulation. Thus

$$\frac{z^{(v)\prime}}{z^{(v)}} = \frac{z^{(l)\prime}}{z^{(l)}} = \frac{a}{a + \delta x}$$

From this it is clear that the volumes of the vapor phase and of the liquid remain unchanged by the whole process. It is, therefore, a change at constant volume (and also a change at constant pressure, since the vapor pressure is constant in an isothermal process), in which the amounts of the two phases are unchanged. It should be noticed that this result is a direct consequence of the definition of the equimolecular dividing surface and is not true for other dividing surfaces.

Let us now consider the contributions of the surface layer to the thermodynamic functions in a two-phase system. Each of the thermodynamic properties of the entire system can be considered to be the sum of three contributions: that due to the liquid, that due to the vapor, and that due to the surface. For example, the Helmholtz free energy of a two-phase system is

$$A = A^{(l)} + A^{(v)} + A^{(s)} \tag{5.1–5}$$

Here $A^{(l)}$ is the free energy per unit volume of the homogeneous liquid (that is, in the body of the liquid) multiplied by the volume of the system contained below the equimolecular dividing surface. $A^{(v)}$ is defined similarly for the vapor phase. Since the free energy of the total system, A, is well defined, Eq. 5.1–5 is used as the defining equation for $A^{(s)}$.

We now examine the thermodynamics of the two-phase system. The element of work, δw, which appears in the first law is

$$\delta w = p\, dV - \gamma\, d\alpha \tag{5.1–6}$$

Thus the change in the Helmholtz free energy of the system is

$$dA = dU - d(TS) = -S\, dT - p\, dV + \gamma\, d\alpha \tag{5.1–7}$$

For the liquid and vapor phases

$$dA^{(l)} = -S^{(l)}\, dT - p\, dV^{(l)} \tag{5.1–8}$$

$$dA^{(v)} = -S^{(v)}\, dT - p\, dV^{(v)} \tag{5.1–9}$$

Combining these last three relations and making use of the fact that $V^{(l)} + V^{(v)} = V$, we obtain

$$dA^{(s)} = -S^{(s)}\, dT + \gamma\, d\alpha \tag{5.1–10}$$

Because of the additivity of the volumes,[6] $A^{(s)} = G^{(s)}$, and thus the surface tension is[7]

$$\gamma = \left(\frac{\partial A^{(s)}}{\partial \alpha}\right)_T = \left(\frac{\partial G^{(s)}}{\partial \alpha}\right)_T \tag{5.1–11}$$

[6] The equality of $A^{(S)}$ and $G^{(S)}$ depends upon the use of the equimolecular dividing surface for the definition of the liquid-vapor interface. For example, this would not quite be true if the liquid-vapor interface were specified by the "surface of tension" discussed later in this section in connection with curved surfaces.

[7] R. H. Fowler, *Proc. Roy. Soc.* (*London*), **A159**, 229 (1937), and *Physica*, **5**, 39 (1938), pointed out that the surface tension is not the increase in the potential energy of the surface as assumed by Bradley, *Phil. Mag.*, **11**, 846 (1936), and Margenau, *Phys. Rev.*, **38**, 365 (1931).

Other thermodynamical quantities of the interfacial film can be expressed in terms of γ and its derivatives. For example, from the Gibbs-Helmholtz equation an expression can be obtained for the internal energy of the surface:

$$U^{(s)} = -T^2 \frac{\partial}{\partial T}\left(\frac{\gamma}{T}\right) \tag{5.1–12}$$

This quantity can clearly be obtained from surface tension measurements, and is frequently used for making comparisons between theory and experiment. The thermodynamic development just given is restricted to the equimolecular dividing surface and single-component systems.

The surface tension may also be considered from the corresponding states standpoint discussed in § 4.1. In terms of reduction of the variables by the use of critical constants, we would expect that the reduced surface tension $\gamma_r = \gamma V_c^{2/3}(kT_c)^{-1}$ would be a universal function of the reduced temperature $T_r = T/T_c$. When the variables are reduced by using molecular units (for example, the σ and ϵ of the Lennard-Jones potential) the reduced surface tension $\gamma^* = \gamma\sigma^2/\epsilon$ is a universal function of the reduced temperature $T^* = kT/\epsilon$. For purposes of correlating data and predicting the surface tension of substances which have not been studied experimentally the principle of corresponding states may be of use, inasmuch as rigorous theories have not yet been developed to the stage where extensive practical calculations have been made.

b. Surface tension from free-volume methods

Lennard-Jones and Corner[8,9] have developed a theory of surface tension, beginning with Eq. 5.1–11. Their work is an extension of the Lennard-Jones–Devonshire free-volume theory of liquids to include a surface layer. By this approach they were able to calculate the Helmholtz free energy associated with a unit area of surface. The following assumptions are made in their development:

(i) The vapor density is so low that the molecules in the vapor phase can be neglected in calculating the surface tension.

(ii) The liquid and its surface forms a semi-infinite column. The structure of the liquid is considered to be of a lattice-like form, the lattice points being the positions of equilibrium of the molecules. The surface tension then depends upon which crystal plane is exposed. Calculations of the surface tension have been made assuming the different faces are

[8] J. E. Lennard-Jones and J. Corner, *Trans. Faraday Soc.*, **36**, 1156 (1940).

[9] J. Corner, *Trans. Faraday Soc.*, **44**, 1036 (1948).

exposed. Actually the liquid would be expected to expose that face which leads to the lowest surface tension.

(iii) The lattice points for the surface layer are shifted slightly towards the main body of the liquid so as to minimize the potential energy of the system consisting of all the molecules located at their lattice points in the semi-infinite column. Except for the surface layer, the lattice points are considered to be unaffected by the presence of the surface.

(iv) The free volumes of the molecules in the interior of the liquid are assumed to be unaffected by the presence of the surface. The free volume of a molecule in the surface layer is calculated by assuming that all the neighboring molecules are fixed in their lattice points and that the molecule under consideration wanders in the resulting potential field.

To calculate the free energy of the surface film, Lennard-Jones and Corner calculated the free energy of a mole of liquid bounded by a surface film of area α and subtracted from this the free energy of a mole of liquid in the interior of the liquid phase. The latter quantity, which is unaffected by the surface film, is given by the Lennard-Jones–Devonshire theory:

$$A^{(l)} = \Phi^{(l)} - NkT \ln \lambda^{-3} - NkT \ln v_f^{(l)} - NkT \qquad (5.1\text{–}13)$$

where $\lambda^2 = h^2/2\pi mkT$, and the superscript $^{(l)}$ indicates quantities calculated for the interior of the liquid phase. $\Phi^{(l)}$ is just the total potential energy of N molecules located at their lattice positions.

For a mole of liquid which is bounded by a surface film the total potential energy of the molecules is designated by $\Phi^{(l')}(z)$. This depends on the distance, z, by which the surface layer of molecules is displaced towards the body of liquid. A displacement z_0 may be found, for which $\Phi^{(l')}(z)$ is a minimum,[10] and henceforth this displacement defines the position of the lattice points in the surface layer. Accordingly the free energy per mole of the liquid bounded by the surface film is:

$$A^{(l')} = \Phi^{(l')}(z_0) - NkT \ln \lambda^{-3} - (N - N^{(s)})kT \ln v_f^{(l)}$$
$$- N^{(s)}kT \ln v_f^{(s)} - NkT \qquad (5.1\text{–}14)$$

The superscript $^{(l')}$ denotes properties of the liquid phase which is bounded by the surface film. $N^{(s)}$ is the number of molecules exposed in the

[10] It would be more correct to choose the distance z_0 so as to minimize the Helmholtz free energy (or the calculated surface tension). However, this process would be considerably more difficult to do and would not lead to results appreciably different.

surface film and $v_f^{(s)}$ is the free volume of a surface molecule. The surface tension is then given by[11]

$$\gamma = \frac{A^{(l')} - A^{(l)}}{\alpha} = \frac{1}{\alpha}\left[(\Phi^{(l')}(z_0) - \Phi^{(l)}) + N^{(s)}kT \ln\left(\frac{v_f^{(l)}}{v_f^{(s)}}\right)\right] \quad (5.1\text{–}15)$$

according to Eq. 5.1–11.

Corner[9] used this result to calculate the surface tension of a liquid made up of spherical non-polar molecules interacting according to the Lennard-Jones potential and arranged in a face-centered cubic lattice. It is first necessary to decide which face of the lattice is exposed. This is the face which corresponds to the lowest surface free energy or surface tension. Of the three principal planes in this lattice, the (100) can be excluded immediately[14] as it corresponds to breaking four nearest neighbor bonds per a^2 surface area (a is the distance between nearest neighbors), whereas the (110)-plane corresponds to breaking 3.54, and the (111)-plane corresponds to breaking 3.56. The breaking of nearest neighbor bonds requires considerable energy and therefore the (110)-plane or the (111)-plane is more probably the exposed face. Careful calculations show that the (111)-plane is slightly preferred, and therefore the remaining discussion is limited to this case.

Some of the results of these calculations are given in Table 5.1–1. First is given the displacement, z_0, of the surface layer toward the interior of the liquid. Also given is the potential energy of a surface molecule, $\chi(z_0)$, when the surface layer has been displaced by z_0, the quantity $\chi(0)$ is the potential energy of a surface molecule in the absence of

[11] The law of Eötvös follows directly from this equation. Eötvös' law is

$$\gamma V^{2/3} = K(T_0 - T) \quad (5.1\text{–}15a)$$

Here K and T_0 are constants. The value of K is usually 2.1 ergs per degree, and T_0 is approximately the critical temperature. To obtain the relation it is assumed that the ratio of the free volumes $[v_f^{(l)}/v_f^{(s)}]$ is independent of temperature. It is clear that $[\Phi^{(l')}(z_0) - \Phi^{(l)}]$ and $N^{(s)}$ are proportional to the number of molecules on a unit of surface, and of course this is proportional to $V^{2/3}$. However, a better empirical relation for the surface tension of simple molecules has been given by Guggenheim:[12, 13]

$$\gamma = \gamma_0 \left[1 - \frac{T}{T_c}\right]^{11/9} \quad (5.1\text{–}15b)$$

Here γ_0 is such a value that $\gamma_0 \tilde{V}_c^{2/3}/T_c = 4.4$ ergs deg^{-1} mole$^{-2/3}$.

[12] E. A. Guggenheim, *J. Chem. Phys.*, **13**, 253 (1945).

[13] E. A. Guggenheim, *Thermodynamics*, North Holland Publishing Co. (1950), 2nd Ed., p. 168.

[14] A. Harasima [*Proc. Phys. Math. Soc. Japan*, **22**, 825 (1940)] calculated $[\Phi^{(l')}(z_0) - \Phi^{(l)}]$ but unfortunately only for the (100)-plane.

such a displacement. The quantity $[\Phi^{(l')}(z_0) - \Phi^{(l)}]$ in Eq. 5.1–15 (which is just the increase in the potential energy of the perfect lattice when two semi-infinite blocks of liquid with plane surfaces are moved from zero to infinite separation) is given in the last column. These values were calculated by painstakingly summing the contributions of over 400 lattice points and approximating the contributions of all those molecules at distances greater than $5a$ from the surface.

TABLE 5.1–1

SUMMARY OF SOME INTERMEDIATE RESULTS IN THE FREE-VOLUME CALCULATIONS OF SURFACE TENSION[9]

$\epsilon, \sigma =$ parameters in Lennard-Jones potential

$a =$ distance between nearest neighbors

$a\sqrt{3}/2 =$ distance between (111)-planes

$\left(\frac{\sigma^3}{v}\right)^2$	$\frac{z_0}{(a\sqrt{3}/2)}$	$-\frac{\chi(z_0)}{\epsilon}$	$-\frac{\chi(0)}{\epsilon}$	$\frac{[\Phi^{(l')}(z_0) - \Phi^{(l)}]}{\alpha} \cdot \frac{\sigma^2}{\epsilon}$
0.7	0.075	10.6524	10.1361	1.550
0.8	0.054	11.1648	10.8585	1.990
0.9	0.036	11.5496	11.3994	2.377
1.0	0.020	11.8077	11.7589	2.703

The free volume of the molecules in the surface layer $v_f^{(s)}$ was calculated by a modification of the Lennard-Jones–Devonshire procedure. The symmetry of the hexagonal packing in the surface layer enables the potential to be replaced to a good approximation by one having cylindrical symmetry. The potential was calculated for each individual case, one example of which is shown in Fig. 5.1–3.

In order to make numerical calculations of surface tension it is necessary to know the density of the liquid (in equilibrium with its vapor) as a function of the temperature. For simple liquids, Guggenheim[12] showed empirically that this relation can be represented by the following equation in terms of the reduced variables $V_r = V/V_c$, $T_r = T/T_c$:

$$\frac{1}{V_r} = 1 + \tfrac{3}{4}(1 - T_r) + \tfrac{7}{4}(1 - T_r)^{1/3} \qquad (5.1\text{–}16)$$

Corner[9] made use of the empirical relations $kT_c/\epsilon \doteq 1.29$ and $\tilde{V}_c/N\sigma^3 \doteq 3.05$ and Eq. 5.1–16 to obtain v^* as a function of T^*. The values of T^* in Table 5.1–2 were calculated from such a relation. In this table are given some of the results of the free-volume calculations. It is interesting to note that when the temperature gets larger than $0.62T_c$ the free volume for the surface molecules actually become less than for the molecules in the interior of the liquid. For liquid argon at 90°K, where $T/T_c = 0.60$, the surface tension is $1.63\epsilon/\sigma^3 = 23.1$ dynes per cm. The experimental value[15, 16] is 11.9 dynes per cm. According to the calculations of Kirkwood and Buff, which are discussed in § 5.1c, the radial distribution function approach gives a calculated value of 14.9 dynes per cm, which is considerably more in agreement with the experimental value.

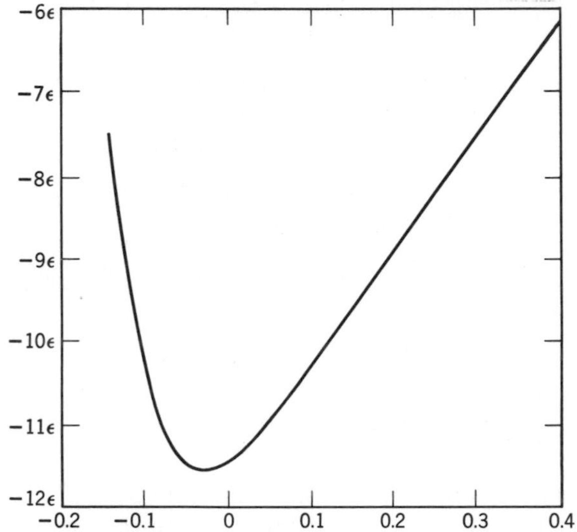

Fig. 5.1–3. Potential energy of a molecule on the surface as a function of its distance from its undisplaced lattice position outward in units of the average distance between (111) planes. This curve is for $(1/v^*)^2 = 0.9$. [From J. Corner, *Trans. Faraday Soc.*, **44**, 1036 (1948).]

TABLE 5.1–2

SUMMARY OF RESULTS OF THE FREE-VOLUME CALCULATIONS OF SURFACE TENSION[9]

(Based on the Lennard-Jones (6-12) Potential)

$\frac{1}{v^{*2}}$	T_r	$\frac{1}{T^*}$	$\ln \frac{v_f^{(s)}}{v_f^{(l)}}$	$\gamma^* = \frac{\gamma\sigma^2}{\epsilon}$
0.7	0.620	1.2495	0.009	1.545
0.8	0.521	1.4871	0.153	1.902
0.9	0.421	1.8432	0.295	2.236
1.0	0.319	2.4280	0.427	2.542

15 Baly and Donnan, *J. Chem. Soc.*, **81**, 907 (1902).
16 G. Rudorf, *Ann. Physik*, **29**, 751 (1909).

The free-volume theory of surface tension provides an interesting viewpoint and a simple qualitative picture of surface phenomena. However, it is too crude to provide a means for making accurate numerical calculations. Furthermore, it is not suitable for considerations of the effect of the curvature of the surface on the value of the surface tension. At the present time it would seem that the theories based on the radial distribution function (discussed in the next subsection) show greater promise.

c. Surface tension from the radial distribution function[17]

The pressure in a homogeneous phase is given in terms of the radial distribution function by Eq. 3.1–13,

$$p = nkT - \tfrac{1}{6}n^2 \int g(r) \frac{d\varphi}{dr} r\, dr \tag{5.1–17}$$

It is shown in § 9.4 that, in general, the pressure tensor may be expressed in terms of the radial distribution function by the relation

$$\mathsf{p}(\boldsymbol{r}_1) = n(\boldsymbol{r}_1)kT\mathsf{U} - \tfrac{1}{2}n(\boldsymbol{r}_1) \int n(\boldsymbol{r}_2)g(\boldsymbol{r}_1, \boldsymbol{r}_{21}) \frac{d\varphi}{dr_{21}} \frac{\boldsymbol{r}_{21}\boldsymbol{r}_{21}}{r_{21}}\, d\boldsymbol{r}_{21} \tag{5.1–18}$$

In this case, the radial distribution function depends parametrically on the position of molecule 1. That is, $n(\boldsymbol{r}_2)g(\boldsymbol{r}_1, \boldsymbol{r}_{21})\, d\boldsymbol{r}_{21}$ is the number of molecules lying in the volume element $d\boldsymbol{r}_{21}$ about a molecule at $\boldsymbol{r}_1$. The vector $\boldsymbol{r}_1$ is measured from a fixed origin whereas $\boldsymbol{r}_{21}$ is measured from the point $\boldsymbol{r}_1$. This expression applies to the non-homogeneous region of transition between the two homogeneous phases. (It also applies equally well to non-equilibrium situations.)

From Eq. 5.1–18 an expression for $p_{xx}(z)$ may be obtained which may be substituted into Eq. 5.1–4 for the surface tension. The result is

$$\gamma = -kT\,\Gamma_0^{(1)} + \tfrac{1}{2} \int \Gamma_0^{(2)}(\boldsymbol{r}_{21}) \frac{d\varphi}{dr_{21}} \frac{x_{21}{}^2}{r_{21}}\, d\boldsymbol{r}_{21} \tag{5.1–19}$$

$\Gamma_0^{(1)}$ and $\Gamma_0^{(2)}$ are called the *superficial number density* and the *superficial pair density* and are special cases of the following functions:

$$\Gamma_j^{(1)} = \int_{-\infty}^{0} z_1{}^j [n(z_1) - n^{(l)}]\, dz_1 + \int_{0}^{\infty} z_1{}^j [n(z_1) - n^{(v)}]\, dz_1 \tag{5.1–20}$$

[17] J. G. Kirkwood and F. P. Buff, *J. Chem. Phys.*, **17**, 338 (1949).

$$\Gamma_j^{(2)} = \int_{-\infty}^{0} z_1^{\,j}[n(z_1)n(z_2)g(z_1, \boldsymbol{r}_{21}) - n^{(l)^2}g^{(l)}(r_{21})]\, dz_1$$
$$+ \int_{0}^{\infty} z_1^{\,j}[n(z_1)n(z_2)g(z_1, \boldsymbol{r}_{21}) - n^{(v)^2}g^{(v)}(r_{21})]\, dz_1 \qquad (5.1\text{–}21)$$

$g^{(l)}$ and $g^{(v)}$ are the ordinary radial distribution functions in the liquid and vapor phases away from the surface.

The surface tension for a multicomponent system is a generalization of Eq. 5.1–19:

$$\gamma = -kT \sum_i (\Gamma_0^{(1)})_i + \tfrac{1}{2} \sum_{i>j} \int (\Gamma_0^{(2)}(\boldsymbol{r}_{21}))_{ij} \frac{d\varphi_{ij}}{dr_{21}} \frac{x_{21}^{\,2}}{r_{21}}\, d\boldsymbol{r}_{21} \qquad (5.1\text{–}22)$$

Here $(\Gamma_0^{(1)})_i$ is the superficial number density for molecules of the ith species defined by an equation similar to Eq. 5.1–20. $(\Gamma_0^{(2)})_{ij}$ is the superficial pair density for molecules of types i and j defined by an equation similar to Eq. 5.1–21, where now one member of the pair of molecules is of species i and the other is of species j. $\varphi_{ij}(r_{21})$ is the energy of interaction between molecules 1 and 2, which are of species i and j.

Up to this point nothing has been said about the location of the dividing surface between liquid and vapor, that is the origin of the z-coordinate. The value of the calculated surface tension clearly does not depend upon the choice of the dividing surface. For the equimolecular dividing surface defined in Eq. 5.1–1 (which simply states that $\Gamma_0^{(1)} = 0$) the expression for the surface tension simplifies to

$$\gamma = \tfrac{1}{2} \int \Gamma_0^{(2)}(\boldsymbol{r}_{21}) \frac{d\varphi}{dr_{21}} \frac{x_{21}^{\,2}}{r_{21}}\, d\boldsymbol{r}_{21} \qquad (5.1\text{–}23)$$

This is a rigorous expression for the surface tension. It is completely free of the assumptions introduced in the free-volume approach. The difficulty, of course, is that our knowledge of the density and the pair distribution function in the neighborhood of the interface is incomplete. Nevertheless, this approach seems quite promising as a method for investigating surface phenomena. In § 5.1e we summarize some simple calculations based upon the technique just described.

d. Effect of radius of curvature on surface tension

A thermodynamical theory of the effect of the radius of curvature on surface tension has been developed by Tolman[18] and subsequently extended

[18] R. C. Tolman, *J. Chem. Phys.*, **16**, 758 (1948); **17**, 118, 333 (1949).

by Kirkwood and Buff.[19, 20] The theory describes the thermodynamical properties of extremely small droplets or clusters such as occur in the nucleation of supersaturated vapors. In the future it should be useful in helping to solve the mysteries of the critical phenomena where very large clusters are prevalent.

For droplets it turns out that the *equimolecular dividing surface* is not the most convenient one. Gibbs[4] showed that there is a dividing surface called the *surface of tension* which, when used for the calculation of thermodynamic properties, gives simpler results for droplets.[21, 22]

For spherical surfaces, Buff and Kirkwood[19] have concluded that the surface of tension has a radius smaller by z_0 than the equimolecular dividing surface, and z_0 is given by

$$\int_{-\infty}^{+\infty} (z + z_0)\,[p_0 - p_{xx}(z)]\,dz = 0 \tag{5.1–24}$$

Using the expression for surface tension given in Eq. 5.1–19 and the definitions of the functions $\Gamma_j^{(1)}$ and $\Gamma_j^{(2)}$, we obtain for z_0

$$z_0 = \frac{1}{\gamma}\left[kT\,\Gamma_1^{(1)} - \tfrac{1}{2}\int \Gamma_1^{(2)}(\boldsymbol{r}_{21})\,\frac{d\varphi}{dr_{21}}\,\frac{z_{21}^{\,2}}{r_{21}}\,d\boldsymbol{r}_{21}\right] \tag{5.1–25}$$

In § 4.9 we described the Kirkwood and the Born-Green-Yvon approximate integro-differential equations, which relate the pair distribution function to the number density. From these equations it follows that[19]

$$\Gamma_j^{(1)} = -\frac{1}{(j+1)kT}\int \Gamma_{j+1}^{(2)}(\boldsymbol{r}_{21})\,\frac{d\varphi}{dr_{21}}\,\frac{z_{21}}{r_{21}}\,d\boldsymbol{r}_{21} \tag{5.1–26}$$

[19] J. G. Kirkwood and F. P. Buff, *J. Chem. Phys.*, **17**, 338 (1949). F. P. Buff and J. G. Kirkwood, *J. Chem. Phys.*, **18**, 991 (1950).

[20] F. P. Buff, *J. Chem. Phys.*, **19**, 1591 (1951).

[21] The work of formation of a spherical droplet is a well-defined quantity. It is equal to the surface tension times the surface area,

$$W = -\Delta A = 4\pi r^2\gamma$$

In this section, r is the radius of curvature of the surface of tension, and γ is the surface tension defined with respect to this dividing surface. For any other dividing surface having a radius of curvature, r' and a surface area $4\pi r'^2$, the surface tension is γ'. To a good approximation

$$4\pi r^2\gamma = 4\pi r'^2\gamma'$$

It is only for very small droplets that γ and γ' are significantly different.

[22] The precise definition of this surface of tension is founded on somewhat lengthy thermodynamic arguments. We do not give the definition here but refer the interested reader to the discussion given by Tolman in Ref. 18.

Substitution of this result for $j = 1$ into the preceding equation gives

$$z_0 = -\frac{1}{2\gamma}\int [z_{21}{}^2\,\Gamma_1^{(2)}(\boldsymbol{r}_{21}) + z_{21}\,\Gamma_2^{(2)}(\boldsymbol{r}_{21})]\,\frac{d\varphi}{dr_{21}}\,\frac{1}{r_{21}}\,d\boldsymbol{r}_{21} \quad (5.1\text{–}27)$$

These expressions for z_0 apply, strictly speaking only in the case of plane surfaces. If the surfaces are curved, the $\Gamma_j^{(1)}$ and $\Gamma_j^{(2)}$ should be modified by replacing the integration over the cartesian coordinate by a similar integration over the radial coordinate. This effect has been ignored, and, up to the present time, z_0 has been assumed to be independent of the radius of curvature.

However, in evaluating the superficial number density, $\Gamma_0^{(1)}$, the effect of the curvature is important. For a droplet whose surface of tension has a radius of curvature, r, the superficial density $\Gamma_0^{(1)}$ (which is the difference, per unit area of dividing surface, between the actual amount of fluid in the two-phase system and the amount it would contain if the liquid and and vapor phases retained uniform densities up to the dividing surface) is

$$\Gamma_0^{(1)} = \int_{-r}^{0} [n(z) - n^{(l)}]\left(1 + \frac{z}{r}\right)^2 dz + \int_{0}^{\infty} [n(z) - n^{(v)}]\left(1 + \frac{z}{r}\right)^2 dz \quad (5.1\text{–}28)$$

If the surface of tension is taken to be a distance, z_0, beneath the surface for which $\Gamma_0^{(1)}$ is zero, it follows that relative to the surface of tension as origin the value of the superficial density is

$$\Gamma_0^{(1)} = \Gamma^* = z_0\,[n^{(l)} - n^{(v)}]\left[1 + \frac{z_0}{r} + \frac{1}{3}\left(\frac{z_0}{r}\right)^2\right] \quad (5.1\text{–}29)$$

Gibbs derived an equation for the change of the surface tension with the chemical potential, μ, in the following form:

$$d\gamma = -\Gamma^*\,d\mu \quad (5.1\text{–}30)$$

For isothermal changes which preserve the equilibrium between the two phases,

$$d\mu = \frac{dp^{(l)}}{n^{(l)}} = \frac{dp^{(v)}}{n^{(v)}} \quad (5.1\text{–}31)$$

Here $p^{(v)}$ is the pressure in the vapor, and $p^{(l)}$ is the pressure in the liquid or droplet. In addition, the familiar Gibbs-Kelvin equation gives the excess of the pressure within the droplet over the pressure on the outside,

$$p^{(l)} - p^{(v)} = \frac{2\gamma(r)}{r} \quad (5.1\text{–}32)$$

Differentiating this last expression and making use of the three previous equations, we get the Gibbs-Tolman-Koenig[23] relation:

$$\frac{r}{\gamma}\frac{d\gamma}{dr} = \frac{\dfrac{2z_0}{r}\left[1 + \dfrac{z_0}{r} + \dfrac{1}{3}\left(\dfrac{z_0}{r}\right)^2\right]}{1 + \dfrac{2z_0}{r}\left[1 + \dfrac{z_0}{r} + \dfrac{1}{3}\left(\dfrac{z_0}{r}\right)^2\right]} \tag{5.1–33}$$

Integrating Eq. 5.1–33 from $r = \infty$ (corresponding to a plane surface) to any radius of curvature of the droplet, r, leads to the result

$$\ln \frac{\gamma}{\gamma_0} = -\int_r^\infty \frac{\dfrac{2z_0}{r^2}\left[1 + \dfrac{z_0}{r} + \dfrac{1}{3}\left(\dfrac{z_0}{r}\right)^2\right]}{1 + \dfrac{2z_0}{r}\left[1 + \dfrac{z_0}{r} + \dfrac{1}{3}\left(\dfrac{z_0}{r}\right)^2\right]}\, dr \tag{5.1–34}$$

Here γ_0 is the surface tension of a plane surface. Table 5.1–3 gives the ratio of (γ/γ_0) for small radii of curvature.

To the first approximation,

$$\frac{\gamma}{\gamma_0} = 1 - \frac{2z_0}{r} \tag{5.1–35}$$

It is doubtful that the value of z_0 remains constant and independent of the radius of curvature for droplets so small that r is of the same order as z_0. On this account the numerical values shown in Table 5.1–3 should not be regarded as accurate. Surface tension of very small drops containing as few as one hundred molecules is of considerable interest in connection with theories of nucleation. A great deal of work remains to be done on the variation of surface tension with drop size before the theory can be regarded as satisfactory.

TABLE 5.1–3

CHANGE IN SURFACE TENSION WITH RADIUS OF CURVATURE OF THE SURFACE OF TENSION, r

z_0/r	γ/γ_0	z_0/r	γ/γ_0
0.00	1.00	0.40	0.52
0.01	0.98	0.50	0.46
0.02	0.96	0.60	0.41
0.05	0.91	0.70	0.36
0.10	0.83	0.80	0.33
0.20	0.70	0.90	0.30
0.30	0.60	1.00	0.28

[23] F. O. Koenig, *J. Chem. Phys.*, **18**, 449 (1950).

e. First-order calculations of surface tension

The calculation of surface tension requires a detailed knowledge of the density distribution, $n(\boldsymbol{r})$, and the radial distribution function, $g(\boldsymbol{r}_1, \boldsymbol{r}_{21})$, in the neighborhood of the surface, Kirkwood and Buff[19] indicate that these can be calculated in principle by the use of the Born and Green[24] theory of liquids. However, let us consider here two very simplified models.

(i) *Liquid with normal density up to Gibbs' dividing surface in contact with a vacuum.* In this case,

$$\begin{aligned} n(z_1) &= n^{(l)} \qquad && z_1 \leq 0 \\ n(z_1) &= 0 && z_1 \geq 0 \\ g(z_1, \boldsymbol{r}_{21}) &= g^{(l)}(r_{21}) && z_1 + z_{21} \leq 0 \end{aligned} \tag{5.1–36}$$

and the only part of $\Gamma^{(2)}$ which is different from zero arises from the integration between $z_1 = -z_{21}$ and $z_1 = 0$, provided that z_{21} is positive. Thus

$$\begin{aligned} \Gamma_j^{(2)} &= (-1)^{j+1} \frac{z_{21}^{j+1}}{j+1} n^{(l)^2} g^{(l)}(r_{21}) \qquad && z_{21} > 0 \\ \Gamma_j^{(2)} &= 0 && z_{21} < 0 \end{aligned} \tag{5.1–37}$$

Consequently, Eqs. 5.1–23 and 27 give for the surface tension and the location of the surface of tension

$$\gamma = \frac{\pi}{8} n^{(l)^2} \int_0^\infty g^{(l)}(r) \frac{d\varphi}{dr} r^4 \, dr \tag{5.1–38}$$

$$z_0 = \frac{4}{15} \frac{\int_0^\infty g^{(l)}(r) \frac{d\varphi}{dr} r^5 \, dr}{\int_0^\infty g^{(l)}(r) \frac{d\varphi}{dr} r^4 \, dr} \tag{5.1–39}$$

It is easy to show that the surface internal energy $U^{(s)}$ is given by

$$U^{(s)} = \tfrac{1}{2} \int \Gamma_0^{(2)} \varphi(r_{21}) \, d\boldsymbol{r}_{21} \tag{5.1–40}$$

(here, $\Gamma_0^{(2)}$ is referred to the equimolecular dividing surface) so that $U^{(s)}$ reduces to

$$U^{(s)} = -\frac{\pi}{2} n^{(l)^2} \int_0^\infty g^{(l)}(r) \varphi(r) r^3 \, dr \tag{5.1–41}$$

[24] M. Born and H. S. Green, *Proc. Roy. Soc.* (*London*), **A188**, 10 (1946). H. S. Green, *Proc. Roy. Soc.* (*London*), **A189**, 103 (1947).

Kirkwood and Buff[19] used these equations to calculate the surface properties of liquid argon. They used a Lennard-Jones potential and the $g^{(l)}(r)$ curve experimentally determined by Eisenstein and Gingrich.[25] At 90°K, they calculated

$$\gamma = 14.9 \text{ dynes/cm} \qquad \text{(Exptl: 11.9)}$$

$$U^{(s)} = 27.2 \text{ dynes/cm} \qquad \text{(Exptl: 35)}$$

$$\Gamma^* = 4.99 \times 10^{-8} \text{ g/cm}^2$$

$$z_0 = 3.63 \times 10^{-8} \text{ cm}$$

The values in parentheses are the experimental values of Baly and Donnan.[15, 16] The agreements are surprisingly good. It will be remembered that Corner[9] used the cell method to calculate $\gamma = 23.1$ dynes per cm for this case. Thus the radial distribution function method shows much greater promise for the calculation of surface tensions.

(ii) *Liquid with normal density up to an equimolecular dividing surface in contact with a gas of constant density.* In this case,

$$\begin{aligned} n(z_1) &= n^{(l)} \qquad z_1 < 0 \\ n(z_1) &= n^{(v)} \qquad z_1 > 0 \end{aligned} \tag{5.1–42}$$

$$\begin{aligned} g(z_1, \boldsymbol{r}_{21}) &= g^{(l)}(r_{21}) \qquad z_1 < 0 \text{ and } z_1 + z_{21} < 0 \\ g(z_1, \boldsymbol{r}_{21}) &= g^{(v)}(r_{21}) \qquad z_1 > 0 \text{ and } z_1 + z_{21} > 0 \\ g(z_1, \boldsymbol{r}_{21}) &= g^{(l,v)}(r_{21}) \qquad \text{Either } z_1 < 0 \text{ and } z_1 + z_{21} > 0 \text{ or } z_1 > 0 \\ &\qquad\qquad \text{and } z_1 + z_{21} < 0 \end{aligned} \tag{5.1–43}$$

It is clear that $g^{(l)}(r_{21})$ and $g^{(v)}(r_{21})$ are the normal radial distribution functions characteristic of the bulk liquid and gas, respectively. However, the function $g^{(l,v)}(r_{21})$ is some sort of correlation between the molecules in the liquid and those in the gas phase which cannot be precisely specified in the present crude approximation.

From Eq. 5.1–21 we obtain

$$\begin{aligned} \Gamma_j^{(2)} &= (-1)^{j+1} \frac{z_{21}^{j+1}}{j+1} [n^{(l)^2} g^{(l)}(r_{21}) - n^{(l)} n^{(v)} g^{(l,v)}(r_{21})] \qquad z_{21} > 0 \\ \Gamma_j^{(2)} &= (-1)^{j+1} \frac{z_{21}^{j+1}}{j+1} [n^{(l)} n^{(v)} g^{(l,v)}(r_{21}) - n^{(v)^2} g^{(v)}(r_{21})] \qquad z_{21} < 0 \end{aligned} \tag{5.1–44}$$

[25] A. Eisenstein and N. H. Gingrich, *Phys. Rev.*, **62**, 261 (1942).

Then, using polar coordinates to evaluate the angular parts of the triple integral over $\boldsymbol{r}_{21}$, we obtain from Eqs. 5.1–23 and 40 the following expressions for the surface tension and the surface internal energy:

$$\gamma = \frac{\pi}{8} \int_0^\infty r^4 \frac{d\varphi}{dr} [n^{(l)^2} g^{(l)}(r) - 2n^{(l)} n^{(v)} g^{(l,v)}(r) + n^{(v)^2} g^{(v)}(r)] \, dr \quad (5.1\text{–}45)$$

$$U^{(s)} = -\frac{\pi}{2} \int_0^\infty r^3 \varphi(r) [n^{(l)^2} g^{(l)}(r) - 2n^{(l)} n^{(v)} g^{(l,v)}(r) + n^{(v)^2} g^{(v)}(r)] \, dr \quad (5.1\text{–}46)$$

These are the same results which Fowler[7] obtained making a direct calculation applicable only to this model. Equation 5.1–46 forms the basis for Fowler's theory of the parachor, which we discuss presently.

f. Macleod's equation and the parachor

Macleod[26] proposed an empirical equation for the surface tension,

$$\gamma = \text{constant } (\rho^{(l)} - \rho^{(v)})^4 \quad (5.1\text{–}47)$$

Here the $\rho^{(l)}$ and $\rho^{(v)}$ are the actual densities of the liquid and vapor. Sugden[27] has expressed this result in the form

$$P = \frac{M\gamma^{1/4}}{\rho^{(l)} - \rho^{(v)}} = \frac{\gamma^{1/4}}{n^{(l)} - n^{(v)}} \quad (5.1\text{–}48)$$

The constant P is called the parachor. To a good approximation, the parachor is the sum of constants characteristic of the individual atoms or groups within the molecule. Sugden thought of the parachor as being associated with the molecular volume. In any case, the parachor for any given substance remains very nearly independent of temperature over a wide temperature range.

Fowler[7] derived the Macleod equation in the following manner. The general equation of state can be expanded in the neighborhood of the critical point in the form

$$p = p_c + (T - T_c)\left(\frac{\partial p}{\partial T}\right)_c + \tfrac{1}{2}(T - T_c)(\tilde{V} - \tilde{V}_c)\left(\frac{\partial^2 p}{\partial T\, \partial \tilde{V}}\right)_c + \tfrac{1}{6}(\tilde{V} - \tilde{V}_c)^3\left(\frac{\partial^3 p}{\partial \tilde{V}^3}\right)_c \quad (5.1\text{–}49)$$

The terms omitted are negligible compared to the terms retained. Eq. 5.1–49 is a cubic equation in the volume so that for any pressure there are

[26] Macleod, *Trans. Faraday Soc.*, **19**, 38 (1923).

[27] S. Sugden, *The Parachor and Valency*, George Routledge and Sons, London (1930).

three values of $\tilde{V}$ which satisfy the equation. In the region of two phases all three roots are real: $\tilde{V}^{(l)}$, $\tilde{V}^{(v)}$, and an extraneous third volume resulting from the S-shape of the equation of state isotherms. The thermodynamic relation,

$$\int_{\tilde{V}^{(l)}}^{\tilde{V}^{(v)}} p\, d\tilde{V} = p[\tilde{V}^{(v)} - \tilde{V}^{(l)}] \tag{5.1–50}$$

may then be used to fix the vapor pressure for a given temperature (see § 5.2b). From these relations Fowler showed that in the neighborhood of the critical point, to a first approximation,

$$[n^{(l)} - n^{(v)}]^2 = \frac{24\alpha}{\beta \tilde{V}_c^3} n_c^2(T_c - T) \tag{5.1–51}$$

Here $\tilde{V}_c$ is the molar volume at the critical point; n_c is the number density at the critical point; $\alpha = (\partial p/\partial T)_c$; and $\beta = (\partial^3 p/\partial \tilde{V}^3)_c$.

Now, the radial distribution functions for the liquid, gas, and mixed regions approach each other at the critical point so that

$$\begin{aligned} g^{(l)}(r) &= g_c(r) + [(T_c - T)/T_c]G^{(l)}(r) + \cdots \\ g^{(v)}(r) &= g_c(r) + [(T_c - T)/T_c]G^{(v)}(r) + \cdots \\ g^{(l,v)}(r) &= g_c(r) + [(T_c - T)/T_c]G^{(l,v)}(r) + \cdots \end{aligned} \tag{5.1–52}$$

Here $G(r)$ is a function about which we know very little.

Substituting these expressions into Eq. 5.1–46, we may write the surface energy in the neighborhood of the critical point as

$$\begin{aligned} U^{(s)} = {} & [n^{(l)} - n^{(v)}]^2 \frac{\pi}{2} \int_0^\infty g_c(r)\varphi(r)r^3\, dr \\ & - \left(\frac{T_c - T}{T_c}\right) \frac{\pi}{2} n_c^2 \int_0^\infty r^3\varphi(r)[G^{(l)}(r) + G^{(v)}(r) - 2G^{(l,v)}(r)]\, dr \end{aligned} \tag{5.1–53}$$

Thus, making use of Eq. 5.1–51, we obtain

$$U^{(s)} = B(T_c - T) \tag{5.1–54}$$

where

$$\begin{aligned} B = {} & -\frac{12\pi\alpha}{\beta \tilde{V}_c^3} n_c^2 \int_0^\infty g_c(r)\varphi(r)r^3\, dr \\ & + \frac{\pi n_c^2}{T_c} \int_0^\infty r^3\varphi(r)[G^{(l)}(r) + G^{(v)}(r) - 2G^{(l,v)}(r)]\, dr \end{aligned} \tag{5.1–55}$$

Substituting $U^{(s)}$ from Eq. 5.1–54 into the Gibbs-Helmholtz equation, integrating from T to T_c to obtain the surface tension, and expanding in the neighborhood of the critical point, we obtain the surface tension:

$$\gamma = BT\left[\frac{T_c}{T} - 1 - \ln\frac{T_c}{T}\right] = \tfrac{1}{2}BT_c\left(\frac{T_c - T}{T_c}\right)^2 \qquad (5.1\text{–}56)$$

and, from Eq. 5.1–51,

$$\gamma = \tfrac{1}{2}\,\frac{B}{T_c n_c^{\,4}}\left(\frac{\beta\tilde{V}_c^{\,3}}{24\alpha}\right)^2 (n^{(l)} - n^{(v)})^4 \qquad (5.1\text{–}57)$$

Thus the parachor is

$$P = \frac{\tilde{V}_c}{2n_c}\left[\frac{B\beta^2\tilde{V}_c^{\,2}}{72T_c\alpha^2}\right]^{1/4} \qquad (5.1\text{–}58)$$

The values of the parachor as given by Sugden for a few substances are given in Table 5.1–4.

Lennard-Jones and Corner[8] show, as seen from Table 5.1–4, that for simple molecules the parachor is given empirically to within 3.6 per cent by the equation

$$P = (7.1 \times 10^{23})\,\epsilon^{1/4}\sigma^{5/2} \qquad (5.1\text{–}59)$$

in which σ and ϵ are the parameters in the Lennard-Jones (6-12) potential, in cm and ergs, respectively. They suggest therefore, that the parachor may provide a sensitive method to obtain the molecular collision diameter σ (since $\epsilon^{1/4}$ is always easy to estimate). The fact that P is almost proportional to σ^3 bears out Sugden's contention that it is almost the molecular volume. Fowler has calculated the parachor for a number of examples, using a set of simplifying assumptions which make the results semi-empirical. At the present time there is no satisfactory explanation of why the parachor remains independent of temperature.

TABLE 5.1–4

THE PARACHOR IN TERMS OF PHYSICAL CONSTANTS[27]

Substance	*Parachor, P*		$\left(\frac{P \times 10^{-23}}{\sigma^{5/2}\epsilon^{1/4}}\right)$
A	54		7.0
Ne	25		7.6
N_2	60.4		7.0
CO	61.6		6.8
CH_4	73.2		7.1
		Average	7.1

2. Phase Behavior of One-Component Systems

The greater part of this section is devoted to a discussion of phase transitions and critical phenomena in pure substances from a macroscopic viewpoint. The approach presented here is based upon the geometrical analysis of the surface $p = p(\tilde{V}, T)$ which represents the equation of state. Both the experimental surfaces and those described by simple analytical equations of state receive attention here. A molecular approach to critical phenomena has been developed by means of statistical mechanics. The theory is an extension of the development of the equation of state given in § 3.2. This section concludes with a brief account of the present status of this theory.

a. Methods of determining the critical point

The equation of state of a one-component system may be represented geometrically by the surface $p = p(\tilde{V}, T)$. Such a surface is sketched in Fig. 5.2–1, where the p-$\tilde{V}$-T behavior in the liquid and vapor phases is shown. The curve *ADCEB* is called the *coexistence line.* The point on this curve for which the temperature is greatest is the *critical point.* The portion of the coexistence curve *ADC* on one side of the critical point is called the "liquidus," and the other portion is called the "vaporus." The tongue-shaped region bounded by the coexistence line describes the conditions under which a system breaks up into a liquid and a vapor phase which coexist in equilibrium.

Inasmuch as the three-dimensional representation of the p-V-T behavior is somewhat inconvenient to use, it is customary to discuss the phase behavior of a system by means of the three two-dimensional diagrams shown in Fig. 5.2–1. The upper right projection shows the familiar *isotherms* on a p-$\tilde{V}$ diagram. These are formed by slicing the surface $p = p(\tilde{V}, T)$ with planes perpendicular to the T-axis, and then projecting the curves of intersection (the isotherms) onto the p-$\tilde{V}$ plane. The isotherm passing through C is called the "critical isotherm", and at the critical point (C) on this isotherm, $(\partial p/\partial \tilde{V})_T = (\partial^2 p/\partial \tilde{V}^2)_T = 0$. The upper left projection is a p-T plot showing the *isochores.* It is formed by slicing the surface $p = p(\tilde{V}, T)$ with planes perpendicular to the $\tilde{V}$-axis and then projecting the curves of intersection. The curve $(A, B)\,(D, E)\,(C)$, terminating at C, is the projection of the tongue-shaped coexistence region onto the p-T plane and is the familiar vapor pressure curve. The lower projection shows the *isobars* on a T-$\tilde{V}$ plot, and this plot is obtained by slicing the surface $p = p(\tilde{V}, T)$ by means of planes perpendicular to the p-axis. Any one of these three plots contains sufficient information to reconstruct the original surface in three dimensions. These three

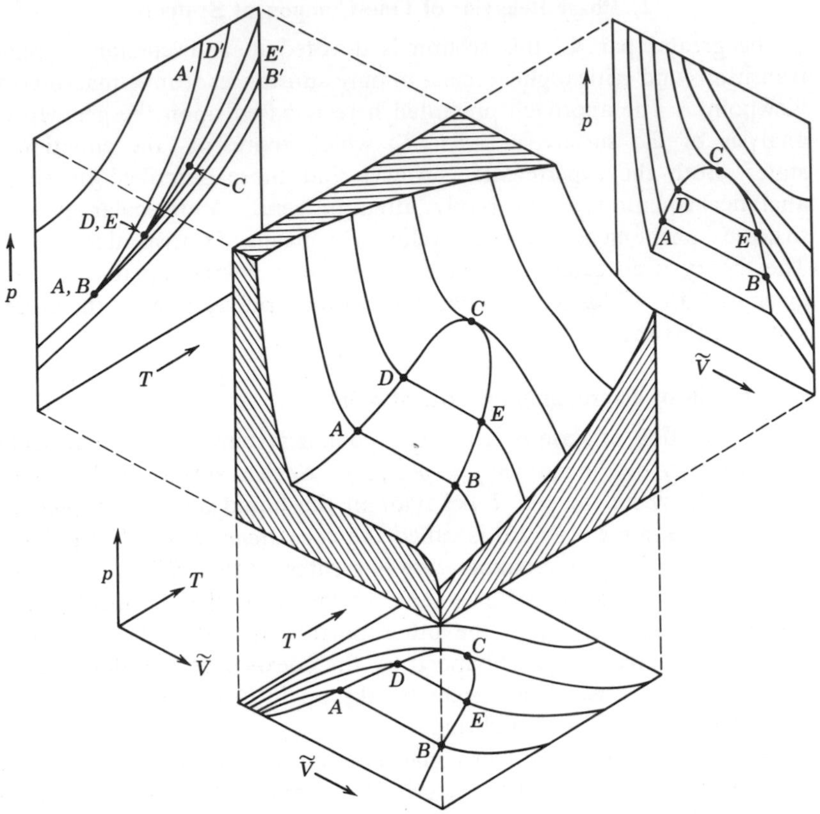

Fig. 5.2–1. The p-$\tilde{V}$-T behavior of the liquid and gas phases of a one-component system. In the center is sketched the surface $p = p(\tilde{V}, T)$. In the upper-right projection is shown the p-$\tilde{V}$ diagram with several *isotherms*. In the upper-left projection the p-T diagram is shown with several *isochores*. The diagram at the bottom shows several *isobars* on a T-$\tilde{V}$ diagram.

projections form the basis of discussions of the methods of determining the critical constants from equation of state measurements.

i. *Determination of the Critical Point from Isotherms*

The critical temperature may be estimated to within a few hundredths of a degree by an analysis of the geometry of the isotherms. This method is illustrated in Fig. 5.2–2a, where the experimental data of Michels, Blaisse, and Michels,[1] for CO_2 are shown. The recent measurements

[1] A. Michels, B. Blaisse, and C. Michels, *Proc. Roy. Soc.* (*London*), **A160**, 358 (1937).

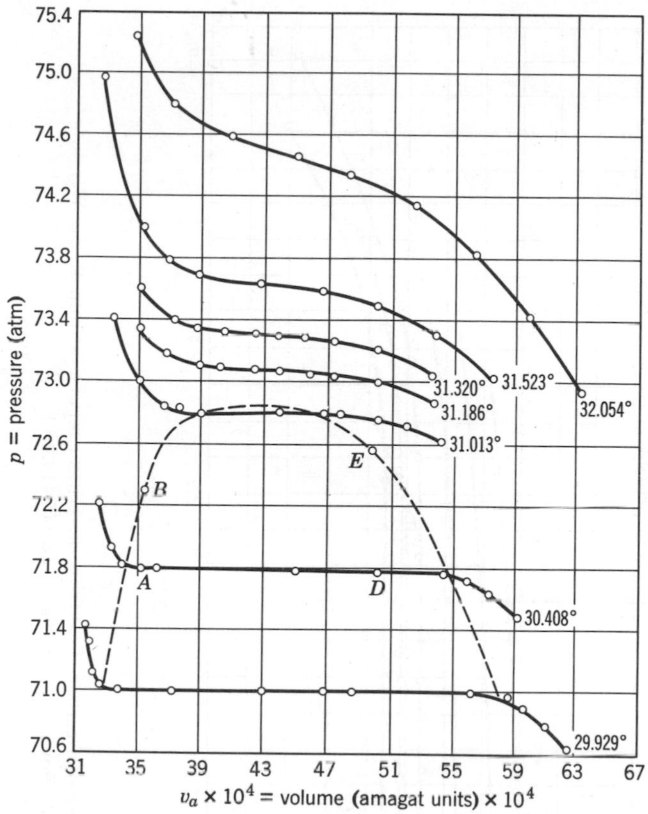

Fig. 5.2–2a. Pressure-volume isotherms of carbon dioxide in the critical region. [From A. Michels, B. Blaisse, and C. Michels, *Proc. Roy. Soc. (London)*, **A160**, 358 (1937).]

of Wentorf and Boyd[2] very close to the critical point are given in Fig. 5.2–2b.

ii. *Determination of the Critical Point from Isochores*

There are two methods for studying the critical phenomena by means of loading a bomb of constant volume with a known weight of the substance and then studying the behavior of the system with change in temperature. In the first method we measure the pressure of the system, that is, actually

[2] R. H. Wentorf and C. A. Boyd, University of Wisconsin Naval Research Laboratory Report, CM-724 (May 1952). R. H. Wentorf, Doctoral Dissertation, University of Wisconsin, December 1951.

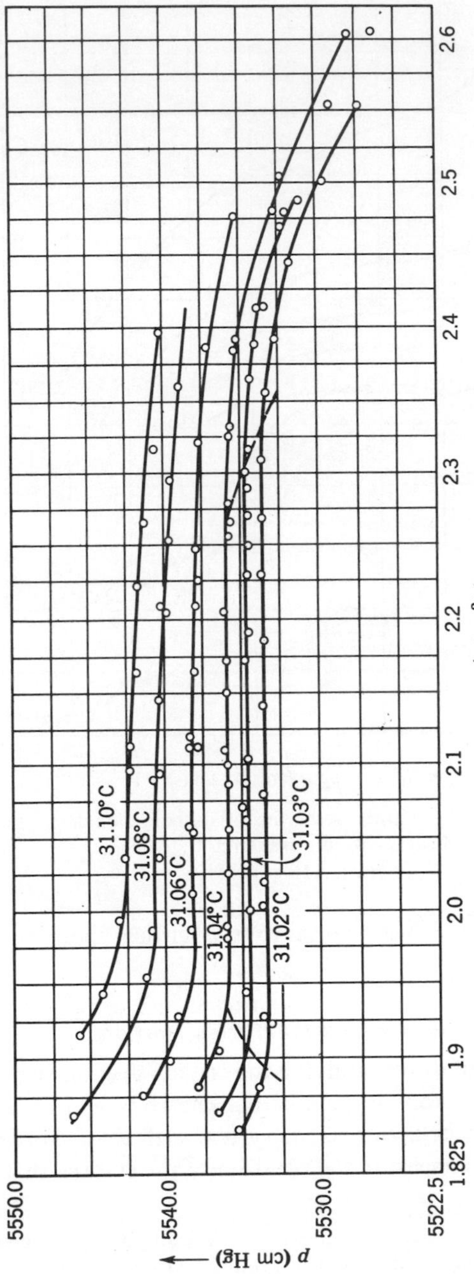

Fig. 5.2–2b. Pressure-volume isotherms of carbon dioxide in the critical region. [From R. H. Wentorf and C. A. Boyd, *J. Chem. Phys.*, **24**, 607 (1956).]

plot the isochores.[3] In the second method we study the behavior of the meniscus[4, 5] as the temperature is changed.

The first method amounts to measuring the isochores shown in Fig. 5.2–1, and the problem is to find the overall density of loading for which the curve p versus T does not exhibit a discontinuity. It can be seen in the figure that the isochores behave quite differently, depending upon whether the overall (gas + liquid) density of loading $\bar{\rho}$ is less than, greater than, or equal to the critical density ρ_c. Examples of the three cases are (see Fig. 5.2–1):

When	the system follows the curve p versus T:
$\bar{\rho} < \rho_c$,	$(A, B)EE'$
$\bar{\rho} > \rho_c$,	$(A, B)DD'$
$\bar{\rho} = \rho_c$,	$(A, B)\,(D, E)C$

The last case represents the limit of discontinuous behavior and gives a measurement of the critical density.

The second method is similar to the first in every way except that, instead of measuring the pressure of the system, we observe the height of the meniscus separating the liquid and gaseous phases.[5] Once again there are three types of behavior, depending upon the overall density of loading:

When:

$\bar{\rho} < \rho_c$	The meniscus falls until the entire vessel is filled with gas.
$\bar{\rho} > \rho_c$	The meniscus rises until the entire vessel is filled with liquid.
$\bar{\rho} = \rho_c$	The meniscus disappears at a point about halfway up the container.

The last condition may be taken as a criterion for the critical point.

The behavior of the meniscus may be explained as follows. Let $\bar{\rho}$ be the average density of the substance in the container and $\rho^{(v)}$ and $\rho^{(l)}$ be the densities of the coexisting vapor and liquid phases. Then the fraction of the volume made up of the liquid phase is $(\bar{\rho} - \rho^{(v)})/(\rho^{(l)} - \rho^{(v)})$. If the bomb is loaded to a density $\bar{\rho} > \rho_c$, as the bomb is heated a temperature is reached at which $\bar{\rho} = \rho^{(l)}$, and the system becomes all liquid.

[3] W. Sajotschewsky, *Ann. phys. Beibl.*, **3**, 741 (1879). Cailletet and Colardeau, *Compt. rend.*, **112**, 563 (1891). Ipatieff and Monroe, *Ind. Eng. Chem.* (Anal. Ed.), **14**, 171 (1942).

[4] D. White, A. Friedman, and H. Johnston, *J. Am. Chem. Soc.*, **72**, 3565 (1950).

[5] Cagnaird de la Tour, *Ann. chim.* (Ser. 2), **21**, 127 (1922).

Similarly, if $\bar{\rho} < \rho_c$, as the bomb is heated a temperature is reached at which $\bar{\rho} = \rho^{(v)}$, and the system becomes all vapor. If the density of loading is chosen so that $\bar{\rho} = \rho_c$, as the bomb is heated a temperature is reached at which $\bar{\rho} = \rho_c = \rho^{(v)} = \rho^{(l)}$. At this temperature the meniscus disappears at a point approximately halfway up the bomb.[6]

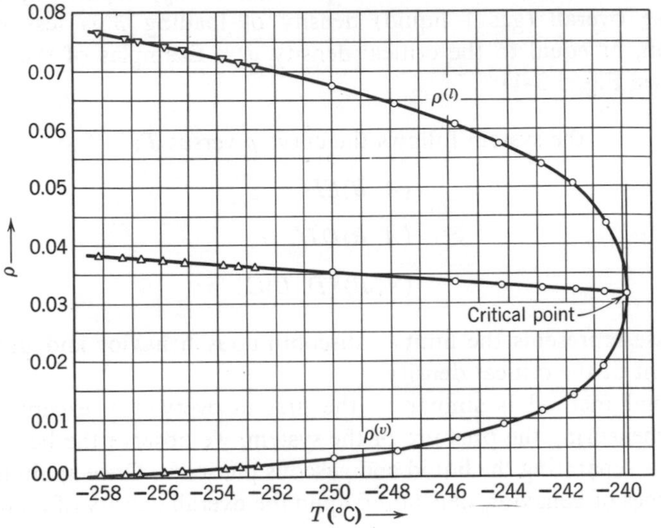

Fig. 5.2–3. Determination of the critical point from measurements of the liquid density $\rho^{(l)}$ and the vapor density $\rho^{(v)}$ according to the method of Cailletet and Mathias. The data plotted here are for hydrogen. [E. Mathias, C. A. Crommelin, and H. Kamerlingh Onnes, *Comm. Phys. Lab. Leiden*, No. 154b (1921).] The critical temperature and density obtained in this manner are in excellent agreement with that determined by visual observation of the meniscus. [D. White, A. S. Friedman, H. L. Johnston, *J. Am. Chem. Soc.*, **72**, 3565 (1950).]

iii. *Determination of the Critical Point from Liquid and Vapor Densities (Law of Cailletet and Mathias)*

Another method of determining the critical point may be discussed in terms of the T-$\tilde{V}$ plot in Fig. 5.2–1. Actually, it is customary to plot the temperature versus the density rather than the volume. To determine the critical density, Cailletet and Mathias[7] suggested plotting the average densities of the coexisting liquid and vapor. This average density,

[6] In the neighborhood of the critical point $\frac{1}{2}(\rho^{(v)} + \rho^{(l)}) \doteq \rho_c + \alpha(T - T_c)$. If $\alpha = 0$ the point at which the meniscus disappears is exactly halfway up the bomb.

[7] Cailletet and Mathias, *Compt. rend.*, **102**, 1202 (1886); **104**, 1563 (1887); *J. Phys.*, **5**, 549 (1886).

$\frac{1}{2}(\rho^{(v)} + \rho^{(l)})$, is known as the *rectilinear diameter*.[8] The point of intersection of the rectilinear diameter with the coexistence curve gives the critical density and temperature. This method is illustrated for hydrogen in Fig. 5.2-3.

b. Stable and metastable states

The tongue-shaped region in Fig. 5.2-1 bounded by the coexistence line requires further consideration. The true equilibrium condition described by the graph is not always the one obtained experimentally. For example, let us imagine that a vapor is being compressed. A state of *supersaturation* can occur in which the homogeneous vapor phase persists, although the phase diagram indicates that a part of this vapor should condense so that a liquid and a vapor phase coexist in equilibrium. This supersaturation is a metastable state, but it may persist for a considerable length of time. In order for the liquid phase to be formed, it is necessary for the substance to condense on nuclei. These nuclei can form spontaneously, they can be formed by ions (as in a Wilson cloud chamber), or they can already be present in the form of dust or other small particles of solid impurities.[9-11] Once the substance begins to condense on nuclei, the vapor-liquid equilibrium is rapidly established.

Another type of metastable condition is obtained by means of the *overexpansion* of a liquid. Let us imagine that a homogeneous liquid is contained in a cylinder at high pressure. Now if the piston is moved in such a way that the liquid is expanded, it would be expected that a vapor phase would be formed when the pressure becomes less than the saturation pressure. Instead, however, the homogeneous liquid phase can persist for a considerable length of time even if the pressure is negative (in the sense of trying to tear the liquid apart). In order for the liquid to vaporize it must evaporate molecules into small bubbles or cavities. These cavities can be formed spontaneously, but more often they are formed by gases dissolved in the liquid or upon the surface of solid impurities which are present.[12, 13]

[8] A very exhaustive discussion of the subject of rectilinear diameters is given by J. R. Partington, *Treatise on Physical Chemistry*, Longman, Green (1949), Vol. I, p. 639. The law of Cailletet and Mathias states that the rectilinear diameter is independent of the temperature and equal to the critical density. This law is only approximately correct. Actually, the rectilinear diameter varies linearly or quadratically with the temperature.

[9] R. Becker and W. Döring, *Ann. Physik* (5), **24**, 719 (1935). R. Becker, *Trans. Faraday Soc.*, **45**, 55 (1949).

[10] H. Reiss, *J. Chem. Phys.*, **18**, 529 (1950).

[11] D. Turnbull and J. Fisher, *J. Chem. Phys.*, **17**, 71 (1949).

[12] A. F. Scott, D. P. Shoemaker, K. N. Tanner, and J. G. Wendel, *J. Chem. Phys.*, **16**, 495 (1948).

[13] M. S. Plesset, *J. Appl. Mech.*, **16**, 277 (1949).

Let us now consider the isotherms on a p-$\tilde{V}$ diagram which describe these metastable states. This may be conveniently done by considering a simple analytical equation of state, such as the van der Waals equation. For this equation the isotherms below the critical isotherm are not characterized by a horizontal section corresponding to vapor-liquid equilibrium, but they have the familiar S-shaped form shown in Fig. 5.2–4. For example, at temperature T_2 the analytical equations give the curve $DQRSE$, whereas the true equilibrium p-$\tilde{V}$ behavior is indicated

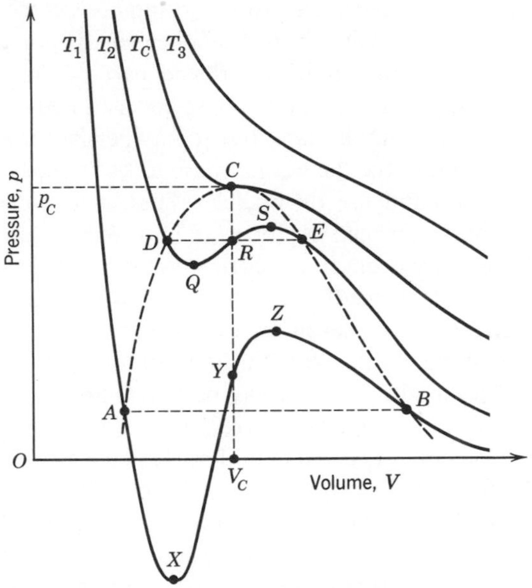

Fig. 5.2–4. The pressure-volume isotherms as given by the approximate simple analytical equations of state such as the van der Waals equation. The equilibrium behavior is given by the tie lines DE and AB. The segments of the curves, DQ and AX, represent states of *overexpansion* of the liquid; SE and ZB represent *supersaturation* of the vapor. The segments QRS and XYZ cannot be given any physical interpretation.

by the dotted line DE. This line indicates the vapor pressure for the temperature T_2. It was Maxwell[14] who suggested a means for finding the vapor pressure (that is, locating the dotted line DE) from the isotherms of the simple analytical equations. When a mole of liquid is transformed into vapor, the change in the Gibbs free energy $\tilde{G} = \tilde{H} - T\tilde{S}$ is given by

$$\tilde{G}^{(v)} - \tilde{G}^{(l)} = \int \tilde{V}\, dp \tag{5.2–1}$$

[14] *The Scientific Papers of James Clerk Maxwell*, Cambridge University Press (1890), Vol. II, p. 425.

where the integration is along the S-shaped portion of the isotherm (such as *DQRSE*). Inasmuch as the liquid and vapor are in equilibrium $G^{(v)}$ equals $G^{(l)}$, and the integral is zero. This means that the tie line *DE* must be chosen so as to make the area bounded by the line *DR* and the curve *DQR* equal to the area bounded by *RE* and *RSE*. It should be noted that this argument does not make use of any particular interpretation of the various regions of the loops (except that they represent an analytical continuation of the physically realizable portions of the isotherms).

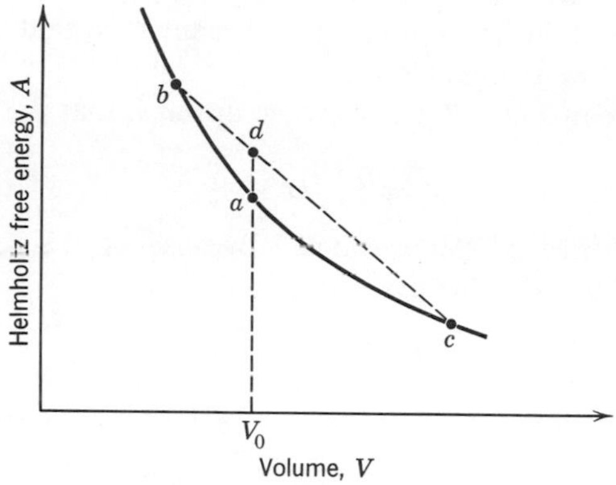

Fig. 5.2–5. Isothermal variation of the Helmholtz free energy, *A*, with volume for a hypothetical stable system.

The true equilibrium behavior is described by the tie lines, such as *DE*. It is possible to interpret the portions *DQ* and *SE* of the S-shaped analytical curve in terms of metastable conditions which are experimentally realizable. The segment *SE* of the isotherm for temperature T_2 corresponds to states of *supersaturation*, and the segment *DQ* corresponds to states of *over-expansion*. It is interesting to note that even the negative pressures of the metastable liquid isotherm for temperature T_1 of Fig. 5.2–4 are not without significance. These metastable states are observed in the laboratory[10] and are of considerable importance in the study of cavitation in liquids.[11] The portions *QRS* and *XYZ* of the isotherms have no physical significance. A more complete interpretation of the various portions of the S-shaped isotherms may be obtained from the thermodynamical arguments which follow.

Let us consider the isothermal variation of the Helmholtz free energy ($A = U - TS$) with volume for a hypothetical system as shown in Fig. 5.2–5. It is a direct consequence of the second law of thermodynamics that a stable state is one having a minimum value of *A* with respect to variations at constant temperature and volume. Let us consider a quantity of the substance in the state represented by the point a. It is possible to alter the state of a system by compressing a portion of the system to state b and expanding the remainder to state c, the amounts of the two portions being such as to maintain the same total volume. Clearly the value of A corresponding to the new state of the system is given by the state point d. Hence, if the curve is concave upward the new state of the system has a larger free energy and is unstable. Conversely, if the curve is concave downward, the new state of the system has a lower free energy and is more stable than the original state. In this latter case the system will actually break up in such a manner so that the Helmholtz free energy is as low as possible.

Since the curve in Fig. 5.2–5 is concave upward, that is,

$$(\partial^2 A/\partial V^2)_T \geqslant 0 \tag{5.2–2}$$

it represents a series of stable states. Because of the relation of the Helmholtz free energy to the pressure

$$(\partial A/\partial V)_T = -p \tag{5.2–3}$$

it follows that an equation of state can represent a series of stable states only if

$$(\partial p/\partial V)_T \leqslant 0 \tag{5.2–4}$$

Unless this condition is satisfied, the system is unstable with respect to infinitesimal density fluctuations.

The variation of the Helmholtz free energy, A, along an S-shaped pV-isotherm is illustrated in Fig. 5.2–6. According to Eq. 5.2–3 the negative of the slope of the curve at any point is the pressure corresponding to this point. Furthermore, from the relation

$$G = A + pV = A - V(\partial A/\partial V)_T \tag{5.2–5}$$

it follows that the intercept of the tangent to the curve at any point with the vertical axis is the Gibbs free energy of the corresponding point. Since the liquid and vapor phases in equilibrium are at the same pressure and have the same value of G, it follows that the tangents to the curve at the points representing the liquid and vapor phases in equilibrium are parallel and have a common intercept. This is illustrated in Fig. 5.2–6 by the dotted line which goes through points D and E.

Let us now consider the various portions of the curve $DQRSE$ in Fig. 5.2–4 (this curve corresponds to the curve $DQRSE$ in Fig. 5.2–6). The portions DQ and SE, which have negative slope, satisfy Eq. 5.2–4 and thus represents states of the system which are stable with respect to small fluctuations in the density. Since these portions of the curve lie inside the tie line, they represent states of the system which are unstable with respect to a phase change involving finite fluctuations in the density. These points represent the metastable states of supersaturation and overexpansion. The portion *QRS* of the isotherm in Fig. 5.2–4 does not meet the requirement of Eq. 5.2–4, and hence the states described by this segment are not even metastable and are completely unobtainable.

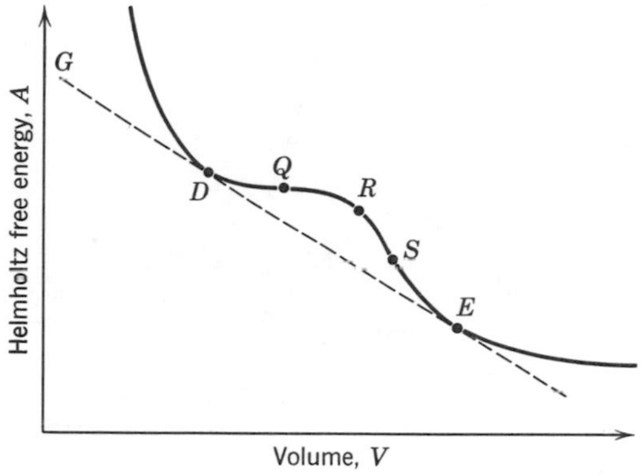

Fig. 5.2–6. Isothermal variation of the Helmholtz free energy with volume for a van der Waals gas below the critical point. The points *D, Q, R, S, E* correspond to the similarly labeled points in Fig. 5.2–4 on isotherm T_2.

c. Thermodynamic properties in the critical region

Now let us examine the thermodynamic properties of a one-component system in the neighborhood of the critical point. The heat capacity at constant pressure, C_p, becomes infinite at the critical point, but the heat capacity at constant volume C_v, the velocity of sound c, and the Joule-Thomson coefficient μ, all remain finite.

i. *Heat Capacity at Constant Volume*

The heat capacity at constant volume can be calculated as the sum of the ideal gas capacity heat, $\tilde{C}_v^0$, and an integral involving the second derivative of the pressure with respect to temperature:

$$C_v = \tilde{C}_v^0 + T \int_{\tilde{V}=\infty}^{\tilde{V}} \left(\frac{\partial^2 p}{\partial T^2}\right)_{\tilde{V}} d\tilde{V} \qquad (5.2\text{–}6)$$

The second term can be evaluated from experimental compressibility data. The results of such calculations for CO_2 in the neighborhood of the critical point[15] are shown in Fig. 5.2–7. The existence of a very pronounced maximum in the neighborhood of the critical point is quite evident. This maximum can be interpreted in terms of fluctuations.

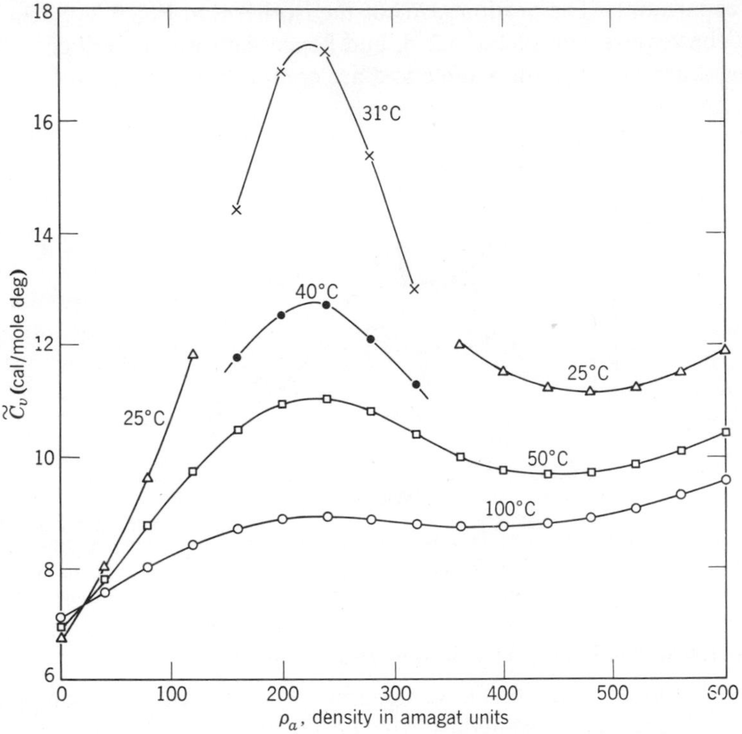

Fig. 5.2–7. The variation of $\tilde{C}_v$ for carbon dioxide with density at various temperatures as calculated from compressibility data. (The critical density is 237 amagat.) [From A. Michels, A. Bijl, and C. Michels, *Proc. Roy. Soc.* (*London*), **A160**, 376 (1937).]

It is shown in § 2.6 that the heat capacity at constant volume is proportional to the mean square deviation of the internal energy:

$$C_v = \frac{1}{kT^2}\overline{(U - \bar{U})^2} \tag{5.2–7}$$

The large fluctuations and formation of molecular clusters in the neighborhood of the critical point therefore result in an abnormally large specific heat.

If a bomb of constant volume containing a mixture of liquid and vapor

[15] A. Michels, A. Bijl, and C. Michels, *Proc. Roy. Soc.* (*London*), **A160**, 376 (1937).

is heated, the energy absorbed is the sum of the energies required to heat the liquid and the vapor phases separately plus the energy required to vaporize enough of the liquid to maintain the phase equilibrium at the higher temperature. If the density of loading of the bomb is either greater than or less than the critical density, the curve of apparent specific heat versus temperature becomes discontinuous at the point where the system becomes a single phase. If, on the other hand, the bomb is filled to the critical density, the apparent heat capacity remains continuous. Recent measurements of the heat capacity of carbon dioxide[16] by means of this procedure led to values of the specific heat more than twice as large as those calculated from p-V-T data. The reason for this discrepancy is not yet known.

ii. *Heat Capacity at Constant Pressure*

The heat capacity at constant pressure may be considered in terms of a bomb equipped with a frictionless piston which applies a constant pressure on the system. Initially the temperature of the system is sufficiently low that the system is entirely liquid. The addition of small amounts of heat results in finite increases in temperature, with a resulting increase in volume, and the value of C_p is finite. Similar considerations apply if the temperature is sufficiently high that the system is entirely vapor. However, when the temperature of the system is increased to a value such that the pressure on the system is the equilibrium vapor pressure, a vapor phase starts to appear. Further small additions of heat are absorbed as latent heat of vaporization with no accompanying increase in temperature. Consequently, at this point the value of C_p becomes infinite, and remains so until the phase transition is complete and the system is entirely in the vapor state. Thus it is seen that for any pressure less than the critical pressure there is a range of volumes (or overall densities) over which C_p is infinite. In the limit of the critical pressure, p_c, the range of volume approaches a single volume (or density), the critical volume (or density). Thus as a system approaches the critical point from the single-phase region, the value of C_p approaches infinity.

iii. *Velocity of Sound*

The velocity of sound at zero frequency[17] is

$$c_0 = \tilde{V}\left[-\frac{1}{M}\left(\frac{\partial p}{\partial \tilde{V}}\right)_S\right]^{1/2} = \tilde{V}\left[-\frac{\gamma}{M}\left(\frac{\partial p}{\partial \tilde{V}}\right)_T\right]^{1/2} \tag{5.2–8}$$

[16] A. Michels and J. C. Strijland, *Physica*, **15**, 813 (1950).

[17] One must distinguish between the velocity of sound at zero frequency, c_0, which is a thermodynamically defined quantity and the velocity of sound at any other frequency, c, which depends upon relaxation times and other rate constants (see § 11.4).

where M is the molecular weight of the material. The second form of this equation becomes indeterminate at the critical point since the ratio $\gamma = \tilde{C}_p/\tilde{C}_v$ becomes infinite while $(\partial p/\partial \tilde{V})_T$ becomes zero. By straightforward thermodynamic manipulation,[18] however, Eq. 5.2–8 can be rearranged into the form

$$c_0 = \tilde{V}\left(\frac{T}{M\tilde{C}_v}\right)^{1/2}\left(\frac{\partial p}{\partial T}\right)_{\tilde{V}}\left[1 - \frac{\tilde{C}_v}{T}\frac{(\partial p/\partial \tilde{V})_T}{(\partial p/\partial T)_{\tilde{V}}^2}\right]^{1/2} \qquad (5.2\text{–}9)$$

Now, since $(\partial p/\partial \tilde{V})_T$ becomes zero at the critical point while the other quantities remain finite, it follows that

$$(c_0)_{\text{critical}} = \tilde{V}\left(\frac{T}{M\tilde{C}_v}\right)^{1/2}\left(\frac{\partial p}{\partial T}\right)_{\tilde{V}} \qquad (5.2\text{–}10)$$

The value of $(\partial p/\partial T)_{\tilde{V}}$ at the critical point may be obtained either from ordinary p-$\tilde{V}$-T data or from the vapor pressure curve. Because of the continuity of the phases, the vapor pressure curve becomes identical with the critical isochore and $(\partial p/\partial T)_{\tilde{V}}$ is its slope.

At the present time there are unfortunately no experimental measurements of the velocity of sound in the critical region at frequencies sufficiently low that $c \approx c_0$. Hence it is not possible to test the validity of Eq. 5.2–10.[19] The behavior of the velocity of sound at finite frequencies in the critical region is illustrated in Fig. 5.2–8a, where the experimental measurements[20] for CO_2 are plotted. The recent measurements of Schneider[21] are shown in Fig. 5.2–8b for SF_6.

iv. *The Joule-Thomson Coefficient*

The Joule-Thomson coefficient may be written in the form

$$\mu = \left(\frac{\partial T}{\partial p}\right)_{\tilde{H}} = \frac{-\tilde{V} + T(\partial \tilde{V}/\partial T)_p}{\tilde{C}_p} \qquad (5.2\text{–}11)$$

This form is indeterminate at the critical point. By straightforward thermodynamic arguments, this expression may be rearranged[18] to give the exact thermodynamic relation:

$$\mu = \frac{[1 + (\tilde{V}/T)(\partial p/\partial \tilde{V})_T/(\partial p/\partial T)_V]}{(\partial p/\partial T)_{\tilde{V}}[1 - (\tilde{C}_v/T)(\partial p/\partial \tilde{V})_T/(\partial p/\partial T)_{\tilde{V}}^2]} \qquad (5.2\text{–}12)$$

[18] C. F. Curtiss, C. A. Boyd, and H. B. Palmer, *J. Chem. Phys.*, **19**, 801 (1951).

[19] W. G. Schneider (private correspondence, March 1952) has measured the velocity and dispersion of sound of xenon in its critical region, using frequencies of 250, 750, 1250, 1750, and 2250 kc. The velocity decreases as the frequency becomes lower. An extrapolation to zero frequency is very rough but is in the right direction to give the value of c_0 predicted from Eq. 5.2–10.

[20] C. M. Herget, *J. Chem. Phys.*, **8**, 537 (1940). Data for C_2H_4 are also given in this publication.

[21] W. G. Schneider, *J. Chem. Phys.*, **18**, 1300 (1950); *Canadian J. Chem.*, **29**, 243 (1951).

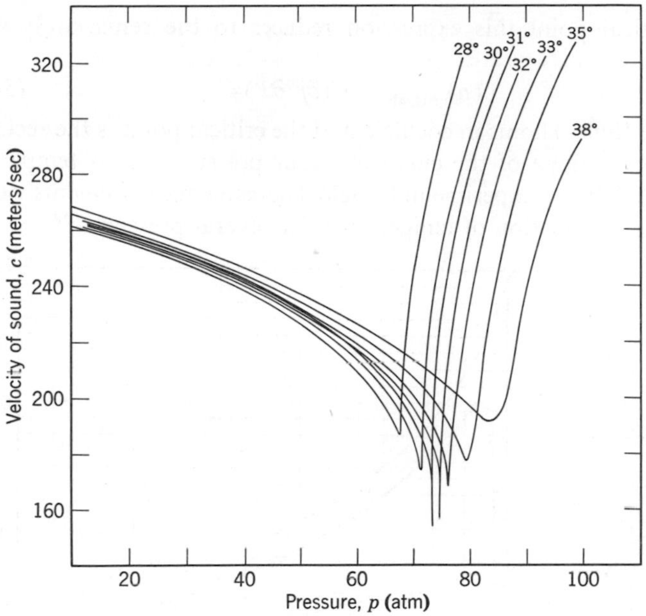

Fig. 5.2-8a. Behavior of the velocity of sound in CO_2 near the critical point, for a frequency of 260 kc. The minimum in the velocity versus pressure curve is the lowest for the critical isotherm. [From C. M. Herget, *J. Chem. Phys.*, **8**, 537 (1940).]

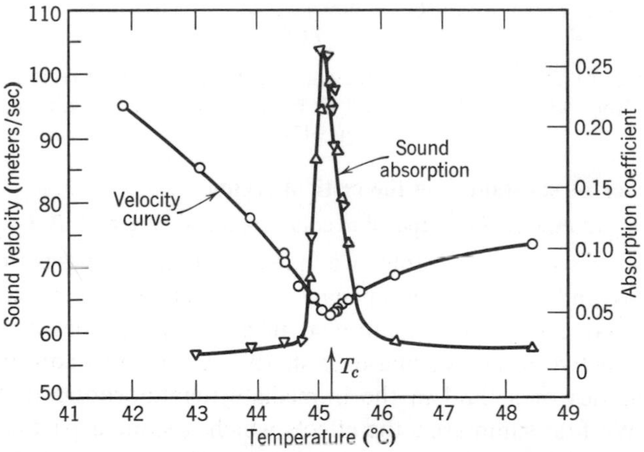

Fig. 5.2-8b. Sound velocity and sound absorption (frequency, 600 kc) in SF_6 in the critical region. Measurements made at critical loading density. The absorption coefficient α is defined by the equation $A = A_0 e^{-\alpha x/\lambda}$, where A and A_0 are amplitudes and λ the wavelength. [From W. G. Schneider, *J. Chem. Phys.*, **18**, 1300 (1950).]

At the critical point this expression reduces to the remarkably simple result

$$(\mu)_{\text{critical}} = 1/(\partial p/\partial T)_{\tilde{V}} \tag{5.2-13}$$

That is, the Joule-Thomson coefficient at the critical point is the reciprocal of the limiting slope of the curve of vapor pressure versus temperature.

In Fig. 5.2-9 the experimental Joule-Thomson measurements on CO_2 are shown as a function of temperature for several pressures.[22]

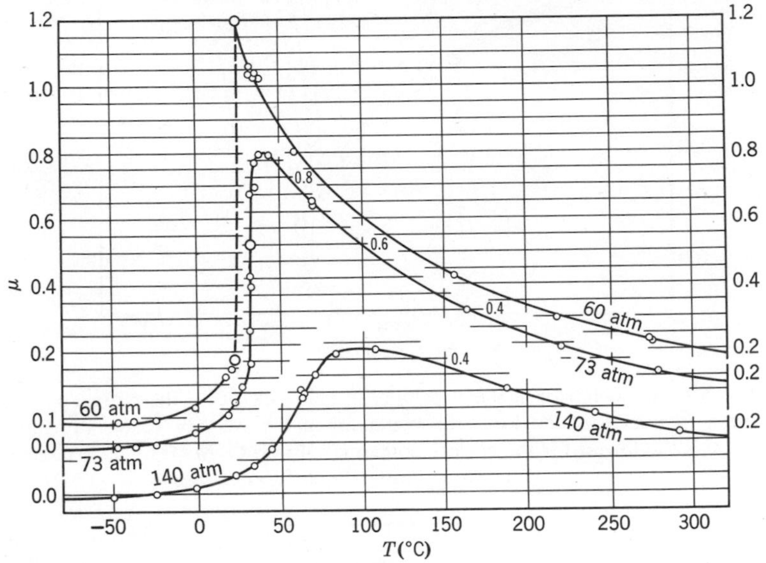

Fig. 5.2-9. Joule-Thomson coefficient of CO_2 in the critical region. [From J. R. Roebuck, T. A. Murrell and E. E. Miller, *J. Am. Chem. Soc.*, **64**, 400 (1942).]

d. Behavior of substances in the critical region

(This discussion was prepared in collaboration with Dr. H. B. Palmer.)

In the previous paragraphs we have discussed the nature of phase transitions and critical phenomena. This discussion is based upon the concept that each phase is uniform in all its properties and that the boundary between the two phases is sharp. Let us now consider in detail the properties of a fluid in the immediate neighborhood of the critical point. We first summarize the effects which assume a particular importance in the vicinity of the critical point, and then we proceed to examine the various observed phenomena in terms of these effects.

The surface, or transition region, between the two phases is diffuse, particularly in the neighborhood of the critical point. The nature of the

[22] J. R. Roebuck, T. A. Murrell, and E. E. Miller, *J. Am. Chem. Soc.*, **64**, 400 (1942).

transition region is discussed in detail in § 5.1. As the substance approaches the critical point, the transition region becomes progressively broader, and at the same time the density difference between the two phases becomes progressively smaller. This lack of a distinct boundary between the liquid and vapor phases is exaggerated by the effects of gravity and the fact that $(\partial p/\partial V)_T$ is small. In a vessel containing a fluid there is slow change in the pressure, with height, due to the change in the hydrostatic head of the fluid above. This fact, coupled with the fact that $(\partial p/\partial V)_T$ is small, leads to a variation of the density of the fluid with height. These two effects, the *diffuseness of the surface* and the importance of *gravity*, are experimentally indistinguishable and lead to macroscopic density gradients.

The statistical theory of fluctuations is discussed in § 2.6. It is there shown that the *fluctuations in the density* become very large in the neighborhood of the critical point. That is, there are large microscopic density gradients in random directions superimposed upon the macroscopic density gradients in the vertical direction discussed above. It is shown in § 12.7 that these microscopic density fluctuations lead to a scattering of light. In the neighborhood of the critical point this scattering is great and is referred to as "critical opalescence."

Experimentally it is observed that in the neighborhood of the critical point it is *difficult to obtain equilibrium conditions* throughout the system. This gives rise to a number of interesting phenomena, such as that illustrated by the inverted *U*-tube experiment. If liquid is placed in one arm of an inverted *U*-tube and the system heated slightly above the critical point, on cooling the liquid tends to recondense in the arm which originally contained the liquid.

Macroscopic density gradients in a fluid near the critical point have been observed by several investigators.[23–26] Maass and coworkers[24, 25] have used a method in which the density of the fluid at various points in the cell is measured by means of the buoyancy of a small bob. A typical density gradient curve obtained by this method is illustrated in Fig. 5.2–10. More recently Palmer[26] has measured the density gradients by means of a Schlieren optical technique. His results are given in Fig. 5.2–11. By both methods it was found that the density gradients depend not only upon the temperature but also on the previous thermal treatment of the system. These "hystereris" effects are discussed in detail presently.

The density gradients in a fluid under the action of gravity may be

[23] P. Hein, *Z. physik. Chem.*, **86**, 385 (1914).
[24] O. Maass, *Chem. Revs.*, **23**, 17 (1938).
[25] R. L. McIntosh, J. R. Dacey, and O. Maass, *Canadian J. Research*, **17B**, 241 (1939).
[26] H. B. Palmer, Doctoral Dissertation, University of Wisconsin (1952).

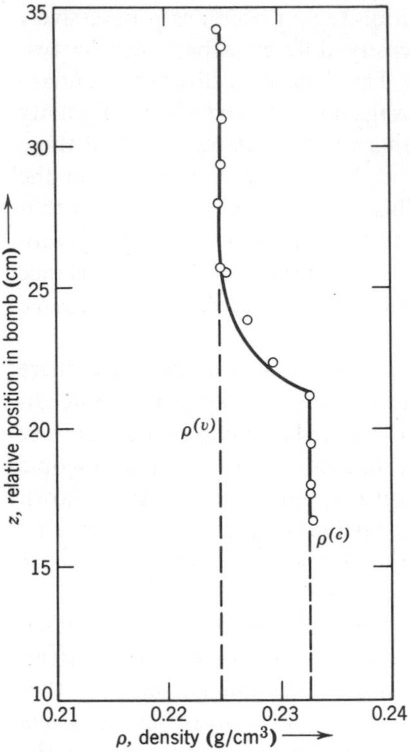

Fig. 5.2–10. Density of methyl ether as a function of height in a bomb. The experimental data are those of C. A. Winkler and O. Maass, *Canadian J. Research*, **9**, 613 (1933). The solid line is the curve calculated from Eq. 5.2–16 on the assumption that the molecular clusters contain 1.8×10^7 molecules.

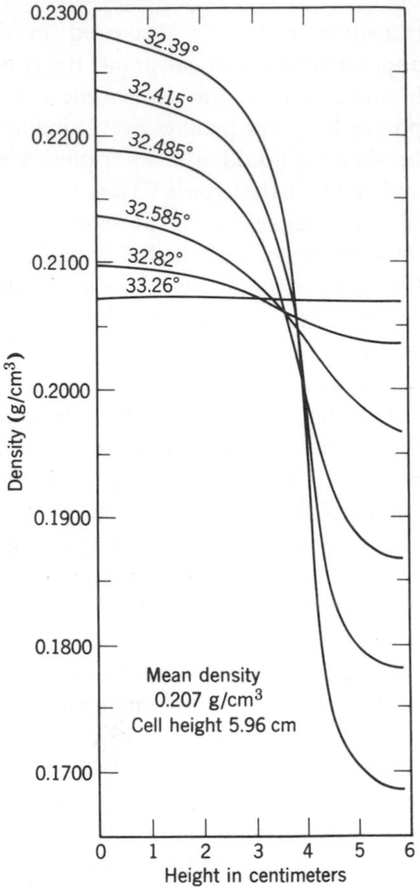

Fig. 5.2–11. Density of ethane as a function of height at several temperatures above the critical temperature. [From H. B. Palmer, Doctoral Dissertation, University of Wisconsin, 1952.]

related simply to the equation of state.[27] The pressure in a fluid varies with the height due to the weight of the fluid above according to the relation

$$dp/dz = -\rho g \tag{5.2–14}$$

Then, since the temperature is constant throughout the fluid, the variation of the density with height is

$$\frac{d\rho}{dz} = -\frac{\rho g}{(\partial p/\partial \rho)_T} \tag{5.2–15}$$

[27] J. Yvon, *Actualités scientifiques and industrielles*, Hermann & $C^{\underline{ie}}$, Paris (1937), p. 542.

Since $(\partial p/\partial \rho)_T$ is small in the neighborhood of the critical point, this expression explains the large density gradients.

Equation 5.2–15 is an expression for the density gradient in terms of macroscopic variables. It is possible to obtain an expression for the density distribution in terms of microscopic quantities by means of crude statistical arguments. A fluid, such as that described by the density distribution in Fig. 5.2–10, may be considered as a liquid phase of density $\rho^{(l)}$ separated from a vapor phase of density $\rho^{(v)}$ by a rather broad transition region. This fluid is made up of a large number of clusters of molecules of various sizes. The system may be idealized by assuming that the liquid consists of clusters of volume $v^{(c)}$, and density $\rho^{(c)}$, that the vapor phase consists of the homogeneous medium of density $\rho^{(v)}$, and that the transition region consists of a barometric distribution of the clusters from the liquid in the vapor phase. If it is further assumed that the liquid phase consists of spherical clusters in a close-packed array, then $\rho^{(c)} = [3\sqrt{2}/\pi]\,\rho^{(l)} = 1.3505\rho^{(l)}$. If the origin of the z-axis is taken to be at the surface of the liquid, the mean density as a function of z is

$$\rho = \rho^{(v)} + (\rho^{(l)} - \rho^{(v)}) \exp\left[-\frac{(\rho^{(c)} - \rho^{(v)})v^{(c)}zg}{kT}\right] \qquad (5.2\text{–}16)$$

The quantity $v^{(c)}$ appearing in this density distribution is an empirical constant which represents a mean cluster size. It may be obtained by fitting Eq. 5.2–16 to the experimental data. The solid curve for methyl ether in Fig. 5.2–10 is that given by this equation with $v^{(c)} = 6 \times 10^{-15}$ cm^3. Clusters of this size have a molecular weight of 8.5×10^8 and contain 2×10^7 methyl ether molecules. The diameter of such clusters is approximately 270 molecular diameters. This cluster size is of the same order of magnitude as that determined by light-scattering experiments on ethylene in the critical region.[28, 29]

Because of the long times required to establish equilibrium, it is very difficult to determine the thermodynamically stable density gradients in a fluid. Figure 5.2–10 shows a typical curve of density plotted as a function of height in the cell. Now let us fix our attention on some point in the lower half of the cell below the level of the normal liquid. Figure 5.2–12 shows how the density at this point varies as the temperature is raised or lowered (at a rate of about 0.01 degree per hour). The top curve shows the behavior with increasing temperature whereas the bottom curve illustrates the behavior with decreasing temperature. Neither of these curves gives evidence of instability. After stirring, the system

[28] H. A. Cataldi and H. G. Drickamer, *J. Chem. Phys.*, **18**, 650 (1950).

[29] See the discussion of light scattering in § 12.7.

resumes its former density distribution, and neither density distribution is appreciably affected by standing for periods of the order of days. This "hysteresis" behavior in the density gradients is probably due to the fact that under equilibrium conditions with increasing temperature the clusters become smaller, whereas with decreasing temperature the clusters grow. With increasing temperature the clusters tend to become smaller at a sufficiently rapid rate that equilibrium is easily attained. With decreasing temperature, on the other hand, the rate of growth of the

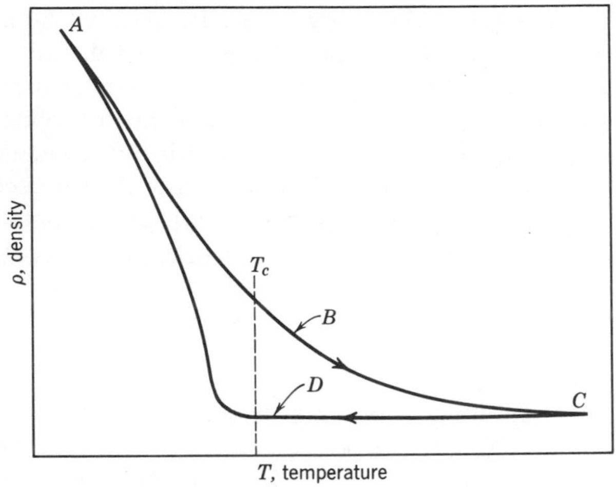

Fig. 5.2–12. A schematic illustration of the variation of density of the liquid phase in the neighborhood of the critical temperature.

clusters is extremely slow, and equilibrium is not obtained in a period of days. Thus the rising-temperature portion of the curve in Fig. 5.2–12 probably represents equilibrium states of the system, whereas the decreasing-temperature portion of the curve represents non-equilibrium states.[30]

e. Statistical mechanical theory of condensation

The discussion thus far has been limited to thermodynamic and empirical considerations. The exact statistical mechanical treatment of the equation of state of fluids should lead to an understanding of the phenomena of

[30] M. A. Weinberger and W. G. Schneider, *Canadian J. Chem.*, **30**, 422 (1952), have measured the relative density distribution with height in xenon in the critical region, using a radioactive tracer technique. They observe density distributions at temperatures above the critical temperature having the general character predicted by the classical theory of the critical point and some of the recent *P-V-T* data in the critical region. Interestingly, they did not find a hysteresis behavior.

phase change and the critical point. Some preliminary developments have been made along these lines, but much work remains to be done before the theory is clear-cut. Mayer[31–34] first proposed a theory of condensation based on the cluster theory of imperfect gases discussed in § 3.2. Later he and his coworkers presented arguments for the existence of an anomalous region above the temperature of the usually observed critical point. In particular, it was predicted that for a finite temperature interval above the temperature at which the meniscus disappears isotherms exist having no variation in pressure over a finite density range, but having at all pressures continuous derivatives with respect to the density. Various objections to this theory of condensation have been raised, and the existence of such an anomalous region near the critical point is an interesting question which requires experimental investigation.

For a system in a finite volume, the isotherms are continuous functions of the density. The discontinuous derivative, indicating a phase change, occurs only in the limit that the volume and the number of molecules become large in such a manner that the volume per molecule remains constant. It is always this limit which is tacitly assumed in the development of equations of state.

In § 3.2, it is shown that

$$p = kT \sum_{l=1}^{N} b_l z^l \tag{3.2–23}$$

Here z is the *active number density*, and the b_l are the *cluster integrals* defined by Eq. 3.2–5. The cluster integrals are integrals over the coordinates of l molecules in a volume V, the integrand of which depends on the potential energy and coordinates of l molecules. For low values of l the b_l are nearly independent of V. For larger, but finite, values of l the b_l approach limits, $b_l^{(0)}$, as V approaches infinity, provided the intermolecular potential approaches zero sufficiently rapidly with increasing separation.

Since the sum in Eq. 3.2–23 is a finite sum, the isotherm represented by the equation is analytic and does not have discontinuous derivatives. The discontinuous first derivative, indicating a phase change, appears only in the limit that V and N approach infinity with $V/N = v$, a constant. The pressure, p_s, at which condensation occurs may therefore be associated

[31] J. E. Mayer, *J. Chem. Phys.*, **5**, 67 (1937).
[32] J. E. Mayer and P. G. Ackermann, *J. Chem. Phys.*, **5**, 74 (1937).
[33] J. E. Mayer and S. F. Harrison, *J. Chem. Phys.*, **6**, 87, (1938).
[34] S. F. Harrison and J. E. Mayer, *J. Chem. Phys.*, **6**, 101 (1938).

with the first singularity (that is, the singularity corresponding to the smallest value of z) of the equation

$$p = kT \lim_{V\to\infty} \sum_{l=1}^{V/v} b_l z^l \tag{5.2–17}$$

Mayer assumed that this is the same as the first singularity of

$$p = kT \sum_{l=1}^{\infty} b_l^{(0)} z^l \tag{5.2–18}$$

Katsura and Fujita[35] point out that since the active number density z depends on V (as well as T and $v = V/N$), this is not necessarily correct. They believe that the first singularities of Eqs. 5.2–17 and 18 differ.

By purely formal manipulations, Eq. 5.2–18 may be transformed to the virial form

$$p = nkT\left[1 - \sum_{k=1}^{\infty} \frac{k\beta_k}{(k+1)} n^k\right] \tag{5.2–19}$$

The β_k are defined by Eq. 3.2–25 in terms of the integrals $b_l^{(0)}$ for $l \leq k + 1$. This expression leads directly to

$$\left(\frac{\partial p}{\partial n}\right)_T = kT\left[1 - \sum_{k=1}^{\infty} k\beta_k n^k\right] \tag{5.2–20}$$

for the derivative of the isotherm.

It has been shown[36] that the first singularity of Eq. 5.2–18 occurs at the lowest value of n for which either

$$\sum_{k=1}^{\infty} k\beta_k n^k \tag{5.2–21}$$

is singular or at which

$$\sum_{k=1}^{\infty} k\beta_k n^k = 1 \tag{5.2–22}$$

Mayer defines $\beta_0(T)$ as the limit[37]

$$\beta_0(T) = \lim_{k\to\infty} [\beta_k]^{1/k} \tag{5.2–23}$$

Thus condensation occurs at $n = 1/\beta_0$ unless Eq. 5.2–22 is satisfied for a smaller value of n, in which case condensation occurs at the lower density. In the former case $(\partial p/\partial n)_T > 0$ in the limit at the point of

[35] S. Katsura and H. Fujita, *J. Chem. Phys.*, **19**, 795 (1951).

[36] M. Born and K. Fuchs, *Proc. Roy. Soc.* (*London*), **A166**, 391 (1938).

[37] It should be pointed out that it has only been shown that for finite l the b_l approach finite limits $b_l^{(0)}$. Since the β_k are defined in terms of the $b_l^{(0)}$, it may very well be that the value of $\beta_0(T)$ depends on the order in which the limits are taken.

condensation, and a discontinuity appears in the slope of the isotherm. This corresponds to the usual ideas of condensation below the critical point. If any finite temperature interval exists in which Eq. 5.2–22 determines the density at which condensation occurs, from Eq. 5.2–20, $(\partial p/\partial n)_T$ approaches zero as this density is approached, and these isotherms are continuous.

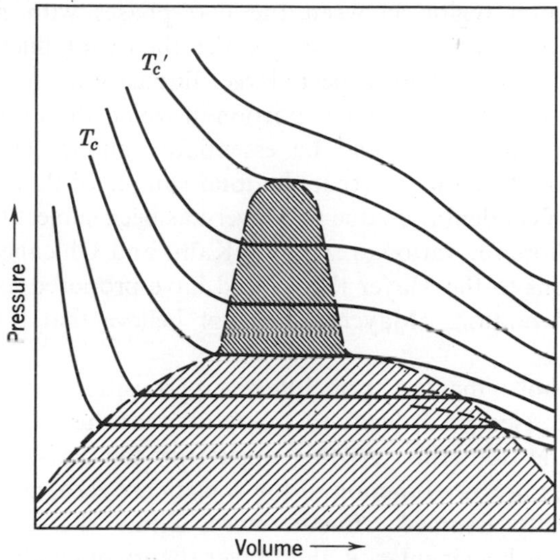

Fig. 5.2–13. The isotherms in neighborhood of the critical point according to the theory of Mayer and co-workers. (From J. E. Mayer and M. G. Mayer, *Statistical Mechanics*, Wiley, 1940, p. 312.)

Such a temperature interval and such an anomalous region exist unless the β_k are such that the following four conditions are simultaneously satisfied:

(1) $\Sigma_k k\beta_k n^k$ is singular.

(2) The position of the singularity is a branch point.

(3) $\Sigma_k k\beta_k n^k \to 1$ as the singularity is approached.

(4) $\Sigma_k k^2\beta_k n^k \to 0$ as the singularity is approached.

The last condition is equivalent to a statement that the second derivative of the pressure with respect to the density along an isotherm is zero. The "plausibility" arguments of Mayer for the existence of the anomalous region are that the four conditions are more than can be expected to be satisfied. If the anomalous region exists the isotherms are of the form indicated in Fig. 5.2–13. Below the temperature, T_c, the isotherms have a discontinuous derivative at the point of condensation; above this temperature and below T_c' the isotherms have at least a point of zero slope but have a continuous slope. Within the shaded region associated with these isotherms the fluid would be expected to have very peculiar properties. Mayer states that there would be no surface tension between the two phases. In view of the effects of gravity on the density distribution within a cell as discussed in § 5.2d we would surely expect to find a broad transition region between the two phases with no apparent discontinuity. Furthermore, in view of the theory of fluctuations discussed in § 2.6, we would expect large fluctuations in the density. Actually if the isotherms have a flat portion in which all of the derivatives are zero, the fluctuations would be essentially infinite (except for the restriction imposed by the fact that the total sample of fluid is finite).

This theory of condensation due to Mayer has been subject to objections by various authors for various reasons. Kahn and Uhlenbeck[38, 39] have offered objections to the Mayer theory and have proposed an alternative theory of condensation. Mayer[40] does not believe that the objections are justified.

Zimm[41] has shown that the "principle of superposition" of the potentials of average force (see § 4.9) leads to the result that the critical point is a singularity in the isotherm. At this singularity the derivatives of every order of the pressure as a function of the density are zero, not just the first two, as is usually assumed. Furthermore, Zimm showed that, if the critical point is such a singularity, the Mayer theory of condensation leads to a single critical temperature and the anomalous region is no longer predicted. Mayer[40] points out that the only conclusion to be drawn from Zimm's argument is that the existence of the anomalous region is inconsistent with the principle of superposition. It is clear that the existence of the anomalous region remains subject to question, both from the point of view of theory and from the point of view of experiment.

3. Phase Behavior of Two-Component Systems[1, 2]

In one-component systems the phenomenon of condensation is associated with lowering the temperature and raising the pressure, and the phenomenon of vaporization is associated with raising the temperature and lowering the pressure. The phase behavior of two-component systems is further complicated by the possibility of *retrograde* phenomena.

[38] B. Kahn and G. E. Uhlenbeck, *Physica*, **5**, 399 (1938).

[39] B. Kahn, Doctoral Dissertation, Utrecht (1938).

[40] J. E. Mayer, *J. Chem. Phys.*, **19**, 1024 (1951).

[41] B. H. Zimm, *J. Chem. Phys.*, **19**, 1019 (1951).

[1] O. A. Hougen and K. M. Watson, *Chemical Process Principles*, Wiley (1947), Part II, Ch. XIV.

[2] C. A. Boyd, *J. Phys. Colloid. Chem.*, **54**, 1347 (1950).

If a gaseous mixture is compressed, a pressure may be reached where a liquid phase appears. Under certain conditions of temperature and composition, however, a further increase in pressure causes the amount of liquid phase to decrease and eventually to disappear completely. This phenomenon was first observed by Cailletet[3] in connection with his studies on the liquefaction of CO_2-air mixtures; it is referred to as *retrograde condensation of the first kind.* A similar phenomenon may occur when the temperature of the system is varied at constant pressure. It is known as *retrograde condensation of the second kind.* These retrograde phenomena may be explained by an analysis of the p-V-T-x diagram for the binary mixture. This section concludes with a thermodynamic analysis of two-phase systems.

a. The critical point and retrograde behavior

In § 5.2a it is shown how the equation of state behavior of a pure substance may be interpreted in terms of three two-dimensional projections of the surface, $p = p(\tilde{V}, T)$, shown in Fig. 5.2–1. When the system is in a state in which there are two coexisting phases in equilibrium, the system is represented by a point on the tongue-shaped region (enclosed by the coexistence curve $ADCEB$). The projection of the tongue-shaped region on the p-T plane is the familiar vapor-pressure curve, $p_{\text{vap}}(T)$, which terminates at the critical point.

The complete phase behavior of a binary system is represented by the surface (in four dimensions) $p = p(\tilde{V}, T, x)$, where x is the mole fraction of one of the two components. This surface may be studied by means of various three-dimensional projections. In particular, for the purpose of studying vapor-liquid equilibria it is convenient to examine in detail the three-dimensional surface, which is the projection of that part of the surface $p = p(\tilde{V}, T, x)$, which represents the states characterized by two coexisting phases in equilibrium. This surface $p_{\text{vap}}(T, x)$ is shown in Fig. 5.3–1[4] and is the two-component analog of the vapor-pressure curve for pure substances.[5] The curve K_1C_1 is the vapor-pressure curve for pure component 1, terminating at C_1, which is the critical point for that component. Similarly, K_2C_2, terminating at C_2, is the vapor-pressure curve for the pure component 2. At any point (p, x, T) within the surface a line may be constructed parallel to the x-axis. This line pierces the

[3] L. Cailletet, *Compt. rend.*, **90**, 210 (1880).

[4] This figure is a drawing of a three-dimensional model made by C. A. Boyd[2] and N. A. Eckstein.

[5] It should be noted that the surface $p_{\text{vap}}(T, x)$ is *not* a representation of the function $p = p(\tilde{V}, T, x)$ at constant $\tilde{V}$, just as $p_{\text{vap}}(T)$ is not the function $p = p(\tilde{V}, T)$ at constant $\tilde{V}$. For this reason the subscript "vap" is used.

surface at two points. These two points of intersection give the composition of the liquid and vapor phases in equilibrium at the given value of p and T. A pressure and temperature (and composition) at which these two points are identical is referred to as a critical point of the mixture.[6] The curve $C_1C_0C_2$ is the locus of the critical points for mixtures

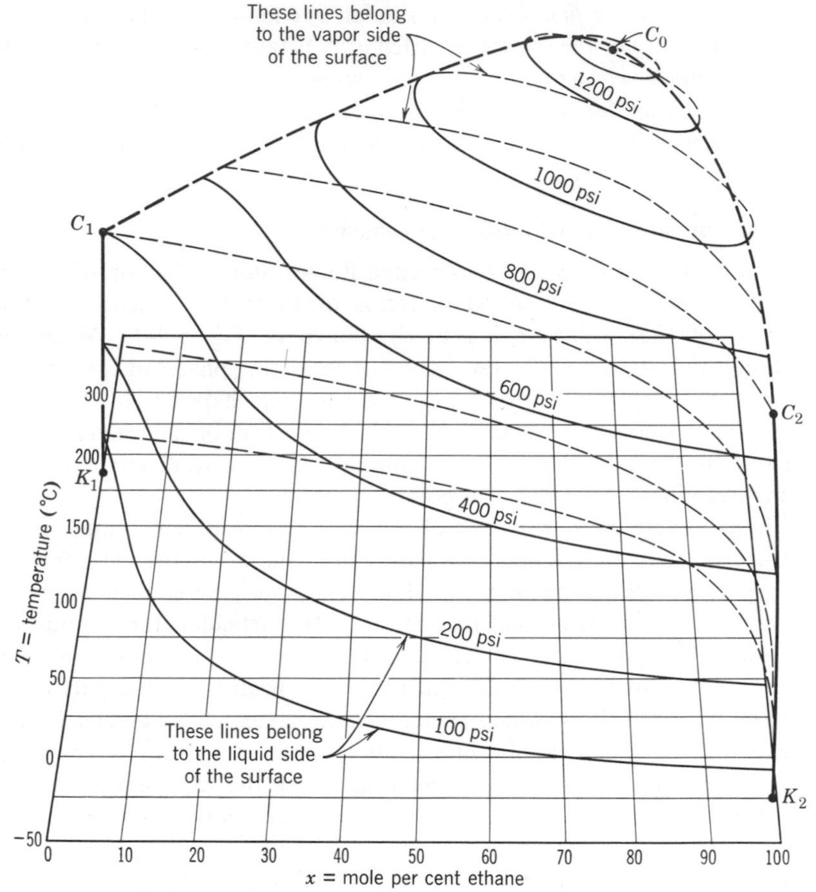

Fig. 5.3–1. Three-dimensional representation[4] of the surface $p_{\text{vap}}(T, x)$ for the system ethane-heptane [from the experimental data of W. B. Kay, *Ind. Eng. Chem.*, **30**, 459 (1938)]. C_1 and C_2 are the critical points of heptane and ethane, respectively. The curves K_1C_1 and K_2C_2 are the corresponding vapor pressure curves. The curve $C_1C_0C_2$ is the locus of critical points for mixtures of various compositions.

[6] A critical point of a mixture, as well as that of a one-component system, may be defined as the limiting condition under which the two phases have the same properties. Note that it is only in the case of a pure substance that the critical point is the highest temperature and pressure at which two phases coexist.

of various compositions. This curve divides the surface into two parts—the liquid side and the vapor side.

In order to facilitate the understanding of the three-dimensional surface shown in Fig. 5.3-1, three two-dimensional projections can be prepared exactly as was done in Fig. 5.2-1. These projections are shown in Figs. 5.3-2, 3, and 4. Let us now discuss the liquid-vapor equilibria of two

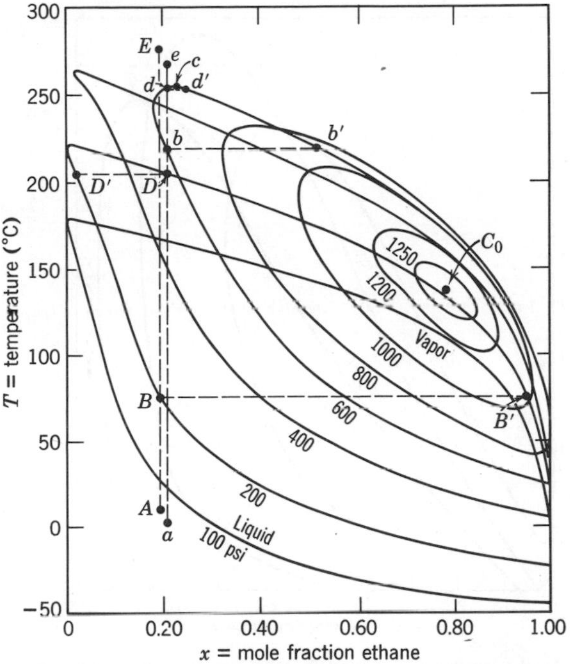

Fig. 5.3-2. Isobars on a T-x plot for the system ethane-heptane. This plot is obtained by slicing the surface $p_{\text{vap}}(T, x)$ with planes perpendicular tc the p-axis and projecting the curves of intersection onto the T-x plane. This plot may be used to illustrate *retrograde condensation of the second kind* along the line *ae* for the 600 psi isobar. (From O. A. Hougen and K. M. Watson, *Chemical Process Principles*, Wiley, 1947.)

phase systems and the phenomenon of retrograde condensation in terms of these various diagrams.

In Fig. 5.3-2 *isobars* are shown on the T–x plane. The curves are obtained by slicing the surface $p_{\text{vap}} = p_{\text{vap}}(T, x)$ with planes parallel to the T–x plane and then projecting the curves of intersection on the T–x plane. These curves are the familiar liquid-vapor equilibrium curves, which are frequently used in the analysis of the phase behavior of binary systems. Let us now discuss several types of behavior in terms of this diagram.

Let us first consider the system in a state represented by point A on the T–x diagram and let the system be at a pressure of 200 psi. As the temperature of the system is increased and the volume increased so that the pressure remains constant, the point representing the system moves up the dotted ordinate until point B is reached. At this temperature, a vapor phase (that is, a phase of lower density) represented by B', appears

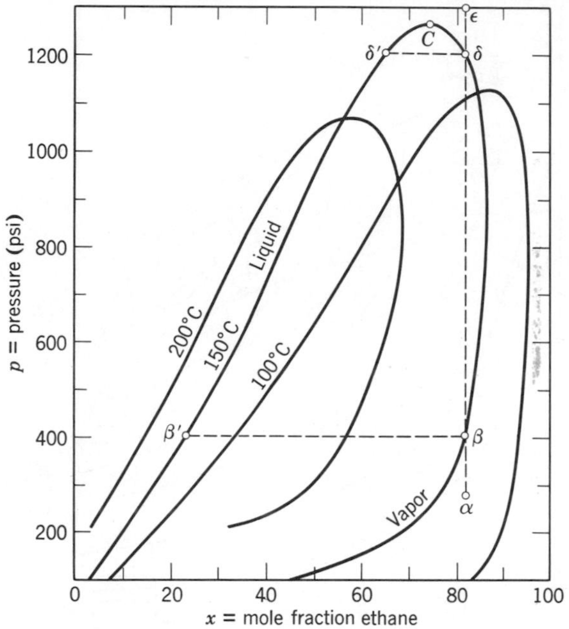

Fig. 5.3–3. Isotherms on a p-x plot for the system ethane-heptane. These curves are obtained by slicing the surface $p_{\text{vap}}(T, x)$ with planes perpendicular to the T-axis and projecting the curves of intersection onto the p-x plane. The line illustrates *retrograde condensation of the first kind* at 150°C.

in equilibrium with the liquid. Further increase in temperature results in an increasing amount of vapor phase and a corresponding decrease in the amount of liquid until point D is reached, where the last trace of liquid having a composition D' disappears.

At higher pressures the liquid and vapor boundaries of the curves occur at higher temperatures. The variation with pressure of the boiling points of the pure components ($x = 0$ and $x = 1$) follows the vapor-pressure curves for the two pure substances. With increasing pressure the boiling points of the pure components continue to increase until the critical temperature for one of them is reached. For the ethane-heptane system under consideration this occurs for heptane at a pressure slightly less than

400 psi. The corresponding critical temperature is approximately 250°C. At or above this temperature two fluid phases cannot exist in the system beyond some limiting composition which is determined by the pressure.

Let us now examine the behavior of the system at 600 psi. The heterogeneous area bounded by the liquid and vapor curves does not extend to the left of about $x = 0.18$. Consequently, if a mixture of

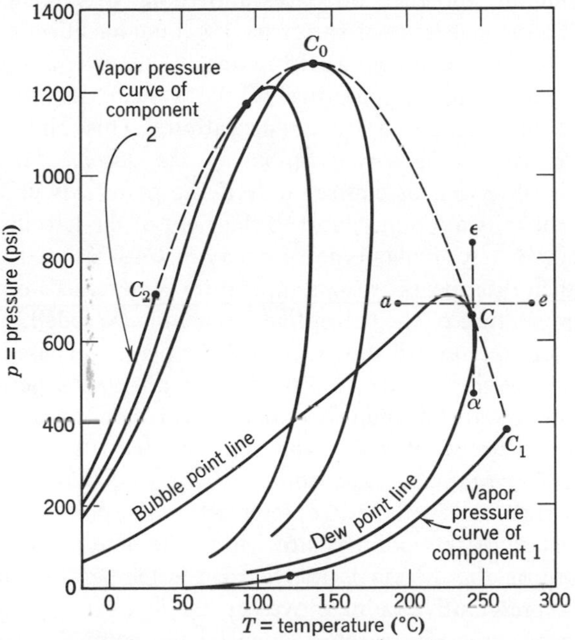

Fig. 5.3–4. Lines of constant composition on a p-T plot. The curves shown here are obtained by slicing the surface shown in Fig. 5.3–1 with planes perpendicular to the x-axis and then projecting the resulting curves of intersection onto the p-T plane. The dotted lines $\alpha\epsilon$ and ae represent the paths followed by the system in retrograde condensation of the first and second kind respectively, for a composition of $x = 0.265$ mole fraction ethane. (From O. A. Hougen and K. M. Watson, *Chemical Process Principles*, Wiley, 1947.)

composition $x = 0.15$ is heated at constant pressure, there is no phase separation such as is observed at 200 psi. The liquid boundary of the 600 psi isobar goes through a minimum in the ethane content with increasing temperature before it joins with the vapor boundary at the point indicated by c. Point c, which is the point at which the boundary curve has a horizontal tangent, is then the critical point for a mixture of approximately 0.22 mole fraction of ethane. At this point only are the vapor and liquid phases indistinguishable in density and composition.

The composition minimum in the liquid boundary gives rise to one type of retrograde condensation. Consider a mixture at 600 psi whose state is represented by point *a* in Fig. 5.3–2. As the temperature is increased while holding the pressure and composition constant, the system point moves upward from *a* to the point *b*, under which condition a vapor phase appears having, a composition given by b'. When the temperature is further increased the amount of liquid phase decreases, reaches a minimum, and then increases until point *d* is reached, under which condition the last trace of vapor having a composition represented by d' disappears and the system again returns to the single liquid phase. Thus, by increasing the temperature of the system, the initial vapor formation has been followed by condensation. This phenomenon is referred to as *retrograde condensation of the second kind.*[7–9] The phenomenon is observed, of course, only if the point *a* is chosen to lie to the left, of the critical point *c*, and to the right of the leftmost point of the liquidus curve. A similar type of behavior (in which a liquid phase appears and then disappears as the temperature is increased) occurs when the critical temperature of the second component is exceeded.

In Fig. 5.3–3 *isotherms* are shown on the p-x plane. These curves are obtained by slicing the surface in Fig. 5.3–1 with planes perpendicular to the T-axis and then projecting the resulting curves of intersection onto the p-x plane. Curves of this type may be used to illustrate the phenomenon of *retrograde condensation of the first kind.*[3,8,9] Let us consider the system at 150°K and represented by the point α. Only one phase is present since this point is not within the heterogeneous region. As the pressure on the system is increased, the temperature being held constant, the representative point moves up the line $\alpha\epsilon$. At the point β a liquid phase of composition represented by the point β' appears. As the pressure is increased further, the amount of liquid first increases and then decreases. At the point δ the last trace of liquid, of composition δ', disappears. This retrograde behavior would of course not be observed with mixtures containing less ethane than the critical mixtures at this pressure (represented by the point C) or with mixtures containing more ethane than the rightmost point on the vaporous curve.

In general, retrograde behavior occurs whenever the path of the representative point in the three-dimensional representation enters and leaves the heterogeneous volume through the same phase boundary surface, whether it be liquid or vapor. The path need not be parallel to the

[7] "Retrograde condensation of the first kind" is the analogous phenomenon which occurs by varying the pressure instead of the temperature. This problem is discussed presently.

[8] J. P. Kuenen, *Arch. Néerland. Sci.*, **26**, 354 (1893).

[9] D. L. Katz and F. Kurata, *Ind. Eng. Chem.*, **32**, 817 (1946).

temperature axis or to the pressure axis, but can combine changes in both pressure and temperature.

In Fig. 5.3–4 we show the *lines of constant composition* on a pressure-temperature diagram. These curves are formed by slicing the surface in Fig. 5.3–1 with planes perpendicular to the x-axis, and then projecting the resulting curves of intersection onto the p-T plane. That portion of the curve which is formed by the intersection of the plane with the liquidus surface is usually referred to as the *bubble-point line* and the intersection with the vaporus surface as the *dew-point line*. The critical point for the mixture of a given composition is then the point of juncture of the dew-point and bubble-point lines. As the point representing a system moves into the two-phase region across the dew-point line, a liquid phase of some other composition appears. If it enters across the bubble-point line, a vapor phase appears. The two types of retrograde condensation are illustrated in Fig. 5.3–4 by means of the lines a–e and α–ϵ.

In recent years the petroleum industry has given much attention to these problems of retrograde phenomena, since they are of importance in the high-pressure distillation of hydrocarbons. Furthermore, the phenomena are regularly employed to increase the yield of petroleum from wells. By maintaining a moderate pressure in the condensate reservoir one avoids losses of the higher boiling components which would occur if the pressure were allowed to decrease.

The physical properties of solutions of non-volatile solutes in the neighborhood of the critical region of the solvent are quite interesting. The following phenomena have been observed:

(1) The usual ionic condition in the liquid persists in alcohol above the critical point.[10] This was shown by studying the absorption spectrum of cobalt chloride-alcohol solutions above and below the critical temperature. The absorption spectrum of the ionized salt remained the same.

(2) Iodine molecules remain solvated by carbon tetrachloride molecule when such a solution passes through the critical point of the solvent.[11] This was shown by the fact that the absorption spectrum of the iodine remained that of the iodine dissolved in liquid rather than becoming that of gaseous iodine. This demonstrates the persistence of solvent action above the critical point.

(3) The electrical conductivity of methyl alcohol solutions of either KI or NH_4Cl shows a discontinuous temperature derivative in passing through the critical point.[12] As can be seen from Fig. 5.3–5, in the

[10] V. B. Hannay, *Proc. Roy. Soc.* (*London*), **30**, 478, 484 (1880). V. B. Hannay and J. Hogarth, *Proc. Roy. Soc.* (*London*), **29**, 324 (1879); **30**, 178 (1880).

[11] P. Villard, *Compt. rend.*, **120**, 182 (1895).

[12] C. A. Kraus, *Phys. Rev.*, **18**, 40, 89 (1904).

neighborhood of the critical point the electrical conductivity of the vapor increases and the electrical conductivity of the liquid decreases. Above the critical point, the conductivity gradually decreases.

(4) For dilute solutions, the elevation of the critical point is proportional to the molar concentration of the solute.[13] For example, for liquid CO_2 the raising of the critical point is 8.8°C per mole per cent of solute; for liquid ammonia, 13.0°C per mole per cent of solute.

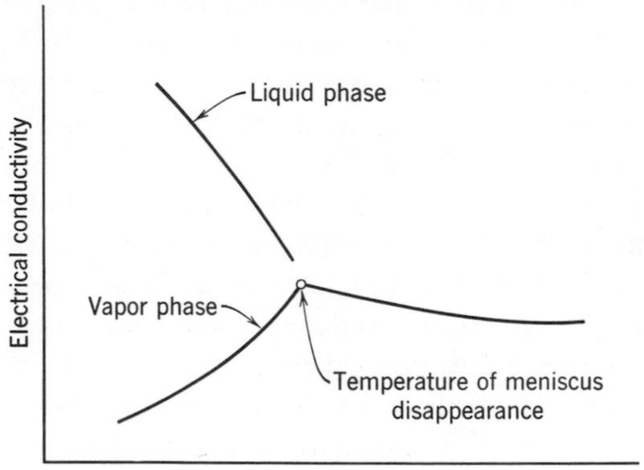

Fig. 5.3–5. Variation of electrical conductivity of solutions of NH_4Cl in CH_3OH in the neighborhood of the critical point. [From C. A. Kraus, *Phys. Rev.*, **18**, 40, 89 (1904).]

b. Thermodynamic considerations

An empirical equation of state of a mixture may be used to obtain information about the phase behavior of the mixture. In § 5.2b it was pointed out that the vapor pressure of a single component may be estimated from the empirical equations of state by drawing a horizontal line on the p–$\tilde{V}$ diagram in such a manner that the areas bounded by the isotherm on the two sides of the line are equal. The generalization of this idea to a binary mixture is straightforward but not so simple.

If several phases of a multicomponent mixture are in equilibrium, thermodynamic conditions require that the chemical potential (that is, the partial molar Gibbs free energy) of the *i*th chemical species be the same in each of the phases. In the special case of liquid-vapor equilibrium in a binary system the requirement is

$$\mu_1^{(l)} = \mu_1^{(v)} \qquad \mu_2^{(l)} = \mu_2^{(v)} \tag{5.3–1}$$

where the superscripts l and v refer to the liquid and vapor phases and the subscripts 1 and 2 refer to the components.

[13] H. S. Booth and R. M. Bidwell, *Chem. Revs.*, **44**, 477 (1949).

In a mixture of perfect gases, the chemical potential of component i is

$$\mu_i(T, p) = \mu_i^{(0)}(T) + RT \ln p + RT \ln x_i \tag{5.3–2}$$

Here x_i is the mole fraction of component i and $\mu_i^{(0)}(T)$ is the chemical potential or Gibbs free energy per mole of pure i at the temperature of the mixture and at unit fugacity. Deviations of the behavior of real gases from this expression may be written in terms of the equation of state of the mixture. From thermodynamic arguments it follows that

$$\left(\frac{\partial \mu_i}{\partial p}\right)_T = \bar{V}_i \tag{5.3–3}$$

where $\bar{V}_i$ is the partial molar volume of component i. Thus, in a mixture of real gases, the chemical potential of component i is

$$\mu_i(T, p) = \mu_i^{(0)}(T) + RT \ln (px_i) + \int_0^p \left[\bar{V}_i - \frac{RT}{p}\right] dp \tag{5.3–4}$$

the integral being taken at constant temperature.

The composition of a binary mixture may be specified by the mole fraction of one component. Let us use x_1 and define

$$\begin{aligned} \ln f_i(T, p, x_1) &= [\mu_i(T, p) - \mu_i^{(0)}(T)]/RT \\ &= \ln p + \ln x_i + \frac{1}{RT}\int_0^p \left[\bar{V}_i - \frac{RT}{p}\right] dp \end{aligned} \tag{5.3–5}$$

Since the partial molar volume $\bar{V}_i$ may be evaluated in terms of the equation of state of the mixture, the function $f_i(T, p, x_1)$ may also be determined from a knowledge of the equation of state. As was pointed out in § 5.2, empirical equations of state are such that some of the isotherms are S-shaped. Thus in a certain range of conditions there may be three points on an isotherm corresponding to a particular pressure, and $f_i(T, p, x_1)$ is a triple-valued function. The middle value is meaningless, but it is necessary to distinguish between the value associated with the vapor side of the isotherm, $f_i^{(v)}(T, p, x_1)$, and the value associated with the liquid side of the isotherm, $f_i^{(l)}(T, p, x_1)$.

In terms of the functions just defined the conditions for equilibrium between two phases of a binary mixture (Eq. 5.3–1) become

$$\begin{aligned} f_1^{(l)}(T, p, x_1^{(l)}) &= f_1^{(v)}(T, p, x_1^{(v)}) \\ f_2^{(l)}(T, p, x_1^{(l)}) &= f_2^{(v)}(T, p, x_1^{(v)}) \end{aligned} \tag{5.3–6}$$

For specified values of temperature and pressure, this is a pair of equations for $x_1^{(l)}$ and $x_1^{(v)}$, the mole fractions of component "1" in the liquid and vapor phases. In general, the compositions of the two phases are different.

The critical composition for a particular temperature and pressure is defined as the value of x_1 such that $x_1^{(v)} = x_1^{(l)}$. Below the critical temperatures of both components there is no such composition. As discussed in the previous subsection, at higher temperatures there may be 0, 1, or 2 such points.

The analytic form of the functions $f_i(T, p, x_1)$ for a mixture obeying the van der Waals equation of state is given in Appendix A, at the end of this chapter. The nature of these functions is indicated in Fig. 5.3–6.

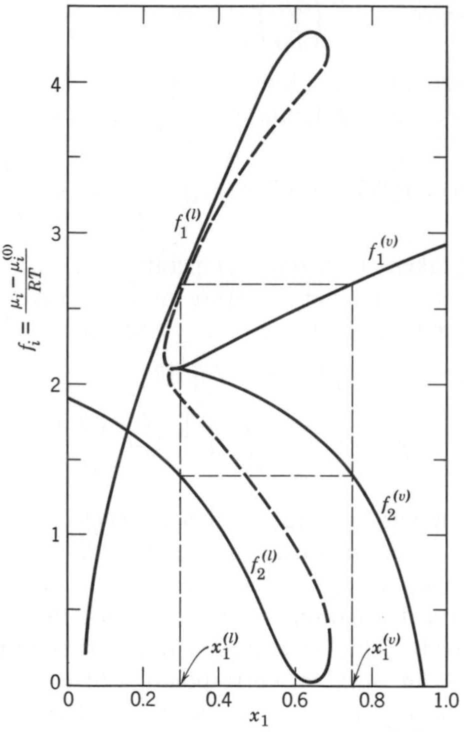

Fig. 5.3–6. An illustration of the form of the functions $f_i^{(l)}$ and $f_i^{(v)}$ which determine the coexistence surface for two component mixtures.

These curves are drawn with constants characteristic of the ethane-heptane system for a temperature of 400°K and a pressure of 20 atm. The dotted portions of the curves arise from the unattainable center portions of the van der Waals isotherms. The solutions to the Eqs. 5.3–6 are indicated at $x_1^{(v)} = 0.30$ and $x_1^{(l)} = 0.75$. It is evident from the nature of the heterogeneous region, as indicated in Fig. 5.3–1, that under some conditions of temperature and pressure no solutions to the equation exist.

APPENDIX A. THE CHEMICAL POTENTIAL OF A VAN DER WAALS MIXTURE

The van der Waals equation of state is

$$p = \frac{RT}{\tilde{V} - b} - \frac{a}{\tilde{V}^2} \tag{5.A–1}$$

Although this equation was originally proposed to account for the p-V-T relations in a pure gas, van der Waals also applied the equation to mixtures. In applications to a binary mixture the constants a and b are taken to depend upon the composition according to Eqs. 4.2–5, 6.

Using this equation of state, we may evaluate the functions $f_i(T, p, x_1)$ defined by Eq. 5.3–5. The result is

$$f_i(T, p, x_1) = \ln \frac{x_i RT}{(\tilde{V} - b)} + \frac{B_i}{(\tilde{V} - b)} - \frac{A_i}{\tilde{V}RT} \tag{5.A–2}$$

The quantities A_i and B_i are defined by the relations

$$\begin{aligned} A_1 &= 2(x_1 a_{11} + x_2 a_{12}) \\ B_1 &= b_{11} - x_2^2(b_{11} - 2b_{12} + b_{22}) \end{aligned} \tag{5.A–3}$$

with analogous relations for A_2 and B_2.

PROBLEMS

1. Use the van der Waals equation to find the specific volume of the vapor, the specific volume of the liquid, and the vapor pressure for a one-component system when the temperature is $\frac{8}{9}T_c$.

2. Suppose that a set of isotherms has been determined in the neighborhood of the critical point by experimental measurements of the pressure and temperature at various values of the density in a cell of height h. How would you correct the isotherms to take into account the variation of pressure and density in the cell due to the force of gravity? [See R. H. Wentorf and C. A. Boyd, University of Wisconsin Naval Research Laboratory, CM 724 (1952).]

3. For a mixture containing an equal number of moles of ethane and heptane at 100°C, calculate the composition and specific volume of both the liquid and the vapor phases. Use the van der Waals equation, together with the mixing law given by Eqs. 4.2–5 and 6. Assume that $a_{12} = (a_{11} + a_{22})/2$ and $b_{12} = (b_{11}b_{22})^{1/2}$. Take $b = \frac{1}{3}\tilde{V}_c$ and $a = 3p_c\tilde{V}_c^2$. [See C. A. Boyd, *J. Phys. and Coll. Chem.*, **54**, 1347 (1950). Experimental data for the ethane-heptane system are given by W. B. Kay, *Ind. Eng. Chem.*, **30**, 459 (1938).]

· 6 ·

Quantum Theory and the Equation of State

by J. de Boer[1] and R. Byron Bird

Thus far the discussion of the equilibrium properties of gases has been restricted to those substances and those conditions for which classical mechanics provides an adequate description of the system. There are two types of quantum effects which have to be considered under certain conditions: (i) *diffraction effects*, which result from the wave nature of the molecules and are important when the de Broglie wavelength associated with the molecules is of the order of magnitude of the molecular diameter; (ii) *symmetry effects*, which result from the statistics of the particles and are of importance when the de Broglie wavelength of the molecules is of the order of magnitude of the average distance between the molecules in the gas. At room temperatures the diffraction effects are measurable in helium and hydrogen but unimportant for heavier gases. At lower temperatures the quantum deviations associated with these effects are quite appreciable for helium and hydrogen and of some importance for the heavier gases. Symmetry effects are important only at high densities or very low temperatures.

This chapter deals with the calculation of these quantum effects and, except for the final section, concerns itself only with monatomic gases. After a brief discussion of the canonical ensemble in quantum mechanics, we discuss the development of the equation of state according to the two general methods which were described in Chapter 3 in connection with the classical equation of state. From these results may be obtained the equation of state of perfect gases, for which the various equilibrium properties may be expressed in closed form. This gives us information about the "symmetry effects" mentioned above and also about the phenomenon of Bose-Einstein condensation. We then consider in detail the quantum mechanical calculation of the second virial coefficient and

[1] Director of the *Instituut voor Theoretische Physica*, University of Amsterdam, The Netherlands.

the zero-pressure Joule-Thomson coefficient. Wherever possible comparisons are made between the calculated and experimental values.

At the beginning of Chapter 4 we discuss the principle of corresponding states in classical mechanics. The analogous principle in quantum mechanics has the form $p^* = p^*(V^*, T^*; \Lambda^*)$. Thus this principle states that deviations from classical behavior depend on the magnitude of the quantity $\Lambda^* = h/\sigma\sqrt{m\epsilon}$. This quantity is the ratio of the de Broglie wavelength (corresponding to a system of reduced mass $\mu = m/2$ and energy ϵ) to the collision diameter σ, and is characteristic for each substance. In this chapter this principle of corresponding states is used to discuss the quantum effects in liquids and dense gases.

1. Statistical Mechanical Preliminaries

Before beginning with the discussion of the development of the equation of state, we summarize briefly some information about the canonical ensemble in quantum mechanics. First, several forms for the probability density matrix are set forth, and then the partition function, average values, and the "Slater sum" are discussed. The Slater sum is the quantum mechanical analog of the Boltzmann factor. It is shown that the Slater sum approaches the Boltzmann factor in the correspondence limit.

a. The probability density matrix for a canonical ensemble

For a closed system in equilibrium at temperature T the probability density operator is given by

$$\mathscr{P}^{(N)} = Z_{Nq}^{-1} e^{-\mathscr{H}/kT} \tag{6.1-1}$$

in which $\mathscr{H}$ is the quantum mechanical Hamiltonian operator for a system of N particles and the operator $\exp(-\mathscr{H}/kT)$ is defined to be $\Sigma_j(-\mathscr{H}/kT)^j/j!$. The factor Z_{Nq}^{-1} is a normalizing constant.

According to Eq. 2.2-19 the probability density matrix $\mathscr{P}(\boldsymbol{r}^N; \boldsymbol{r}'^N)$ in Hilbert space is given by

$$\begin{aligned}\mathscr{P}^{(N)}(\boldsymbol{r}^N; \boldsymbol{r}'^N) &= Z_{Nq}^{-1}(e^{-\mathscr{H}/kT})(\boldsymbol{r}^N; \boldsymbol{r}'^N) \\ &= Z_{Nq}^{-1}\, \Sigma_\rho \phi_\rho^*(\boldsymbol{r}'^N)\, e^{-\mathscr{H}/kT} \phi_\rho(\boldsymbol{r}^N)\end{aligned} \tag{6.1-2}$$

The diagonal element

$$\mathscr{P}^{(N)}(\boldsymbol{r}^N; \boldsymbol{r}^N) = Z_{Nq}^{-1}\, \Sigma_\rho \phi_\rho^*(\boldsymbol{r}^N)\, e^{-\mathscr{H}/kT} \phi_\rho(\boldsymbol{r}^N) \tag{6.1-3}$$

is the quantum mechanical expression for the probability density of a configuration $\boldsymbol{r}^N$. Z_{Nq} is the quantum mechanical partition function as obtained from Eq. 2.2-22 and given in Eq. 2.4-2. The functions $\phi_\rho(\boldsymbol{r}^N)$ are a complete orthonormal set of eigenfunctions which have been properly symmetrized. An important property of the density matrices in these last two expressions is that they are independent of the set of orthonormal functions $\phi_p(\boldsymbol{r}^N)$, chosen for the expansion of the system wave function (see § 2.2). There are two sets of functions which are used in connection with subsequent derivations:

i. *Energy Eigenfunctions*

The system wave function $\Psi(\boldsymbol{r}^N)$ (Eq. 2.2–1) may be expanded in terms of the eigenfunctions $\psi_\sigma(\boldsymbol{r}^N)$ of the Hamiltonian operator $\mathscr{H}$. Then the probability density matrix in Eq. 6.1–3 becomes

$$\mathscr{P}^{(N)}(\boldsymbol{r}^N; \boldsymbol{r}^N) = Z_{Nq}{}^{-1}\Sigma_\sigma \mid \psi_\sigma(\boldsymbol{r}^N) \mid^2 e^{-E_\sigma/kT} \tag{6.1–4}$$

Here $\exp(-E_\sigma/kT)$ represents the probability of an energy state $\{\sigma\}$, and $\mid \psi_\sigma(\boldsymbol{r}^N) \mid^2$ denotes the probability density in that state. In this form the interpretation of $\mathscr{P}^{(N)}(\boldsymbol{r}^N; \boldsymbol{r}^N)$ as the probability of a configuration $\boldsymbol{r}^N$ is easy to understand. It is shown later on that this expression approaches the classical expression $P^{(N)}(\boldsymbol{r}^N) = \int P^{(N)}(\boldsymbol{r}^N, \boldsymbol{p}^N)\, d\boldsymbol{p}^N$ at high temperatures, where the deviations from the classical behavior are small.

ii. *Momentum Eigenfunctions*

The system wave function $\Psi(\boldsymbol{r}^N)$ (Eq. 2.2–1) may be expanded in terms of the momentum eigenfunctions $\exp\left[-\frac{i}{\hbar}(\boldsymbol{p}^N \cdot \boldsymbol{r}^N)\right]$. If the system is contained in a cubical box of side-length L, the values which $\boldsymbol{p}_j$ may assume are limited to a certain number of discrete values. It is therefore convenient to introduce the dimensionless vector $\boldsymbol{\sigma}^N = (L/h)\boldsymbol{p}^N$, which may assume all positive or negative *integral* values. The set of functions used in the expansion of the system wave function must of course be consistent with the symmetry requirements of the system. Consequently, the set of symmetrized momentum eigenfunctions which should be used is

$$\phi(\boldsymbol{r}^N, \boldsymbol{\sigma}^N) = \frac{1}{(L^{3N}\, N!)^{1/2}} \Sigma_P (\pm 1)^p\, e^{\frac{2\pi i}{L}(\boldsymbol{\sigma}^N \cdot P\boldsymbol{r}^N)} \tag{6.1–5}$$

P is any permutation (of order p)[2] of the N particles, that is, any permutation of the indices of $\boldsymbol{r}^N \equiv \boldsymbol{r}_1, \boldsymbol{r}_2, \cdots, \boldsymbol{r}_N$. The plus sign is for Bose-Einstein statistics, and the minus sign for Fermi-Dirac statistics.

[2] Here p is the number of interchanges between pairs of molecules required to bring the permuted state back to the initial arrangement.

The expression in Eq. 6.1–2 for the density matrix then becomes

$$\mathscr{P}^{(N)}(\boldsymbol{r}^N; \boldsymbol{r}'^N)$$

$$= \frac{1}{Z_{Nq}L^{3N}N!^2} \int \Sigma_P \Sigma_{P'} (\pm 1)^{p+p'} e^{-\frac{2\pi i}{L}(\boldsymbol{\sigma}^N \cdot P'\boldsymbol{r}'^N)} e^{-\mathscr{H}/kT} e^{+\frac{2\pi i}{L}(\boldsymbol{\sigma}^N \cdot P\boldsymbol{r}^N)} d\boldsymbol{\sigma}^N$$

$$= \frac{1}{Z_{Nq}L^{3N}N!} \int \Sigma_P (\pm 1)^p e^{-\frac{2\pi i}{L}(\boldsymbol{\sigma}^N \cdot P\boldsymbol{r}'^N)} e^{-\mathscr{H}/kT} e^{\frac{2\pi i}{L}(\boldsymbol{\sigma}^N \cdot \boldsymbol{r}^N)} d\boldsymbol{\sigma}^N$$

$$= \frac{1}{Z_{Nq}h^{3N}N!} \int \Sigma_P (\pm 1)^p e^{-\frac{2\pi i}{h}(\boldsymbol{p}^N \cdot P\boldsymbol{r}'^N)} e^{-\mathscr{H}/kT} e^{\frac{2\pi i}{h}(\boldsymbol{p}^N \cdot \boldsymbol{r}^N)} d\boldsymbol{p}^N \qquad (6.1\text{–}6)$$

The second expression given here for $\mathscr{P}^{(N)}(\boldsymbol{r}^N; \boldsymbol{r}'^N)$ is made possible by the invariance of the Hamiltonian operator under the permutation operation P. The third expression results from changing back to $\boldsymbol{p}^N$ from $\boldsymbol{\sigma}^N$. The summation over ρ in Eq. 6.1–2, which is to be carried out for all *different* sets of quantum numbers, is here replaced by an integration over $\boldsymbol{\sigma}^N$. However, this is an independent integration over *all* possible momentum components from $-\infty$ to $+\infty$. Hence an additional factor $N!$ has been included in Eq. 6.1–6 to compensate for the fact that, owing to the identity of the particles, all momentum states resulting simply from permutations of the particles are included inherently in the integration.

The probability matrix may also be written in the form of Eq. 2.2–20:

$$\mathscr{P}^{(N)}_{\rho\rho'} = \frac{1}{Z_{Nq}} \int \phi_\rho(\boldsymbol{r}^N) e^{-\mathscr{H}/kT} \phi_{\rho'}(\boldsymbol{r}^N)\, d\boldsymbol{r}^N \qquad (6.1\text{–}7)$$

This matrix depends upon the system of orthonormal functions which is chosen as a basis. The change to another system has been indicated in Eq. 2.2–11. If, in particular, energy wave functions are selected (that is those satisfying $\mathscr{H}\psi_\sigma = E_\sigma \psi_\sigma$), then $\mathscr{P}^{(N)}_{\rho\rho'}$ assumes the diagonal form:

$$\mathscr{P}^{(N)}_{\sigma\sigma'} = \frac{\delta_{\sigma\sigma'}}{Z_{Nq}} e^{-E_\sigma/kT} \qquad (6.1\text{–}8)$$

and $\mathscr{P}^{(N)}_{\sigma\sigma}$ is the probability that the system finds itself in the eigenstate $\{\sigma\}$ with energy E_σ. Z_{Nq} is the quantum mechanical partition function as obtained from the normalizing condition in Eq. 2.2–22 and given in Eq. 2.4–1.

b. The probability density matrix in the classical limit

The diagonal element of the quantum mechanical probability density matrix and the corresponding classical expression are

$$\mathscr{P}^{(N)}(\boldsymbol{r}^N; \boldsymbol{r}^N) = \frac{1}{Z_{Nq}} [\Sigma_\rho \phi_\rho^*(\boldsymbol{r}^N) e^{-\mathscr{H}/kT} \phi_\rho(\boldsymbol{r}^N)] \qquad (6.1\text{–}9)$$

and[3]

$$P^{(N)}(\boldsymbol{r}^N) = \frac{1}{Z_N N! \lambda^{3N}} e^{-\Phi(\boldsymbol{r}^N)/kT} \qquad (6.1\text{–}10)$$

[3] This comes from Eqs. 2.1–3 and 20.

Here $\Phi(\boldsymbol{r}^N)$ is the potential energy of the system, and $\lambda^2 = h^2/2\pi mkT$. The factor λ^{-3N} arises from the integration over the momenta. These two equations may be written in the following form in order to bring out the similarity between the classical and quantum formulations:

$$\mathscr{P}^{(N)}(\boldsymbol{r}^N; \boldsymbol{r}^N) = \frac{1}{Z_{N_Q} N! \lambda^{3N}} \mathscr{W}_N(\boldsymbol{r}^N) \tag{6.1–11}$$

$$P^{(N)}(\boldsymbol{r}^N) = \frac{1}{Z_N N! \lambda^{3N}} W_N(\boldsymbol{r}^N) \tag{6.1–12}$$

$\mathscr{W}_N(\boldsymbol{r}^N)$ is known as the *Slater sum*,[4] and its classical counterpart, $W_N(\boldsymbol{r}^N)$, is commonly referred to as the *Boltzmann factor*. These quantities are defined by

$$\mathscr{W}_N(\boldsymbol{r}^N) = N! \lambda^{3N} \Sigma_\rho \phi_\rho^* (\boldsymbol{r}^N)\, e^{-\mathscr{H}/kT}\, \phi_\rho(\boldsymbol{r}^N) \tag{6.1–13}$$

$$W_N(\boldsymbol{r}^N) = e^{-\Phi(\boldsymbol{r}^N)/kT} \tag{6.1–14}$$

We now show[5] that the Slater sum approaches the Boltzmann factor in the correspondence limit, that is, in the high-temperature region, where the deviation from classical behavior is small.

For the purpose of this proof it is convenient to use as the expansion functions, $\phi(\boldsymbol{r}^N)$, the properly symmetrized momentum eigenfunctions given in Eq. 6.1–5. Accordingly, the following expression may be obtained for the Slater sum:

$$\mathscr{W}_N(\boldsymbol{r}^N) = \left(\frac{\lambda}{h}\right)^{3N} \int \Sigma_P (\pm 1)^p\, e^{-\frac{i}{\hbar}(\boldsymbol{p}^N \cdot P\boldsymbol{r}^N)}\, e^{-\mathscr{H}/kT}\, e^{+\frac{i}{\hbar}(\boldsymbol{p}^N \cdot \boldsymbol{r}^N)}\, d\boldsymbol{p}^N \tag{6.1-15}$$

The application of the operator $e^{-\mathscr{H}/kT}$ to its operand in this equation is somewhat difficult because the operators for kinetic energy and potential energy do not commute. Hence we resort to another method of evaluating the function:

$$X(\boldsymbol{r}^N, \boldsymbol{p}^N; T) = e^{-\mathscr{H}/kT}\, e^{+\frac{i}{\hbar}(\boldsymbol{p}^N \cdot \boldsymbol{r}^N)} \tag{6.1–16}$$

which occurs in the integrand. This function may be shown to satisfy the Bloch differential equation,

$$\mathscr{H} X(\boldsymbol{r}^N, \boldsymbol{p}^N; T) = -\frac{\partial}{\partial (1/kT)} X(\boldsymbol{r}^N, \boldsymbol{p}^N; T) \tag{6.1–17}$$

[4] Slater sums for a few simple systems are calculated in problem 1 at the end of this chapter.

[5] This proof is due to J. G. Kirkwood, *Phys. Rev.*, **44**, 31 (1933).

and must have as asymptotic solution for $T \to \infty$ the form $X = \exp[(i/\hbar)(\mathbf{p}^N \cdot \mathbf{r}^N)]$. For $T < \infty$ a solution of the following form is assumed:

$$X = e^{+\frac{i}{\hbar}(\mathbf{p}^N \cdot \mathbf{r}^N)} e^{-\frac{H(\mathbf{r}^N, \mathbf{p}^N)}{kT}} Y(\mathbf{r}^N, \mathbf{p}^N; T) \tag{6.1–18}$$

Substitution of this expression into the Bloch differential equation gives a differential equation for Y which must be solved with the boundary condition that Y approach unity when $T \to \infty$. This equation has been solved[6] by substituting for Y the series development:

$$Y = \Sigma_j h^j y_j(\mathbf{r}^N, \mathbf{p}^N) \tag{6.1–19}$$

The y_j are determined by substituting this expression for Y into the differential equation for Y and equating terms on both sides containing equal powers of Planck's constant. This having been done, the expression for Y is substituted back into Eq. 6.1–15, and the integration over the momenta is performed. (During the last operation terms containing odd powers of Planck's constant vanish.) The final expression for the Slater sum is then:[7, 8]

$$\begin{aligned}\mathscr{W}_N(\mathbf{r}^N) \\ = W_N(\mathbf{r}^N)\end{aligned} \left[\begin{aligned}&\{1 + \lambda^2 \textstyle\sum_j w_2^{(j)} + \lambda^4 \sum_j w_4^{(j)} \\ &+ \text{terms with higher powers of } h\} \\ &\pm \{\tfrac{1}{2} \textstyle\sum_j \sum_k{}' \exp\left[-\frac{2\pi}{\lambda^2}(\mathbf{r}_j - \mathbf{r}_k)^2\right][1 + s_1^{(j,k)} + s_2^{(j,k)} + \cdots]\} \\ &+ \{\text{other terms involving higher permutations}\}\end{aligned}\right] \tag{6.1–20}$$

in which $\lambda^2 = h^2/2\pi mkT$, and

$$w_2^{(j)}(\mathbf{r}^N) = -\frac{1}{24\pi kT}\left[\left(\frac{\partial}{\partial \mathbf{r}_j} \cdot \frac{\partial}{\partial \mathbf{r}_j}\Phi\right) - \frac{1}{2kT}\left(\frac{\partial \Phi}{\partial \mathbf{r}_j} \cdot \frac{\partial \Phi}{\partial \mathbf{r}_j}\right)\right] \tag{6.1–21}$$

$$s_1^{(j,k)}(\mathbf{r}^N) = \frac{1}{2kT}\left((\mathbf{r}_j - \mathbf{r}_k) \cdot \left(\frac{\partial \Phi}{\partial \mathbf{r}_i} - \frac{\partial \Phi}{\partial \mathbf{r}_j}\right)\right) \tag{6.1–22}$$

[6] Other ways have been suggested for solving this equation. See, for example, K. Husimi, *Proc. Phys.-Math. Soc. Japan*, Ser. 3, **22**, 264 (1940), Part I, Sect. 7. Also J. E. Mayer and W. Band, *J. Chem. Phys.*, **15**, 141 (1947).

[7] $\Sigma_j \Sigma_k$ means summation over all j and k, excluding those terms for which $j = k$.

[8] To understand the meaning of the terms in this expression, let us consider the case where $N = 3$. Then in Eq. 6.1–15 the summing over all permutations would amount to

$$\Sigma_P (\pm 1)^p = P_{123} \pm [P_{213} + P_{132} + P_{321}] + [P_{231} + P_{312}]$$

The terms in the first {} in Eq. 6.1–20 result from the application of the identity permutation P_{123}. The next three permutation operators give rise to the second {} in Eq. 6.1–18, that is, interchanges of two molecules only are involved. The third {} results from the last two permutation operators which involve third-order permutations.

Equation 6.1–20 may be used to calculate the deviations from the classical behavior of the Boltzmann function, provided that the temperature is sufficiently high, so that the quantum effects are quite small; for lower temperatures the series expansion in powers of Planck's constant diverges. The terms involving the higher order permutations would have to be considered in the third and higher virial coefficients but do not affect the second virial coefficient.

From the above results it is clear that the Slater sum $\mathscr{W}_N(\boldsymbol{r}^N)$ approaches the Boltzmann factor $W_N(\boldsymbol{r}^N)$ in the high-temperature limit. It also follows that the quantum mechanical sum over states (given by Eq. 2.4–1 or 2) goes over into the classical partition function (given in Eq. 2.4–3). As was mentioned in the introduction to this chapter, deviations from classical behavior result from the wave nature of the molecules ("diffraction effects") and from the statistics of the molecules ("symmetry effects"). These two contributions manifest themselves in Eq. 6.1–20. The terms contained in the first set of braces result solely from the diffraction effects; the remaining terms have their origin in the symmetry requirements for the wave functions of a system of N particles.

2. Development of the Equation of State from Statistical Mechanics

This section parallels quite closely the discussion given in § 3.1 on classical systems. We show that the equation of state[1] may be obtained from the quantum mechanical partition function and also from the quantum mechanical virial theorem, and that the results from the two procedures are the same. In this chapter we do not give the detailed derivation of the virial form of the equation of state as was done in § 3.2 and 3.3, inasmuch as the development is almost identical. We do indicate how the final classical results of § 3.4 have to be modified in order to be applicable in quantum statistics.

a. The method of the partition function

As was shown in Chapter 2 the pV-product is related to the partition function by:

$$pV = kT(\partial \ln Z_{Nq}/\partial \ln V)_T \tag{6.2–1}$$

And the quantum mechanical partition function Z_{Nq} may be written in either of the two forms:

$$Z_{Nq} = \textstyle\sum_\sigma e^{-E_\sigma/kT} \tag{2.4–1}$$

$$Z_{Nq} = \int [\textstyle\sum_\rho \phi_\rho^*(\boldsymbol{r}^N)\, e^{-\mathscr{H}/kT} \phi_\rho(\boldsymbol{r}^N)]\, d\boldsymbol{r}^N \tag{2.4–2}$$

[1] As in Chapter 3 we confine the discussion to the *thermal* equation of state [$p = p(V, T)$]. The *caloric* equation of state [$U = U(V, T)$] is discussed in problem 2 at the end of this chapter.

where $\mathscr{H} = \mathscr{K} + \Phi$, the sum of the kinetic energy and potential energy operators. The first expression is the usual "sum-over-states" form for the partition function. In this form the volume dependence of Z_{Nq} is contained in the energy levels E_σ, which depend in a complicated way on the external mechanical parameters of the system. The second expression for Z_{Nq} is of such a form that its volume dependence is contained in the limits of integration and also in the boundary conditions which the functions $\phi_\rho(\mathbf{r}^N)$ must satisfy. In terms of this second formulation we may write

$$pV = \frac{1}{Z_{Nq}} VkT \frac{\partial}{\partial V} \int [\Sigma_\rho \phi_\rho^*(\mathbf{r}^N) e^{-\mathscr{H}/kT} \phi_\rho(\mathbf{r}^N)]\, d\mathbf{r}^N \qquad (6.2\text{–}2)$$

for the equation of state.

b. The method based on the virial theorem of quantum mechanics

The pV-product may also be calculated from an ensemble average according to Eqs. 2.3–33. In order to make use of this expression we must have an expression for the pV-operator. From the quantum mechanical virial theorem given in § 1.6f, the following expression is obtained analogous to Eq. 3.1–11:

$$(pV)_{\text{op}} = \tfrac{2}{3}[\mathscr{K} - \Xi_i]$$

$$= \frac{2}{3}\left[-\frac{\hbar^2}{2m}\Sigma\left(\frac{\partial}{\partial \mathbf{r}_i}\cdot\frac{\partial}{\partial \mathbf{r}_i}\right) - \frac{1}{2}\Sigma\left(\mathbf{r}_i \cdot \frac{\partial}{\partial \mathbf{r}_i}\Phi(\mathbf{r}^N)\right)\right] \qquad (6.2\text{–}3)$$

in which $\mathscr{K}$ and Ξ_i are respectively the kinetic energy operator and the operator corresponding to the virial of the intermolecular forces of the system. The pV-product is then

$$pV = \frac{1}{Z_{Nq}} \int [\Sigma \phi_\rho^*(\mathbf{r}^N)(pV)_{\text{op}}\, e^{-\mathscr{H}/kT} \phi_\rho(\mathbf{r}^N)]\, d\mathbf{r}^N \qquad (6.2\text{–}4)$$

When the assumption of two-body forces is made, this may be written in the form

$$pV = NkT - \tfrac{1}{6} \iint \mathscr{N}^{(2)}(\mathbf{r}_1, \mathbf{r}_2; \mathbf{r}_1, \mathbf{r}_2) r_{12}\, (d\varphi_{12}/dr_{12})\, d\mathbf{r}_1\, d\mathbf{r}_2 \qquad (6.2\text{–}5)$$

which is exactly like Eq. 3.1–13 except that the classical pair distribution function $n^{(2)}$ has been replaced by its quantum mechanical analogue, $\mathscr{N}^{(2)}$, defined in Eq. 2.2–24.

c. The equivalence of the equation of state from the partition function and that from the virial theorem[2]

If in Eq. 6.2–2 we use the momentum eigenfunctions given in Eq. 6.1–5, the expression for pV from the partition function becomes

$$pV = \frac{kT}{N!Z_{Nq}} \frac{L}{3} \frac{\partial}{\partial L} \iint \Sigma_P(\pm 1)^p e^{-2\pi i(\mathbf{k}^N \cdot P\mathbf{r}^N)} e^{-\mathscr{H}/kT} e^{+2\pi i(\mathbf{k}^N \cdot \mathbf{r}^N)} d\mathbf{k}^N \, d\mathbf{r}^N \tag{6.2–6}$$

Here we have used wave numbers $\mathbf{k}_j = \mathbf{p}_j/h$ rather than momenta, and we have let $V = L^3$ [so that $V(\partial/\partial V) = \frac{1}{3}L(\partial/\partial L)$]. In order to perform the differentiation,[3] we introduce the reduced variables $\bar{\mathbf{r}}_j = \mathbf{r}_j/L$ and $\bar{\mathbf{k}}_j = \mathbf{k}_j/L$. Then the last expression becomes[4]

$$pV = \frac{1}{N!Z_{Nq}} \iint \Sigma_P(\pm 1)^p e^{-2\pi i(\bar{\mathbf{k}}^N \cdot P\bar{\mathbf{r}}^N)} \left[-\frac{L}{3}\left(\frac{\partial \mathscr{H}}{\partial L}\right) e^{-\mathscr{H}/kT} \right] e^{+2\pi i(\bar{\mathbf{k}}^N \cdot \bar{\mathbf{r}}^N)} \, d\bar{\mathbf{k}}^N \, d\bar{\mathbf{r}}^N \tag{6.2–7}$$

The differential operator has been brought inside the integral sign since the only L-dependence is in the Hamiltonian operator:

$$\mathscr{H} = \mathscr{K} + \Phi = -\frac{\hbar^2}{2mL^2} \Sigma_i \left(\frac{\partial}{\partial \bar{\mathbf{r}}_i} \cdot \frac{\partial}{\partial \bar{\mathbf{r}}_i} \right) + \Phi(L\bar{\mathbf{r}}^N) \tag{6.2–8}$$

It is easy to show that the differentiation with respect to L yields

$$-\frac{L}{3}\frac{\partial \mathscr{H}}{\partial L} = \frac{2}{3}[\mathscr{K} - \Xi_i] \tag{6.2–9}$$

Substitution of this result into Eq. 6.2–7 and transformation back to the original variables give exactly Eq. 6.2–4, which was obtained from the virial theorem.

d. Final expressions for the quantum mechanical equation of state

The partition function method may be used to get the equation of state in virial form in a manner exactly analogous to that used in § 3.2. The only difference is that Z_N and $W_N(\mathbf{r}^N)$ must everywhere be replaced by

[2] The proof outlined here is due to J. de Boer, *Physica*, **15**, 843 (1949). A similar proof based on the "sum-over-states" representation of the partition function has been given by C. R. Yvon, *Acad. Sci.* (*Paris*), **227**, 763 (1948).

[3] This method was introduced in the analogous classical proof (see § 3.1c) by H. S. Green, *Proc. Roy. Soc.* (*London*), **A189**, 103 (1947).

[4] Use is here made of the fact that, although the operators $\partial\mathscr{H}/\partial L$ and $\exp(-\mathscr{H}/kT)$ do not in general commute, the order of the operators is immaterial in computing the trace. (See J. de Boer, *Physica*, **15**, 843 (1949), appendix.)

Z_{Nq} and $\mathscr{W}_N(\boldsymbol{r}^N)$. The final expressions for the second and third virial coefficients given in Eq. 3.4–5 and 6 are also valid in quantum mechanics when the same changes are effected (the formulae in terms of the f_{ij} are not, however, applicable in quantum theory).

The method based upon the virial theorem may also be developed just as in the classical case in § 3.3. The power-series development of $n^{(2)}$ given in Eq. 3.3–8 applies equally well for $\mathscr{N}^{(2)}$. The only change is that in all the formulae the Boltzmann factor must be replaced by the Slater sum.[5, 6]

3. The Properties of a Perfect Gas

We now consider the special case of a perfect gas for which there is no energy of interaction between the molecules[1] ($\Phi(\boldsymbol{r}^N) = 0$). The indistinguishability of the molecules imposes certain symmetry restrictions on the form of the system wave function, as is discussed in § 1.6d. For systems composed of molecules in which there is an odd number of nucleons and electrons, the system wave function must be antisymmetrical in the interchange of any two molecules. For systems of molecules with even numbers of nucleons and electrons, the system wave function must be symmetrical.[2] Most molecules belong to the latter category, notable exceptions being He^3 and HD.

Throughout the discussion of the Slater sum and the equation of state of a perfect gas it should be noted that, although there are no forces between perfect gas molecules, Fermi-Dirac gases deviate from classical perfect gas behavior in somewhat the same way as gases composed of molecules which repel one another. The opposite behavior is found in Bose-Einstein gases. Consequently, it is convenient to speak of the *apparent repulsion* between molecules of a gas having antisymmetric wave functions (that is, which satisfy the Pauli principle) and the *apparent attraction* between molecules of a gas having symmetric wave functions. This latter behavior is closely related to the phenomenon of Bose-Einstein condensation.

a. The Slater sum for a perfect gas composed of molecules with zero spin

The Hamiltonian operator for a perfect gas is just the kinetic energy operator $\mathscr{H} = -\dfrac{\hbar^2}{2m}\sum\left(\dfrac{\partial}{\partial \boldsymbol{r}_i}\cdot\dfrac{\partial}{\partial \boldsymbol{r}_i}\right)$. Since the exponential functions in Eq. 6.1–15 are just the eigenfunctions of the linear momentum operator,

[5] J. de Boer, *Nuovo Cimento*, Suppl. al Vol. VI, Ser. IX (1949).

[6] See problem 3 at the end of this chapter.

[1] Quantities associated with such a system are designated by the superscript 0.

[2] P. Ehrenfest and J. R. Oppenheimer, *Phys. Rev.*, 37, 333 (1931).

the operator $\mathscr{H} = \mathscr{K}$ may just be replaced by its eigenvalue $\Sigma p_j^2/2m$. When the integration is performed, the Slater sum becomes[3]

$$\mathscr{W}^0(\boldsymbol{r}^N) = \Sigma_P(\pm 1)^p e^{-\frac{\pi}{\lambda^2}\Sigma_k(\boldsymbol{r}_k - \boldsymbol{r}_{P_k})^2} \qquad \begin{matrix}\text{(Upper sign = B.E.)} \\ \text{(Lower sign = F.D.)}\end{matrix} \tag{6.3–1}$$

The symbol $\boldsymbol{r}_{Pk}$ gives the position of that particle which corresponds to the permutation P applied to the kth particle. The identity permutation operator makes the argument of the exponent zero. Hence in the absence of symmetry effects $\mathscr{W}^0 = 1$, which is the value of the classical Boltzmann factor when $\Phi(\boldsymbol{r}^N) = 0$.

In a system of two particles Eq. 6.3–1 reduces to

$$\mathscr{W}^0(\boldsymbol{r}_1, \boldsymbol{r}_2) = 1 \pm e^{-2\pi r_{12}^2/\lambda^2} \qquad \begin{matrix}\text{(Upper sign = B.E.)} \\ \text{(Lower sign = F.D.)}\end{matrix} \tag{6.3–2}$$

The positive sign is to be used when the system wave function is symmetric in the interchange of the two particles, and the negative sign is to be used for antisymmetric wave functions. For the symmetric wave functions the Slater sum of two molecules as a function of the distance r_{12} rises above unity as r_{12} decreases and approaches 2 as r_{12} approaches zero—an example of the "apparent attraction" between molecules in Bose-Einstein systems. For the antisymmetric wave functions the Slater sum of the two molecules decreases with decreasing distance and approaches zero as r_{12} approaches zero. Thus the probability of finding two Fermi-Dirac molecules in exactly the same place is zero, although for the ideal gas the molecules have no extension in space (that is, there are no intermolecular forces). This is an example of the "apparent repulsion" between the molecules of the gas having antisymmetrical wave functions (that is, which satisfy the Pauli principle).

In both cases the distance over which the molecules influence each other due to the required symmetry of the wave function is of the order of magnitude of $\lambda = h/\sqrt{2\pi mkT}$. This distance is, aside from a numerical factor of the order of unity, the de Broglie wavelength associated with molecules in a system at temperature T. If the average distance between the molecules is of the order of magnitude of this de Broglie wavelength,

[3] The integration reduces to the evaluation of

$$\int_{-\infty}^{+\infty} \exp(ibx) \exp(-a^2x^2)\, dx = \frac{\sqrt{\pi}}{a} \exp(-b^2/4a^2)$$

the "symmetry effects" are of importance, and the system is said to be "degenerate" or "in a state of degeneracy."

b. The Slater sum for a perfect gas composed of molecules with non-zero spin

Thus far the atoms have been treated as mass points. It frequently occurs, however, that the atoms of a gas possess an intrinsic, constant angular momentum. This "nuclear spin" has an influence on the weights and symmetry properties of the different states.

Consider, for the sake of simplicity, a system of two identical particles, each with an angular momentum $s\hbar$. This spin can have $(2s + 1)$ different directions with respect to a fixed axis, and all these orientations have the same energy. In Boltzmann statistics, where the two spins may be chosen independently, the existence of spin merely has the effect that each state of the two-particle system is $(2s + 1)^2$-fold degenerate, and consequently the partition function is simply multiplied by this factor. In practice, we sometimes redefine the partition function (and Slater sum) by dividing it by this factor, so that the factor does not appear in any of the formulae. The spin has no influence upon the thermodynamical properties of the system. In Bose-Einstein and Fermi-Dirac statistics, however, the effect of spin may not be neglected.

The Slater sums for molecules with spin, $\mathscr{W}^{(s)}(\boldsymbol{r}_1, \boldsymbol{r}_2)$, can be expressed in terms of Slater sums for molecules without spin, $\mathscr{W}^{(0)}(\boldsymbol{r}_1, \boldsymbol{r}_2)$, in the following manner. Let us consider once again a two-particle system, but this time particles which obey Bose-Einstein statistics. The total wave function of the system must then be symmetrical with respect to the interchange of the two particles. If the particles possess no intrinsic spin, this means that the space wave function must be symmetrical. When the particles possess spin, however, it is the product of the space and spin wave functions which must be symmetrical. From the $(2s + 1)^2$ different spin functions we can form $(s + 1)(2s + 1)$ symmetrical and $s(2s + 1)$ antisymmetrical combinations. In order to form symmetrical total wave functions, the latter spin function must be multiplied by a symmetrical space function and the former by an antisymmetrical one. Hence in the expression for the Slater sum, the states with symmetrical space functions appear with weight $(s + 1)/(2s + 1)$, and the states with antisymmetrical space functions with weight $s/(2s + 1)$. In this way we obtain for Bose-Einstein particles:

$$\mathscr{W}^{(s)}_{\text{B.E.}}(\boldsymbol{r}_1, \boldsymbol{r}_2) = \left(\frac{s + 1}{2s + 1}\right) \mathscr{W}^{(0)}_{\text{B.E.}}(\boldsymbol{r}_1, \boldsymbol{r}_2) + \left(\frac{s}{2s + 1}\right) \mathscr{W}^{(0)}_{\text{F.D.}}(\boldsymbol{r}_1, \boldsymbol{r}_2) \tag{6.3–3}$$

in which the upper index on $\mathscr{W}(\boldsymbol{r}_1, \boldsymbol{r}_2)$ denotes the value of the spin quantum number, s. Similarly, for Fermi-Dirac particles:

$$\mathscr{W}^{(s)}_{\text{F.D.}}(\boldsymbol{r}_1, \boldsymbol{r}_2) = \left(\frac{s+1}{2s+1}\right) \mathscr{W}^{(0)}_{\text{F.D.}}(\boldsymbol{r}_1, \boldsymbol{r}_2) + \left(\frac{s}{2s+1}\right) \mathscr{W}^{(0)}_{\text{B.E.}}(\boldsymbol{r}_1, \boldsymbol{r}_2) \tag{6.3–4}$$

We note that if the spin angular momentum is very large, $\mathscr{W}^{(0)}_{\text{F.D.}}(\boldsymbol{r}_1, \boldsymbol{r}_2)$ and $\mathscr{W}^{(0)}_{\text{B.E.}}(\boldsymbol{r}_1, \boldsymbol{r}_2)$ are mixed in almost equal proportions, and we obtain very nearly the Slater sum for Boltzmann statistics. Qualitatively, then, the effect of the non-zero spin is to diminish the influence of the exclusion principle.

c. The equation of state for a perfect gas[4, 5]

The cluster integrals for an ideal gas may be obtained from Eq. 3.2–10, when the expression for $\mathscr{W}^0$ in Eq. 6.3–1 is used. The result is

$$b_l^0 = (\pm 1)^{l-1} l^{-5/2} \lambda^{3(l-1)} \tag{6.3–5}$$

From these cluster integrals are obtained the pressure and the number density as power series expansions in the "active number density," z, defined in § 3.2c:

$$p^0/kT = \lambda^{-3} \sum_{l=1}^{\infty} (\pm 1)^{l-1} l^{-5/2} [\lambda^3 z]^l \tag{6.3–6}$$

$$n^0 = \lambda^{-3} \sum_{l=1}^{\infty} (\pm 1)^{l-1} l^{-3/2} [\lambda^3 z]^l \tag{6.3–7}$$

In all these equations the upper sign is to be used for symmetrical eigenfunctions (Bose-Einstein statistics) and the lower for antisymmetrical eigenfunctions (Fermi-Dirac statistics).

Of particular interest is the second virial coefficient:

$$B^0(T) = -\tilde{N} b_2^0 = \mp \tilde{N} \lambda^3 2^{-5/2} = \mp \tilde{N} 2^{-5/2} \left[\frac{h^2}{2\pi mkT}\right]^{3/2}$$

(Upper sign = B.E.)

(Lower sign = F.D.) (6.3–8)

We see thus that the second virial coefficient is proportional to $(mT)^{-3/2}$ and can be important only for particles of small mass and low temperatures. For Bose-Einstein statistics, $B^0(T)$ is negative; and for Fermi-Dirac statistics, it is positive. This is consistent with the notions of apparent attraction and repulsion.

[4] B. Kahn and G. E. Uhlenbeck, *Physica*, **5**, 399 (1938).

[5] B. Kahn, Doctoral Dissertation, Utrecht (1938).

d. Bose-Einstein condensation[4–8]

Let us now examine the results in Eqs. 6.3–6 and 7 for Bose-Einstein statistics and study their behavior as the gas density is increased. At sufficiently low densities the product $\lambda^3 z$ is less than unity, and there is no question of the convergence of the two series. As the density is increased, the product $\lambda^3 z$ becomes unity, and these equations become

$$p_s^0/kT = \lambda^{-3} \sum_{l=1}^{\infty} l^{-5/2} = 1.34\lambda^{-3} \qquad (6.3\text{–}9)$$

$$n_c^0 = \lambda^{-3} \sum_{l=1}^{\infty} l^{-3/2} = 2.61\lambda^{-3} \qquad (6.3\text{–}10)$$

As the density is further increased, the product $\lambda^3 z$ becomes greater than unity, and the series diverge. According to Einstein,[8] who was the first to study this phenomenon, n_c^0 is the maximum number density which can be reached for a given temperature T. By further compression of the gas, some of the molecules "condense" into a state of zero energy and contribute neither to the pressure nor to the density of the system, the pressure remaining p_s^0. We have thus a sort of condensation phenomenon: for all temperatures there exists a number density, n_c^0, at which "condensation" begins to occur, and, associated with this, a saturation pressure, p_s^0. There is no temperature above which this condensation will not occur, as may be seen from Eqs. 6.3–9 and 10. That is to say, there is no critical point such as is associated with the condensation of real gases.

In real gas condensation the derivative $(\partial p/\partial \tilde{V})_T$ is discontinuous at the transition point. From Eqs. 6.3–6 and 7 it may be seen that for the perfect Bose-Einstein gas this derivative is

$$\left(\frac{\partial p}{\partial \tilde{V}}\right)_T = -\frac{kT}{\lambda^3 \tilde{V}} \frac{\left[\sum_{l=1}^{\infty} l^{-3/2}(\lambda^3 z)^l\right]^2}{\left[\sum_{l=1}^{\infty} l^{-1/2}(\lambda^3 z)^l\right]} \qquad (6.3\text{–}11)$$

which exhibits no discontinuity at the condensation point. For $\lambda^3 z = 1$ this derivative becomes 0 and remains so for $\lambda^3 z > 1$ because of the divergence of the series $\Sigma l^{-1/2}$. With this information we may plot the isotherms of the ideal Bose-Einstein gas which are shown in Fig. 6.3–1. We see that the p-V-T behavior of the system predicts a condensed phase with zero volume.

[6] F. London, *Phys. Rev.*, **54**, 948 (1938).

[7] F. London, *International Conference Report*, Vol. II (Physical Society, London), 1947. This is a rather complete review article on the subject, and complete references are given to the theory and applications of Bose-Einstein condensation.

[8] A. Einstein, *Berl. Ber.*, p. 261 (1924); p. 3 (1925).

Let us now examine the condensing system from the thermodynamic standpoint. First, we write the expressions for a number of thermodynamic properties and specialize them where $\lambda^3 z = 1$:

$$\tilde{A}^0 = RT \ln (z\lambda^3) - p^0\tilde{V}^0 \rightarrow p_s{}^0\tilde{V}^0$$
$$\tilde{S}^0 = \tfrac{5}{2}p^0\tilde{V}^0/T - R \ln (z\lambda^3) \rightarrow \tfrac{5}{2}(p_s{}^0\tilde{V}^0/T)$$
$$\tilde{G}^0 = RT \ln (z\lambda^3) \rightarrow 0 \qquad (6.3\text{–}12)$$
$$\tilde{U}^0 = \tfrac{3}{2}p^0\tilde{V}^0 \rightarrow \tfrac{3}{2}p_s{}^0\tilde{V}^0$$
$$\tilde{C}_v{}^0 = \tfrac{15}{4}(p^0\tilde{V}^0/T) - \tfrac{9}{4}(\tilde{N}k)\,[\Sigma(\lambda^3 z)^l l^{-3/2}]\,[\Sigma(\lambda^3 z)^l l^{-1/2}]^{-1} \rightarrow \tfrac{15}{4}(p^0\tilde{V}^0/T)$$

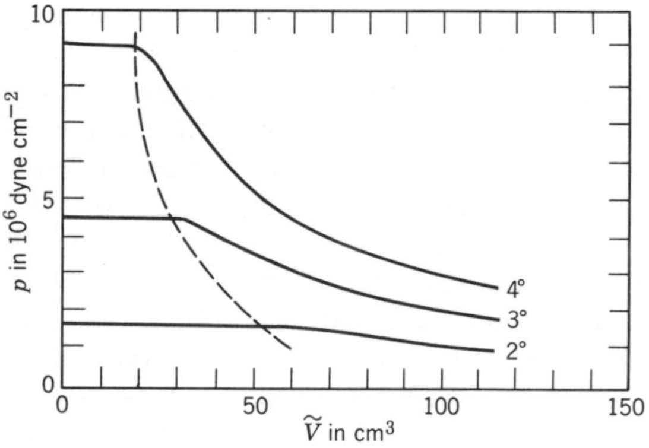

Fig. 6.3–1. Isotherms of He[4] to illustrate the behavior of the perfect Bose-Einstein gas. (From B. Kahn, Dissertation, Utrecht, 1938.)

The difference between the values of the thermodynamic quantities for the two phases are obtained from the last group of formulae by putting $\tilde{V} = \tilde{V}_c$ and $\tilde{V} = 0$ for the vapor and "liquid" phases, respectively. We see, first, that $\Delta\tilde{G}^0 = 0$, which is the thermodynamic requirement that the vapor and liquid phases be in equilibrium. From Eq. 6.3–9 it follows that

$$(dp_s{}^0/dT) = \tfrac{5}{2}(p_s{}^0/T) = \Delta\tilde{S}^0/\Delta\tilde{V}^0 \qquad (6.3\text{–}13)$$

which is consistent with the difference in entropy and volume between the liquid and vapor phases; that is, Clapeyron's equation is satisfied.

Thus we see that the thermodynamic requirements of a condensation phenomenon are satisfied. But we have seen that

(i) The volume of the condensed phase is zero.
(ii) A critical temperature does not exist.
(iii) $(\partial p/\partial \tilde{V})_T$ suffers no discontinuity at $\tilde{V} = \tilde{V}_c$.
(iv) $\tilde{C}_v$ has no discontinuity for $\tilde{V} = \tilde{V}_c$.

In these points this phenomenon differs from the condensation of real gases. The Fermi-Dirac gas does not exhibit a condensation phenomenon. In Fig. 6.3–2 the graphs of $\tilde{C}_v$ versus T for the perfect Fermi-Dirac and Bose-Einstein gases are compared.

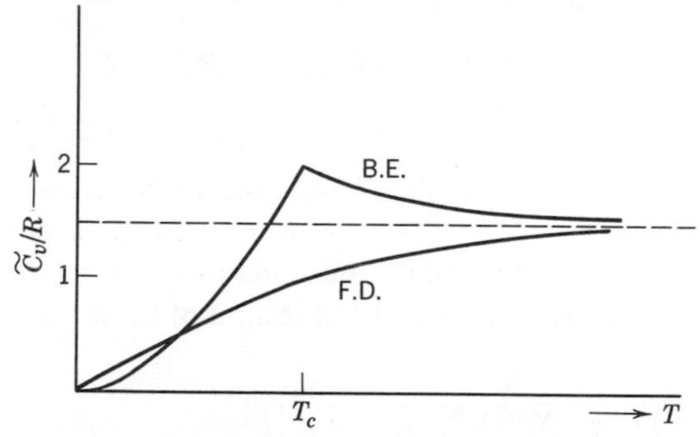

Fig. 6.3–2. Qualitative behavior of the specific heat at constant volume as a function of the temperature. The dotted line is the classical value for monatomic gases. [From J. de Boer, *Nederlands Tijdschrift voor Natuurkunde*, **16**, 89 (1950), p. 96.]

4. The Second Virial Coefficient for Real Gases at Very Low Temperatures[1]

The second virial coefficient in quantum mechanics depends on the partition function of two interacting molecules. The energy levels to be used in the partition function are obtained from the solution of the two-particle Schrödinger wave equation. Two types of solutions are obtained: solutions corresponding to the pair of molecules being trapped in the potential well as "double molecules", and solutions corresponding to the pair of molecules undergoing a collision. These two types of solutions are discussed in § 1.7 and shown in Fig. 1.7–1. In this section we show how the two-molecule partition function (and hence the second virial coefficient) can be expressed in terms of stationary energy states (corresponding to double molecules) and the "phase-shifts" in the radial wave equation (corresponding to collisions). We describe briefly the calculation of phase shifts for some simple potentials and for the Lennard-Jones potential. At the end of the section we summarize the low-temperature calculation of $B(T)$ for the isotopes of helium and hydrogen.

a. The second virial coefficients in terms of phase shifts and stationary states

The second virial coefficient in classical statistical mechanics is given in Eq. 3.4–5 in terms of the classical partition function. It has been

[1] A knowledge of the quantum mechanics of two-body systems and the quantum theory of binary collisions is needed for the understanding of this section. This information has been given in the introductory chapter in § 1.7.

mentioned that this formula is also valid in the quantum mechanical theory of the equation of state when the classical partition functions, Z_1 and Z_2, are replaced by the quantum mechanical partition functions, Z_{1q} and Z_{2q}. Accordingly, we may write for the non-ideal gas and for the ideal gas (in which $\Phi(\boldsymbol{r}^N) = 0$):

$$\text{Non-ideal:}\quad B(T) = -(\tilde{N}/2V)\lambda^6[2Z_{2q} - Z_{1q}^{\ 2}] \tag{6.4–1}$$

$$\text{Ideal:}\quad B^0(T) = -(\tilde{N}/2V)\lambda^6[2Z_{2q}^{\ 0} - (Z_{1q}^{\ 0})^2] \tag{6.4–2}$$

in which $\lambda^2 = h^2/2\pi mkT$. Z_{1q} is the sum-over-states for a single molecule and is the same as $Z_{1q}^{\ 0}$. Z_{2q} is the sum-over-states for a pair of interacting molecules; $Z_{2q}^{\ 0}$ is the analogous quantity for a pair of non-interacting molecules. Subtraction of the second of these equations from the first gives

$$\begin{aligned} B(T) - B^0(T) &= -(\tilde{N}/V)\lambda^6[Z_{2q} - Z_{2q}^{\ 0}] \\ &= -(\tilde{N}/V)\lambda^6[\Sigma_\sigma e^{-E_\sigma/kT} - \Sigma_\sigma e^{-E_\sigma{}^0/kT}] \end{aligned} \tag{6.4–3}$$

The E_σ are the eigenstates of a two-molecule system with molecular interaction $\varphi(r)$ and the $E_\sigma^{\ 0}$ are the eigenstates when $\varphi(r) = 0$. Each eigenstate is characterized by a set of six quantum numbers, $\{\sigma\}$.

As described in § 1.7, the wave function for a system of two particles may be written as a product of a translational wave function (representing the overall translatory motion of the system) and the wave function for the relative motion:

$$\begin{aligned} \Psi(\boldsymbol{r}_1, \boldsymbol{r}_2) &= \psi^{(\text{tr})}(\boldsymbol{r}_c)\psi^{(\text{rel})}(\boldsymbol{r}_{12}) \\ &= \psi^{(\text{tr})}(\boldsymbol{r}_c)\psi_{nl}(r_{12})\, Y_l^{\,m}(\theta, \phi) \end{aligned} \tag{6.4–4}$$

Here $\boldsymbol{r}_c = \frac{1}{2}(\boldsymbol{r}_1 + \boldsymbol{r}_2)$ is the coordinate of the center of mass, and $\boldsymbol{r}_{12} = (\boldsymbol{r}_1 - \boldsymbol{r}_2)$ is the coordinate of relative motion. The wave function of relative motion has been separated into a radial wave function, ψ_{nl}, and an angular part, $Y_l^{\,m}$, the latter being the spherical harmonics. Writing the wave function as a product corresponds to writing the energy as a sum:

$$E = E^{(\text{tr})} + E^{(\text{rel})} \tag{6.4–5}$$

Hence the sums-over-states in Eq. 6.4–3 can be written

$$Z_{2q} = Z_2^{(\text{tr})}\, \Sigma_{n,l,m} e^{-E_{nlm}/kT} = 2^{3/2} V\lambda^{-3}\, \Sigma_l(2l+1)\, \Sigma_n e^{-E_{nl}/kT} \tag{6.4–6}$$

$$Z_{2q}^{\ 0} = Z_2^{(\text{tr})}\, \Sigma_{n,l,m} e^{-E^0_{nlm}/kT} = 2^{3/2} V\lambda^{-3}\, \Sigma_l(2l+1)\, \Sigma_n e^{-E_{nl}{}^0/kT} \tag{6.4–7}$$

Here we have inserted the proper expression for the translational partition function from Eq. 2.5–28. The factor $2^{3/2}$ appears since we are dealing with a system of mass $2m$. The energy levels of the relative motion do not depend upon the quantum number m, but the existence of these states must be taken into account in the partition function by giving each state a multiplicity $(2l + 1)$ as has been done in these last two equations. The state of the two-molecule system is then specified by the two quantum numbers, n and l, which give the energy and angular momentum of the system.

Substitution of these expressions for the partition functions into the expression for the second virial coefficient gives

$$[B(T) - B^0(T)] = -\tilde{N}2^{3/2}\lambda^3\Sigma_l(2l+1)[\Sigma_n e^{-E_{nl}/kT} - \Sigma_n e^{-E_{nl}^0/kT}] \tag{6.4–8}$$

The contributions to the sums over n may now be separated into those due to the negative energy states and those due to the positive energy states: The *negative energy spectrum* is discrete and represents "double molecule" formation with discrete levels. There is, of course, no contribution of this sort for non-interacting molecules, and hence the second summation over n in Eq. 6.4–8 can be ignored. The sum over n becomes simply

$$\Sigma_n e^{-E_{nl}^-/kT} \tag{6.4–9}$$

The values of the discrete negative energy states E_{nl}^- are obtained from the solution of the radial wave equation for $\psi_{nl}(r_{12})$. The *positive energy spectrum* is continuous and arises from the transitory collisions between two molecules. The energy of relative motion is just the relative kinetic energy of a system of reduced mass μ: $E = p^2/2\mu = \hbar^2\kappa^2/2\mu$. The summations over n have then to be replaced by integrations over κ; hence the term in the square bracket on the right-hand side of Eq. 6.4–8 becomes

$$\int e^{-\hbar^2\kappa^2/2\mu kT}\left[\left(\frac{dn}{d\kappa}\right) - \left(\frac{dn}{d\kappa}\right)^0\right] d\kappa = \int e^{-\hbar^2\kappa^2/2\mu kT}\left[\frac{1}{\pi}\frac{d\eta_l(\kappa)}{d\kappa}\right] d\kappa \tag{6.4–10}$$

Equation 1.7–14 has been used to introduce the phase shifts, $\eta_l(\kappa)$, which are determined from the solution of the radial wave equation for positive energies.

The final quantum mechanical expression for the second virial coefficient is obtained by combining the last three relations:

$$\begin{aligned} B(T) = {} & \pm\tilde{N}2^{-5/2}\lambda^3 \\ & -\tilde{N}2^{+3/2}\lambda^3\,\Sigma_l(2l+1)\,\Sigma_n e^{-E_{nl}^-/kT} \\ & -\tilde{N}2^{+3/2}\lambda^3\,\Sigma_l(2l+1)\int e^{-\hbar^2\kappa^2/2\mu kT}\left[\frac{1}{\pi}\frac{d\eta_l(\kappa)}{d\kappa}\right] d\kappa \end{aligned} \tag{6.4–11}$$

Here we have written out the expression for $B^0(T)$ explicitly, which was obtained in Eq. 6.3–8. The minus sign is to be used for Bose-Einstein statistics and the plus sign for Fermi-Dirac statistics. It should also be pointed out that in the summations over l, only the even l-values are used in Bose-Einstein statistics and only odd l-values are used in Fermi-Dirac statistics.[2]

We see in Eq. 6.4–11 that the expression for $B(T)$ consists of three parts, each of which has a definite physical significance. The first term shows how the "apparent attraction" (or repulsion) decreases (or increases) the pressure in the gas. The second contribution shows how the pressure is diminished by the formation of double molecules. The integral over κ indicates the contributions to non-ideality resulting from bimolecular collisions in the gas.

The results up to this point are valid only for molecules with zero spin. For molecules with spin, s, we must write [analogously to Eqs. 6.3–3 and 4]:

$$B^{(s)}_{\text{B.E.}} = \left[\frac{s+1}{2s+1}\right] B^{(0)}_{\text{B.E.}} + \left[\frac{s}{2s+1}\right] B^{(0)}_{\text{F.D.}} \tag{6.4–12}$$

$$B^{(s)}_{\text{F.D.}} = \left[\frac{s+1}{2s+1}\right] B^{(0)}_{\text{F.D.}} + \left[\frac{s}{2s+1}\right] B^{(0)}_{\text{B.E.}} \tag{6.4–13}$$

The $B^{(0)}$ are those calculated for zero spin, that is, from Eq. 6.4–11. In § 6.4c the second virial coefficient of He^3 is discussed. This atom has an odd number of nucleons and a spin of $\frac{1}{2}$, and hence Eq. 6.4–13 must be used.

b. Phase shifts for simple potentials

The phase shifts needed for the calculation of the second virial coefficient have been obtained formally in Eq. 1.7–10. In order to make calculations of phase shifts it is necessary to specify the intermolecular potential function in the radial wave equation. It is not in general possible to obtain analytical expressions for the phase shifts in terms of the intermolecular potential. However, solutions in closed form may easily be obtained for rigid spheres and for the square-well potential (for $l = 0$). From the results of calculations based on these simple potentials, a certain amount of insight may be obtained about the nature of the phase shifts.

[2] The reason for this is as follows: When we sum over the states of relative motion in Eq, 6.4–8 only those states are to be included for which the eigenfunctions are either symmetrical or antisymmetrical in the interchange of the two particles. Interchanging of the particles means replacement of ϕ by $(\phi + \pi)$ and of θ by $(\pi - \theta)$. The angular part of the wave function, Y_l^m, remains unchanged under this substitution for even l, but changes sign for odd l. Hence for Bose-Einstein particles we sum over the even l-states and for Fermi-Dirac particles we sum over the odd l-states.

i. *Rigid Spheres*

Since for rigid spheres of collision diameter σ the potential is zero for $r > \sigma$, we may use Eq. 1.7–8 for the radial wave function in this region. The ratio $[B_l(\kappa)/A_l(\kappa)]$ may be determined from the boundary condition that $\sigma\psi(\sigma) = 0$. Hence, according to Eq. 1.7–10, the phase shifts are given by

$$\eta_l(\kappa) = \arctan\left[(-1)^{l+1}\frac{J_{l+1/2}(\kappa\sigma)}{J_{-l-1/2}(\kappa\sigma)}\right] \tag{6.4–14}$$

which for $l = 0$ reduces to $\eta_0(\kappa) = -\kappa\sigma$. The phase shifts for rigid spheres are shown graphically in Fig. 6.4–1. That the phase shift for rigid spheres should always be negative can easily be understood by considering its geometrical meaning. Also $d\eta_l/d\kappa$ is everywhere negative, which makes the density of energy states in the partition function of two interacting molecules everywhere smaller than that of the non-interacting molecules. This, in turn, makes the contribution of the interaction to the second virial coefficient positive as may be seen from Eqs. 6.4–10 and 11. Introduction of Eq. 6.4–14 into Eq. 6.4–11 gives the following expressions for the reduced second virial coefficients $B^\star = B/\frac{2}{3}\pi\tilde{N}\sigma^3$ for Bose-Einstein and Fermi-Dirac statistics:[3]

$$B^\star_{\text{B.E.}} = -\frac{3\sqrt{2}}{16\pi}\left(\frac{\lambda}{\sigma}\right)^3 + \frac{3}{\pi}\left(\frac{\lambda}{\sigma}\right)^2 - 22\pi\left(\frac{\sigma}{\lambda}\right)^2 + O\left[\left(\frac{\sigma}{\lambda}\right)^6\right] \tag{6.4–15}$$

$$B^\star_{\text{F.D.}} = +\frac{3\sqrt{2}}{16\pi}\left(\frac{\lambda}{\sigma}\right)^3 + 9 + \frac{1921\pi^2}{15}\left(\frac{\sigma}{\lambda}\right)^4 + O\left[\left(\frac{\sigma}{\lambda}\right)^8\right] \tag{6.4–16}$$

From this it may be seen that when the de Broglie wavelength (approximately given by $\lambda = h/\sqrt{2\pi mkT}$) is greater than the diameter of the molecules the predominant contribution is that due to statistics.

ii. *Square-Well Potential*

Let us now consider the square-well potential of Eq. 1.3–24, with $R = \frac{3}{2}$. For this potential we wish to find a solution to the radial wave equation (Eq. 1.7–3) which describes the relative motion of two particles with relative energy E and with $l = 0$. Since the wave function must vanish at $r = \sigma$, the solution may be written as

$$r\psi(r) = A\sin\kappa'(r - \sigma) \qquad \sigma < r < \tfrac{3}{2}\sigma \tag{6.4–17}$$

$$r\psi(r) = B\sin(\kappa r + \eta_0) \qquad r > \tfrac{3}{2}\sigma \tag{6.4–18}$$

where

$$\hbar^2\kappa^2 = 2\mu E \qquad \hbar^2\kappa'^2 = 2\mu(E + \epsilon) \tag{6.4–19}$$

[3] J. de Boer, Doctoral Dissertation, University of Amsterdam (1940).

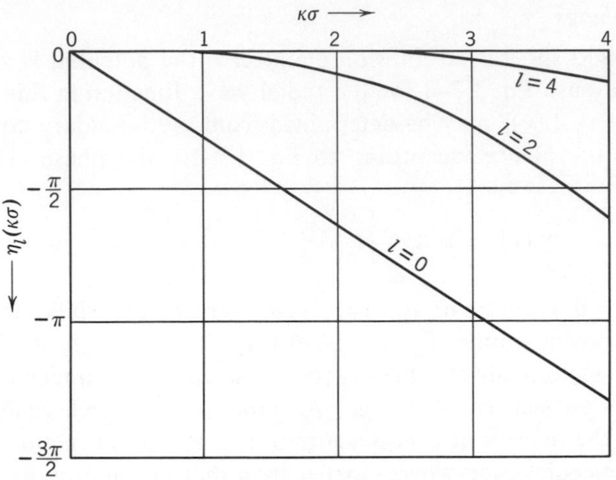

Fig. 6.4–1. Phase shifts for rigid spheres. (From J. de Boer, Dissertation, Amsterdam, 1940, p. 53.)

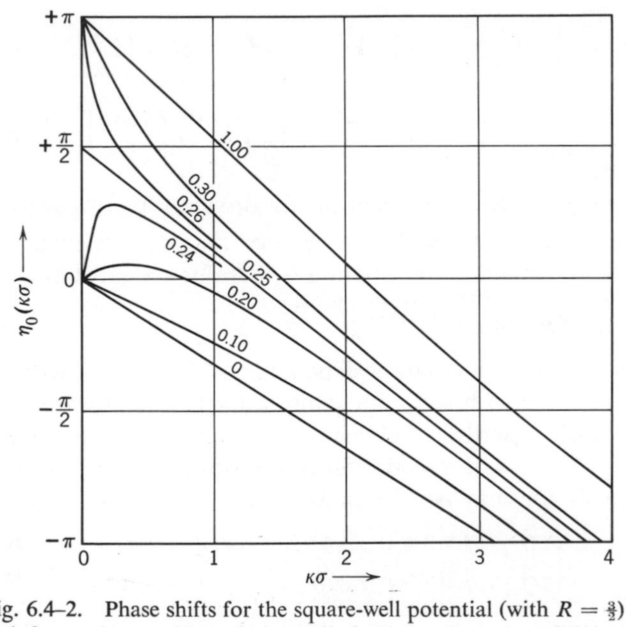

Fig. 6.4–2. Phase shifts for the square-well potential (with $R = \frac{3}{2}$) for $l = 0$, and for various values of the well depth, ϵ (in units of $h^2/m\sigma^2$). $\epsilon = 0$ corresponds to the rigid-sphere model. (From J. de Boer, Dissertation, Amsterdam, 1940, p. 55.)

in which ϵ is the depth of the square potential well. The requirement that $r\psi(r)$ and $d(r\psi(r))/dr$ be continuous at $r = \frac{3}{2}\sigma$ leads directly to

$$\eta_0(\kappa) = \arctan\left[\frac{\kappa}{\kappa'}\tan\frac{\kappa'\sigma}{2}\right] - \tfrac{3}{2}\kappa\sigma \qquad (6.4\text{–}20)$$

The phase shifts as functions of $\kappa\sigma$ are given graphically in Fig. 6.4–2 for various values of the depth of the potential well.

In Fig. 6.4–2 we may examine the behavior of the phases as we increase the depth of the well. When the depth of the well, ϵ, is less than $\frac{1}{4}h^2/m\sigma^2$, the phase shift curves begin at zero at $\kappa\sigma = 0$. When the well depth is between $\frac{1}{4}h^2/m\sigma^2$ and $\frac{9}{4}h^2/m\sigma^2$ the phase shift curves have the value π at $\kappa\sigma = 0$. In general the phase shifts at $\kappa\sigma = 0$ jump discontinuously to a value π larger, when $[\tan \kappa'\sigma/2]_{E=0} = \infty$ or $\epsilon = (n - \frac{1}{2})^2h^2/m\sigma^2$. It may be shown that at these values of ϵ a discrete level exists just exactly at the brim of the square well (that is, at $E = 0$). Hence the behavior of the phases at $\kappa\sigma = 0$ may be useful for ascertaining whether one or more discrete levels exist for the colliding pair of molecules.

Another interesting thing may be deduced from Fig. 6.4–2. It can there be seen that, with increasing depth of the potential well, the phases become more and more positive for low-energy collisions. That is, under these circumstances there is great deviation from the rigid-sphere behavior because the interacting system feels the dip in the potential. For high-energy collisions the system does not feel the potential hole so strongly, and the phase shifts approach those of rigid spheres, as would be expected.

c. Calculations for the Lennard-Jones potential

For potential functions which are more realistic than those just discussed, the phase shifts must be evaluated by numerical integration of the radial wave equation (Eq. 1.7–3), starting from the boundary condition that $r\psi(r) = 0$ for $r = 0$. The integration must be extended up to the region for which the potential energy is essentially zero. In this region we know that the wave function has the form given in Eq. 1.7–8. Hence, by joining the wave function obtained by numerical integration smoothly with that given in Eq. 1.7–8, the values of the coefficients $A_l(\kappa)$ and $B_l(\kappa)$ may be determined. From these coefficients the phase shifts may be calculated from Eq. 1.7–10. For each value of l this procedure must be carried out for a considerable number of values of κ.

For the Lennard-Jones (6-12) potential, the radial wave equation, Eq. 1.7–3, may be written in the reduced form:

$$\frac{d^2}{dr^{*2}}(r^*\psi) + \left[\kappa^{*2} - \frac{l(l+1)}{r^{*2}} - \frac{16\pi^2}{\Lambda^{*2}}\left(\frac{1}{r^{*12}} - \frac{1}{r^{*6}}\right)\right](r^*\psi) = 0 \quad (6.4\text{–}21)$$

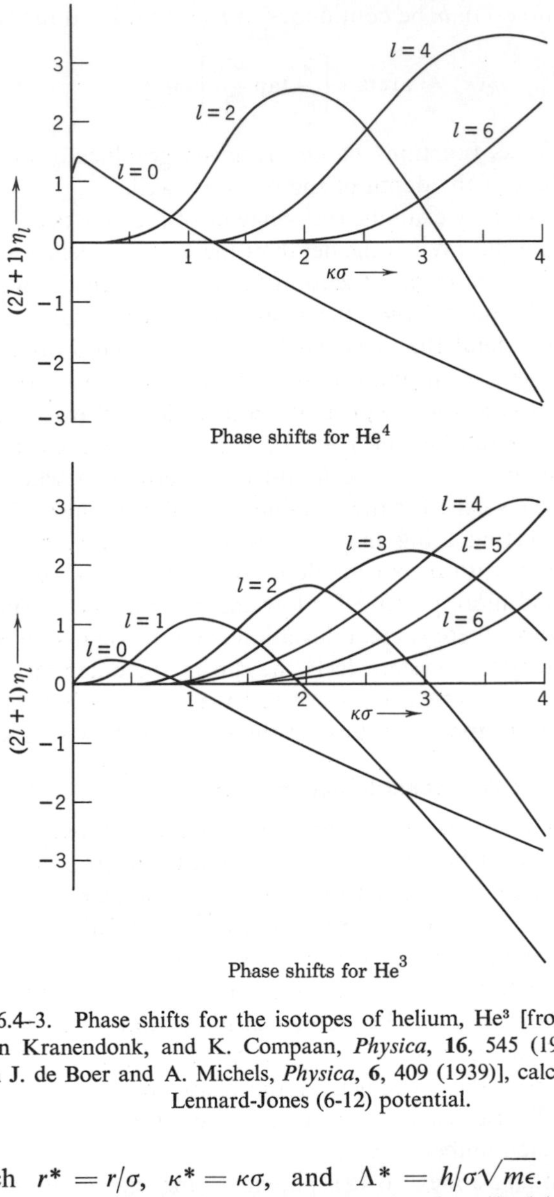

Phase shifts for He^4

Phase shifts for He^3

Fig. 6.4–3. Phase shifts for the isotopes of helium, He^3 [from J. de Boer, J. van Kranendonk, and K. Compaan, *Physica*, **16**, 545 (1950)] and He^4 [from J. de Boer and A. Michels, *Physica*, **6**, 409 (1939)], calculated for the Lennard-Jones (6-12) potential.

in which $r^* = r/\sigma$, $\kappa^* = \kappa\sigma$, and $\Lambda^* = h/\sigma\sqrt{m\epsilon}$. The collisions between particles of any chemical species are described by the differential equation above. The value of Λ^* varies, of course, from substance to substance. This is consistent with the principle of corresponding states which is discussed in § 6.6. The method for determining the parameter

Λ^* is given in § 6.5c, and a tabulation of values of Λ^* for various substances is given in Table 6.5–2.

Extensive calculations of phase shifts have been made for He^3 for the Lennard-Jones potential[4] and for He^4 for several potential fields.[5–7] Since He^4 has an even number of nucleons and electrons and zero spin, only phase shifts with even l need be calculated. For He^3, which has an odd number of nucleons and electrons and spin $\frac{1}{2}$, phase shifts for both even and odd l are required. The phase shifts for the helium isotopes are shown in Fig. 6.4–3, and a complete tabulation of calculated results is given in Tables I–F and I–G.

These results may now be interpreted in the light of the discussion of the results for the rigid-sphere and square-well models. For both He^3 and He^4 the phase shifts resemble the rigid-sphere behavior for high energies. They do not approach the rigid-sphere phase shifts asymptotically inasmuch as the Lennard-Jones potential allows for a certain amount of penetration at high relative energies. The positive phase shifts result from the attractive part of the potential. From the behavior of the phase shifts for He^3 as $\kappa\sigma$ approaches zero, it is evident that no stationary states exist for two interacting He^3 atoms. For He^4, on the other hand, it is difficult to decide whether or not there is a discrete level very near to $E = 0$. It is rather probable that no discrete level exists[8] for the particular form of the potential chosen, but a slight alteration of this potential might well bring one into existence.

From these phase shifts the second virial coefficients of the isotopes of helium have been calculated for very low temperatures. It is only for temperatures below about $T^* = 1$ that the sums over l in Eq. 6.4–11 converge sufficiently rapidly to make the series suitable for numerical calculation. For He^4, a Bose-Einstein gas with zero spin, we use Eq. 6.4–11. For He^3, a Fermi-Dirac gas with spin $\frac{1}{2}$, we use Eq. 6.4–13. The calculated results for the Lennard-Jones potential are given for both gases in Table 6.4–1. The same results are also given graphically in Fig. 6.4–4, where the available experimental data for He^4 are plotted.

[4] J. de Boer, J. van Kranendonk, and K. Compaan, *Physica*, **16**, 545 (1950).

[5] J. de Boer and A. Michels, *Physica*, **6**, 409 (1939). Calculations based on the Lennard-Jones (6-12) potential.

[6] H. S. W. Massey and R. A. Buckingham, *Proc. Roy. Soc.* (*London*), **A168**, 378 (1938); *ibid.*, **A169**, 205 (1939). Calculations based on the Buckingham potential.

[7] R. A. Buckingham, J. Hamilton, and H. S. W. Massey, *Proc. Roy. Soc.* (*London*), **A179**, 103 (1941). Calculations based on the Buckingham-Corner potential.

[8] For a discussion of the discrete energy levels associated with the Lennard-Jones (6-12) potential, see J. E. and M. F. Kilpatrick, *J. Chem. Phys.*, **19**, 930 (1951).

TABLE 6.4–1

CALCULATED SECOND VIRIAL COEFFICIENTS FOR THE ISOTOPES OF HELIUM AT VERY LOW TEMPERATURE[3]

(Lennard-Jones (6-12) Potential)

T (°K)	$B(T)$ (He^3)	$B(T)$ (He^4)
0.51	−293.0	−1066
1.02	−199.3	−389
2.04	−113.5	−164
3.07	−76.52	−101
4.09	−56.70	−71.6
5.11	−44.24	−54.1
6.13	−35.67	−42.4
7.15	−29.35	−34.2

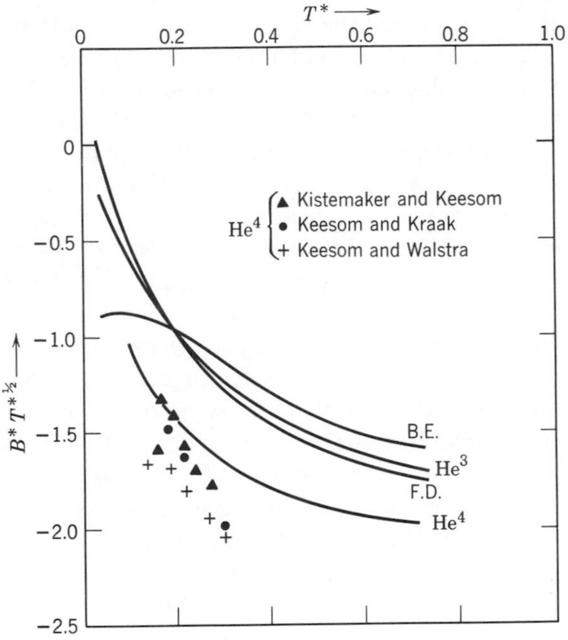

Fig. 6.4–4. Quantum mechanical low-temperature calculations of the second virial coefficients of He^4 and He^3. The Bose-Einstein and Fermi-Dirac contributions to the second virial coefficient of He^3 are also shown. [The calculated curves are from J. de Boer, J. van Kranendonk, and K. Compaan, *Physica*, **16**, 545 (1950). The sources of the experimental data are: J. Kistemaker and W. H. Keesom, *Physica*, **12**, 227 (1946); W. H. Keesom and H. H. Kraak, *Physica*, **2**, 37 (1935); W. H. Keesom and W. K. Walstra; *Physica*, **6**, 1146 (1939)].

In Fig. 6.4–5 we compare the various calculations which have been made for He^4. This enables us to get some idea of the sensitivity of $B(T)$ at low temperatures to the form of the intermolecular potential function. In order to make a comparison of the results for these various potential fields, a Lennard-Jones (6-12) potential has been selected for each of them which fits the potential curve as closely as possible. The values of the constants, σ and ϵ, so determined for these potential fields are shown in

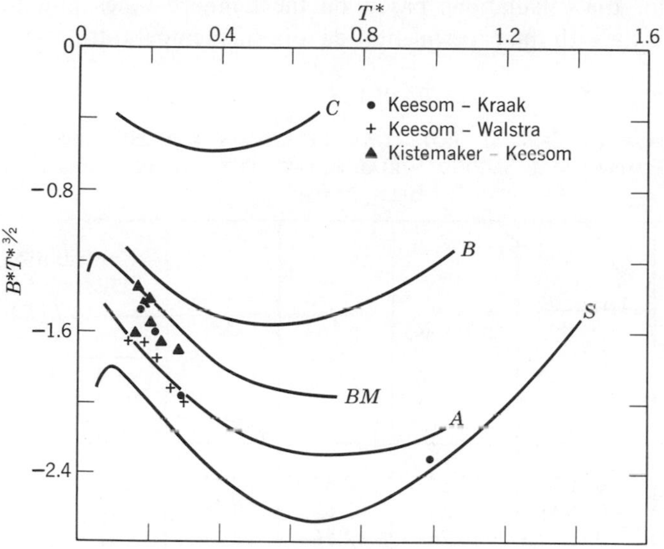

Fig. 6.4–5. Comparison of the various low-temperature second virial coefficient calculations for He^4. [This figure is taken from J. de Boer, *Reports on Progress in Physics*, **12**, 305 (1949). The sources of the experimental data are given in Fig. 6.4–4.]

Curve BM: (Calculation of de Boer and Michels.[5]) Lennard-Jones (6-12) potential with the parameters, σ and ϵ, so adjusted as to give experimental second virial coefficients in the high-temperature range, where quantum effects are small.

Curve S: (Calculation of Massey and Buckingham.[6]) Potential function 1.3 times as large as that calculated theoretically by Slater, being of the form:

$$\varphi(r) = b \exp(-ar) - c/r^6$$

with $b = 10^{-9}$ erg, $c = 1.91 \times 10^{-12}$ erg Å^6 and $a = 4.60$ Å^{-1}.

Curve A: (Calculation of Buckingham, Hamilton, and Massey.[7]) Potential function including a term for the induced-dipole–induced-quadrupole interaction:

$$\varphi(r) = b \exp(-ar) - cr^{-6} - c'r^{-8}$$

with $b = 9.77 \times 10^{-10}$ erg, $c = 1.50 \times 10^{-12}$ erg Å^6, $c' = 2.51 \times 10^{-12}$ erg Å^8, and $a = 4.60$ Å^{-1}.

Curve B: (Calculation of Buckingham, Hamilton, and Massey.[7]) Same potential function as used for curve *A*, with the constants multiplied by a factor 0.83. This leaves the minimum of the potential curve in the same place and changes the depth.

Curve C: (Calculation of Buckingham, Hamilton, and Massey.[7]) Same potential function as used for curve *A*, with the constants multiplied by 0.67.

Table 6.4–2,[9] where various features of these potential functions are compared. With the values of these force constants Λ^* may be calculated. In the table is also given information about the stationary states found for the various potential functions, and their contributions to the virial coefficients at 1°K and 7°K. It seems from this analysis of the data that it would be necessary to decrease Λ^* for He^4 by about 5 per cent in order for the calculations based on the Lennard-Jones potential to agree perfectly with the experimental data in this temperature region.

TABLE 6.4–2

COMPARISON OF SEVERAL POTENTIAL FUNCTIONS FOR He^4 FOR WHICH LOW-TEMPERATURE SECOND VIRIAL COEFFICIENT CALCULATIONS HAVE BEEN MADE[9]

Curve of Fig. 6.4–5	Discrete Level, E^-/ϵ	(ϵ/k) (°K)	σ (Å)	Λ^*	Contribution of Discrete Level to $B(T)$	
					at 1°K	at 7°K
S	−0.0058	11.84	2.62	2.42	12%	1.3%
A	−0.0004	10.64	2.62	2.56	1%	0.1%
BM	0	10.24	2.56	2.67	—	—
B	—	8.87	2.62	2.80	—	—
C	—	7.10	2.62	3.14	—	—

Low-temperature calculations of the second virial coefficient have also been made for hydrogen and deuterium by Miyako.[10] His calculations are based on the monatomic gas theory discussed thus far and hence the effects of the quantized rotational states are not taken into account. Miyako has, however, taken into account the fact that hydrogen molecules exist in ortho and para states. This means that the gas must be considered as a binary mixture of two types of hydrogen molecules, and consequently symmetry requirements are applicable only to a certain fraction of the total number of collisions.[11] The calculated values are not in very good agreement with the experimental values, perhaps because the nature of the rotational quantum effects was not considered exactly. A brief discussion of these rotational quantum effects is given in § 6.7.

[9] J. de Boer, *Reports on Progress in Physics*, **12**, 305 (1949).
[10] R. Miyako, *Proc. Phys. Math. Soc. Japan* (Ser. 3), **24**, 852 (1942).
[11] O. Halpern and E. Gwathmey, *Phys. Rev.*, **52**, 944 (1937).

5. The Second Virial Coefficient for Real Gases at "Intermediate Temperatures"

In the last section it was shown how the quantum mechanical expression for the second virial coefficient given in Eq. 6.4–11 has been used for the computation of the equation of state at *very low temperatures.* In Chapter 3 the classical expression for the second virial coefficient was derived, which is valid for *high temperatures.* We now wish to discuss the behavior of the equation of state in that *intermediate temperature* region for which the quantum deviations from classical behavior are small. We show that the quantum mechanical second virial coefficient may be written as the classical mechanical second virial coefficient plus a correction term.

It was pointed out in § 1.6e that the WKB method is convenient to use when a system deviates only slightly from classical behavior. The first WKB approximation gives exactly the classical result, the second WKB approximation gives the first quantum correction, and so forth. Kahn[1] applied this method to the calculation of the discrete negative energy states E_{nl}^- and the phase shifts $\eta_l(\kappa)$ of Eq. 6.4–11. He was thus able to obtain the correct classical limiting expression for the second virial coefficient and also the first quantum correction. We do not present a discussion of this approach here, inasmuch as the same expression for the quantum corrections to $B(T)$ may be obtained more simply from Eq. 6.1–20, which gives the quantum deviations of the Slater sum. Furthermore, the use of the WKB technique is described in detail in connection with the quantum deviations of the transport properties in Chapter 10.

a. General expressions for the quantum deviations of the second virial[2]

The second virial coefficient in classical statistical mechanics is given in Eq. 3.4–5 in terms of the Boltzmann factor, $W_2(\boldsymbol{r}_1, \boldsymbol{r}_2)$. It has been pointed out that this formula is also true in the quantum mechanical theory of the equation of state when the Boltzmann factor is replaced by its quantum mechanical analog, the Slater sum, $\mathscr{W}_2(\boldsymbol{r}_1, \boldsymbol{r}_2)$. Accordingly, we may write for the non-ideal gas and for the ideal gas:

$$\text{Non-ideal:}\quad B(T) = -(\tilde{N}/2V)\iint [\mathscr{W}_2(\boldsymbol{r}_1, \boldsymbol{r}_2) - 1]\, d\boldsymbol{r}_1\, d\boldsymbol{r}_2 \qquad (6.5\text{–}1a)$$

$$\text{Ideal:}\quad B^0(T) = -(\tilde{N}/2V)\iint [\mathscr{W}_2^0(\boldsymbol{r}_1, \boldsymbol{r}_2) - 1]\, d\boldsymbol{r}_1\, d\boldsymbol{r}_2 \qquad (6.5\text{–}1b)$$

[1] B. Kahn, Dissertation, Utrecht (1938), Ch. IV, Sections 6 and 7.
[2] G. E. Uhlenbeck and E. Beth, *Physica*, **3**, 729 (1936).

Subtraction of the second of these equations from the first and integration over the coordinates of one molecule gives

$$[B(T) - B^0(T)] = -(\tilde{N}/2) \int [\mathscr{W}_2(\mathbf{r}_{12}) - \mathscr{W}_2^0(\mathbf{r}_{12})]\, d\mathbf{r}_{12} \qquad (6.5\text{–}2)$$

When the expression given in Eq. 6.1–20 for the Slater sum is written for two particles and substituted into this last equation, the second virial coefficient assumes the form[3]

$$B(T) = \left[B_{\text{cl}}(T) + \left(\frac{h^2}{m}\right) B_{\text{I}}(T) + \left(\frac{h^2}{m}\right)^2 B_{\text{II}}(T) + \cdots\right] \mp \left(\frac{h^2}{m}\right)^{3/2} B_0(T) \qquad (6.5\text{–}3)$$

in which

$$B_{\text{cl}}(T) = -2\pi\tilde{N} \int_0^\infty [e^{-\varphi(r)/kT} - 1]\, r^2\, dr \qquad (6.5\text{–}4)$$

$$B_{\text{I}}(T) = +2\pi\tilde{N} \left(\frac{1}{48\pi^2k^3T^3}\right) \int_0^\infty e^{-\varphi(r)/kT} \varphi'^2 r^2\, dr \qquad (6.5\text{–}5)$$

$$B_{\text{II}}(T) = -2\pi\tilde{N}\left(\frac{1}{1920\pi^4k^4T^4}\right) \int_0^\infty e^{-\varphi(r)/kT} \times \left[\varphi''^2 + \frac{2}{r^2}\varphi'^2 + \frac{10}{9kT}\frac{1}{r}\varphi'^3 - \frac{5}{36k^2T^2}\varphi'^4\right] r^2\, dr \qquad (6.5\text{–}6)$$

$B_{\text{cl}}(T)$ is just the ordinary classical expression for the second virial coefficient and $B^0(T) = \mp\left(\frac{h^2}{m}\right)^{3/2} B_0(T)$ is the second virial coefficient of the ideal gas as obtained in Eq. 6.3–8.

b. Series expressions for the quantum deviations of $B(T)$ (Lennard-Jones potential)[4, 5]

It was shown in § 3.6a that the expression for $B_{\text{cl}}(T)$ for the Lennard-Jones potential could be expanded in a rapidly converging infinite series of gamma-functions. A similar development may be made for the functions $B_{\text{I}}(T)$ and $B_{\text{II}}(T)$. Using ϵ/k and $b_0 = \frac{2}{3}\pi\tilde{N}\sigma^3$ for reducing the temperature and the contributions to $B(T)$, we get for the Lennard-Jones potential

$$B^\star = [B_{\text{cl}}^\star + \Lambda^{*2}B_{\text{I}}^\star + \Lambda^{*4}B_{\text{II}}^\star + \cdots] \mp \Lambda^{*3}B_0^\star \qquad (6.5\text{–}7)$$

[3] When this substitution is made, only the terms in the first set of braces in Eq. 6.1–20 are used.

[4] J. de Boer, Dissertation, Amsterdam (1940).

[5] J. de Boer and A. Michels, *Physica*, **5**, 945 (1938).

in which

$$B_{cl}^{\star}(T^*) = \sum_{j=0}^{\infty} b^{(j)} T^{*-(3+6j)/12} \tag{6.5–8}$$

$$B_{I}^{\star}(T^*) = \sum_{j=0}^{\infty} b_{I}^{(j)} T^{*-(13+6j)/12} \tag{6.5–9}$$

$$B_{II}^{\star}(T^*) = \sum_{j=0}^{\infty} b_{II}^{(j)} T^{*-(23+6j)/12} \tag{6.5–10}$$

$$B_{0}^{\star}(T^*) = \left(\frac{3}{32\pi^{5/2}}\right) T^{*-3/2} \tag{6.5–11}$$

The expansion coefficients $b^{(j)}$, $b_{I}^{(j)}$, and $b_{II}^{(j)}$ are given by[5]

$$b^{(j)} = -\left(\frac{2^{j+\frac{3}{6}}}{4j!}\right) \Gamma\left(\frac{6j-3}{12}\right) \tag{6.5–12}$$

$$b_{I}^{(j)} = -\left(\frac{11-36j}{768\pi^2}\right)\left(\frac{2^{j+\frac{13}{6}}}{j!}\right) \Gamma\left(\frac{6j-1}{12}\right) \tag{6.5–13}$$

$$b_{II}^{(j)} = -\left(\frac{767+4728j+3024j^2}{491520\pi^4}\right)\left(\frac{2^{j+\frac{23}{6}}}{j!}\right) \Gamma\left(\frac{6j+1}{12}\right) \tag{6.5–14}$$

Values of the $b^{(j)}$, $b_{I}^{(j)}$, and $b_{II}^{(j)}$ are tabulated in Table I–E. The functions $B_{cl}^{\star}$, $B_{I}^{\star}$, $B_{II}^{\star}$, and $B_{0}^{\star}$ are given in Table 6.5–1.[6]

The quantity Λ^* which appears in the above expressions is the de Broglie wavelength of the relative motion of two molecules, with relative kinetic energy ϵ, divided by the collision diameter σ:

$$\Lambda^* = \Lambda/\sigma = h/\sigma\sqrt{m\epsilon} \tag{6.5–15}$$

Hence we see that the reduced second virial coefficient depends not only on the reduced temperature T^* but also on the value of the quantum mechanical parameter Λ^*. This is in agreement with the quantum mechanical principle of corresponding states, which is discussed in detail in the next section. The larger the value of Λ^* for a substance, the greater the quantum deviations in the bulk properties.

[6] R. J. Lunbeck, Doctoral Dissertation, Amsterdam (1951). The quantities $B_{cl}^{\star}$, $B_{I}^{\star}$, $B_{II}^{\star}$ are related to the corresponding quantities B_{cl}^{*}, B_{I}^{*}, B_{II}^{*} used by de Boer and Lunbeck by the equation $B^{\star} = (3/2\pi)B^{*}$ as explained in the Note on Notation at the front of the book.

TABLE 6.5–1

CLASSICAL AND QUANTUM MECHANICAL CONTRIBUTIONS TO THE REDUCED SECOND VIRIAL COEFFICIENT[5, 6]

$$B^\star = [B_{cl}^\star + \Lambda^{*2}B_{I}^\star + \Lambda^{*4}B_{II}^\star + \ldots] \mp \Lambda^{*3}B_0^\star$$

T^*	$B_{cl}^\star$	$B_{I}^\star$	$B_{II}^\star$	$B_0^\star$
1	−2.538	0.4145	−0.09463	0.0^25359
2	−0.6274	0.08203	−0.01095	0.0^21895
4	+0.1154	0.03247	-0.0^21176	0.0^36699
6	0.3229	0.01826	-0.0^34227	0.0^33646
9	0.4406	0.01057	-0.0^31372	0.0^31985
12	0.4759	0.0^27324	-0.0^46761	0.0^31289
25	0.5290	0.0^23025	-0.0^4117	0.0^44287
100	0.4640	0.0^36126	—	0.0^55359

Note: $0.0^36126 = 0.0006126$.

c. Calculations for the Lennard-Jones potential

In order to make use of the results of the last section it is necessary to know the "force constants" σ and ϵ/k for the molecules under consideration. To obtain the proper values of these parameters for use in quantum mechanical calculations, we fit the experimental second virial coefficient data (or Joule-Thomson coefficient data) with Eq. 6.5–7. This is accomplished by successive approximation as follows: First, values of the parameters σ and ϵ/k are determined by using only the classical contribution to the second virial coefficient. With these parameters a trial value of Λ^* can be calculated. Then, using this trial value of Λ^*, we may obtain new values of σ and ϵ/k from the experimental data and Eq. 6.5–7. This process is repeated until a consistent set of values of σ, ϵ/k, and Λ^* is obtained. The values so obtained for a large number of gases are shown in Table 6.5–2.[6, 7]

Once the parameters have been thus determined, the second virial coefficient and the zero-pressure Joule-Thomson coefficient may easily be calculated. The expansion in powers of Planck's constant in Eq. 6.5–3 converges less rapidly as the deviations from classical behavior become greater. This means that Eq. 6.5–3 may not be used below about 40°K for helium and below 75°K and 45°K for hydrogen and deuterium, respectively. Values for the various terms in the second virial coefficient expansion are shown in Table 6.5–3 for four gases.

[7] When the values of σ, ϵ, and Λ^* have been determined for one isotope of a molecule, the value of Λ^* for any other isotope may be calculated at once, since σ and ϵ are essentially the same for the various isotopes of a substance. In this way the parameters * for He^3 and some of the hydrogen isotopes were determined.

TABLE 6.5–2[6]

VALUES OF THE QUANTUM MECHANICAL PARAMETER Λ^*

Noble Gases		*Hydrogen Isotopes*		*Other Gases*	
He^3	3.08	H_2	1.729	CH_4	0.239
He^4	2.67	HD	1.412	N_2	0.226
Ne	0.593	D_2	1.223	CO	0.220
A	0.186	HT	1.223	O_2	0.201
Kr	0.102	DT	1.095		
Xe	0.064	T_2	1.00		

In Fig. 3.6–1 are shown the calculated curves of the second virial coefficient along with the experimental values. It may there be seen that the theory predicts quite nicely the quantum deviations in the low density equation of state. A similar comparison is made in Fig. 3.6–3 for the zero-pressure Joule-Thomson coefficient, which may be written in the quantum mechanical form:

$$\mu^0 = \left[\mu_{cl}{}^0 + \left(\frac{h^2}{m}\right)\mu_{\mathrm{I}}{}^0 + \left(\frac{h^2}{m}\right)^2 \mu_{\mathrm{II}}{}^0 + \cdots\right] \mp \left(\frac{h^2}{m}\right)^{3/2} \mu_0{}^0 \qquad (6.5\text{–}16)$$

which is analogous to Eq. 6.5–3

In Table I–A there are given two sets of force constants for the lighter gases. The parameters designated by Qu were obtained from the experimental data and Eq. 6.5–7. These are the true force constants appropriate for the Lennard-Jones potential. It is, however, possible to fit the experimental data with the classical formula given in Eq. 3.6–3. By this means the parameters labeled Cl were determined. These quantities must, however, be regarded as "effective" force constants. For accurate calculations, high-temperature extrapolations, and very low-temperature computations the Qu parameters should be used.

TABLE 6.5–3

ORDER OF MAGNITUDE OF THE VARIOUS CONTRIBUTIONS[5] TO $B(T)$

Gas	T(°K)	B_{cl}	B^0	$(h^2/m)B_{\mathrm{I}}$	$(h^2/m)^2B_{\mathrm{II}}$
He^4	27.3	−4.87	−0.50	9.16	−4.05
	83.5	8.87	−0.093	1.82	−0.19
	256.0	11.13	−0.017	0.48	−0.01
H_2	49.2	−47.1	−0.57	20.68	−8.63
	182.8	7.55	−0.080	2.26	−0.19
	592.	15.7	−0.014	0.49	−0.01
D_2	37.0	−78.94	−0.31	19.60	−10.21
	182.8	7.55	−0.029	1.13	−0.05
	592.0	15.7	−0.004	0.25	0
Ne	35.6	−66.2	−0.03	3.80	−0.47
	95.0	−6.23	−0.007	0.55	−0.01
	392.0	12.1	−0.0008	0.07	0

d. Calculations for the Buckingham-Corner potential[8]

Buckingham and Corner[9] have evaluated the second virial coefficient and the Joule-Thomson coefficient for the potential function given in Eq. 1.3–29. They have expressed their results in the form;

$$B_{\text{cl}} = (2\pi\tilde{N} r_m{}^3)\, F_0(\alpha, \beta; T^*)$$

$$B_{\text{I}} = (\tilde{N} r_m/kT)\, F_1(\alpha, \beta; T^*) \qquad (6.5\text{–}17)$$

$$\mu_{\text{cl}}{}^0 C_p{}^0 = (2\pi\tilde{N} r_m{}^3)\, G_0(\alpha, \beta; T^*)$$

$$\mu_{\text{I}}{}^0 C_p{}^0 = (\tilde{N} r_m/kT)\, G_1(\alpha, \beta; T^*) \qquad (6.5\text{–}18)$$

The functions F_0, G_0, F_1, G_1 are given in Tables VI–A, B, C, D. The tables cover a wide temperature range and are given for five values of α and two values of β. These tables have not been used for computing the force constants for the Buckingham-Corner potential taking into account the quantum effects in the lighter gases.

6. The Principle of Corresponding States in Quantum Mechanics

This discussion parallels to some extent the discussion given in § 4.1, in which the principle of corresponding states for classical systems was discussed. Here we want to formulate the analogous principle for systems in which quantum deviations are observed. Then we show how this principle can be used for summarizing the nature of quantum effects in the liquid phase and for predicting the properties of some of the isotopes of hydrogen and helium. The transport coefficients are discussed from the stand-point of the quantum mechanical principle of corresponding states in § 10.4.

a. Statement of the principle of corresponding states in quantum mechanics

The principle of corresponding states has developed in quantum mechanics in much the same manner as in classical theory: first came the statement in terms of the reduction of variables in terms of critical constant (bulk properties) and later in terms of parameters in the intermolecular potential (molecular properties).

It was first suggested by Byk[1] that there should be quantum deviations from the principle of corresponding states at high pressures and low temperatures. He suggested that the reduced equation of state, as given by Eq. 4.1–6, should be modified in such a way that Planck's constant

[8] The symbols used in this discussion have been defined in § 3.7.

[9] R. A. Buckingham and J. Corner, *Proc. Roy. Soc.* (*London*), **A189**, 118 (1947).

[1] A. Byk, *Ann. Physik*, **66**, 157 (1921); **69**, 161 (1922).

appears in dimensionless form. Consequently, according to Byk the equation of state assumes the form:

$$p_r = p_r(V_r, T_r; \Lambda_r) \tag{6.6–1}$$

Here the quantity Λ_r is the dimensionless combination

$$\Lambda_r = \frac{h}{(\tilde{V}_c/\tilde{N})^{1/3}(mkT_c)^{1/2}} \tag{6.6–2}$$

The inclusion of the parameter Λ_r allows then for deviations from the classical principle of corresponding states. Actually this parameter is not too well-suited for the study of quantum effects, inasmuch as Λ_r is itself influenced by the quantum effects through the quantities V_c and T_c. Nevertheless, it is seen that the quantum deviations are greatest for gases which are of low molecular weight and have small critical temperatures and volumes.

A corresponding states relationship based on molecular parameters, analogous to Eq. 4.1–16 may also be developed for the quantum mechanical equation of state.[2–4] Quite generally the equation of state may be written in the form

$$p = p(\tilde{V}/\tilde{N}, kT; h, m, \sigma, \epsilon) \tag{6.6–3}$$

provided that the intermolecular potential function is of the form of Eq. 4.1–13. If the molecular parameters σ and ϵ are then used for the reduction of the variables, the equation of state assumes the reduced form

$$p^* = p^*(V^*, T^*; \Lambda^*) \tag{6.6–4}$$

The reduced pressure $p^* = p\sigma^3/\epsilon$ can depend only on the dimensionless quantities $V^* = \tilde{V}/\tilde{N}\sigma^3$ and $T^* = kT/\epsilon$ and on a dimensionless combination Λ^*, which is defined by

$$\Lambda^* = \frac{h}{\sigma\sqrt{m\epsilon}} \tag{6.6–5}$$

This must be true, inasmuch as V^*, T^*, and Λ^* are the only dimensionless quantities which can be formed by various combinations of $\tilde{V}/\tilde{N}$, kT, h, m, ϵ, and σ. Equation 6.6–4 is the statement of the principle of corresponding states in quantum mechanics as applied to the equation of state. The result does not depend on any limitation as to the density or temperature of the system and must consequently be valid for gases, liquids, and solids.

[2] J. de Boer, *Physica*, **14**, 139 (1948).
[3] J. de Boer and B. S. Blaisse, *Physica*, **14**, 149 (1948).
[4] J. de Boer and R. J. Lunbeck, *Physica*, **14**, 520 (1948).

Thus in general the reduced pressure becomes a function of the reduced volume and temperature and depends parametrically on the parameter Λ^*. It should be pointed out that this function is different for molecules which obey Bose-Einstein statistics and for those obeying Fermi-Dirac statistics. This must be so, because in the summation over all quantum states in the expression for the partition function, only symmetrical states should be considered in the first case and only antisymmetrical states in the second case. Under conditions of temperature and density, however, for which the de Broglie wavelength is small compared with the average distance between the molecules, this difference between the sum over symmetrical states and the one over antisymmetrical states becomes of minor importance, and consequently both reduced equations of state approach one and the same reduced quantum mechanical equation of state.

The principle of corresponding states has already been illustrated for several equilibrium properties of gases. In Fig. 3.6–1 is shown the classical curve of $B^\star$ versus T^*. There are also shown the calculated $B^\star$-curves and the experimental points for several of the light gases. It is quite clear that the quantum deviations are greater for those substances with larger Λ^* values. Similar behavior has been observed for the third virial coefficient (Fig. 3.6–2) and for the zero-pressure Joule-Thomson coefficient (Fig. 3.6–3).

b. Quantum effects in the liquid phase[3, 4, 5]

It has been shown that the theoretical investigations of the quantum deviations in the gas-phase properties give a satisfactory quantitative description of the phenomena. In the liquid phase, however, such refined theoretical results have not yet been obtained. Consequently, we content ourselves with a semi-empirical investigation of the quantum effects in liquids based on the principle of corresponding states in quantum mechanics. We make use of the principle in the form given in Eq. 6.6–4 and use the values of the parameter Λ^* given in Table 6.5–2 based on the Lennard-Jones (6-12) potential. To illustrate the general nature of the quantum effects, we consider briefly the experimental observations of critical properties, liquid volumes, liquid-vapor and solid-vapor equilibria, and surface tension.

i. *The Critical Properties*

In Fig. 6.6–1 the reduced critical constants of the noble gases and hydrogen are plotted as a function of Λ^*. From this plot the limiting

[5] R. J. Lunbeck, Doctoral Dissertation, Amsterdam (1950).

values of the critical constants for $\Lambda^* = 0$ have been found to be

$$\begin{aligned} T_c^* &= kT_c/\epsilon &&= 1.26 \\ p_c^* &= p_c\sigma^3/\epsilon &&= 0.117 \\ V_c^* &= \tilde{V}_c/\tilde{N}\sigma^3 &&= 3.16 \end{aligned} \tag{6.6–6}$$

For lighter gases large deviations from the classical behavior may be observed, the deviations increasing for the larger values of Λ^*.

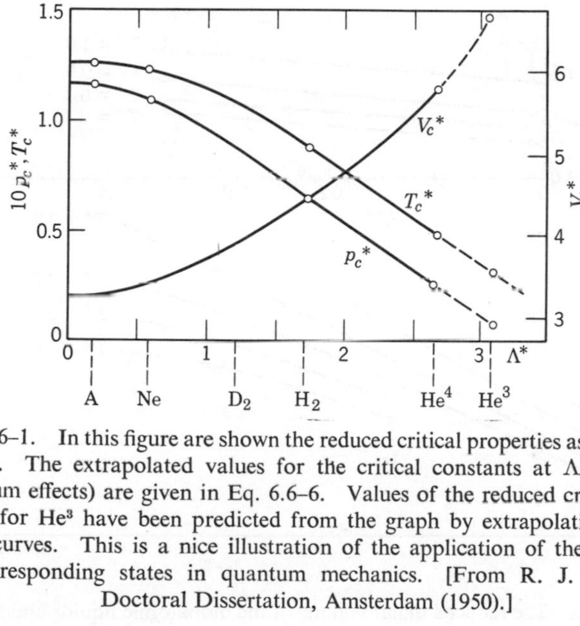

Fig. 6.6–1. In this figure are shown the reduced critical properties as functions of Λ^*. The extrapolated values for the critical constants at $\Lambda^* = 0$ (no quantum effects) are given in Eq. 6.6–6. Values of the reduced critical constants for He^3 have been predicted from the graph by extrapolation of the three curves. This is a nice illustration of the application of the principle of corresponding states in quantum mechanics. [From R. J. Lunbeck, Doctoral Dissertation, Amsterdam (1950).]

ii. *Liquid Volumes*

The molar volume of the liquid phase exhibits quite clearly deviations due to quantum effects. As may be seen in Fig. 6.6–2, the deviation of the reduced molar volume from the classical limiting value is, for not too large values of Λ^*, clearly proportional to Λ^{*2}. This proportionality has been investigated theoretically,[4, 6] using the Lennard-Jones–Devonshire theory (§ 4.7) for the equation of state of the liquid. It may be recalled that in this theory the partition function for a single molecule in the liquid

[6] The problem of quantum effects in the liquid phase has also been studied by S. D. Hamann, *Trans. Faraday Soc.*, **48**, 303 (1952), and by H. G. David and S. D Hamann, *Trans. Faraday Soc.*, **49**, 711 (1953).

is, aside from certain volume-independent factors, of the form

$$z \sim \int_{\Delta} e^{-\omega(\boldsymbol{r})/kT} \, d\boldsymbol{r} \tag{6.6–7}$$

Here $\omega(\boldsymbol{r})$ is the average potential field of the molecule in its cell of volume Δ. In order to make the Lennard-Jones–Devonshire theory apply in quantum mechanics, the Boltzmann factor, $\exp(-\omega(\boldsymbol{r})/kT)$, must be replaced by its quantum mechanical analog, the Slater sum. The Slater

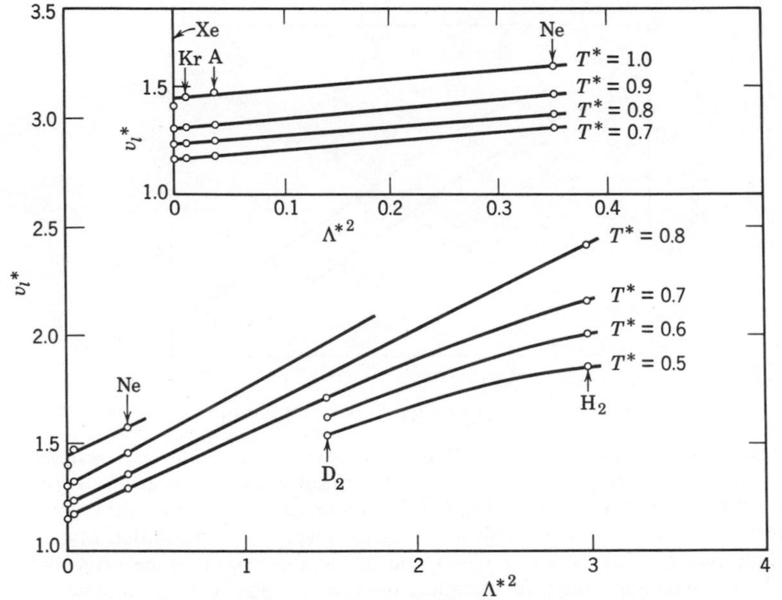

Fig. 6.6–2. The reduced molar volume of the monatomic liquids and isotopes of hydrogen at several reduced temperatures. It may be seen here that the reduced molar volume of liquids is almost a linear function of Λ^{*2}. [From J. de Boer and R. J. Lunbeck, *Physica*, **14**, 520 (1948).]

sum, in turn, may be expanded as indicated by Eq. 6.1–20. The result is that the partition function for the single molecule becomes

$$z_q \sim \int_{\Delta} e^{-\omega(\boldsymbol{r})/kT} [1 + \lambda^2 w_2(\boldsymbol{r}, T) + \lambda^4 w_4(\boldsymbol{r}, T) + \cdots] \, d\boldsymbol{r} \tag{6.6–8}$$

When this expression is substituted into Eq. 4.4–32, we finally obtain the reduced equation of state in the form

$$p^* = p_{\text{cl}}^* + \Lambda^{*2} p_{\text{I}}^* + \Lambda^{*4} p_{\text{II}} + \cdots \tag{6.6–9}$$

From this quantum mechanical treatment, we may thus show that the quantum deviations of various properties of liquids are directly proportional to Λ^{*2} for small values of Λ^*. The value of $(\partial v_l^*/\partial \Lambda^{*2})$ has been calculated[4] from this theory, but the calculated value differs by about a factor 2 from the slope of the experimental v_l^* versus Λ^{*2} curves in Fig. 6.6–2. This is not bad, however, considering the approximate nature of the Lennard-Jones–Devonshire treatment.

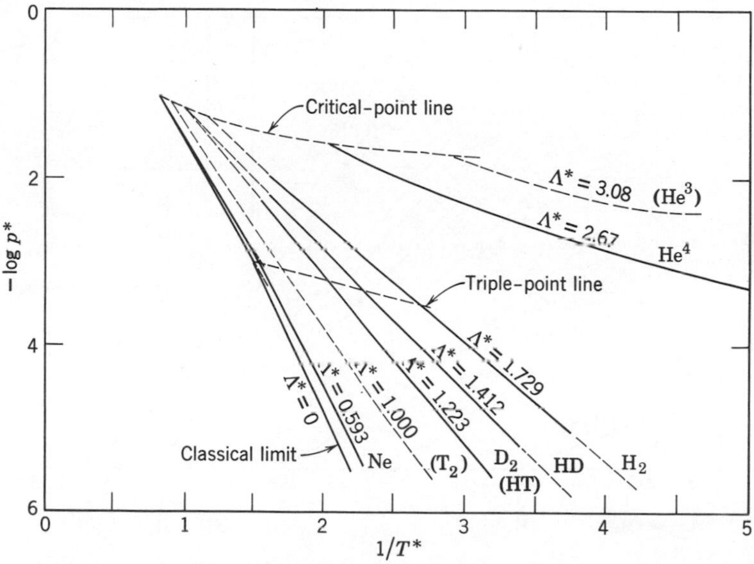

Fig. 6.6–3. Reduced vapor pressure for several gases. This figure shows that for the lighter molecules He, H_2, Ne, the quantum deviations may not be neglected and that the quantum effects become more appreciable for larger Λ^*-values. [From R. J. Lunbeck, Doctoral Dissertation, Amsterdam (1950).]

iii. *Vapor-Liquid and Vapor-Solid Equilibrium*

According to the classical theory of corresponding states the reduced vapor pressure should be a universal function of the reduced temperature. For the heavy noble gases (A, Kr, Xe) this is indeed corroborated by recent experimental data,[7] as may be seen in Fig. 6.6–3. In this figure are also shown the vapor pressure curves for the lighter noble gases[8] and three

[7] A. Michels and T. Wassenaar, *Physica*, **16**, 253 (1950), Xenon. A. M. Clark, F. Din, J. Robb, A. Michels, T. Wassenaar, and Th. Zwietering, *Physica*, **17**, 876 (1951), Argon. A. Michels, T. Wassenaar, and Th. Zwieterling, *Physica*, **18**, 63 (1952), Krypton.

[8] R. W. Ditchburn and J. C. Gilmour, *Revs. Mod. Phys.*, **13**, 310 (1941). Landolt-Börnstein, *Physikalisch-Chemische Tabellen*, Berlin (1936).

isotopes of hydrogen.[9] We see that the quantum deviations for these lighter gases are appreciable, even for neon. We see also that the vapor pressure curves for the three isotopes of hydrogen are distinctly different, an effect which is of course not predicted by classical theory at all. It is clear that the greater the value of Λ^*, the greater is the deviation from classical behavior. An interpretation of this effect may be given[5] in terms of the Debye theory of solids and the Lennard-Jones–Devonshire theory

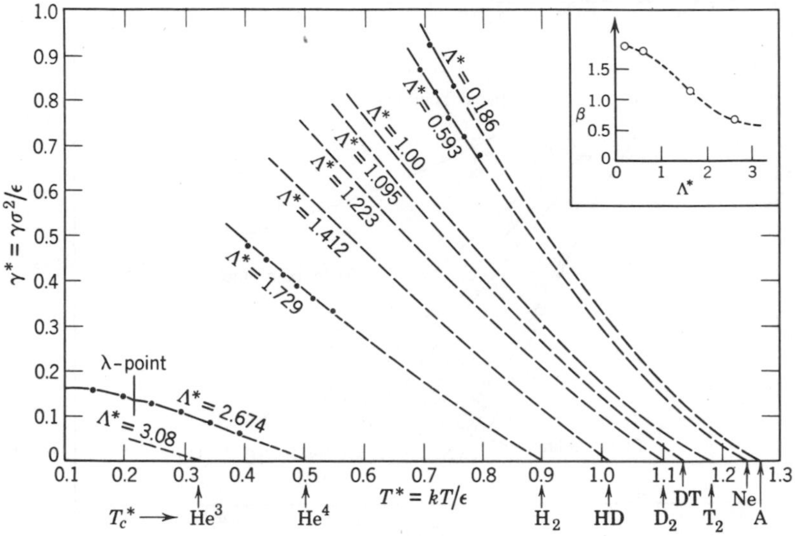

Fig. 6.6–4. The reduced surface tension γ^* as a function of the reduced temperature T^* and the quantum mechanical parameter, Λ^*. The arrows above the atomic and molecular symbols are pointing to the reduced critical temperatures of the various substances.

of liquids. The vapor-solid equilibrium comes out to be in satisfactory agreement with the experiments since the solid and gas phases are fairly well understood. Quantitative conclusions about the liquid-vapor equilibrium are, of course, rather unsatisfactory because of the present unsatisfactory status of our knowledge of the liquid state.

iv. *Surface Tension*

The classical theory of surface tension has been discussed in § 5.1, but as yet the quantum deviations have not been studied from the theoretical standpoint. It is clear from Fig. 6.6–4 that quantum effects

[9] H. W. Woolley, R. B. Scott, and F. G. Brickwedde, *J. Research Natl. Bur. Standards*, **41**, 379 (1948).

are quite prominent in the surface tension of the lighter substances. According to the classical principle of corresponding states we should expect that the reduced surface tension, $\gamma^* = \gamma\sigma^2/\epsilon$ would be a universal function of the reduced temperature $T^* = kT/\epsilon$, for those substances which are described adequately by the Lennard-Jones potential. The available experimental data indicate that γ^* depends parametrically on the quantum mechanical parameter Λ^*.

c. The properties of the isotopes of helium and hydrogen

There is at present a great deal of interest in the separation of isotopes and their properties. Among the more interesting are the two isotopes of helium and the six isotopes of molecular hydrogen for which very limited data are available. In this section we indicate how various properties for He^3, D_2, T_2, HD, HT, and DT may be estimated.

i. *Properties*[10] *of* He^3

He^3 has recently become interesting because it does not seem to exhibit the unusual properties of He^{II}. Inasmuch as σ and ϵ are the same for both species, and since the mass of He^3 is three-fourths that of He^4, Λ^* for He^3 is $\sqrt{4/3}$ of Λ^* for He^4, or 3.08. This is the largest value of Λ^* thus far known.

If we know any reduced physical property as a function of Λ^*, we may now extrapolate the curve out to $\Lambda^* = 3.08$ and get an estimation of the value for He^3 which should be good to within 10 to 20 per cent. By thus extrapolating the curves of the critical constants of Fig. 6.6–1, the critical constants for He^3 were predicted in 1948.[10] The following year the critical constants were measured.[11] The experimental results and the results predicted from the quantum mechanical principle of corresponding states are compared in Table 6.6–1.

In a similar way the vapor pressure curve for He^3 was computed[10] in 1948. Two years later measurements were made of this property.[12] Experimental and theoretical results are compared in Table 6.6–2, and the agreement is seen to be exceptionally good.

The surface tension of He^3 has also been estimated by means of the principle of corresponding states. This was done by fitting the surface tension data of H_2, He^4, Ne, and A with the equation

$$\gamma^* = \beta(T_c^* - T^*)^{11/9} \tag{6.6–10}$$

The values of β were plotted as a function of Λ^* (see insert Fig. 6.6–4),

[10] J. de Boer and R. J. Lunbeck, *Physica*, **14**, 510 (1948).

[11] S. G. Sydoriak, E. R. Grilly, and E. F. Hammel, *Phys. Rev.*, **75**, 303, 1103 (1949).

[12] B. M. Abraham, D. W. Osborne, and B. Weinstock, *Phys. Rev.*, **80**, 366 (1950).

and a value of $\beta = 0.56$ for He^3 was found by extrapolation. From this value of β and the value of $T_c^* = 0.32$, the surface tension curve may be constructed. This property of He^3 has not yet been measured.

TABLE 6.6–1

CRITICAL PROPERTIES OF THE ISOTOPES OF HELIUM

Gas	T_c(°K)	p_c(atm)	$\tilde{V}_c$(cm³/mole)	T_c^*	p_c^*	V_c^*
He^4	5.20	2.26	57.76	0.509	0.0271	5.742
He^3 Extrap[10]	3.37	1.12	70.	0.33	0.0135	7.0
He^3 Exptl[11]	3.34	1.15	72.			

TABLE 6.6–2

VAPOR PRESSURE OF THE ISOTOPES OF HELIUM

(Measured in cm Hg.)

Gas \ T^*	1.21	1.33	1.52	1.63	1.8	2.0	2.4	2.8	3.0	3.2	3.3
He^4	0.07	0.14	0.39	0.64	1.23	2.34	6.26	13.27	18.12	24.05	27.48
He^3 Extrap[10]						14.	27.	48.	59.	75.	82.
He^3 Exptl[12]	2.07	3.10	5.35	7.04		15.2	29.1	49.11	61.79	76.40	84.47

ii. *Properties of H_2-Isotopes*

The determination of properties of He^3 rested on an extrapolation, but for the H_2-isotopes an interpolation process may be used. There is, however, an uncertainty in this interpolation, for we must assume that (i) the H_2-isotopes, which are diatomic molecules, still fit into the series of noble gases, and (ii) that the various H_2-isotopes obey the same intermolecular potential field. Since we are dealing here with rotating diatomic molecules, we may expect deviations from the principle of corresponding states, which is here set up for spherical molecules. Moreover there are several reasons why assumption (ii), which is rigorously valid for the isotopes of helium, might not be valid for the isotopes of hydrogen. The first effect, which is very small, is the fact that the difference in zero-point energy would make the force fields of H_2, D_2, and T_2 somewhat unequal.[13] The second effect, which is more serious, is the fact that HD, HT, and DT rotate around a center of gravity which is not situated halfway between the two atoms as is the case with H_2, D_2, and T_2. Experiments will have to show whether these effects have any influence on the agreement between the experimental data and the calculations based on assumptions (i) and (ii).

By means of interpolating the physical properties plotted as functions of Λ^{*2} several properties of the various isotopes of hydrogen have been computed.[5, 14] In Tables 6.6–3 and 6.6–4 are given the thus calculated values of the critical constants and the vapor pressure curves. The available experimental data for the critical constants are also given.[15, 16] The accuracy of the interpolation process cannot be claimed to be larger than 5 per cent. Hence the existing data cannot be said to show quite definitely deviations from the interpolated values. This suggests that the effects mentioned above are not too serious in causing deviations from the interpolated values. Similar calculations have been performed for some other properties.[5]

TABLE 6.6–3

CRITICAL PROPERTIES OF HYDROGEN ISOTOPES

Substance		H_2	HD	D_2; HT	DT	T_2
Λ^*		1.729	1.412	1.223	1.095	1.00
T_c^*		0.897	1.03	1.10	1.14	1.17
$p_c^* \cdot 10^2$		6.46	7.8	8.6	9.2	9.6
V_c^*		4.42	4.1	3.9	3.8	3.7
T_c (°K)	Theor[5]	(33.18)	38.	41.	42.	43.
	Exptl	33.18	35.9[14]	38.3[14, 15]	—	—
p_c (atm)	Theor[5]	(12.98)	15.5	17.5	18.5	19.
	Exptl	12.98	14.6[14]	16.3[14, 15]	—	—
V_c (cc/mole)	Theor[5]	(66.95)	62.	59.	57.	56.
	Exptl	66.95	62.8[14]	60.3[14]	—	—

[13] R. P. Bell, *Proc. Roy. Soc.* (*London*), **A174**, 504 (1940).
[14] E. F. Hammel, *J. Chem. Phys.*, **18**, 228 (1950).
[15] R. D. Arnold and H. J. Hoge, *J. Chem. Phys.*, **18**, 1295 (1950).
[16] A. S. Friedman, D. White, and H. L. Johnston, *J. Chem. Phys.*, **19**, 126 (1951).

TABLE 6.6–4

COMPUTED VAPOR PRESSURE OF HYDROGEN ISOTOPES[5]

(in mm Hg.)

T(°K)	H_2	HD	D_2; HT	DT	T_2
10	1.7_3	0.28	0.05		
12	12.7	2.94	0.73	0.21	0.09
14	55.4	16.8	5.44	1.85	0.98
16	153.3	65.2	25.4	11.5	7.43
18	345.9	176.4	87.2	43.5	31.6
20	675.7	382.8	219.9	130.	106.
25	2525.	1630.	1040.	770.	700.
30	6200.	4415.	3180.	2540.	2345.
35		8060.	6650.	5790.	5400.

7. Quantum Effects in Diatomic Gases

The theoretical developments given thus far in this chapter are rigorous only for monatomic gases. It is true that we have discussed the equation of state of hydrogen at very low temperatures and the quantum deviations of hydrogen and deuterium at intermediate temperatures, making use of the results of the monatomic gas theory. We now wish to examine more closely the quantum mechanical effects associated with the rotational motion of these molecules. First, a discussion is given of the theoretical approach to the problem, and then the rotational quantum effects in H_2 are discussed. Calculations have been made for the intermediate temperature region (analogous to § 6.5), but no computational work has been done at very low temperatures (analogous to § 6.4).

a. Brief summary of the theoretical development

The quantum statistical theory of the equilibrium bulk properties of diatomic molecules has been worked out by Wang Chang.[1] She assumed that diatomic molecules may be represented by rigid three dimensional rotators of mass m and moment of inertia I, each with five degrees of freedom—three translational and two rotational. The Hamiltonian operator for a system of N such molecules is the quantum mechanical analog of the classical Hamiltonian given in Eq. 3.4–10. Similarly the quantum mechanical partition function for the system is very much like the classical partition function given in Eq. 3.4–13, except of course that the Boltzmann factor must be replaced by the Slater sum. Wang Chang showed that the latter may be expanded in terms of U-functions in a manner similar to that described in § 3.2a. In this way expressions for the virial coefficients were obtained.

[1] C. S. Wang Chang, Doctoral Dissertation, University of Michigan (1944).

Wang Chang showed that the expressions for the virial coefficients thus derived reduce to those given in Eqs. 3.4–15, 16 for rotating diatomic molecules in classical theory. She then proceeded to obtain the quantum deviations in the second virial coefficient by a scheme analogous to that described in § 6.5a for monatomic gases. It was found that there are two types of quantum deviations: those proportional to successive powers of (h^2/m) due to the translational contributions, and those proportional to successive powers of (h^2/I) due to the rotational contributions. The final result (analogous to Eq. 6.5–3) is

$$B(T) = B_{\text{cl}} + \left[\left(\frac{h^2}{m}\right) B_{\text{I}}^{(\text{tr})} + \left(\frac{h^2}{m}\right)^2 B_{\text{II}}^{(\text{tr})} + \cdots\right] + \left[\left(\frac{h^2}{I}\right) B_{\text{I}}^{(\text{rot})} + \left(\frac{h^2}{I}\right)^2 B_{\text{II}}^{(\text{rot})} + \cdots\right] \tag{6.7–1}$$

in which

$$B_{\text{cl}}(T) = -\frac{\tilde{N}}{4}\iint (e^{-\varphi/kT} - 1)\, r^2\, dr\, d\Omega \tag{6.7–2}$$

$$B_{\text{I}}^{(\text{tr})}(T) = +\frac{\tilde{N}}{4}\left(\frac{1}{48\pi^2k^3T^3}\right)\iint e^{-\varphi/kT}\left(\frac{\partial\varphi}{dr}\right)^2 r^2\, dr\, d\Omega \tag{6.7–3}$$

$$B_{\text{I}}^{(\text{rot})}(T) = +\frac{\tilde{N}}{4}\left(\frac{1}{96\pi^2k^3T^3}\right)\iint e^{-\varphi/kT}\left[\left(\frac{\partial\varphi}{\partial\theta_1}\right)^2 + \left(\frac{\partial\varphi}{\partial\theta_2}\right)^2 + \csc^2\theta_1\left(\frac{\partial\varphi}{\partial\phi_1}\right)^2 + \csc^2\theta_2\left(\frac{\partial\varphi}{\partial\phi_2}\right)^2\right] r^2\, dr\, d\Omega \tag{6.7–4}$$

In these expressions:

$$\varphi = \varphi(r, \theta_1, \theta_2, \phi_2 - \phi_1)$$

$$\int \cdots d\Omega = \int_0^{2\pi}\int_0^{\pi}\int_0^{\pi} \cdots \sin\theta_1\, d\theta_1 \sin\theta_2\, d\theta_2\, d(\phi_2 - \phi_1) \tag{6.7–5}$$

The next higher order corrections (proportional to h^4) have also been worked out. They are not given here because of their length and because they have been published elsewhere.[1] The expressions given in Eqs. 6.7–1 through 5 are not the most general expressions for the second virial coefficient. Wang Chang[1] has also given more complex formulae in which the ortho-para content of a homopolar diatomic gas is taken into account. We do not present the formulae here, but the results are discussed briefly.

b. Comparison of theory and experiment for hydrogen

In order to calculate the influence of rotational quantum effects in hydrogen, Wang Chang assumed that the intermolecular potential of hydrogen could be represented approximately by the function

$$\varphi(r, \theta_1, \theta_2, \phi) = -\frac{a}{r^6} + \frac{b}{r^{12}} + \frac{c}{r^{12}}(\cos^2 \theta_1 + \cos^2 \theta_2) \qquad (6.7\text{–}6)$$

She adjusted the constants *a*, *b*, and *c* so as to give the best possible agreement with the various quantum mechanical calculations which have been made for the non-spherical potential field of hydrogen.[2–4]

Computations of the second virial coefficient have been made using the potential given in Eq. 6.7–6. In Table 6.7–1 the results are summarized up through the first quantum corrections. A graph of *B* versus *T* makes the agreement between theory and experiment seem better at the low temperatures where the slope dB/dT is large. This is due to the fact that the second-order corrections are always negative, and they are not small at the lower temperatures, as may be seen in Table 6.7–2. The second rotational quantum corrections have signs opposite to the first-order corrections as is also the case for the translational quantum corrections (see Table 6.5–3). From the order of magnitude of the functions $B_{\mathrm{I}}^{(\mathrm{rot})}$ and $B_{\mathrm{II}}^{(\mathrm{rot})}$ it can be seen that the convergence of the series expansion is slow at low temperatures, and hence that the development in powers of h^2/I is valid only at relatively high temperatures.

TABLE 6.7–1[1]

CONTRIBUTIONS TO THE SECOND VIRIAL COEFFICIENT OF H_2

T (°K)	B_{cl} (cc/mole)	$(h^2/m)\,B_{\mathrm{I}}^{(\mathrm{tr})}$ (cc/mole)	$(h^2/I)\,B_{\mathrm{I}}^{(\mathrm{rot})}$ (cc/mole)	$B_{\mathrm{calcd}}{}^a$ (cc/mole)	B_{exptl} (cc/mole)
123	−3.06	4.23	1.00	2.17	2.56
173	+5.68	2.58	0.46	8.72	9.14
223	9.49	1.76	0.28	11.53	12.08
323	13.15	1.13	0.15	14.43	15.14
373	14.06	0.97	0.12	15.15	15.55
423	15.22	0.64	0.08	15.94	15.68

[a] $B_{\mathrm{calcd}} = B_{\mathrm{cl}} + \dfrac{h^2}{m} B_{\mathrm{I}}^{(\mathrm{tr})} + \dfrac{h^2}{I} B_{\mathrm{I}}^{(\mathrm{rot})}$

[2] J. de Boer, *Physica*, **9**, 363 (1943).
[3] H. Margenau, *Phys. Rev.*, **64**, 131 (1943).
[4] The values thus found are: $a = 1.25 \times 10^{-11}$ erg Å^6; $b = 4.438 \times 10^{-9}$ erg Å^{12}; $c = 4.784 \times 10^{-9}$ erg Å^{12}.

TABLE 6.7–2

FIRST- AND SECOND-ORDER ROTATIONAL QUANTUM CORRECTIONS[1]

T (°K)	$(h^2/I)\,B_{\rm I}^{(\rm rot)}$ (cc/mol)	$(h^2/I)^2\,B_{\rm II}^{(\rm rot)}$ (cc/mol)
123	1.00	−0.42
173	0.46	−0.14
223	0.28	−0.07
323	0.15	−0.02

Wang Chang[1] has estimated the difference between the second virial coefficients of normal and para hydrogen at 173° and 223°K. She has found for these temperatures that $B_{\rm H_2} - B_{\rm para}$ is 0.19 cc/mole and 0.11 cc/mole, respectively. These values indicate that the difference $(B_{\rm H_2} - B_{\rm para})$ at temperatures as low as 173°K, is small compared to the experimental error of existing equation of state measurements.

PROBLEMS

1. Derive the expressions for the *Slater sums* for the following simple systems:[1]
   a. Freely moving mass point in one-dimensional "box" of length L:

$$\mathscr{W}(x) = \lambda \frac{2}{L} \sum_{n=1}^{\infty} e^{-n^2h^2/8mkTL^2} \sin^2 \frac{n\pi x}{L} = 1 - e^{-4\pi x^2/\lambda^2}$$

   b. Linear harmonic oscillator[2] of frequency ν:

$$\mathscr{W}(x) = \left(\frac{2\theta}{1 - e^{2\theta}}\right)^{1/2} e^{-\frac{1}{2}\theta - y^2 \tanh \frac{1}{2}\theta}, \text{ where } y = 2\pi x \sqrt{\frac{m\nu}{h}} \text{ and } \theta = h\nu/kT$$

   c. Two non-interacting mass-points in a one-dimensional box of length L; use Boltzmann, Bose-Einstein, and Fermi-Dirac statistics:

$$\mathscr{W}_{\rm B.}(x) = (1 - e^{-4\pi x_1^2/\lambda^2})(1 - e^{-4\pi x_2^2/\lambda^2})$$

$$\left.\begin{matrix}\mathscr{W}_{\rm B.E.}(x) \\ \mathscr{W}_{\rm F.D.}(x)\end{matrix}\right\} = \mathscr{W}_{\rm B.}(x) \pm \left(e^{-\frac{\pi}{\lambda^2}(x_1 - x_2)^2} - e^{-\frac{\pi}{\lambda^2}(x_1 + x_2)^2}\right)$$

Discuss the behavior of the Slater sums in the classical limit.

[1] B. Kahn, Dissertation, Utrecht (1938), pp. 12 *et seq.*

[2] Use needs to be made of the relation:

$$\sum_{n=0}^{\infty} e^{-n\theta} \, [H_n^2(y)/2^n n!] = (1 - e^{-2\theta})^{-1/2} \, e^{+y^2(1 - \tanh \frac{1}{2}\theta)}$$

where $H_n(y)$ are the Hermite polynomials. This relation is given by G. E. Uhlenbeck and L. S. Ornstein, *Phys. Rev.*, **36**, 823 (1930).

2. Show how the following expressions for the *caloric equation of state* may be derived, and prove that they are equivalent:

$$U = \frac{1}{Z_{Nq}} \int (\mathscr{H} e^{-\mathscr{H}/kT}) (\mathbf{r}^N; \mathbf{r}^N) \, d\mathbf{r}^N$$

$$U = -\frac{1}{Z_{Nq}} \frac{\partial}{\partial(1/kT)} \int (e^{-\mathscr{H}/kT}) (\mathbf{r}^N; \mathbf{r}^N) \, d\mathbf{r}^N$$

3. Derive the following quantum mechanical expression for the *pair distribution function* of an ideal gas:

$$\mathscr{N}^{(2)}(r_{12}) = n^2(1 \pm e^{-2\pi r_{12}^2/\lambda^2})$$

Interpret this equation in terms of apparent repulsion and attraction of the molecules.

PART II

NON-EQUILIBRIUM PROPERTIES

· 7 ·

The Kinetic Theory Ⓝ of Dilute Gases

The preceding chapters are concerned with the properties of systems in equilibrium. In this and the following chapters, statistical methods are applied to the description of the non-equilibrium properties, in particular the transport phenomena. An elementary discussion of the transport phenomena is presented in § 1.2. A summary is given there of the rigorous kinetic theory approach used in this chapter, along with the assumptions involved in the theory and the limitations to its application. In this chapter we arrive at expressions for the hydrodynamical equations and formulae for the transport coefficients at low densities. Chapter 8 deals with the evaluation of and the practical computation of the transport coefficients. The present status of the work on high-pressure transport phenomena is discussed in Chapter 9, and the quantum theory of transport phenomena is discussed in Chapter 10. In Chapter 11 the hydrodynamical equations are discussed, and several applications of these equations receive detailed consideration. For the most part the theoretical developments given in these chapters are restricted to monatomic gases. It is pointed out in Chapter 8, however, that the coefficients of ordinary diffusion and shear viscosity are not very much affected by the internal degrees of freedom. Hence some of the results are in practice more generally applicable than is indicated by the derivations. On the other hand, the coefficient of thermal conductivity is quite dependent on the interchange of energy between translational and internal degrees of freedom. The theory of transport phenomena in gases made up of molecules with internal degrees of freedom is given brief consideration in § 7.6.

We begin by showing that the properties of a dilute gas are completely described by the distribution function $f(\boldsymbol{r}, \boldsymbol{v}, t)$. This distribution function is given as the solution of an integro-differential equation, known as the Boltzmann equation. This equation is valid at densities sufficiently low that the effect of collisions involving more than two molecules is negligible. If the mean free path of the molecules in the gas is short compared with all the macroscopic dimensions, the gas behaves as a continuum. Under such conditions the Boltzmann equation leads to the Navier-Stokes equations of hydrodynamics and expressions for the flux vectors. The transport coefficients are defined in terms of the flux vectors. Expressions for the transport coefficients are obtained in terms of a set of integrals $\Omega^{(l,s)}$, which involve the intermolecular potential function.

1. The Kinetic Theory Distribution Functions[1]

The kinetic theory in this chapter is based on the Boltzmann equation, which specifies the distribution function $f(\boldsymbol{r}, \boldsymbol{v}, t)$. We give here two derivations of the Boltzmann equation. The first, a simple physical derivation, gives physical interpretation to the various terms. The second, a more rigorous derivation, is based on the integration of the Liouville equation. Before presenting these derivations, we discuss some of the properties of the various kinetic theory distribution functions and their use in describing non-equilibrium systems.

a. Physical description of non-equilibrium systems[2]

The exact dynamical state of a system of particles is given by specifying the complete set of position and momentum coordinates of all the individual particles. According to the laws of classical mechanics a knowledge of the exact dynamical state at a particular time permits an exact prediction of the state at any future time.

It is virtually impossible to give a complete description of the state of a complex macroscopic system. We must content ourselves with descriptions of the system which are considerably less than complete. The problem of predicting the probable behavior of a system from incomplete information about the system at some specified time is a statistical one. It is useful to employ the technique of representing the system by means of an ensemble consisting of a large number of replicas of the single system. The state of the ensemble is then described by a distribution function $f^{(N)}(\boldsymbol{r}^N, \boldsymbol{p}^N, t)$, in the phase space of the single system. This distribution function is so chosen that averages over the ensemble are in exact agreement with the incomplete (macroscopic) knowledge of the state of the system at some specified time. Then the probable behavior of the system at subsequent times is taken to be the average behavior of members of the representative ensemble. There are, of course, many different ways in which the ensemble could be formed, and therefore the distribution function is not uniquely specified. In the equilibrium case the ensemble is

[1] The distribution functions used in this section have been defined in § 2.1.

[2] The discussion presented here is similar to that of H. Grad, *Communications on Pure and Applied Mathematics*, **2**, 331 (1949).

specified by the ergodic theorem of Birkhoff. Such a theorem has not yet been developed in the non-equilibrium case. However, this offers no difficulties, since the study of non-equilibrium statistical mechanics is principally concerned with the lower-order distribution functions $f^{(1)}$ and $f^{(2)}$. Equations for the lower-order distribution functions are derived by introducing restrictions, such as the concept of "molecular chaos," which effectively restrict the consideration to certain types of distribution functions $f^{(N)}$.

The variation of the distribution function $f^{(N)}(\boldsymbol{r}^N, \boldsymbol{p}^N, t)$ with time is described by the Liouville equation, which is derived in § 1.4b. This equation, involving $6N$ variables, is difficult to solve. Fortunately we are usually not interested in a description of the system so complete as that afforded by $f^{(N)}$. Rather we are satisfied with the less complete description given by one of the lower-order distribution functions $f^{(h)}(\boldsymbol{r}^h, \boldsymbol{p}^h, t)$ These functions are obtained by integrating $f^{(N)}$ over the $N - h$ molecules not included in the group $1, 2, 3, \cdots h$, as described[3] in § 2.1. Of particular interest are the distribution functions with $h = 1$ and $h = 2$.

In this chapter we are concerned primarily with the function $f^{(1)}(\boldsymbol{r}, \boldsymbol{p}, t)$ which gives the probability of finding one particular molecule with the specified position and momentum. The configuration and momenta of the other $N - 1$ molecules remain unspecified. In considering a system made up of identical molecules, the distribution function $f^{(N)}$ is symmetric in the coordinates of all the molecules, inasmuch as no physical experiment differentiates among them. Consequently, in obtaining $f^{(1)}$ it is immaterial which molecule is singled out as special. Clearly $f^{(1)}$ is adequate for the description of all the properties of gases which do not depend upon the relative positions of two or more molecules. This means that the level of information corresponding to $f^{(1)}$ is sufficient for studying the behavior of moderately dilute gases.

For gases at higher density a knowledge of higher-order distribution functions is required. If, however, two-body forces can be assumed (that is, $\Phi(\boldsymbol{r}^N) = \frac{1}{2} \Sigma_{ij}\varphi_{ij}$), the distribution function of order $h = 2$ is sufficient to determine all the macroscopic properties of the system. The distribution function $f^{(2)}(\boldsymbol{r}_1, \boldsymbol{r}_2, \boldsymbol{p}_1, \boldsymbol{p}_2, t)$ is the distribution in the phase space of pairs. The use of this pair distribution function in the study of the behavior of dense gases is discussed in § 9.4. It may be recalled that it was shown in § 3.1b that, as a result of the assumption of additivity of forces, the equilibrium properties of dense gases may be expressed solely in terms of the equilibrium pair distribution function.

Let us now consider the time dependence of the various distribution

[3] For the definitions and normalizations of these distribution functions see § 2.1b.

functions. As already mentioned, the manner in which $f^{(N)}$ changes with time is given by the Liouville equation. That is, to each $f^{(N)}$ at an initial time, t_0, there corresponds uniquely a function $f^{(N)}$ at a later time, t_1. However, for the lower-order distribution functions, it is not possible to predict from a knowledge of $f^{(h)}(t_0)$ a unique value of $f^{(h)}(t_1)$. For example, at t_0 it is possible that there are a number of functions $f^{(N)}(t_0)$, $f^{(N)\prime}(t_0)$, $f^{(N)\prime\prime}(t_0)$, $\cdots$ which, when integrated over the variables corresponding to $N - 1$ molecules, all give the same function $f^{(1)}(t_0)$. Later on, the group of Nth order functions becomes $f^{(N)}(t_1)$, $f^{(N)\prime}(t_1)$, $f^{(N)\prime\prime}(t_1)$, $\cdots$, and there correspond to these functions the single distribution functions $f^{(1)}(t_1)$, $f^{(1)\prime}(t_1)$, $f^{(1)\prime\prime}(t_1)$, $\cdots$, which are in general different from one another. This means that no unique integro-differential equation exists for $f^{(1)}$. In order to remove this ambiguity it is necessary to invoke an additional condition which restricts the possible functions $f^{(N)}$. This is the condition of *molecular chaos*, which is introduced into the derivation of the Boltzmann equation for $f^{(1)}$.

b. Physical derivation of the Boltzmann equation

Let us consider a monatomic gas mixture in a non-equilibrium state. The gas is assumed to be sufficiently dilute that two-body but not three-body collisions are important. For generality we suppose that the molecules of the ith species are subject to an external force $\boldsymbol{X}_i$. In this discussion $\boldsymbol{X}_i$ may be a function of position and time, but not of velocity. The effect of velocity-dependent forces are considered in a somewhat different manner.[4] The external force is assumed to be much smaller than the forces which act on the molecules during an encounter. The intermolecular forces are generally many powers of ten larger than the force of gravity and act only during the very short time of an encounter.

As discussed above, we are interested in the description of the gas in terms of the distribution function in the phase space of the single molecule (μ-space). For each component of a mixture there is a distribution function $f_i^{(1)}(\boldsymbol{r}, \boldsymbol{p}_i, t)$ such that the probable number of molecules of kind i with position coordinates in the range $d\boldsymbol{r}$ about $\boldsymbol{r}$ and with momentum coordinates in the range $d\boldsymbol{p}_i$ about $\boldsymbol{p}_i$ is $f_i^{(1)}(\boldsymbol{r}, \boldsymbol{p}_i, t)\, d\boldsymbol{r}\, d\boldsymbol{p}_i$. The discussion of equilibrium statistical mechanics of Chapter 2 indicates that at equilibrium the function $f_i^{(1)}$ is independent of time and space and that the velocity-distribution is Maxwellian. Now it is desired to ascertain the manner in which $f_i^{(1)}(\boldsymbol{r}, \boldsymbol{p}_i, t)$ depends upon the variables in non-equilibrium situations. That is, we wish to determine the nature of the

[4] S. Chapman and T. G. Cowling, *The Mathematical Theory of Non-uniform Gases*, Cambridge University Press (1939), Chapter 18.

flow of phase points through a six-dimensional phase space, where each phase point represents one molecule and the molecules interact with one another. If there were no interaction between the individual molecules, the behavior of the function $f_i^{(1)}(\boldsymbol{r}, \boldsymbol{p}_i, t)$, would be given by a Liouville equation for points in μ-space. We shall find, in fact, that the assumption of interaction simply modifies the Liouville equation by the addition of terms which account for molecular collisions.

We visualize a region of volume $d\boldsymbol{r}\, d\boldsymbol{p}_i$ located about a point $(\boldsymbol{r}, \boldsymbol{p}_i)$. In this element of volume there are $f_i^{(1)}\, d\boldsymbol{r}\, d\boldsymbol{p}_i$ phase points associated with particles of the ith kind. In the absence of collisions in the gas, the molecules corresponding to these phase points move in such a way that at time $t + dt$, their position vectors[5] are $[\boldsymbol{r} + (\boldsymbol{p}_i/m_i)\, dt]$ and their momentum vectors are $[\boldsymbol{p}_i + \boldsymbol{X}_i\, dt]$. No other phase points arrive at this latter position (in absence of collisions), so that

$$f_i^{(1)}(\boldsymbol{r}, \boldsymbol{p}_i, t)\, d\boldsymbol{r}\, d\boldsymbol{p}_i = f_i^{(1)}\left(\left[\boldsymbol{r} + \frac{\boldsymbol{p}_i}{m_i}\, dt\right], [\boldsymbol{p}_i + \boldsymbol{X}_i\, dt], [t + dt]\right) d\boldsymbol{r}\, d\boldsymbol{p}_i \tag{7.1–1}$$

But, since collisions are taking place in the gas, not all the phase points at $(\boldsymbol{r}, \boldsymbol{p}_i)$ arrive at $\left\{\left(\boldsymbol{r} + \frac{\boldsymbol{p}_i}{m_i}\, dt\right), (\boldsymbol{p}_i + \boldsymbol{X}_i\, dt)\right\}$ after the interval dt, for the molecules associated with those phase points which are deflected from their course by collisions suffer changes in momentum. There are also some phase points which did not begin at $(\boldsymbol{r}, \boldsymbol{p}_i)$ but which, as a result of colliding with other molecules, arrive at $\left\{\left(\boldsymbol{r} + \frac{\boldsymbol{p}_i}{m_i}\, dt\right), (\boldsymbol{p}_i + \boldsymbol{X}_i\, dt)\right\}$. Let the number of molecules of the ith kind lost from the momentum range $\boldsymbol{p}_i$ to $\boldsymbol{p}_i + d\boldsymbol{p}_i$ in the position range $\boldsymbol{r}$ to $\boldsymbol{r} + d\boldsymbol{r}$ because of collisions with molecules of type j during the time interval dt be $\Gamma_{ij}^{(-)}\, d\boldsymbol{r}\, d\boldsymbol{p}_i\, dt$. Similarly the number of molecules of the ith kind which in a time dt join the group of points which started from $(\boldsymbol{r}, \boldsymbol{p}_i)$ because of collision with molecules of type j is denoted by $\Gamma_{ij}^{(+)}\, d\boldsymbol{r}\, d\boldsymbol{p}_i\, dt$. When the equation for the flow of phase points takes into account the effects of collisions, it becomes

$$\begin{aligned} f_i^{(1)}&\left(\left[\boldsymbol{r} + \frac{\boldsymbol{p}_i}{m_i}\, dt\right], [\boldsymbol{p}_i + \boldsymbol{X}_i\, dt], [t + dt]\right) d\boldsymbol{r}\, d\boldsymbol{p}_i \\ &= f_i^{(1)}(\boldsymbol{r}, \boldsymbol{p}_i, t)\, d\boldsymbol{r}\, d\boldsymbol{p}_i + \Sigma_j[\Gamma_{ij}^{(+)} - \Gamma_{ij}^{(-)}]\, d\boldsymbol{r}\, d\boldsymbol{p}_i\, dt \end{aligned} \tag{7.1–2}$$

[5] Here we use explicitly the properties of Cartesian coordinate systems.

The term on the left-hand side of this equation may be expanded in a Taylor series about the point $(\boldsymbol{r}, \boldsymbol{p}_i, t)$:

$$f_i^{(1)}\left(\left[\boldsymbol{r} + \frac{\boldsymbol{p}_i}{m_i}\,dt\right], [\boldsymbol{p}_i + \boldsymbol{X}_i\,dt], [t + dt]\right) d\boldsymbol{r}\,d\boldsymbol{p}_i$$

$$= \left[f_i^{(1)}(\boldsymbol{r}, \boldsymbol{p}_i, t) + \frac{1}{m_i}\left(\boldsymbol{p}_i \cdot \frac{\partial f_i^{(1)}}{\partial \boldsymbol{r}}\right) dt + \left(\boldsymbol{X}_i \cdot \frac{\partial f_i^{(1)}}{\partial \boldsymbol{p}_i}\right) dt + \left(\frac{\partial f_i^{(1)}}{\partial t}\right) dt + \cdots\right] d\boldsymbol{r}\,d\boldsymbol{p}_i \quad (7.1\text{–}3)$$

These two equations may be combined to give the Boltzmann equation:

$$\frac{\partial f_i^{(1)}}{\partial t} + \frac{1}{m_i}\left(\boldsymbol{p}_i \cdot \frac{\partial f_i^{(1)}}{\partial \boldsymbol{r}}\right) + \left(\boldsymbol{X}_i \cdot \frac{\partial f_i^{(1)}}{\partial \boldsymbol{p}_i}\right) = \Sigma_j(\Gamma_{ij}^{(+)} - \Gamma_{ij}^{(-)}) \quad (7.1\text{–}4)$$

which describes the time rate of change of the function $f_i^{(1)}$. This equation has the same form as the Liouville equation except for the addition of the collision terms on the right side.

It should be mentioned that the quantities $\Gamma_{ij}^{(+)}$ and $\Gamma_{ij}^{(-)}$ do not include the contributions resulting from the molecules colliding with the walls. This is taken into account in the boundary conditions which are imposed on the hydrodynamical equations as considered in Chapter 11.

An explicit expression for the terms on the right side of the Boltzmann equation—the *collision integrals*—can be found from the following arguments. First we examine $\Gamma_{ij}^{(-)}\,d\boldsymbol{r}\,d\boldsymbol{p}_i\,dt$, the number of molecules of type i which are removed from the volume element $d\boldsymbol{r}\,d\boldsymbol{p}_i$ by collisions with the molecules of type j during an element of time dt. Let us consider a molecule of type i, located at the position $\boldsymbol{r}$, and having a momentum $\boldsymbol{p}_i$. We wish to find the probability that this molecule will experience a collision with a molecule of type j, in the time interval dt, with the impact parameter[6] in a range db about b. If molecule i is considered to be fixed, molecule j approaches it with a relative momentum $(\boldsymbol{p}_j - \boldsymbol{p}_i)$. This way of looking at the collision is pictured in Fig. 7.1–1. It is assumed that the intermolecular force is negligible for distances of separation greater than a distance A, which is small compared to the mean free path.

In Fig. 7.1–1 any molecule of type j within a sector of the cylindrical shell will undergo an encounter with molecule i during the time interval dt, characterized by an *impact parameter* b and an *initial relative velocity*:

$$\boldsymbol{g}_{ji} = \frac{\boldsymbol{p}_j}{m_j} - \frac{\boldsymbol{p}_i}{m_i} \quad (7.1\text{–}5)$$

[6] The geometry of collisions is discussed in § 1.5.

The probable number of molecules of type j within this sector is

$$f_j^{(1)}(\mathbf{r}, \mathbf{p}_j, t)g_{ij}b\,db\,d\epsilon\,dt \tag{7.1–6}$$

where

$$g_{ij} = g_{ji} = |\,\mathbf{g}_{ji}\,| \tag{7.1–7}$$

Now the total number of collisions experienced by this molecule i with molecules of type j is obtained by adding together the number of collisions characterized by all values of the parameters b and ϵ and all relative velocities g_{ji}. The result is

$$dt \iiint f_j^{(1)}(\mathbf{r}, \mathbf{p}_j, t)g_{ij}b\,db\,d\epsilon\,d\mathbf{p}_j \tag{7.1–8}$$

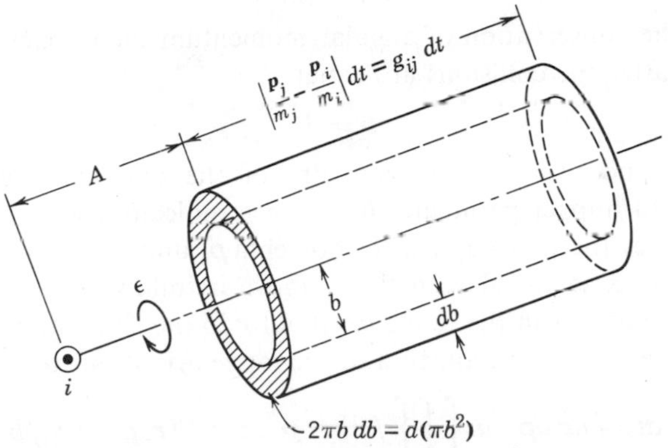

Fig. 7.1–1. Collisions of molecules of type j with one molecule of type i, in which the impact parameter is b. The distance A is essentially the intermolecular distance at which the potential begins to "take hold." Any molecule of type j which is initially located in the cylinder of base $2\pi b\,db$ and height $g_{ij}\,dt$ will undergo a collision with the molecule i during the short time interval dt.

Since the probable number of molecules of type i in the volume element $d\mathbf{r}$ about $\mathbf{r}$ with momentum in the range $d\mathbf{p}_i$ about $\mathbf{p}_i$ is $f_i^{(1)}(\mathbf{r}, \mathbf{p}_i, t)\,d\mathbf{r}\,d\mathbf{p}_i$, it follows that

$$\Gamma_{ij}^{(-)}\,d\mathbf{r}\,d\mathbf{p}_i\,dt = d\mathbf{r}\,d\mathbf{p}_i\,dt \iiint f_j^{(1)}(\mathbf{r}, \mathbf{p}_j, t) f_i^{(1)}(\mathbf{r}, \mathbf{p}_i, t)g_{ij}\,b\,db\,d\epsilon\,d\mathbf{p}_j \tag{7.1–9}$$

Hence

$$\Gamma_{ij}^{(-)} = \iiint f_i^{(1)} f_j^{(1)} g_{ij} b\,db\,d\epsilon\,d\mathbf{p}_j \tag{7.1–10}$$

represents the contribution to $\partial f_i^{(1)}/\partial t$ due to the removal from the group of molecules i by collisions with molecules of j. [In the last equation $f_i^{(1)}$ and $f_j^{(1)}$ are abbreviations for $f_i^{(1)}(\boldsymbol{r}, \boldsymbol{p}_i, t)$ and $f_j^{(1)}(\boldsymbol{r}, \boldsymbol{p}_j, t)$.]

The remaining portion of the collision integral, $\Gamma_{ij}^{(+)}$, may be evaluated in a similar manner. Let us consider a collision characterized by an impact parameter b between molecules with momenta $\boldsymbol{p}_i$ and $\boldsymbol{p}_j$. The momenta of the molecules after collision are denoted by $\boldsymbol{p}_i'$ and $\boldsymbol{p}_j'$. The values of the momenta after the collision are determined by the values of the momenta before the collision, the impact parameter, and the nature of the intermolecular force. For potential functions which are spherically symmetric it follows from the conservation of energy that the absolute values of the relative velocity before and after the collision are equal:

$$g_{ij} = g_{ij}' \tag{7.1-11}$$

And from the conservation of angular momentum the impact parameters before and after the collisions are equal:

$$b = b' \tag{7.1-12}$$

Furthermore because of the symmetry of the dynamical equations a collision, with impact parameter b, between molecules with momenta $\boldsymbol{p}_i'$ and $\boldsymbol{p}_j'$ leaves the molecules with momenta $\boldsymbol{p}_i$ and $\boldsymbol{p}_j$.

By arguments identical with those above it follows that the probable number of collisions in the range $d\boldsymbol{r}$ about $\boldsymbol{r}$ in the time interval dt which result in molecules with momenta in the range $d\boldsymbol{p}_i$ about $\boldsymbol{p}_i$ is

$$\Gamma_{ij}^{(+)}\, d\boldsymbol{r}\, d\boldsymbol{p}_i\, dt = d\boldsymbol{r}\, d\boldsymbol{p}_i'\, dt \iiint f_i^{(1)}(\boldsymbol{r}, \boldsymbol{p}_i', t) f_j^{(1)}(\boldsymbol{r}, \boldsymbol{p}_j', t) g_{ij}' b'\, db'\, d\epsilon'\, d\boldsymbol{p}_j' \tag{7.1-13}$$

Here the primed quantities are functions of the unprimed quantities, the functional relationship being determined by the nature of the intermolecular force. It is a direct consequence of the Liouville theorem that[7]

$$d\boldsymbol{p}_i'\, d\boldsymbol{p}_j' = d\boldsymbol{p}_i\, d\boldsymbol{p}_j \tag{7.1-14}$$

This fact may be used, along with the equivalence before and after collision of both g_{ij} and b, to obtain $\Gamma_{ij}^{(+)}$

$$\Gamma_{ij}^{(+)} = \iiint f_i^{(1)\prime} f_j^{(1)\prime} g_{ij} b\, db\, d\epsilon\, d\boldsymbol{p}_j \tag{7.1-15}$$

[7] A transformation which transforms a point in phase space to a point on the same trajectory a fixed time interval removed from the original point is a *contact* transformation. The theorem of conservation of extension in phase space, discussed in § 2.1c, is closely related to the theorem which states that the Jacobian of a contact transformation is unity. Since it is assumed that the position vectors of the two molecules are not changed in the collision, the transformation $(p_i, p_j) \rightarrow (p_i', p_j')$ is a contact transformation, and the Jacobian is unity.

where $f_i^{(1)\prime}$ and $f_j^{(1)\prime}$ represent $f_i^{(1)}(\boldsymbol{r}, \boldsymbol{p}_i', t)$ and $f_j^{(1)}(\boldsymbol{r}, \boldsymbol{p}_j', t)$, respectively. This expression gives the contribution to $\partial f_i^{(1)}/\partial t$ due to additions to the group of molecules by collision processes.

Now the expressions for $\Gamma_{ij}^{(+)}$ and $\Gamma_{ij}^{(-)}$ are substituted into the Boltzmann equation as it appears in Eq. 7.1–4, and the following equation for $f_i^{(1)}(\boldsymbol{r}, \boldsymbol{p}_i, t)$ results:

$$\frac{\partial f_i^{(1)}}{\partial t} + \frac{1}{m_i}\left(\boldsymbol{p}_i \cdot \frac{\partial f_i^{(1)}}{\partial \boldsymbol{r}_i}\right) + \left(\boldsymbol{X}_i \cdot \frac{\partial f_i^{(1)}}{\partial \boldsymbol{p}_i}\right)$$

$$= \Sigma_j \iiint (f_i^{(1)\prime} f_j^{(1)\prime} - f_i^{(1)} f_j^{(1)}) g_{ij} b \, db \, d\epsilon \, d\boldsymbol{p}_j \qquad (7.1\text{–}16)$$

This is the important Boltzmann integro-differential equation for the distribution function. Such an equation may be written for all the components in the gas mixture. In each of these equations, the distribution functions for all the components appear on the right-hand side of the equation under the integral sign. It should be kept in mind that the law of force enters these integrals implicitly. The functions $f_i^{(1)\prime}$ and $f_j^{(1)\prime}$ are functions of $\boldsymbol{p}_i'$ and $\boldsymbol{p}_j'$ which can be calculated from dynamical principles when $\boldsymbol{p}_i$, $\boldsymbol{p}_j$, and b are given, along with the intermolecular potential energy.

This derivation of the Boltzmann equation has the advantage of simplicity and direct physical interpretation. However, some aspects of this treatment present logical difficulties, because of the finite extension of the molecules and because of the finite duration of a collision.[8] To introduce greater rigor Kirkwood[9] has derived the Boltzmann equation directly from the Liouville theorem.

c. The Boltzmann equation derived from the Liouville theorem

A gas made up of N molecules may be represented by an ensemble described by the distribution function $f^{(N)}(\boldsymbol{r}^N, \boldsymbol{p}^N, t)$ in the γ-space of $6N$ dimensions. According to the Liouville equation discussed in § 1.4, the time variation of the distribution function, $f^{(N)}$, is given by the equation

$$\frac{\partial f^{(N)}}{\partial t} + \left(\frac{\partial H}{\partial \boldsymbol{p}^N} \cdot \frac{\partial f^{(N)}}{\partial \boldsymbol{r}^N}\right) - \left(\frac{\partial H}{\partial \boldsymbol{r}^N} \cdot \frac{\partial f^{(N)}}{\partial \boldsymbol{p}^N}\right) = 0 \qquad (7.1\text{–}17)$$

or

$$\frac{\partial f^{(N)}}{\partial t} + \sum_{k=1}^{N}\left\{\frac{1}{m_k}\left(\boldsymbol{p}_k \cdot \frac{\partial f^{(N)}}{\partial \boldsymbol{r}_k}\right) + \left((\boldsymbol{F}_k + \boldsymbol{X}_k) \cdot \frac{\partial f^{(N)}}{\partial \boldsymbol{p}_k}\right)\right\} = 0 \qquad (7.1\text{–}18)$$

[8] H. S. Green, *Molecular Theory of Fluids*, Interscience, New York, 1952, p. 218.
[9] J. G. Kirkwood, *J. Chem. Phys.*, **15**, 72 (1947).

where m_k is the mass of molecule k, $\boldsymbol{F}_k$ is the force on molecule k due to all the other molecules, and $\boldsymbol{X}_k$ is the force on molecule k due to an external field.

As stated earlier in this section, the macroscopic behavior of a gas is usually described with sufficient accuracy by a distribution function of lower order. For example, the macroscopic behavior of a gas at sufficiently low densities is described by the set of distribution functions $f_i^{(1)}$. These functions are defined as the integral of $f^{(N)}$ over the coordinates and momenta of all but one of the molecules. Because of the symmetry of $f^{(N)}$, this function depends only upon the species of the remaining molecule, indicated by the subscript i, and does not depend upon which molecule of the particular kind is chosen as special.

An equation for $f_i^{(1)}$ may be obtained from the Liouville equation (Eq. 7.1–18), by integrating over the coordinates of $(N - 1)$ molecules. When such an integration is performed and use is made of the fact that $f_i^{(1)}$ vanishes when $|\boldsymbol{p}_i| \to \infty$ and also at the walls of the containing vessel, we obtain

$$\frac{\partial f_i^{(1)}}{\partial t} + \frac{1}{m_i}\left(\boldsymbol{p}_i \cdot \frac{\partial f_i^{(1)}}{\partial \boldsymbol{r}}\right) + \left(\boldsymbol{X}_i \cdot \frac{\partial f_i^{(1)}}{\partial \boldsymbol{p}_i}\right)$$

$$= -\frac{1}{(N-1)!}\iint \left(\boldsymbol{F}_i \cdot \frac{\partial f^{(N)}}{\partial \boldsymbol{p}_i}\right) d\boldsymbol{r}^{N-1}\, d\boldsymbol{p}^{N-1} \qquad (7.1\text{–}19)$$

This equation does not in itself define the behavior of $f_i^{(1)}$. As discussed above, whenever we lower the level of description it is necessary to introduce a condition which effectively restricts the nature of the systems under consideration. In this case, in order to obtain the Boltzmann equation it is necessary to introduce the concept of "molecular chaos."

Kirkwood[8] showed that, in the derivation of the Boltzmann equation, the assumption is made implicitly that the distribution functions, $f_i^{(1)}(t)$, do not change appreciably during the duration of a collision. This may be seen in the following way. For a gas containing a single component and having only two body forces between the molecules, Eq. 7.1–19 reduces to

$$\frac{\partial f_1^{(1)}}{\partial t} + \frac{1}{m}\left(\boldsymbol{p}_1 \cdot \frac{\partial f_1^{(1)}}{\partial \boldsymbol{r}}\right) + \left(\boldsymbol{X}_1 \cdot \frac{\partial f_1^{(1)}}{\partial \boldsymbol{p}_1}\right) = -\iint \left(\boldsymbol{F}_{12} \cdot \frac{\partial f_{12}^{(2)}}{\partial \boldsymbol{p}_1}\right) d\boldsymbol{r}_2\, d\boldsymbol{p}_2 \qquad (7.1\text{–}20)$$

If the intermolecular forces are short range, we can define a collision diameter r_0, such that $\boldsymbol{F}_{12}$ is effectively zero when $|\boldsymbol{r}_1 - \boldsymbol{r}_2| \geqslant r_0$. All the contributions to the integral of Eq. 7.1–20 come from regions where $|\boldsymbol{r}_1 - \boldsymbol{r}_2| < r_0$. The principle of molecular chaos assumes that, outside this interaction sphere,

$$f_{12}^{(2)}(t) = f_1^{(1)}(t) f_2^{(1)}(t) \qquad |\boldsymbol{r}_1 - \boldsymbol{r}_2| \geqslant r_0 \tag{7.1–21}$$

But inside the interaction sphere, the pair distribution function, $f_{12}^{(2)}(t)$, is not known explicitly. Let us propose a scheme by which $f_{12}^{(2)}(t)$ could be calculated in principle.

If we neglect the possibility of three-body collisions, there is only one trajectory in two-particle phase space passing through the point $(\boldsymbol{r}_1, \boldsymbol{p}_1; \boldsymbol{r}_2, \boldsymbol{p}_2)$. Thus, following the trajectory backwards in time, if the system is at $(\boldsymbol{r}_1, \boldsymbol{p}_1; \boldsymbol{r}_2, \boldsymbol{p}_2)$ at the time t, we see that it must have been at a well-defined point $(\boldsymbol{r}_1', \boldsymbol{r}_2'; \boldsymbol{p}_1', \boldsymbol{p}_2')$ at time $t - \delta t$. Let us define the time $\delta t(\boldsymbol{r}_1, \boldsymbol{r}_2; \boldsymbol{p}_1, \boldsymbol{p}_2; t)$ as the interval of time such that $|\boldsymbol{r}_1' - \boldsymbol{r}_2'| = r_0$. At this time,

$$f_{12}^{(2)}(\boldsymbol{r}_1', \boldsymbol{r}_2'; \boldsymbol{p}_1', \boldsymbol{p}_2', t - \delta t) = f_1^{(1)}(\boldsymbol{r}_1', \boldsymbol{p}_1', t - \delta t)\, f_2^{(1)}(\boldsymbol{r}_2', \boldsymbol{p}_2', t - \delta t).$$

Thus it follows that

$$f_{12}^{(2)}(\boldsymbol{r}_1, \boldsymbol{r}_2; \boldsymbol{p}_1, \boldsymbol{p}_2, t) = f_1^{(1)}(\boldsymbol{r}_1', \boldsymbol{p}_1', t - \delta t) f_2^{(1)}(\boldsymbol{r}_2', \boldsymbol{p}_2', t - \delta t) \tag{7.1–22}$$

Thus, for every point $(\boldsymbol{r}_2, \boldsymbol{p}_2)$ in the integral of Eq. 7.1–20, the pair distribution function is related to one particle distribution functions at a time $t - \delta t$, and for each point there is a different δt. The magnitude of δt is of the order of the duration of a collision and is small compared with the times involved in macroscopic measurements.

Kirkwood corrected for the existence of the various δt corresponding to different points $(\boldsymbol{r}_2, \boldsymbol{p}_2)$ by time averaging Eq. 7.1–19 over an interval somewhat longer than the duration of a collision. This time averaging is denoted by a bar so that the time averaged distribution function is $\bar{f}_i^{(1)}$. In this manner he obtained

$$\frac{\partial \bar{f}_i^{(1)}}{\partial t} + \frac{1}{m_i}\left(\boldsymbol{p}_i \cdot \frac{\partial \bar{f}_i^{(1)}}{\partial \boldsymbol{r}}\right) + \left(\boldsymbol{X}_i \cdot \frac{\partial \bar{f}_i^{(1)}}{\partial \boldsymbol{p}_i}\right)$$

$$= \Sigma_j \iiint \overline{(f_i^{(1)\prime} f_j^{(1)\prime}} - \overline{f_i^{(1)} f_j^{(1)}}) g_{ij} b\, db\, d\epsilon\, d\boldsymbol{p}_j \tag{7.1–23}$$

This equation would be the same as the simple Boltzmann equation derived in the previous subsection if $\overline{f_i^{(1)} f_j^{(1)}} = \bar{f}_i^{(1)} \bar{f}_j^{(1)}$. This condition is satisfied provided that the distribution functions do not change appreciably in the interval of time τ_0 (comparable to the duration of a collision) over which they are time averaged. This may be seen in the following way:

$$\overline{f_i^{(1)}f_j^{(1)}} = \frac{1}{\tau_0}\int_{-\tau_0/2}^{\tau_0/2} f_i(t+\tau)f_j(t+\tau)d\tau = f_i^{(1)}(t)f_j^{(1)}(t)$$
$$+\frac{\tau_0^{\,2}}{24}\left(f_i^{(1)}\frac{\partial^2 f_j^{(1)}}{\partial t^2} + 2\,\frac{\partial f_i^{(1)}}{\partial t}\frac{\partial f_j^{(1)}}{\partial t} + f_j^{(1)}\frac{\partial^2 f_i^{(1)}}{\partial t^2}\right) \tag{7.1-24}$$
$$\bar{f}_i^{(1)}\bar{f}_j^{(1)} = \left(\frac{1}{\tau_0}\int_{-\tau_0/2}^{\tau_0/2} f_i^{(1)}(t+\tau)d\tau\right)\left(\frac{1}{\tau_0}\int_{-\tau_0/2}^{\tau_0/2} f_j^{(1)}(t+\tau)d\tau\right)$$
$$= f_i^{(1)}(t)f_j^{(1)}(t) + \frac{\tau_0^{\,2}}{24}\left(f_i^{(1)}\frac{\partial^2 f_j^{(1)}}{\partial t^2} + f_j^{(1)}\frac{\partial^2 f_i^{(1)}}{\partial t^2}\right)$$

In the usual derivations of the Boltzmann equation δt is neglected, and it is argued that the error introduced thereby is comparable to the error introduced by neglecting in the distribution function the distance between the centers of the molecules on collision. Both errors should be negligible, provided that the distribution functions do not change appreciably in times of the order of the collision duration or in distances of the order of a molecular diameter.

d. The distribution in velocities

In most kinetic theory problems it is more convenient to work in terms of velocities than momenta. Hence in the remainder of this chapter we shall use the distribution function in coordinate-velocity space, $f_i(\mathbf{r}, \mathbf{v}_i, t)$, rather than the distribution function in phase space, $f_i^{(1)}(\mathbf{r}, \mathbf{p}_i, t)$. In terms of this function the Boltzmann equation is[10]

$$\frac{\partial f_i}{\partial t} + \left(\mathbf{v}_i \cdot \frac{\partial f_i}{\partial \mathbf{r}}\right) + \frac{1}{m_i}\left(\mathbf{X}_i \cdot \frac{\partial f_i}{\partial \mathbf{v}_i}\right)$$
$$= \Sigma_j \iiint (f_i'f_j' - f_if_j)g_{ij}b\, db\, d\epsilon\, d\mathbf{v}_j \tag{7.1-25}$$

This equation forms the basis for the discussion of the transport properties of gases.

[10] We omit the superscript (1) when the distribution function is written in terms of the velocities rather than the momenta.

2. The Equations of Change

The hydrodynamic equations of change—the equations of conservation of mass, momentum, and energy—may be derived directly from the Boltzmann equation. Certain expressions involving the distribution function appear in the derivation of these equations. These expressions may be shown to represent the fluxes of mass, momentum, and energy and are directly related to the diffusion velocity, the pressure tensor, and the heat flux. These relations are derived in the present section. The approximate solutions of the Boltzmann equation and evaluation of the fluxes are discussed in subsequent sections. We begin this section by presenting a set of definitions of the various velocities needed to discuss the hydrodynamic equations.

a. Molecular velocities and stream velocities[1]

The *linear velocity* of a molecule of species j with respect to a coordinate system fixed in space is denoted by $\boldsymbol{v}_j$, with components v_{jx}, v_{jy}, v_{jz}. Its magnitude, $|\boldsymbol{v}_j| = v_j$, is called the molecular speed. For chemical species j present at a number density, n_j, we define an average velocity $\bar{\boldsymbol{v}}_j$ by

$$\bar{\boldsymbol{v}}_j(\boldsymbol{r}, t) = \frac{1}{n_j} \int \boldsymbol{v}_j f_j(\boldsymbol{r}, \boldsymbol{v}_j, t)\, d\boldsymbol{v}_j \tag{7.2–1}$$

The average velocity is a function of position and time and represents the macroscopic rate of flow of the chemical species j. The bar denotes, in general, the average value of a function of the velocity, for example,

$$\bar{\alpha}(\boldsymbol{r}, t) = \frac{1}{n_j} \int \alpha(\boldsymbol{v}_j) f_j(\boldsymbol{r}, \boldsymbol{v}_j, t)\, d\boldsymbol{v}_j \tag{7.2–2}$$

is the average value of $\alpha(\boldsymbol{v}_j)$.

[1] Inasmuch as the notation for velocities differs from that of S. Chapman and T. G. Cowling (*Mathematical Theory of Non-uniform Gases*, Cambridge University Press, 1939), we summarize the two notations here:

Velocity	*Chapman and Cowling*	*This Book*
Molecular velocity	$\boldsymbol{c}$	$\boldsymbol{v}$
Components of molecular velocity	u, v, w	v_x, v_y, v_z
Mass average velocity	$\boldsymbol{c}_0$	$\boldsymbol{v}_0$
Number average velocity	– – –	$\boldsymbol{\omega}$
Peculiar velocity	$\boldsymbol{C}$	$\boldsymbol{V}$
Diffusion velocity	$\bar{\boldsymbol{C}}$	$\bar{\boldsymbol{V}}$
Reduced velocity	$\mathscr{C}$	$\boldsymbol{W}$
Initial relative velocity	$\boldsymbol{g}$	$\boldsymbol{g}$
Reduced initial relative velocity	$\mathscr{g}$	$\boldsymbol{\gamma}$

The *mass average velocity*[2] is defined by:

$$\boldsymbol{v}_0(\boldsymbol{r}, t) = \frac{1}{\rho} \sum_j n_j m_j \overline{\boldsymbol{v}}_j \tag{7.2–3}$$

in which $\rho(\boldsymbol{r}, t)$ is the overall density of the gas at a particular point:

$$\rho(\boldsymbol{r}, t) = \Sigma_j n_j m_j \tag{7.2–4}$$

The mass average velocity is then a weighted mean, with each molecule being given a weight proportional to its mass. The momentum of the gas, per unit volume, is the same as if all the molecules were moving with the mass average velocity $\boldsymbol{v}_0$. This velocity is usually referred to as the *stream velocity* or the *flow velocity.*

The *peculiar velocity* of a molecule of species j is defined as the velocity of the molecule with respect to coordinates moving with the mass average velocity $\boldsymbol{v}_0$:

$$\boldsymbol{V}_j(\boldsymbol{v}_j, \boldsymbol{r}, t) = \boldsymbol{v}_j - \boldsymbol{v}_0 \tag{7.2–5}$$

The *diffusion velocity* of chemical species j is the rate of flow of molecules of j with respect to the mass average velocity of the gas,

$$\overline{\boldsymbol{V}}_j(\boldsymbol{r}, t) = \overline{\boldsymbol{v}}_j - \boldsymbol{v}_0 \tag{7.2–6}$$

Clearly the diffusion velocity is also the average of the peculiar velocity and may be written in the form

$$\overline{\boldsymbol{V}}_j(\boldsymbol{r}, t) = \frac{1}{n_j} \int (\boldsymbol{v}_j - \boldsymbol{v}_0) f_j(\boldsymbol{r}, \boldsymbol{v}_j, t)\, d\boldsymbol{v}_j \tag{7.2–7}$$

as a consequence of the definitions of $\boldsymbol{v}_j$ and $\boldsymbol{V}_j$. (Note that $\boldsymbol{v}_0$ is a function of position and time but not of the velocities $\boldsymbol{v}_j$.) It follows from the definitions of the diffusion velocity and the mass average velocity that

$$\Sigma_j n_j m_j \overline{\boldsymbol{V}}_j = \Sigma_j n_j m_j (\overline{\boldsymbol{v}}_j - \boldsymbol{v}_0) = 0 \tag{7.2–8}$$

Another kind of velocity—the *number average velocity*—is sometimes used. It is defined as

$$\boldsymbol{\omega}(\boldsymbol{r}, t) = \frac{1}{n} \Sigma n_j \overline{\boldsymbol{v}}_j \tag{7.2–9}$$

where $n = \Sigma n_j$ is the total number density of the mixture. It is easy to show that this velocity is simply related to the mass average velocity, thus:

$$\boldsymbol{\omega}(\boldsymbol{r}, t) = \boldsymbol{v}_0(\boldsymbol{r}, t) + \sum_j \frac{n_j}{n} \overline{\boldsymbol{V}}_i \tag{7.2–10}$$

[2] In Chapter 11, where the hydrodynamics of fluids is discussed, we omit the subscript 0 on the symbol $\boldsymbol{v}_0$ for the mass average velocity. This causes no confusion in Chapter 11, inasmuch as the molecular velocities $\boldsymbol{v}$ do not enter into the discussions there.

For the sake of simplicity in writing certain expressions in subsequent sections, a *reduced velocity*, $\boldsymbol{W}_j$, is used frequently. It is defined by

$$\boldsymbol{W}_j = \sqrt{\frac{m_j}{2kT}}\,\boldsymbol{V}_j \qquad (7.2\text{–}11)$$

and its magnitude is designated by W_j.

In addition to the velocities defined here, there are two other velocities which are used in this and subsequent chapters: the *initial relative velocity* $\boldsymbol{g}_{ij}$ of two molecules in a binary encounter (defined in Eq. 7.1–5), and the *reduced initial relative velocity* $\boldsymbol{\gamma}_{ij}$, which is

$$\boldsymbol{\gamma}_{ij} = \sqrt{\frac{\mu_{ij}}{2kT}}\,\boldsymbol{g}_{ij} \qquad (7.2\text{–}12)$$

in which μ_{ij} is the reduced mass of the two colliding molecules.

We define the kinetic theory temperature in terms of the mean peculiar kinetic energy, averaged over all types of molecules:

$$\tfrac{3}{2}\,kT = \frac{1}{n}\,\Sigma_j n_j(\tfrac{1}{2}m_j\overline{V_j^{\,2}}) \qquad (7.2\text{–}13)$$

The concept of temperature is introduced in § 2.4 through thermodynamic arguments. Since, however, the earlier discussion was restricted to equilibrium conditions, the previous definition has meaning only at equilibrium. The present more general definition agrees with the thermodynamic definition in this limit.

b. The flux vectors[3]

In a gas under non-equilibrium conditions gradients exist in one or more of the macroscopic physical properties of the system: composition, mass average velocity, and temperature. The gradients of these properties are the cause of the molecular transport of mass (m_j), momentum ($m_j\boldsymbol{V}_j$), and kinetic energy ($\tfrac{1}{2}m_jV_j^2$) through the gas. Since the mechanism of the transport of each of these molecular properties can be treated similarly, they are designated collectively by ψ_j (as was done in § 1.2a). It may be recalled that these properties have already been discussed in § 1.5a in connection with their importance as summational invariants of an encounter.

Let us now examine the transport of these properties ψ_j on the microscopic level. Imagine in the gas a small element of surface, dS, moving with the mass average velocity $\boldsymbol{v}_0$. The orientation of the surface is

[3] An elementary discussion of flux vectors is given in § 1.2a–iii in connection with a simplified kinetic theory.

designated by a unit vector $\boldsymbol{n}$ normal to the surface. Then the velocity of molecules of the jth species with respect to the surface dS is $\boldsymbol{V}_j$, according to the definition in Eq. 7.2–5. All those molecules of the jth species which have velocity[4] $\boldsymbol{V}_j$ and which cross dS during a time interval dt must at the beginning of this time interval be located in a cylinder with dS as its base and with generators parallel to $\boldsymbol{V}_j$ and of length $|\boldsymbol{V}_j|\,dt$. (See Fig. 7.2–1.) This cylinder has a volume $(\boldsymbol{n} \cdot \boldsymbol{V}_j)dS\,dt$. Since there are $f_j d\boldsymbol{V}_j$ molecules per unit volume which have a velocity $\boldsymbol{V}_j$, the number of molecules which cross dS during a time interval dt is:

$$f_j\,(\boldsymbol{n} \cdot \boldsymbol{V}_j)\,d\boldsymbol{V}_j\,dS\,dt \tag{7.2–14}$$

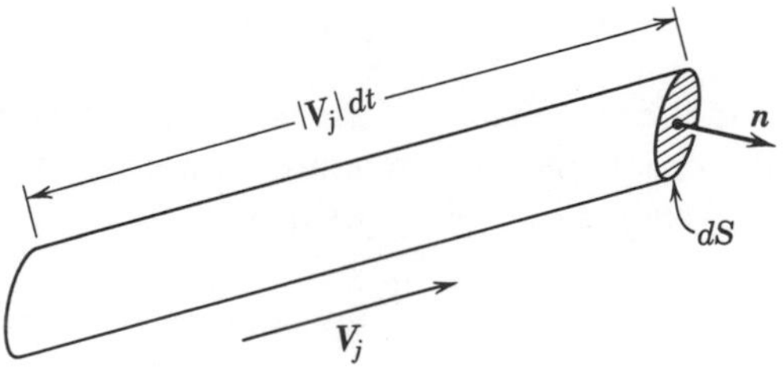

Fig. 7.2–1. The cylinder containing all those molecules of species j with velocity $\boldsymbol{V}_j$ which cross the surface dS during the time interval dt.

If associated with each molecule there is some property ψ_j, the magnitude of which depends on $\boldsymbol{V}_j$, then

$$\psi_j f_j\,(\boldsymbol{n} \cdot \boldsymbol{V}_j)\,d\boldsymbol{V}_j\,dS\,dt \tag{7.2–15}$$

is the amount of this property transported across dS during the time interval dt by molecules with velocities in the range $d\boldsymbol{V}_j$ about $\boldsymbol{V}_j$. The flux of this property (that is, the amount which crosses per unit area per unit time) is then

$$\psi_j f_j\,(\boldsymbol{n} \cdot \boldsymbol{V}_j)\,d\boldsymbol{V}_j \tag{7.2–16}$$

The total flux across the elementary surface is obtained by adding the contributions from molecules within all velocity ranges, and is, accordingly,

$$\int \psi_j f_j\,(\boldsymbol{n}_j \cdot \boldsymbol{V}_j)\,d\boldsymbol{V}_j = \left(\boldsymbol{n} \cdot \int \psi_j f_j \boldsymbol{V}_j\,d\boldsymbol{V}_j\right) \equiv (\boldsymbol{n} \cdot \boldsymbol{\Psi}_j) \tag{7.2–17}$$

The vector

$$\boldsymbol{\Psi}_j = \int \psi_j f_j \boldsymbol{V}_j\,d\boldsymbol{V}_j \tag{7.2–18}$$

[4] Or, more precisely, those molecules whose velocities lie in a small range $d\boldsymbol{V}_j$, about $\boldsymbol{V}_j$.

is called the *flux vector* associated with the property ψ_j. This vector has the physical significance that the component of the vector in any direction $\boldsymbol{n}$ is the flux of the associated physical property across a surface normal to $\boldsymbol{n}$.

Let us now examine the flux vectors related to the transport of mass, momentum, and kinetic energy:

i. *Transport of Mass*

If $\psi_j = m_j$, then[5]

$$\boldsymbol{\Psi}_j = m_j \int f_j \boldsymbol{V}_j \, d\boldsymbol{V}_j = n_j m_j \overline{\boldsymbol{V}}_j = \boldsymbol{j}_j \qquad (7.2\text{–}19)$$

is the *mass flux vector.*

ii. *Transport of Momentum*

If $\psi_j = m_j V_{jx}$, then

$$\boldsymbol{\Psi}_j = m_j \int V_{jx} \boldsymbol{V}_j f_j \, d\boldsymbol{V}_j = n_j m_j \overline{V_{jx} \boldsymbol{V}_j} \qquad (7.2\text{–}20)$$

is the flux vector associated with the transport of the x-component of momentum (relative to $\boldsymbol{v}_0$). This vector has components proportional to $\overline{V_{jx}V_{jx}}$, $\overline{V_{jx}V_{jy}}$, and $\overline{V_{jx}V_{jz}}$. Similar flux vectors can be obtained for the y- and z-components of the momentum, making a total of three flux vectors associated with momentum transfer. The nine components of these three vectors form a symmetric second-order tensor, p:

$$(p_j)_{xx} = m_j \int f_j V_{jx} V_{jx} \, d\boldsymbol{V}_j = n_j m_j \overline{V_{jx} V_{jx}}$$
$$(p_j)_{xy} = (p_j)_{yx} = n_j m_j \overline{V_{jx} V_{jy}}$$
$$\cdots \qquad (7.2\text{–}21)$$

Symbolically,

$$\mathsf{p}_j = n_j m_j \overline{\boldsymbol{V}_j \boldsymbol{V}_j} \qquad (7.2\text{–}22)$$

is the tensor associated with the partial pressure of the jth chemical species in the gas. The sum of the partial pressure tensors over all the species in the gas gives the *pressure tensor* for the mixture:

$$\mathsf{p} = \Sigma_j \mathsf{p}_j = \Sigma_j n_j m_j \overline{\boldsymbol{V}_j \boldsymbol{V}_j} \qquad (7.2\text{–}23)$$

The pressure tensor has the physical significance that it represents the flux of momentum through the gas. The individual components have the following meaning: the diagonal elements p_{xx}, p_{yy}, p_{zz} are *normal stresses*;

[5] It is to be noted that in computing average quantities, integration over $\boldsymbol{V}_i$ is equivalent to integration over $\boldsymbol{v}_i$ since the two differ by a constant, and the integration is over the entire range.

that is, p_{xx} is the force per unit area in the x-direction exerted on a plane surface in the gas which is perpendicular to the x-direction. The non-diagonal elements are *shear stresses*; that is, p_{yx} represents the force per unit area in the x-direction exerted on a plane surface which is perpendicular to the y-direction. The significance of the components, p_{yx}, p_{yy}, p_{yz}, which when combined give a resultant force $\boldsymbol{p}_y$ on a unit area perpendicular to the y-direction is shown in Fig. 7.2–2. The pressure

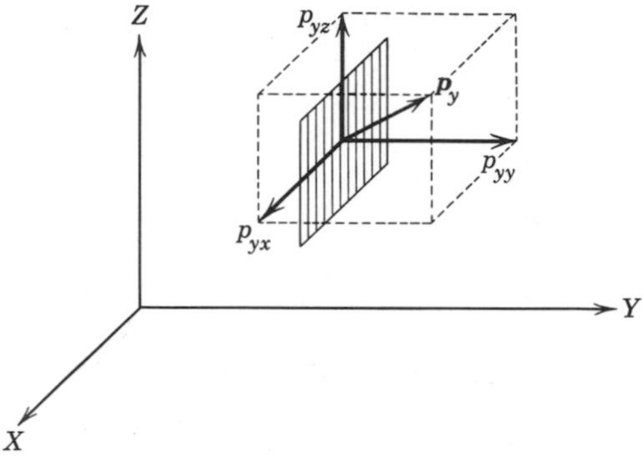

Fig. 7.2–2. Significance of the components of the pressure tensor. In this figure is shown a small element of surface whose normal is in the y-direction. On this element, located in the body of a system of gas, there is a total force per unit area $\boldsymbol{p}_y$. The components of this force are p_{yy} (a normal stress) and p_{yx} and p_{yz} (shear stresses). The nine components of this type make up the pressure tensor.

tensor represents stresses or pressures measured by an instrument moving with the stream velocity $\boldsymbol{v}_0$. The pressure as measured by a stationary gage depends upon $\boldsymbol{v}_0$ and the orientation of the gage.

It is shown in § 7.3 that at equilibrium the shear stresses are zero and the normal stresses are equal. In this case the force on any surface element in the gas is constant and normal to the surface regardless of its orientation, that is,

$$p_{xx} = p_{yy} = p_{zz} = p$$
$$p_{xy} = p_{yz} = \cdots = 0 \qquad (7.2\text{–}24)$$

where p is the equilibrium hydrostatic pressure.

iii. *Transport of Kinetic Energy*

If $\psi_j = \frac{1}{2}m_jV_j^2$, then

$$\boldsymbol{\Psi}_j = \tfrac{1}{2}m_j \int V_j^2\boldsymbol{V}_jf_j\, d\boldsymbol{V}_j = \tfrac{1}{2}n_jm_j\overline{V_j^2\boldsymbol{V}_j} = \boldsymbol{q}_j \qquad (7.2\text{–}25)$$

is the flux vector associated with the transport of kinetic energy of molecules of the jth species. The sum of such vectors over all the components in the gas mixture gives the *heat flux vector*, $\boldsymbol{q}$:

$$\boldsymbol{q} = \Sigma_j \boldsymbol{q}_j = \Sigma_j \tfrac{1}{2} n_j m_j \overline{V_j^2 \boldsymbol{V}_j} \tag{7.2–26}$$

This vector has the physical significance that its components, q_x, q_y, q_z, represent the flux of kinetic energy in the x, y, and z directions, respectively.

It should be noted that these are the correct expressions for the flux vectors in a dilute gas only. In a more dense gas there are additional terms due to *collisional transfer*. When two molecules undergo a collision, a certain amount of momentum and energy is transferred almost instantaneously from the center of one molecule to the center of the other. Now if in Fig. 7.2–1 the centers of two molecules should be on the opposite sides of the surface element, dS, the resulting "collisional transfer" provides a contribution to the fluxes which is not included in the above expressions.[6] This limitation is not of importance in this chapter inasmuch as the effect of collisional transfers is negligible under conditions for which the Boltzmann equation that we use is valid.

c. The general equations of change[7]

The fundamental hydrodynamic equations of continuity, motion, and energy balance may be derived from the Boltzmann equation without actually determining the form of the distribution functions, f_i. If the Boltzmann equation (Eq. 7.1–25) for the ith component is multiplied by the quantity, ψ_i, associated with the ith species and if the equation is integrated over $\boldsymbol{v}_i$, we obtain

$$\int \psi_i \left\{ \frac{\partial f_i}{\partial t} + \left(\boldsymbol{v}_i \cdot \frac{\partial f_i}{\partial \boldsymbol{r}} \right) + \frac{1}{m_i} \left(\boldsymbol{X}_i \cdot \frac{\partial f_i}{\partial \boldsymbol{v}_i} \right) \right\} d\boldsymbol{v}_i$$

$$= \Sigma_j \int\!\!\int\!\!\int\!\!\int \psi_i (f_i' f_j' - f_i f_j) g_{ij} b \, db \, d\epsilon \, d\boldsymbol{v}_i \, d\boldsymbol{v}_j \tag{7.2–27}$$

The three terms on the left-hand side of Eq. 7.2–27 may be transformed by simple manipulations:

$$\int \psi_i \frac{\partial f_i}{\partial t} d\boldsymbol{v}_i = \frac{\partial}{\partial t} \int \psi_i f_i \, d\boldsymbol{v}_i - \int f_i \frac{\partial \psi_i}{\partial t} d\boldsymbol{v}_i = \frac{\partial (n_i \overline{\psi_i})}{\partial t} - n_i \overline{\frac{\partial \psi_i}{\partial t}} \tag{7.2–28}$$

[6] A detailed discussion of this has been given by J. G. Kirkwood, *J. Chem. Phys.*, **18**, 817 (1950). (See §§ 9.3 and 9.4.)

[7] Although the derivation given here is valid only for dilute gases, the form of the equations of change as derived in this section is valid even for dense gases and liquids. (See § 9.4.)

$$\int \psi_i v_{ix} \frac{\partial f_i}{\partial x} d\boldsymbol{v}_i = \frac{\partial}{\partial x} \int \psi_i v_{ix} f_i \, d\boldsymbol{v}_i - \int f_i v_{ix} \frac{\partial \psi_i}{\partial x} d\boldsymbol{v}_i$$

$$= \frac{\partial}{\partial x} (n_i \overline{\psi_i v_{ix}}) - n_i \overline{v_{ix} \frac{\partial \psi_i}{\partial x}} \tag{7.2–29}$$

$$\int \psi_i \frac{\partial f_i}{\partial v_{ix}} d\boldsymbol{v}_i = \iint \Big[\psi_i f_i \Big]_{v_{ix}=-\infty}^{v_{ix}=+\infty} dv_{iy}\, dv_{iz} - \int f_i \frac{\partial \psi_i}{\partial v_{ix}} d\boldsymbol{v}_i$$

$$= - n_i \overline{\frac{\partial \psi_i}{\partial v_{ix}}} \tag{7.2–30}$$

The last two equations have been written for only the x-components.[8] In Eq. 7.2–30 the first term produced by the partial integration vanishes because the product $f_i \psi_i$ is assumed to diminish sufficiently rapidly for large v_i. We may use these last three equations to obtain

$$\frac{\partial (n_i \bar{\psi}_i)}{\partial t} + \left(\frac{\partial}{\partial \boldsymbol{r}} \cdot n_i \overline{\psi_i \boldsymbol{V}_i} \right) - n_i \left\{ \overline{\frac{\partial \psi_i}{\partial t}} + \left(\overline{\boldsymbol{v}_i \cdot \frac{\partial \psi_i}{\partial \boldsymbol{r}}} \right) + \left(\frac{\boldsymbol{X}_i}{m_i} \cdot \overline{\frac{\partial \psi_i}{\partial \boldsymbol{v}_i}} \right) \right\}$$

$$= \Sigma_j \iiiint \psi_i (f_i' f_j' - f_i f_j) g_{ij} b \, db \, d\epsilon \, d\boldsymbol{v}_i \, d\boldsymbol{v}_j \tag{7.2–31}$$

This is known as Enskog's *general equation of change* for a physical quantity ψ_i associated with the ith kind of molecule. Summation over i gives the equation of change for the property ψ for the entire gas.

d. Vanishing of the collision integrals for the summational invariants

The equations of the type shown in Eq. 7.2–31 are not particularly useful for a general ψ_i because of the very complex integrals which occur on the right side. However, if ψ_i is the mass of the ith molecule, then because the masses of the individual molecules are unchanged in a collision, it may be shown that

$$\iiiint m_i (f_i' f_j' - f_i f_j) g_{ij} b \, db \, d\epsilon \, d\boldsymbol{v}_i \, d\boldsymbol{v}_j = 0 \tag{7.2–32}$$

Furthermore, since mass, momentum, and energy are conserved during a collision, it may be shown that, if ψ_i is m_i, $m_i \boldsymbol{V}_i$, or $\frac{1}{2} m_i V_i^2$, then

$$\Sigma_{ij} \iiiint \psi_i (f_i' f_j' - f_i f_j) g_{ij} b \, db \, d\epsilon \, d\boldsymbol{v}_i \, d\boldsymbol{v}_j = 0 \tag{7.2–33}$$

These equations enable us to simplify the general equation of change.

[8] The quantity ψ_i may depend on $\boldsymbol{r}$ and t through $\boldsymbol{v}_0 (\boldsymbol{r}, t)$. The quantities $\boldsymbol{r}$, $\boldsymbol{V}_i$, and t are taken as independent variables.

The validity of these last two equations may be justified by the following arguments: The integral,

$$\iiiint \psi_i(f_i'f_j' - f_i f_j) g_{ij} b \, db \, d\epsilon \, d\mathbf{v}_i \, d\mathbf{v}_j \tag{7.2–34}$$

is equal to the integral

$$\iiiint \psi_i'(f_i f_j - f_i'f_j') g_{ij}' b' \, db' \, d\epsilon' \, d\mathbf{v}_i' \, d\mathbf{v}_j' \tag{7.2–35}$$

which is written in terms of inverse encounters. In § 7.1, it is stated that

$$g_{ij} = g_{ij}' \; ; b = b' \; ; d\mathbf{v}_i \, d\mathbf{v}_j = d\mathbf{v}_i' \, d\mathbf{v}_j' \tag{7.2–36}$$

so that Eq. 7.2–35 may be rewritten as

$$- \iiiint \psi_i'(f_i'f_j' - f_i f_j) g_{ij} b \, db \, d\epsilon \, d\mathbf{v}_i \, d\mathbf{v}_j \tag{7.2–37}$$

Since the integrals of Eqs. 7.2–34 and 37 are equal, they are also each equal to one-half the sum of the two. The result of this symmetrizing operation is that

$$\iiiint \psi_i(f_i'f_j' - f_i f_j) g_{ij} b \, db \, d\epsilon \, d\mathbf{v}_i \, d\mathbf{v}_j$$
$$= \tfrac{1}{2} \iiiint (\psi_i - \psi_i')(f_i'f_j' - f_i f_j) g_{ij} b \, db \, d\epsilon \, d\mathbf{v}_i \, d\mathbf{v}_j \tag{7.2–38}$$

For the case when $\psi_i = m_i$, this equation shows immediately the validity of Eq. 7.2–32, for $(\psi_i - \psi_i') = 0$ expresses the fact that the masses of the individual molecules are not changed during an encounter.

Equation 7.2–38 may be summed over both i and j; then the dummy indices may be interchanged to give the two equivalent expressions:

$$\tfrac{1}{2} \Sigma_{i,j} \iiiint (\psi_i - \psi_i')(f_i'f_j' - f_i f_j) g_{ij} b \, db \, d\epsilon \, d\mathbf{v}_i \, d\mathbf{v}_j$$
$$= \tfrac{1}{2} \Sigma_{i,j} \iiiint (\psi_j - \psi_j')(f_i'f_j' - f_i f_j) g_{ij} b \, db \, d\epsilon \, d\mathbf{v}_i \, d\mathbf{v}_j \tag{7.2–39}$$

so that

$$\Sigma_{i,j} \iiiint \psi_i(f_i'f_j' - f_i f_j) g_{ij} b \, db \, d\epsilon \, d\mathbf{v}_i \, d\mathbf{v}_j$$
$$= \tfrac{1}{4} \Sigma_{i,j} \iiiint (\psi_i + \psi_j - \psi_i' - \psi_j')(f_i'f_j' - f_i f_j) g_{ij} b \, db \, d\epsilon \, d\mathbf{v}_i \, d\mathbf{v}_j \tag{7.2–40}$$

The vanishing of the expression $(\psi_i + \psi_j - \psi_i' - \psi_j')$ is used to define the invariants of the encounter (see Eq. 1.5–5). Consequently, Eq. 7.2–33 is valid for the properties m_i, $m_i\mathbf{V}_i$, and $\frac{1}{2}m_iV_i^2$.

e. Explicit expressions for the equations of change

Now that the validity of Eqs. 7.2–32 and 7.2–33 has been demonstrated, this information may be used to derive the equations of change for specific molecular properties. This is done by letting ψ_i in Eq. 7.2–31 be m_i, $m_i\mathbf{V}_i$, and $\frac{1}{2}m_iV_i^2$, and then summing on the index i.

When $\psi_i = m_i$, following this procedure and using the vanishing of the collision integrals just established, we obtain

$$\frac{\partial n_i}{\partial t} + \left(\frac{\partial}{\partial \boldsymbol{r}} \cdot n_i \bar{\boldsymbol{v}}_i\right) = 0 \tag{7.2-41}$$

or, in terms of the diffusion velocity, this becomes

$$\frac{\partial n_i}{\partial t} + \left(\frac{\partial}{\partial \boldsymbol{r}} \cdot n_i(\boldsymbol{v}_0 + \bar{\boldsymbol{V}}_i)\right) = 0 \tag{7.2-42}$$

These last two equations represent two forms of the equation of continuity for the ith chemical species. If in the last expression each of the equations is multiplied by m_i and the equations added, then, since $\Sigma_i n_i m_i \bar{\boldsymbol{V}}_i = 0$,

$$\frac{\partial \rho}{\partial t} + \left(\frac{\partial}{\partial \boldsymbol{r}} \cdot \rho \boldsymbol{v}_0\right) = 0 \tag{7.2-43}$$

This is the *equation of continuity* for the gas as a whole.

If we put $\psi_i = m_i \boldsymbol{V}_i$ in Eq. 7.2-31 and sum over i, the collision integrals on the right side of the equation vanish so that we obtain

$$\Sigma_i m_i \left\{\frac{\partial n_i \bar{\boldsymbol{V}}_i}{\partial t} + \left(\frac{\partial}{\partial \boldsymbol{r}} \cdot n_i \overline{\boldsymbol{v}_i \boldsymbol{V}_i}\right) - n_i \frac{\overline{\partial \boldsymbol{V}_i}}{\partial t} - n_i \overline{\left(\boldsymbol{v}_i \cdot \frac{\partial}{\partial \boldsymbol{r}} \boldsymbol{V}_i\right)} - \frac{n_i}{m_i} \left(\boldsymbol{X}_i \cdot \overline{\frac{\partial}{\partial \boldsymbol{v}_i} \boldsymbol{V}_i}\right)\right\} = 0 \tag{7.2-44}$$

This equation may be simplified by using the relation among the diffusion velocities (Eq. 7.2-8) and the definition of the pressure tensor (Eq. 7.2-23). It should be noted that in the differentiations $\boldsymbol{r}$ and $\boldsymbol{v}_i$ are considered as the independent variables. After some manipulation, we obtain

$$\frac{\partial \boldsymbol{v}_0}{\partial t} + \left(\boldsymbol{v}_0 \cdot \frac{\partial}{\partial \boldsymbol{r}} \boldsymbol{v}_0\right) = -\frac{1}{\rho}\left(\frac{\partial}{\partial \boldsymbol{r}} \cdot \mathsf{P}\right) + \frac{1}{\rho} \Sigma_i n_i \boldsymbol{X}_i \tag{7.2-45}$$

for the *equation of motion of the gas.*

If for the case when $\psi_i = \frac{1}{2} m_i V_i^2$ in the general equation of change we perform the manipulations just described, this relation results:

$$\Sigma_i \tfrac{1}{2} m_i \left\{\frac{\partial n_i \overline{V_i^2}}{\partial t} + \left(\frac{\partial}{\partial \boldsymbol{r}} \cdot n_i \overline{V_i^2 \boldsymbol{v}_i}\right) - n_i \frac{\overline{\partial V_i^2}}{\partial t} - n_i \overline{\left(\boldsymbol{v}_i \cdot \frac{\partial V_i^2}{\partial \boldsymbol{r}}\right)} - n_i \left(\frac{\boldsymbol{X}_i}{m_i} \cdot \overline{\frac{\partial V_i^2}{\partial \boldsymbol{v}}}\right)\right\} = 0 \tag{7.2-46}$$

This equation may be transformed, using the same methods as in the treatment of the equation of motion. If we introduce the pressure tensor, defined by Eq. 7.2–23, and the heat flux vector, defined by Eq. 7.2–26 we obtain the *equation of energy balance*:

$$\frac{\partial}{\partial t}(\rho \hat{U}^{(\mathrm{tr})}) + \left(\frac{\partial}{\partial \boldsymbol{r}} \cdot \rho \hat{U}^{(\mathrm{tr})} \boldsymbol{v}_0\right) + \left(\frac{\partial}{\partial \boldsymbol{r}} \cdot \boldsymbol{q}\right) + \left(\mathsf{p} : \frac{\partial}{\partial \boldsymbol{r}} \boldsymbol{v}_0\right) - \Sigma_i n_i (\boldsymbol{X}_i \cdot \overline{\boldsymbol{V}}_i) = 0 \qquad (7.2\text{–}47)$$

where $\hat{U}^{(\mathrm{tr})}$ is the translational contribution to the internal energy per unit mass defined by [9]

$$\hat{U}^{(\mathrm{tr})} = \frac{1}{\rho} \Sigma_i \tfrac{1}{2} n_i m_i \overline{V_i^2} \qquad (7.2\text{–}48)$$

This quantity represents the total energy of a unit mass of gas in a coordinate frame moving with the mass average velocity, $\boldsymbol{v}_0$ (that is, the kinetic energy of the overall flow is not included), excluding the potential energy due to an external field.[10] If we use the equation of continuity (Eq. 7.2–43), the equation of energy balance (Eq. 7.2–47) may be written in a somewhat different form:

$$\rho \frac{\partial \hat{U}^{(\mathrm{tr})}}{\partial t} + \rho \left(\boldsymbol{v}_0 \cdot \frac{\partial \hat{U}^{(\mathrm{tr})}}{\partial \boldsymbol{r}}\right) = -\left(\frac{\partial}{\partial \boldsymbol{r}} \cdot \boldsymbol{q}\right) - \left(\mathsf{p} : \frac{\partial}{\partial \boldsymbol{r}} \boldsymbol{v}_0\right) + \Sigma_i n_i (\boldsymbol{X}_i \cdot \overline{\boldsymbol{V}}_i) \qquad (7.2\text{–}49)$$

This may be restated in terms of the temperature by using the definitions of $\hat{U}^{(\mathrm{tr})}$ and T:

$$\frac{3}{2} nk \left[\frac{\partial T}{\partial t} + \left(\boldsymbol{v}_0 \cdot \frac{\partial T}{\partial \boldsymbol{r}}\right)\right] = -\left(\frac{\partial}{\partial \boldsymbol{r}} \cdot \boldsymbol{q}\right) - \left(\mathsf{p} : \frac{\partial}{\partial \boldsymbol{r}} \boldsymbol{v}_0\right) + \Sigma_i n_i (\boldsymbol{X}_i \cdot \overline{\boldsymbol{V}}_i) + \frac{3}{2} kT \left(\frac{\partial}{\partial \boldsymbol{r}} \cdot \Sigma_i n_i \overline{\boldsymbol{V}}_i\right) \qquad (7.2\text{–}50)$$

Both of these equations apply only to a non-reacting mixture of particles with no internal degrees of freedom. Note, however, that if $\hat{U}^{(\mathrm{tr})}$ is replaced by $\hat{U}$ in Eq. 7.2–49, then it is valid for a reacting mixture of polyatomic molecules (cf. § 7.6).

[9] For molecules without internal degrees of freedom, such as being considered here, this is the only contribution to the internal energy. In general, however, there are other contributions. This is discussed in § 7.6.

[10] Some authors have written the energy balance equation in terms of an energy which includes either the kinetic energy associated with $\boldsymbol{V}_0$ or the potential energy associated with the external force, or both. The definition of $\hat{U}$ given here is used throughout this book.

3. Enskog's solution of the Boltzmann equation

Various attempts have been made to obtain approximate solutions to the Boltzmann equation. We consider here the perturbation technique of Enskog, which is a modification of a method due to Hilbert. This method of successive approximations can in principle be extended to systems in which the gradients of the thermodynamic quantities are quite large. In the zeroth approximation, the distribution function is locally Maxwellian, and we obtain the *Euler equations* of change. The first-order perturbation leads to the *Navier-Stokes*[1] *equations*; the second-order perturbation gives the *Burnett equations*. From the higher approximations more complicated equations result in which the flux vectors depend progressively on higher derivatives of the thermodynamic quantities and higher powers of the lower derivatives. The results of the higher-order perturbations are seldom used.

A gas in any initial state which is permitted to remain undisturbed for a sufficient length of time approaches a stationary state. If the gas is isolated adiabatically and not subject to an external force, the stationary state is a uniform condition in which all the distribution functions are Maxwellian. The proof that the equilibrium distribution functions are Maxwellian (the H-theorem) is discussed below. The remaining portion of the section is devoted to a discussion of Enskog's solution of the Boltzmann equation, and includes a detailed consideration of the results of the first-order perturbation. This method involves the solution of a set of integral equations by a variational procedure which leads to a rapidly converging series.

Recently a new solution has been developed by Grad which is more powerful for studying systems in states far removed from equilibrium. In the first approximation the results are identical with those of Enskog, but different expressions are obtained in the higher approximations. This second solution is discussed in § 7.5.

a. The *H*-theorem (the equilibrium solution)

The distribution functions describing the behavior of a gaseous mixture are the solutions of the set of Boltzmann equations, one for each component. From these equations, which are derived in § 7.1 and are given in final form in Eq. 7.1–25, we find that in the absence of external forces and under uniform conditions the time rate of change of the

[1] The Navier-Stokes equations apply to systems in which the gradients in the physical properties are small, that is, in which the physical properties do not change appreciably in a distance of mean free path.

distribution function f_i is given by

$$\frac{\partial f_i}{\partial t} = \Sigma_j \iiint (f_i'f_j' - f_if_j)g_{ij}b\, db\, d\epsilon\, d\mathbf{v}_j \qquad (7.3\text{–}1)$$

That these functions approach a limiting form which is the Maxwellian distribution function is evident from the treatment of equilibrium statistical mechanics of Chapter 2. It is, however, of interest to show that the Boltzmann equations lead to an identical set of equilibrium distribution functions.

In order to examine the equilibrium solution it is convenient to introduce a function $H(t)$, defined by

$$H(t) = \Sigma_i \int f_i(\mathbf{v}_i, t) \ln f_i(\mathbf{v}_i, t)\, d\mathbf{v}_i \qquad (7.3\text{–}2)$$

This function is a generalization of the entropy defined in Chapter 2 (see problem 11 at the end of that chapter), and the proof of the H-theorem given here is a special case of the general statistical proof of the second law of thermodynamics. Differentiating $H(t)$ and making use of the Boltzmann equation for $\partial f_i/\partial t$, we obtain

$$\frac{dH}{dt} = \Sigma_{ij} \iiiint (1 + \ln f_i)\,(f_i'f_j' - f_if_j)g_{ij}b\, db\, d\epsilon\, d\mathbf{v}_i\, d\mathbf{v}_j \qquad (7.3\text{–}3)$$

The integral on the right side of this equation may be symmetrized by the method explained in § 7.2d to give

$$\frac{dH}{dt} = -\frac{1}{4}\Sigma_{ij} \iiiint \left[\ln \frac{f_i'f_j'}{f_if_j}\right] (f_i'f_j' - f_if_j)g_{ij}b\, db\, d\epsilon\, d\mathbf{v}_i\, d\mathbf{v}_j \qquad (7.3\text{–}4)$$

Each of the integrands is of the form $(x - y) \ln (x/y)$, where in each case $x = f_i'f_j'$ and $y = f_if_j$. If $x > y$, both $(x - y)$ and $\ln (x/y)$ are positive; if $x < y$, both $(x - y)$ and $\ln (x/y)$ are negative. Therefore, the integrand of each of the integrals on the right of this equation is always positive or zero. Hence dH/dt is negative or zero so that $H(t)$ can never increase. From the basic definition (Eq. 7.3–2) it follows that $H(t)$ is bounded and thus approaches a limit[2] for large values of t. In this limit the distribution functions are such that integrands of each of the integrals on the right of Eq. 7.3–4 are identically zero. That is, at equilibrium,

$$\ln f_i + \ln f_j = \ln f_i' + \ln f_j' \qquad (7.3\text{–}5)$$

[2] For simplicity consider a single pure component rather than a mixture. The function H can equal $-\infty$ only if the integral $(a) = -\int f \ln f\, d\mathbf{v}$ fails to converge. If f decreases faster than $\exp(-\frac{1}{2}mv^2/kT)$ the integral (a) clearly converges. On the other hand, if f decreases more slowly than $\exp(-\frac{1}{2}mv^2/kT)$, then (a) still converges for the following reason. The integrand, $-f \ln f$, is then asymptotically less than $\frac{1}{2}mv^2 f$. Now, in any case, the integral $(b) = \int \frac{1}{2}mv^2 f\, d\mathbf{v}$, which corresponds to the total kinetic energy of the molecules, must converge. Chapman and Cowling consider this problem carefully. (See S. Chapman and T. G. Cowling, *Mathematical Theory of Non-uniform Gases*, Cambridge University Press, 1939, p. 70.)

and the logarithms of the distribution functions are summational invariants of a molecular collision.

It can be shown that the only summational invariants are linear combinations of the three invariants discussed in § 1.5, the mass m_i, the momentum $m_i\boldsymbol{v}_i$, and the kinetic energy $\frac{1}{2}m_iv_i^2$. Thus at equilibrium the most general expression for $\ln f_i$ is of the form

$$\ln f_i = a_i m_i + (\boldsymbol{b} \cdot (m_i\boldsymbol{v}_i)) + c(\tfrac{1}{2}m_iv_i^2) \tag{7.3–6}$$

where a_i, $\boldsymbol{b}$, and c are constants, depending (through the initial distribution functions) on the total number of molecules of kind i, the total momentum, and the total energy of the system. It is convenient to write this expression in terms of the physical parameters: n_i, the number density of molecules of kind i; $\boldsymbol{v}_0$, the mass average velocity, defined by Eq. 7.2–3; and the temperature T, defined by Eq. 7.2–13. In terms of these quantities the equilibrium distribution function is

$$f_i = n_i \left(\frac{m_i}{2\pi kT}\right)^{3/2} \exp\left(-m_iV_i^2/2kT\right) \tag{7.3–7}$$

where $\boldsymbol{V}_i = (\boldsymbol{v}_i - \boldsymbol{v}_0)$ is the peculiar velocity defined in Eq. 7.2–5.

At equilibrium f_i is independent of time, and hence the term on the right of Eq. 7.3–1 is zero. This constitutes a state of overall balance in the collision processes: the number of molecules of kind i in a particular velocity range which are lost due to collisions is exactly compensated by the number created by the collision processes. However, the H-theorem states that the only equilibrium solution[3] to the Boltzmann equations is one in which not only the term on the right of Eq. 7.3–1 is zero but also the integrand of each integral is identically zero. This is proof of the statistical principle of "detailed balance." That is, at equilibrium the number of molecules of kind i in a particular velocity range which are lost due to collisions of a particular kind with molecules of kind j is exactly balanced by the number of reverse collisions.

b. The Enskog series[4]

The Boltzmann equations (Eq. 7.1–25) may be written as

$$\frac{\partial f_i}{\partial t} + \left(\boldsymbol{v}_i \cdot \frac{\partial f_i}{\partial \boldsymbol{r}}\right) + \frac{1}{m_i}\left(\boldsymbol{X}_i \cdot \frac{\partial f_i}{\partial \boldsymbol{v}_i}\right) = \textstyle\sum_j J(f_i, f_j) \tag{7.3–8}$$

[3] The proof of this rests basically on the proof that the only summational invariants are linear combinations of the five scalars mentioned above.

[4] D. Enskog, *Archiv för Matematik, Astronomi, och Fysik*, **16**, § 16 (1922) *in German*; *Kinetische Theorie der Vorgänge in mäßig verdünnten Gasen*, Inaugural Dissertation, Uppsala (Sweden), Almqvist and Wiksell, 1917.

where $J(f_i, f_j)$ is the bilinear form

$$J(f_i, f_j) = \iiint (f_i'f_j' - f_if_j)g_{ij}b\, db\, d\epsilon\, d\mathbf{v}_j \tag{7.3–9}$$

representing the collision integrals.

The series solution to the Boltzmann equation is obtained by introducing a perturbation parameter ξ into the Boltzmann equation in such a manner that the frequency of collisions can be varied in an arbitrary manner without affecting the relative number of collisions of a particular kind. Thus we consider a hypothetical problem in which the Boltzmann equation is

$$\frac{\partial f_i}{\partial t} + \left(\mathbf{v}_i \cdot \frac{\partial f_i}{\partial \mathbf{r}}\right) + \frac{1}{m_i}\left(\mathbf{X}_i \cdot \frac{\partial f_i}{\partial \mathbf{v}_i}\right) = \frac{1}{\xi} \sum_j J(f_i, f_j) \tag{7.3–10}$$

and $1/\xi$ measures the frequency of collisions. If ξ were small, collisions would be very frequent and the gas would behave like a continuum in which local equilibrium is everywhere maintained. The distribution function is expanded[5] in a series in ξ,

$$f_i = f_i^{[0]} + \xi f_i^{[1]} + \xi^2 f_i^{[2]} + \cdots \tag{7.3–11}$$

If this series is introduced into the modified Boltzmann equation, Eq. 7.3–10, and the coefficients of equal powers of ξ equated, we obtain the following set of equations for the functions $f_i^{[0]}, f_i^{[1]}, f_i^{[2]}, \ldots$:

$$0 = \sum_j J(f_i^{[0]}, f_j^{[0]})$$

$$\frac{\partial f_i^{[0]}}{\partial t} + \left(\mathbf{v}_i \cdot \frac{\partial f_i^{[0]}}{\partial \mathbf{r}}\right) + \frac{1}{m_i}\left(\mathbf{X}_i \cdot \frac{\partial f_i^{[0]}}{\partial \mathbf{v}_i}\right) = \sum_j [J(f_i^{[0]}, f_j^{[1]}) + J(f_i^{[1]}, f_j^{[0]})]$$

$$\frac{\partial f_i^{[1]}}{\partial t} + \left(\mathbf{v}_i \cdot \frac{\partial f_i^{[1]}}{\partial \mathbf{r}}\right) + \frac{1}{m_i}\left(\mathbf{X}_i \cdot \frac{\partial f_i^{[1]}}{\partial \mathbf{v}_i}\right) = \sum_j [J(f_i^{[0]}, f_j^{[2]}) + J(f_i^{[1]}, f_j^{[1]}) + J(f_i^{[2]}, f_j^{[0]})] \tag{7.3–12}$$

These equations for the $f_i^{[r]}$ serve to determine the distribution function uniquely in the manner described below.

The first expression of the Eqs. 7.3–12 is the set of coupled integral equations considered in the discussion of the equilibrium solution of the

[5] The superscripts indicating the degree of approximation are enclosed in brackets to avoid any possible confusion with the notation $f^{(1)}$, $f^{(2)}$, etc., where the superscripts enclosed in parentheses denote the order of the distribution function.

Boltzmann equation and the H-theorem (§ 7.3a). From the arguments presented there, it is clear that the most general solution of these equations is

$$f_i^{[0]} = n_i \left(\frac{m_i}{2\pi kT}\right)^{3/2} \exp\{-m_i(\boldsymbol{v}_i - \boldsymbol{v}_0)^2/2kT\} \qquad (7.3\text{–}13)$$

The quantities

$$n_i = n_i(\boldsymbol{r}, t); \quad \boldsymbol{v}_0 = \boldsymbol{v}_0(\boldsymbol{r}, t); \quad T = T(\boldsymbol{r}, t) \qquad (7.3\text{–}14)$$

are arbitrary functions of space and time insofar as this set of equations is concerned. In order for these functions to represent the local values of the physical quantities, number density, mass average velocity, and temperature, it is necessary for the solutions of the remaining equations to be such that

$$\int f_i \, d\boldsymbol{v}_i = n_i \qquad (7.3\text{–}15)$$

$$\Sigma_i m_i \int \boldsymbol{v}_i f_i \, d\boldsymbol{v}_i = \rho \boldsymbol{v}_0 \qquad (7.3\text{–}16)$$

$$\tfrac{1}{2}\Sigma_i m_i \int (\boldsymbol{v}_i - \boldsymbol{v}_0)^2 f_i \, d\boldsymbol{v}_i = \tfrac{3}{2}nkT \qquad (7.3\text{–}17)$$

It may be shown[6] that each of the remaining integral equations of Eqs. 7.3–12 along with the auxiliary conditions,

$$\int f_i^{[r]} \, d\boldsymbol{v}_i = 0 \qquad r = 1, 2, 3, \cdots \qquad (7.3\text{–}18)$$

$$\Sigma_i m_i \int \boldsymbol{v}_i f_i^{[r]} \, d\boldsymbol{v}_i = 0 \qquad r = 1, 2, 3, \cdots \qquad (7.3\text{–}19)$$

$$\tfrac{1}{2}\Sigma_i m_i \int (\boldsymbol{v}_i - \boldsymbol{v}_0)^2 f_i^{[r]} \, d\boldsymbol{v}_i = 0 \qquad r = 1, 2, 3, \cdots \qquad (7.3\text{–}20)$$

specify uniquely a set of functions $f_i^{[r]}$. Since the set of distribution functions so defined satisfies the conditions of Eqs. 7.3–15, 16, and 17, it is used as the solution to the Boltzmann equation.

c. The first-order perturbation solution

The equation for the $f_i^{[1]}$ may be written in terms of a perturbation function ϕ_i, defined thus:

$$f_i^{[1]}(\boldsymbol{r}, \boldsymbol{v}_i, t) = f_i^{[0]}(\boldsymbol{r}, \boldsymbol{v}_i, t)\phi_i(\boldsymbol{r}, \boldsymbol{v}_i, t) \qquad (7.3\text{–}21)$$

[6] S. Chapman and T. G. Cowling, *The Mathematical Theory of Non-uniform Gases*, Cambridge University Press (1939).

In terms of this function the second of Eqs. 7.3-12 becomes

$$\frac{\partial f_i^{[0]}}{\partial t} + \left(\boldsymbol{v}_i \cdot \frac{\partial f_i^{[0]}}{\partial \boldsymbol{r}}\right) + \frac{1}{m_i}\left(\boldsymbol{X}_i \cdot \frac{\partial f_i^{[0]}}{\partial \boldsymbol{v}_i}\right)$$
$$= \Sigma_j \iiint f_i^{[0]} f_j^{[0]} (\phi_i' + \phi_j' - \phi_i - \phi_j) g_{ij} b \, db \, d\epsilon \, d\boldsymbol{v}_j \qquad (7.3\text{-}22)$$

The preceding auxiliary conditions, in terms of ϕ_i, are

$$\int f_i^{[0]} \phi_i \, d\boldsymbol{v}_i = 0 \qquad (7.3\text{-}23)$$

$$\Sigma_i m_i \int \boldsymbol{v}_i f_i^{[0]} \phi_i \, d\boldsymbol{v}_i = 0 \qquad (7.3\text{-}24)$$

$$\tfrac{1}{2} \Sigma_i m_i \int (\boldsymbol{v}_i - \boldsymbol{v}_0)^2 f_i^{[0]} \phi_i \, d\boldsymbol{v}_i = 0 \qquad (7.3\text{-}25)$$

As stated above, this set of equations is just sufficient to define the perturbation functions ϕ_i uniquely.

The differentiations of the function $f_i^{[0]}$ indicated in Eq. 7.3-22 may be carried out. The resulting expressions involve space and time derivatives of the functions $n_i(\boldsymbol{r}, t)$, $\boldsymbol{v}_0(\boldsymbol{r}, t)$, and $T(\boldsymbol{r}, t)$. The time derivatives are eliminated by means of the equations of change (Eqs. 7.2-42, 45, 50). It is consistent with this approximation to replace f_i by $f_i^{[0]}$ in the integrals for the flux vectors which occur in the equations of change (that is, we use $\boldsymbol{j}_i = 0$, $\mathsf{p} = p\mathsf{U}$, $\boldsymbol{q} = 0$). The resulting equation for the perturbation function ϕ_i is

$$f_i^{[0]} \left[\frac{n}{n_i} (\boldsymbol{V}_i \cdot \boldsymbol{d}_i) + \left(\mathsf{b}_i : \frac{\partial}{\partial \boldsymbol{r}} \boldsymbol{v}_0\right) - (\tfrac{5}{2} - W_i^2)\left(\boldsymbol{V}_i \cdot \frac{\partial \ln T}{\partial \boldsymbol{r}}\right)\right]$$
$$= \Sigma_j \iiint f_i^{[0]} f_j^{[0]} (\phi_i' + \phi_j' - \phi_i - \phi_j) g_{ij} b \, db \, d\epsilon \, d\boldsymbol{v}_j \qquad (7.3\text{-}26)$$

The quantities $\boldsymbol{d}_i$ and b_i are defined by

$$\boldsymbol{d}_i = \frac{\partial}{\partial \boldsymbol{r}}\left(\frac{n_i}{n}\right) + \left(\frac{n_i}{n} - \frac{n_i m_i}{\rho}\right) \frac{\partial \ln p}{\partial \boldsymbol{r}} - \left(\frac{n_i m_i}{p\rho}\right)\left[\frac{\rho}{m_i} \boldsymbol{X}_i - \Sigma_j n_j \boldsymbol{X}_j\right] \qquad (7.3\text{-}27)$$

$$\mathsf{b}_i = 2[\boldsymbol{W}_i \boldsymbol{W}_i - \tfrac{1}{3} W_i^2 \mathsf{U}] \qquad (7.3\text{-}28)$$

The dimensionless velocity $\boldsymbol{W}_i$ is defined by Eq. 7.2-11.

d. The integral equations

The perturbation function ϕ_i depends upon space and time only through the quantities n_i, $\boldsymbol{v}_0$, and T and their space derivatives. It is clear from the form of the integral equation for ϕ_i that this quantity is linear in the derivatives and has the form

$$\phi_i = -\left(\boldsymbol{A}_i \cdot \frac{\partial \ln T}{\partial \boldsymbol{r}}\right) - \left(\mathsf{B}_i : \frac{\partial}{\partial \boldsymbol{r}} \boldsymbol{v}_0\right) + n \, \Sigma_j (\boldsymbol{C}_i^{(j)} \cdot \boldsymbol{d}_j) \qquad (7.3\text{-}29)$$

where the $\boldsymbol{A}_i$, B_i, and $\boldsymbol{C}_i^{(j)}$ are functions of the dimensionless velocity, $\boldsymbol{W}_i$, the local composition, and the local temperature. If there are ν components to the chemical mixture, there are only $(\nu - 1)$ independent vectors $\boldsymbol{d}_i$, since, according to the definition of the $\boldsymbol{d}_i$,

$$\Sigma_i \boldsymbol{d}_i = 0 \tag{7.3–30}$$

This fact enables us to set one of the $\boldsymbol{C}_i^{(j)}$ equal to zero for each i. To retain the symmetry we let

$$\boldsymbol{C}_i^{(i)} = 0 \tag{7.3–31}$$

When the expression for ϕ_i in Eq. 7.3–29 is inserted into Eq. 7.3–26 and the coefficients of similar gradients are equated, separate integral equations result[7] for the functions $\boldsymbol{C}_i^{(j)}$, B_i, and $\boldsymbol{A}_i$:

$$\begin{aligned}\frac{1}{n_i} f_i^{[0]} (\delta_{ih} - \delta_{ik}) \boldsymbol{V}_i \\ = \Sigma_j \iiint \{\boldsymbol{C}_i^{(h)\prime} + \boldsymbol{C}_j^{(h)\prime} - \boldsymbol{C}_i^{(k)\prime} - \boldsymbol{C}_j^{(k)\prime} - \boldsymbol{C}_i^{(h)} - \boldsymbol{C}_j^{(h)} + \boldsymbol{C}_i^{(k)} + \boldsymbol{C}_j^{(k)}\} \\ \times f_i^{[0]} f_j^{[0]} g_{ij} b\, db\, d\epsilon\, d\boldsymbol{v}_j\end{aligned} \tag{7.3–32}$$

$$f_i^{[0]} \mathsf{b}_i = - \Sigma_j \iiint \{\mathsf{B}_i' + \mathsf{B}_j' - \mathsf{B}_i - \mathsf{B}_j\} f_i^{[0]} f_j^{[0]} g_{ij} b\, db\, d\epsilon\, d\boldsymbol{v}_j \tag{7.3–33}$$

$$f_i^{[0]} (\tfrac{5}{2} - W_i^2) \boldsymbol{V}_i = \Sigma_j \iiint \{\boldsymbol{A}_i' + \boldsymbol{A}_j' - \boldsymbol{A}_i - \boldsymbol{A}_j\} f_i^{[0]} f_j^{[0]} g_{ij} b\, db\, d\epsilon\, d\boldsymbol{v}_j \tag{7.3–34}$$

[7] Equation 7.3–32 is obtained in the following way. We have by inserting from Eq. 7.3–29 into Eq. 7.3–26:

$$\begin{aligned}\frac{1}{n_i} f_i^{[0]} (\boldsymbol{V}_i \cdot \boldsymbol{d}_i) = \Sigma_{j,h} \iiint (\{\boldsymbol{C}_i^{(h)\prime} + \boldsymbol{C}_j^{(h)\prime} - \boldsymbol{C}_i^{(h)} - \boldsymbol{C}_j^{(h)}\} \cdot \boldsymbol{d}_h) \\ \times f_i^{[0]} f_j^{[0]} g_{ij} b\, db\, d\epsilon\, d\boldsymbol{v}_j\end{aligned}$$

Then, making use of the fact that $\sum_j \boldsymbol{d}_j = 0$, and making algebraic rearrangements, we have

$$\begin{aligned}\frac{1}{n_i} f_i^{[0]} (\boldsymbol{V}_i \cdot \Sigma_h \delta_{ih} \boldsymbol{d}_h) \\ = \sum_{h \neq k} \boldsymbol{d}_h \cdot \Sigma_j \iiint [\boldsymbol{C}_i^{(h)\prime} + \boldsymbol{C}_j^{(h)\prime} - \boldsymbol{C}_i^{(k)\prime} - \boldsymbol{C}_j^{(k)\prime} - \boldsymbol{C}_i^{(h)} - \boldsymbol{C}_j^{(h)} + \boldsymbol{C}_i^{(k)} + \boldsymbol{C}_j^{(k)}] \\ \times f_i^{[0]} f_j^{[0]} g_{ij} b\, db\, d\epsilon\, d\boldsymbol{v}_j\end{aligned}$$

The left-hand side may now be rewritten as $\frac{1}{n_i} f_i^{[0]} (\boldsymbol{V}_i \cdot \sum_{h \neq k} (\delta_{ih} - \delta_{ik}) \boldsymbol{d}_h)$ and coefficients of $\boldsymbol{d}_h$ may now be equated to give Eq. 7.3–32.

In these equations the only variables involved are $n_i(\boldsymbol{r}, t)$, $T(\boldsymbol{r}, t)$ and $\boldsymbol{V}_i(\boldsymbol{r}, t)$ [actually we choose to work with $\boldsymbol{W}_i(\boldsymbol{r}, t)$ rather than $\boldsymbol{V}_i(\boldsymbol{r}, t)$]. The spatial coordinates (or derivatives) do not occur explicitly. Consequently, $\boldsymbol{A}_i$, B_i and $\boldsymbol{C}_i^{(j)}$ are functions of the space coordinates only through the variables mentioned above. It may be shown that any vector function of $\boldsymbol{W}_i$, the only vector variable, is the vector itself multiplied by some scalar function of the absolute value of the vector $\boldsymbol{W}_i$. Hence $\boldsymbol{A}_i$ and $\boldsymbol{C}_i^{(j)}$ are of the form

$$\boldsymbol{C}_i^{(j)} = \boldsymbol{W}_i C_i^{(j)}(W_i) \qquad (7.3\text{–}35)$$

$$\boldsymbol{A}_i = \boldsymbol{W}_i A_i(W_i) \qquad (7.3\text{–}36)$$

where $C_i^{(j)}$ and A_i are functions of W_i which depend parametrically on T and all of the n_j. It may also be shown that the only tensor B_i, which is consistent with the form of the integral equation for B_i (Eq. 7.3–33), is of the form

$$\mathsf{B}_i = \{\boldsymbol{W}_i\boldsymbol{W}_i - \tfrac{1}{3}W_i^2\mathsf{U}\}B_i(W_i) \qquad (7.3\text{–}37)$$

The integral equations for the $\boldsymbol{A}_i$, B_i, and $\boldsymbol{C}_i^{(j)}$ (Eqs. 7.3–32, 33, and 34) are, of course, to be solved in conjunction with the auxiliary conditions imposed by Eqs. 7.3–23, 24, and 25. In terms of these quantities the auxiliary relations become

$$\Sigma_i\sqrt{m_i}\int([\boldsymbol{C}_i^{(j)} - \boldsymbol{C}_i^{(k)}] \cdot \boldsymbol{W}_i) f_i^{[0]}\, d\boldsymbol{v}_i = 0 \qquad (7.3\text{–}38)$$

$$\Sigma_i\sqrt{m_i}\int(\boldsymbol{A}_i \cdot \boldsymbol{W}_i) f_i^{[0]}\, d\boldsymbol{v}_i = 0 \qquad (7.3\text{–}39)$$

There is no auxiliary equation for the B_i analogous to these equations inasmuch as the functions of the form defined by Eq. 7.3–37 automatically satisfy the constraints (Eqs. 7.3–23, 24, and 25) for any arbitrary function $B_i(W_i)$.

Solutions to these integral equations have been obtained by two equivalent methods, that of Chapman and Cowling[6] and a variational method.[8] In both methods the scalar functions $C_i^{(j)}(W_i)$, $B_i(W_i)$, and $A_i(W_i)$ are expanded in a series of Sonine polynomials.[9] Chapman and Cowling used an *infinite series of these polynomials*, with the result that the transport coefficients are expressed in terms of ratios of infinite determinants. To get numerical values it is necessary to consider only a few elements of these determinants since the convergence of the ratios of determinants is quite rapid as additional rows and columns are included. Here we discuss the problem from the standpoint of the variational method.

[8] C. F. Curtiss and J. O. Hirschfelder, *J. Chem. Phys.*, **17**, 550 (1949).

[9] See Eq. 7.3–57 for the definition of these polynomials.

Because the integral equations (Eqs. 7.3–32, 33, and 34) are quite similar in form, it is possible to write one general equation for a tensor $\mathsf{T}_i^{(h,k)}$ which includes all three of these equations:[10]

$$\mathsf{R}_i^{(h,k)} = \Sigma_j \iiint [\mathsf{T}_i^{(h,k)\prime} + \mathsf{T}_j^{(h,k)\prime} - \mathsf{T}_i^{(h,k)} - \mathsf{T}_j^{(h,k)}] f_i^{[0]} f_j^{[0]} g_{ij} b \, db \, d\epsilon \, d\boldsymbol{v}_j \tag{7.3–40}$$

The correspondence between the symbols $\mathsf{R}_i^{(h,k)}$ and $\mathsf{T}_i^{(h,k)}$ and their counterparts in Eqs. 7.3–32, 33, and 34 is given in the following table:

Equation	$\mathsf{R}_i^{(h,k)}$	$\mathsf{T}_i^{(h,k)}$
7.3–32	$\frac{1}{n_i} f_i^{[0]} (\delta_{ih} - \delta_{ik}) \boldsymbol{V}_i$	$\boldsymbol{C}_i^{(h)} - \boldsymbol{C}_i^{(k)}$
7.3–33	$-2f_i^{[0]} (\boldsymbol{W}_i \boldsymbol{W}_i - \frac{1}{3} W_i^2 \mathsf{U})$	B_i
7.3–34	$f_i^{[0]} (\frac{5}{2} - W_i^2) \boldsymbol{V}_i$	$\boldsymbol{A}_i$

It should be kept in mind that the subscript i in the symbol $\mathsf{T}_i^{(h,k)}$ indicates that the tensor is a function of the velocity vector $\boldsymbol{W}_i$. The subscripts on the other symbols, R, $\boldsymbol{A}$, B, $\boldsymbol{C}$, have the same significance. We shall seek an approximate solution to the integral equation for $\mathsf{T}_i^{(h,k)}$ in Eq. 7.3–40 by a variational method. This equation, together with the auxiliary equation

$$\Sigma_i \sqrt{m_i} \int (\mathsf{T}_i^{(h,k)} \cdot \boldsymbol{W}_i) f_i^{[0]} d\boldsymbol{v}_i = 0 \tag{7.3–41}$$

which is equivalent to Eqs. 7.3–38 and 39, serves to specify $\mathsf{T}_i^{(h,k)}$ uniquely.

e. Several important integral theorems

In the following development several abbreviations in the notation will be useful. Let G_{ij} and H_{ij} be any two tensors, in general functions of both $\boldsymbol{W}_i$ and $\boldsymbol{W}_j$. Then let us define $[\mathsf{G}_{ij}; \mathsf{H}_{ij}]_{ij}$ by [11]

$$[\mathsf{G}_{ij}; \mathsf{H}_{ij}]_{ij} = -\frac{1}{n_i n_j} \iiiint (\mathsf{G}_{ij} : (\mathsf{H}_{ij}' - \mathsf{H}_{ij})) f_i^{[0]} f_j^{[0]} g_{ij} b \, db \, d\epsilon \, d\boldsymbol{v}_i \, d\boldsymbol{v}_j \tag{7.3–42}$$

[10] Two of the equations involve the vector quantities (tensors of order one) $\boldsymbol{A}_i$ and $\boldsymbol{C}_i^{(h)} - \boldsymbol{C}_i^{(k)}$.

[11] The subscript ij on the bracket indicates an integration over the variables $\boldsymbol{v}_i$ and $\boldsymbol{v}_j$.

From symmetry arguments similar to those introduced in § 7.2d it follows that

$$[\mathsf{G}_{ij}; \mathsf{H}_{ij}]_{ij} = \frac{1}{2n_i n_j} \iiiint ((\mathsf{G}_{ij}' - \mathsf{G}_{ij}) : (\mathsf{H}_{ij}' - \mathsf{H}_{ij})) \times f_i^{[0]} f_j^{[0]} g_{ij} b \, db \, d\epsilon \, d\boldsymbol{v}_i \, d\boldsymbol{v}_j \quad (7.3\text{–}43)$$

Hence the bracket expression is symmetrical with respect to the interchange of G_{ij} and H_{ij} and also of the i and j subscripts on the bracket:

$$[\mathsf{G}_{ij}; \mathsf{H}_{ij}]_{ij} = [\mathsf{H}_{ij}; \mathsf{G}_{ij}]_{ij} = [\mathsf{G}_{ij}; \mathsf{H}_{ij}]_{ji} = [\mathsf{H}_{ij}; \mathsf{G}_{ij}]_{ji} \quad (7.3\text{–}44)$$

This operator [ ] is a linear operator. If G_{ij} and H_{ij} have the form

$$\mathsf{G}_{ij} = \mathsf{K}_i + \mathsf{L}_j; \quad \mathsf{H}_{ij} = \mathsf{M}_i + \mathsf{N}_j \quad (7.3\text{–}45)$$

where K_i and M_i depend only on $\boldsymbol{W}_i$, and L_j and N_j depend only on $\boldsymbol{W}_j$, then

$$\begin{aligned}[\mathsf{K}_i + \mathsf{L}_j; \mathsf{M}_i + \mathsf{N}_j]_{ij} &= [\mathsf{K}_i; \mathsf{M}_i + \mathsf{N}_j]_{ij} + [\mathsf{L}_j; \mathsf{M}_i + \mathsf{N}_j]_{ij} \\ &= [\mathsf{K}_i; \mathsf{M}_i]_{ij} + [\mathsf{K}_i; \mathsf{N}_j]_{ij} \quad (7.3\text{–}46) \\ &\quad + [\mathsf{L}_j; \mathsf{M}_i]_{ij} + [\mathsf{L}_j; \mathsf{N}_j]_{ij}\end{aligned}$$

It should be noted that the subscripts on the symbols within the bracket indicate the functional dependence of the tensors on the velocities $\boldsymbol{W}_i$ and $\boldsymbol{W}_j$. The subscript ij on the bracket itself indicates that the integral is evaluated for collisions between molecules i and j.

Let us consider two sets of tensor functions, K_i and L_i and define an additional quantity in terms of these sets by

$$\{\mathsf{K}; \mathsf{L}\} = \Sigma_{ij} n_i n_j [\mathsf{K}_i + \mathsf{K}_j; \mathsf{L}_i + \mathsf{L}_j]_{ij} \quad (7.3\text{–}47)$$

These brace expressions satisfy the following relations:

$$\{\mathsf{K}; \mathsf{L}\} = \{\mathsf{L}; \mathsf{K}\} \quad (7.3\text{–}48)$$

$$\{\mathsf{K}; \mathsf{L} + \mathsf{M}\} = \{\mathsf{K}; \mathsf{L}\} + \{\mathsf{K}; \mathsf{M}\} \quad (7.3\text{–}49)$$

Inasmuch as $\{\mathsf{K}; \mathsf{K}\}$ represents a sum of integrals, all of which have non-negative integrands, it follows that

$$\{\mathsf{K}; \mathsf{K}\} \geqslant 0 \quad (7.3\text{–}50)$$

It can easily be shown that $\{\mathsf{K}; \mathsf{K}\}$ vanishes if and only if K_i is a linear combination of the summational invariants. The only linear combination of the summational invariants which satisfies the auxiliary condition (Eq. 7.3–41) is identically zero. Hence if we restrict the consideration to sets of tensor functions, K_i, which satisfy the auxiliary condition, it follows that $\{\mathsf{K}; \mathsf{K}\}$ vanishes if and only if each of the K_i are identically zero.

f. A variational principle

A variational principle may be employed now to obtain approximate solutions to the integral equations (Eq. 7.3–40). Let us use as trial functions a set of functions $\mathsf{t}_i^{(h,k)}$, which satisfy the equations

$$\int (\mathsf{t}_i^{(h,k)} : \mathsf{R}_i^{(h,k)})\, d\boldsymbol{v}_i = -\Sigma_j n_i n_j [\mathsf{t}_i^{(h,k)}; \mathsf{t}_i^{(h,k)} + \mathsf{t}_j^{(h,k)}]_{ij} \qquad (7.3\text{–}51)$$

and contain as many arbitrary parameters as is convenient.

If $\mathsf{t}_i^{(h,k)}$ is "double-dotted" into the integral equation for $\mathsf{T}_i^{(h,k)}$ (Eq. 7.3–40) and an integration is carried out over $\boldsymbol{v}_i$, we obtain

$$\int (\mathsf{t}_i^{(h,k)} : \mathsf{R}_i^{(h,k)})\, d\boldsymbol{v}_i = -\Sigma_j n_i n_j [\mathsf{t}_i^{(h,k)}; \mathsf{T}_i^{(h,k)} + \mathsf{T}_j^{(h,k)}]_{ij} \qquad (7.3\text{–}52)$$

where the $\mathsf{t}_i^{(h,k)}$ are the trial functions and the $\mathsf{T}_i^{(h,k)}$ are the exact solutions to the integral equations. Equating the right sides of the last two equations and summing over i, we obtain (after making use of the symmetry relations in Eq. 7.3–44 and the definition of the brace expressions in Eq. 7.3–47).

$$\{\mathsf{t}^{(h,k)}; \mathsf{T}^{(h,k)}\} = \{\mathsf{t}^{(h,k)}; \mathsf{t}^{(h,k)}\} \qquad (7.3\text{–}53)$$

Since the brace expression written for two identical sets of functions is non-negative (Eq. 7.3–50),

$$\{\mathsf{T}^{(h,k)} - \mathsf{t}^{(h,k)}; \mathsf{T}^{(h,k)} - \mathsf{t}^{(h,k)}\} \geqslant 0 \qquad (7.3\text{–}54)$$

Then, making use of the linear operator property of the operator $\{\,\}$ (Eq. 7.3–49) and the relation between the trial functions and the exact solutions (Eq. 7.3–53), we find that

$$\{\mathsf{t}^{(h,k)}; \mathsf{t}^{(h,k)}\} \leqslant \{\mathsf{T}^{(h,k)}; \mathsf{T}^{(h,k)}\} \qquad (7.3\text{–}55)$$

This is the statement of the variational method[12] of obtaining approximations to the solutions, $\mathsf{T}_i^{(h,k)}$. Specifically, the method of solution is as follows. We begin by choosing a set of trial functions, $\mathsf{t}_i^{(h,k)}$, which contain a number of arbitrary parameters. Then, if only those trial functions are considered which satisfy the auxiliary condition (Eq. 7.3–41), the equality sign in Eq. 7.3–55 applies only when $\mathsf{T}_i^{(h,k)}$ and $\mathsf{t}_i^{(h,k)}$ are identical. Thus the best approximation to the true solution of the integral equation is obtained by maximizing the brace on the left of Eq. 7.3–55 with respect to all the available parameters in the set of trial functions. That is, for the best approximation

$$\delta\{\mathsf{t}^{(h,k)}; \mathsf{t}^{(h,k)}\} = -2\delta\, \Sigma_i \int (\mathsf{t}_i^{(h,k)} : \mathsf{R}_i^{(h,k)})\, d\boldsymbol{v}_i = 0 \qquad (7.3\text{–}56)$$

This, along with the Eq. 7.3–51, which restricts the choice of the trial functions, forms the basis of the variational method of solution of the integral equations (Eqs. 7.3–40).

[12] A statement of the variational principle was first made by E. J. Hellund and E. A. Uehling, *Phys. Rev.*, **56**, 818 (1939).

g. Application of the variational principle (the Sonine polynomial expansion)

Let us now consider the implications of the variational principle discussed above when the trial functions are taken to be finite series of polynomials in the square of the velocity, W_i^2. It is convenient to make use of the Sonine polynomials, $S_n^{(m)}$, defined by[13]

$$S_n^{(m)}(x) = \sum_j \frac{(-1)^j(m+n)!}{(n+j)!(m-j)!j!} x^j \tag{7.3–57}$$

These polynomials satisfy the orthogonality condition,

$$\int_0^\infty x^n e^{-x} S_n^{(m)}(x) S_n^{(m')}(x)\, dx = \frac{(n+m)!}{m!} \delta_{mm'} \tag{7.3–58}$$

and are convenient, for as two special cases of this orthogonality relation we have

$$\int f_i^{[0]} S_{3/2}^{(m)}(W_i^2) V_i^2 \, d\mathbf{V}_i = \frac{3n_i kT}{m_i} \delta_{m0} \tag{7.3–59}$$

$$\int f_i^{[0]} S_{5/2}^{(m)}(W_i^2) V_i^4 \, d\mathbf{V}_i = 15n_i \left(\frac{kT}{m_i}\right)^2 \delta_{m0} \tag{7.3–60}$$

As the trial functions, $\mathsf{t}_i^{(h,k)}$, we now take a *finite* linear combination of the Sonine polynomials $S_n^{(m)}(W_i^2)$

$$\mathsf{t}_i^{(h,k)}(\boldsymbol{W}_i) = \mathsf{W}_i \sum_{m=0}^{\xi-1} t_{im}^{(h,k)}(\xi) S_n^{(m)}(W_i^2) \tag{7.3–61}$$

in which the values of the index n and the meaning of the tensor W_i are as follows:

When $\mathsf{T}_i^{(h,k)}$ is:	The value of the index n is:	The quantity W_i is:	The Sonine expansion coefficients $t_{im}^{(h,k)}$ are designated by:
$\boldsymbol{A}_i$	3/2	$\boldsymbol{W}_i$	$a_{im}(\xi)$
B_i	5/2	$\boldsymbol{W}_i\boldsymbol{W}_i - \frac{1}{3}W_i^2\mathsf{U}$	$b_{im}(\xi)$
$\boldsymbol{C}_i^{(h)} - \boldsymbol{C}_i^{(k)}$	3/2	$\boldsymbol{W}_i$	$c_{im}^{(h,k)}(\xi)$

[13] Except for the normalization, these polynomials are the same as the associated Laguerre polynomials. The first two Sonine polynomials are

$$S_m^{(0)}(x) = 1$$

$$S_m^{(1)}(x) = m + 1 - x$$

For reasons which will become apparent later we have indicated the dependence of the expansion coefficients on the number of terms, ξ, used in the finite series trial function. These coefficients are *not* coefficients in an *infinite series* expansion and therefore do depend upon the number of terms used.

Let us define

$$R_{im}^{(h,k)} = \int (\mathsf{R}_i^{(h,k)} : \mathsf{W}_i) S_n^{(m)}(W_i^2)\, dV_i \tag{7.3–62}$$

and

$$g^{(h,k)} = \Sigma_{i,m}\, t_{im}^{(h,k)} R_{im}^{(h,k)} \tag{7.3–63}$$

In terms of these quantities the constraints on the trial functions (Eq. 7.3–51) become

$$w_i^{(h,k)} = 0 \tag{7.3–64}$$

where

$$\begin{aligned} w_i^{(h,k)} &= \sum_{m=0}^{\xi-1} t_{im}^{(h,k)} R_{im}^{(h,k)} \\ &+ \sum_j \sum_{m=0}^{\xi-1} \sum_{m'=0}^{\xi-1} n_i n_j t_{im}^{(h,k)} \Big[t_{im'}^{(h,k)} [\mathsf{W}_i S_n^{(m)}(W_i^2); \mathsf{W}_i S_n^{(m')}(W_i^2)]_{ij} \\ &\qquad + t_{jm'}^{(h,k)} [\mathsf{W}_i S_n^{(m)}(W_i^2); \mathsf{W}_j S_n^{(m')}(W_j^2)]_{ij} \Big] \end{aligned} \tag{7.3–65}$$

and the statement of the variational criterion (Eq. 7.3–56) becomes

$$\delta g^{(h,k)} = 0 \tag{7.3–66}$$

The problem then is to find the extremum of $g^{(h,k)}$ subject to the constraints of Eq. 7.3–64. This extremum is determined by the method of the Lagrangian multipliers. Let $\lambda_i^{(h,k)}$ be the multipliers. Then the Eq. 7.3–64 and the equations

$$\left(\frac{\partial g^{(h,k)}}{\partial t_{im}^{(h,k)}}\right) + \Sigma_r \lambda_r^{(h,k)} \left(\frac{\partial w_r^{(h,k)}}{\partial t_{im}^{(h,k)}}\right) = 0 \tag{7.3–67}$$

are sufficient to determine the $\lambda_i^{(h,k)}$ and the expansion coefficients, $t_{im}^{(h,k)}(\xi)$. Performing the indicated differentiations, we get

$$\begin{aligned} &[1 + \lambda_i^{(h,k)}] R_{im}^{(h,k)} \\ &+ \sum_j \sum_{m'=0}^{\xi-1} n_i n_j \Big[2\lambda_i^{(h,k)} t_{im'}^{(h,k)} [\mathsf{W}_i S_n^{m}(W_i^2); \mathsf{W}_i S_n^{(m')}(W_i^2)]_{ij} \\ &\qquad + (\lambda_i^{(h,k)} + \lambda_j^{(h,k)}) t_{jm'}^{(h,k)} [\mathsf{W}_i S_n^{(m)}(W_i^2); \mathsf{W}_j S_n^{(m')}(W_j^2)]_{ij} \Big] = 0 \end{aligned} \tag{7.3–68}$$

$$i = 1, 2, \cdots, \nu$$

$$m = 0, 1 \cdots, \xi - 1$$

The only solution to this set of equations together with the Eq. (7.3–64) is:

$$\lambda_i^{(h,k)} = 1 \qquad i = 1, 2, 3, \cdots, \nu \tag{7.3–69}$$

with the constants, $t_{im}^{(h,k)}(\xi)$, determined by Eq. 7.3–68, with $\lambda_i^{(h,k)} = 1$. The equations may be rewritten in the form

$$\sum_j \sum_{m'=0}^{\xi-1} Q_{ij}^{mm'} t_{jm'}^{(h,k)}(\xi) = -R_{im}^{(h,k)} \tag{7.3–70}$$

where

$$Q_{ij}^{mm'} = \sum_l n_i n_l \left[\delta_{ij}[\mathsf{W}_i S_n^{(m)}(W_i^2); \mathsf{W}_i S_n^{(m')}(W_i^2)]_{il} \atop + \delta_{jl}[\mathsf{W}_i S_n^{(m)}(W_i^2); \mathsf{W}_l S_n^{(m')}(W_l^2)]_{il} \right] \tag{7.3–71}$$

When $\mathsf{T}_i^{(h,k)}$ is B_i (and $t_{im}^{(h,k)}$ is $b_{im}^{(h,k)}$), the equations (Eqs. 7.3–70) are all linearly independent, and hence all the $b_{im}^{(h,k)}$ can be determined from these equations. However, when $\mathsf{T}_i^{(h,k)}$ is either $\boldsymbol{A}_i$ or $(\boldsymbol{C}_i^{(h)} - \boldsymbol{C}_i^{(k)})$ then it may be shown that the set of equations for $m = 0$ includes one redundant equation. For these we make use of the auxiliary relation, Eq. 7.3–41, which, in terms of the $t_{im}^{(h,k)}$, is

$$\sum_i \sum_{m=0}^{\xi-1} \sqrt{m_i}\, t_{im}^{(h,k)}(\xi) \int W_i^2 S_{3/2}^{(m)}(W_i^2) f_i^{[0]}\, d\boldsymbol{V}_i = 0 \tag{7.3–72}$$

Because of the orthogonality relation (Eq. 7.3–59) the terms in this sum for $m \neq 0$ are zero. Thus the auxiliary condition becomes

$$\sum_i \sqrt{m_i}\, t_{i0}^{(h,k)} (2n_i/\sqrt{\pi}) \Gamma(\tfrac{5}{2}) = 0 \tag{7.3–73}$$

Consequently, when $\mathsf{T}_i^{(h,k)}$ is either $\boldsymbol{A}_i$ or $(\boldsymbol{C}_i^{(h)} - \boldsymbol{C}_i^{(k)})$, the trial function must be chosen so that

$$\sum_i n_i \sqrt{m_i}\, t_{i0}^{(h,k)} = 0 \tag{7.3–74}$$

This supplies the additional information needed for the specification of all the coefficients $t_{im}^{(h,k)}(\xi)$. Equation 7.3–70 may be modified to include this statement. The result is

$$\sum_j \sum_{m'=0}^{\xi-1} \tilde{Q}_{ij}^{mm'} t_{jm'}^{(h,k)}(\xi) = -R_{im}^{(h,k)} \tag{7.3–75}$$

where

$$\tilde{Q}_{ij}^{mm'} = \begin{cases} Q_{ij}^{mm'}, & \text{when } t_{jm'}^{(h,k)} = b_{jm'} \\[2ex] Q_{ij}^{mm'} - \dfrac{n_j\sqrt{m_j}}{n_i\sqrt{m_i}} Q_{ii}^{mm'}\, \delta_{m0}\, \delta_{m'0}, & \text{when } t_{jm'}^{(h,k)} = a_{jm'} \text{ or } c_{jm'}^{(h,k)} \end{cases} \tag{7.3–76}$$

From Eq. 7.3–75 we can obtain the $t_{im}^{(h,k)}(\xi)$, which give the functions $\boldsymbol{A}_i$, B_i, and $\boldsymbol{C}_i^{(j)}$. These, in turn, give the function ϕ_i and the distribution function f_i correct to the first order. The knowledge of the non-equilibrium distribution function f_i then provides the information needed for the evaluation of the transport coefficients. Fortunately, it turns out that only a few terms in the Sonine expansion are needed. For viscosity and diffusion, one term gives a good approximation; the result of using two terms differs by only a few per cent. For diffusion the use of one term alone does not describe the dependence of the diffusion coefficient on concentration; the slight concentration-dependence is brought out when the first two terms in the Sonine expansion are used. The transfer of mass due to a temperature gradient (that is, thermal diffusion) does not appear at all in the expression for the diffusion velocity if only one term in the Sonine polynomial expansion is used. It is also necessary to consider two terms in the Sonine expansion to obtain the expression for the first approximation to the thermal conductivity.

4. The Formulation of the Transport Coefficients

The integral expressions for the flux vectors, which describe the flux of mass, momentum, and energy, are derived in § 7.2. The evaluation of these integrals requires a knowledge of the distribution function f_i. An approximation to the distribution function in the form $f_i = f_i^{[0]}(1 + \phi_i)$ is derived in the previous section. If the expression for ϕ_i, given by Eq. 7.3–29, is used in the integrals for the flux vectors, we obtain expressions for the diffusion velocity, the pressure tensor, and the heat flux vector in terms of integrals of the functions $A_i(W_i)$, $B_i(W_i)$, and $C_i^{(j)}(W_i)$. It is these relations for the flux vectors which we shall now derive and discuss.

a. Diffusion and thermal diffusion coefficients in terms of Sonine expansion coefficients

The integral for the diffusion velocity (Eq. 7.2–7) rewritten in terms of ϕ_i is

$$\bar{\boldsymbol{V}}_i = \frac{1}{n_i}\int \boldsymbol{V}_i f_i \, d\boldsymbol{V}_i = \frac{1}{n_i}\int \boldsymbol{V}_i \phi_i f_i^{[0]} \, d\boldsymbol{V}_i \qquad (7.4\text{–}1)$$

Using Eq. 7.3–29, and noting that the term involving B_i vanishes on integration, we may write $\bar{\boldsymbol{V}}_i$ as

$$\bar{\boldsymbol{V}}_i = \frac{1}{n_i}\int \left\{ n\Sigma_j(\boldsymbol{C}_i^{(j)} \cdot \boldsymbol{d}_j) - \left(\boldsymbol{A}_i \cdot \frac{\partial \ln T}{\partial \boldsymbol{r}}\right)\right\} \boldsymbol{V}_i f_i^{[0]} \, d\boldsymbol{V}_i \qquad (7.4\text{–}2)$$

Then, making use of the form of the functions $\boldsymbol{A}_i$ and $\boldsymbol{C}_i^{(j)}$, indicated in Eqs. 7.3–35 and 36, we obtain[1]

$$\bar{\boldsymbol{V}}_i = \left(\frac{n^2}{n_i\rho}\right) \Sigma_j m_j D_{ij}\boldsymbol{d}_j - \frac{1}{n_i m_i} D_i^T \frac{\partial \ln T}{\partial \boldsymbol{r}} \tag{7.4–3}$$

In this expression $\boldsymbol{d}_j$ is defined in Eq. 7.3–27, and D_{ij} and D_i^T are

$$D_{ij} = \frac{\rho}{3nm_j}\sqrt{\frac{2kT}{m_i}}\int C_i^{(j)}(W_i)W_i^2 f_i^{[0]}\, d\boldsymbol{V}_i \tag{7.4–4}$$

$$D_i^T = \frac{m_i}{3}\sqrt{\frac{2kT}{m_i}}\int A_i(W_i)W_i^2 f_i^{[0]}\, d\boldsymbol{V}_i \tag{7.4–5}$$

These are the *multicomponent diffusion coefficients* and the *multicomponent thermal diffusion coefficients*, respectively.[2]

Thus we see that the diffusion velocity, $\bar{\boldsymbol{V}}_i$, contains terms proportional to the concentration gradient, the pressure gradient, the difference in the external forces acting on the various species of molecules, and the gradient in the temperature. Before the work of Chapman and Enskog thermal diffusion in the gas phase had been unknown theoretically and unobserved experimentally. Subsequent experiments of Chapman and Dootson[3] revealed that the theoretical prediction of this phenomenon was quite correct. This is one of a number of historically interesting instances of the prediction of experimentally observable phenomena by rigorous theoretical analysis. Experiments for the measurement of D_{ij} are usually arranged so that the contributions to the diffusion velocity resulting from pressure gradients, external forces, and thermal gradients are negligible.

By means of the Sonine polynomial expansions (Eq. 7.3–61) the expressions for the diffusion coefficients become

$$D_{ij}(\xi) = \left(\frac{\rho}{3nm_j}\right)\sqrt{\frac{m_i}{2kT}}\sum_{m=0}^{\xi-1} c_{im}^{(j,i)}(\xi)\int V_i^2 S_{3/2}^{(m)}(W_i^2) f_i^{[0]}\, d\boldsymbol{V}_i \tag{7.4–6}$$

[1] Here we use a theorem which may be proved by symmetry arguments. If $F(r)$ is any function of the absolute value of $\boldsymbol{r}$, then

$$\int F(r)\boldsymbol{rr}\, d\boldsymbol{r} = \tfrac{1}{3}\mathsf{U}\int F(r)r^2\, d\boldsymbol{r}$$

[2] There is a considerable variation among authors in the nomenclature and definition of these quantities. The D_{ij} defined here are such that for a two-component mixture the D_{ij} reduce to the usual *binary diffusion coefficients*, $\mathscr{D}_{ij}$. The quantities D_i^T have not been previously defined. In the case of two components, the D_i^T defined here do *not* reduce to the *binary thermal diffusion coefficients* as defined in Chapman and Cowling. The relation is discussed in § 8.1.

[3] S. Chapman and F. W. Dootson, *Phil. Mag.*, **33**, 248 (1917).

$$D_i^T(\xi) = \frac{m_i}{3}\sqrt{\frac{m_i}{2kT}}\sum_{m=0}^{\xi-1} a_{im}(\xi)\int V_i^2 S_{3/2}^{(m)}(W_i^2) f_i^{[0]}\, d\boldsymbol{V}_i \tag{7.4–7}$$

the argument ξ of $D_{ij}(\xi)$ and $D_i^T(\xi)$ being the number of terms used in the Sonine expansions. Subsequent use of Eq. 7.3–59 to evaluate the integrals then gives

$$D_{ij}(\xi) = \frac{\rho n_i}{2nm_j}\sqrt{\frac{2kT}{m_i}}\, c_{i0}^{(j,\,i)}(\xi) \tag{7.4–8}$$

$$D_i^T(\xi) = \frac{n_i m_i}{2}\sqrt{\frac{2kT}{m_i}}\, a_{i0}(\xi) \tag{7.4–9}$$

We have thus expressed D_{ij} and D_i^T in terms of the zeroth Sonine expansion coefficient alone. No matter how many terms are used in the expansion (that is, regardless of the value of ξ), it is only the zeroth coefficient which remains after the integrations have been performed. However, the values of the coefficients $c_{i0}^{(j,\,i)}(\xi)$ and $a_{i0}(\xi)$ which are determined by Eq. 7.3–75 depend upon the number of terms considered in the expansion.

In the case of D_{ij}, letting $\xi = 1$ gives quite good results; if $\xi = 2$, we obtain a small correction term. Except in very unusual cases it is unnecessary to use any approximations beyond $\xi = 2$. However, when $\xi = 1$, the coefficients D_i^T vanish identically. This happens because the function $\mathsf{R}_i^{(h,\,k)} = f_i^{[0]}[\frac{5}{2} - W_i^2]\,\boldsymbol{V}_i$, when used in Eq. 7.3–62 with $n = \frac{3}{2}$, causes this integral to vanish since $(\frac{5}{2} - W_i^2)$ is in reality $S_{3/2}^{(1)}(W_i^2)$ and is therefore orthogonal to $S_{3/2}^{(0)}(W_i^2)$. Hence, in order to get the coefficient of thermal diffusion, it is necessary to take at least two terms in the Sonine expansion (that is, $\xi = 2$). For realistic potential functions this approximation is in error by about 5 to 10 per cent.

b. Coefficient of viscosity in terms of Sonine expansion coefficients

The integral for the pressure tensor (Eq. 7.2–23) in terms of the perturbation function ϕ_i is

$$\mathsf{p} = \Sigma_j m_j \int \boldsymbol{V}_j \boldsymbol{V}_j f_j\, d\boldsymbol{V}_j \tag{7.4–10}$$

$$= \Sigma_j m_j \left\{\int \boldsymbol{V}_j \boldsymbol{V}_j f_j^{[0]}\, d\boldsymbol{V}_j + \int \boldsymbol{V}_j \boldsymbol{V}_j f_j^{[0]}\phi_j\, d\boldsymbol{V}_j\right\} \tag{7.4–11}$$

$$= p\mathsf{U} + \Sigma_j m_j \int \boldsymbol{V}_j \boldsymbol{V}_j f_j^{[0]}\phi_j\, d\boldsymbol{V}_j \tag{7.4–12}$$

where

$$p = nkT \tag{7.4–13}$$

is the equilibrium hydrostatic pressure at the local temperature and density. Then, using the form of the perturbation function ϕ_i as given by Eq. 7.3–29, we find that

$$\mathsf{p} = p\mathsf{U} - \Sigma_j m_j \int \boldsymbol{V}_j\boldsymbol{V}_j\left(\mathsf{B}_j : \frac{\partial}{\partial \boldsymbol{r}} \boldsymbol{v}_0\right) f_j^{[0]}\, d\boldsymbol{V}_j \tag{7.4–14}$$

The terms in $\boldsymbol{A}_i$ and $\boldsymbol{C}_i^{(j)}$ can be shown to be zero on the basis of symmetry arguments. Then, using the form of the tensor B_i as given in Eq. 7.3–37 and further symmetry arguments, we obtain

$$\mathsf{p} = p\mathsf{U} - \left\{\frac{2}{15}\Sigma_j \frac{m_j^2}{2kT}\int B_j(W_j)V_j^4 f_j^{[0]}\, dV_j\right\}\mathsf{S} \tag{7.4–15}$$

where S is the *rate of shear tensor*, defined by

$$S_{\alpha\beta} = \frac{1}{2}\left[\frac{\partial v_{0\beta}}{\partial x_\alpha} + \frac{\partial v_{0\alpha}}{\partial x_\beta}\right] - \frac{1}{3}\,\delta_{\alpha\beta}\left(\frac{\partial}{\partial \boldsymbol{r}}\cdot \boldsymbol{v}_0\right) \tag{7.4–16}$$

The coefficient of viscosity η is defined by the relation

$$\mathsf{p} = p\mathsf{U} - 2\eta\mathsf{S} \tag{7.4–17}$$

From Eq. 7.4–15 it follows that the coefficient of viscosity is

$$\eta = \frac{1}{15}\Sigma_j \frac{m_j^2}{2kT}\int B_j(W_j)V_j^4 f_j^{[0]}\, dV_j \tag{7.4–18}$$

Then, making use of the Sonine polynomial expansion (Eq. 7.3–61), we obtain

$$\eta(\xi) = \frac{1}{15}\Sigma_j \frac{m_j^2}{2kT}\sum_{m=0}^{\xi-1} b_{jm}(\xi)\int S_{5/2}^{(m)}(W_j^2)V_j^4 f_j^{[0]}\, dV_j \tag{7.4–19}$$

Again the argument of $\eta(\xi)$ indicates the order of the approximation. The orthogonality relation in Eq. 7.3–60 can now be employed to evaluate the integral, and we obtain

$$\eta(\xi) = \tfrac{1}{2}kT\,\Sigma_j n_j b_{j0}(\xi) \tag{7.4–20}$$

as the coefficient of viscosity of a mixture in terms of the Sonine expansion coefficients $b_{j0}(\xi)$. As for ordinary diffusion, the first approximation is the predominant contribution. Actual calculations show that there is very little change in η when additional terms in the expansion are used.

c. Coefficient of thermal conductivity in terms of Sonine expansion coefficients

The integral for the energy flux vector $\boldsymbol{q}$ (Eq. 7.2–26) is given in terms of the perturbation function ϕ_j by

$$\boldsymbol{q} = \tfrac{1}{2}\,\Sigma_j m_j \int V_j^2 \boldsymbol{V}_j f_j^{[0]}\phi_j\, d\boldsymbol{V}_j \tag{7.4–21}$$

When the expression for ϕ_j (Eq. 7.3–29) is used in this equation, the term containing B_j does not contribute and we have

$$\boldsymbol{q} = \tfrac{1}{2}\textstyle\sum_j m_j \displaystyle\int \left\{ n \textstyle\sum_k (\boldsymbol{C}_j^{(k)} \cdot \boldsymbol{d}_k) - \left(\boldsymbol{A}_j \cdot \dfrac{\partial \ln T}{\partial \boldsymbol{r}}\right)\right\} V_j^2 \boldsymbol{V}_j f_j^{[0]}\, d\boldsymbol{V}_j \qquad (7.4\text{–}22)$$

The energy flux may be separated into two parts, that due to the flux of molecules relative to the mass velocity and that due to other causes. Using the forms of the functions $\boldsymbol{A}_i$ and $\boldsymbol{C}_i^{(j)}$ given by Eqs. 7.3–35 and 36, we obtain

$$\begin{aligned}\boldsymbol{q} &= \tfrac{5}{2}kT \textstyle\sum_j n_j \overline{\boldsymbol{V}}_j \\ &\quad -kT \textstyle\sum_j \displaystyle\int \left\{ n \textstyle\sum_k C_j^{(k)}(W_j)\,(\boldsymbol{W}_j \cdot \boldsymbol{d}_j) - A_j(W_j)\left(\boldsymbol{W}_j \cdot \dfrac{\partial \ln T}{\partial \boldsymbol{r}}\right)\right\} \\ &\qquad\qquad \times (\tfrac{5}{2} - W_j^2)\boldsymbol{V}_j f_j^{[0]}\, d\boldsymbol{V}_j \end{aligned} \qquad (7.4\text{–}23)$$

Then according to the symmetry arguments discussed above it follows that

$$\begin{aligned}\boldsymbol{q} &= \tfrac{5}{2}kT \textstyle\sum_j n_j \overline{\boldsymbol{V}}_j - \lambda' \dfrac{\partial T}{\partial \boldsymbol{r}} \\ &\quad - \frac{\sqrt{2}}{3} n (kT)^{3/2} \textstyle\sum_k \boldsymbol{d}_k \textstyle\sum_j \dfrac{1}{\sqrt{m_j}} \displaystyle\int C_j^{(k)}(W_j)\,(\tfrac{5}{2} - W_j^2)\, W_j^2 f_j^{[0]}\, d\boldsymbol{V}_j \end{aligned} \qquad (7.4\text{–}24)$$

where

$$\lambda' = -\frac{\sqrt{2}}{3} k\sqrt{kT} \textstyle\sum_j \dfrac{1}{\sqrt{m_j}} \displaystyle\int A_j(W_j)\,(\tfrac{5}{2} - W_j^2) W_j^2 f_j^{[0]}\, d\boldsymbol{V}_j \qquad (7.4\text{–}25)$$

The first term represents the flux of energy incident to mass transport; the second, that due to a temperature gradient; and the third, an additional effect due directly to the concentration gradients. The last term is analogous to the effect of temperature gradients on diffusion, that is, thermal diffusion.

The expression for $\boldsymbol{q}$ can be rearranged as follows. From the integral equation for the $\boldsymbol{A}_i$ (Eq. 7.3–34) we may obtain the relation

$$\begin{aligned}&\sqrt{\frac{2kT}{m_j}} \int C_j^{(k)}(W_j)\,(\tfrac{5}{2} - W_j^2) W_j^2 f_j^{[0]}\, d\boldsymbol{V}_j \\ &\quad = \textstyle\sum_i \displaystyle\iiiint ([\boldsymbol{A}_i' + \boldsymbol{A}_j' - \boldsymbol{A}_i - \boldsymbol{A}_j] \cdot \boldsymbol{C}_j^{(k)}) f_i^{[0]} f_j^{[0]} g_{ij} b\, db\, d\epsilon\, d\boldsymbol{V}_i\, d\boldsymbol{V}_j \end{aligned}$$

(7.4–26)

which can be used to rewrite the expression for $\boldsymbol{q}$ (Eq. 7.4–24). Then, "symmetrizing" the sum over i and j and making use of the fact that $\Sigma_k \boldsymbol{d}_k = 0$, we obtain

$$\boldsymbol{q} = \tfrac{5}{2}kT \textstyle\sum_j n_j \overline{\boldsymbol{V}}_j - \lambda' \dfrac{\partial T}{\partial \boldsymbol{r}}$$

$$- \tfrac{1}{6}nkT \textstyle\sum_k \boldsymbol{d}_k \sum_{i,j} \displaystyle\iiiint ([\boldsymbol{A}_i' + \boldsymbol{A}_j' - \boldsymbol{A}_i - \boldsymbol{A}_j]$$

$$\cdot [\boldsymbol{C}_i^{(k)} + \boldsymbol{C}_j^{(k)} - \boldsymbol{C}_i^{(h)} - \boldsymbol{C}_j^{(h)}]) f_i^{[0]} f_j^{[0]} g_{ij} b \, db \, d\epsilon \, d\boldsymbol{V}_i \, d\boldsymbol{V}_j \qquad (7.4\text{–}27)$$

But from the integral equation for $\boldsymbol{C}_i^{(k)}$ (Eq. 7.3–32) it follows that

$$(\delta_{ih} - \delta_{ik}) \frac{1}{n_i} \sqrt{\frac{2kT}{m_i}} \int A_i(W_i) W_i^2 f_i^{[0]} \, d\boldsymbol{V}_i = \textstyle\sum_j \displaystyle\iiiint \Bigg(\boldsymbol{A}_i$$

$$\cdot \begin{bmatrix} \boldsymbol{C}_i^{(h)\prime} + \boldsymbol{C}_j^{(h)\prime} - \boldsymbol{C}_i^{(k)\prime} - \boldsymbol{C}_j^{(k)\prime} \\ - \boldsymbol{C}_i^{(h)} - \boldsymbol{C}_j^{(h)} + \boldsymbol{C}_i^{(k)} + \boldsymbol{C}_j^{(k)} \end{bmatrix} \Bigg) f_i^{[0]} f_j^{[0]} g_{ij} b \, db \, d\epsilon \, d\boldsymbol{V}_i \, d\boldsymbol{V}_j \qquad (7.4\text{–}28)$$

Summing Eq. 7.4–28 over i and "symmetrizing" results in

$$\textstyle\sum_i (\delta_{ih} - \delta_{ik}) \dfrac{1}{n_i} \sqrt{\dfrac{2kT}{m_i}} \displaystyle\int A_i(W_i) W_i^2 f_i^{[0]} d\boldsymbol{V}_i = -\tfrac{1}{2} \textstyle\sum_{i,j} \displaystyle\iiiint \left(\begin{bmatrix} \boldsymbol{A}_i' + \boldsymbol{A}_j' \\ -\boldsymbol{A}_i - \boldsymbol{A}_j \end{bmatrix} \right.$$

$$\left. \cdot \begin{bmatrix} \boldsymbol{C}_i^{(k)} + \boldsymbol{C}_j^{(k)} \\ -\boldsymbol{C}_i^{(h)} - \boldsymbol{C}_j^{(h)} \end{bmatrix} \right) f_i^{[0]} f_j^{[0]} g_{ij} b \, db \, d\epsilon \, d\boldsymbol{V}_i \, d\boldsymbol{V}_j \qquad (7.4\text{–}29)$$

Then, with the definition of D_j^T (Eq. 7.4–5) and the fact that $\Sigma_k \boldsymbol{d}_k = 0$, the energy flux becomes

$$\boldsymbol{q} = \tfrac{5}{2}kT \textstyle\sum_j n_j \overline{\boldsymbol{V}}_j - \lambda' \dfrac{\partial T}{\partial \boldsymbol{r}} - nkT \textstyle\sum_j \dfrac{1}{n_j m_j} D_j^T \, \boldsymbol{d}_j \qquad (7.4\text{–}30)$$

The coefficient λ' is *not* the coefficient of thermal conductivity as it is usually defined. It is conventional to eliminate the gradients, $\boldsymbol{d}_j$, from the expression for $\boldsymbol{q}$ by means of the equation for the diffusion velocities (Eq. 7.4–3). The energy flux is then given in terms of the diffusion velocities and the temperature gradient. Because of the thermal diffusion term in the expression for the diffusion velocity a small term adds to λ' to result in the quantity λ, which is the usual coefficient of thermal conductivity. The final expression for λ (Eq. 7.4–65) is derived later in this section.

If the functions $A_i(W_i)$ are expressed as a series of Sonine polynomials as in Eq. 7.3–61, the expression for λ' (Eq. 7.4–25) becomes

$$\lambda'(\xi) = -\frac{\sqrt{2}}{3} k\sqrt{kT} \sum_j \sum_{m=0}^{\xi-1} \frac{1}{\sqrt{m_j}} a_{jm}(\xi) \int S_{3/2}^{(m)}(W_j^2) \left(\tfrac{5}{2} - W_j^2\right) W_j^2 f_j^{[0]} \, d\mathbf{V}_j \tag{7.4–31}$$

Then, since

$$S_{3/2}^{(1)}(W_j^2) = \tfrac{5}{2} - W_j^2 \tag{7.4–32}$$

we obtain from the condition of orthogonality of the polynomials, (Eq. 7.3–58),

$$\lambda'(\xi) = -\tfrac{5}{4}k \textstyle\sum_j n_j \sqrt{\dfrac{2kT}{m_j}}\, a_{j1}(\xi) \tag{7.4–33}$$

d. The integrals $\Omega^{(l,s)}$

The transport coefficients have been expressed in terms of the Sonine polynomial expansion coefficients. It will be recalled that these expansion coefficients are obtained by the solution of sets of simultaneous equations given in Eq. 7.3–75. It can be seen that the expansion coefficients $t_{jm}^{(h,k)}(\xi)$ are complicated combinations of the bracket integrals, which are defined by Eq. 7.3–42. Chapman and Cowling have shown that these integrals may be written as linear combinations of a set of integrals[4] $\Omega^{(l,s)}$. For collisions between molecules of type i and type j, these integrals are defined by

$$\Omega_{ij}^{(l,s)} = \sqrt{\frac{2\pi kT}{\mu_{ij}}} \int_0^\infty \int_0^\infty e^{-\gamma_{ij}^2} \gamma_{ij}^{2s+3} (1 - \cos^l \chi) b \, db \, d\gamma_{ij} \tag{7.4–34}$$

In these integrals μ_{ij} is the reduced mass of colliding molecules i and j (defined by Eq. 1.5–9), γ_{ij} is the reduced initial relative speed of the colliding molecules (defined in Eq. 7.2–12), χ is the angle by which the molecules are deflected in the center of gravity coordinate system, and b is the *impact parameter*. (b and χ are shown graphically in Fig. 1.5–3.) A tabulation of the most frequently needed bracket expressions in terms of the $\Omega^{(l,s)}$ is given in Appendix A at the end of the chapter. With this table and Eq. 7.3–75, we may calculate any of the Sonine expansion coefficients, $t_{im}^{(h,k)}$.

[4] S. Chapman and T. G. Cowling, *The Mathematical Theory of Non-uniform Gases*, Cambridge University Press, 1939. The integrals $\Omega^{(l,s)}$ in this book are the same as the $\Omega^{(l)}(s)$ of Chapman and Cowling. They are *not*, however, the same as the $\Omega^{(l,s)}$ of D. Enskog, *Archiv. för Mathematik, Astronomi och Fysik*, **16**, § 16 (1922).

The dynamics of the collisions enters into the description of the transport coefficients through the collision integrals defined by Eq. 7.4-34. For, in order to evaluate the $\Omega^{(l,s)}$, we must know χ as a function of the initial relative velocity g_{ij} and the impact parameter b. Such a relation is given by Eq. 1.5-26. In this equation the potential energy of interaction $\varphi(r)$ appears explicitly. Thus, given the interaction potential, we can calculate the $\Omega^{(l,s)}$ integrals and hence the expansion coefficients $t_{im}^{(h,k)}(\xi)$.

The formulae for the transport coefficients in terms of the $\Omega^{(l,s)}$ integrals are discussed in the next subsection. The actual evaluation of the angles $\chi(g, b)$, the integrals $\Omega^{(l,s)}$, and the transport coefficients for several intermolecular laws of force is performed in Chapter 8. The most satisfactory and usable calculations are those made on the basis of either the Lennard-Jones (6-12) potential or the modified Buckingham potential, which describe reasonably well the interaction between spherical, non-polar molecules. Equations and tables are given in Chapter 8 which enable us to make practical applications of the theory. It is shown that the agreement between calculated and experimental results is quite satisfactory.

e. Explicit formulae for the transport coefficients in terms of the $\Omega^{(l,s)}$

The method of obtaining formulae for the transport coefficients in terms of the intermolecular forces and the dynamics of binary collisions is discussed in this and the preceding sections. The algebraic detail of the development of the expressions in terms of the integrals $\Omega^{(l,s)}$ is rather lengthy and is omitted, except to indicate briefly how the results obtained thus far may be used to obtain the lowest approximation to the various transport coefficients.

i. *The Coefficient of Diffusion*

The coefficient of diffusion in a multicomponent mixture can be obtained to a very good approximation by considering only one term in the Sonine polynomial expansion. The equations specifying the $c_{j0}^{(h,k)}(1)$ (Eq. 7.3-75) are then

$$\Sigma_j \tilde{Q}_{ij}^{00} c_{j0}^{(h,k)}(1) = -R_{i0}^{(h,k)} \tag{7.4-35}$$

In terms of the $\Omega^{(l,s)}$ these equations become

$$\Sigma_j c_{j0}^{(h,k)}(1) \, \Sigma_l \frac{n_l m_l}{(m_i + m_l)\sqrt{m_j}} \, [n_i m_i(\delta_{ij} - \delta_{jl}) - n_j m_j(1 - \delta_{il})] \, \Omega_{il}^{(1,1)}$$

$$= -(\delta_{ih} - \delta_{ik}) \, \tfrac{3}{16} \sqrt{2kT} \tag{7.4-36}$$

For a binary mixture we immediately obtain from this equation,

$$c_{i0}^{(h,k)}(1) = (\delta_{jh} - \delta_{jk}) \frac{3(m_i + m_j)}{16 n_i \rho} \sqrt{\frac{2kT}{m_i}} \frac{1}{\Omega_{ij}^{(1,1)}} \tag{7.4–37}$$

So that the first approximation to the coefficient of diffusion[5] of a binary mixture is (from Eq. 7.4–8)

$$\mathscr{D}_{ij}(1) = \frac{3(m_i + m_j)}{16 n m_i m_j} \frac{kT}{\Omega_{ij}^{(1,1)}} \tag{7.4–38}$$

From the definitions (or from the form of Eq. 7.4–37),

$$c_{j0}^{(h,k)} = c_{j0}^{(h,j)} - c_{j0}^{(k,j)} \tag{7.4–39}$$

Using this result, the expressions for the diffusion constants, and the above relation for the binary diffusion constants, we get for the equation for the general diffusion constants (Eq. 7.4–36):

$$\Sigma_j F_{ij}\{m_h D_{jh}(1) - m_k D_{jk}(1)\} = (\delta_{ih} - \delta_{ik}) \tag{7.4–40}$$

where

$$F_{ij} = \left\{\frac{n_i}{\rho \mathscr{D}_{ij}(1)} + \sum_{l \neq i} \frac{n_l m_j}{\rho m_i \mathscr{D}_{il}(1)}\right\}(1 - \delta_{ij}) \tag{7.4–41}$$

A formal solution of this set of equations can be obtained easily. Let us define F^{ij} as the cofactor of F_{ij} in the determinant $|F|$ of the F_{ij}, that is,

$$F^{ij} = (-1)^{i+j} \begin{vmatrix} F_{11} & \cdots & F_{1,j-1} & F_{1,j+1} & \cdots & F_{1\nu} \\ \cdot & & \cdot & \cdot & & \cdot \\ \cdot & & \cdot & \cdot & & \cdot \\ \cdot & & \cdot & \cdot & & \cdot \\ F_{i-1,1} & \cdots & F_{i-1,j-1} & F_{i-1,j+1} & \cdots & F_{i-1\,\nu} \\ F_{i+1,1} & \cdots & F_{i+1,j-1} & F_{i+1,j+1} & \cdots & F_{i+1,\nu} \\ \cdot & & \cdot & \cdot & & \cdot \\ \cdot & & \cdot & \cdot & & \cdot \\ \cdot & & \cdot & \cdot & & \cdot \\ F_{\nu,1} & \cdots & F_{\nu,j-1} & F_{\nu,j+1} & \cdots & F_{\nu,\nu} \end{vmatrix} \tag{7.4–42}$$

Then, solving the Eq. 7.4–40, we get

$$m_h D_{ih}(1) - m_k D_{ik}(1) = \frac{F^{hi} - F^{ki}}{|F|} \tag{7.4–43}$$

[5] In a binary mixture we denote D_{ij} by $\mathscr{D}_{ij}$.

Thus, since $D_{ii} \equiv 0$, it follows that

$$D_{ij}(1) = \frac{F^{ji} - F^{ii}}{m_j \,|\, F \,|} \tag{7.4–44}$$

The set of Eqs. 7.4–44 relates the generalized diffusion coefficients of a mixture to the binary diffusion coefficients of the various pairs. The form of the result, however, is usually difficult to handle in actual problems. For this reason it may often be advantageous to make use of an alternate formulation of the problem. From Eq. 7.4–3, we find that

$$\Sigma_j \frac{n_i n_j}{\mathscr{D}_{ij}(1)} (\bar{\boldsymbol{V}}_i - \bar{\boldsymbol{V}}_j) = \frac{n^2}{\rho} \sum_{\substack{j,k \\ j \neq i}} \frac{m_k}{\mathscr{D}_{ij}(1)} \{n_j D_{ik} - n_i D_{jk}\} \boldsymbol{d}_k$$

$$- \frac{\partial \ln T}{\partial \boldsymbol{r}} \Sigma_j \frac{1}{\mathscr{D}_{ij}(1)} \left[\frac{n_j}{m_i} D_i^T - \frac{n_i}{m_j} D_j^T \right] \tag{7.4–45}$$

This expression can be simplified considerably by making use of a special form of Eq. 7.4–40. The auxiliary conditions on the coefficients $c_{i0}^{(h,k)}$ (Eq. 7.3–74) can be written in terms of the diffusion coefficients. The result is

$$\Sigma_i \{m_i m_h D_{ih}(1) - m_i m_k D_{ik}(1)\} = 0 \tag{7.4–46}$$

Making use of this, we find that Eq. 7.4–40 becomes[6]

$$\sum_{j \neq i} \frac{1}{\mathscr{D}_{ij}(1)} \{n_i m_h D_{jh}(1) - n_i m_k D_{jk}(1) - n_j m_h D_{ih}(1) + n_j m_k D_{ik}(1)\}$$

$$= (\delta_{ih} - \delta_{ik}) \rho \tag{7.4–47}$$

This set of equations is not linearly independent and hence could not be used without Eq. 7.4–46 to obtain the coefficients. Nevertheless, they are valid relations. Because of Eq. 7.4–47 and the fact that $\Sigma_k \boldsymbol{d}_k = 0$, Eq. 7.4–45, in the approximation that the D_{jk} may be replaced by the first approximation $D_{jk}(1)$, becomes

$$\Sigma_j \frac{n_i n_j}{n^2 \mathscr{D}_{ij}(1)} (\bar{\boldsymbol{V}}_j - \bar{\boldsymbol{V}}_i) = \boldsymbol{d}_i - \frac{\partial \ln T}{\partial \boldsymbol{r}} \Sigma_j \frac{n_i n_j}{n^2 \mathscr{D}_{ij}(1)} \left(\frac{D_j^T}{n_j m_j} - \frac{D_i^T}{n_i m_i} \right) \tag{7.4–48}$$

[6] This set of equations is a special case of the general relations, Eqs. 7.3–70.

This is a set of $(\nu - 1)$ independent equations which is often directly applicable to hydrodynamic problems.

ii. *The Coefficient of Thermal Diffusion*

To obtain the coefficients of thermal diffusion, it is necessary to evaluate the functions A_i. In this case two terms in the Sonine polynomial expansion must be considered. Use of a single term results in a zero thermal diffusion coefficient; for this reason thermal diffusion is frequently referred to as a "second-order" effect. In this case Eq. 7.3–75 becomes

$$\sum_j \sum_{m'=0}^{1} \tilde{Q}_{ij}^{mm'} a_{jm'}(2) = -R_{im} \tag{7.4–49}$$

In terms of the $\Omega^{(l,s)}$ the $\tilde{Q}_{ij}^{mm'}$ are

$$\tilde{Q}_{ij}^{00} = 8\sum_k \frac{n_k m_k}{\sqrt{m_i m_j}(m_i + m_k)} [n_i m_i(\delta_{ij} - \delta_{jk}) - n_j m_j(1 - \delta_{ik})]\Omega_{ik}^{(1,1)} \tag{7.4–50}$$

$$\tilde{Q}_{ij}^{01} = -8\left(\frac{m_i}{m_j}\right)^{3/2} \sum_k \frac{n_i n_k m_k^2}{(m_i + m_k)^2}(\delta_{ij} - \delta_{kj})[\Omega_{ik}^{(1,2)} - \tfrac{5}{2}\Omega_{ik}^{(1,1)}] \tag{7.4–51}$$

$$\tilde{Q}_{ij}^{10} = \frac{m_j}{m_i}\tilde{Q}_{ij}^{01} \tag{7.4–52}$$

$$\tilde{Q}_{ij}^{11} = 8\left(\frac{m_i}{m_j}\right)^{3/2} \sum_k \frac{n_i n_k m_k}{(m_i + m_k)^3} \left[(\delta_{ij} - \delta_{jk})\left[\begin{matrix} \tfrac{5}{4}(6m_j^2 + 5m_k^2)\Omega_{ik}^{(1,1)} \\ -5m_k^2\Omega_{ik}^{(1,2)} \\ +m_k^2\Omega_{ik}^{(1,3)} \end{matrix}\right] + (\delta_{ij} + \delta_{jk})2m_j m_k \Omega_{ik}^{(2,2)}\right] \tag{7.4–53}$$

and

$$R_{im} = \delta_{m1}\frac{15}{4} n_i \sqrt{2kT/m_i} \tag{7.4–54}$$

The expressions in Eq. 7.4–49 form a set of linear equations for the coefficients a_{j0} and a_{j1}, which can be solved by Cramer's rule.[7] Then

[7] Cramer's rule states that the solution of a set of linear equations can be expressed as the ratio of determinants of the coefficients.

from Eq. 7.4–9 we obtain the expression for the coefficient of thermal diffusion:

$$D_i^T(2) = n_i\sqrt{\frac{m_ikT}{2}}\;\frac{\begin{vmatrix} \tilde{Q}^{00}_{11} & \tilde{Q}^{00}_{12} & \cdots & \tilde{Q}^{01}_{1\nu} & \tilde{Q}^{01}_{11} & \tilde{Q}^{01}_{12} & \cdots & \tilde{Q}^{01}_{1\nu} & 0 \\ \tilde{Q}^{00}_{21} & \tilde{Q}^{00}_{22} & \cdots & \tilde{Q}^{00}_{2\nu} & \tilde{Q}^{01}_{21} & \tilde{Q}^{01}_{22} & \cdots & \tilde{Q}^{01}_{2\nu} & 0 \\ \cdot & \cdot & \cdots & \cdot & \cdot & \cdot & \cdots & \cdot & \cdot \\ \cdot & \cdot & \cdots & \cdot & \cdot & \cdot & \cdots & \cdot & \cdot \\ \cdot & \cdot & \cdots & \cdot & \cdot & \cdot & \cdots & \cdot & \cdot \\ \tilde{Q}^{00}_{\nu 1} & \tilde{Q}^{00}_{\nu 2} & \cdots & \tilde{Q}^{00}_{\nu\nu} & \tilde{Q}^{01}_{\nu 1} & \tilde{Q}^{01}_{\nu 2} & \cdots & \tilde{Q}^{01}_{\nu\nu} & 0 \\ \tilde{Q}^{10}_{11} & \tilde{Q}^{10}_{12} & \cdots & \tilde{Q}^{10}_{1\nu} & \tilde{Q}^{11}_{11} & \tilde{Q}^{11}_{12} & \cdots & \tilde{Q}^{11}_{1\nu} & R_{11} \\ \tilde{Q}^{10}_{21} & \tilde{Q}^{10}_{22} & \cdots & \tilde{Q}^{10}_{2\nu} & \tilde{Q}^{11}_{21} & \tilde{Q}^{11}_{22} & \cdots & \tilde{Q}^{11}_{2\nu} & R_{21} \\ \cdot & \cdot & \cdots & \cdot & \cdot & \cdot & \cdots & \cdot & \cdot \\ \cdot & \cdot & \cdots & \cdot & \cdot & \cdot & \cdots & \cdot & \cdot \\ \cdot & \cdot & \cdots & \cdot & \cdot & \cdot & \cdots & \cdot & \cdot \\ \tilde{Q}^{10}_{\nu 1} & \tilde{Q}^{10}_{\nu 2} & \cdots & \tilde{Q}^{10}_{\nu\nu} & \tilde{Q}^{11}_{\nu 1} & \tilde{Q}^{11}_{\nu 2} & \cdots & \tilde{Q}^{11}_{\nu\nu} & R_{\nu 1} \\ \delta_{i1} & \delta_{i2} & \cdots & \delta_{i\nu} & 0 & 0 & \cdots & 0 & 0 \end{vmatrix}}{\begin{vmatrix} \tilde{Q}^{00}_{11} & \cdots & \tilde{Q}^{00}_{1\nu} & \tilde{Q}^{01}_{11} & \cdots & \tilde{Q}^{01}_{1\nu} \\ \cdot & \cdots & \cdot & \cdot & \cdots & \cdot \\ \cdot & \cdots & \cdot & \cdot & \cdots & \cdot \\ \cdot & \cdots & \cdot & \cdot & \cdots & \cdot \\ \tilde{Q}^{00}_{\nu 1} & \cdots & \tilde{Q}^{00}_{\nu\nu} & \tilde{Q}^{01}_{\nu 1} & \cdots & \tilde{Q}^{01}_{\nu\nu} \\ \tilde{Q}^{10}_{11} & \cdots & \tilde{Q}^{10}_{1\nu} & \tilde{Q}^{11}_{11} & \cdots & \tilde{Q}^{11}_{1\nu} \\ \cdot & \cdots & \cdot & \cdot & \cdots & \cdot \\ \cdot & \cdots & \cdot & \cdot & \cdots & \cdot \\ \cdot & \cdots & \cdot & \cdot & \cdots & \cdot \\ \tilde{Q}^{10}_{\nu 1} & \cdots & \tilde{Q}^{10}_{\nu\nu} & \tilde{Q}^{11}_{\nu 1} & \cdots & \tilde{Q}^{11}_{\nu\nu} \end{vmatrix}} \qquad (7.4\text{–}55)$$

iii. *The Coefficient of Viscosity*

For a ν-component mixture the first approximation to the viscosity is (according to Eq. 7.4–20):

$$\eta(1) = \tfrac{1}{2}kT\,\Sigma_j n_j b_{j0}(1) \qquad (7.4\text{–}56)$$

The $b_{j0}(1)$ are then determined by the ν equations (according to Eq. 7.3–75):

$$\Sigma_j\left(\frac{Q^{00}_{ij}}{R_{io}}\right) b_{j0}(1) = -1 \qquad i = 1, 2, 3, \cdots, \nu \qquad (7.4\text{–}57)$$

with

$$Q^{00}_{ij} = \Sigma_l n_i n_l \{\delta_{ij}[\mathsf{W}_i\,;\,\mathsf{W}_i]_{il} + \delta_{jl}[\mathsf{W}_i;\,\mathsf{W}_l]_{il}\} \qquad (7.4\text{–}58)$$

In this case W_i and R_{i0} are

$$\mathsf{W}_i = \boldsymbol{W}_i\boldsymbol{W}_i - \tfrac{1}{3}W_i^2\mathsf{U} \qquad (7.4\text{–}59)$$

$$R_{i0} = \int 2(\mathsf{W}_i : \mathsf{W}_i)f_i^{[0]}\,d\boldsymbol{V}_i$$

$$= -\tfrac{4}{3}\int W_i^4 f_i^{[0]}\,d\boldsymbol{V}_i = -5n_i \qquad (7.4\text{–}60)$$

From Eq. 7.4–57 we can, of course, obtain the $b_{j0}(1)$ as ratios of two determinants of order ν by Cramer's rule. However, the only quantity which appears in the expression for the coefficient of viscosity is $\Sigma_j n_j b_{j0}(1)$. This can be written as a ratio of two determinants—the one in the numerator being of order $(\nu + 1)$ and that in the denominator of order ν. Specifically we obtain

$$\eta(1) = -\frac{\begin{vmatrix} H_{11} & H_{12} & \cdots & H_{1\nu} & n_1/n \\ H_{21} & H_{22} & \cdots & H_{2\nu} & n_2/n \\ \cdot & \cdot & & \cdot & \cdot \\ \cdot & \cdot & & \cdot & \cdot \\ \cdot & \cdot & & \cdot & \cdot \\ H_{\nu1} & H_{\nu2} & \cdots & H_{\nu\nu} & n_\nu/n \\ n_1/n & n_2/n & \cdots & n_\nu/n & 0 \end{vmatrix}}{|H_{ij}|} \qquad (7.4\text{–}61)$$

with

$$H_{ij} = -\frac{2n_i Q_{ij}^{00}}{n^2kTR_{i0}} = \frac{2}{5}\frac{1}{kT}\Sigma_l\frac{n_i n_l}{n^2}\{\delta_{ij}[\mathsf{W}_i;\mathsf{W}_i]_{il} + \delta_{jl}[\mathsf{W}_i;\mathsf{W}_l]_{il}\} \qquad (7.4\text{–}62)$$

The H_{ij} may be rewritten in terms of the $\Omega^{(l,s)}$:

$$H_{ij} = \frac{32}{15}\frac{n_i m_i}{n^2 m_j kT}\Sigma_l\frac{n_l m_l}{(m_i + m_l)^2}\begin{bmatrix} 5m_j(\delta_{ij} - \delta_{jl})\Omega_{il}^{(1,1)} \\ +\tfrac{3}{2}m_l(\delta_{ij} + \delta_{jl})\Omega_{il}^{(2,2)} \end{bmatrix} \qquad (7.4\text{–}63)$$

This result can easily be extended to include the effect of more terms in the Sonine polynomial expansion. The formal results can be simplified considerably for binary mixtures and pure gases (see § 8.2b).

iv. *The Coefficient of Thermal Conductivity*

The expression for the energy flux is usually written in terms of the diffusion velocities and the temperature gradient. Combining Eqs. 7.4–30 and 48 gives

$$\boldsymbol{q} = -\lambda\frac{\partial T}{\partial \boldsymbol{r}} + \frac{5}{2}kT\,\Sigma_i n_i\overline{\boldsymbol{V}}_i + \frac{kT}{n}\Sigma_{i,j}\frac{n_j D_i^T}{m_i\mathscr{D}_{ij}(1)}(\overline{\boldsymbol{V}}_i - \overline{\boldsymbol{V}}_j) \qquad (7.4\text{–}64)$$

In this expression

$$\lambda = \lambda' - \frac{k}{2n}\sum_{i,j} \frac{n_i n_j}{\mathscr{D}_{ij}(1)}\left[\frac{D_i^T}{n_i m_i} - \frac{D_j^T}{n_j m_j}\right]^2 \tag{7.4-65}$$

is the usual coefficient of thermal conductivity. The quantity λ' is expressed in terms of the Sonine expansion coefficients by Eq. 7.4-33 from which, on applying the methods and results described above, we obtain

$$\lambda'(2) = -\frac{75}{8}k^2T \frac{\begin{vmatrix} q_{11}^{00} & \cdots & q_{1\nu}^{00} & q_{11}^{01} & \cdots & q_{1\nu}^{01} & 0 \\ \cdot & \cdots & \cdot & \cdot & \cdots & \cdot & \cdot \\ \cdot & \cdots & \cdot & \cdot & \cdots & \cdot & \cdot \\ \cdot & \cdots & \cdot & \cdot & \cdots & \cdot & \cdot \\ \cdot & \cdots & \cdot & \cdot & \cdots & \cdot & \cdot \\ q_{\nu 1}^{00} & \cdots & q_{\nu\nu}^{00} & q_{\nu 1}^{01} & \cdots & q_{\nu\nu}^{01} & 0 \\ q_{11}^{10} & \cdots & q_{1\nu}^{10} & q_{11}^{11} & \cdots & q_{1\nu}^{11} & 1 \\ \cdot & \cdots & \cdot & \cdot & \cdots & \cdot & \cdot \\ \cdot & \cdots & \cdot & \cdot & \cdots & \cdot & \cdot \\ \cdot & \cdots & \cdot & \cdot & \cdots & \cdot & \cdot \\ \cdot & \cdots & \cdot & \cdot & \cdots & \cdot & \cdot \\ q_{\nu 1}^{10} & \cdots & q_{\nu\nu}^{10} & q_{\nu 1}^{11} & \cdots & q_{\nu\nu}^{11} & 1 \\ 0 & \cdots & 0 & 1 & \cdots & 1 & 0 \end{vmatrix}}{\begin{vmatrix} q_{11}^{00} & \cdots & q_{1\nu}^{00} & q_{11}^{01} & \cdots & q_{1\nu}^{01} \\ \cdot & \cdots & \cdot & \cdot & \cdots & \cdot \\ \cdot & \cdots & \cdot & \cdot & \cdots & \cdot \\ \cdot & \cdots & \cdot & \cdot & \cdots & \cdot \\ \cdot & \cdots & \cdot & \cdot & \cdots & \cdot \\ q_{\nu 1}^{00} & \cdots & q_{\nu\nu}^{00} & q_{\nu 1}^{01} & \cdots & q_{\nu\nu}^{01} \\ q_{11}^{10} & \cdots & q_{1\nu}^{10} & q_{11}^{11} & \cdots & q_{1\nu}^{11} \\ \cdot & \cdots & \cdot & \cdot & \cdots & \cdot \\ \cdot & \cdots & \cdot & \cdot & \cdots & \cdot \\ \cdot & \cdots & \cdot & \cdot & \cdots & \cdot \\ q_{\nu 1}^{10} & \cdots & q_{\nu\nu}^{10} & q_{\nu 1}^{11} & \cdots & q_{\nu\nu}^{11} \end{vmatrix}} \tag{7.4-66}$$

Here

$$q_{ij}^{mm'} = \frac{\sqrt{m_i m_j}}{n_i n_j}\tilde{Q}_{ij}^{mm'} \tag{7.4-67}$$

where the $\tilde{Q}_{ij}^{mm'}$ are those given by Eqs. 7.4-50, 51, 52, and 53.

5. Grad's Solution of the Boltzmann Equation

As discussed in § 7.1, the state of a gas may be described in varying degrees of completeness. The level of information provided by the distribution function $f(\mathbf{r}, \mathbf{v}, t)$ of single molecules is adequate to describe completely the behavior of gases at low density, where the effect of more than two body collisions is unimportant. The variation of the distribution function $f(\mathbf{r}, \mathbf{v}, t)$ with time is given by the Boltzmann equation. This equation cannot be solved exactly, but for most purposes we are satisfied with the hydrodynamic description of the state of the gas in terms of the macroscopic variables: density, velocity, and temperature. The equations describing the time variation of these quantities are the equations of change derived in § 7.2. In the derivation of these equations, certain additional quantities (the flux vectors) were introduced: the diffusion velocities, the pressure tensor, and the heat flux vector. The values of these quantities depend upon the perturbation of the distribution function from the equilibrium Maxwellian distribution.

The Enskog method of solution of the Boltzmann equation yields expressions for the flux vectors in terms of the space derivatives of the macroscopic quantities. The first approximation, which is discussed in detail in the previous section, yields expressions involving the first derivatives. The higher approximations involve the higher derivatives and powers of the lower derivatives.

A knowledge of the macroscopic variables (density, mass-average velocity, and temperature) is equivalent to a knowledge of the first three velocity moments of the distribution function. The Enskog solution of the Boltzmann equation then provides a complete description of the future of a gas in terms of a knowledge, at a particular time, of the first three moments of the distribution function at each point in space. Clearly, many functions, $f(\mathbf{r}, \mathbf{v}, t)$, have the same first three moments at a particular time and each leads to a different distribution corresponding to a different set of first three moments at a later time. Thus the Enskog series does not provide a general solution but in some manner restricts the consideration to a particular class of distribution functions. This is characteristic of the process of lowering the completeness of the description of the state of the system. Each time we lower the level of description it is necessary to introduce a condition which restricts the possible states under consideration. In this case it is not clear how the restriction has been imposed. Also it is not clear that a solution has actually been obtained since the convergence of the Enskog series has often been questioned.

Grad[1] has introduced a method of solution of the Boltzmann equation

[1] H. Grad, *Communications on Pure and Applied Mathematics*, **2**, 331 (1949).

which justifies the first approximation of Enskog and permits any level of description between the complete description in terms of $f(\mathbf{r}, \mathbf{v}, t)$ and the hydrodynamic description. The results of this treatment are of value in the study of gases at sufficiently low density that the gas no longer behaves as a continuous medium. The solutions permit the use of considerably more general boundary conditions in the solution of hydrodynamic problems. The method of solution is discussed briefly below. For simplicity we restrict our attention to a gas consisting of a single component, in which case there is only one distribution function and only one Boltzmann equation, and the problems of diffusion do not arise.

a. The moment equations

Let us form a tensor of order n from the components of the velocity $\mathbf{v}$:

$$v_{ijk\cdots}^{(n)} = v_i v_j v_k \cdots \qquad (7.5\text{–}1)$$

Here the subscript specifies the component of $\mathbf{v}$. Corresponding to each velocity tensor, an nth order moment tensor of the distribution function may be defined:

$$S_{ijk\cdots}^{(n)} = \int v_{ijk\cdots}^{(n)} f(\mathbf{r}, \mathbf{v}, t)\, d\mathbf{v} \qquad (7.5\text{–}2)$$

It is clear that the zeroth moment is the number density n. The first moment is the macroscopic flux $n\mathbf{v}_0$. The macroscopic temperature is related to a contraction of the second moment:[2]

$$\tfrac{3}{2}nkT = \tfrac{1}{2}nm\overline{V^2} = \frac{m}{2}\,\Sigma_i S_{ii}^{(2)} - \tfrac{1}{2}nm{v_0}^2 \qquad (7.5\text{–}3)$$

The pressure tensor is related to the full second moment, thus:

$$p_{ij} = mS_{ij}^{(2)} - nmv_{0i}v_{0j} \qquad (7.5\text{–}4)$$

The energy flux vector is related to a contraction of the third moment,

$$q_i = \tfrac{1}{2}m\,\Sigma_j\,S_{ijj}^{(3)} - \tfrac{1}{2}nmv_{0i}{v_0}^2 - \tfrac{3}{2}nkTv_{0i} - \Sigma_j v_{0j}p_{ij} \qquad (7.5\text{–}5)$$

If the Boltzmann equation is multiplied successively by each of the $\mathbf{v}^{(n)}$ and integrated over the velocities, we obtain successive equations for the moments. In the absence of external forces these equations are

$$\frac{\partial}{\partial t}S_{ijk\cdots}^{(n)} + \Sigma_l \frac{\partial}{\partial x_l}S_{lijk\cdots}^{(n+1)} = \iiint v_{ijk\cdots}^{(n)}(f'f'_1 - ff_1)gb\,db\,d\epsilon\,d\mathbf{v}\,d\mathbf{v}_1 \qquad (7.5\text{–}6)$$

[2] A contraction of a tensor is a tensor whose rank is lower by two. It is formed by taking components of the original tensor in which two of the indices are alike and summing over this index.

The first two equations and a contraction of the third are the usual equations of change derived in § 7.2. In these equations the collision terms on the right are zero because of the properties of the summational invariants. We see that in general the equation for each moment involves the moment of one higher order explicitly and the entire distribution function in the collision integral. This set of equations is equivalent to the original Boltzmann equation.

The method of solution is as follows. A trial function representing the distribution function is set up in which a number, ν, of arbitrary parameters are included. These parameters may be written in terms of the first ν (scalar) moments. The remaining moments may then be written in terms of the lower moments. The first ν (scalar) equations of the set of moment equations (Eqs. 7.5–6) are then assumed to describe the time variation of the parameters and consequently the behavior of the gas.

Grad used as a trial function a Maxwellian distribution multiplied by a finite series of multidimensional Hermite polynomials. He showed that the series obtained by considering progressively more terms in the series of Hermite polynomials converged to a true solution of the Boltzmann equation.

b. The "thirteen-moment" approximation

Let us consider in detail the "thirteen-moment" approximation. A distribution function with thirteen scalar parameters is set up. The thirteen parameters are related to the thirteen independent scalars defining the moments $S^{(0)}$, $S^{(1)}$, and $S^{(2)}$ and a contraction of the third moment $\Sigma_j S^{(3)}_{ijj}$. The time variation of the thirteen parameters is obtained by using the corresponding moment equations, that is, Eq. 7.5–6 with $n = 0, 1, 2$, and a sum of the equations obtained by setting $n = 3$.

The $n = 0, 1$, and the sum of the "diagonal" $n = 2$ equations are the equation of continuity, equation of motion, and equation of energy balance, respectively, if we relate the moments to the density, velocity, temperature, pressure tensor, and heat flux as described above. However, in this approximation the pressure tensor and heat flux vector are taken to be independent functions satisfying their own differential equations—the remaining moment equations. These equations are

$$\frac{\partial P_{ij}}{\partial t} + \Sigma_k \frac{\partial}{\partial x_k} (v_{0k} P_{ij}) + 2 \left\{ \Sigma_k P_{ik} \frac{\partial v_{0j}}{\partial x_k} \right\} + 2p \left\{ \frac{\partial v_{0i}}{\partial x_k} \right\}$$

$$+ \frac{4}{5} \left\{ \frac{\partial q_i}{\partial x_j} \right\} + \frac{p}{\eta} P_{ij} = 0 \tag{7.5–7}$$

and

$$\frac{\partial q_i}{\partial t} + \sum_k \frac{\partial}{\partial x_k}(v_{0k}q_i) + \frac{5}{2}\frac{pk}{m}\frac{\partial T}{\partial x_i} + \frac{kT}{m}\sum_k \frac{\partial}{\partial x_k} P_{ik}$$
$$+ \frac{7}{2}\frac{k}{m}\sum_k P_{ik}\frac{\partial T}{\partial x_k} - \frac{1}{\rho}\sum_{j,k} P_{ij}\frac{\partial}{\partial x_k} p_{jk} + \frac{9}{5}\sum_k q_k \left\{\frac{\partial v_{0i}}{\partial x_k}\right\}$$
$$+ \frac{1}{2}\sum_k q_k\left(\frac{\partial v_{0i}}{\partial x_k} - \frac{\partial v_{0k}}{\partial x_i}\right) + q_i \sum_k \frac{\partial v_{0k}}{\partial x_k} + \frac{5pk}{2\lambda m} q_i = 0 \qquad (7.5\text{–}8)$$

In these expressions the { } denotes

$$\{A_{ij}\} = \tfrac{1}{2}(A_{ij} + A_{ji}) - \tfrac{1}{3}\delta_{ij}\sum_k A_{kk} \qquad (7.5\text{–}9)$$

P is defined by

$$\mathsf{P} = \mathsf{p} - p\mathsf{U} \qquad (7.5\text{–}10)$$

and η and λ represent integral expressions which are formally identical with the coefficients of viscosity and conductivity derived in the previous section.

Equations 7.5–7 and 8, along with the usual equations of change, form a set of equations for the macroscopic variables n, $\boldsymbol{v}_0$, and T, and in addition p and $\boldsymbol{q}$. The solutions of these equations require a more complete description of the boundary condition than is required for the solution of the Navier-Stokes equation; and hence more general problems may be solved. However, it may be shown that, if the flow is such that the properties of a small element of gas do not change appreciably in a collision time (that is, the mean time between collisions), then within a few collision times p and $\boldsymbol{q}$ approach values given by the equations

$$\mathsf{P} = \mathsf{p} - p\mathsf{U} = -2\eta\left\{\frac{\partial}{\partial \boldsymbol{r}}\boldsymbol{v}_0\right\} - \frac{4}{5}\frac{\eta}{p}\left\{\frac{\partial}{\partial \boldsymbol{r}}\boldsymbol{q}\right\} \qquad (7.5\text{–}11)$$

$$\boldsymbol{q} = -\lambda\frac{\partial T}{\partial \boldsymbol{r}} - \frac{2\lambda}{nk}\left(\frac{\partial}{\partial \boldsymbol{r}}\cdot\mathsf{P}\right) \qquad (7.5\text{–}12)$$

These relations are valid under many conditions, although they do not apply to such extreme situations as the passage of a gas through a shock wave.

If the variation of velocity and temperature with position are known, Eqs. 7.5–11 and 12 are a pair of coupled equations for $\boldsymbol{q}$ and P. The coupling terms (the second terms on the right-hand side of both equations) are essentially second derivative terms. If the velocity and temperature of the gas do not vary appreciably in a mean free path, these coupling terms are negligible, and the equations reduce to the Navier-Stokes relations. The added terms are of importance in the study of gases at low densities, where the mean free path is long and the gas no longer behaves as a continuous medium.

6. Effects of Chemical Reactions and the Internal Degrees of Freedom of the Molecules

The discussion of kinetic theory presented in this chapter has thus far been limited to non-reacting mixtures of simple molecules. It has been assumed that the molecules are spherical and have no internal degrees of freedom. We begin this section by discussing the modifications necessary in the equations of change when chemical reactions are taking place in a polyatomic gas mixture.[1] Then we discuss the general theory of transport properties for molecules which have internal degrees of freedom. In this connection an appraisal of the Eucken correction is given. No extensive calculations have been made for polyatomic molecules. However, the material presented in this section is helpful in indicating the extent to which the theory of monatomic gases can be safely employed for polyatomic gas calculations.

a. The equations of change for a reacting gas mixture

In § 7.1b it is shown that the terms on the right side of the Boltzmann equation represent the net number of molecules of a particular kind gained by a "group" of molecules in phase space because of collisions. Consequently, if collisions result in a chemical reaction, the right side of the Boltzmann equation must be modified. It is clear that the modifications of the Boltzmann equation affect the integral properties used in obtaining the equations of change. The integral

$$\int [\Gamma_{ij}^{(+)} - \Gamma_{ij}^{(-)}] \, d\mathbf{v}_i \tag{7.6–1}$$

is the *total* rate of gain of molecules of species i due to collision with molecules of j per unit volume. (In the absence of chemical reactions this term is of course zero.) Hence for reacting gas mixtures the total rate of increase (per unit volume) resulting from collisions of molecules i with all types of molecules (including i itself) is

$$\Sigma_j \int (\Gamma_{ij}^{(+)} - \Gamma_{ij}^{(-)}) \, d\mathbf{v}_i = K_i \tag{7.6–2}$$

where K_i is the total increase of molecules i per unit volume per unit time due to chemical reactions. Inasmuch as the total mass is conserved in a chemical reaction,

$$\Sigma_i m_i K_i = 0 \tag{7.6–3}$$

[1] The diffusion of excited or ionized molecules through molecules of the same species in the ground state is anomalous because of the strong resonance forces. See § 13.6a, § 14.6a, and R. Buckingham and A. Dalgarno, *Proc. Roy. Soc.* (*London*), **A213**, 506 1952).

Equation 7.6–2 is used to replace Eq. 7.2–32 in the development of the equations of continuity. However, even in a collision which produces a chemical reaction, mass, momentum, and energy are conserved. Hence, Eq. 7.2–33 remains valid except that the summational invariants are now m_i, $m_i\mathbf{V}_i$, and $\frac{1}{2}m_iV_i^2 + u_i^{(\mathrm{int})}$, where $u_i^{(\mathrm{int})}$ is the energy in the internal degrees of freedom of a molecule of i.

Making use of Eq. 7.6–2, we obtain the *individual equations of continuity*:

$$\frac{\partial n_i}{\partial t} + \left(\frac{\partial}{\partial \mathbf{r}} \cdot n_i[\mathbf{v}_0 + \overline{\mathbf{V}}_i]\right) = K_i \tag{7.6–4}$$

which replace Eq. 7.2–42. The term K_i represents a source strength due to the production of molecules of i in the chemical reactions. The *equation of continuity for the entire system* (Eq. 7.2–43)

$$\frac{\partial \rho}{\partial t} + \left(\frac{\partial}{\partial \mathbf{r}} \cdot \rho \mathbf{v}_0\right) = 0 \tag{7.6–5}$$

remains valid (since m_i is still a summational invariant). The same expression can be obtained from Eq. 7.6–4 by multiplying each of the equations by m_i and summing over i.

The momentum of a system of two colliding molecules is conserved in any collision in which a chemical reaction occurs. Consequently, we have as before

$$\frac{\partial \mathbf{v}_0}{\partial t} + \left(\mathbf{v}_0 \cdot \frac{\partial}{\partial \mathbf{r}} \mathbf{v}_0\right) = -\frac{1}{\rho}\left(\frac{\partial}{\partial \mathbf{r}} \cdot \mathsf{p}\right) + \frac{1}{\rho}\Sigma_i n_i \mathbf{X}_i \tag{7.6–6}$$

for the *equation of motion.*

The energy balance equation can be obtained in a manner quite similar to that described in § 7.2. For polyatomic molecules, however, the quantity ψ_i, which appears in the general equation of change, is not the translational energy of the molecule but the total energy—translational plus internal. This modification leads to an equation like Eq. 7.2–49 in which $\hat{U}^{(\mathrm{tr})}$ is replaced by $\hat{U}$. The *energy balance equation* is, accordingly

$$\rho\frac{\partial \hat{U}}{\partial t} + \rho\left(\mathbf{v}_0 \cdot \frac{\partial}{\partial \mathbf{r}} \hat{U}\right) = -\left(\frac{\partial}{\partial \mathbf{r}} \cdot \mathbf{q}\right) - \left(\mathsf{p} : \frac{\partial}{\partial \mathbf{r}} \mathbf{v}_0\right) + \Sigma_i n_i\,(\mathbf{X}_i \cdot \overline{\mathbf{V}}_i) \tag{7.6–7}$$

Here $\hat{U}$ is the thermodynamic internal energy per gram of the mixture

$$\hat{U} = \frac{1}{\rho}\Sigma_i n_i m_i \hat{U}_i \tag{7.6–8}$$

The $\hat{U}_i$ are the energies per gram of each of the chemical species.

We may also write the energy balance equation in terms of the temperature, as we did in Eq. 7.2–50. The resulting equation assumes a form slightly different from that for the monatomic gases. Using Eq. 7.6–4 to eliminate $(\partial n_i/\partial t)$ which results from differentiating $\hat{U}$, we obtain

$$\rho\hat{C}_v\left[\frac{\partial T}{\partial t} + \left(\boldsymbol{v}_0 \cdot \frac{\partial}{\partial \boldsymbol{r}} T\right)\right] = -\left(\frac{\partial}{\partial \boldsymbol{r}} \cdot \boldsymbol{q}\right) - \left(\mathsf{P} : \frac{\partial}{\partial \boldsymbol{r}} \boldsymbol{v}_0\right)$$
$$+ \Sigma_i n_i(\overline{\boldsymbol{V}}_i \cdot \boldsymbol{X}_i) - \Sigma_i m_i K_i \hat{U}_i + \Sigma_i \hat{U}_i \left(\frac{\partial}{\partial \boldsymbol{r}} \cdot n_i m_i \overline{\boldsymbol{V}}_i\right) \qquad (7.6\text{–}9)$$

In this equation

$$\hat{C}_v = \frac{1}{\rho} \Sigma_i n_i m_i \left(\frac{\partial \hat{U}_i}{\partial T}\right)_V = \frac{1}{\rho} \Sigma_i n_i m_i (\hat{C}_v)_i \qquad (7.6\text{–}10)$$

is the average heat capacity per gram at constant volume.

The expressions for the fluxes in terms of the distribution function are unaffected by the fact that chemical reactions are taking place in the gas mixture. However, the occurrence of collisions in which chemical reactions occur perturbs the distribution function if the system is not in equilibrium. This effect is small and unimportant in most cases.[2–4]

b. The effect of internal degrees of freedom on the transport phenomena (the Eucken correction)

The presence of internal degrees of freedom in the molecules does not affect the expressions for the coefficients of diffusion and viscosity in terms of the distribution function. The heat flux vector, on the other hand, is clearly influenced, inasmuch as $\frac{1}{2}m_iV_i^2 + u_i^{(\text{int})}$ now replaces the simple transitional kinetic energy term in the derivation of the energy balance equation. Hence for polyatomic molecules Eq. 7.2–26 must be replaced by

$$\boldsymbol{q} = \tfrac{1}{2} \Sigma_i n_i m_i \overline{V_i^2 \boldsymbol{V}_i} + \Sigma_i n_i \overline{u_i^{(\text{int})} \boldsymbol{V}_i} \qquad (7.6\text{–}11)$$

The vector $\boldsymbol{q}$ then represents the total energy flux. An immediate effect of this difference can be seen by noting that to a good approximation $u_i^{(\text{int})}$ is independent of $\boldsymbol{V}_i$ and hence the second term in this expression simply adds to the second term in Eq. 7.4–64 for the heat flux. Thus

$$\boldsymbol{q} = -\lambda \frac{\partial T}{\partial \boldsymbol{r}} + \Sigma_i n_i h_i \overline{\boldsymbol{V}}_i + \frac{kT}{n} \Sigma_{i,j} \frac{n_j D_i^T}{m_i \mathscr{D}_{ij}(1)} (\overline{\boldsymbol{V}}_i - \overline{\boldsymbol{V}}_j) \qquad (7.6\text{–}12)$$

[2] I. Prigogine and E. Xhrouet, *Physica*, **15**, 913 (1949).

[3] I. Prigogine and M. Mahieu, *Physica*, **16**, 51 (1950).

[4] C. F. Curtiss, Ph.D Dissertation (University of Wisconsin, 1948), published as University of Wisconsin Naval Research Report CM-476.

where h_i is the enthalpy per molecule of component, i,

$$h_i = \tfrac{5}{2}kT + u_i^{(\mathrm{int})} \tag{7.6–13}$$

However, the presence of the internal degrees of freedom has an additional effect due to the time lag in the transfer of energy from the translational to the internal degrees of freedom.

Because of the possibility of inelastic collisions, the coefficient of thermal conductivity is sensitive to the nature of the internal degrees of freedom of the molecules. The exact expression for the coefficient of thermal conductivity depends upon the transition probabilities for the transfer of energy among the various degrees of freedom of the molecule, particularly on the probability of transfer from the translational to the internal degrees of freedom. In view of the difficulty of treating this problem exactly, we discuss briefly the "Eucken assumption," which permits a quick estimation of the effect on the thermal conductivity due to internal degrees of freedom.

Eucken[5] introduced an approximation which is applicable when the rate of transfer is fast—that is, when the rate of transfer is sufficiently fast that the distribution of molecules among the various states is essentially the equilibrium distribution corresponding to the local temperature.[6] Let us consider a gas made up of molecules of a single chemical species. Then, according to Eqs. 8.2–10, 11, the first approximation to the coefficient of thermal conductivity is

$$\lambda = \tfrac{5}{2}\,\eta\hat{C}_v \tag{7.6–14}$$

However, this expression applies only to a gas composed of molecules without internal degrees of freedom. The molecules of the gas can exist in various internal quantum states.[7] Let us now regard the molecules in a particular quantum state as molecules of a particular chemical species. With this interpretation the gas can be considered as a reacting mixture of a large number of chemical components, each of which is devoid of internal degrees of freedom. The inelastic collisions are considered to be chemical reactions. Furthermore, the masses of all the

[5] A. Eucken, *Physik. Z.*, **14**, 324 (1913).

[6] In § 13.7 it is shown from an experimental study of the pressure broadening of microwaves that for most molecules, the rate of transfer by collision of rotational energy is comparable to the rate of transfer of translational energy. Then the Eucken assumption appears reasonable for the rotational degrees of freedom but not for the vibrational degrees of freedom where energy transitions are known to require a large number of collisions (50 to 5000).

[7] The concept of a quantum state is introduced here, not for accuracy, but rather for convenience of discussion.

molecules are alike, and to a good approximation all the intermolecular potentials are alike.

For a mixture of molecules of the same mass and with the same law of force between any pair, the coefficient of thermal diffusion is zero. Hence, from Eq. 7.6–12 the energy flux vector for such a mixture is

$$\boldsymbol{q} = -\lambda^{(0)} \frac{\partial T}{\partial \boldsymbol{r}} + \Sigma_i n_i (\tfrac{5}{2}kT + u_i^{(\text{int})}) \overline{\boldsymbol{V}}_i \tag{7.6–15}$$

Here $u_i^{(\text{int})}$ is the energy in the internal degrees of freedom of a molecule in quantum state i, and $\lambda^{(0)}$ is the coefficient of thermal conductivity of the system, considered as a mixture. From Eq. 7.6–14,

$$\lambda^{(0)} = \frac{15}{4} \frac{k\eta}{m} \tag{7.6–16}$$

where $\hat{C}_v$, the heat capacity per gram, has been set equal to $(3k/2m)$.

The diffusion velocity is given by Eq. 7.4–3, which for this simple mixture becomes

$$\overline{\boldsymbol{V}}_i = -\frac{n}{n_i} \mathscr{D} \frac{\partial}{\partial \boldsymbol{r}} \left(\frac{n_i}{n}\right) \tag{7.6–17}$$

where $\mathscr{D}$ is the coefficient of self-diffusion. The quantity (n_i/n) here has the significance of being the fraction of molecules in quantum state i. In general this quantity depends in a rather complicated way upon all the gradients. To obtain the Eucken approximation we assume that the fraction of molecules in state i is given by the equilibrium (Maxwellian) distribution characteristic of the local temperature. Then

$$\frac{\partial}{\partial \boldsymbol{r}} \left(\frac{n_i}{n}\right) = \left[\frac{d}{dT}\left(\frac{n_i}{n}\right)\right] \frac{\partial T}{\partial \boldsymbol{r}} \tag{7.6–18}$$

Substituting this into the expression for the diffusion velocity and making use of the fact that $\Sigma n_i \overline{\boldsymbol{V}}_i = 0$ (when all the m_i are equal), we obtain for the energy flux vector of Eq. 7.6–15:

$$\boldsymbol{q} = -\left[\frac{15}{4} \frac{k\eta}{m} + \rho \mathscr{D} \, \Sigma_j \hat{U}_j^{(\text{int})} \frac{d}{dT}\left(\frac{n_j}{n}\right)\right] \frac{\partial T}{\partial \boldsymbol{r}} \tag{7.6–19}$$

Here $\hat{U}_j^{(\text{int})} = u_j^{(\text{int})}/m$ is the internal energy per unit mass in the internal degrees of freedom of a molecule in state j.

Let us now introduce $\hat{U}^{(\text{int})}$, the average energy per gram in the internal degrees of freedom, and $\hat{C}_v^{(\text{int})}$, the contribution of the internal motion to the heat capacity per gram:

$$\hat{U}^{(\text{int})} = \Sigma_i \left(\frac{n_i}{n}\right) \hat{U}_i^{(\text{int})} \tag{7.6–20}$$

$$\hat{C}_v^{(\text{int})} = \hat{C}_v - \frac{3k}{2m} = \Sigma_i \hat{U}_i^{(\text{int})} \frac{d}{dT}\left(\frac{n_i}{n}\right) \tag{7.6–21}$$

Then the expressions for the energy flux vector and the coefficient of thermal conductivity of the system become

$$\boldsymbol{q} = -\lambda \frac{\partial}{\partial \boldsymbol{r}} T \tag{7.6–22}$$

$$\begin{aligned}\lambda &= \left[\left(\frac{15}{4} - \frac{3\rho\mathscr{D}}{2\eta}\right)\frac{k}{m} + \frac{\rho\mathscr{D}}{\eta}\,\hat{C}_v\right]\eta \\ &= \frac{1}{4}\left[\left(15 - 6\,\frac{\rho\mathscr{D}}{\eta}\right)\gamma - \left(15 - 10\,\frac{\rho\mathscr{D}}{\eta}\right)\right]\hat{C}_v\eta\end{aligned} \tag{7.6–23}$$

In this last expression for the thermal conductivity, the ratio of heat capacities, $\gamma = \hat{C}_p/\hat{C}_v = 1 + k/\hat{C}_v m$, has been introduced.

The dimensionless ratio $\rho\mathscr{D}/\eta$ is a function of temperature which is of the order of unity. Letting this quantity be exactly 1, we may write the coefficient of thermal conductivity as

$$\lambda = \frac{15}{4}\frac{k}{m}\eta\left(\frac{4}{15}\frac{m\hat{C}_v}{k} + \frac{3}{5}\right) \tag{7.6–24}$$

The factor in the parentheses is the *Eucken correction* for the thermal conductivity of polyatomic molecules. Eucken originally derived this correction factor by simple arguments. Because of the difficulty of transferring energy from translation to the internal degrees of freedom, the preceding equations for λ (Eqs. 7.6–23 and 24) do not fit the experimental data accurately at moderate (room) temperatures. At sufficiently high temperatures, however, Eq. 7.6–23 should be applicable.

c. The formal kinetic theory of polyatomic molecules[8]

The formal treatment of the kinetic theory of gases has been extended to polyatomic molecules or to molecules with internal quantum states. As is appropriate the translational motion is considered classically and the internal motions quantum mechanically. We introduce a distribution function $f_i(\boldsymbol{r}, \boldsymbol{v}, t)$ for each quantum state i. The single index i refers to the entire set of quantum numbers $\{i\} \equiv i_1, i_2, i_3 \cdots$ necessary to specify the internal state of the molecule.[9] Each distribution function then satisfies its own Boltzmann equation.

[8] The discussion given here is a summary of the work of C. S. Wang-Chang and G. E. Uhlenbeck, *Transport Phenomena in Polyatomic Molecules*, University of Michigan publication, CM-681 (1951). A very similar treatment has also been given independently by J. de Boer (unpublished).

[9] In previous sections $f_i(\boldsymbol{r}, \boldsymbol{v}, t)$ indicated the distribution function for the ith chemical species. Since this discussion is restricted to gases of a single component, the use of the subscript i to indicate a quantum state should cause no confusion.

The collision integrals are written in terms of a set of differential cross-sections, $I_{ij}^{kl}(g, \theta, \phi)$. The cross-section $I_{ij}^{kl}(g, \theta, \phi)$ refers to a collision in which the molecules, initially in states i and j, end up in states k and l. The magnitude of the initial asymptotic relative velocity is g. The direction of the initial relative velocity is taken as the axis of a polar coordinate system. Then $I_{ij}^{kl}(g, \theta, \phi)$ is the cross-section for scattering at the angle, θ, ϕ. Now we can make use of the arguments presented in § 7.1b to develop a more general Boltzmann equation. In terms of the cross-sections, it is clear that the number of molecules lost to the group in state i due to collisions with molecules in state j is (in analogy with Eq. 7.1–10)

$$\Gamma_{ij}^{(-)}\, d\mathbf{v}_i = \Sigma_{k,l} \iiint f_i f_j g_{ij} I_{ij}^{kl} \sin\theta \, d\theta \, d\phi \, d\mathbf{v}_i \, d\mathbf{v}_j \qquad (7.6\text{–}25)$$

Similarly the number of molecules gained by a group in state i due to collisions in which the other product molecule is in state j is

$$\Gamma_{ij}^{(+)}\, d\mathbf{v}_i = \Sigma_{k,l} \iiint f_k' f_l' g_{kl}' I_{kl}^{ij} \sin\theta \, d\theta \, d\phi \, d\mathbf{v}_k' \, d\mathbf{v}_l' \qquad (7.6\text{–}26)$$

Here $\mathbf{v}_k'$ and $\mathbf{v}_l'$ are the velocities before a collision in which the final velocities are $\mathbf{v}_i$ and $\mathbf{v}_j$. Then, making use of the fact that inverse collisions exist,[10] we may write

$$\Gamma_{ij}^{(+)} = \Sigma_{k,l} \iiint f_k' f_l' g_{ij} I_{ij}^{kl} \sin\theta \, d\theta \, d\phi \, d\mathbf{v}_j \qquad (7.6\text{–}27)$$

Thus the generalized Boltzmann equation becomes

$$\frac{\partial f_i}{\partial t} + \left(\mathbf{v}_i \cdot \frac{\partial}{\partial \mathbf{r}} f_i\right) + \frac{1}{m}\left(\mathbf{X}_i \cdot \frac{\partial f_i}{\partial \mathbf{v}_i}\right)$$
$$= \Sigma_{j,\,k,\,l} \iiint (f_k' f_l' - f_i f_j) g_{ij} I_{ij}^{kl}(g, \theta, \phi) \sin\theta \, d\theta \, d\phi \, d\mathbf{v}_j \qquad (7.6\text{–}28)$$

This generalized Boltzmann equation has been solved by perturbation methods for two limiting cases. One applies to gases in which the transfer of energy between the translational motion and the internal degrees of freedom takes place with ease. The other applies to gases in which the transitions take place with difficulty. The theoretical development and the results are quite similar to the simple case of monatomic molecules. We discuss here some of the results for a gas consisting of a single component.

[10] It is noted that $g_{kl}' I_{kl}^{ij}\, dv_k'\, dv_l' = g_{ij} I_{ij}^{kl}\, dv_i\, dv_j$. However it should be further noted that this relation has been proven only if the internal states are non-degenerate.

i. *Energy Exchange between Translational and Internal Motion Is Not Difficult*

Let us consider the case in which the transitions take place with ease. The equations of change are, of course, identical in form with those obtained for a monatomic gas. The pressure tensor, however, becomes

$$\mathsf{p} = p\mathsf{U} - 2\eta\mathsf{S} - \kappa\left(\frac{\partial}{\partial \boldsymbol{r}} \cdot \boldsymbol{v}_0\right)\mathsf{U} \tag{7.6–29}$$

where S is the stress tensor defined by Eq. 7.4–16.

The coefficient η is closely related to the corresponding coefficient of viscosity appearing in the treatment of monatomic molecules and is called the *coefficient of shear viscosity*. The coefficient κ is an additional transport coefficient, the *coefficient of bulk viscosity*[11] which is closely related to a "relaxation time"—a characteristic time required for the transfer of energy from the translational to the internal degrees of freedom.

It is convenient to consider each of the internal modes of motion or degrees of freedom separately and define a relaxation time τ_l characteristic of each mode. It may be shown that the bulk viscosity is related to the relaxation times by

$$\kappa = \frac{nk^2T}{c_v^{\,2}} \Sigma_l\, c_v^{(l)} \tau_l \tag{7.6–30}$$

where the $c_v^{(l)}$ is the contribution of the particular degree of freedom to the specific heat per molecule, c_v.

The expression for the energy flux is identical with that obtained in the simple case. However, it is convenient to consider the coefficient of thermal conductivity as the sum of terms representing the effects of the translational motion and of the internal degrees of freedom,

$$\boldsymbol{q} = -(\lambda^{(\mathrm{tr})} + \lambda^{(\mathrm{int})}) \frac{\partial T}{\partial \boldsymbol{r}} \tag{7.6–31}$$

The detailed expressions for the transport coefficients are

(i) *The Coefficient of Shear Viscosity*

$$\frac{1}{\eta} = \frac{8}{5\sqrt{\pi mkT}} \frac{1}{(\Sigma_i e^{-\epsilon_i})^2} \sum_{\substack{i,\,j\\k,\,l}} e^{-\epsilon_i - \epsilon_j}$$
$$\times \iiint [\gamma^4 \sin^2\theta + \tfrac{2}{3}\gamma^2\, \Delta\epsilon\, (1 - \tfrac{3}{2}\sin^2\theta)]\gamma^3 e^{-\gamma^2} I_{ij}^{kl}(g, \theta, \phi) \sin\theta\, d\theta\, d\phi\, d\gamma \tag{7.6–32}$$

[11] Sometimes called the *coefficient of dilatation viscosity.*

Here ϵ_i is

$$\epsilon_i = E_i/kT \tag{7.6–33}$$

where E_i is the energy of the ith state and

$$\Delta\epsilon = \epsilon_k + \epsilon_l - \epsilon_i - \epsilon_j \tag{7.6–34}$$

The dimensionless relative initial velocity is defined in Eq. 7.2–12.

(ii) *The Coefficient Thermal Conductivity*

$$\lambda^{(\text{tr})} = \frac{5k^2T}{2m}\left[\frac{\dfrac{15}{4}a + \dfrac{3c_v^{(\text{int})}}{2k}b}{ac - b^2}\right] \tag{7.6–35}$$

$$\lambda^{(\text{int})} = \frac{kTc_v^{(\text{int})}}{m}\left[\frac{\dfrac{3c_v^{(\text{int})}}{2k}c + \dfrac{15}{4}b}{ac - b^2}\right] \tag{7.6–36}$$

where

$$a = \frac{1}{2}\sqrt{\frac{kT}{\pi m}}\frac{1}{(\Sigma_i e^{-\epsilon_i})^2}\sum_{\substack{i,j\\k,l}} e^{-\epsilon_i-\epsilon_j} \tag{7.6–37}$$
$$\times \iiint \{3(\Delta\epsilon)^2 + 2[(\epsilon_i - \epsilon_j)\boldsymbol{\gamma} - (\epsilon_k - \epsilon_l)\boldsymbol{\gamma}']^2\}\gamma^3 e^{-\gamma^2} I_{ij}^{kl}(g, \theta, \phi)\sin\theta\, d\theta\, d\phi\, d\gamma$$

$$b = \frac{5}{2}\sqrt{\frac{kT}{\pi m}}\frac{1}{(\Sigma_i e^{-\epsilon_i})^2}\sum_{\substack{i,j\\k,l}} (\Delta\epsilon)^2 e^{-\epsilon_i-\epsilon_j}$$
$$\times \iiint \gamma^3 e^{-\gamma^2} I_{ij}^{kl}(g, \theta, \phi)\sin\theta\, d\theta\, d\phi\, d\gamma \tag{7.6–38}$$

$$c = 4\sqrt{\frac{kT}{\pi m}}\frac{1}{(\Sigma_i e^{-\epsilon_i})^2}\sum_{\substack{i,j\\k,l}} e^{-\epsilon_i-\epsilon_j} \tag{7.6–39}$$
$$\times \iiint \{\gamma^4\sin^2\theta + \gamma^2(\Delta\epsilon)(\tfrac{7}{4} + \cos^2\theta)\}\gamma^3 e^{-\gamma^2} I_{ij}^{kl}(g, \theta, \phi)\sin\theta\, d\theta\, d\phi\, d\gamma$$

and where

$$\gamma'^2 = \gamma^2 - \Delta\epsilon \tag{7.6–40}$$

and $c_v^{(\text{int})}$ is the contribution of the internal degrees of freedom to the heat capacity per molecule.

(iii) *Relaxation Time*

$$\frac{1}{\tau} = 2nc_v^{(\text{int})}\sqrt{\frac{kT}{\pi m}}\frac{1}{(\Sigma_i e^{-\epsilon_i})^2}\sum_{\substack{i,j\\k,l}} (\Delta\epsilon)^2 e^{-\epsilon_i-\epsilon_j}$$
$$\times \iiint \gamma^3 e^{-\gamma^2} I_{ij}^{kl}(g, \theta, \phi)\sin\theta\, d\theta\, d\phi\, d\gamma \tag{7.6–41}$$

ii. *Energy Interchange between Translational and Internal Motions Is Difficult*

The results for the case in which the transitions take place relatively seldom are expressed in a somewhat different manner. For simplicity let us confine our attention to molecules which have only one internal degree of freedom. The discussion may be easily extended to molecules with many internal degrees of freedom. Because of the slowness with which equilibrium is established, there are two different temperatures: a temperature characteristic of the translational energy, $T^{(\mathrm{tr})}$, and a temperature characteristic of the internal energy, $T^{(\mathrm{int})}$.

The two temperatures are related by an equation which is essentially an additional equation of change,

$$nc_v^{(\mathrm{int})}\left[\frac{\partial T^{(\mathrm{int})}}{\partial t}+\left(\mathbf{v}_0\cdot\frac{\partial T^{(\mathrm{int})}}{\partial \mathbf{r}}\right)\right]=\frac{\partial}{\partial \mathbf{r}}\left(\lambda^{(\mathrm{int})}\frac{\partial T^{(\mathrm{int})}}{\partial \mathbf{r}}\right)+\frac{nc_v^{(\mathrm{int})}}{\tau}(T^{(\mathrm{tr})}-T^{(\mathrm{int})}) \tag{7.6–42}$$

Here, as above, $c_v^{(\mathrm{int})}$ is the contribution of the internal degree of freedom to the capacity heat, τ is a relaxation time, and $\lambda^{(\mathrm{int})}$ is the coefficient of conductivity of the energy in the internal degrees of freedom. This equation states that, aside from the effect of the conductivity term, the internal temperature $T^{(\mathrm{int})}$ approaches the translational temperature $T^{(\mathrm{tr})}$ exponentially with a characteristic time τ.

The ordinary equations of change are unchanged. In this case the pressure tensor does not contain the bulk viscosity term. The energy flux is the sum of two terms,

$$\mathbf{q}=-\lambda^{(\mathrm{tr})}\frac{\partial}{\partial \mathbf{r}}T^{(\mathrm{tr})}-\lambda^{(\mathrm{int})}\frac{\partial}{\partial \mathbf{r}}T^{(\mathrm{int})} \tag{7.6–43}$$

The detailed expressions for the transport coefficients are

(i) *The Coefficient of Shear Viscosity*

$$\frac{1}{\eta}=\frac{8}{5\sqrt{\pi mkT}}\frac{1}{(\Sigma_i e^{-\epsilon_i})^2}\sum_{\substack{i,\,j\\k,\,l}} e^{-\epsilon_i-\epsilon_j}$$
$$\times\iiint \gamma^7 e^{-\gamma^2} I_{\mathrm{el}}(g,\theta,\phi)\sin^3\theta\, d\theta\, d\phi\, d\gamma \tag{7.6–44}$$

where I_{el} is the elastic cross-section, and only elastic collisions enter into the sum.

(ii) *The Coefficient of Thermal Conductivity*

$$\frac{1}{\lambda^{(\text{tr})}} = \frac{32}{75\sqrt{\pi m k^3 T}} \frac{1}{(\Sigma_i e^{-\epsilon_i})^2} \sum_{\substack{i,\,j\\k,\,l}} e^{-\epsilon_i - \epsilon_j}$$
$$\times \iiint \gamma^7 e^{-\gamma^2} I_{\text{el}}(g, \theta, \phi) \sin^3\theta \, d\theta \, d\phi \, d\gamma \qquad (7.6\text{–}45)$$

$$\frac{1}{\lambda^{(\text{int})}} = \frac{3}{8c_v^{(\text{int})}\sqrt{\pi m k T}} \frac{k/c_v^{(\text{int})}}{(\Sigma_i e^{-\epsilon_i})^2} \sum_{\substack{i,\,j\\k,\,l}} \epsilon_i(\epsilon_i - \epsilon_j) e^{-\epsilon_i - \epsilon_j}$$
$$\times \iiint \gamma^5 e^{-\gamma^2} I_{\text{el}}(g, \theta, \phi) \sin\theta \, d\theta \, d\phi \, d\gamma \qquad (7.6\text{–}46)$$

(iii) *Relaxation Time*

$$\frac{1}{\tau} = \frac{2nk}{c_v^{(\text{int})}} \sqrt{\frac{kT}{\pi m}} \frac{1}{(\Sigma_i e^{-\epsilon_i})^2} \sum_{\substack{i,\,j\\k,\,l}} (\Delta\epsilon)^2 e^{-\epsilon_i - \epsilon_j}$$
$$\times \iiint \gamma^3 e^{-\gamma^2} I_{ij}^{kl}(g, \theta, \phi) \sin\theta \, d\theta \, d\phi \, d\gamma \qquad (7.6\text{–}47)$$

In order to use these formulae and those given in Eqs. 7.6–32 through 41, it is of course necessary to know the differential cross-sections for some assumed model. These have never been calculated for any realistic molecular model.

d. Several special models (rigid ovaloids, rough spheres, loaded spheres)

Prior to the development of the general formal theory outlined in the preceding subsection, the transport phenomena had been studied for several molecular models with internal degrees of freedom. Because no numerical results have yet been obtained from the formal theory, we summarize some of the results for rigid ovaloids, perfectly rough spheres, and loaded spheres.

i. *Rigid Ovaloids*

Ishida[12] has studied the kinetic theory of molecules which are rigid and non-spherical, but possess no other internal degrees of freedom. He developed a generalization of the Boltzmann equation which applies to this type of model. The thus modified Boltzmann equation leads to the ordinary equations of change and, in addition, to an equation expressing the conservation of angular momentum:

$$\mathsf{M} \cdot \left\{\frac{\partial \boldsymbol{\omega}_0}{\partial t} + \left(\boldsymbol{v}_0 \cdot \frac{\partial}{\partial \boldsymbol{r}} \boldsymbol{\omega}_0\right)\right\} + \frac{1}{n}\frac{\partial}{\partial \boldsymbol{r}} \cdot \{n\overline{\boldsymbol{V}}(\boldsymbol{\omega}_0 \cdot \mathsf{M}) + n\,\overline{\boldsymbol{V}(\boldsymbol{\Omega} \cdot \mathsf{M})}\} - \boldsymbol{G} = 0 \qquad (7.6\text{–}48)$$

[12] Y. Ishida, *Phys. Rev.*, **10**, 305 (1917). Ishida's results are formally correct, but the specific variables used and the Jacobians involved in the integrations require further clarification.

Here $\boldsymbol{G}$ is the external torque applied to the individual molecules, and M is the moment of inertia tensor. $\boldsymbol{\omega}_0$ is the (number) *average angular velocity* of the molecules, and $\boldsymbol{\Omega} = \boldsymbol{\omega} - \boldsymbol{\omega}_0$ is the *peculiar angular velocity* of a molecule. If the molecules are spherical, this additional equation is not interesting since all the angular momentum is present in the form of the macroscopic motion of the gas (or at least there is no mechanism for an interchange of the macroscopic angular momentum with that associated with the rotation of the molecules). However, if the molecules are non-spherical, the possibility of interchange of the angular momenta introduces some interesting consequences. It is at this point that the additional transport property related to the relaxation time appears. However, this model has not been considered to a sufficient extent to lead to any numerical results for the transport coefficients.

ii. *Perfectly Rough Spherical Molecules*[13]

One of the simplest idealized models for which numerical values have been obtained is the perfectly rough elastic sphere model suggested by Bryan.[14] The methods of Chapman and Enskog, discussed in this chapter were extended to this model by Pidduck.[15, 16] The concept of the perfectly rough sphere implies that the molecules do not slip with respect to each other when they collide. More precisely, the rough-sphere model is such that the relative velocity of the points of contact is reversed on collision. These molecules may exchange angular momentum with one another and with the translational motion on collision. That is, the forces are not strictly central forces. However, the theory is simplified by the fact that no additional coordinates are needed to describe the orientation of the molecules. In this case the distribution function $f(\boldsymbol{r}, \boldsymbol{v}, \boldsymbol{\omega}, t)$ depends on the space and linear velocity coordinates and on the angular velocity of the molecule, $\boldsymbol{\omega}$.

The solution of the Boltzmann equation for $f(\boldsymbol{r}, \boldsymbol{v}, \boldsymbol{\omega}, t)$ can be obtained by much the same method as is used for the solution of the analogous problem for point molecules with central forces. The results can be expressed in terms of α, the dimensionless radius of gyration:

$$\alpha = 4I/m\sigma^2 \tag{7.6-49}$$

where m, σ, and I are the mass, diameter, and moment of inertia of the

[13] This model may be treated by the method of Wang Chang and Uhlenbeck discussed in § 7.6c. The results are identical with those given here.

[14] G. H. Bryan, *Brit. Assoc. Reports*, p. 83 (1894).

[15] F. B. Pidduck, *Proc. Roy. Soc.* (*London*), **A101** (1922).

[16] S. Chapman and T. G. Cowling, *The Mathematical Theory of Non-uniform Gases*, Cambridge University Press (1939).

rough spherical molecule. The value of α ranges from zero, when all the mass is concentrated at the center of the sphere, to two-thirds, when all the mass is on the surface of the sphere. For a sphere of uniform density, α has the value two-fifths.

We summarize the results for the rough-sphere model by quoting the first approximation to the transport coefficients. In order to compare them with those for smooth spheres, we write the expressions as the smooth-sphere values[17] (between brackets) multiplied by a correction factor (between braces):[18]

$$\mathscr{D}_{12}(1) = \left[\frac{3}{8n\sigma_{12}{}^2}\sqrt{\frac{kT}{2\pi\mu_{12}}}\right]\left\{\frac{m_1\alpha_1 + m_2\alpha_2 + (m_1 + m_2)\alpha_1\alpha_2}{m_1\alpha_1 + m_2\alpha_2 + 2(m_1 + m_2)\alpha_1\alpha_2}\right\} \tag{7.6–50}$$

$$\mathscr{D}(1) = \left[\frac{3}{8n\sigma^2}\sqrt{\frac{kT}{\pi m}}\right]\left\{\frac{1+\alpha}{1+2\alpha}\right\} \tag{7.6–51}$$

$$\eta(1) = \left[\frac{5}{16\sigma^2}\sqrt{\frac{mkT}{\pi}}\right]\left\{\frac{(1+\alpha)^2}{1+\frac{13}{6}\alpha}\right\} \tag{7.6–52}$$

$$\lambda(2) = \left[\frac{75}{64\sigma^2}\sqrt{\frac{k^3T}{\pi m}}\right]\left\{\frac{12(1+\alpha)^2(37+151\alpha+50\alpha^2)}{25(12+75\alpha+101\alpha^2+102\alpha^3)}\right\} \tag{7.6–53}$$

By way of illustrating the nature of the deviations due to the roughness of the molecules, the correction factors for self-diffusion and for viscosity are given in Fig. 7.6–1 as functions of α. It should be noted from the equations that, when $\alpha = 0$, the value of the ratio $m\lambda(2)/k\eta(1)$ becomes 5.55 as compared with $15/4 = 3.75$ for smooth spheres. This difference results from the fact that the rough-sphere model permits interchange of rotational and translational energy.

The expression for the coefficient of thermal conductivity may be written in the following form to show its relation to the coefficient of viscosity:

$$\lambda(2) = \frac{k}{m}\,\eta(1)\left\{\frac{3(6+13\alpha)(37+151\alpha+50\alpha^2)}{10(12+75\alpha+101\alpha^2+102\alpha^3)}\right\} \tag{7.6–54}$$

It is interesting to compare this expression with the one we obtain from the formula in Eq. 7.6–23, which assumes rapid transfer of energy. If in the latter equation we let $\hat{C}_v = 3k/m$ and use the value of $\rho\mathscr{D}/\eta$ for

[17] Transport properties for smooth spheres are discussed in § 8.3a.

[18] σ_{12} and μ_{12} are the collision diameter and reduced mass of two colliding molecules defined by $\sigma_{12} = \frac{1}{2}(\sigma_1 + \sigma_2)$; and $(1/\mu_{12}) = (1/m_1) + (1/m_2)$.

rough spheres (as given by Eqs. 7.6–51, 52), the coefficient of thermal conductivity is given by

$$\lambda(2) = \frac{k}{m}\,\eta(1)\left\{\frac{3(37 + 101\alpha + 50\alpha^2)}{20(1 + 3\alpha + 2\alpha^2)}\right\} \tag{7.6–55}$$

The ratio of the rough-sphere value in Eq. 7.6–54 to the value given by Eq. 7.6–55 is plotted in Fig. 7.6–2. It is seen that the ratio is unity for $\alpha = 0$, since in this case it is easy to transfer energy, and equilibrium is

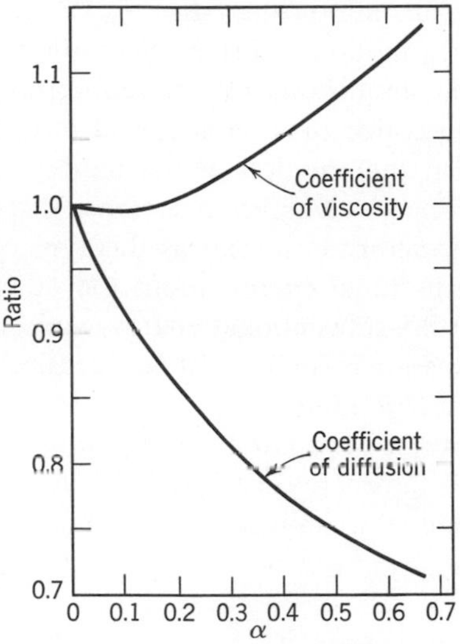

Fig. 7.6–1. The ratio of the rough sphere to the smooth sphere values of the coefficients of viscosity and self-diffusion.

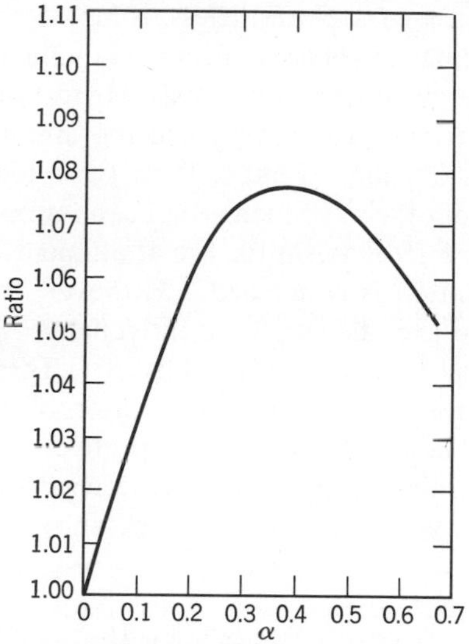

Fig. 7.6–2. The ratio of the thermal conductivity of rough spheres to that predicted by the modified Eucken approximation.

established immediately. For other values of α the deviation from unity gives a measure of the effect of the relaxation time on the thermal conductivity. It is also clear from this comparison that we would expect the Eucken correction to be satisfactory to within 10 per cent or less. The latter is also borne out by thermal conductivity calculations which are given in Chapter 8.

iii. *Loaded Spheres*

The relaxation time (the time required for equilibrium to be established between the translational and internal energies of the molecules) has not yet been calculated for a gas made up of rough-sphere molecules. The corresponding calculation, however, has been made by Jeans[19] for a gas

[19] J. H. Jeans, *Dynamical Theory of Gases*, Cambridge University Press (1904).

made up of molecules which are regarded as "loaded spheres." This model is a spherical molecule of diameter σ and mass m, in which the center of gravity lies a short distance δ from the geometrical center. It is assumed that $\delta \ll \sigma$ and that the mass distribution has an axis of symmetry. The molecule has a moment of inertia I about an axis through the center of mass perpendicular to the symmetry axis. The treatment used by Jeans made use of an earlier development of kinetic theory due to Maxwell, and hence his results are not directly comparable to those just discussed. Nevertheless, some of his results are of interest.

Loaded-sphere molecules wobble in their motion and transfer rotational energy during collisions. Hence we can inquire as to the equilibrium distribution of energy and the time required for the establishment of this equilibrium. First it is to be noted that the rotation of the molecules about their symmetry axes cannot be affected by a collision. Hence there is no mechanism for the attainment of equilibrium insofar as this type of rotation is concerned. However, the rotational energy about the other two axes can undergo interchange with the translational energy, and an equilibrium can be established. This situation is similar, but not identical, to the two-dimensional rotation of a diatomic molecule.

Let $u^{(\mathrm{tr})}$ and $u^{(\mathrm{rot})}$ be, respectively, the mean translational and rotational energies per molecule (the latter excludes the energy of the rotation about the symmetry axis). Jeans showed that in a uniform gas of number density n,

$$\frac{d}{dt} \ln \left| u^{(\mathrm{rot})} - \tfrac{2}{3}u^{(\mathrm{tr})} \right| = - \tfrac{5}{2}n\beta\sqrt{u^{(\mathrm{tr})}} \tag{7.6–56}$$

Here β is a constant depending only on the structure of the molecules:

$$\beta = \frac{16\delta^2\sigma^2}{3I}\sqrt{2\pi m/3} \tag{7.6–57}$$

Equation 7.6–56 shows that $\left| u^{(\mathrm{rot})} - \tfrac{2}{3}u^{(\mathrm{tr})} \right|$ is monotone, decreasing to zero. This is consistent with the known equilibrium values of $u^{(\mathrm{tr})} = \tfrac{3}{2}kT$ and $u^{(\mathrm{rot})} = kT$ for a two-dimensional rotator. Furthermore, Eq. 7.6–56 shows that the system approaches equilibrium. The value of $\left| u^{(\mathrm{rot})} - \tfrac{2}{3}u^{(\mathrm{tr})} \right|$ decreases exponentially with time, dropping to $1/e$ of its value in a time ("the relaxation time"):

$$\tau = \frac{3}{5\beta n\sqrt{u^{(\mathrm{tr})}}} \tag{7.6–58}$$

In this expression we have made use of Eq. 7.6–57 for β.

According to Eq. 1.2-1 the mean time between collisions of rigid sphere molecules is

$$\tau_c = \frac{1}{4n\sigma^2}\sqrt{m/\pi kT} \tag{7.6–59}$$

This number under standard conditions is of the order of 10^{-10} second. The relaxation time is

$$\tau = \frac{9}{20}\left(\frac{I}{m\delta^2}\right)\tau_c \tag{7.6–60}$$

It can thus be seen that, if the moment of inertia is small, energy is transferred very readily, and the relaxation time is short. But if the moment of inertia is large, many collisions are needed to effect the transfer of energy, and the time required to reach equilibrium is long. The larger the asymmetry δ, the easier it is to transfer energy, and the smaller is the relaxation time. It should be mentioned, however, that this model is of doubtful value, since in most cases the transfer of energy probably occurs because of the non-spherical nature of the potential rather than because of an asymmetry of the mass distribution.

Jeans also considered the propagation of sound through a gas made up of loaded sphere molecules by methods similar to those discussed in § 11.4. He showed that for frequencies, ν, small compared to $1/\tau$, the velocity of propagation is that characteristic of a perfect gas with a ratio of specific heats $\gamma = 7/5$. This is the true ratio of specific heats for loaded spheres. Hence at low frequencies the rotational motion follows the changes due to the passage of the wave. However, at high frequencies, $\nu \gg 1/\tau$, the velocity is that characteristic of a gas with $\gamma = 5/3$. This value of γ corresponds to a gas whose molecules have only translational energy. Hence at frequencies large compared to the reciprocal of the relaxation time, the rotational motion does not follow the changes. If the frequency is of the order $1/\tau$, there is resonance absorption of the sound. Similar calculations could be made for rough spheres.

APPENDIX A. BRACKET EXPRESSIONS IN TERMS OF THE $\Omega^{(l,s)}$ WHICH ARE USED IN DERIVING THE EXPRESSIONS FOR THE TRANSPORT COEFFICIENTS[1]

$$[W_i; W_j]_{ij} = -8\frac{\sqrt{m_i m_j}}{(m_i + m_j)}\Omega_{ij}^{(1,1)} \tag{7.A–1}$$

[1] The results given in Eqs. 7.A–1, 2, 3, 6, 7, 9, 12, and 13 are from S. Chapman and T. G. Cowling, *The Mathematical Theory of Non-uniform Gases*, Cambridge (1939). The results given in Eqs. 7.A–4, 5, 8, 10, and 11 are from E. A. Mason, *J. Chem. Phys.*, **22** (1954).

$$[\boldsymbol{W}_i;\ S^{(1)}_{3/2}(W_j^2)\boldsymbol{W}_j]_{ij} = 8\,\frac{m_i\sqrt{m_i m_j}}{(m_i+m_j)^2}\,\{\Omega^{(1,2)}_{ij} - \tfrac{5}{2}\,\Omega^{(1,1)}_{ij}\} \tag{7.A-2}$$

$$[S^{(1)}_{3/2}(W_i^2)\boldsymbol{W}_i;\ S^{(1)}_{3/2}(W_j^2)\boldsymbol{W}_j]_{ij}$$
$$= -8\,\frac{(m_i m_j)^{3/2}}{(m_i+m_j)^3}\,\{\tfrac{55}{4}\,\Omega^{(1,1)}_{ij} - 5\Omega^{(1,2)}_{ij} + \Omega^{(1,3)}_{ij} - 2\Omega^{(2,2)}_{ij}\} \tag{7.A-3}$$

$$[S^{(1)}_{3/2}(W_i^2)\boldsymbol{W}_i;\ S^{(2)}_{3/2}(W_j^2)\boldsymbol{W}_j]_{ij}$$
$$= -8\,\frac{m_i(m_i m_j)^{3/2}}{(m_i+m_j)^4}\begin{bmatrix}\tfrac{595}{16}\,\Omega^{(1,1)}_{ij} - \tfrac{189}{8}\,\Omega^{(1,2)}_{ij} + \tfrac{19}{4}\,\Omega^{(1,3)}_{ij}\\ -\tfrac{1}{2}\Omega^{(1,4)}_{ij} - 7\Omega^{(2,2)}_{ij} + 2\Omega^{(2,3)}_{ij}\end{bmatrix} \tag{7.A-4}$$

$$[S^{(2)}_{3/2}(W_i^2)\boldsymbol{W}_i;\ S^{(2)}_{3/2}(W_j^2)\boldsymbol{W}_j]_{ij}$$
$$= -\,\frac{(m_i m_j)^{5/2}}{(m_i+m_j)^5}\begin{bmatrix}\tfrac{8505}{64}\,\Omega^{(1,1)}_{ij} - \tfrac{833}{8}\,\Omega^{(1,2)}_{ij} + \tfrac{241}{8}\,\Omega^{(1,3)}_{ij} - \tfrac{7}{2}\,\Omega^{(1,4)}_{ij}\\ +\tfrac{1}{4}\,\Omega^{(1,5)}_{ij} - \tfrac{77}{2}\,\Omega^{(2,2)}_{ij} + 14\Omega^{(2,3)}_{ij} - 2\Omega^{(2,4)}_{ij} + 2\Omega^{(3,3)}_{ij}\end{bmatrix} \tag{7.A-5}$$

$$[\boldsymbol{W}_i;\ \boldsymbol{W}_i]_{ij} = 8\,\frac{m_j}{(m_i+m_j)}\,\Omega^{(1,1)}_{ij} \tag{7.A-6}$$

$$[\boldsymbol{W}_i;\ S^{(1)}_{3/2}(W_i^2)\boldsymbol{W}_i]_{ij} = -8\,\frac{m_j^2}{(m_i+m_j)^2}\,\{\Omega^{(1,2)}_{ij} - \tfrac{5}{2}\,\Omega^{(1,1)}_{ij}\} \tag{7.A-7}$$

$$[\boldsymbol{W}_i;\ S^{(2)}_{3/2}(W_i^2)\boldsymbol{W}_i]_{ij} = 4\,\frac{m_j^3}{(m_i+m_j)^3}\,[\tfrac{35}{4}\,\Omega^{(1,1)}_{ij} - 7\Omega^{(1,2)}_{ij} + \Omega^{(1,3)}_{ij}] \tag{7.A-8}$$

$$[S^{(1)}_{3/2}(W_i^2)\boldsymbol{W}_i;\ S^{(1)}_{3/2}(W_i^2)\boldsymbol{W}_i]_{ij}$$
$$= 8\,\frac{m_j}{(m_i+m_j)^3}\begin{bmatrix}\tfrac{5}{4}\,(6m_i^2 + 5m_j^2)\Omega^{(1,1)}_{ij} - 5m_j^2\Omega^{(1,2)}_{ij}\\ + m_j^2\Omega^{(1,3)}_{ij} + 2m_i m_j\Omega^{(2,2)}_{ij}\end{bmatrix} \tag{7.A-9}$$

$$[S^{(1)}_{3/2}(W_i^2)\boldsymbol{W}_i;\ S^{(2)}_{3/2}(W_i^2)\boldsymbol{W}_i]_{ij}$$
$$= 8\,\frac{m_j^2}{(m_i+m_j)^4}\begin{bmatrix}\tfrac{35}{16}\,(12m_i^2 + 5m_j^2)\Omega^{(1,1)}_{ij} - \tfrac{21}{8}\,(4m_i^2 + 5m_j^2)\Omega^{(1,2)}_{ij}\\ +\tfrac{19}{4}\,m_j^2\Omega^{(1,3)}_{ij} - \tfrac{1}{2}\,m_j^2\Omega^{(1,4)}_{ij} + 7m_i m_j\Omega^{(2,2)}_{ij} - 2m_i m_j\Omega^{(2,3)}_{ij}\end{bmatrix} \tag{7.A-10}$$

$$[S_{3/2}^{(2)}(W_i^2)\boldsymbol{W}_i;\ S_{3/2}^{(2)}(W_i^2)\boldsymbol{W}_i]_{ij}$$

$$= 8\,\frac{m_j}{(m_i+m_j)^5}\left[\begin{aligned}&\tfrac{35}{64}(40m_i^4+168m_i^2m_j^2+35m_j^4)\Omega_{ij}^{(1,1)}\\&-\tfrac{7}{8}\,m_j^2(84m_i^2+35m_j^2)\Omega_{ij}^{(1,2)}\\&+\tfrac{1}{8}\,m_j^2(108m_i^2+133m_j^2)\Omega_{ij}^{(1,3)}\\&-\tfrac{7}{2}\,m_j^4\Omega_{ij}^{(1,4)}+\tfrac{1}{4}\,m_j^4\Omega_{ij}^{(1,5)}\\&+\tfrac{7}{2}\,m_im_j(4m_i^2+7m_j^2)\Omega_{ij}^{(2,2)}\\&-14m_im_j^3\Omega_{ij}^{(2,3)}\\&+2m_im_j^3\Omega_{ij}^{(2,4)}\\&+2m_i^2m_j^2\Omega_{ij}^{(3,3)}\end{aligned}\right] \tag{7.A–11}$$

and if $\mathsf{W}_i = \boldsymbol{W}_i\boldsymbol{W}_i - \frac{1}{3}W_i^2\mathsf{U}$

$$[\mathsf{W}_i\,;\mathsf{W}_j]_{ij} = -\frac{16}{3}\,\frac{m_im_j}{(m_i+m_j)^2}\{5\Omega_{ij}^{(1,1)} - \tfrac{3}{2}\Omega_{ij}^{(2,2)}\} \tag{7.A–12}$$

$$[\mathsf{W}_i\,;\mathsf{W}_i]_{ij} = \frac{16}{3}\,\frac{m_j}{(m_i+m_j)^2}\{5m_i\Omega_{ij}^{(1,1)} + \tfrac{3}{2}m_j\Omega_{ij}^{(2,2)}\} \tag{7.A–13}$$

PROBLEMS

1. Obtain an explicit expression for the coefficients of diffusion of a ternary mixture.
2. Obtain an explicit expression for the coefficient of thermal conductivity of a binary mixture.
3. Find the transport coefficients of a gas made up of rough-sphere molecules which are of uniform density.

· 8 ·

Transport Phenomena of Dilute Gases

(This chapter was prepared in collaboration with Dr. Ellen L. Spotz, formerly of the University of Wisconsin.)

In the preceding chapter a detailed account is given of the development of a rigorous kinetic theory for monatomic gases.[1] The final result of this development is the expression of the various transport coefficients in terms of a set of integrals $\Omega_{ij}^{(l,s)}$ which, in turn, depend upon the force law which is assumed for the molecular interaction. In this chapter we discuss the evaluation of these integrals and the calculation of the transport coefficients for five spherically symmetrical potential functions. The most useful potential function for which such calculations have been made is the Lennard-Jones (6-12) potential. Considerable space is devoted to the discussion of the calculations for this potential, sample computations for applications to practical problems, and the determination of the intermolecular potential parameters from experimental transport property measurements. Generally speaking, the transport phenomena of molecules with spherically symmetric force fields are well understood.

For molecules in which this spherical symmetry is lacking, however, much work remains to be done. At the end of the last chapter it was pointed out that some calculations have been made for special models such as rigid ovaloids, rough spheres, and loaded spheres. The general theory for molecules with internal degrees of freedom has been worked out (see § 7.6c). Up to the present time, however, this theory has not been applied to the study of transport phenomena of long molecules and polar molecules. It is, however, possible to make some approximate calculations of the transport coefficients of polar gases and of mixtures which contain one polar component. These calculations are discussed at the end of this chapter.

[1] In § 1.2 the elementary theory of transport phenomena is discussed. Also the main restrictions and assumptions of the Chapman-Enskog theory of Chapter 7 are summarized and discussed there. This chapter is based on the results of the *monatomic* theory described in Chapter 7.

1. The Flux Vectors and the Transport Coefficients

In § 1.2 it is shown that, in the simple kinetic theory, the transport coefficients are defined in terms of the fluxes and the gradients of the various physical properties. In the preceding chapter similar relationships were obtained on the basis of a rigorous mathematical development of gas kinetic theory. Before we examine the various transport property calculations which have been made, it seems advisable to summarize at this point the definitions of the transport coefficients according to the rigorous theory and to extend the discussion to include some items of information which are of practical interest. It should be mentioned that the expressions given here for the flux vectors contain only the *first* spatial derivatives of the various physical properties—temperature, concentration, and mass-average velocity. In general the flux vectors contain higher derivatives and hence the results quoted in this section are applicable only to situations in which the gradients of these physical properties are small. Also, the expressions for the flux vectors and the transport coefficients given here are valid only at densities sufficiently low that three-body collisions can be ignored. Strictly speaking, the expressions for the fluxes given here are valid only for monatomic gases, but little error is involved in applying them to polyatomic gases. The *flux of mass* (diffusion) and the *flux of momentum* (viscosity) are not appreciably affected by the internal degrees of freedom. Hence the coefficients of diffusion and viscosity of polyatomic molecules may be adequately described by the formulae given in this chapter. The *flux of energy* (thermal conductivity), on the other hand, includes both the energy of translation and the energy of the internal degrees of freedom. The formula for the thermal conductivity is modified to take this into account (the Eucken correction).

There is one important difference which should be pointed out between the expressions for the flux vectors given here and those given in § 1.2. According to the simple kinetic theory the transport of mass results from a concentration gradient and the transport of energy from a temperature gradient. According to the rigorous kinetic theory there are, in addition to these phenomena, a transport of mass due to a temperature gradient (the Soret effect or thermal diffusion) and a transport of energy due to a concentration gradient (the Dufour effect or the diffusion-thermo effect). These additional effects have been studied extensively from the standpoint of the so-called reciprocal relationships of Onsager, which are discussed in § 11.2. The expressions for the flux of momentum and the viscosity coefficient given by the rigorous kinetic theory are essentially the same as those given in the elementary treatment in § 1.2.

This section is devoted to a discussion of the rigorous kinetic theory expressions for monatomic gases analogous to the simple expressions for the flux vectors which are given in Eqs. 1.2–9, 10, and 11. The notation used in Chapter 7 for discussing the fluxes may be summarized in the following table:

Flux, Ψ_i	*Statistical Expression for Flux*	*Symbol*	$\Sigma_i \Psi_i$
$\Psi_i(m)$	$n_i m_i \overline{\boldsymbol{V}}_i$	$\boldsymbol{j}_i$	$\boldsymbol{j} = 0$
$\Psi_i(m\boldsymbol{V})$	$n_i m_i \overline{\boldsymbol{V}_i \boldsymbol{V}_i}$	p_i	p
$\Psi_i(\frac{1}{2}mV^2)$	$\frac{1}{2} n_i m_i \overline{V_i^2 \boldsymbol{V}_i}$	$\boldsymbol{q}_i$	$\boldsymbol{q}$

The fluxes are expressed by the symbol Ψ, the quantity in parentheses gives the property associated with the flux, and the subscript i refers to the chemical species. The symbols $\boldsymbol{j}_i$, p_i, and $\boldsymbol{q}_i$ are the mass flux vector, the pressure tensor, and the heat flux vector associated with the ith chemical species in the multicomponent mixture. The corresponding symbols without the index i are the fluxes for the entire gas. The total mass flux vector is identically zero because the diffusion velocity $\overline{\boldsymbol{V}}_i$ is defined as the rate of flow of molecules of species i with respect to the mass average velocity of the gas.[2]

a. Mass transfer and the diffusion coefficients

In the simple kinetic theory the coefficient of diffusion is defined in terms of the flux of molecules due to a gradient in the concentration as shown in Eq. 1.2–9. In the rigorous kinetic theory of ν-component gas mixtures the analogous expression for the *mass flux vector* is considerably more complicated:

$$\boldsymbol{j}_i = n_i m_i \overline{\boldsymbol{V}}_i = \frac{n^2}{\rho} \sum_{j=1}^{\nu} m_i m_j D_{ij} \boldsymbol{d}_j - D_i^T \frac{\partial \ln T}{\partial \boldsymbol{r}} \qquad i = 1, 2, 3, \cdots \nu \tag{8.1–1}$$

The symbol $\boldsymbol{d}_j$ includes the gradients of the mole fraction and pressure and also the effects of the external forces, $\boldsymbol{X}_k$, acting on the molecules:

$$\boldsymbol{d}_j = \frac{\partial}{\partial \boldsymbol{r}}\left(\frac{n_j}{n}\right) + \left(\frac{n_j}{n} - \frac{n_j m_j}{\rho}\right)\frac{\partial \ln p}{\partial \boldsymbol{r}} - \left(\frac{n_j m_j}{p\rho}\right)\left[\frac{\rho}{m_j}\boldsymbol{X}_j - \sum_{k=1}^{\nu} n_k \boldsymbol{X}_k\right] \tag{8.1–2}$$

[2] The various types of molecular velocities which are used in the kinetic theory discussion in this book are defined in § 7.2a. The definitions of the pressure tensor, the heat flux vector, and the kinetic theory temperature are given in § 7.2b. Particular caution should be taken in connection with the diffusion velocity. Some authors prefer to define this quantity with respect to the *number* average velocity $\boldsymbol{\omega}$ rather than the *mass* average velocity $\boldsymbol{v}_0$. In this book we use the latter convention.

The n_i are the number densities (that is, number of molecules per cubic centimeter) of the various components, and n and ρ are the overall number density and mass density, respectively. The D_{ij} and the D_i^T are the *multicomponent diffusion coefficients*[3] and *multicomponent thermal diffusion coefficients*, respectively.

Equation 8.1–1 indicates that a flux of mass may arise in four different ways: (i) the flux due to the gradient in the concentration, as is considered in simple kinetic theory; (ii) the flux due to a pressure gradient, as for example in a rotating gas, where the heavy molecules are forced to the part of the container most distant from the axis of rotation;[4] (iii) flux due to external forces, such as occurs in the diffusion of electrically charged particles in an ionized gas under the influence of an electric field;[5, 6] and (iv) flux due to a temperature gradient, giving rise to thermal diffusion. It is the first of these effects which is measured experimentally to determine diffusion coefficients. The thermal diffusion coefficient is usually measured by allowing the effects (i) and (iv) to proceed until the establishment of an equilibrium condition.

For certain hydrodynamic applications it is sometimes convenient to replace the ν relations given in Eq. 8.1–1 by a set of $\nu - 1$ independent equations:[7]

$$\sum_{\substack{j=1 \\ j\neq i}}^{\nu} \frac{n_i n_j}{n^2[\mathscr{D}_{ij}]_1}(\overline{\boldsymbol{V}}_j - \overline{\boldsymbol{V}}_i) = \boldsymbol{d}_i - \frac{\partial \ln T}{\partial \boldsymbol{r}} \sum_{\substack{j=1 \\ j\neq i}}^{\nu} \frac{n_i n_j}{n^2[\mathscr{D}_{ij}]_1}\left(\frac{D_j^T}{n_j m_j} - \frac{D_i^T}{n_i m_i}\right) \tag{8.1-3}$$

Here the $\mathscr{D}_{ij}$ are the usual *binary diffusion coefficients.*

In many laboratory experiments designed for the study of diffusion in non-reacting gas mixtures, the conditions are simplified in the following manner. The system is maintained at constant temperature and pressure, there are no external forces, $\boldsymbol{X}_k$, acting on the molecules, and the diffusion takes place in one direction only. Under such conditions Eq. 8.1–1 may be combined with the equations of continuity for the gas mixture to obtain for the concentration a differential equation which is second-order in

[3] The D_{ij} are related to the usual binary diffusion coefficients, $\mathscr{D}_{ij}$, by Eq. 7.4–44. For three-component mixtures Eq. 7.4–44 simplifies to Eq. 11.2–41.

[4] Gravitational accelerations lead to pressure diffusion but not to external force diffusion. The force on a molecule due to an acceleration $\boldsymbol{a}$ is $\boldsymbol{X}_i = m_i\boldsymbol{a}$. Substituting this force into Eq. 8.1–2 makes the external force term vanish.

[5] S. Chapman and T. A. Cowling, *The Mathematical Theory of Non-uniform Gases*, Cambridge University Press (1939), Ch. 18.

[6] K. F. Herzfeld, *Freie Weglänge und Transporterscheinungen in Gasen*, Hand- und Jahrbuch der Chemischen Physik, Band 3, Teil 2, Abschnitt IV, Leipzig (1939).

[7] The derivation of this relation is presented in § 7.4e–i. See footnote 2 of § 8.2 concerning the notation.

position and first-order in time. If the equations of continuity (given in Eq. 7.2–42 are added together for all the chemical species, the resultant equation may be simplified by using the fact that $n = \Sigma n_i$ is a constant as a result of the constant temperature and pressure. If the diffusion is taking place in the x-direction only, the result is

$$\frac{\partial}{\partial x} \sum_{i=1}^{\nu} n_i(v_0 + \bar{V}_i) = \frac{\partial}{\partial x} \omega(x, t) = 0 \tag{8.1–4}$$

Thus the number average velocity $\omega(x, t) = (1/n)\Sigma_i n_i(v_0 + \bar{V}_i)$ is independent of position and a function of the time alone.[8] The equations of continuity in Eq. 7.2–42 may then be written in terms of the number-average velocity thus:

$$\frac{\partial n_i}{\partial t} = -\frac{\partial}{\partial x}\left[n_i \sum_{j=1}^{\nu}\left(\delta_{ij} - \frac{n_j}{n}\right)\bar{V}_j\right] - \omega(t)\frac{\partial n_i}{\partial x} \tag{8.1–5}$$

When the expression for the diffusion velocity in Eq. 8.1–1 is substituted into this expression, this set of equations results:

$$\frac{\partial n_i}{\partial t} = -\frac{\partial}{\partial x}\left[\sum_{k=1}^{\nu}\sum_{j=1}^{\nu}\left(\delta_{ij} - \frac{n_j}{n}\right)\frac{n_i n}{n_j \rho} m_k D_{jk} \frac{\partial n_k}{\partial x}\right] - \omega(t)\frac{\partial n_i}{\partial x} \tag{8.1–6}$$

This is the multicomponent generalization of *Fick's second law of diffusion.*

All the results quoted thus far are for multicomponent systems. For two-component systems these formulae may be considerably simplified. Equation 8.1–1 may be written for component 1 of a two-component mixture thus:

$$\boldsymbol{j}_1 = n_1 m_1 \bar{\boldsymbol{V}}_1 = \frac{n^2}{\rho} m_1 m_2 \mathscr{D}_{12} \boldsymbol{d}_2 - D_1^T \frac{\partial \ln T}{\partial \boldsymbol{r}} \tag{8.1–7}$$

Since $\boldsymbol{d}_1 = -\boldsymbol{d}_2$ and $\boldsymbol{j}_1 = -\boldsymbol{j}_2$, it follows that

$$\mathscr{D}_{12} = \mathscr{D}_{21} \qquad D_1^T = -D_2^T \tag{8.1–8}$$

From Eq. 8.1–7 the two-component analog of the general expression given in Eq. 8.1–3 may be obtained:

$$\bar{\boldsymbol{V}}_1 - \bar{\boldsymbol{V}}_2 = -\frac{n^2}{n_1 n_2} \mathscr{D}_{12} \left\{\boldsymbol{d}_1 + k_T \frac{\partial \ln T}{\partial \boldsymbol{r}}\right\} \tag{8.1–9}$$

[8] If the diffusion is taking place in any arbitrary direction, Equation 8.1–4 must be written as

$$\left(\frac{\partial}{\partial \boldsymbol{r}} \cdot \boldsymbol{\omega}(\boldsymbol{r}, t)\right) = 0$$

However, it is important to note that it does *not* follow from this equation that the number average velocity is independent of the space coordinate, unless the velocity is irrotational.

Here we have introduced the quantity k_T, defined by

$$k_T = \frac{\rho}{n^2 m_1 m_2} \frac{D_1^{\,T}}{\mathscr{D}_{12}} \qquad (8.1\text{–}10)$$

This quantity, which is a measure of the relative importance of the thermal and ordinary diffusion, is known as the *thermal diffusion ratio*. The quantity k_T is so defined that when $k_T > 0$ component 1 moves to the cold region, and when $k_T < 0$ component 1 moves to the hot region.

First let us consider the ordinary diffusion which results when there are no temperature gradients. When Eq. 8.1–6 is written for two components and the fact that $D_{11} = D_{22} = 0$ is taken into account, we obtain two equations of this form:

$$\frac{\partial n_1}{\partial t} = \frac{\partial}{\partial x}\left(\mathscr{D}_{12}\frac{\partial n_1}{\partial x}\right) - \omega(t)\frac{\partial n_1}{\partial x} \qquad (8.1\text{–}11)$$

This relation applies to any non-reacting binary gas mixture under conditions of constant temperature and pressure, in which diffusion is occurring in the x-direction only. For a system within a stationary closed vessel, the number average velocity $\omega(t)$ is zero, and Eq. 8.1–11 simplifies to

$$\frac{\partial n_1}{\partial t} = \frac{\partial}{\partial x}\left(\mathscr{D}_{12}\frac{\partial n_1}{\partial x}\right) \qquad (8.1\text{–}12)$$

This is the well-known Fick's second law of diffusion.[9] It is this equation which is used in the analysis of closed diffusion-cell data[10] for the determination of $\mathscr{D}_{12}$. It should be pointed out, however, that there are many practical cases, such as problems involving evaporation, in which $\omega(t)$ is not zero and the more general expression in Eq. 8.1–11 must be used.

Next let us consider the thermal diffusion in a binary gas mixture in the absence of external forces and gradients in the pressure. Then Eq. 8.1–9 assumes the form

$$\bar{\boldsymbol{V}}_1 - \bar{\boldsymbol{V}}_2 = -\frac{n^2}{n_1 n_2}\mathscr{D}_{12}\left\{\frac{\partial}{\partial \boldsymbol{r}}\left(\frac{n_1}{n}\right) + k_T \frac{\partial}{\partial \boldsymbol{r}} \ln T\right\} \qquad (8.1\text{–}13)$$

When equilibrium has been established so that the diffusion velocities are zero, this simplifies to

$$\frac{\partial}{\partial \boldsymbol{r}}\left(\frac{n_1}{n}\right) = -k_T \frac{\partial}{\partial \boldsymbol{r}} \ln T \qquad (8.1\text{–}14)$$

[9] In the first approximation the diffusion coefficient is independent of the concentration, and this equation assumes the form $\partial n_1/\partial t = \mathscr{D}_{12}\partial^2 n_1/\partial x^2$.

[10] See, for example, C. A. Boyd, N. Stein, V. Steingrimsson, and W. F. Rumpel, *J. Chem. Phys.*, **19**, 548 (1951).

This equation may be integrated to give

$$\Delta\left(\frac{n_1}{n}\right) = \left(\frac{n_1}{n}\right)_{T'} - \left(\frac{n_1}{n}\right)_T = -\int_T^{T'} \frac{k_T(T)}{T}\, dT \qquad (8.1\text{–}15)$$

Since k_T is a function of composition as well as temperature, this result does not constitute a true solution of the previous equation. However, in practice the composition change is usually so small that the variation in k_T due to this variation may be neglected, although the variation due to the temperature variation may not be neglected. Because of the complex temperature dependence of the thermal diffusion ratio, the indicated integration is avoided by use of the mean-value theorem of the integral calculus. This enables us to write

$$-k_T(\bar{T}) = \frac{\Delta(n_1/n)}{\ln(T'/T)} \qquad (8.1\text{–}16)$$

The temperature $\bar{T}$ is some mean value of the temperature[11] lying between T and T'. It is Eq. 8.1–16 which is usually used in the analysis of thermal diffusion experiments. The value of k_T is found by analyzing the equilibrium composition in two connected vessels, one maintained at a temperature T and the other at a higher temperature T'.

Experimental data are sometimes given in terms of quantities denoted[12] by $k_T^\star$ or α. These are defined by

$$k_T^\star = \frac{(k_T)_{\text{exptl}}}{(k_T)_{\text{rig sph}}} \qquad \alpha = \frac{(k_T)_{\text{exptl}}}{x_1 x_2} \qquad (8.1\text{–}17)$$

In order to tabulate experimental $k_T^\star$ values, it is necessary to choose arbitrarily a "rigid sphere collision diameter." Clearly when experimental and calculated $k_T^\star$ values are compared, care should be taken that the same collision diameter is used in the reduction of the experimental and the calculated k_T values. $k_T^\star$ is introduced so as to obtain a quantity which is slowly varying in temperature and concentration. The quantity α is used because it is very nearly concentration-independent.

[11] H. Brown, *Phys. Rev.*, **58**, 661 (1940), has suggested the following relation for $\bar{T}$:

$$\bar{T} = \left(\frac{TT'}{T' - T}\right) \ln\left(\frac{T'}{T}\right)$$

[12] The quantity $k_T^\star$ has been designated as R_T in the literature. We prefer the symbol $k_T^\star$ since it is consistent with the notation for reduced quantities used in this book.

b. Momentum transfer and the viscosity coefficient

The simple kinetic theory expression for the flux of momentum and the definition of the coefficient of viscosity is given by Eq. 1.2–10. The expression for the *pressure tensor* given by rigorous kinetic theory development is[13]

$$\mathsf{p} = p\mathsf{U} - 2\eta\mathsf{S} \tag{8.1–18}$$

Here η is the coefficient of viscosity, and S is the rate of shear tensor[14] defined by

$$\mathsf{S} = \tfrac{1}{2}\left\{\left(\frac{\partial}{\partial \boldsymbol{r}}\boldsymbol{v}_0\right) + \left(\frac{\partial}{\partial \boldsymbol{r}}\boldsymbol{v}_0\right)^{\dagger} - \tfrac{2}{3}\left(\frac{\partial}{\partial \boldsymbol{r}}\cdot\boldsymbol{v}_0\right)\mathsf{U}\right\} \tag{8.1–19}$$

The symbol † denotes the transpose of the tensor, which is obtained by interchanging the rows and columns. Typical diagonal and non-diagonal elements of the pressure tensor are

$$\begin{aligned} p_{xx} &= p - \tfrac{2}{3}\eta\left(2\frac{\partial v_{0x}}{\partial x} - \frac{\partial v_{0y}}{\partial y} - \frac{\partial v_{0z}}{\partial z}\right) \\ p_{xy} &= -\eta\left(\frac{\partial v_{0y}}{\partial x} + \frac{\partial v_{0x}}{\partial y}\right) \end{aligned} \tag{8.1–20}$$

The physical significance of the components of the pressure tensor is shown in Fig. 7.2–2.

The definition of momentum flux and the coefficient of viscosity given in Eq. 8.1–18 is a straightforward generalization of the simple kinetic theory definition given in § 1.2. For the situation pictured in Fig. 8.1–1, the pressure tensor simplifies to

$$\mathsf{p} = \begin{bmatrix} p & 0 & -\eta\dfrac{\partial v_{0x}}{\partial z} \\ 0 & p & 0 \\ -\eta\dfrac{\partial v_{0x}}{\partial z} & 0 & p \end{bmatrix} \tag{8.1–21}$$

[13] A more general discussion of the pressure tensor (which applies to dense gases and liquids) is given in Chapter 11. It is shown there that the pressure tensor contains three terms: the hydrostatic pressure, a term involving the *shear viscosity* η, and another term containing the *bulk viscosity* κ. For dilute monatomic gases κ is equal to zero, and Eq. 8.1–18 is valid. For dense monatomic gases κ is not equal to zero. Also for polyatomic molecules κ is generally small but not zero and depends upon the relaxation times (§ 7.6c).

[14] Some authors define the pressure tensor as the negative of that used in this book. This other convention has arisen from the notion in the theory of elasticity that tension is positive and compression is negative.

The element of the pressure tensor p_{xz} is the x-component of the force on a unit area of surface perpendicular to the z-direction. Hence from Eq. 8.1–21 the usual elementary defining equation for viscosity may be obtained:

$$\frac{F}{A} = \eta \frac{u}{s} \tag{8.1–22}$$

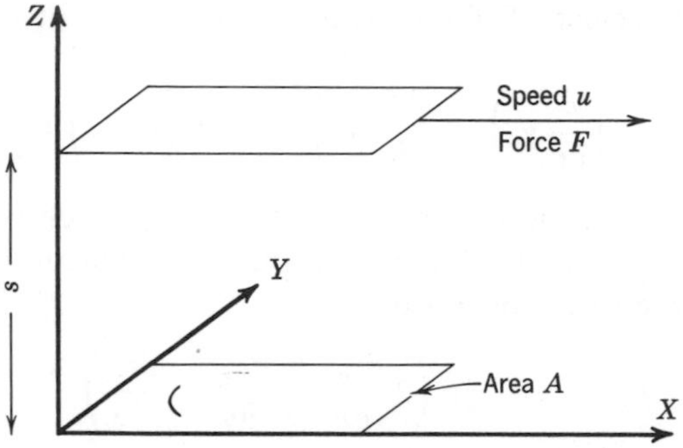

Fig. 8.1–1. The physical situation which corresponds to the pressure tensor given in Eq. 8.1–21.

Here s is the separation between two plates of area A parallel to the XY-plane, one of which is being moved with a force F at a speed u.

c. Energy transfer and the thermal conductivity coefficient

The simple kinetic theory definition of the coefficient of thermal conductivity, λ, in terms of the energy flux is given in Eq. 1.2–11. The analogous expression for a ν-component mixture of monatomic gases obtained by the rigorous methods described in Chapter 7 is the following:[15]

$$\boldsymbol{q} = -\lambda \frac{\partial T}{\partial \boldsymbol{r}} + \tfrac{5}{2}kT \sum_{i=1}^{\nu} n_i \overline{\boldsymbol{V}}_i + \frac{kT}{n} \sum_{i=1}^{\nu} \sum_{\substack{j=1 \\ j\neq i}}^{\nu} \frac{n_j D_i^T}{m_i \mathscr{D}_{ij}} (\overline{\boldsymbol{V}}_i - \overline{\boldsymbol{V}}_j) \tag{8.1–23}$$

According to this expression energy may be transported through a multicomponent gas by three mechanisms: (i) the transport due to the temperature gradient, as is explained by simple kinetic theory; (ii) the transport due to the flux of $\Sigma n_i \overline{\boldsymbol{V}}_i$ molecules per unit time relative to the mass velocity, each of which carries with it, on the average, a quantity $(5/2)kT$

[15] This expression is derived for monatomic gases. It is shown in § 7.6b that for polyatomic gases the heat flux vector has the same general form. The only difference is that the term $\frac{5}{2}kT\Sigma n_i \overline{\boldsymbol{V}}_i$ has to be replaced by the term $\Sigma n_i h_i \overline{\boldsymbol{V}}_i$, in which h_i is the enthalpy per molecule of the ith component defined as $(m_i \hat{U}_i + kT)$. In some problems it is quite important to include in the expression for the heat flux vector the heat lost or gained by radiation effects. This contribution is discussed in § 11.3.

of thermal energy; and (iii) an added term due to the "reciprocal process" to thermal diffusion known as the *Dufour effect*. It is only the first of these effects which is ordinarily measured in laboratory experiments.

The thermal conductivity is determined experimentally by considering stationary systems (in which the $\overline{V}_i$ are zero) and which are arranged in such a fashion that the heat flux is in only one direction. Then Eq. 8.1–23 simplifies to:

$$q = -\lambda\left(\frac{T' - T}{x' - x}\right) \tag{8.1-24}$$

The temperatures T and T' are those of the two boundary surfaces, and $(x' - x)$ is the distance between them.

In a static system (where all the velocities are zero), according to Eqs. 7.6–7 and 8.1–23,

$$\rho\frac{\partial\hat{U}}{\partial t} = -\left(\frac{\partial}{\partial \boldsymbol{r}}\cdot\boldsymbol{q}\right) = \left(\frac{\partial}{\partial \boldsymbol{r}}\cdot\lambda\frac{\partial T}{\partial \boldsymbol{r}}\right) \tag{8.1-25}$$

If the heat capacity, c_v, is constant (as is the case of a monatomic gas where $c_v = (3/2)k$) $\hat{U} = c_v T/m$, so that

$$\rho\hat{C}_v\frac{\partial T}{\partial t} = \left(\frac{\partial}{\partial \boldsymbol{r}}\cdot\lambda\frac{\partial T}{\partial \boldsymbol{r}}\right) \tag{8.1-26}$$

There is a strong analogy between this equation and Eq. 8.1–12.

2. Summary of Kinetic Theory Formulae for Pure Gases and Multicomponent Mixtures

In the preceding chapter it is shown that the transport coefficients may be expressed in terms of a set of integrals $\Omega^{(l,s)}$, the molecular masses m_i, and the number densities of the various components n_i. In this section we present these formulae again, but in such a form that they are more immediately applicable to practical calculations. These results are used in the remainder of the chapter to discuss transport property calculations for various potential functions. The formulae are written in terms of the molecular weights M_i, the mole fractions x_i, and a set of quantities $\Omega^{(l,s)\star}$, which are just the $\Omega^{(l,s)}$ for the potential under consideration divided by the analogous quantities for rigid spherical molecules. The formulae are given for the first approximation to the transport coefficients only; the explicit expressions for the second approximations may be found in Appendix A at the end of this chapter.

a. The quantities $\Omega^{(l,s)\star}$

In order to make calculations of transport coefficients for any potential function, $\varphi(r)$, the angle of deflection in a collision, χ, must first be calculated[1] according to Eq. 1.5–26. For rigid spherical molecules it is easy to write an analytical expression for χ, but for any realistic potential function numerical methods must be used. Once χ has been evaluated for a large number of values of g and b, the double integrals in Eq. 7.4–34 may be evaluated numerically to obtain the $\Omega^{(l,s)}$. The transport properties may then be calculated as functions of the temperature. The $\Omega^{(l,s)}$ which are needed for the calculation of the transport coefficients in the first and second approximation[2] are

Property	*Pure Substance* (1*st Approximation*)	*Mixture* (1*st Approximation*)	*Pure Substance* (2*nd Approximation*)
η	$\Omega^{(2,2)}$	$\Omega^{(2,2)}$, $\Omega^{(1,1)}$	$\Omega^{(2,s)}$ $s = 2, 3, 4$
λ	$\Omega^{(2,2)}$	$\Omega^{(2,2)}$, $\Omega^{(1,s)}$ $s = 1, 2, 3$	$\Omega^{(2,s)}$ $s = 2, 3, 4$
$\mathscr{D}$	$\Omega^{(1,1)}$	$\Omega^{(1,1)}$	$\Omega^{(2,2)}$, $\Omega^{(1,s)}$ $s = 1, 2, 3$
k_T	...	$\Omega^{(2,2)}$, $\Omega^{(1,s)}$ $s = 1, 2, 3$	$\Omega^{(2,t)}$ $\Omega^{(1,s)}$ $\Omega^{(3,3)}$ $s = 1, 2, 3, 4, 5$ $t = 2, 3, 4$

Explicit formulae for the transport coefficients in terms of the $\Omega^{(l,s)}$ are given later in this section.

Inasmuch as the expression for χ in Eq. 1.5–26 and that for the integrals $\Omega^{(l,s)}$ in Eq. 7.4–34 form the starting point for the transport calculations

[1] This discussion makes use of the results of a dynamical analysis of two-body collisions. Such an analysis is presented in § 1.5, and the various symbols used in connection with binary collisions are carefully defined there.

[2] In the preceding chapter it was convenient to denote the degree of approximation for the various transport coefficients by indicating the number of terms in the Sonine polynomial expansion which are used. Thus $\eta(\xi)$ indicates the coefficient of viscosity when ξ terms in the Sonine polynomial expansion are employed. In this notation the lowest order approximations to the viscosity, thermal conductivity, and thermal diffusion are $\eta(1)$, $\lambda(2)$, $\mathscr{D}(1)$, $k_T(2)$. This indicates that for thermal conductivity and thermal diffusion two terms in the Sonine polynomial expansion (Eq. 7.3–61) must be used in order to get the lowest order expressions for these properties.

In this chapter we adopt the notation of Chapman and Cowling [*The Mathematical Theory of Non-uniform Gases*, Cambridge University Press (1939), p. 157] for the convenience of those already familiar with their treatise. These authors choose to designate the first non-zero approximation as the first approximation. Accordingly, the symbols written above in the notation of Chapter 7 are in the notation of Chapman and Cowling and this chapter: $[\eta]_1$, $[\lambda]_1$, $[\mathscr{D}]_1$, $[k_T]_1$. The higher approximations are designated by: $[\eta]_2 = \eta(2)$, $[\lambda]_2 = \lambda(3)$, etc.

discussed in this chapter, they are written again here for convenience but in a slightly different form, and additional quantities $Q^{(l)}$, the *cross-sections*, are defined:

$$\chi(g, b) = \pi - 2b \int_{r_m}^{\infty} \frac{dr/r^2}{\sqrt{1 - \dfrac{b^2}{r^2} - \dfrac{\varphi(r)}{\frac{1}{2}\mu g^2}}} \tag{8.2–1}$$

$$Q^{(l)}(g) = 2\pi \int_0^{\infty} (1 - \cos^l\chi)\, b\, db \tag{8.2–2}$$ [3]

$$\Omega^{(l,s)}(T) = \sqrt{kT/2\pi\mu} \int_0^{\infty} e^{-\gamma^2}\gamma^{2s+3} Q^{(l)}(g)\, d\gamma \tag{8.2–3}$$ [4]

Here $\gamma^2 = \frac{1}{2}\mu g^2/kT$, and μ is the reduced mass of two colliding molecules. If collisions between two molecules of different chemical species i and j are being considered, the potential function φ_{ij} is that characteristic of collisions between unlike pairs of molecules. The reduced mass is then given by $(1/\mu_{ij}) = (1/m_i) + (1/m_j)$ and we write $\Omega_{ij}^{(l,s)}(T)$ to indicate the integral associated with the interaction between species i and j. For collisions between molecules of the same species i, these quantities become respectively, φ_{ii}, $\mu_{ii} = \frac{1}{2}m_i$, and $\Omega_{ii}^{(l,s)}(T)$. In transport property calculations involving pure substances where only i-i type collisions occur it is unnecessary to indicate the chemical species by means of subscripts, but care should be taken that the proper reduced mass is used. In calculations of transport properties of multicomponent mixtures where there are both i-i and i-j collisions, extreme care should be taken to indicate explicitly which interactions are involved.

For rigid spherical molecules[5] of diameter σ, Eqs. 8.2–2 and 3 simplify to

$$[Q^{(l)}]_{\text{rig sph}} = \left[1 - \frac{1}{2}\,\frac{1 + (-1)^l}{1 + l}\right] \pi\sigma^2 \tag{8.2–4}$$

$$[\Omega^{(l,s)}]_{\text{rig sph}} = \sqrt{\frac{kT}{2\pi\mu}}\,\frac{(s+1)!}{2}\,[Q^{(l)}]_{\text{rig sph}} \tag{8.2–5}$$

[3] The quantity $Q^{(l)}(g)$ is Chapman and Cowling's function $\phi^{(l)}(g)$ multiplied by $2\pi/g$. We prefer to use this quantity $Q^{(l)}(g)$ since it has the dimensions of a cross-section. The quantities $\Omega^{(l,s)}$ are the same as the $\Omega^{(l)}(s)$ of Chapman and Cowling. They should not be confused with the $\Omega^{(l,s)}$ of Enskog. [See S. Chapman and T. A. Cowling, *The Mathematical Theory of Non-Uniform Gases*, Cambridge University Press (1939), Ch. 9.]

[4] Note that

$$T\frac{\partial\Omega^{(l,s)}}{\partial T} + \left(s + \frac{3}{2}\right)\Omega^{(l,s)} = \Omega^{(l,s+1)}.$$

[5] The rigid-sphere model is discussed in detail in § 8.3a. We present these results at this point for use in the reduction of the $\Omega^{(l,s)}$ in terms of rigid-sphere values. It is only for rigid spheres that $\sqrt{2\pi\mu/kT}\,\Omega^{(l,s)}$ is proportional to $Q^{(l)}$.

For this simple model the cross-sections are independent of g. For diffusion the appropriate cross-section is $Q^{(1)} = \pi\sigma^2$, and for viscosity and thermal conductivity $Q^{(2)} = \frac{2}{3}\pi\sigma^2$ is to be used.

All the potential functions discussed in this chapter may be characterized by two parameters, σ and ϵ. All these potential functions may be written in the form

$$\varphi(r) = \epsilon f(r/\sigma) \tag{8.2-6}$$

in which $f(r/\sigma)$ is assumed to be the same function for all substances. The various kinetic theory variables may now be made dimensionless by dividing by the proper combinations of the parameters appearing in the potential functions. In this way we define the following reduced variables:

$$r^* = r/\sigma \quad = \text{reduced intermolecular distance}$$

$$b^* = b/\sigma \quad = \text{reduced impact parameter}$$

$$\varphi^* = \varphi/\epsilon \quad = \text{reduced intermolecular potential energy}$$

$$T^* = kT/\epsilon \quad = \text{reduced temperature}$$

$$g^{*2} = \tfrac{1}{2}\mu g^2/\epsilon = \text{reduced relative kinetic energy}$$

It is convenient to reduce $Q^{(l)}(g)$ and $\Omega^{(l,s)}(T)$ by dividing them by their corresponding rigid-sphere values,[6] thus:

$$Q^{(l)\star} = \frac{[Q^{(l)}]}{[Q^{(l)}]_{\text{rig sph}}} = \frac{Q^{(l)}}{\left[1 - \frac{1}{2}\,\dfrac{1+(-1)^l}{1+l}\right]\pi\sigma^2} \tag{8.2-7}$$

$$\Omega^{(l,s)\star} = \frac{[\Omega^{(l,s)}]}{[\Omega^{(l,s)}]_{\text{rig sph}}} = \frac{\Omega^{(l,s)}\sqrt{2\pi\mu/kT}}{\frac{1}{2}(s+1)!\left[1 - \frac{1}{2}\,\dfrac{1+(-1)^l}{1+l}\right]\pi\sigma^2} \tag{8.2-8}$$

The quantities $\Omega^{(l,s)\star}$ and $Q^{(l)\star}$ have then the physical significance that they indicate the deviation of any particular molecular model from the idealized rigid-sphere model. In terms of these quantities, to a first

[6] This is consistent with the convention used in this book for the reduction of the second virial coefficient, that is,

$$B^\star(T^*) = B(T)/\tfrac{2}{3}\pi\tilde{N}\sigma^3 = B(T)/b_0$$

approximation the rigorous kinetic theory formulae for the transport properties of a pure substance are[7]

$$[\mathscr{D}]_1 = \frac{3}{8}\left(\frac{\sqrt{\pi mkT}}{\pi\sigma^2\,\Omega^{(1,1)\star}}\right)\left(\frac{1}{\rho}\right) = \frac{3}{16}\frac{\sqrt{2\pi k^3T^3/\mu}}{p\pi\sigma^2\,\Omega^{(1,1)\star}} \tag{8.2–9}$$

$$[\eta]_1 = \frac{5}{16}\left(\frac{\sqrt{\pi mkT}}{\pi\sigma^2\,\Omega^{(2,2)\star}}\right) \tag{8.2–10}$$

$$[\lambda]_1 = \frac{25}{32}\left(\frac{\sqrt{\pi mkT}}{\pi\sigma^2\,\Omega^{(2,2)\star}}\right)\left(\frac{c_v}{m}\right) \tag{8.2–11}$$

These results should be compared with the simple kinetic theory results (see Eqs. 1.2–12, 13, 14).

The three basic starting formulae for the transport calculations given in Eqs. 8.2–1, 2, 3, may now be rewritten in terms of reduced units:

$$\chi(g^*, b^*) = \pi - 2b^* \int_{r_m^*}^{\infty} \frac{dr^*/r^{*2}}{\sqrt{1 - \dfrac{b^{*2}}{r^{*2}} - \dfrac{\varphi^*(r^*)}{g^{*2}}}} \tag{8.2–12}$$

$$Q^{(l)\star}(g^*) = \frac{2}{\left[1 - \frac{1}{2}\dfrac{1+(-1)^l}{1+l}\right]} \int_0^{\infty} (1 - \cos^l\chi) b^*\, db^* \tag{8.2–13}$$

$$\Omega^{(l,s)\star}(T^*) = \frac{2}{(s+1)!\,T^{*s+2}} \int_0^{\infty} e^{-g^{*2}/T^*} g^{*2s+3} Q^{(l)\star}(g^*)\, dg^* \tag{8.2–14}$$

Three combinations of the $\Omega^{(l,s)\star}$ occur frequently enough in the expressions for the transport coefficients of pure gases and mixtures to make it

[7] The formula for $\mathscr{D}$ is also valid for the coefficient of binary diffusion when the proper interpretation of the symbols is made. The formulae for η and λ may *not* be simply generalized to binary mixtures.

worth while giving them special symbols.[8] They are

$$\text{A}^{\star} = \Omega^{(2,2)\star}/\Omega^{(1,1)\star} \tag{8.2–15}$$ [9]

$$\text{B}^{\star} = \{5\Omega^{(1,2)\star} - 4\Omega^{(1,3)\star}\}/\Omega^{(1,1)\star} \tag{8.2–16}$$

$$\text{C}^{\star} = \Omega^{(1,2)\star}/\Omega^{(1,1)\star} \tag{8.2–17}$$ [10]

These three quantities are all very nearly unity.

b. The coefficient of viscosity

The coefficient of viscosity for a pure substance or a mixture may be obtained to any degree of approximation from Eq. 7.4–20. First we discuss the viscosity of a pure gas, then the viscosity of a binary mixture, and finally the viscosity of multicomponent mixtures.

i. *The Coefficient of Viscosity of a Pure Gas*

To a first approximation the viscosity of a pure gas is given by

$$[\eta]_1 \times 10^7 = 266.93 \frac{\sqrt{MT}}{\sigma^2\,\Omega^{(2,2)\star}(T^*)} \tag{8.2–18}$$

where

η = viscosity in g/cm sec,

T = temperature in °K,

T^* = reduced temperature = kT/ϵ,

M = molecular weight,

σ = collision diameter in Å,

ϵ/k = potential parameter in °K.

In the kth approximation, the coefficient of viscosity is given by

$$[\eta]_k = [\eta]_1 f_\eta^{(k)} \tag{8.2–19}$$

[8] The quantities A★, B★, and C★ given here are just the quantities A, B, and C of Chapman and Cowling (*The Mathematical Theory of Non-uniform Gases*, p. 164) divided by their rigid-sphere values; that is, $\text{A}^\star = \text{A}/(0.4)$, $\text{B}^\star = \text{B}/(0.6)$, and $\text{C}^\star = \text{C}/(1.2)$.

[9] The quantity A★ is closely related to the ratio $\rho[\mathscr{D}]_1/[\eta]_1$. See Eq. 8.2–48.

[10] The quantity C★ is closely related (E. M. Holleran and H. M. Hulburt, *J. Chem. Phys.*, **19**, 232 (1951) to the temperature derivative $[\mathscr{D}]_1$ at constant pressure:

$$\text{C}^\star = 1 + \tfrac{1}{3}\frac{d\ln\Omega^{(1,1)\star}}{d\ln T^*} = \tfrac{3}{2} - \tfrac{5}{6}\left(\frac{\partial \ln[\mathscr{D}]_1}{\partial \ln T}\right)_p$$

This relation may easily be derived from the recursion relation between $\Omega^{(l,s)}$ given in the footnote to Eq. 8.2–3. B★ may be expressed in terms of the first and second derivatives of the diffusion coefficient.

The function $f_\eta^{(k)}$ is a very slowly varying function of T^* and differs only slightly from unity.[11] This function through the third approximation ($k = 3$) is given explicitly in terms of the $\Omega^{(l\ s)\star}$ in Appendix A at the end of this chapter.

The viscosities of a large number of gases have been measured at atmospheric pressure as a function of temperature. From these data it is possible to obtain a certain amount of information concerning the intermolecular forces in the gas. Once a potential function of the form in Eq. 8.2–6 has been chosen, and the $\Omega^{(2\ 2)\star}(T^*)$ have been evaluated, Eq. 8.2–19 may be used along with experimental viscosity data to determine the parameters σ and ϵ in an assumed potential function. An illustration of the method of determining the intermolecular forces from viscosity is given in § 8.4b, where the Lennard-Jones (6-12) potential is discussed.

ii. *The Coefficient of Viscosity for Binary Mixtures*

In order to discuss the viscosity of a binary mixture it is convenient to define a quantity $[\eta_{12}]_1$ thus:

$$[\eta_{12}]_1 = \frac{5}{16}\left(\frac{\sqrt{2\pi m_1 m_2 kT/(m_1 + m_2)}}{\pi\sigma_{12}{}^2\,\Omega_{12}^{(2,\,2)\star}(T_{12}{}^*)}\right) \tag{8.2–20}$$

or, in practical units,

$$[\eta_{12}]_1 \times 10^7 = 266.93\,\frac{\sqrt{2M_1M_2T/(M_1 + M_2)}}{\sigma_{12}{}^2\,\Omega_{12}^{(2,\,2)\star}(T_{12}{}^*)} \tag{8.2–21}$$

where T = temperature in °K,

$T_{12}{}^* = kT/\epsilon_{12}$ = reduced temperature,

M_1, M_2 = molecular weights of species 1 and 2,

$\sigma_{12}, \epsilon_{12}/k$ = parameters in the potential function characteristic, of 1–2 interaction (in Å and °K, respectively).

This quantity may be regarded as the coefficient of viscosity of a hypothetical pure substance, the molecules of which have a molecular weight $2M_1M_2/(M_1 + M_2)$ and interact according to a potential curve specified by the interaction parameters σ_{12} and ϵ_{12}. (In connection with the calculation of the second virial coefficient of a mixture a similar artificial quantity B_{12} was defined.) If in Eq. 8.2–21 the subscript 2 is replaced by 1, the resulting expression is identical with the formula given in Eq. 8.2–18 for the pure component 1.

[11] For the Lennard-Jones potential $f_\eta^{(3)}$ is given in Table I–P and differs from unity by less than 0.8 per cent.

We may now write the viscosity of a binary mixture in terms of the quantities defined in Eqs. 8.2–18 and 8.2–21:

$$\frac{1}{[\eta_{\text{mix}}]_1} = \frac{X_\eta + Y_\eta}{1 + Z_\eta} = X_\eta \left[\frac{1 + (Y_\eta/X_\eta)}{1 + Z_\eta}\right] \tag{8.2–22}$$

$$X_\eta = \frac{x_1^2}{[\eta_1]_1} + \frac{2x_1x_2}{[\eta_{12}]_1} + \frac{x_2^2}{[\eta_2]_1}$$

$$Y_\eta = \tfrac{3}{5}\,\mathrm{A}_{12}^\star \left\{\frac{x_1^2}{[\eta_1]_1}\left(\frac{M_1}{M_2}\right) + \frac{2x_1x_2}{[\eta_{12}]_1}\left(\frac{(M_1+M_2)^2}{4M_1M_2}\right)\left(\frac{[\eta_{12}]_1^2}{[\eta_1]_1[\eta_2]_1}\right) + \frac{x_2^2}{[\eta_2]_1}\left(\frac{M_2}{M_1}\right)\right\}$$

$$Z_\eta = \tfrac{3}{5}\,\mathrm{A}_{12}^\star \left\{x_1^2\left(\frac{M_1}{M_2}\right) + 2x_1x_2\left[\left(\frac{(M_1+M_2)^2}{4M_1M_2}\right)\left(\frac{[\eta_{12}]_1}{[\eta_1]_1} + \frac{[\eta_{12}]_1}{[\eta_2]_1}\right) - 1\right] + x_2^2\left(\frac{M_2}{M_1}\right)\right\}$$

where x_1, x_2 = mole fractions of species 1 and 2,
M_1, M_2 = molecular weights of species 1 and 2,
$\mathrm{A}_{12}^\star$ = a function of kT/ϵ_{12}, defined in Eq. 8.2–15.

In general the quantity $\left[\dfrac{1 + Y_\eta/X_\eta}{1 + Z_\eta}\right]$ is far different from unity and may contribute as much as 50 per cent to the final result. If the molecular weights of species 1 and 2 are not very different from one another, and if the forces between unlike and like pairs are very nearly the same, the quantity X_η is the predominant contribution. For a binary mixture of heavy isotopes the coefficient of viscosity is given to a good approximation by

$$\frac{1}{\sqrt{[\eta_{\text{mix}}]_1}} = \frac{x_1}{\sqrt{[\eta_1]_1}} + \frac{x_2}{\sqrt{[\eta_2]_1}} \tag{8.2–23}$$

It should be pointed out that the quantity η_{12} is closely related to the coefficient of diffusion:

$$[\eta_{12}]_1 = \frac{5}{3}\frac{m_1m_2}{(m_1+m_2)}\frac{n[\mathscr{D}_{12}]_1}{\mathrm{A}_{12}^\star} = \frac{5}{3}\frac{M_1M_2}{(M_1+M_2)}\frac{p[\mathscr{D}_{12}]_1}{\mathrm{A}_{12}^\star RT} \tag{8.2–24}$$

If diffusion data were available it would be better to make use of them to obtain the quantity $[\eta_{12}]_1$ rather than to use the formula given in Eq. 8.2–20 or 8.2–21. In view of the lack of diffusion data, it seems better at the present time to write Eq. 8.2–22 in terms of the quantity $[\eta_{12}]_1$. This also has the advantage that the expression for the viscosity of a binary mixture assumes a form somewhat better for computational purposes.

There is a considerable amount of experimental data on the viscosity of mixtures of two gases. From these data and Eq. 8.2–22 it is possible, in principle, to determine the potential parameters between unlike pairs of molecules. In practice, however, this turns out to be virtually impossible, because the interactions between unlike molecules are masked by the interaction between pairs of similar molecules. It is also pointed out in § 3.6b that measurements of the second virial coefficients for binary mixtures are equally unsatisfactory for determining the force laws between pairs of dissimilar molecules.

iii. *The Coefficient of Viscosity of Multicomponent Mixtures*[12]

According to the rigorous kinetic theory of multicomponent gas mixtures, the coefficient of viscosity of a ν-component mixture is given by Eq. 7.4–61. For computational purposes, this equation may be written in the form:

$$[\eta_{\text{mix}}]_1 = -\frac{\begin{vmatrix} H_{11} & H_{12} & H_{13} & \cdots & H_{1\nu} & x_1 \\ H_{12} & H_{22} & H_{23} & \cdots & H_{2\nu} & x_2 \\ H_{13} & H_{23} & H_{33} & \cdots & H_{3\nu} & x_3 \\ \cdot & \cdot & \cdot & & \cdot & \cdot \\ \cdot & \cdot & \cdot & & \cdot & \cdot \\ \cdot & \cdot & \cdot & & \cdot & \cdot \\ H_{1\nu} & H_{2\nu} & H_{3\nu} & \cdots & H_{\nu\nu} & x_\nu \\ x_1 & x_2 & x_3 & \cdots & x_\nu & 0 \end{vmatrix}}{\begin{vmatrix} H_{11} & H_{12} & H_{13} & \cdots & H_{1\nu} \\ H_{12} & H_{22} & H_{23} & \cdots & H_{2\nu} \\ H_{13} & H_{23} & H_{33} & \cdots & H_{3\nu} \\ \cdot & \cdot & \cdot & & \cdot \\ \cdot & \cdot & \cdot & & \cdot \\ \cdot & \cdot & \cdot & & \cdot \\ H_{1\nu} & H_{2\nu} & H_{3\nu} & \cdots & H_{\nu\nu} \end{vmatrix}} \qquad (8.2\text{–}25)$$

[12] C. F. Curtiss and J. O. Hirschfelder, *J. Chem. Phys.*, **17**, 550 (1949).

The elements H_{ij} may be written in terms of the $[\eta_{ij}]_1$ or in terms of the diffusion coefficients $[\mathscr{D}_{ij}]_1$:

$$H_{ii} = \frac{x_i^2}{[\eta_i]_1} + \sum_{\substack{k=1\\k\neq i}}^{\nu} \frac{2x_ix_k}{[\eta_{ik}]_1} \frac{M_iM_k}{(M_i + M_k)^2}\left[\frac{5}{3A_{ik}^\star} + \frac{M_k}{M_i}\right]$$

$$= \frac{x_i^2}{[\eta_i]_1} + \sum_{\substack{k=1\\k\neq i}}^{\nu} \frac{2x_ix_k}{(M_i + M_k)}\frac{RT}{p[\mathscr{D}_{ik}]_1}\left[1 + \frac{3}{5}\frac{M_k}{M_i}A_{ik}^\star\right] \qquad (8.2\text{–}26)$$

$$H_{ij} = -\frac{2x_ix_j}{[\eta_{ij}]_1}\frac{M_iM_j}{(M_i + M_j)^2}\left[\frac{5}{3A_{ij}^\star} - 1\right] \quad i \neq j$$

$$= -\frac{2x_ix_j}{(M_i + M_j)}\frac{RT}{p[\mathscr{D}_{ij}]_1}\left[1 - \frac{3}{5}A_{ij}^\star\right] \quad i \neq j \qquad (8.2\text{–}27)$$

where $[\eta_i]_1$ = coefficient of viscosity given in Eq. 8.2–18,

$[\eta_{ik}]_1$ = quantity defined in Eq. 8.2–20,

$[\mathscr{D}_{ik}]_1$ = coefficient of diffusion defined in Eq. 8.2–44,

$A_{ik}^\star$ = function defined in Eq. 8.2–15,

x_i, M_i = mole fraction and molecular weight of ith component.

The ratio of determinants in Eq. 8.2–25 may be expanded thus:

$$[\eta_{\text{mix}}]_1 = \sum_{i=1}^{\nu}\frac{x_i^2}{H_{ii}} - \sum_{i=1}^{\nu}\sum_{\substack{j=1\\j\neq i}}^{\nu}\frac{x_ix_jH_{ij}}{H_{ii}H_{jj}} + \sum_{i=1}^{\nu}\sum_{\substack{j=1\\j\neq i}}^{\nu}\sum_{\substack{k=1\\k\neq i}}^{\nu}\frac{x_jx_kH_{ij}H_{ik}}{H_{ii}H_{jj}H_{kk}} - \cdots \qquad (8.2\text{–}28)$$

Since the off-diagonal elements H_{ij} are small in comparison with the diagonal elements H_{ii}, the primary contribution to the viscosity of a multicomponent gas mixture is given by the first term of this expansion. In order to make the off-diagonal elements vanish exactly, it is necessary to assume that $A^\star = 5/3$. When the same assumption is made in the diagonal elements, Eq. 8.2–28 becomes

$$[\eta_{\text{mix}}]_1 \doteq \sum_{i=1}^{\nu}\frac{x_i^2}{H_{ii}} \doteq \sum_{i=1}^{\nu}\frac{x_i^2}{\dfrac{x_i^2}{[\eta_i]_1} + \sum\limits_{\substack{k=1\\k\neq i}}^{\nu} 2x_ix_k\dfrac{RT}{pM_i[\mathscr{D}_{ik}]_1}} \qquad (8.2\text{–}29)$$

This equation does not describe the viscosity of mixtures very well because of neglect of higher terms in the expansion of Eq. 8.2–28 and because of the unrealistic value assumed for $A^{\star}$. It has been shown,[13] however, by an extensive analysis of experimental data that Eq. 8.2–29 describes the behavior of the coefficient of viscosity of multicomponent systems if the numerical constant 2 is replaced by the empirical value 1.385. Consequently, a very good approximation to Eq. 8.2–25 may be taken to be

$$[\eta_{\text{mix}}]_1 = \sum_{i-1}^{\nu} \frac{x_i^{\,2}}{\dfrac{x_i^{\,2}}{[\eta_i]_1} + 1.385 \sum\limits_{\substack{k=1\\k\neq i}}^{\nu} x_i x_k \dfrac{RT}{pM_i[\mathscr{D}_{ik}]_1}} \qquad (8.2\text{–}30)$$

This relation enables us to calculate quite simply the viscosity of a multicomponent mixture from the viscosities of the pure components and the diffusion coefficients for the various pairs of chemical species. In the absence of experimental data, Eq. 8.2–18 may be used to calculate the $[\eta_i]_1$ and Eq. 8.2–44 may be used to calculate the $[\mathscr{D}_{ik}]_1$.

The form of Eq. 8.2–30 was not originally derived by Buddenberg and Wilke[13] from the rigorous kinetic theory of multicomponent gases.[12] They based their work on the earlier formulae given by Sutherland,[14] Thiesen,[15] and Schudel.[16] Buddenberg and Wilke recognized the necessity of introducing the diffusion coefficient into the formula to take into account the collisions between unlike pairs, and then evaluated the constant 1.385 by a careful analysis of the experimental data.

c. The coefficient of thermal conductivity

The coefficient of thermal conductivity for a pure monatomic substance or a mixture of monatomic gases may be obtained to any degree of approximation from Eqs. 7.4–65 and 66. For polyatomic gases the monatomic gas formulae must not be used, since the effect of internal degrees of freedom on the thermal conductivity is considerable. At the present time the best way to correct the monatomic gas formulae so as to make them applicable to polyatomic gases is to use the Eucken correction, which is discussed in § 7.6b. Accordingly, the formulae given in this section for monatomic gases are the result of rigorous kinetic theory developments, but those for polyatomic gases must be regarded as approximate.

[13] J. W. Buddenberg and C. R. Wilke, *Ind. Eng. Chem.*, **41**, 1345 (1949).
[14] W. Sutherland, *Phil. Mag.*, **40**, 421 (1895).
[15] M. Thiesen, *Verhandl. deutschen physik. Gesellschaft*, **4**, 348 (1902).
[16] W. Schudel, *Schweiz. Ver. Gas- u. Wasserfach. Monats-Bull.*, **22**, 112, 131 (1942).

i. *The Coefficient of Thermal Conductivity for a Pure Gas*

The coefficient of thermal conductivity for a pure gas is given in the first approximation by

$$[\lambda]_1 \times 10^7 = 1989.1 \frac{\sqrt{T/M}}{\sigma^2 \Omega^{(2,2)\star}(T^*)}$$
$$= \frac{15}{4}\frac{R}{M}[\eta]_1 \times 10^7 \tag{8.2–31}$$

where λ = thermal conductivity in cal/cm sec °K,
T = temperature in °K,
T^* = kT/ϵ = reduced temperature,
M = molecular weight,
$\sigma, \epsilon/k$ = parameters in potential function Å and °K, respectively.

Thus, in the first approximation, the coefficient of thermal conductivity is proportional to the coefficient of viscosity. This is in agreement with the results of the simple kinetic theory approach.

The higher approximations to the coefficient of thermal conductivity are given by

$$[\lambda]_k = [\lambda]_1 f_\lambda^{(k)} = \frac{15}{4}\frac{[\eta]_k R}{M}\frac{f_\lambda^{(k)}}{f_\eta^{(k)}} \tag{8.2–32}$$

The functions $f_\lambda^{(k)}$ and $f_\eta^{(k)}$ differ but slightly from unity and vary slowly with T^*. In Appendix A at the end of this chapter the functions $f_\lambda^{(3)}$ and $f_\eta^{(3)}$ are given explicitly in terms of the $\Omega^{(l,s)\star}$.

For polyatomic molecules, Eq. 8.2–31, should be replaced by the following relation, which takes into account approximately the transfer of energy between translational and internal degrees of freedom in the molecules (see Eq. 7.6–24):

$$[\lambda]_1^{\text{Eucken}} = \frac{15}{4}\frac{R}{M}[\eta]_1\left(\frac{4}{15}\frac{\tilde{C}_v}{R} + \frac{3}{5}\right) \tag{8.2–33}$$

For monatomic gases, for which the heat capacity per mole is $\tilde{C}_v = 3R/2$, this expression simplifies to that given in Eq. 8.2–31.

ii. *The Coefficient of Thermal Conductivity for Binary Mixtures*

In order to discuss the thermal conductivity of binary mixtures it is convenient to define a quantity $[\lambda_{12}]_1$ analogous to the quantity $[\eta_{12}]_1$ defined in Eq. 8.2–20:

$$[\lambda_{12}]_1 = \frac{25}{32}\left(\frac{\sqrt{(m_1+m_2)\pi kT/2m_1m_2}}{\pi\sigma_{12}{}^2\,\Omega_{12}^{(2,2)\star}(T_{12}{}^*)}\right)\left(\frac{3}{2}k\right) = \frac{15}{4}k\left(\frac{m_1+m_2}{2m_1m_2}\right)[\eta_{12}]_1 \tag{8.2–34}$$

or, in practical units,

$$[\lambda_{12}]_1 \times 10^7 = 1989.1 \frac{\sqrt{T(M_1 + M_2)/2M_1M_2}}{\sigma_{12}{}^2\,\Omega_{12}^{(2,\,2)\star}(T_{12}{}^*)} \tag{8.2-35}$$

where T = temperature in °K,

$T_{12}{}^* = kT/\epsilon_{12}$ = reduced temperature,

M_1, M_2 = molecular weights of species 1 and 2,

$\sigma_{12}, \epsilon_{12}/k$ = parameters in the potential function characteristic of 1-2 interaction (in Å and °K, respectively).

In terms of this quantity and the thermal conductivities of the pure components, the thermal conductivity of a mixture of monatomic gases may be written as

$$\frac{1}{[\lambda_{\text{mix}}]_1} = \frac{X_\lambda + Y_\lambda}{1 + Z_\lambda} = X_\lambda\left[\frac{1 + (Y_\lambda/X_\lambda)}{1 + Z_\lambda}\right] \tag{8.2-36}$$

$$X_\lambda = \frac{x_1{}^2}{[\lambda_1]_1} + \frac{2x_1x_2}{[\lambda_{12}]_1} + \frac{x_2{}^2}{[\lambda_2]_1}$$

$$Y_\lambda = \frac{x_1{}^2}{[\lambda_1]_1}U^{(1)} + \frac{2x_1x_2}{[\lambda_{12}]_1}U^{(Y)} + \frac{x_2{}^2}{[\lambda_2]_1}U^{(2)}$$

$$Z_\lambda = x_1{}^2U^{(1)} + 2x_1x_2U^{(Z)} + x_2{}^2U^{(2)}$$

$$U^{(1)} = \frac{4}{15}\text{A}_{12}{}^\star - \frac{1}{12}\left(\frac{12}{5}\text{B}_{12}{}^\star + 1\right)\frac{M_1}{M_2} + \frac{1}{2}\frac{(M_1 - M_2)^2}{M_1M_2}$$

$$U^{(2)} = \frac{4}{15}\text{A}_{12}{}^\star - \frac{1}{12}\left(\frac{12}{5}\text{B}_{12}{}^\star + 1\right)\frac{M_2}{M_1} + \frac{1}{2}\frac{(M_2 - M_1)^2}{M_1M_2}$$

$$U^{(Y)} = \frac{4}{15}\text{A}_{12}{}^\star\left(\frac{(M_1 + M_2)^2}{4M_1M_2}\right)\frac{[\lambda_{12}]_1{}^2}{[\lambda_1]_1[\lambda_2]_1} - \frac{1}{12}\left(\frac{12}{5}\text{B}_{12}{}^\star + 1\right) - \frac{5}{32\text{A}_{12}{}^\star}\left(\frac{12}{5}\text{B}_{12}{}^\star - 5\right)\frac{(M_1 - M_2)^2}{M_1M_2}$$

$$U^{(Z)} = \frac{4}{15}\text{A}_{12}{}^\star\left[\left(\frac{(M_1 + M_2)^2}{4M_1M_2}\right)\left(\frac{[\lambda_{12}]_1}{[\lambda_1]_1} + \frac{[\lambda_{12}]_1}{[\lambda_2]_1}\right) - 1\right] - \frac{1}{12}\left(\frac{12}{5}\text{B}_{12}{}^\star + 1\right)$$

where x_1, x_2 = mole fractions of species 1 and 2,

M_1, M_2 = molecular weights of species 1 and 2,

$\text{A}_{12}{}^\star, \text{B}_{12}{}^\star$ = functions of $T_{12}{}^* = kT/\epsilon_{12}$ defined in Eqs. 8.2-15 and 16.

For mixtures of heavy isotopes to a good approximation this expression reduces to

$$\frac{1}{\sqrt{[\lambda_{\text{mix}}]_1}} = \frac{x_1}{\sqrt{[\lambda_1]_1}} + \frac{x_2}{\sqrt{[\lambda_2]_1}} \tag{8.2–37}$$

The quantity $[\lambda_{12}]_1$ is closely related to the coefficient of diffusion $[\mathscr{D}_{12}]_1$, thus:

$$[\lambda_{12}]_1 = \frac{25}{8}\frac{p[\mathscr{D}_{12}]_1}{\text{A}_{12}{}^\star T} \tag{8.2–38}$$

If diffusion data were available it would be better to use them in connection with the calculation of λ for binary and multicomponent mixtures. Since very few diffusion measurements have been made, we have written Eq. 8.2–36 in terms of the $[\lambda_{12}]_1$.

There is at present no rigorous method for calculating the thermal conductivity of mixtures of polyatomic gases. However, the coefficient of thermal conductivity for a binary mixture of polyatomic gases can be estimated by the following empirical method.[17] First, we calculate for the mixture, assuming that the molecules are effectively monatomic, the quantity given by Eq. 8.2–36. This result is denoted by λ_{mon}. If the experimental values of λ are known for the pure gases, then, for each of the components, we may compute the ratio

$$E_i = \frac{(\lambda_i)_{\text{exptl}}}{(\lambda_i)_{\text{mon}}} = \frac{(\lambda_i)_{\text{exptl}}}{[\lambda_i]_1} \tag{8.2–39}$$

An empirical expression for the coefficient of thermal conductivity for the mixture is then

$$\lambda_{\text{mix}} = \lambda_{\text{mon}}\,[x_1E_1 + x_2E_2] \tag{8.2–40}$$

For pure substances, the thermal conductivity is proportional to the viscosity. The prediction of the thermal conductivity of mixtures would be much easier if the thermal conductivity of mixtures were still proportional to the viscosity with an easily calculated proportionality constant.

[17] There is an alternate empirical method which also gives good agreement with experimental values of the coefficient of thermal conductivity for binary mixtures of polyatomic gases. If force constants for the pure components are known from viscosity data, and if the experimental value of λ is known for the pure gases, we may make the following computation. For each of the substances, we use only the parameter, ϵ_i/k as obtained from viscosity data. We then substitute the corresponding value of T_i^* and the experimentally observed value of λ_i into Eq. 8.2–31 in order to obtain an adjusted σ_i'. The geometric mean of the ϵ_i/k and the arithmetic mean of the adjusted σ_i' are used to compute $[\lambda_{12}]_1$ from Eq. 8.2–35. Using the adjusted σ_i', or the experimental value of λ_i in place of $[\lambda_i]_1$, we find that Eq. 8.2–36 reproduces well the concentration dependence of the coefficient of thermal conductivity.

The best empirical relationship of this type is

$$\frac{1}{[\lambda_{\text{mix}}]_1} = \frac{1}{[\eta_{\text{mix}}]_{\text{exptl}}} \left(\frac{x_1^{\,2}}{\alpha_1} + \frac{2x_1x_2}{\sqrt{\alpha_1\alpha_2}} + \frac{x_2^{\,2}}{\alpha_2} \right) \tag{8.2–41}$$

where $\alpha_i = (\lambda_i/\eta_i)_{\text{exptl}}$. However, from the discrepancies between the experimental values and the values calculated on this basis, it is clear that this relation is not nearly so reliable as that given in Eq. 8.2–39.

iii. *The Coefficient of Thermal Conductivity for Multicomponent Mixtures*

The coefficient of thermal conductivity of a multicomponent mixture is given by Eq. 7.4–65, which may be written in the form:

$$[\lambda_{\text{mix}}]_1 = [\lambda'_{\text{mix}}]_1 - \tfrac{1}{2}R \sum_{i=1}^{\nu} \sum_{\substack{j=1 \\ j\neq i}}^{\nu} \frac{RTx_ix_j}{p[\mathscr{D}_{ij}]_1} \left[\frac{[D_i^{\,T}]_1}{x_iM_i} - \frac{[D_j^{\,T}]_1}{x_jM_j} \right]^2 \tag{8.2–42}$$

Here the $[\mathscr{D}_{ij}]_1$ are the first approximations to the binary diffusion constants as given by Eq. 8.2–44, the $[D_i^{\,T}]_1$ are the thermal diffusion constants of Eq. 8.2–53, and

$$[\lambda'_{\text{mix}}]_1 = 4 \frac{\begin{vmatrix} L_{11}^{00} & \cdots & L_{1\nu}^{00} & L_{11}^{01} & \cdots & L_{1\nu}^{01} & 0 \\ \vdots & & \vdots & \vdots & & \vdots & \vdots \\ L_{\nu1}^{00} & \cdots & L_{\nu\nu}^{00} & L_{\nu1}^{01} & \cdots & L_{\nu\nu}^{01} & 0 \\ L_{11}^{10} & \cdots & L_{1\nu}^{10} & L_{11}^{11} & \cdots & L_{1\nu}^{11} & x_1 \\ \vdots & & \vdots & \vdots & & \vdots & \vdots \\ L_{\nu1}^{10} & \cdots & L_{\nu\nu}^{10} & L_{\nu1}^{11} & \cdots & L_{\nu\nu}^{11} & x_\nu \\ 0 & \cdots & 0 & x_1 & \cdots & x_\nu & 0 \end{vmatrix}}{\begin{vmatrix} L_{11}^{00} & \cdots & L_{1\nu}^{00} & L_{11}^{01} & \cdots & L_{1\nu}^{01} \\ \vdots & & \vdots & \vdots & & \vdots \\ L_{\nu1}^{00} & \cdots & L_{\nu\nu}^{00} & L_{\nu1}^{01} & \cdots & L_{\nu\nu}^{01} \\ L_{11}^{10} & \cdots & L_{1\nu}^{10} & L_{11}^{11} & \cdots & L_{1\nu}^{11} \\ \vdots & & \vdots & \vdots & & \vdots \\ L_{\nu1}^{10} & \cdots & L_{\nu\nu}^{10} & L_{\nu1}^{11} & \cdots & L_{\nu\nu}^{11} \end{vmatrix}} \tag{8.2–43}$$

where

$$L_{ii}^{00} = 0$$

$$L_{ij}^{00} = \frac{2x_i x_j}{\mathrm{A}_{ij}^\star [\lambda_{ij}]_1} + \sum_{k \neq i} \frac{2x_j x_k M_j}{M_i \mathrm{A}_{ik}^\star [\lambda_{ik}]_1} \qquad i \neq j$$

$$= \frac{16T}{25p} \left[\frac{x_i x_j}{[\mathscr{D}_{ij}]_1} + \sum_{k \neq i} \frac{x_j x_k M_j}{M_i [\mathscr{D}_{ik}]_1} \right] \qquad i \neq j$$

$$L_{ii}^{01} = 5 \sum_{k \neq i} \frac{x_i x_k M_k (\frac{6}{5}\mathrm{C}_{ik}^\star - 1)}{(M_i + M_k)\mathrm{A}_{ik}^\star [\lambda_{ik}]_1}$$

$$= \frac{8T}{5p} \sum_{k \neq i} \frac{x_i x_k M_k (\frac{6}{5}\mathrm{C}_{ik}^\star - 1)}{(M_i + M_k)\, [\mathscr{D}_{ik}]_1}$$

$$L_{ij}^{01} = -\, 5 x_i x_j \frac{M_i (\frac{6}{5}\mathrm{C}_{ij}^\star - 1)}{(M_i + M_j)\mathrm{A}_{ij}^\star [\lambda_{ij}]_1} \qquad i \neq j$$

$$= -\frac{8T}{5p} x_i x_j \frac{M_i (\frac{6}{5}\mathrm{C}_{ij}^\star - 1)}{(M_i + M_j)[\mathscr{D}_{ij}]_1} \qquad i \neq j$$

$$L_{ij}^{10} = \frac{M_j}{M_i} L_{ij}^{01}$$

$$L_{ii}^{11} = -\frac{4x_i^2}{[\lambda_i]_1} - \sum_{k \neq i} \frac{2x_i x_k [\frac{15}{2} M_i^2 + \frac{25}{4} M_k^2 - 3M_k^2 \mathrm{B}_{ik}^\star + 4M_i M_k \mathrm{A}_{ik}^\star]}{(M_i + M_k)^2 \mathrm{A}_{ik}^\star [\lambda_{ik}]_1}$$

$$= -\frac{4x_i^2}{[\lambda_i]_1} - \frac{16T}{25p} \sum_{k \neq i} \frac{x_i x_k [\frac{15}{2} M_i^2 + \frac{25}{4} M_k^2 - 3M_k^2 \mathrm{B}_{ik}^\star + 4M_i M_k \mathrm{A}_{ik}^\star]}{(M_i + M_k)^2 [\mathscr{D}_{ik}]_1}$$

$$L_{ij}^{11} = \frac{2x_i x_j M_i M_j}{(M_i + M_j)^2 \mathrm{A}_{ij}^\star [\lambda_{ij}]_1} [\tfrac{55}{4} - 3\mathrm{B}_{ij}^\star - 4\mathrm{A}_{ij}^\star] \qquad i \neq j$$

$$= \frac{16T}{25p} \frac{x_i x_j M_i M_j}{(M_i + M_j)^2 [\mathscr{D}_{ij}]_1} [\tfrac{55}{4} - 3\mathrm{B}_{ij}^\star - 4\mathrm{A}_{ij}^\star] \qquad i \neq j$$

d. The coefficient of diffusion

We begin by giving the expression for the coefficient of diffusion in a binary gas mixture. Then we show that under certain conditions a limiting form can be obtained for the coefficient of diffusion, which is called the coefficient of "self-diffusion." Finally the expression for the coefficient of diffusion in multicomponent gas systems is presented.

i. *Coefficient of Diffusion in a Binary Mixture*

The coefficient of diffusion of a binary mixture may be obtained from Eq. 7.4–4. In the first approximation the result is

$$[\mathscr{D}_{12}]_1 = 0.0026280 \frac{\sqrt{T^3(M_1 + M_2)/2M_1M_2}}{p\sigma_{12}{}^2\,\Omega_{12}^{(1,1)\star}(T_{12}{}^*)} \tag{8.2–44}$$

where $\mathscr{D}_{12}$ = diffusion coefficient in cm^2/sec,
p = pressure in atmospheres,
T = temperature in °K,
$T_{12}{}^* = kT/\epsilon_{12}$,
M_1, M_2 = molecular weights of species 1 and 2,
$\sigma_{12}, \epsilon_{12}/k$ = molecular potential energy parameters characteristic of 1-2 interaction in Å and °K, respectively.

The higher approximations to the coefficient of diffusion are given by

$$[\mathscr{D}_{12}]_k = [\mathscr{D}_{12}]_1 f_{\mathscr{D}_{12}}^{(k)} \tag{8.2–45}$$

The function $f_{\mathscr{D}_{12}}^{(2)}$ is a function of the molecular weights, the mole fractions, and the viscosities of the two components, and also of the temperature. An explicit expression for this function which varies only slightly from unity[18] is given in Appendix A of this chapter. The dependence of the diffusion coefficient on the composition of a mixture of gases is hence only slight.

We note that in the first approximation the only interactions which enter into the expression for the diffusion coefficient are those between unlike molecules. The forces between like pairs of molecules do not enter except in the second approximation. This means that the coefficient of diffusion as a function of temperature affords an excellent means of obtaining the force law between dissimilar pairs of molecules from the measurement of bulk properties. It is unfortunate that there are at the present time few experimental data of this sort.

ii. *The Coefficient of Self-diffusion*

When Eq. 8.2–44 is written for a single component the formula for "self-diffusion" is obtained:

$$[\mathscr{D}]_1 = 0.0026280 \frac{\sqrt{T^3/M}}{p\sigma^2\Omega^{(1,1)\star}(T^*)} \tag{8.2–46}$$

where $\mathscr{D}$ = coefficient of self-diffusion in cm^2/sec,
p = pressure in atmospheres,
T = temperature,
T^* = reduced temperature = kT/ϵ,
M = molecular weight,
$\sigma, \epsilon/k$ = parameters in potential function in Å and °K, respectively.

18 For most binary mixtures this quantity varies from 1.00 to 1.03 for the Lennard-Jones potential.

The higher approximations for the coefficient of self-diffusion are given by

$$[\mathscr{D}]_k = [\mathscr{D}]_1 f_{\mathscr{D}}^{(k)} \tag{8.2–47}$$

The correction factor $f_{\mathscr{D}}^{(2)}$, which is a function of the reduced temperature T^* alone, is given in Appendix A at the end of the chapter.

Let us now inquire as to the meaning of the coefficient of self-diffusion. Clearly, if the molecules in a gas are all physically identical, it is impossible to measure their interdiffusion. It is, however, possible to measure quantities experimentally which are very nearly coefficients of self-diffusion.

(i) *Interdiffusion of Isotopes.* If one isotopic form of a gas is allowed to diffuse into another isotopic form, the progress of the diffusion can be followed by standard tracer techniques. Inasmuch as the number of neutrons in the atomic nuclei has essentially no influence upon the intermolecular forces, $\sigma_{12} = \sigma_1 = \sigma_2$ and $\epsilon_{12} = \epsilon_1 = \epsilon_2$. Furthermore, if the molecules are sufficiently large $2M_1M_2/(M_1 + M_2)$ is very nearly M_1 or M_2. Consequently, Eq. 8.2–44 simplifies directly to Eq. 8.2–46. With the increasing availability of isotopes, this should prove an interesting method for getting information about intermolecular forces.

(ii) *Interdiffusion of Ortho and Para Forms.* If the ortho form of a molecule is allowed to diffuse into the para form, the progress of diffusion can be followed.[19] Since the ortho and para forms of the substance are experimentally distinguishable only when the molecules are quite small, such techniques are essentially applicable only to the isotopes of hydrogen. For these molecules the interactions between ortho and ortho, ortho and para, and para and para can be considered as being described by the same sets of force constants, although the interaction does of course depend to a very slight extent upon the rotational states of the molecule. Also $2(M_1M_2)/(M_1 + M_2) = M_1 = M_2$. Consequently Eq. 8.2–44 once again simplifies to Eq. 8.2–46.

It is apparent that the coefficient of self-diffusion must be regarded as somewhat artificial. It is more correct simply to consider it as a limiting form of the coefficient of binary diffusion. It is interesting to note that in this limit of equal masses and equal intermolecular forces Eq. 8.2–24 simplifies to

$$\frac{\rho[\mathscr{D}]_1}{[\eta]_1} = \frac{6}{5}\,\mathrm{A}^\star \tag{8.2–48}$$

The function $\mathrm{A}^\star$, defined in Eq. 8.2–15, is a very slowly varying function of T^*, and hence $\rho[\mathscr{D}]_1/[\eta]_1$ is very nearly a constant.

[19] Experimentally this can be followed by the electrical resistance of a heated wire, from which heat is conducted at different rates by ortho and para forms.

iii. *The Coefficient of Diffusion in Multicomponent Gas Systems*

The coefficients of diffusion in a multicomponent mixture are given in Eq. 7.4–44, which may be written in the form

$$D_{ij} = \frac{1}{M_j} (\Sigma_k x_k M_k) \frac{K^{ji} - K^{ii}}{|K|} \tag{8.2–49}$$

where $K_{ii} = 0$

$$K_{ij} = \frac{x_i}{[\mathscr{D}_{ij}]_1} + \frac{M_j}{M_i} \sum_{k \neq i} \frac{x_k}{[\mathscr{D}_{ik}]_1}; \quad i \neq j$$

$|K|$ is the determinant of the K_{ij} and the K^{ji} are the minors:

$$K^{ji} = (-1)^{i+j} \begin{vmatrix} 0 & \cdots & K_{1,\, i-1} & K_{1,\, i+1}, & \cdots & K_{1,\, \nu} \\ \vdots & & \vdots & \vdots & & \vdots \\ K_{j-1,\, 1} & \cdots & K_{j-1,\, i-1} & K_{j-1,\, i+1} & \cdots & K_{j-1,\, \nu} \\ K_{j+1,\, 1} & \cdots & K_{j+1,\, i-1} & K_{j+1, i+1} & \cdots & K_{j+1,\, \nu} \\ \vdots & & \vdots & \vdots & & \vdots \\ K_{\nu,\, 1} & \cdots & K_{\nu,\, i-1} & K_{\nu,\, i+1} & \cdots & K_{\nu,\, \nu} \end{vmatrix}$$

e. The coefficient of thermal diffusion

The coefficients of thermal diffusion D_i^T for a multicomponent system may be obtained from the rigorous kinetic theory formulae in Eq. 7.4–55. Also, the thermal diffusion ratio k_T for two-component systems may be obtained. We give the latter expression in its general form for use in calculating the thermal diffusion ratio for any gas pair and also in the special form appropriate for the thermal diffusion of isotopes.

i. *The Thermal Diffusion Ratio in Binary Gas Mixtures*

The first approximation to the thermal diffusion ratio k_T is given by the following expression:

$$[k_T]_1 = \frac{x_1 x_2}{6[\lambda_{12}]_1} \frac{S^{(1)} x_1 - S^{(2)} x_2}{X_\lambda + Y_\lambda} (6\text{C}_{12}{}^\star - 5)$$

$$S^{(1)} = \frac{M_1 + M_2}{2M_2} \frac{[\lambda_{12}]_1}{[\lambda_1]_1} - \frac{15}{4\text{A}_{12}{}^\star} \left(\frac{M_2 - M_1}{2M_1} \right) - 1 \tag{8.2–50}$$

$$S^{(2)} = \frac{M_2 + M_1}{2M_1} \frac{[\lambda_{12}]_1}{[\lambda_2]_1} - \frac{15}{4\text{A}_{12}{}^\star} \left(\frac{M_1 - M_2}{2M_2} \right) - 1$$

where x_1, x_2 = mole fractions of species 1, 2,
M_1, M_2 = molecular weights of species 1, 2,
$[\lambda_1]_1, [\lambda_2]_1$ = thermal conductivities calculated from Eq. 8.2–31,
$[\lambda_{12}]_1$ = quantity defined in Eq. 8.2–34,
$\text{A}_{12}^\star, \text{C}_{12}^\star$ = functions of $T_{12}^* = kT/\epsilon_{12}$ defined in Eqs. 8.2–15, 17,
X_λ, Y_λ = functions defined in Eq. 8.2–36.

The thermal diffusion ratio is thus a very complex function of temperature, concentration, and the molecular weights, and depends parametrically on the force law of the molecules. The primary concentration dependence is given by x_1x_2 and to a lesser extent by $[S^{(1)}x_1 - S^{(2)}x_2]$. The main dependence on the masses of the molecules is given by $S^{(1)}$ and $S^{(2)}$. The principal temperature dependence is given by $(6\text{C}_{12}^\star - 5)$. The thermal diffusion ratio can be positive or negative. A positive value of k_T signifies that component 1 tends to move into the cooler region and 2 towards the warmer region.[20] The temperature at which the thermal diffusion ratio undergoes a change of sign is referred to as the *inversion temperature*.

The next higher approximation for the thermal diffusion ratio may be obtained from the formulae in Appendix A. The few calculations for $[k_T]_2$ which have been made indicate that the error in the first approximation is greater for k_T than for any of the other transport coefficients.[21]

ii. *The Thermal Diffusion Ratio in Binary Isotopic Gas Mixtures*[22]

Equation 8.2–50 may be considerably simplified for the special case of heavy isotopes. When this expression is expanded in powers of $(M_1 - M_2)/(M_1 + M_2)$, the following formula for k_T results:

$$[k_T]_1 = \frac{15(2\text{A}^\star + 5)(6\text{C}^\star - 5)}{2\text{A}^\star(16\text{A}^\star - 12\text{B}^\star + 55)} \frac{(M_1 - M_2)}{(M_1 + M_2)} x_1 x_2 \qquad (8.2\text{–}51)$$

The quantity frequently reported in the literature[23] is $k_T^\star$, defined in

[20] The significance of the sign of k_T depends on the sign convention adopted in the definition of this quantity. The convention used in this book is the same as that used by Chapman and Cowling [*The Mathematical Theory of Non-uniform Gases*, Cambridge University Press (1939)].

[21] See Table 8.3–2 for summary of results for rigid spheres. See also E. A. Mason *J. Chem. Phys.*, **22** (1954), for recent calculations of $[k_T]_2$ for the modified Buckingham, potential.

[22] R. Clark Jones, *Phys. Rev.*, **58**, 111 (1940).

[23] This quantity $k_T^\star$ is usually called R_T in the literature. We use the symbol $k_T^\star$ to be consistent with the convention used in this book that quantities divided by rigid sphere quantities be denoted by a 5-pointed star.

Eq. 8.1-17. The first approximation to this quantity is given by

$$[k_T]_1^\star = \frac{[k_T]_1}{[k_T]_1^{\text{rig sph}}} = \frac{59}{7}\,\frac{(2\text{A}^\star + 5)\,(6\text{C}^\star - 5)}{\text{A}^\star(16\text{A}^\star - 12\text{B}^\star + 55)} \tag{8.2-52}$$

and is thus a universal function of T^*. This expression has been shown to be valid[24] for values of $(M_1 - M_2)/(M_1 + M_2)$ up to 0.15.

iii. *The Coefficient of Thermal Diffusion in Multicomponent Gas Mixtures*

The coefficient of thermal diffusion in a multicomponent mixture is given by Eq. 7.4-55. The expression may be written in the form:

$$[D_k^T]_1 = -\frac{8M_k}{5R}\,\frac{\begin{vmatrix} L_{11}^{00} & \cdots & L_{1\nu}^{00} & L_{11}^{01} & \cdots & L_{1\nu}^{01} & 0 \\ \cdot & & \cdot & \cdot & & \cdot & \cdot \\ \cdot & & \cdot & \cdot & & \cdot & \cdot \\ \cdot & & \cdot & \cdot & & \cdot & \cdot \\ L_{\nu 1}^{00} & \cdots & L_{\nu\nu}^{00} & L_{\nu 1}^{01} & \cdots & L_{\nu\nu}^{01} & 0 \\ L_{11}^{10} & \cdots & L_{1\nu}^{10} & L_{11}^{11} & \cdots & L_{1\nu}^{11} & x_1 \\ \cdot & & \cdot & \cdot & & \cdot & \cdot \\ \cdot & & \cdot & \cdot & & \cdot & \cdot \\ \cdot & & \cdot & \cdot & & \cdot & \cdot \\ L_{\nu 1}^{10} & \cdots & L_{\nu\nu}^{10} & L_{\nu 1}^{11} & \cdots & L_{\nu\nu}^{11} & x_\nu \\ x_1\delta_{1k} & \cdots & x_\nu\delta_{\nu k} & 0 & \cdots & 0 & 0 \end{vmatrix}}{\begin{vmatrix} L_{11}^{00} & \cdots & L_{1\nu}^{00} & L_{11}^{01} & \cdots & L_{1\nu}^{01} \\ \cdot & & \cdot & \cdot & & \cdot \\ \cdot & & \cdot & \cdot & & \cdot \\ \cdot & & \cdot & \cdot & & \cdot \\ L_{\nu 1}^{00} & \cdots & L_{\nu\nu}^{00} & L_{\nu 1}^{01} & \cdots & L_{\nu\nu}^{01} \\ L_{11}^{10} & \cdots & L_{1\nu}^{10} & L_{11}^{11} & \cdots & L_{1\nu}^{11} \\ \cdot & & \cdot & \cdot & & \cdot \\ \cdot & & \cdot & \cdot & & \cdot \\ \cdot & & \cdot & \cdot & & \cdot \\ L_{\nu 1}^{10} & \cdots & L_{\nu\nu}^{10} & L_{\nu 1}^{11} & \cdots & L_{\nu\nu}^{11} \end{vmatrix}} \tag{8.2-53}$$

where the $L_{ij}^{mm'}$ are defined by Eqs. 8.2-43.

3. Transport Coefficient Calculations for Simple Potentials

In Chapter 3 it is shown that the second virial coefficient can be evaluated analytically for a number of simple potentials. Such is not, however, the case for the transport coefficients. It is possible to evaluate analytically the collision cross-sections for the rigid-sphere potential, but for the

[24] E. R. S. Winter, *Trans. Faraday Soc.*, **46**, 81 (1950).

other simple potential functions discussed in this section numerical integrations have to be used. The results of this numerical work are given here, inasmuch as they may be useful for rough calculations and for interpolation of data over small temperature ranges. The inverse power model $\varphi(r) = dr^{-\delta}$ is handy because it is differentiable and also because the double integral over b and g may be manipulated into a single integral. The Sutherland model (rigid sphere surrounded by an attractive field) has in the past been widely used for correlating experimental data, and the "Sutherland constants" for many substances are recorded in the literature. The square-well model may be of use for some complex molecules because it affords three adjustable constants. For accurate numerical work based on a realistic interaction potential the best calculations available at the present time are those based on the Lennard-Jones (6-12) potential and the modified Buckingham (6-exp) potential, which are discussed in § 8.4. All these potential functions have the form specified by Eq. 8.2–6.

a. Rigid elastic spheres

The results of the rigid-sphere calculations are used in the preceding section for the reduction of the collision cross-sections. For the rigid-sphere model [$\varphi(r) = \infty$ for $r < \sigma$, $\varphi(r) = 0$ for $r > \sigma$] the integral for the angle of deflection may be integrated easily. The distance of closest approach for two colliding molecules is $r_m = \sigma$ if $b \leqslant \sigma$ and is $r_m = b$ for $b \geqslant \sigma$. Consequently, we get at once from Eq. 8.2–1:

$$\chi(g, b) = 2 \arc\cos (b/\sigma) \qquad b \leqslant \sigma \tag{8.3–1}$$

$$\chi(g, b) = 0 \qquad b \geqslant \sigma$$

These results may also be obtained quite easily from simple geometrical considerations. As is to be expected for impenetrable spheres the angle of deflection for this model is independent of the relative kinetic energy. Substitutions of the expression for χ just obtained into Eqs. 8.2–2 and 3 give the expressions for $Q^{(l)}$ and $\Omega^{(l,s)}$ which were quoted in Eqs. 8.2–4 and 5. The reduced quantities $Q^{(l)\star}$ and $\Omega^{(l,s)\star}$ were then defined in such a way that they are exactly 1 for the rigid-sphere model. This means that all the formulae for transport coefficients given in the last section may be used for rigid spheres simply by setting the $\Omega^{(l,s)\star}$ equal to unity.

The expressions for the viscosity and self-diffusion given in Eqs. 8.2–18 and 46 with the $\Omega^{(l,s)\star}$ equal to 1 may be used to analyze experimental data to obtain the molecular diameters σ or the molecular cross-sections

$\pi\sigma^2$. In Table 8.3–1 the molecular diameters calculated from these two properties are compared. It is clear from this tabulation that the values of the rigid-sphere collision diameter from viscosity are higher than those from self-diffusion. From this it may be concluded that $\Omega^{(2,2)\star}$ for real molecules is slightly greater than $\Omega^{(1,1)\star}$. Calculations of the collision cross-sections for more realistic potentials substantiate this fact.

TABLE 8.3–1

RIGID-SPHERE MOLECULAR DIAMETERS CALCULATED FROM VISCOSITY[a] AND SELF-DIFFUSION[b] MEASUREMENTS AT 0°C AND 1 ATM

$$[\eta]_1 \times 10^7 = 266.93 \frac{\sqrt{MT}}{\sigma^2} \qquad [\mathscr{D}]_1 = 0.0026280 \frac{\sqrt{T^3/M}}{p\sigma^2}$$

Gas	$[\eta]_1 \times 10^7$ (gm/cm sec)	$[\mathscr{D}]_1$ (cm²/sec)	σ in Å	
			From Viscosity	From Diffusion
A	2099	0.156	3.64	3.47
Ne	2967	0.452	2.58	2.42
N_2	1663	0.185	3.75	3.48
O_2	1918	0.187	3.61	3.35
CH_4	1030	0.206	4.14	3.79
CO_2	1366	0.0974	4.63	4.28

[a] H. L. Johnston and K. E. McCloskey, *J. Phys. Chem.*, **44**, 1038 (1939)—Ne, A. H. L. Johnston and E. R. Grilly, *J. Phys. Chem.*, **46**, 948 (1942)—N_2, O_2, CH_4, CO_2.
[b] E. B. Winn, *Phys. Rev.*, **80**, 1024 (1950).

Important information has been obtained from the rigid-sphere model regarding the rate of convergence of the Sonine polynomial expansion used in deriving the expressions for the transport coefficients. This information is summarized[1] in Table 8.3–2, where the percentage of the true value of the transport coefficients in the kth approximation is given. The error in the thermal diffusion ratio is considerably larger than that for any of the other coefficients. Generally speaking, the errors in the first approximation are greater for rigid spheres than for more realistic molecular models.

[1] S. Chapman and T. G. Cowling, *The Mathematical Theory of Non-uniform Gases*, Cambridge University Press (1939), p. 169 and 196.

TABLE 8.3–2[1]

FRACTION OF THE TRUE VALUE OF THE TRANSPORT COEFFICIENTS IN THE kth APPROXIMATION (BASED ON THE RIGID-SPHERE MODEL)

$[P]_k$ = k^{th} approximation to the coefficient P
$[P]$ = true value of the coefficient P

P	$[P]_1/[P]$	$[P]_2/[P]$	$[P]_3/[P]$
η	0.984	0.999	0.999+
λ	0.976	0.998	0.999+
$\mathscr{D}$	0.883	0.957	0.978
k_T	0.77	0.88	...

b. Point centers of repulsion

At very high temperatures the repulsive forces play a much more important role than the attractive forces. It is then possible to represent molecules as point centers of repulsive forces with a potential energy of interaction $\varphi(r) = dr^{-\delta}$ (see Eq. 1.3–23). The index δ is a measure of the hardness or softness of the molecules. For $\delta = \infty$ this model reduces to the rigid-sphere model. The model with δ finite allows for the natural "squishiness" of the molecules. For most molecules δ lies between 9 ("soft" molecules) and 15 ("hard" molecules).

A point in favor of this potential function is that the angle of deflection, which is a function of b and g, may be expressed in terms of a single combination of these two variables. If we define the quantities y, y_m, and y_0 by

$$y = \frac{b}{r} \qquad y_m = \frac{b}{r_m} \qquad y_0 = b\left[\frac{\frac{1}{2}\mu g^2}{\delta d}\right]^{1/\delta} \tag{8.3–2}$$

the angle of deflection may be written thus:

$$\chi(y_0) = \pi - 2\int_0^{y_m(y_0)}\left[1 - y^2 - \frac{1}{\delta}\left(\frac{y}{y_0}\right)^{\delta}\right]^{-1/2} dy \tag{8.3–3}$$

The limit y_m is that value of y for which the radical in the denominator of the integrand vanishes. The angle of deflection as a function of y_0 is shown in Fig. 8.3–1 for $\delta = 12$; a numerical tabulation of $y_m(y_0)$ and $\chi(y_0)$ is given in Table III. These quantities have to be evaluated numerically.

Substitution of the angles of deflection in Eqs. 8.2–2 and 3 gives the following formulae for the collision cross-sections:

$$Q^{(l)} = 2\pi \left(\frac{\delta d}{\frac{1}{2}\mu g^2}\right)^{2/\delta} \int_0^\infty [1 - \cos^l \chi] y_0 \, dy_0 = 2\pi \left(\frac{\delta d}{\frac{1}{2}\mu g^2}\right)^{2/\delta} A^{(l)}(\delta) \quad (8.3\text{–}4)$$

$$\sqrt{\mu/2\pi kT}\, \Omega^{(l,s)} = \tfrac{1}{2} A^{(l)}(\delta) \left(\frac{\delta d}{kT}\right)^{2/\delta} \Gamma\left(s + 2 - \frac{2}{\delta}\right) \quad (8.3\text{–}5)$$

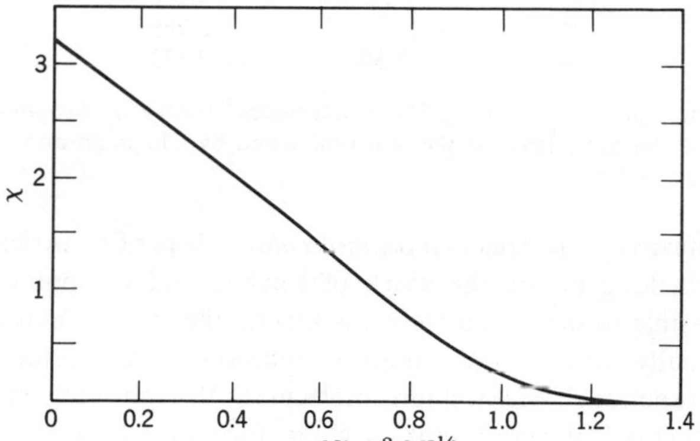

Fig. 8.3–1. The angle of deflection as a function of the single parameter y_0 for the potential of interaction $\phi(r) = dr^{-12}$. (From unpublished calculations of R. B. Bird.)

Values of the integrals $A^{(l)}(\delta)$ are given in Table 8.3–3. When the $\Omega^{(l,s)}$ given above are used, the following relations are obtained for the transport coefficients:

$$[\eta]_1 = \frac{5}{8}\sqrt{\frac{km}{\pi}} \left(\frac{k}{\delta d}\right)^{2/\delta} T^{(1/2)+(2/\delta)} \Big/ \Gamma\left(4 - \frac{2}{\delta}\right) A^{(2)}(\delta)$$

$$[\lambda]_1 = \frac{5}{2} [\eta]_1 \hat{C}_v \quad (8.3\text{–}6)$$

$$[\mathscr{D}_{12}]_1 = \frac{3}{16}\sqrt{\frac{2k^3}{\pi\mu}} \left(\frac{k}{d_{12}\delta_{12}}\right)^{2/\delta_{12}} T^{(3/2)+(2/\delta_{12})} \Big/ p A^{(1)}(\delta_{12}) \Gamma\left(3 - \frac{2}{\delta_{12}}\right)$$

These relations are useful for curve-fitting transport coefficients data at high temperatures, where the contributions due to the repulsive forces are far more important than those due to the attractive forces.

There are two special cases of this type of interaction which deserve mention. Molecules which interact according to a repulsion law with

TABLE 8.3–3[a]

VALUES OF THE $A^{(l)}(\delta)$ FOR POINT CENTERS OF REPULSION

δ	$A^{(1)}(\delta)$	$A^{(2)}(\delta)$
4	0.298	0.308
6	0.306	0.283
8	0.321	0.279
10	0.333	0.278
12	0.346	0.279
14	0.356	0.280
20	...	0.286
24	...	0.289
∞	0.500	0.333

[a] S. Chapman and T. G. Cowling, *The Mathematical Theory of Non-uniform Gases*, p. 172. The $A^{(l)}(\delta)$ are related to the $A_l(\delta)$ tabulated by Chapman and Cowling by $A^{(l)}(\delta) = A_l(\delta + 1)/2^{2/\delta}$.

$\delta = 4$ are referred to as *Maxwellian molecules*. It is of historical interest that Maxwell, long before the work of Enskog and Chapman, realized that it is possible to develop a rigorous kinetic theory for such molecules without actually solving the integral equation which determines the Boltzmann function. Maxwellian molecules, though very satisfactory from a mathematical standpoint, are far too unreal to be physically important. For these molecules the thermal diffusion coefficient is identically zero.[1]

A second special case is that for $\delta = 1$ and $d = e_1e_2$, which is the Coulombic interaction[2] characteristic of the potential between two charges e_1 and e_2 (see § 12.1). For this case the angle of deflection may be obtained analytically:

$$\chi(y_0) = 2 \arcsin \frac{1}{\sqrt{1 + 4y_0^2}} \tag{8.3–7}$$

When we substitute this expression into Eq. 8.3–4, we find that the integral diverges at the upper limit. The physical explanation for this mathematical difficulty is that the force field falls off so slowly that it is not clear how a binary encounter should be defined—in fact, all encounters should, in a sense, be regarded as multiple. In a dilute gas, however, it is possible to obtain approximate expressions for the transport coefficients by ignoring the fact that multiple collisions do occur to some extent.

In a dilute gas the values of b for which an appreciable angle of deflection occurs are considerably smaller than the mean distance D between the particles in the gas. Under such conditions then it seems reasonable to

[2] The subject of transport phenomena in ionized gases has been discussed by T. Kihara, *Revs. Mod. Phys.*, **24**, 45 (1952).

take as the upper limit $b = D$ or $y_0 = D(\frac{1}{2}\mu g^2/e_1e_2) \equiv y_0'$. Then the following expressions for the cross-sections may be obtained:

$$Q^{(1)} = \frac{\pi}{2}\left(\frac{e_1e_2}{\frac{1}{2}\mu g^2}\right)^2 \ln(1 + 4y_0'^2) \tag{8.3–8}$$

$$Q^{(2)} = \pi\left(\frac{e_1e_2}{\frac{1}{2}\mu g^2}\right)^2 \left[\ln(1 + 4y_0'^2) - \frac{4y_0'^2}{1 + 4y_0'^2}\right] \tag{8.3–9}$$

In order to obtain the $\Omega^{(l,s)}$ these expressions must be integrated over the relative velocity g, which appears explicitly as g^{-4} and implicitly in the y_0'. Inasmuch as the $Q^{(l)}$ are slowly varying functions of y_0', it is convenient to introduce the additional simplifying assumption that $\frac{1}{2}\mu g^2$ be replaced by its average value over all collisions, which may be shown[3] to be $2kT$. Then the first approximations to the transport coefficients of a gas consisting of a single component become

$$[\mathscr{D}]_1 = \frac{3}{8}\sqrt{\frac{mkT}{\pi}}\left(\frac{2kT}{e^2}\right)^2\left(\frac{1}{\rho}\right) \Big/ [\ln(1 + 4y_0''^2)] \tag{8.3–10}$$

$$[\eta]_1 = \frac{5}{16}\sqrt{\frac{mkT}{\pi}}\left(\frac{2kT}{e^2}\right)^2 \Big/ \left[\ln(1 + 4y_0''^2) - \frac{4y_0''^2}{1 + 4y_0''^2}\right] \tag{8.3–11}$$

$$[\lambda]_1 = \frac{25}{32}\sqrt{\frac{mkT}{\pi}}\left(\frac{2kT}{e^2}\right)^2\left(\frac{c_v}{m}\right) \Big/ \left[\ln(1 + 4y_0''^2) - \frac{4y_0''^2}{1 + 4y_0''^2}\right] \tag{8.3–12}$$

in which $y_0'' = 2DkT/e^2$.

c. The Sutherland model[4, 5]

The Sutherland model represents the molecules as rigid spheres of diameter σ surrounded by an inverse-power attractive force, with maximum energy of attraction ϵ. The interaction potential is given by

$$\begin{aligned} \varphi(r) &= \infty & r &< \sigma \\ \varphi(r) &= -\epsilon\,(\sigma/r)^\gamma & r &> \sigma \end{aligned} \tag{1.3–25}$$

An exact evaluation of the angles of deflection and the collision cross-sections requires a major numerical effort. If, however, it is assumed that the attractive portion of the potential is weak, the higher powers of ϵ which appear in the exact treatment can be neglected. This gives the

[3] S. Chapman and T. G. Cowling, *loc. cit.*, p. 93.
[4] M. Kotani, *Proc. Physico-Mathematical Soc. Japan*, **24**, 76 (1942).
[5] S. Chapman and T. G. Cowling, *loc. cit.*, p. 182 et seq.

Sutherland formulae for viscosity and diffusion which have been used extensively for curve fitting data:

$$[\eta]_1 = [\eta_{\text{rig sph}}]_1 \Big/ \left(1 + \frac{S_\eta}{T}\right) \tag{8.3–13}$$

$$[\mathscr{D}]_1 = [\mathscr{D}_{\text{rig sph}}]_1 \Big/ \left(1 + \frac{S_\mathscr{D}}{T}\right) \tag{8.3–14}$$

The Sutherland constants, S_η and $S_\mathscr{D}$, which are proportional to the energy of interaction of the two molecules when in contact, are given by

$$S_\mathscr{D} = i^{(1)}(\gamma)\,(\epsilon/k) \tag{8.3–15}$$

$$S_\eta = i^{(2)}(\gamma)\,(\epsilon/k) \tag{8.3–16}$$

The constants of proportionality $i^{(l)}(\gamma)$ for several indices of attraction are shown in Table 8.3–4. The results of this approximate treatment are valid only at very high temperatures where the attractive forces would be expected to play only a small role in the molecular interaction.

TABLE 8.3–4

CONSTANTS OF PROPORTIONALITY FOR THE SUTHERLAND CONSTANTS[5]

γ	$i^{(1)}(\gamma)$	$i^{(2)}(\gamma)$
2	0.2662	0.2336
3	0.2276	0.2118
4	0.2010	0.1956
6	0.1667	0.1736
8	0.1444	0.1556

If the energy of attraction varies as $1/r^6$, the potential function assumes the form:

$$\begin{aligned} \varphi(r) &= \infty & r &< \sigma \\ \varphi(r) &= -\epsilon(\sigma/r)^6 & r &> \sigma \end{aligned} \tag{8.3–17}$$

where once again ϵ is the maximum energy of attraction and σ is the diameter of the hard core.

A complete evaluation of the angles of deflection and the collision cross-sections for this potential, without any assumption as to the smallness of the attractive forces, has been performed by Kotani.[4] The integrals $\Omega^{(l,\,s)\star}(T^*)$ which he has calculated numerically are given in Table V. With these tabulations, the first and second approximations to the transport properties of pure gases and their mixtures may be calculated by means of the formulae given in § 8.2. These formulae may be used to obtain the force constants ϵ and σ for the Sutherland potential. The force constants for neon and nitrogen determined from viscosity and also from diffusion measurements, and for carbon dioxide obtained from viscosity data, are shown in Table 8.3–5.

TABLE 8.3–5

FORCE CONSTANTS FOR THE SUTHERLAND POTENTIAL CALCULATED FROM VISCOSITY AND SELF-DIFFUSION MEASUREMENTS[a] BETWEEN 200°K AND 300°K

Gas	From Viscosity		From Self-diffusion	
	σ(Å)	ϵ/k(°K)	σ(Å)	ϵ/k(°K)
Ne	2.33	192	2.20	196
N_2	3.07	416	3.17	202
CO_2[b]	3.43	638	...	...

[a] See Table 8.3–1 for source of experimental data.
[b] V. Vasilesco, *Annales de physique* (Paris) (11), **20**, 292 (1945).

d. The square-well potential[6]

The simplest three-constant potential for which transport coefficient calculations have been made is the square-well potential:

$$\begin{aligned} \varphi(r) &= \infty & r &< \sigma \\ \varphi(r) &= -\epsilon & \sigma &< r < R\sigma \\ \varphi(r) &= 0 & r &> R\sigma \end{aligned} \tag{1.3–24}$$

For this potential function the angles of deflection and the collision cross-sections have to be evaluated numerically. The integrals $\Omega^{(l,s)\star}$ so obtained[6] are given in Table IV. The potential parameters (determined from viscosity) to be used in conjunction with these tables are given in Table 8.3–6. When these parameters and the tabulated functions are used, the experimental data can be rather well reproduced, and other transport properties may be calculated.

Because of the unrealistic shape of the potential functions, however, it is not possible to use the parameters obtained from transport coefficients for the calculation of second virial coefficients. In Table 8.3–7 the force constants obtained from viscosity and second virial coefficients are compared. The considerable discrepancy between the two sets of constants results from the fact that the viscosity emphasizes the repulsive parts of the potential function to a greater extent than does the second virial coefficient.

[6] E. M. Holleran and H. M. Hulburt, *J. Chem. Phys.*, **19**, 232 (1951).

TABLE 8.3–6

FORCE CONSTANTS FOR THE SQUARE-WELL POTENTIAL OBTAINED FROM VISCOSITY DATA[6]

Substance	ϵ/k(°K)	σ(Å)	$1/R$
He	232	1.90	0.720
Ne	101	2.38	0.650
A	167	2.98	0.510
H_2	94	2.57	0.700
O_2	94	3.16	0.470
N_2	80	3.36	0.480
CO	91	3.29	0.440
CO_2	200	3.46	0.450
CH_4	174	3.35	0.510
Air	87	3.30	0.480

TABLE 8.3–7

COMPARISON OF FORCE CONSTANTS FOR THE SQUARE-WELL OBTAINED FROM VISCOSITY[a] AND FROM THE SECOND VIRIAL COEFFICIENT[b]

Substance	ϵ/k(°K)	From Viscosity		From the Second Virial Coefficient	
		σ(Å)	$1/R$	σ(Å)	$1/R$
Ethane	244	3.81	0.437	3.54	0.606
Propane	347	4.21	0.480	4.42	0.683
n-Butane	387	4.50	0.460	4.82	0.678
Ethene	222	3.70	0.440	3.35	0.597
Propene	339	4.02	0.450	4.32	0.685

[a] E. M. Holleran and H. M. Hulburt, *J. Chem. Phys.*, **19**, 232 (1951).
[b] J. O. Hirschfelder, F. T. McClure, and I. F. Weeks, *J. Chem. Phys.*, **10**, 201 (1942).

4. Transport Coefficient Calculations for the Lennard-Jones (6-12) Potential[1]

The four simple potential functions discussed in the preceding section give rather good results for the transport properties over limited temperature ranges and indicate the primary nature of the temperature dependence of these properties. A more realistic potential function for which the

[1] The viscosity for molecules which obey a Lennard-Jones (4-8) potential has been calculated by H. R. Hassé and W. R. Cook, *Phil. Mag.*, **3**, 977 (1927), and *Proc. Roy. Soc.* (*London*), **125**, 196 (1929). These results have also been applied to the study of thermal diffusion by R. C. Jones, *Phys. Rev.*, **59**, 1019 (1941).

transport properties of non-polar molecules have been calculated is the Lennard-Jones (6-12) potential:

$$\varphi(r) = 4\epsilon\left[\left(\frac{\sigma}{r}\right)^{12} - \left(\frac{\sigma}{r}\right)^{6}\right] \tag{8.4-1}$$

Here ϵ is the depth of the potential well (the maximum energy of attraction) and σ is the collision diameter for low energy collisions (that is, the value of r for which $\varphi(r) = 0$). The calculations for this potential function have been carried out independently by workers in four different countries.[2-5] Because of the excellent numerical agreement between these results we may be confident that there is little computational error in the tabulated functions. The details of the calculations may be found in the original publications, but the significant results are given here. First we discuss the calculation of the angle of deflection and the collision cross-sections. Then we discuss the calculation of the various transport coefficients and the agreement between calculated and experimental results.

Recently Mason[6] has calculated the set of integrals $\Omega^{(l,s)\star}$ for the modified Buckingham potential, Eq. 1.3-30, using methods similar to those described in this section. Tables of these collision integrals and related quantities are given in Appendix VII. The work has been completed so recently that up to the present time the force constants for only a few molecules have been determined (see Table 3.7-2), and no other applications have yet been made.

a. The dynamics of a binary collision[7] and the calculation of the collision cross-sections

In § 1.5b it was pointed out that the dynamics of a binary collision may be studied in terms of the *effective potential energy*, $\varphi_{eff}(r)$, which is defined in Eq. 1.5-22 as the sum of the intermolecular potential energy and the centrifugal potential energy. In terms of the reduced quantities the effective potential energy function for the Lennard-Jones (6-12) potential is

$$\varphi^*_{\text{eff}} = \varphi^*(r^*) + \frac{g^{*2}b^{*2}}{r^{*2}} \tag{8.4-2}$$

[2] T. Kihara and M. Kotani, *Proc. Phys. Math. Soc. Japan*, **25**, 602 (1943).

[3] J. de Boer and J. van Kranendonk, *Physica*, **14**, 442 (1948).

[4] J. S. Rowlinson, *J. Chem. Phys.*, **17**, 101 (1949).

[5] J. O. Hirschfelder, R. B. Bird, and E. L. Spotz, *J. Chem. Phys.*, **16**, 968 (1948); **17**, 149 (1950); *Chem. Revs.*, **44**, 205 (1949).

[6] E. A. Mason, *J. Chem. Phys.*, **22**, 169 (1954).

[7] Molecular collisions in classical dynamics are discussed in detail in § 1.5. The specific results for the Lennard-Jones potential discussed in this section are based on this previous discussion.

The reduced effective potential energy is then a function of r^* which depends parametrically on the quantity $g^{*2}b^{*2}$. In Fig. 8.4–1 are shown curves of φ^*_{eff} for several values of $g^{*2}b^{*2}$. The humps in the curves

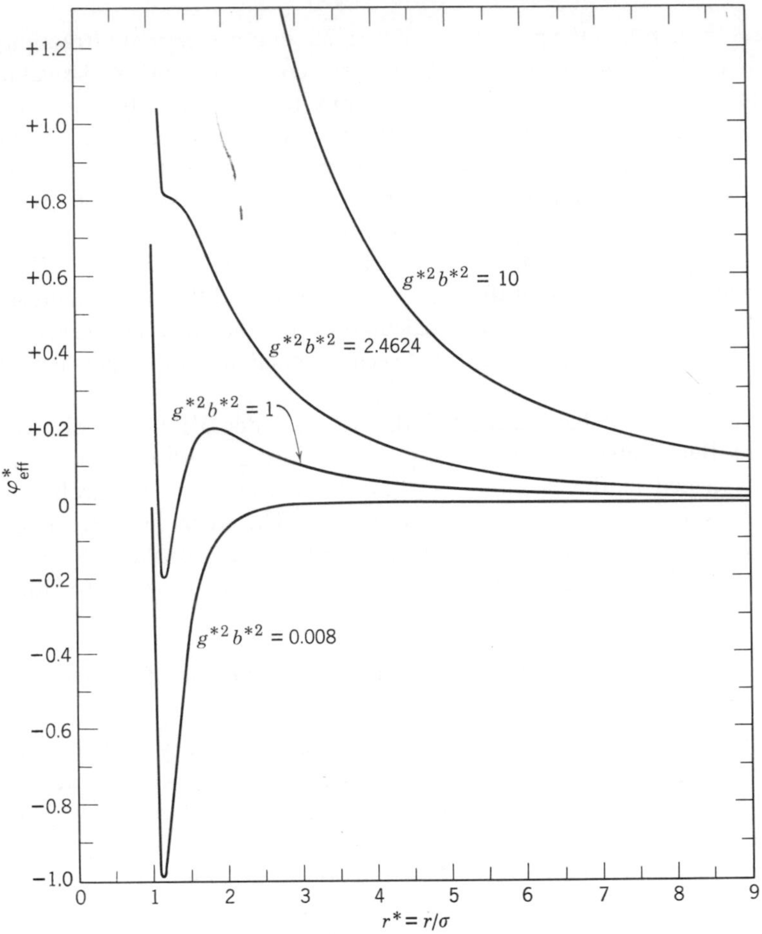

Fig. 8.4–1. The reduced effective potential, defined by Eq. 8.4–2, for the Lennard-Jones (6-12) potential, for several values of $g^{*2}b^{*2}$.

occur roughly at the point where the attractive van der Waals forces balance the centrifugal repulsion. There is a critical value of $g^{*2}b^{*2} = \frac{36}{25}(5^{\frac{1}{3}})$ for which there is an inflection point at a reduced energy of 0.8. For values above this critical value the effective potential curves are monotone decreasing.

We may use the curves in Fig. 8.4–1 to analyze the dynamics of a collision. If a pair of colliding molecules has an initial reduced kinetic energy g^{*2} less than 0.8, several types of collisions are dynamically possible, depending upon the value of $g^{*2}b^{*2}$ characterizing the collision. Several possibilities may be illustrated by the specific case where g^{*2} is approximately 0.2. (a) If b^* is such that $g^{*2}b^{*2} = 10$, there is only a gradual deflection of one molecule with respect to the other—that is, a "grazing collision"—the repulsive part of the potential having a negligible effect on the collision. (b) If b^* is such that $g^{*2}b^{*2} = 0.008$—that is, almost a "head-on collision"—both the attractive forces at large separations and the repulsive forces at small separations influence the trajectory. (c) If b^* is such that the system cannot quite get over the hump, the phenomenon of "orbiting" takes place. Then the system spends a great deal of time in the vicinity of the separation corresponding to the hump, the molecules meanwhile spinning around one another,[8] with an angular velocity given by Eq. 1.5–19. These three types of collisions are shown in Fig. 8.4–2.

The angle of deflection is computed by evaluating the integral in Eq. 8.2–12 by numerical methods.[9] The results are given in tabular form[5] in Table I–R and graphically in Fig. 8.4–3, where $(1 - \cos \chi)$ is plotted as a function of b^{*2} for four values of g^{*2}. The areas under these curves give the cross-section $Q^{(1)\star}$. For small values of the relative kinetic

[8] These collisions in which orbiting takes place should not be confused with the "bound molecules" in periodic orbits discussed by J. G. Kirkwood [*J. Chem. Phys.*, **15**, 72 (1947)]. The latter are pairs of molecules which find themselves trapped in the potential well and accordingly spin around one another separated by a distance of the same order of magnitude as the molecular dimensions. If it is assumed that two-body collisions take place in the gas but that no higher-order collisions occur, such "bound molecules" cannot exist inasmuch as a three-body collision is required for their formation and their dissolution. The Boltzmann equation, from which the kinetic theory is developed, provides no mechanism for three-body collisions. Kirkwood has shown that in the limit of low densities, which is the approximation considered here, these bound molecules do not contribute to the transport properties. However, these bound states do affect the transport properties at somewhat higher densities. This point receives further attention in the introduction to Chapter 9. The collisions in which orbiting occurs do make a small contribution to the cross-sections. The effect is quite small, however, and is practically negligible at high temperatures. In connection with the bound molecules, it should be pointed out that they *are* taken into account in the second virial coefficient. This comes about essentially because of the fact that in the theoretical development from the partition function, a mechanism is provided whereby molecule pairs may be trapped in the potential well.

[9] Several methods have been used for the calculation of the angle of deflection. One method is to curve fit a slowly varying part of the integrand, which allows the integration then to be performed analytically.[5] Another method, the so-called goniometric method, has been used recently by J. de Boer and J. van Kranendonk, *Physica*, **14**, 442 (1948).

energy g^{*2} these curves exhibit rapid oscillations, which correspond to orbiting. For collisions taking place with $g^{*2} \leq 0.8$ there is for each g^* one value of b^* for which the energy of the top of the hump coincides

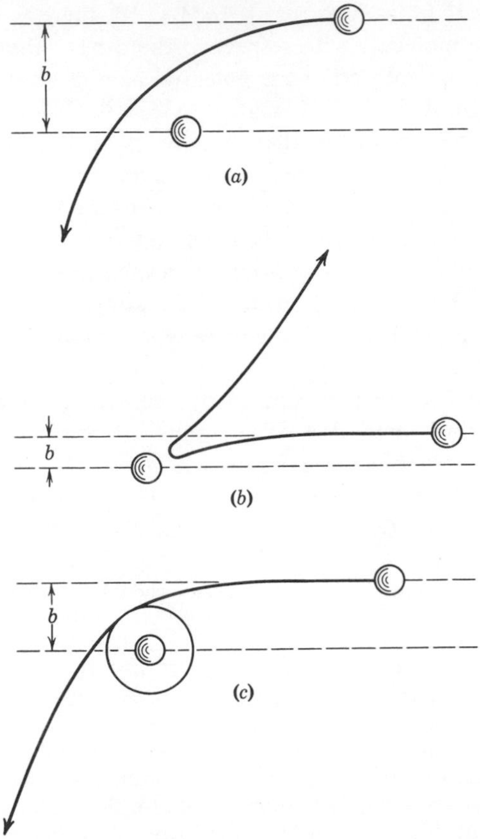

Fig. 8.4–2. Types of collisions which occur for Lennard-Jones molecules. (*a*) Grazing collisions in which attractive forces are most important. (*b*) Almost head-on collisions in which the strong repulsive forces come into play. (*c*) Types of collisions in which "orbiting" takes place. This phenomenon results from the hump in the effective potential energy curve caused by the counterbalancing of the attractive force and the centrifugal force.

precisely with the energy of the system. For this value $b^* = b_0^*$, the angle of deflection is infinite, as can be seen in the tabulation of χ in Table I–R.

The hump in the $(1 - \cos \chi)$ curve gradually disappears with increasing energy of collision because the colliding system feels the dip in the potential

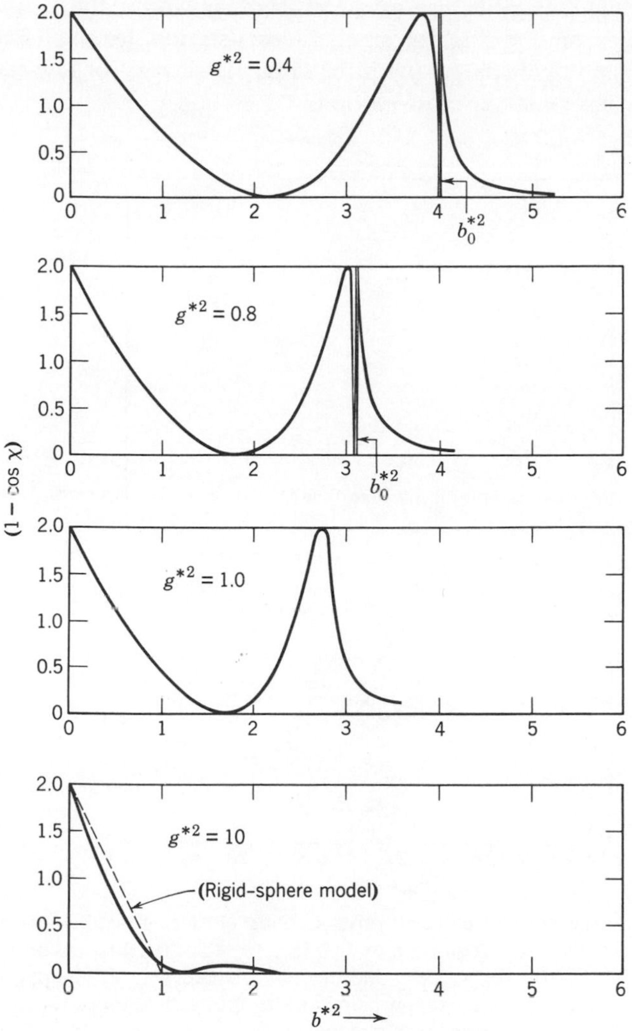

Fig. 8.4-3. The angle of deflection for the Lennard-Jones potential. Here $(1 - \cos\chi)$ is plotted against b^{*2} for several values of the reduced kinetic energy g^{*2}. In the region around b_0^{*2} the value of $(1 - \cos\chi)$ oscillates an infinite number of times between zero and two.

energy curve less and less. When $g^{*2} = 10$, this hump, due to the attractive forces, has almost completely disappeared. In fact the $(1 - \cos\chi)$ curve very nearly approximates the curve for rigid spheres. Actually the Lennard-Jones curve lies slightly below the curve for rigid spheres, since the r^{-12} repulsion allows for the interpenetration of the molecules in high energy collisions. Or, in other words, the Lennard-Jones molecules have a slightly smaller cross-section for high-energy collisions, than do rigid spheres (with the same σ), whereas for low-energy collisions they have a larger cross-section.

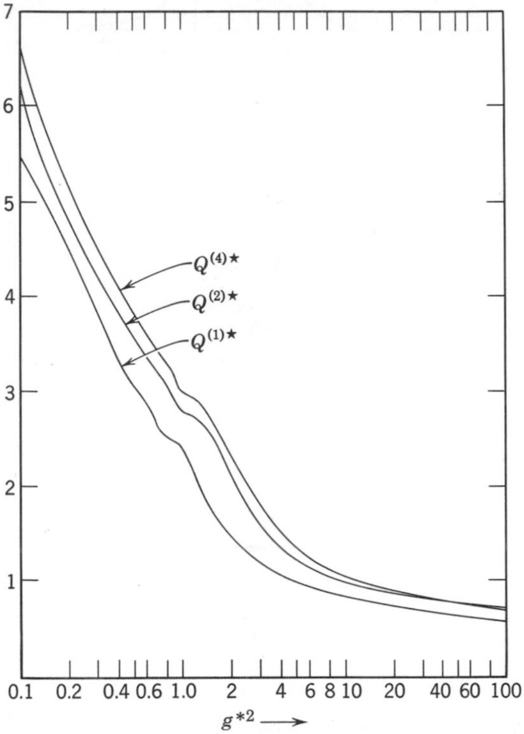

Fig. 8.4–4. The reduced collision cross-sections $Q^{(l)\star}$ as functions of the reduced kinetic energy of relative motion g^{*2}. $Q^{(1)\star}$ is the cross-section for diffusion, $Q^{(2)\star}$ is that for viscosity and thermal conductivity. $Q^{(4)\star}$ appears in the expressions for the third approximation to the coefficients of viscosity and thermal conductivity.

From these angles of deflection as a function of b^* and g^* the cross-sections $Q^{(l)\star}(g^{*2})$ and the quantities $\Omega^{(l,s)\star}(T^*)$ have been obtained by numerical integration of the expressions given in Eqs. 8.2–13 and 14. The dependence of the $Q^{(l)\star}$ on the reduced relative kinetic energy, g^{*2}, and the dependence of the $\Omega^{(l,s)\star}$ on the reduced temperature are shown in Figs. 8.4–4 and 5, respectively. By definition all these quantities are unity for the rigid-sphere model. As was previously mentioned, the deviation of these quantities from unity is an indication of the deviation of any particular model from rigid-sphere behavior. In Fig. 8.4-4 it is clear that the cross-sections for Lennard-Jones molecules are smaller than those for rigid spheres at high energies because of the softness of the repulsive portion of the potential. Also the cross-sections are several times their rigid-sphere values at low energies because of the influence of the attractive forces. The behavior of the $\Omega^{(l,s)\star}$ shown in Fig. 8.4-5 may be explained in the same way, since the averaging process emphasizes the low-energy collisions at low temperatures and the high-energy collisions at high temperatures.

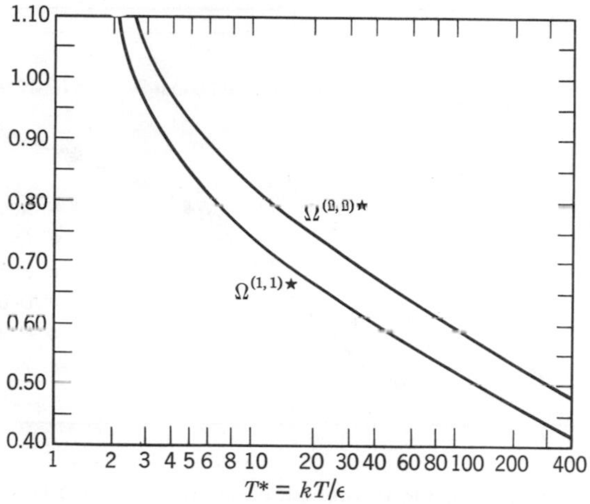

Fig. 8.4-5. The temperature dependence of the $\Omega^{(l,s)\star}$.

For the purposes of making calculations of transport properties, extensive tables of the collision cross-sections and related quantities have been prepared: In Tables I-M, N, P in the Appendix[5] at the end of the book the following quantities are tabulated as functions of T^* from $T^* = 0.30$ to $T^* = 400$: all the $\Omega^{(l,s)\star}$ needed for calculating the third approximation to the viscosity and thermal conductivity, the second approximation to the diffusion, and the first approximation to the thermal diffusion ratio; the quantities $\text{A}^\star$, $\text{B}^\star$, $\text{C}^\star$ defined in Eqs. 8.2-15, 16, 17; and the factors $f_\eta^{(3)}$, $f_\lambda^{(3)}$, and $f_{\mathscr{D}}^{(2)}$ defined in Eqs. 8.2-19, 32, 47. With these tables and the formulae in § 8.2 the transport properties may be calculated for the Lennard-Jones (6-12) potential. In the remainder of this section the various transport properties are discussed, both from the standpoint of calculating the transport coefficients from intermolecular forces, and vice versa. Illustrative examples are given to demonstrate the use of the tabulated functions.

b. The coefficient of viscosity of pure gases

To calculate the coefficient of viscosity from Eq. 8.2–18 or 19 it is necessary to know the values of the force constants, ϵ and σ, appropriate for the given substance. These parameters may be obtained from an analysis of the experimental data for viscosity and self-diffusion (as described later in this section) and from second virial coefficients and Joule-Thomson coefficients (as described in § 3.6). Rough estimates may be obtained from constants characteristic of the critical, melting, or boiling points (as given in § 4.1). The force constants for a few

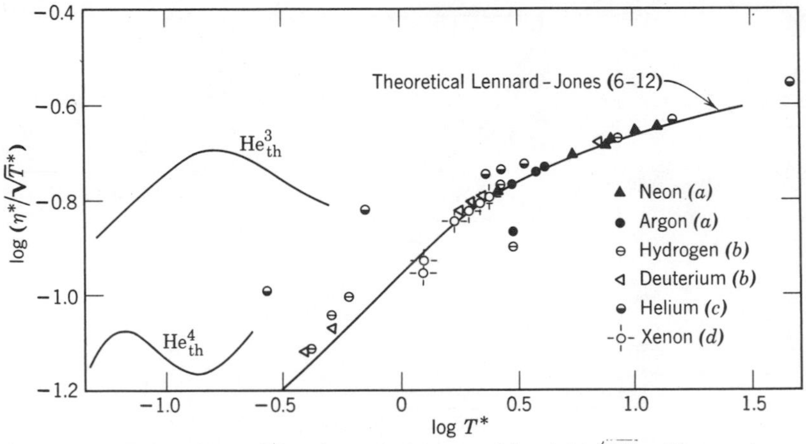

Fig. 8.4–6. Comparison of the theoretical curve of $\log(\eta^*/\sqrt{T^*})$ with experimental data. The experimental values are reduced according to the relation $\eta^* = \eta\sigma^2/\sqrt{m\epsilon}$, using the values of σ and ϵ given in Tables I–A. The curves He^4_{th} [from J. de Boer *Physica*, **10**, 348 (1943)] and He^3_{th} [from E. G. D. Cohen, *Physica*, **17**, 993 (1951)] were calculated, using a quantum mechanical treatment (see § 10.2). (*a*) M. Trautz and H. Zimmerman, *Ann. Physik* (5), **22**, 189 (1935). (*b*) A. van Itterbeek and A. Claes, *Physica*, **5**, 938 (1938). (*c*) A. van Itterbeek and W. H. Keesom, *Physica*, **5**, 257 (1938). (*d*) M. Trautz and R. Heberling, *Ann. Physik* (5), **20**, 118 (1934).

gases are given in Table 8.4–1; these were determined from viscosity measurements. A more complete table of force constants may be found in Table I–A. In that table force constants are given which have been obtained from the data of various investigations and from various properties. Whenever possible it is advisable to use the parameters determined from viscosity for making transport property calculations.

In Fig. 8.4–6 the viscosity for several substances is plotted in reduced units. The theoretical curve based upon the Lennard-Jones (6-12) potential is also shown. In order to illustrate further the excellent agreement between the experimental and calculated values a numerical comparison is made in Table 8.4–2. Let us now consider a numerical example to illustrate the use of the $\Omega^{(l,s)\star}$ tables and the formula for the coefficient of viscosity given in Eq. 8.2–19.

Illustrative Example

Problem. Calculate the viscosity of CH_4 at 450°K. What is the viscosity of CD_4 at the same temperature?

Solution. From Table 8.4–1 the force constants for methane are $\epsilon/k = 137$°K and $\sigma = 3.822$ Å. The reduced temperature is then $T^* = kT/\epsilon = (450/137) = 3.28$. From Table I–M, it can be found that at $T^* = 3.28$, $\Omega^{(2,2)\star} = 1.016$ and from Table I–P, $f_\eta^{(3)} = 1.004$. The molecular weight of CH_4 is 16.04. Hence from Eq. 8.2–19:

$$CH_4\text{:}\quad [\eta]_3 \times 10^7 = 266.93\,\frac{\sqrt{(16.04)\,(450)}}{(3.822)^2(1.016)}\cdot(1.004) = 1534 \text{ g/cm sec}$$

For the heavy isotope of methane, CD_4 (mol. wt. 20.07), the force constants are the same as those for light methane. Hence, we can calculate the viscosity of CD_4 simply by multiplying that of CH_4 by the ratio of the square root of the molecular weights:

$$CD_4\text{:}\quad [\eta]_3 \times 10^7 = 1534\sqrt{\frac{20.07}{16.04}} = 1716 \text{ g/cm sec}$$

TABLE 8.4–1

FORCE CONSTANTS FOR THE LENNARD-JONES (6-12) POTENTIAL DETERMINED FROM VISCOSITY COEFFICIENTS[a]

Gas	ϵ/k(°K)	σ(Å)	*Experimental Data*
Ne	35.7	2.789	*b*
A	124	3.418	*b*
Kr	190	3.61	*c*
Xe	229	4.055	*d*
N_2	91.5	3.681	*e*
O_2	113	3.433	*e*
CH_4	137	3.822	*e*
CO_2	190	3.996	*e*

[a] A more complete table of force constants for the Lennard-Jones (6-12) potential is given in the Appendix in Table I–A. In the same table there are also given the force constants determined from the second virial coefficient.

[b] H. L. Johnston and E. R. Grilly, *J. Phys. Chem.*, **46**, 938 (1942).

[c] Landolt-Börnstein, *Physikalisch-Chemische Tabellen.*

[d] M. Trautz and R. Heberling, *Ann. Physik* (5), **20**, 118 (1934).

[e] H. L. Johnston and K. E. McCloskey, *J. Phys. Chem.*, **44**, 1038 (1940).

TABLE 8.4–2

COMPARISON OF EXPERIMENTAL AND CALCULATED VISCOSITIES[a]
[LENNARD-JONES (6-12) POTENTIAL]

$\eta \times 10^7$ in g $cm^{-1}sec^{-1}$

T (°K)	A		Ne		N_2		CH_4		O_2		CO_2	
	Exptl	Calcd	Exptl	Calcd	Exptl	Calcd	Exptl	Calcd	Exptl	Calcd	Exptl	Calcd
80	688	649	1198	1212								
100	839	814	1435	1451	698	687	403	393	768	757		
120	993	979	1646	1665	826	820	478	472	917	910		
140	1146	1142	1841	1867	948	947	560	553	1061	1059		
160	1298	1300	2026	2054	1068	1070	629	630	1202	1203		
180	1447	1454	2204	2231	1183	1186	703	707	1341	1342		
200	1594	1601	2376	2396	1295	1296	778	780	1476	1474	1015	1014
220	1739	1744	2544	2558	1403	1402	850	852	1604	1602	1112	1114
240	1878	1882	2708	2713	1505	1503	919	921	1728	1726	1209	1212
260	2014	2014	2867	2862	1603	1600	986	987	1845	1845	1303	1308
280	2145	2143	3021	3008	1696	1693	1053	1052	1958	1959	1400	1402
300	2270	2269	3173	3149	1786	1785	1116	1116	2071	2070	1495	1495
400		2839		3812		2202		1405		2578		1923
500		3347		4383		2570		1661		3031		2309
800	4621	4641	5918	5945	3493	3528		2312	4115	4183	3391	3285
1000	5302	5391	6800	6872	4011	4068		2687	4720	4853	3935	3839
1200	5947	6083			4452	4554		3034		5457	4453	4348
1500	6778	6983			5050	5268		3498		6264	5139	5052

[a] The force constants and the references to experimental data are given in Table 8.4–1.

The two adjustable parameters in the Lennard-Jones potential may be obtained from viscosity data by a method similar to that used in § 3.6b for the analysis of the second virial coefficient data. The values of σ and ϵ may be determined from experimental viscosity measurements at two temperatures, T_1 and T_2. The procedure is outlined as follows. First one defines a quantity k_η by

$$k_\eta = \left[\frac{\eta(T_2)}{\eta(T_1)}\right]_{\text{exptl}} \left(\frac{T_1}{T_2}\right)^{1/2} \tag{8.4–3}$$

Then, according to Eq. 8.2–19, ϵ/k may be determined by trial and error solution of the equation:

$$k_\eta = \left(\frac{\Omega^{(2,2)\star}(T_1^*)}{\Omega^{(2,2)\star}(T_2^*)}\right)\left(\frac{f_\eta^{(3)}(T_2^*)}{f_\eta^{(3)}(T_1^*)}\right) \tag{8.4–4}$$

where $T_i^* = kT_i/\epsilon$. As a first approximation to ϵ/k we may use the value calculated from the boiling temperature or critical temperature according to the relations given in § 4.1. Once the value of ϵ/k has been determined, the collision diameter is obtained from

$$\sigma^2 = \frac{266.93 \sqrt{MT_i} f_\eta^{(3)}(T_i^*)}{[\eta(T_i) \times 10^7] \, \Omega^{(2,2)\star}(T_i^*)} \qquad (8.4\text{-}5)$$

in which T_i is either T_1 or T_2. Slightly different sets of parameters are obtained from different choices of T_1 and T_2 because the Lennard-Jones (6-12) potential is an empirical function and does not give an exact description of the dependence of the intermolecular force on the separation between the molecules. To illustrate the determination of force constants from viscosity measurements, we give the following numerical examples.

Illustrative Example

Problem. The experimental viscosity data for Xe are given in Table 8.4-3. From these data obtain the parameters ϵ and σ for the Lennard-Jones (6-12) potential. Compare the values of the force constants so obtained with those obtained from the second virial coefficient in § 3.6b. (The critical temperature of Xe is 289.8°K.)

Solution. If we let $T_1 = 293$°K, and $T_2 = 500$°K, the quantity k_η defined in Eq. 8.4-3 is $k_\eta = 1.2370$. Since $(kT_c/\epsilon) \doteq 1.3$, from $T_c = 289.8$°K the first trial value is $\epsilon/k = 223$°K. The calculation of k_η from Eq. 8.4-4 for this and for successive choices of ϵ/k is shown by the following tabulation:

ϵ/k(°K)	T_1^*	$\Omega^{(2,2)\star}(T_1^*)$	$f_\eta^{(3)}(T_1^*)$	T_2^*	$\Omega^{(2,2)\star}(T_2^*)$	$f_\eta^{(3)}(T_2^*)$	k_η
223	1.3139	1.3923	1.0001	2.2422	1.1312	1.0019	1.2330
230	1.2739	1.4121	1.0001	2.1739	1.1427	1.0018	1.2379
229	1.2795	1.4093	1.0001	2.1834	1.1410	1.0018	1.2373
228	1.2851	1.4065	1.0001	2.1930	1.1393	1.0018	1.2366

The best agreement of the calculated value with the experimental value of k_η is obtained for $\epsilon/k = 229$°K. Now σ can be found from Eq. 8.4-5 for either T_1 or T_2: $\sigma^2 = 16.440$ and $\sigma = 4.055$ Å. From the second virial coefficient measurements of Xe of Beattie, Barriault, and Brierley, we find that $\sigma = 4.10$ Å and $\epsilon/k = 221$°K.

There are given in Table I-A the force constants for a number of gases which do not fall under the category of spherical and non-polar molecules. It was possible to fit the experimental data for these substances with the theoretical results for the Lennard-Jones potential, inasmuch as the coefficient of viscosity is not too much affected by the internal degrees of freedom. It seemed worth while to tabulate the force constants for all these substances, simply for the purpose of providing a means for the

TABLE 8.4–3

EXPERIMENTAL[a] AND CALCULATED VALUES OF $\eta(T)$ FOR XENON

Temperature (°K)	$\eta \times 10^7$ (Exptl) g $cm^{-1}sec^{-1}$	$\eta \times 10^7$ (Calcd) g $cm^{-1}sec^{-1}$
289.7	2235	2236
293	2260	2260
400	3009	3016
450	3351	3341
500	3652	3653
550	3954	3951

[a] M. Trautz and R. Heberling, *Ann Physik* (5), **20**, 118 (1934).

extrapolation of the existing data into regions of higher or lower temperature. It was found, however, that for certain gases the temperature-dependence of the viscosity is considerably different from that predicted by the Lennard-Jones potential. For such substances it is impossible to find parameters for the Lennard-Jones (6-12) potential. We now discuss these anomalous substances and indicate why their properties should exhibit such deviations:[10]

(i) *Polar Molecules:* H_2O, NH_3, HBr, HCN, HI; $HgCl_2$

The energy of interaction of polar molecules is quite different from that of non-polar molecules, in that the potential function contains a strongly angular dependent term proportional to the inverse third power of the intermolecular separation. Hence it is not at all surprising that these molecules behave anomalously with respect to the Lennard-Jones (6-12) potential.

(ii) *Long Molecules: n*-Heptane

The transport properties and, in particular, viscosity are not very sensitive to the shape of the molecules. However, if the ratio of the length to the diameter becomes too great, all the physical properties are affected. Thus the temperature dependence of the viscosity of *n*-heptane is greater than would be expected for spherical molecules.

(iii) *Free Radicals or Molecules in Excited States*

As explained in Chapter 13, the valence unsaturated molecules behave quite differently from those compounds in which the total resultant electron spin is zero. For large separation, where there is essentially no

[10] L. Epstein and M. Marion, *J. Phys. and Coll. Chem.*, **57**, 336 (1953), have succeeded in explaining the temperature dependence of the viscosity of mercury and the metal vapors in terms of Lennard-Jones (6-9) potentials.

overlap of the electronic wave functions for the two molecules, there is the usual inverse seventh-power van der Waals force of attraction. As the molecules come together the potential curve at small separations may assume various forms, depending upon whether the "collision complex" formed by the two molecules is in one of the repulsive or attractive states. These types of interaction are the result of the Pauli principle, which places certain restrictions upon the symmetry properties of the electronic and spin wave functions. From quantum mechanics we can calculate *a priori* the probability that the collision complex will be in a particular attractive or repulsive state.

By way of elaboration we may consider the simplest case of two colliding hydrogen atoms. For large separations, the two atoms attract one another with an interaction potential proportional to $1/r^6$. As the two atoms come closer, the symmetry requirements of the total wave function allow the formation of either a $^1\Sigma$ or a $^3\Sigma$ state. The singlet (attractive) state corresponds to the usual homopolar binding and has force constants, $\sigma = 0.5°$ Å and $\epsilon/k = 51{,}000°$K. One collision out of every four follows this potential curve. The triplet state corresponds to the first excited state of the hydrogen molecule (a state in which the molecules repel one another except at large separations) and has force constants,[11] $\sigma = 3.5$ Å and $\epsilon/k = 3.8°$K. Three out of every four collisions follow this potential.

Inasmuch as the transport properties of these gases cannot be described by the Lennard-Jones (6-12) potential it is convenient to discuss them in terms of the results for simple potentials. In § 8.3 it is shown that for molecules which repel each other according to an inverse power law, the coefficient of viscosity assumes the simple form:

$$\eta = k'T^s \tag{8.4–6}$$

The constants k' and s (the "temperature index") are determined by fitting the experimental data. Also, for molecules which obey the Sutherland model, it is shown that the viscosity is given approximately by

$$\eta = k_S\sqrt{T}/[1 + (S/T)] \tag{8.4–7}$$

in which k_S and S (the *Sutherland constant*) are adjustable parameters. The values of k' and s as well as k_S and S are given in Table 8.4–4 for a number of substances for which it was impossible to find Lennard-Jones potential parameters.

A better understanding of the formulae given in Eqs. 8.4–6 and 7 may be obtained by comparing them with the results for the Lennard-Jones potential. It is thus possible to obtain the variation of s and S with the

[11] Rough quantum mechanical calculation of J. O. Hirschfelder (unpublished).

reduced temperature, T^*. The results of such a comparison are shown in Fig. 8.4–7. The wide variation of the "constants," s and S, with temperature certainly indicates that these simple formulae should not be used for more than interpolation over small ranges in temperature, particularly if force constants for the Lennard-Jones (6-12) potential are known for the gas under consideration. It is also clear that if S/T is greater than 1.1 or if s is greater than 1.01, it is impossible to choose an ϵ/k which can be used in the Lennard-Jones (6-12) potential. There are a number of such gases, some of which are listed in Table 8.4–4.

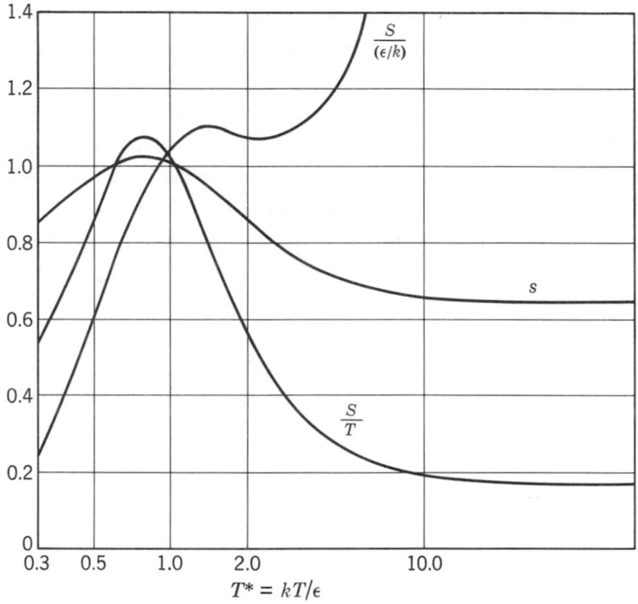

Fig. 8.4–7. Temperature dependence of Sutherland's constant S and the temperature index s.

c. The coefficient of viscosity for mixtures

In order to calculate the viscosity of a binary mixture with Eq. 8.2–22 it is necessary to know the force constants, ϵ and σ, describing the interaction between pairs of like molecules and pairs of unlike molecules. The forces between like molecules may be obtained from the experimental viscosity measurements of pure substances, and, in principle, it is possible to calculate the forces between the unlike pairs of molecules from the viscosity of a binary mixture. However, as in the determination of forces between dissimilar pairs from virial coefficients of mixtures, it is necessary to have extremely accurate data for both the pure components and their

TABLE 8.4–4

VISCOSITY OF ANOMALOUS GASES

$\eta \times 10^7 = k'T^s$

$\eta \times 10^7 = k_S T^{\frac{1}{2}} / [1 + (S/T)]$

Gas	Temperature Range (°K)	k'	s	k_S	S	S/T (*a*)	Reference for Viscosity Data
H_2O	300–400	2.039	1.079	140.2	459.4	1.313	*b*
	500–600	1.227	1.164	235.8	1051.	1.911	
	600–700	1.598	1.123	244.4	1108.	1.705	
NH_3	300–400	1.203	1.181	202.7	740.7	2.116	*b*
	500–600	2.576	1.053	189.4	684.3	1.244	
	600–700	5.207	0.9427	164.7	518.7	0.7980	
HI	300–400	6.889	0.9837	221.9	312.9	0.8940	*c*
	400–500	10.42	0.9152	229.4	334.4	0.7431	
HBr	300–400	5.004	1.040	245.3	376.2	1.075	*b*
HCN	300–400	0.7443	1.215	166.3	836.2	2.389	*b*
	500–600	1.131	1.144	185.4	999.1	1.817	
$HgCl_2$	500–600	1.521	1.180	351.6	1191.	2.165	*b*
	600–700	4.841	1.000	248.1	656.5	1.010	
	750–850	3.406	1.057	314.1	982.8	1.229	
n-C_7H_{16}	350–450	2.163	0.9789	72.73	363.2	0.9080	*c*
	450–550	0.6715	1.172	133.1	1022.	2.044	

[a] Sutherland constant divided by the temperature in the middle of the indicated temperature range.

[b] H. Braune and R. Linke, *Z. physik. Chem.*, **A148** (1930) p. 195.

[c] Landolt-Börnstein, *Physikalisch-Chemische Tabellen.*

mixtures. The easiest and most accurate way to get force constants between unlike molecules is from the coefficient of diffusion as a function of temperature. Since practically no measurements of this sort have ever been made, it is customary to make use of the empirical "combining laws" which relate the force constants between unlike molecules to those between like molecules:

$$\sigma_{ij} = \tfrac{1}{2}(\sigma_i + \sigma_j) \tag{8.4–8}$$

$$\epsilon_{ij} = \sqrt{\epsilon_i \epsilon_j} \tag{8.4–9}$$

These relations are discussed in § 3.6b in connection with the calculation of the second virial coefficient for mixtures. To indicate the sort of agreement which we can expect in calculating the viscosity of mixtures with these combining laws, a comparison between calculated and experimental results is given in Table 8.4–5 for two gas mixtures. A numerical example is given to illustrate how the calculations of the viscosities of binary mixtures are made.

TABLE 8.4–5

VISCOSITIES OF BINARY GAS MIXTURES[a]

$\eta \times 10^7$ g cm^{-1}sec^{-1}

Argon-Neon

T(°K)	%A	0.0	26.80	60.91	74.20	100.0
293.16	Exptl[b]	3092	2808	2504	2401	2213
	Calcd	3070	2795	2493	2390	2208
373.16	Exptl	3623	3313	2990	2885	2693
	Calcd	3566	3281	2963	2853	2660
473.16	Exptl	4220	3890	3529	3413	3222
	Calcd	4170	3847	3495	3375	3164

Oxygen-Carbon Monoxide

T(°K)	%O_2	0.0	23.37	42.01	77.33	100.0
300.06	Exptl[c]	1776	1841	1900	1998	2057
	Calcd	1771	1840	1896	2003	2073
400.06	Exptl	2183	2268	2343	2482	2568
	Calcd	2178	2263	2331	2464	2550
500.06	Exptl	2548	2650	2741	2908	3017
	Calcd	2539	2638	2717	2871	2972

[a] Extensive comparisons of experimental and calculated results have been given by J. O. Hirschfelder, R. B. Bird, and E. L. Spotz, *Chem. Rev.*, **44**, 205 (1949).

[b] M. Trautz and H. E. Binkele, *Ann. Physik* (5) **5**, 561 (1930).

[c] M. Trautz and A. Melster, *Ann. Physik* (5), **7**, 409 (1930).

Illustrative Example

Problem. Calculate the viscosity of a mixture of 23.37 mole per cent N_2 and 76.63 mole per cent CO at 226.9°C.

Solution. From Table I–A the force constants for the pure substances may be obtained. The force constants for the interaction between unlike pairs are obtained from the empirical combining laws given in Eqs. 8.4–8, 9. The force constants needed in the calculation may be summarized thus:

$$N_2: \quad \sigma_1 = 3.681\ \text{Å} \qquad \epsilon_1/k = 91.5°\text{K}$$

$$CO: \quad \sigma_2 = 3.706\ \text{Å} \qquad \epsilon_2/k = 88.0°\text{K}$$

$$N_2\text{-}CO: \quad \sigma_{12} = 3.694\ \text{Å} \qquad \epsilon_{12}/k = 89.7°\text{K}$$

For $T = 226.9°\text{C} = 500.1°\text{K}$ the reduced temperatures are $T_1^* = 5.466$, $T_2^* = 5.683$, $T_{12}^* = 5.575$. From the tabulated functions for the Lennard-Jones (6-12) potential (Tables I–M and I–N) we find:

$$\Omega_1^{(2,2)\star}(5.466) = 0.9127$$

$$\Omega_2^{(2,2)\star}(5.683) = 0.9060$$

$$\Omega_{12}^{(2,2)\star}(5.575) = 0.9093$$

$$\text{A}_{12}^{\star}(5.575) = 1.102$$

From these quantities the following η's may be found:

$$[\eta_1]_1 \times 10^7 = 2555 \qquad \text{(Eq. 8.2–18)}$$

$$[\eta_2]_1 \times 10^7 = 2539 \qquad \text{(Eq. 8.2–18)}$$

$$[\eta_{12}]_1 \times 10^7 = 2546 \qquad \text{(Eq. 8.2–21)}$$

The concentration dependence of the viscosity of N_2-CO mixtures at 226.9°C is then given by

$$[\eta_{\text{mix}}]_1 \times 10^7 = \frac{16613x_1^2 + 33214x_1x_2 + 16611x_2^2}{6.5023x_1^2 + 13.0455x_1x_2 + 6.5423x_2^2}$$

For $x_1 = 0.2337$ and $x_2 = 0.7663$, it is found that $[\eta_{\text{mix}}]_1 \times 10^7 = 2542\ \text{g cm}^{-1}\ \text{sec}^{-1}$. The experimental válue given in Landolt-Börnstein, *Physikalisch-Chemische Tabellen* is $\eta \times 10^7 = 2550\ \text{g cm}^{-1}\ \text{sec}^{-1}$.

Equation 8.2–25 is a formula for the coefficient of viscosity for a multicomponent mixture. In order to use this, we need the tables of $\Omega^{(l,s)\star}$ and $\text{A}^\star$ and also the force constants between all pairs of like and unlike molecules. A comparison of the calculated and experimental results for a ternary mixture is made in Table 8.4–6, where it may be seen that the agreement is within about 1 per cent. In Table 8.4–7 a further comparison is made for some industrial gas mixtures. The agreement in more than half the cases is excellent. For some of the mixtures discrepancies may be due to errors in the gas analysis. The calculated values for these multicomponent gas systems are accurate to within approximately 1 per cent.

TABLE 8.4–6

VISCOSITY OF A TERNARY GAS MIXTURE

T(°K)	Composition in Volume Per Cent			$[\eta]_1 \times 10^7$ in g cm^{-1} sec^{-1}	
	Ne	A	He	Calculated[a]	Experimental[b]
193	55.76	26.70	17.54	2718	2740
	31.93	32.13	35.94	2562	2569
	21.66	58.51	19.83	2429	2411
	21.89	23.82	54.29	2500	2504
373	55.76	26.70	17.54	3205	3237
	31.93	32.13	35.94	3025	3044
	21.66	58.51	19.83	2895	2886
	21.89	23.82	54.29	2938	2957
473	55.76	26.70	17.54	3752	3790
	31.93	32.13	35.94	3551	3574
	21.66	58.51	19.83	3425	3415
	21.89	23.82	54.29	3449	3470

[a] Calculated according to Eq. 8.2–25.

[b] M. Trautz and K. F. Kipphan, *Ann. Physik*, **2**, 746 (1929).

Illustrative Example

Problem. Compute the coefficient of viscosity for the ternary gaseous mixture 50 per cent CH_4, 35 per cent N_2, and 15 per cent O_2, at one atmosphere pressure and $T = 380$°K. Use both Eq. 8.2–25 and Eq. 8.2–30 and compare the results obtained by the two methods.

Solutions. (a) In order to use Eq. 8.2–25 it is necessary to compute the elements H_{ij} from Eqs. 8.2–26 and 27. To do this the six possible interactions between the three chemical species must be considered. The force constants needed for the calculations, the tabulated functions, and some of the intermediate calculations are shown in Table 8.4–8. This table illustrates how problems of this sort may be organized for computation. After the H_{ij} have been computed the evaluation of the ratio of determinants gives $[\eta_{\text{mix}}]_1 \times 10^7 = 1776$ g/cm sec.

(b) The information contained in Table 8.4–8 may also be used to compute the viscosity according to Eq. 8.2–30, when the latter is rewritten in the form:

$$[\eta_{\text{mix}}]_1 = \sum_{i=1}^{\nu} \frac{x_i^2}{\dfrac{x_i^2}{[\eta_i]_1} + 2.308 \displaystyle\sum_{\substack{k=1 \\ k \neq i}}^{\nu} \frac{x_i x_k}{A_{ik}^\star [\eta_{ik}]_1} \frac{M_k}{M_i + M_k}} \tag{8.2–30a}$$

in which for this problem $\nu = 3$. This formula gives $[\eta_{\text{mix}}]_1 \times 10^7 = 1756$ g/cm sec.

TABLE 8.4-7

VISCOSITIES OF MULTICOMPONENT MIXTURES INDUSTRIAL GASES

Composition (Volume %)							Temp. (°K)	$\eta \times 10^7$		Ref.
CO_2	O_2	CO	H_2	CH_4	N_2	Heavier Hydro-carbons		Exptl	Calcd[a]	
8.6	2.3				89.1		293	1756	1761	*b*
13.3	3.9				82.8		293	1749	1765	*b*
6.2	10.7				83.1		293	1793	1789	*b*
10.4		28.5	1.6		59.5		293	1738	1798	*b*
10.80	2.00		2.20		85.00		300.5	1827	1792	*c*
							524.5	2715	2661	
							973	4117	4008	
							1279	4856	4753	
6.70	0.10	7.80	2.20		83.20		307.5	1842	1835	*c*
							519	2655	2653	
							975	4048	4019	
							1285	4808	4783	
6.40	3.00	0.30	0.70		89.60		314	1904	1856	*c*
							518	2706	2644	
							974.5	4113	4017	
							1287	4895	4777	
6.0	0.10	25.70	11.50		56.70		302	1823	1829	*c*
							526	2686	2696	
							976	4041	4042	
							1283	4777	4821	
10.6		29.8	3.9	0.3	55.4		293	1743	1794	*b*
8.9		30.7	3.3	0.4	56.7		293	1747	1797	*b*
8.7		32.8	1.5	0.2	56.8		293	1749	1802	*b*
3.70	0.30	27.10	9.50	1.60	57.80		300.5	1815	1816	*c*
							565.5	2819	2823	
							981	4045	4041	
							1282	4792	4803	
1.7	0.9	6.0	57.5	24.0	7.8	2.1	293	1262	1254	*b*
2.1	0.9	5.7	53.0	24.3	11.7	2.3	293	1304	1290	*b*
2.0	1.4	4.6	54.9	23.5	11.6	2.0	293	1310	1398	*b*
3.3	0.6	3.8	51.3	29.6	10.0	1.4	293	1332	1269	*b*
2.2	0.6	4.1	53.1	29.5	9.2	1.3	293	1306	1254	*b*
2.2	1.0	4.0	52.3	29.9	9.4	1.2	293	1307	1261	*b*
2.5	0.8	14.9	53.0	18.1	9.1	1.6	293	1355	1373	*b*
4.8	0.3	26.4	17.2	2.6	48.2	0.5	293	1714	1743	*b*
3.5	0.3	27.3	14.4	3.7	50.0	0.8	293	1712	1732	*b*
3.1	0.5	28.6	17.7	4.2	45.0	0.9	293	1715	1719	*b*

[a] Calculated according to Eq. 8.2-25.

[b] F. Herning and L. Zipperer, *Gas- und Wasserfach*, **79**, 49–54, 69–73 (1936).

[c] Schmid, *Gas- und Wasserfach*, **85**, 92 (1942).

TABLE 8.4–8

CALCULATION OF THE VISCOSITY OF A TERNARY GAS MIXTURE FROM EQ. 8.2–25 FOR THE LENNARD-JONES (6-12) POTENTIAL

Components	*Mole Fractions*	*Molecular Weights*
1 = CH_4	$x_1 = 0.50$	$M_1 = 16.04$
2 = N_2	$x_2 = 0.35$	$M_2 = 28.02$
3 = O_2	$x_3 = 0.15$	$M_3 = 32.00$

i	j	σ_{ij} (Å)	ϵ_{ij}/k (°K)	$T_{ij}^* = kT/\epsilon_{ij}$	$\Omega_{ij}^{(2,2)\star}$ [c]	$\frac{2M_iM_j}{(M_i+M_j)}$ [d]	$\sqrt{\frac{2M_iM_jT}{(M_i+M_j)}}$ [e]	$[\eta_{ij}]_1 \times 10^7$ (g/cm sec)	$A_{ij}^\star$ [h]	$\frac{M_j}{M_i}$	$\frac{M_iM_j}{(M_i+M_j)^2}$	H_{ij}
1	1	3.822[a]	136.5[a]	2.784	1.060	16.04	78.07	1346[f]	—	—	—	+4118[i]
1	2	3.752[b]	111.7[b]	3.402	1.007	20.40	88.05	1658[g]	1.096	1.747	0.2315	−254[j]
1	3	3.628[b]	124.3[b]	3.057	1.034	21.37	90.11	1767[g]	1.095	1.995	0.2224	−99[j]
2	2	3.681[a]	91.46[a]	4.155	0.9622	28.02	103.2	2113[f]	—	—	—	+1923[i]
2	3	3.557[b]	101.8[b]	3.733	0.9851	29.88	106.6	2283[g]	1.097	1.142	0.2489	−59[j]
3	3	3.433[a]	113.2[a]	3.357	1.010	32.00	110.3	2473[f]	—	—	—	+754[i]

[a] Tabulated in Table I–A: Force constants from viscosity.
[b] Use the empirical combining laws in Eqs. 8.4–8 and 9.
[c] Tabulated in Table I–M.
[d] This equals M_i for $i = j$.
[e] This equals $\sqrt{M_iT}$ for $i = j$.
[f] From Eq. 8.2–18.
[g] From Eq. 8.2–21.
[h] Tabulated in Table I–N.
[i] From Eq. 8.2–26.
[j] From Eq. 8.2–27.

d. The coefficient of thermal conductivity

The coefficient of thermal conductivity for monatomic gases may be calculated from Eq. 8.2–31 in the first approximation and from Eq. 8.2–32 in the third approximation. The correction factor, $f_\lambda^{(3)}$, is given for the Lennard-Jones (6-12) potential in Table I–P. If the parameters σ and ϵ are known, then $[\lambda]_3$ may be readily computed. For the noble gases, a comparison of the values of the coefficient of thermal conductivity calculated using the force constants obtained from viscosity data (Table I–A) with some experimental values is made in Table 8.4–9.

TABLE 8.4–9

THERMAL CONDUCTIVITY OF MONATOMIC GASES: COMPARISON OF EXPERIMENTAL VALUES WITH THOSE CALCULATED FOR THE LENNARD-JONES (6-12) POTENTIAL

$\lambda \times 10^7$ in cal cm^{-1} sec^{-1} deg^{-1}

T (°K)	He		Ne		A		Kr		Xe	
	Calcd[a]	Exptl[b]	Calcd	Exptl	Calcd	Exptl	Calcd	Exptl	Calcd	Exptl
90.2	1711	1655	498	489	137	141	68		40	
194.7	2817	2706	878	876	292	293	148	152	85	91
273.2	3507	3390[c] 3406 3438[d] 3510[e]	1105	1092[f] 1110	392	385[d] 390[g] 394	206	190[f] 208	120	123 124[f]
373.2	4296	4165	1356	1357	504	506	273	272	161	168
491.2	5135	4947	1608	1595	619	614	343	340	204	208
579.1	5711	5504	1791	1789	696	685	390	388	234	237

[a] Calculated values are for $[\lambda]_3$ according to Eq. 8.2–32. Force constants used are those listed in Table I–A from viscosity data.

[b] Unless otherwise indicated the experimental values are those of W. G. Kannuluik and E. H. Carman, *Proc. Phys. Soc.* (*London*), **65B**, 701 (1952).

[c] H. L. Johnston and E. R. Grilly, *J. Chem. Phys.*, **14**, 233 (1946).

[d] S. Weber, *Ann. Physik* (4), **54**, 325 (1917).

[e] B. G. Dickins, *Proc. Roy. Soc.* (*London*), **A143**, 517 (1934).

[f] Landolt-Börnstein, *Physikalisch-Chemische Tabellen.*

[g] T. L. Ibbs and A. A. Hirst, *Proc. Roy. Soc.* (*London*), **A123**, 134 (1929).

For polyatomic gases, Eq. 8.2–33, which includes the factor $\left(\frac{4}{15}\frac{\tilde{C}_v}{R} + \frac{3}{5}\right)$ to take into account approximately the transfer of energy between translational and internal degrees of freedom, offers the best means at present of computing $[\lambda]_1$. In Table 8.4–10 a comparison is given of experimental values of λ for several polyatomic gases with values of $[\lambda]_1$ calculated from Eq. 8.2–33. The force constants used for the pure gases are from viscosity data. Also shown there are values of the factor $\left(\frac{4}{15}\frac{\tilde{C}_v}{R} + \frac{3}{5}\right)$.

TABLE 8.4–10

THERMAL CONDUCTIVITY OF POLYATOMIC GASES: COMPARISON OF EXPERIMENTAL VALUES WITH THOSE CALCULATED FOR THE LENNARD-JONES (6-12) MODEL (WITH THE EUCKEN CORRECTION)[a]

Gas	T(°K)	$\lambda \times 10^7$ (cal/cm sec °K)		$\left(\frac{4}{15}\frac{\tilde{C}_v}{R}+\frac{3}{5}\right)$	Ref. to Experimental λ Data
		Calcd[b]	Exptl		
H_2	100	1618	1625	1.057[c]	*d*
	200	3053	3064	1.217[c]	*d*
	273	3878	{3965 4040}	1.255	{*d* *e*
	300	4140	4227	1.1259	*d*
O_2	100	224	216	1.267	*d*
	200	436	438	1.268	*d*
	273	568	{584 577}	1.273	{*d* *f*
	300	615	635	1.278	*d*
CO_2	200	235	227	1.370	*d*
	273	345	{349 360}	1.487	{*d* *e*
	300	386	398	1.527	*d*
CH_4	100	255	254	1.400	*d*
	200	509	522	1.407	*d*
	273	697	{734 720}	1.460	{*d* *f*
	300	764	819	1.479	*d*
NO	150	347	321	1.333	*d*
	200	445	425	1.310	*d*
	273	576	567	1.297	*d*
	300	619	619	1.293	*d*

[a] The values of $\tilde{C}_v$ needed for the calculation of the "Eucken correction factor" $\left(\frac{4}{15}\frac{\tilde{C}_v}{R}+\frac{3}{5}\right)$ were obtained from the National Bureau of Standards Tables, American Petroleum Institute Research Project No. 44, June 30, 1949 (Washington, D.C.)

[b] The calculated values are $[\lambda]_1^{\text{Eucken}}$, computed from Eq. 8.2–33. The force constants from viscosity data (Table I–A) were used for the calculations.

[c] The values of $\tilde{C}_v$ at 100°K and 200°K for H_2 are the values for a fixed ortho-para ratio of 3 : 1, and are not values taken from the National Bureau of Standards Tables, ref. *a*, above.

[d] H. L. Johnston and E. R. Grilly, *J. Chem. Phys.*, **14**, 233 (1946).

[e] T. L. Ibbs and A. A. Hirst, *Proc. Roy. Soc.* (*London*), **A123**, 134 (1929).

[f] S. Weber, *Ann. Physik*. (4), **54**, 437 (1917).

From these it can be seen that, if the heat capacity is known as a function of the temperature, reasonable approximations to the coefficient of thermal conductivity of polyatomic gases may be obtained, using Eq. 8.2–33. The following numerical example illustrates the calculation of the coefficient of thermal conductivity for pure substances.

Illustrative Example

Problem. Calculate the coefficient of thermal conductivity at 273.16°K of (a) pure argon and (b) pure hydrogen.

Solution. (a) The force constants for argon are found in Table I–A to be:

$$\sigma = 3.418 \text{ Å}$$

$$\epsilon/k = 124°\text{K}$$

Then $T^* = 273.16/124 = 2.203$. From the tabulated functions for the Lennard-Jones (6-12) potential (Tables I–M and I–P), we find:

$$\Omega^{(2,2)\star}(2.203) = 1.138$$

$$f_{\lambda}^{(3)}(2.203) = 1.003$$

From Eq. 8.2–31, 32 we get then:

$$[\lambda]_3 \times 10^7 = 393 \text{ cal/cm sec °K}$$

This compares favorably with the experimental values given in Table 8.4–9.

(b) For H_2 the force constants are:

$$\sigma = 2.968 \text{ Å}$$

$$\epsilon/k = 33.3°\text{K}$$

Then $T^* = 273.16/33.3 = 8.203$, for which we find from the tabulated functions:

$$\Omega^{(2,2)\star}(8.203) = 0.8506$$

We then calculate $[\lambda]_1$ from Eq. 8.2–31:

$$[\lambda]_1 \times 10^7 = 3090 \text{ cal/cm sec °K}$$

This has to be multiplied by the Eucken correction factor:

$$\left[\frac{4}{15}\frac{\tilde{C}_v}{R} + \frac{3}{5}\right] = \left[\frac{4}{15}\frac{4.883}{1.987} + \frac{3}{5}\right] = 1.255$$

The final result is then:

$$[\lambda]_1^{\text{Eucken}} \times 10^7 = 3878 \text{ cal/cm sec °K}$$

A comparison with experimental values is given in Table 8.4–10.

The thermal conductivity of a mixture of two monatomic gases is given by Eq. 8.2–36. If force constants for the pure gases, obtained from viscosity data, are known, the combining laws, Eqs. 8.4–8 and 9, may be used to approximate the force constants between the unlike molecules.

In Table 8.4–11, the experimentally observed values of λ for an argon-helium mixture are shown, along with the values calculated according to Eq. 8.2–36. Force constants are from viscosity data (Table I–A) and Eqs. 8.4–8 and 9. The agreement is reasonably good. Also shown there are the experimental values of the viscosity of the mixture and a tabulation of the quantity $\frac{15}{4}\frac{R}{x_1M_1 + x_2M_2}\eta_{\text{exptl}}$. A comparison of the values of this quantity with the observed coefficients of thermal conductivity points up the fact that the thermal conductivity of a mixture is not simply proportional to the viscosity of that mixture.

At present the best method for calculating the coefficient of thermal conductivity of binary mixtures of polyatomic gases is by means of Eq. 8.2–40, that is, by calculating λ_{mix} by means of the monatomic gas-mixture formula and multiplying by a correction factor. A second but less satisfactory method consists of multiplying the viscosity of the mixture by an appropriate factor according to Eq. 8.2–41. We compare the calculated results from these two methods with the experimental data in Table 8.4–11.

TABLE 8.4–11

COMPARISON OF CALCULATED AND EXPERIMENTAL λ VALUES FOR BINARY GAS MIXTURES[a]

Monatomic Gases

Gas Mixture (Temp °K)	Percent of Lighter Constituent	$\eta \times 10^7$ g cm^{-1} sec^{-1}	$\lambda \times 10^7$ cal cm^{-1} sec^{-1} deg^{-1}		$\frac{15}{4}\frac{R}{(x_1M_1+x_2M_2)}\eta_{\text{exptl}} \times 10^7$
		Exptl	Exptl	Calcd acc to Eq 8.2–36	
He-A (273.16)	0.0	2089[b]	389[c]	391	390
	27.04	2173	742	755	536
	45.37	2206	1077	1102	695
	84.68	2118	2320	2439	1660
	94.61	2017	2939	3046	2530
	100.00	1923	3386	3466	3580

[a] Force constants for all calculations are from Table I–A.

[b] M. Trautz and H. E. Binkele, *Ann. Physik* (5), **5**, 561 (1930).

[c] J. Wachsmith, *Phys. Z.*, **9**, 235 (1908).

TABLE 8.4–11 (*continued*)

Polyatomic Gases

Gas Mixture (Temp °K)	Percent of Lighter Constituent	$\eta \times 10^7$ g cm^{-1} sec^{-1}	$\lambda \times 10^7$ cal cm^{-1} sec^{-1} deg^{-1}		
		Exptl	Exptl	Calcd acc to Eq. 8.2–40	Calcd acc to Eq. 8.2–41
H_2-CO_2 (273.16)	0.0	1369[d]	360[e]	360	360
	10.0	1386	510	515	427
	14.2	1392	570	586	461
	25.0	1406	770	785	565
	35.5	1415	1000	1007	701
	50.0	1417	1350	1377	977
	75.0	1341	2270	2301	1936
	90.1	1163	3150	3191	3154
	100.0	854	4040	4040	4040
H_2-CO (273.16)	0.0	1706[f]	530[e]	530	530
	16.3	1715	800	770	690
	27.2	1649	1030	965	805
	56.6	1538	1800	1701	1425
	63.4	1488	2090	1934	1656
	79.4	1303	2700	2633	2416
	100.0	853	4040	4040	4040
H_2-N_2 (273.16)	0.0	1688[f]	550[e]	550	550
	15.9	1670	800	786	698
	39.0	1600	1270	1241	1028
	65.2	1449	1940	2023	1753
	79.5	1285	2520	2655	2449
	80.3	1274	2570	2996	2498
	100.0	853	4040	4040	4040
H_2-N_2O (273.16)	0.0	1358[d]	380[e]	380	380
	7.5	1366	480	502	430
	20.9	1379	710	745	545
	38.6	1388	1070	1131	775
	59.9	1369	1700	1748	1282
	81.2	1273	2720	2671	2397
	100.0	854	4040	4040	4040

[d] M. Trautz and F. Kurz, *Ann. Physik* (5), **9**, 981 (1931).
[e] T. L. Ibbs and A. A. Hirst, *Proc. Roy. Soc.* (*London*), **A123**, 134 (1929).
[f] A. van Itterbeek, O. van Paemel, and J. van Lierde, *Physica*, **13**, 88 (1947).

TABLE 8.4–11 (*continued*)

Gas Mixture (Temp °K)	Percent of Lighter Constituent	$\eta \times 10^7$ g cm^{-1} sec^{-1}	$\lambda \times 10^7$ cal cm^{-1} sec^{-1} deg^{-1}		
		Exptl	Exptl	Calcd acc to Eq. 8.2–40	Calcd acc to Eq. 8.2–41
H_2-O_2 (295)	0.0	2045[f]	625[g]	625	625
	3.36	2044	651	676	657
	25.0	1994	1112	1060	920
	50.0	1855	1827	1675	1441
	75.0	1588	2749	2606	2496
	94.74	1088	3744	3765	3850
	100.0	887	4180	4180	4180
H_2-A (273.16)	0.0	2135[h]	390[e]	390	390
	9.0	2126	550	509	451
	18.0	2111	730	647	527
	40.0	2020	1260	1087	802
	60.0	1863	1870	1676	1272
	80.2	1480	2700	2588	2148
	100.0	854	4040	4040	4040
N_2-A (273.16)	0.0	2097[i]	385[j]	385	385
	20.38	2010	417	440	413
	35.87	1943	444	476	436
	61.08	1833	490	524	480
	78.04	1758	524	547	514
	100.00	1659	566	566	566

[g] A. Wassiljewa, *Phys. Z.*, **5**, 737 (1904).
[h] Landolt-Börnstein, *Physikalisch-Chemische Tabellen.*
[i] The values of the viscosity of the N_2-A mixtures were calculated by Eq. 8.2–22.
[j] S. Weber, *Ann. Physik* (4), **54**, 325 (1917).

e. The coefficient of diffusion[12]

To calculate the coefficient of diffusion $\mathscr{D}_{12}$ for a pair of gases from Eq. 8.2–44 the force constants σ_{12} and ϵ_{12} between the unlike pairs of molecules in the gas must be known. At the present time, the best approximation to these quantities is given by the combining laws, Eqs. 8.4–8 and 9. In Table 8.4–12 a comparison is made between calculated

[12] A complete discussion of the present experimental and theoretical knowledge of ordinary and thermal diffusion in many types of gaseous and liquid systems is given by W. Jost, *Diffusion in Solids, Liquids, and Gases*, New York, Academic Press, 1952.

TABLE 8.4–12

CALCULATED AND OBSERVED DIFFUSION COEFFICIENTS AT 1 ATM.

Note. The σ_{12} and ϵ_{12}/k listed here were calculated, using the combining laws of Eqs. 8.4–8 and 9, and the force constants for the pure components were obtained from experimental viscosity data. Equation 8.2–44 was used for the calculation of the $[\mathscr{D}_{12}]_1$.

Gas Pair	σ_{12} (Å)	ϵ_{12}/k (°K)	T (°K)	Calculated $[\mathscr{D}_{12}]_1$ ($cm^2\ sec^{-1}$)	Experimental $\mathscr{D}_{12}$ ($cm^2\ sec^{-1}$)	Ref. for Experimental Data
A-He	3.059	21.3	273.2	0.653	0.641	*a*
A-H_2	3.193	64.3	293.2	0.770	0.77	*b*
A-N_2	3.550	106	293.2	0.188	0.20	*b*
A-O_2	3.426	118	293.2	0.188	0.20	*b*
A-CO_2	3.707	153	293.2	0.136	0.14	*b*
N_2-H_2	3.325	55.2	273.2	0.656	0.674	*a*
			288.2	0.718	0.743	*c*
			293.2	0.739	0.76	*b*
N_2-O_2	3.557	102	273.2	0.175	0.181	*a*
			293.2	0.199	0.22	*b*
N_2-CO	3.636	100	273.2	0.174	0.192	*a*
N_2-CO_2	3.839	132	273.2	0.130	0.144	*a*
			288.2	0.143	0.158	*c*
			293.2	0.147	0.16	*b*
			298.2	0.152	0.165	*d*
N_2-C_2H_4	3.957	137	298.2	0.156	0.163	*d*
N_2-C_2H_6	4.050	145	298.2	0.144	0.148	*d*
N_2-nC_4H_{10}	4.339	194	298.2	0.0986	0.0960	*d*
N_2-*iso*-C_4H_{10}	4.511	169	298.2	0.0970	0.0908	*d*
N_2-*cis*-butene-2	4.467	188	298.2	0.0947	0.095	*d*
H_2-O_2	3.201	61.4	273.2	0.689	0.697	*a*
H_2-CO	3.279	60.6	273.2	0.661	0.651	*a*
H_2-CO_2	3.482	79.5	273.2	0.544	0.550	*a*
			288.2	0.597	0.619	*c*
			293.2	0.616	0.60	*b*
			298.2	0.634	0.646	*d*
H_2-N_2O	3.424	85.6	273.2	0.552	0.535	*a*
H_2-SF_6	3.922[e]	89.1[e]	298.2	0.473	0.420	*d*
H_2-CH_4	3.425	67.4	273.2	0.607	0.625	*a*
			298.2	0.705	0.726	*d*
H_2-C_2H_4	3.600	82.6	298.2	0.595	0.602	*d*
H_2-C_2H_6	3.693	87.5	298.2	0.556	0.537	*d*
H_2-*cis*-butene-2	4.111[f]	113[f]	298.2	0.413	0.378	*d*
CO-O_2	3.512	112	273.2	0.175	0.185	*a*
CO_2-O_2	3.715	147	273.2	0.128	0.139	*a*
			293.2	0.146	0.16	*b*
CO_2-CO	3.793	145	273.2	0.128	0.137	*a*
CO_2-N_2O	3.938	204	273.2	0.092	0.096	*a*
CO_2-CH_4	3.939	161	273.2	0.138	0.153	*a*

[a] S. Chapman and T. G. Cowling, *Mathematical Theory of Non-uniform Gases*, Cambridge University Press (1939).

[b] L. E. Boardman and N. E. Wild, *Proc. Roy. Soc.* (*London*), **A162**, 511 (1937).

[c] L. Waldman, *Naturwissenschaften*, **32**, 223 (1944).

[d] C. A. Boyd, N. Stein, V. Steingrimsson, and W. F. Rumpel, *J. Chem. Phys.*, **19**, 548 (1951).

[e] Force constants of pure SF_6 estimated from critical data.

[f] Force constants of pure cis-butene-2 estimated from boiling point and second virial coefficient.

diffusion coefficients and the corresponding experimental quantities. The agreement is generally quite satisfactory inasmuch as the combining laws have been used to approximate force constants and, furthermore, since the calculated values are for the first approximation only.

In order to calculate the second approximation to the diffusion coefficient, Eq. 8.2–45 must be used. For the Lennard-Jones potential the second approximation differs from the first by not more than 3 per cent for most gas pairs. In the second approximation the diffusion coefficient depends slightly on the concentration (see Appendix A of this chapter), but there are no experimental data sufficiently accurate to examine this concentration dependence.

In the first approximation to the coefficient of diffusion it is only the forces between unlike molecules which occur. This means that the coefficient of diffusion as a function of temperature affords the best method for obtaining the force constants σ_{12} and ϵ_{12} characteristic of the interaction between unlike molecules. At the present time, unfortunately, such experimental data are not available. As soon as measurements of this type are made, the experiments may be analyzed to obtain the force law between unlike molecules in a manner very similar to that described in § 8.4b for obtaining the force law between like molecules from viscosity.

Illustrative Example

Problem. Calculate the coefficient of diffusion for the gas-pair Ne-Xe at 320°K and 2 atm, using the formula for the first approximation to $\mathscr{D}_{12}$.

Solution. From Table I–A we find (letting neon be component 1) that $\epsilon_1/k = 35.7$°K, $\sigma_1 = 2.789$ Å, and $\epsilon_2/k = 229$°K, $\sigma_2 = 4.055$ Å. From Eqs. 8.4–8 and 9 we obtain $\epsilon_{12}/k = 90.42$°K and $\sigma_{12} = 3.422$ Å. For the temperature $T = 320$°K, $T_{12}^* = 3.539$. The molecular weights are $M_1 = 20.183$, $M_2 = 131.30$. From Table I–M, we obtain $\Omega_{12}^{(1,1)\star}(3.539) = 0.9096$. The first approximation to $\mathscr{D}_{12}$, computed from Eq. 8.2–44, is 0.119 cm² sec⁻¹.

The coefficient of self-diffusion $\mathscr{D}$ may be calculated from Eq. 8.2–46 and the force constants σ and ϵ between a pair of like molecules. In Table 8.4–13 we compare the experimental self-diffusion constants with the values calculated from Eq. 8.2–46 and the force constants between like molecules determined from experimental viscosity measurements. In almost all cases the agreement is quite good. This is an excellent illustration of how the force constants determined from one property may be used to calculate another property. In Fig. 8.4–8 is shown a plot of the calculated curve of log $\mathscr{D}^*p^*T^{*-3/2}$ against log T^* along with the experimental points for several substances. The correction factor $f_{\mathscr{D}}^{(2)}$ given in Eq. 8.2–47 for the higher approximations to $\mathscr{D}$ is tabulated in Table I–P.

TABLE 8.4–13

COMPARISON OF CALCULATED AND OBSERVED SELF-DIFFUSION COEFFICIENTS AT 1 ATM.

Gas	T(°K)	$[\mathscr{D}]_2$ ($cm^2\ sec^{-1}$) [a]	Experimental $\mathscr{D}$ ($cm^2\ sec^{-1}$)	Ref. for Experimental Data
Ne	353.2	0.669	0.703 ± 0.005	*b*
	273.2	0.435	0.452 ± 0.003	*b*
	77.7	0.0491	0.0492 ± 0.0004	*b*
A	353.2	0.245	0.249 ± 0.003	*b*
	273.2	0.154	0.156 ± 0.002	*b*
	273.2	0.154	0.158 ± 0.002	*c*
	77.7	0.0133	0.0134 ± 0.0002	*b*
Kr	293.	0.093	0.093 ± 0.0045	*d*
Xe	300.5	0.0571	0.0576 ± 0.0009	*e*
H_2	273.	1.243	1.285 ± 0.002	*f*
	85.	0.167	0.172 ± 0.008	*f*
	20.4	0.0104	0.00816 ± 0.0002	*f*
N_2	353.2	0.273	0.287 ± 0.009	*b*
	273.2	0.174	0.185 ± 0.006	*b*
	273.2	0.174	0.172 ± 0.002	*g*
	77.7	0.0161	0.0168 ± 0.0003	*b*
O_2	353.2	0.279	0.301 ± 0.004	*b*
	273.2	0.176	0.187 ± 0.003	*b*
	273.2	0.176	0.175 ± 0.001	*g*
	77.7	0.0154	0.0153 ± 0.0002	*b*
CH_4	353.2	0.302	0.318 ± 0.006	*b*
	273.2	0.189	0.206 ± 0.005	*b*
	90.2	0.0215	0.0266 ± 0.0023	*b*
CO_2	362.6	0.157	0.1644	*h*
	312.8	0.119	0.1248	*h*
	273.2	0.0920	0.0970	*h*
	194.8	0.0474	0.0516	*h*
HCl	295.	0.127	0.1246	*i*

[a] Calculated according to Eq. 8.2–46, with force constants obtained from viscosity data.
[b] E. B. Winn, *Phys. Rev.*, **80**, 1024 (1950).
[c] F. Hutchinson, *J. Chem. Phys.*, **17**, 1081 (1949).
[d] W. Groth and P. Harteck, *Z. Elektrochem.*, **47**, 167 (1941).
[e] S. Visner, Rept. K–688 (May, 1951) of K–25 Plant, Carbide and Carbon Chemicals Co.
[f] P. Harteck and H. W. Schmidt, *Z. Physik. Chem.*, **21B**, 447 (1933).
[g] E. R. S. Winter, *Trans. Faraday Soc.*, **47**, 342 (1951).
[h] I. Amdur, J. W. Irvine, Jr., E. A. Mason, and J. Ross, *J. Chem. Phys.*, **20**, 436 (1952).
[i] H. Braune and F. Zehle, *Z. Physik. Chem.*, **49B**, 247 (1941).

It would also be possible to analyze data on self-diffusion as a function of temperature to obtain the force constants. At the present time, however, viscosity measurements are more readily obtainable and somewhat more accurate.

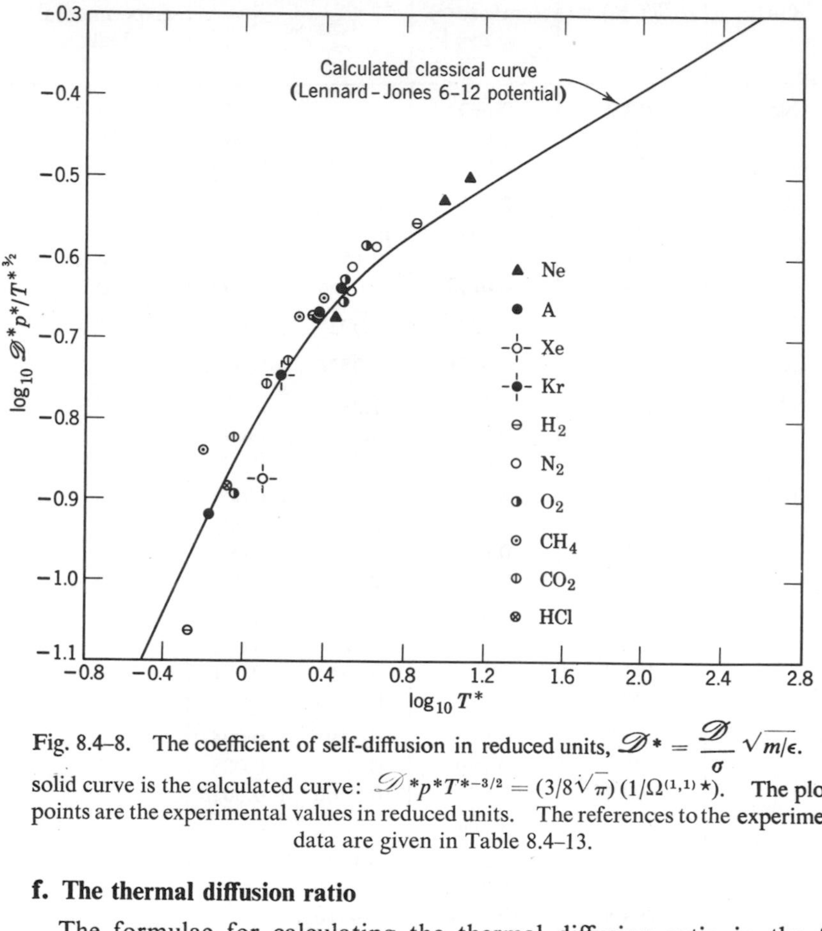

Fig. 8.4–8. The coefficient of self-diffusion in reduced units, $\mathscr{D}^* = \dfrac{\mathscr{D}}{\sigma}\sqrt{m/\epsilon}$. The solid curve is the calculated curve: $\mathscr{D}^*p^*T^{*-3/2} = (3/8\sqrt{\pi})\,(1/\Omega^{(1,1)\star})$. The plotted points are the experimental values in reduced units. The references to the experimental data are given in Table 8.4–13.

f. The thermal diffusion ratio

The formulae for calculating the thermal diffusion ratio in the first approximation are given in Eq. 8.2–50, and the same equations written for heavy isotopic thermal diffusion are given in Eq. 8.2–51. The quantity, $k_T{}^\star$, defined in Eq. 8.1–17, and given for heavy isotopes in Eq. 8.2–52, is tabulated as a function of T^* in Table I–Q. Calculations have not been made for the Lennard-Jones potential for the second approximation to the thermal diffusion. Even in the first approximation, the thermal diffusion is a complicated function of the concentrations and the temperature and depends on the forces between like and unlike pairs of molecules.

When $6c^* - 5$ is zero there is an inversion in the sign of the thermal diffusion ratio. For the Lennard-Jones (6-12) potential it may be seen from Table I–N that there is a temperature inversion at $T^* = 0.4$ and also at $T^* = 0.95$. The latter inversion has been recently observed in the thermal diffusion of H_2-D_2 mixtures.[13]

A comparison of some experimental k_T values with the values calculated by the Lennard-Jones (6-12) potential is given in Table 8.4–14. The agreement is not so good as is obtained for the other transport properties. This probably results from neglecting the higher approximations to k_T, and also from the uncertainty in our knowledge of the forces between the unlike molecules in the gas. In Tables 8.4–15, 16 similar comparisons are made for isotopic thermal diffusion. There the agreement appears to be somwhat better, probably because of the fact that the two inter-diffusing species obey the same force law.

Thermal diffusion data can be used in conjunction with ordinary diffusion data to determine σ_{12} and ϵ_{12} in the Lennard-Jones (6-12) potential which describes the interaction of a pair of dissimilar molecules. This method has been applied by Srivastava and Madan,[14] and the force constants which they obtained for five molecule pairs are given in Table 8.4–17. These parameters are compared with those values obtained by means of the empirical combining laws given in Eqs. 8.4–8 and 9. The rather good agreement serves as additional justification for the use of these combining laws.

Illustrative Example

Problem. A two-bulb thermal diffusion experiment is performed on a gaseous mixture containing 35.6 per cent H_2 and 64.4 per cent Ne.

Calculate the change in concentration produced when one bulb is maintained at 290.4°K and the other at 90.2°K.

Solution. The change in concentration may be obtained from Eq. 8.1–16 or it may be calculated by integrating Eq. 8.1–15 numerically. Both methods are given here.

(a) According to Eq. 8.1–16,

$$\Delta x_1 = -k_T(\bar{T}) \ln (T'/T)$$

in which $\bar{T}$ is a mean temperature which can be approximated by

$$\bar{T} = \frac{TT'}{T' - T} \ln \frac{T'}{T}$$

[13] A. de Troyer, A. van Itterbeek, and A. O. Rietveld, *Physica*, **17**, 938 (1951).

[14] B. N. Srivastava and M. P. Madan, *Proc. Phys. Soc.*, **66**, 27B (1953). Their values of the force constants may be somewhat in error because of the neglect of the second approximation to the thermal diffusion ratio, the expression for which is given in Appendix A of this chapter.

TABLE 8.4–14

COMPARISON OF EXPERIMENTAL k_T VALUES WITH THOSE CALCULATED FOR THE LENNARD-JONES (6-12) POTENTIAL[a,b]

Gas Pair 1-2	Per Cent of Lighter Constituent	$k_T \times 10^2$		$\bar{T}$(°K)	Ref. for Experimental Data
		Exptl	Calcd[c]		
Ne-He	53.8	7.65	8.15	205	*d*
	53.8	7.82	8.28	330	*d*
	53.8	7.83	8.39	365	*d*
	20	5.31	4.53	330	*e*
	30	7.24	6.21	330	*e*
	40	8.64	7.45	330	*e*
	50	9.70	8.15	330	*e*
	60	10.04	8.26	330	*e*
A-He	51.2	9.10	9.44	179	*d*
	51.2	9.20	9.57	205	*d*
	51.2	9.56	9.61	365	*d*
	10	2.50	2.59	330	*e*
	20	4.76	4.94	330	*e*
	30	6.60	6.98	330	*e*
	40	8.10	8.93	330	*e*
	50	9.31	9.79	330	*e*
He-H_2	22.2	2.39	1.98	46	*f*
	81	2.03	2.38	118	*g*
	81	1.79	2.31	358	*g*
	50	4.81	3.74	330	*h*
	60	4.42	3.56	330	*h*
	70	3.50	3.08	330	*h*
	80	2.84	2.31	330	*h*
	90	1.32	1.29	330	*h*
N_2-He	34.5	7.42	7.12	145	*i*
	53.1	9.42	9.23	145	*i*
	34.5	8.31	7.65	261	*i*
	53.1	10.7	9.92	261	*i*
A-Ne	51.2	3.50	3.47	179	*d*
	51.2	3.80	3.85	205	*d*
	51.2	4.15	4.25	261	*d*
	51.2	4.77	4.90	406	*d*
	20	2.33	2.57	324	*e*
	30	3.39	3.53	324	*e*
	40	4.07	4.24	324	*e*
	50	4.57	4.63	324	*e*
	60	4.67	4.68	324	*e*

TABLE 8.4–14 (*continued*)

Gas Pair 1-2	Per Cent of Lighter Constituent	$k_T \times 10^2$		$\bar{T}$(°K)	Ref. for Experimental Data
		Exptl	Calcd[c]		
A-H_2	47	5.14	5.89	167	*j*
	55.6	5.73	6.25	167	*j*
	47	6.35	7.71	258	*j*
	55.6	7.12	8.17	258	*j*
A-N_2	46	1.01	0.624	157	*j*
	62.5	0.842	0.596	157	*j*
	70	0.83	0.536	157	*j*
	46	1.82	1.32	252	*j*
	62.5	1.70	1.28	252	*j*
	70	1.53	1.16	252	*j*
N_2-H_2	29.4	3.95	3.97	143	*j*
	42.0	5.21	5.01	143	*j*
	77.5	4.84	4.44	143	*j*
	29.4	5.48	5.90	264	*j*
	42.0	7.49	7.37	264	*j*
	77.5	6.63	6.36	264	*j*
CO-H_2	24	3.76	3.21	142	*j*
	53	5.83	5.08	142	*j*
	24	4.45	4.81	246	*j*
	53	7.38	7.66	246	*j*
CO_2-H_2	53	6.89	8.39	300	*k*
	53	8.99	9.60	370	*k*

[a] This table is taken from E. R. S Winter, *Trans. of Faraday Soc.*, **46**, Part 2, 81 (1950).

[b] $\bar{T} = \left(\frac{TT'}{T' - T}\right) \ln \left(\frac{T'}{T}\right)$ where T and T' are the temperatures of the cold and hot bulb, respectively. See § 8.1a.

[c] The calculated value is $[k_T]_1$, according to Eq. 8.2–50.

[d] K. E. Grew, *Proc. Roy. Soc.* (*London*), **A189**, 402 (1947).

[e] B. E. Atkins, R. E. Bastick, and T. L. Ibbs, *Proc. Roy. Soc.* (*London*), **A172**, 142 (1939).

[f] A. van Itterbeek, O. van Paemel, and J. van Lierde, *Physica*, **13**, 231 (1947).

[g] B. F. Murphey, *Phys. Rev.*, **72**, 834 (1947).

[h] H. R. Heath, T. L. Ibbs, and N. E. Wild, *Proc. Roy. Soc.* (*London*), **A178**, 380 (1941).

[i] T. L. Ibbs and K. E. Grew, *ibid.*, **43**, 142 (1931).

[j] T. L. Ibbs, K. E. Grew and A. A. Hirst, *Proc. Roy. Soc.* (*London*), **41**, 456 (1929).

[k] R. E. Bastick, H. R. Heath, and T. L. Ibbs, *Proc. Roy. Soc.* (*London*), **A173**, 543 (1939).

TABLE 8.4–15

CONCENTRATION DEPENDENCE OF k_T IN ISOTOPIC THERMAL DIFFUSION OF DEUTERIUM-HYDROGEN MIXTURES AT $\bar{T} = 327$°K

% H_2	$k_T \times 10^2$	
	Exptl[a]	Calcd
10	1.45	1.48
20	2.65	2.66
30	3.56	3.54
40	4.16	4.12
50	4.32	4.34
60	4.16	4.22
70	3.62	3.76
80	2.81	2.91
90	1.66	1.67

[a] Heath, Ibbs, and Wild, *Proc. Roy. Soc.* (*London*), **A178**, 380 (1941).

For this problem $T = 90.2$°K, $T' = 290.4$°K, and hence the mean temperature is $\bar{T} = 153$°K. The first part of the calculation may be organized as shown in Table 8.4–18. We can then calculate $k_T(\bar{T})$ from Eq. 8.2–50. The intermediate results are

$$X_\lambda + Y_\lambda = 3.030 \times 10^{-3}$$

$$S^{(1)} = 12.75$$

$$S^{(2)} = -15.94$$

and the thermal diffusion ratio is

$$k_T(\bar{T}) = 0.0607$$

Then

$$\Delta x_1 = x_1(T') - x_1(T) = -0.0710$$

is the difference in concentration of H_2 in the two bulbs.

(b) To be somewhat more correct we should integrate Eq. 8.1–15 numerically. First of all we have to compute k_T over the temperature range from $T = 90.2$°K to $T' = 290.2$°K. This may be done by the method just given, and the results are

T(°K)	k_T
90.2	0.0444
115.2	0.0532
140.2	0.0589
165.2	0.0626
190.2	0.0653
215.2	0.0672
240.2	0.0685
265.2	0.0694
290.2	0.0699

The integral of (k_T/T) over T may be performed by numerical means. When the integration is performed according to Simpson's rule,[15] it is found that $\Delta x_1 = -0.0707$. The experimental value of A. van Itterbeek, O. van Paemel, and J. van Lierde [*Physica*, **13**, 231 (1947)] is $\Delta x_1 = -0.069$.

TABLE 8.4–16

TEMPERATURE DEPENDENCE OF ISOTOPIC THERMAL DIFFUSION[a, b]

$k_T^\star = (k_T)/(k_T)_{\text{rig. sph.}}$

Gas Pair 1-2	% of Lighter Isotope	$k_T^\star$		$\overline{T}$ (°K)	Refs. for Experimental Data
		Exptl	Calcd[c]		
Ne^{22}-Ne^{20}	90	0.382	0.480	129	*d*
		0.550	0.587	238	
		0.713	0.618	432	
		0.816	0.625	712	
A^{40}-A^{36}	0.307	0.0673	0.030	129	*d*
		0.151	0.096	154	
		0.312	0.359	300	
		0.466	0.528	555	
		0.534	0.572	720	
$O^{16}O^{18}$-$O^{16}O^{16}$	97.5	0.367	0.371	284	*e*
		0.475	0.468	386	
		0.538	0.499	443	

[a] This table is taken from E. R. S. Winter, *Trans. Faraday Soc.*, **46**, 81 (1950).

[b] $\overline{T}$ is defined in § 8.1a. See Table 8.4–14.

[c] $k_T^\star$ is calculated from Table I–Q for various values of $\overline{T}^* = k\overline{T}/\epsilon$.

[d] L. G. Stier, *Phys. Rev.*, **62**, 548 (1942).

[e] E. Whalley and E. R. S. Winter, *Trans. Faraday Soc.*, **45**, 1091 (1949).

Illustrative Example

Problem. Calculate $k_T^\star$ for the isotopic thermal diffusion of A^{36} and A^{40} at a temperature of 300°K.

Solution. According to Table I–A, $\epsilon/k = 124$°K for argon. Hence at $T = 300$°K, $T^* = 300/124 = 2.42$. From Table I–Q it can be found that, for the Lennard-Jones (6-12) potential, $k_T^\star(2.42)$ is 0.359.

[15] For numerical methods of integration see, for example, W. E. Milne, *Numerical Calculus*, Princeton University Press (1949).

TABLE 8.4–17

FORCE CONSTANTS DETERMINED FROM THERMAL DIFFUSION AND ORDINARY DIFFUSION DATA

	ϵ_{12}/k (°K)		σ_{12} (Å)	
	Exptl	Geom. Mean	Exptl	Arith. Mean
He-A	26.65	27.45	3.04	3.06
H_2-A	56.41	64.47	3.24	3.20
H_2-N_2	46.53	53.86	3.34	3.33
H_2-O_2	59.81	60.67	3.19	3.21
H_2-CO	52.02	57.55	3.36	3.31

TABLE 8.4–18

CALCULATION OF CONCENTRATION CHANGE IN THERMAL DIFFUSION

Components	*Mole Fractions*	*Molecular Weights*
1 = Ne	$x_1 = 0.644$	$M_1 = 20.18$
2 = H_2	$x_2 = 0.356$	$M_2 = 2.016$

i j	1 1	2 2	1 2
σ_{ij}(Å)	2.789[a]	2.968[a]	2.878[b]
ϵ_{ij}/k(°K)	35.7[a]	33.3[a]	34.5[b]
T_{ij}^*	4.286	4.595	4.435
$\Omega_{ij}^{(2,2)\star}$	0.9560	0.9424[c]	0.9492
$A_{ij}^\star$	. . .	. . .	1.099[d]
$B_{ij}^\star$	. . .	. . .	1.093[d]
$C_{ij}^\star$	. . .	. . .	0.928[d]
$[\lambda_1]_{ij} \times 10^7$ (cal/cm sec °K)	737[e]	2087[e]	1634[f]

[a] From Table I–A.
[b] Calculated from Eqs. 8.4–8 and 9.
[c] From Table I–M.
[d] From Table I–N.
[e] Calculated from Eq. 8.2–31.
[f] Calculated from Eq. 8.2–35.

5. Comparison of the Results of Transport Coefficient Calculations for Several Spherical Non-polar Potential Functions

In the two preceding sections we have discussed the calculation of the transport coefficients for various molecular models. Calculations for the simpler potentials, including the rigid elastic spheres, point centers of repulsion, the Sutherland model, and the square well are discussed in § 8.3. § 8.4 is given over to the calculations for the Lennard-Jones (6-12) potential. In this section we compare the results of the calculations for these potential functions (with the exception of point centers of repulsion) with the experimental data for the coefficient of viscosity and the coefficient of self-diffusion. The comparison which is made here is analogous to that given for the second virial coefficient in § 3.9.

The experimental[1–3] and theoretical values of $\eta/T^{1/2}$ are summarized for neon, argon, nitrogen, and carbon dioxide in Figs. 8.5–1, 2, 3, 4. The theoretical results are calculated from Eqs. 8.2–18 and 19. The figures in the insets show the potential functions obtained from the experimental viscosity data. Here it can be seen that the temperature dependence of $\eta/T^{1/2}$ is best reproduced by the Lennard-Jones (6-12) potential. The data of Trautz and coworkers are at considerably higher temperatures than those of Johnston and coworkers. Consequently, somewhat different force constants are obtained from an analysis of the two sets of data. Nevertheless, the potential functions from either set of data adequately reproduce the temperature dependence over the entire range for which experimental values are known. On the other hand, for the Sutherland potential good agreement with experiment is obtained for only a comparatively small temperature range. This is shown clearly in Figs. 8.5–1 and 3. For this reason, the Sutherland model should not be used for extensive extrapolations. Fairly good agreement is obtained between observed values and the values calculated for the square-well potential throughout the range for which the collision integrals have been evaluated for this potential. This is partly due to the fact that this potential has three adjustable parameters.

[1] H. L. Johnston and K. E. McCloskey, *J. Phys. Chem.*, **44**, 1038 (1939) (Ne, A). H. L. Johnston and E. R. Grilly, *J. Phys. Chem.*, **46**, 948 (1942) (N_2, CO_2).

[2] M. Trautz and H. E. Binkele, *Ann. Physik* (5), **5**, 561 (1930) (Ne, A). M. Trautz and R. Zink, *Ann. Physik* (5), **7**, 427 (1930) (Ne, A, N_2, CO_2). M. Trautz and H. Zimmerman, *Ann. Physik* (5), **22**, 189 (1935) (Ne). M. Trautz and P. B. Baumann, *Ann. Physik* (5), **2**, 733 (1929) (N_2). M. Trautz and A. Melster, *Ann. Physik* (5), **7**, 409 (1930) (N_2). M. Trautz and F. Kurz, *Ann. Physik* (5), **9**, 981 (1931) (CO_2).

[3] V. Vasilesco, *Ann. Phys.* (Paris) (11), **20**, 292 (1945) (CO_2).

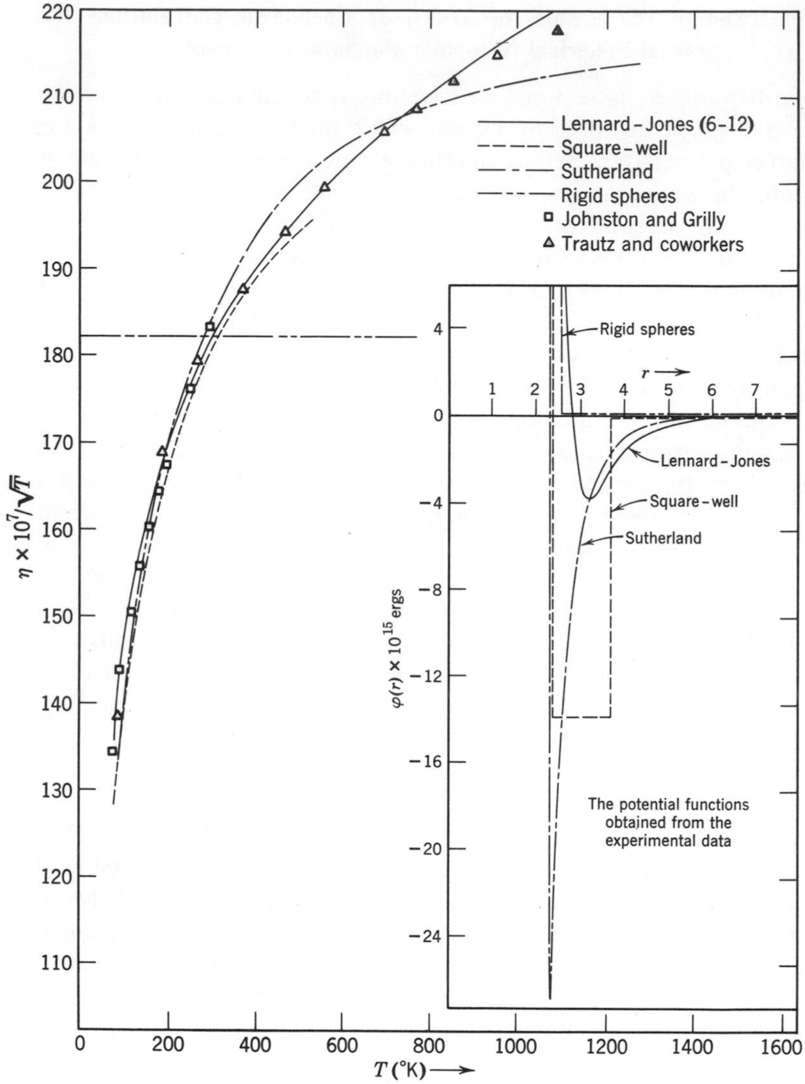

Fig. 8.5–1. The coefficient of viscosity of *neon* as calculated for several molecular models. The experimental data are those of H. L. Johnston and E. R. Grilly, *J. Phys. Chem.*, **46,** 938 (1942); M. Trautz and H. E. Binkele, *Ann. Physik* (5), **5**, 561 (1930); M. Trautz, A. Melster, and R. Zink, *ibid.*, **7**, 409 (1930); M. Trautz and H. Zimmerman, *ibid.*, **22**, 189 (1935).

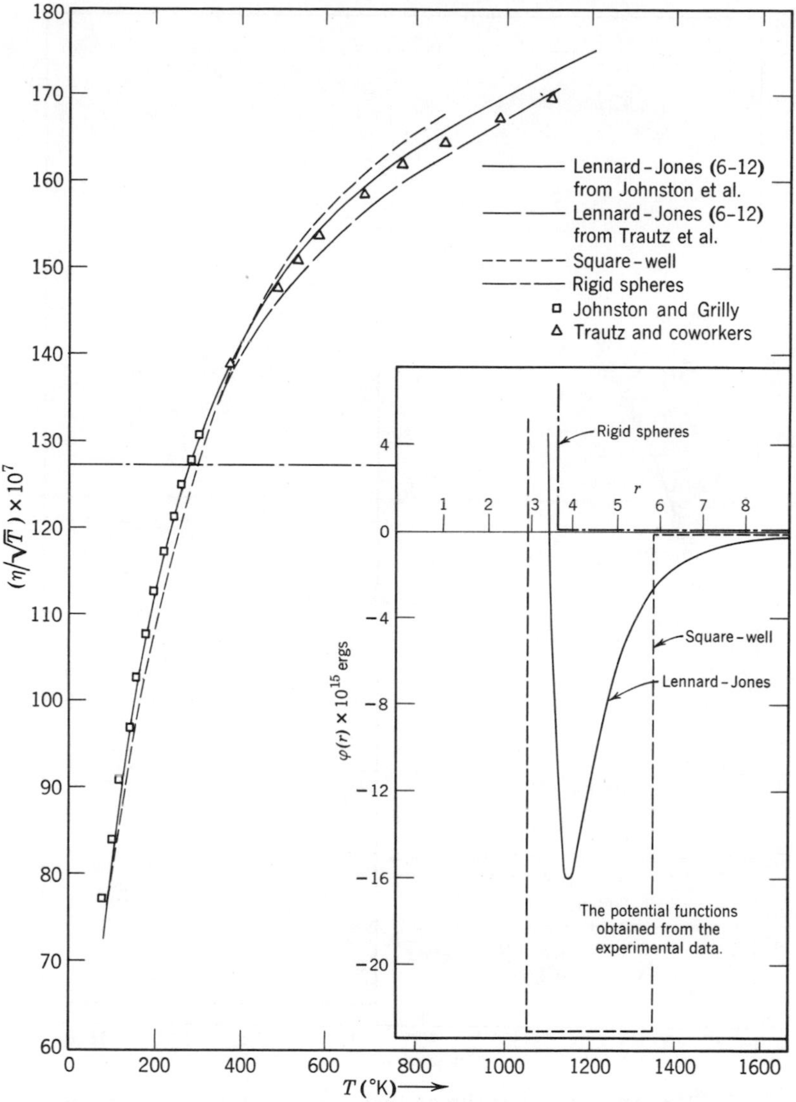

Fig. 8.5–2. The coefficient of viscosity of *argon* as calculated for several molecular models. The experimental data are those of H. L. Johnston and E. R. Grilly, ***J. Phys. Chem.***, **46**, 938 (1942); M. Trautz and H. E. Binkele, *Ann. Physik* (5), **5**, 561 (1930); M. Trautz, A. Melster, and R. Zink, *ibid.*, **7**, 409 (1930).

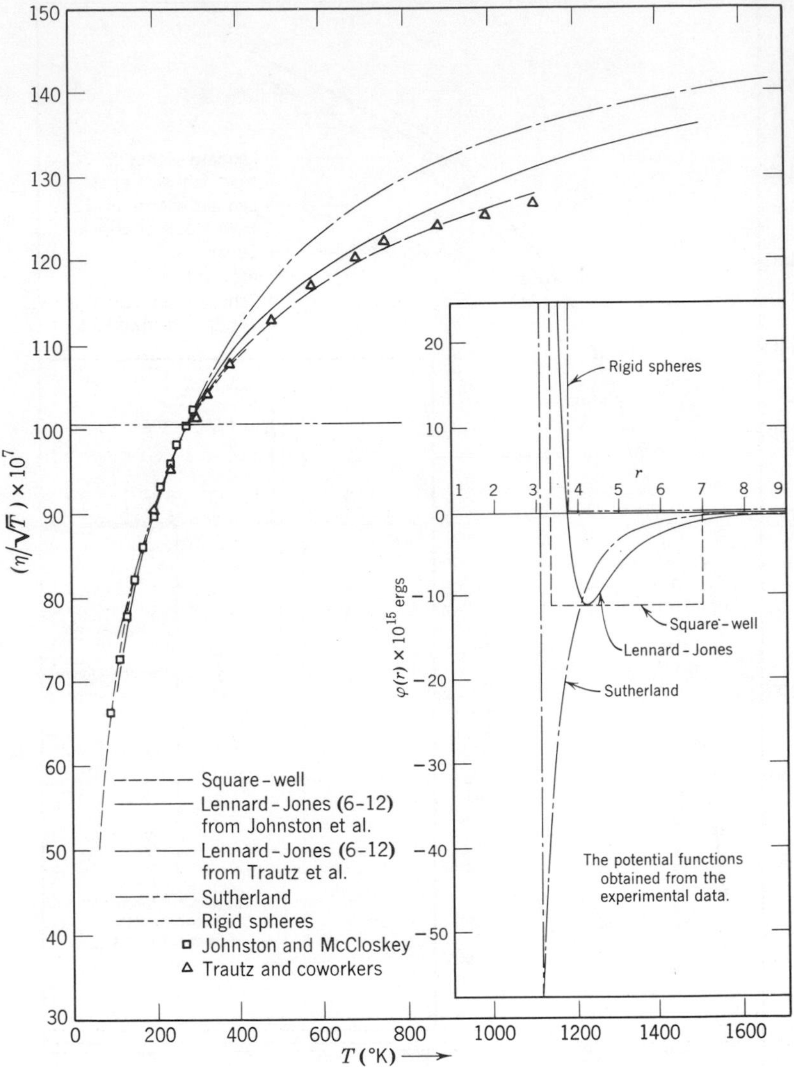

Fig. 8.5–3. The coefficient of viscosity of *nitrogen* as calculated for several molecular models. The experimental data are those of H. L. Johnston and K. E. McCloskey, *J. Phys. Chem.*, **44**, 1038 (1940); M. Trautz and P. B. Baumann, *Ann. Physik* (5), **2**, 733 (1929); M. Trautz, A. Melster, and R. Zink, *ibid.*, **7**, 409 (1930).

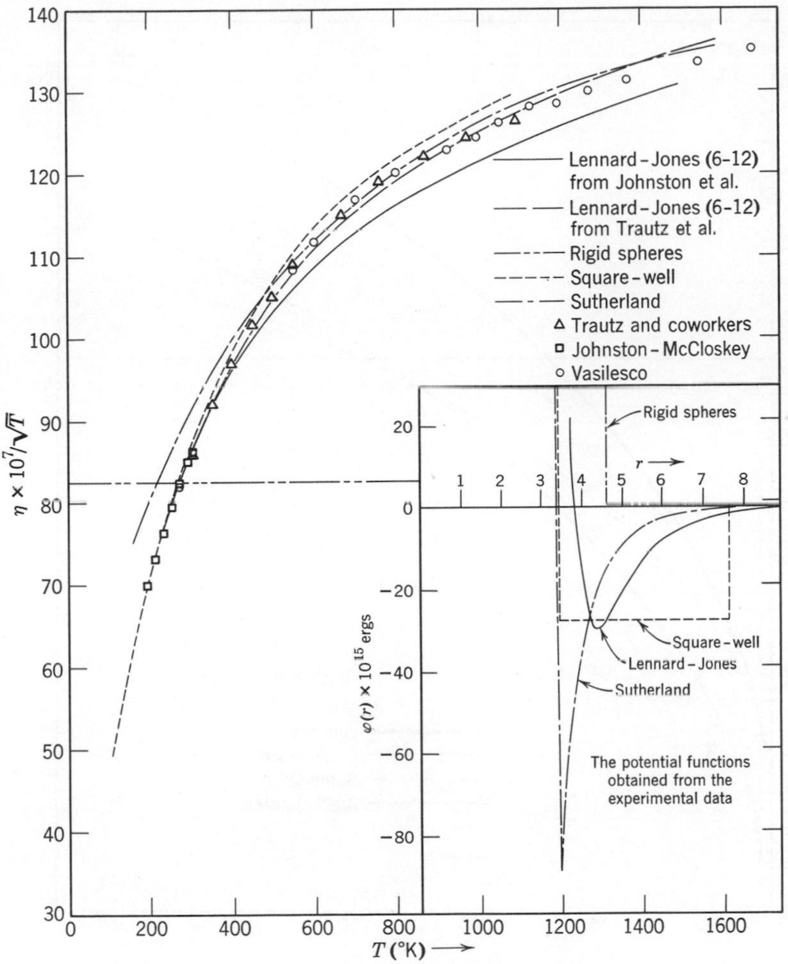

Fig. 8.5–4. The coefficient of viscosity of *carbon dioxide* as calculated for several molecular models. The experimental data are those of H. L. Johnston and K. E. McCloskey, *J. Phys. Chem.*, **44**, 1038 (1940); M. Trautz, A. Melster, and R. Zink, *Ann. Physik* (5), **7**, 409 (1930); M. Trautz and F. Kurz, *ibid.*, **9**, 981 (1931); V. Vasilesco, *Ann. Phys. (Paris)*, *Series* 11, **20**, 292 (1945).

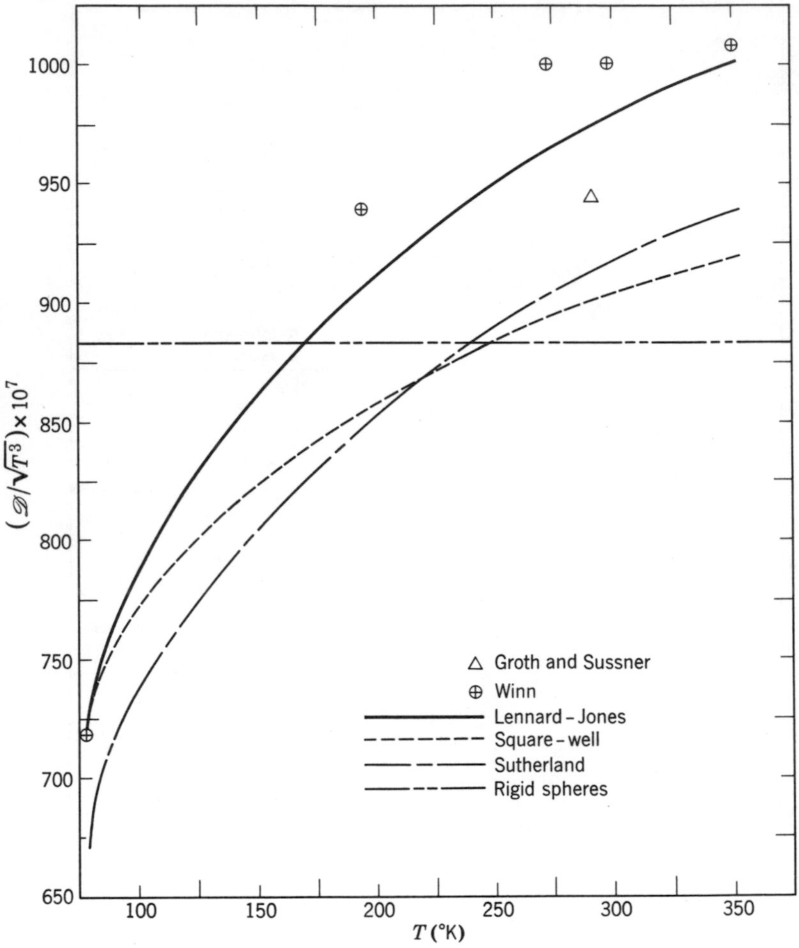

Fig. 8.5–5. The coefficient of self-diffusion for *neon* as calculated for several molecular models. The experimental data are those of W. Groth and E. Sussner, *Z. Physik. Chem.*, **193**, 296 (1944); E. B. Winn, *Phys. Rev.*, **80**, 1024 (1950).

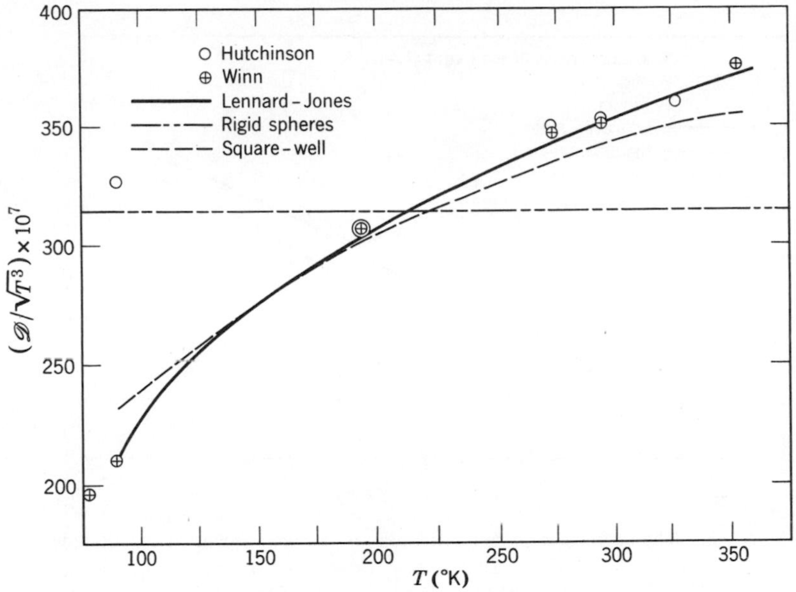

Fig. 8.5-6. The coefficient of self-diffusion for *argon* as calculated for several molecular models. Experimental data: F. Hutchinson, *J. Chem. Phys.*, **17**, 1081 (1949); E. B. Winn, *Phys. Rev.*, **80**, 1024 (1950).

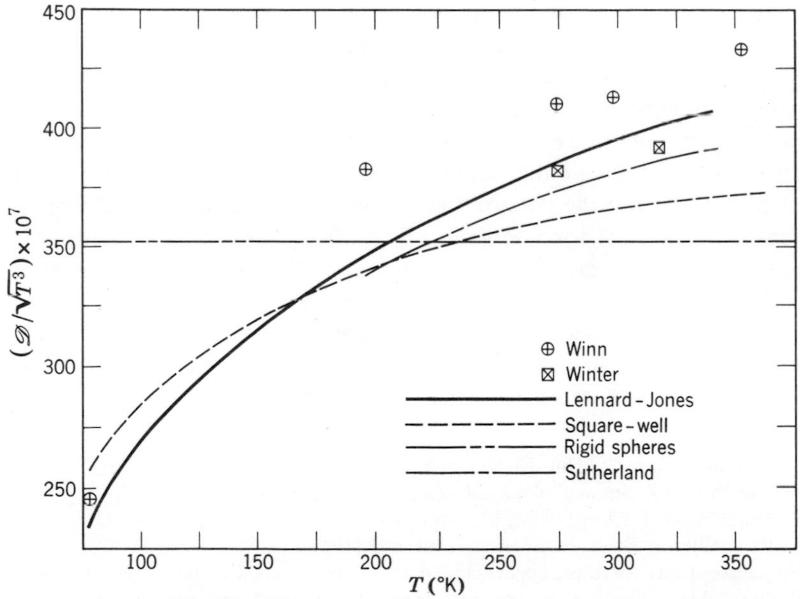

Fig. 8.5-7. The coefficient of self-diffusion for *nitrogen* as calculated for several molecular models. Experimental data: E. B. Winn, *Phys. Rev.*, **80**, 1024 (1950); E. R. S. Winter, *Trans. Faraday Soc.*, **47**, 342 (1951).

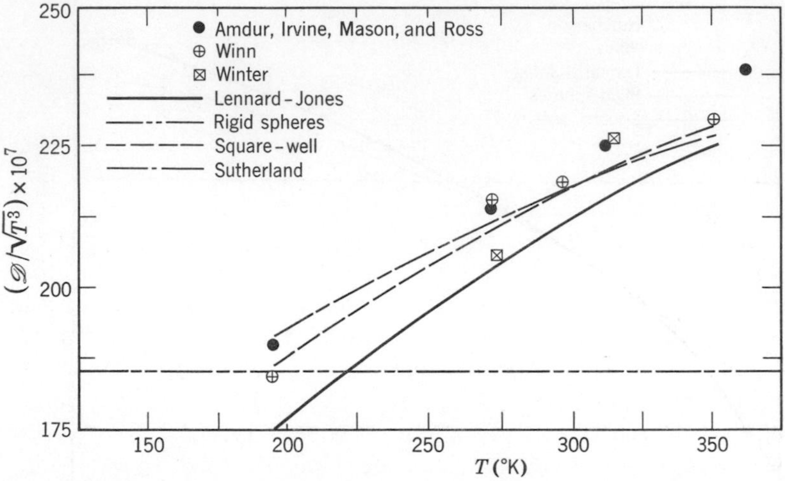

Fig. 8.5–8. The coefficient of self-diffusion for *carbon dioxide* as calculated for several molecular models. Experimental data: E. B. Winn, *Phys. Rev.*, **80**, 1024 (1950); E. R. S. Winter, *Trans. Faraday Soc.*, **47**, 342 (1951).

In Figs. 8.5–5, 6, 7, and 8 a similar comparison between experimental[4–7] and theoretical results is shown for $\mathscr{D}/T^{3/2}$. The theoretical results are calculated from Eq. 8.2–46, using the force constants obtained from the viscosity data for each of the various potential functions.[8] It is thus possible to see the results of using a potential function obtained from one transport property to calculate another. Unfortunately, data for self-diffusion as yet are not available over nearly so great a temperature range as for viscosity nor can they be obtained so accurately. Therefore it is not possible to test the potential functions over as extensive a temperature range as is done for viscosity. For Ne, A, and N_2, the Lennard-Jones (6-12) potential gives a much better reproduction of the temperature dependence of $\mathscr{D}/T^{3/2}$ than do the other potentials. For CO_2, the Sutherland and square-well models give better agreement with the higher set of observed values, and the Lennard-Jones potential is slightly in better agreement with the lower set of observed values.

[4] E. B. Winn, *Phys. Rev.*, **80**, 1024 (1950).

[5] W. Groth and E. Sussner, *Z. physik. Chem.*, **193**, 296 (1944).

[6] F. Hutchinson, *J. Chem. Phys.*, **17**, 1081 (1949).

[7] E. R. S. Winter, *Trans. Faraday Soc.*, **47**, 342 (1941).

[8] Force constants for the Lennard-Jones (6-12) potential are those for references *a* and *c* of Table I–A, since we are interested here in the lower temperature range. (See note 4, Table I–A.)

6. Transport Coefficient Calculations for Polar Gases and Gas Mixtures Containing One Polar Component (an Approximate Treatment)

The theory for transport phenomena of molecules with internal degrees of freedom has not yet been applied to the properties of polar gases. At the present time the only calculations which have been made for polar gases are those described in this section for an effective spherically symmetric potential field. These calculations provide an excellent means for curve-fitting data and should be reasonably good for high-temperature extrapolations. The use of such a spherically symmetric potential for the evaluation of the collision cross-sections means that the results have little meaning as far as interpreting the nature of the intermolecular forces which are strongly angle dependent. Consequently the results discussed here do not enable us to use viscosity data to predict compressibility data, and vice versa, as can be done for spherical non-polar molecules by means of the extensive calculations which have been made for the Lennard-Jones (6-12) potential.

In § 3.10f it is shown how the second virial coefficients for mixtures of polar and non-polar gases may be calculated. In this section we indicate how similar calculations may be performed for the transport properties, if only one polar component is present.

While the treatments described here for polar gases and their mixtures are not rigorous, they are nevertheless the best now available. It seems worth while to include these results because they are useful for calculating the properties of industrial gases, which frequently contain polar components.

a. Viscosity of pure gases[1]

In § 3.10 the calculation of the virial coefficients and the Joule-Thomson coefficient for polar molecules is described. For the calculations described there the Stockmayer potential is used for the interaction between pairs of polar molecules:

$$\varphi(r, \theta_1, \theta_2, \phi_2 - \phi_1) = 4\epsilon\left[\left(\frac{\sigma}{r}\right)^{12} - \left(\frac{\sigma}{r}\right)^{6}\right] - \frac{\mu^2}{r^3} g(\theta_1, \theta_2, \phi_2 - \phi_1)$$

$$g(\theta_1, \theta_2, \phi_2 - \phi_1) = 2\cos\theta_1 \cos\theta_2 - \sin\theta_1 \sin\theta_2 \cos(\phi_2 - \phi_1) \tag{1.3-33}$$

The angle-dependent term proportional to r^{-3} represents the interaction of two "point dipoles" (see § 12.1f–ii). For very high energy collisions, where the repulsive forces are more important than the attractive forces,

[1] F. J. Krieger, "The Viscosity of Polar Gases," Proj. RAND Report, RM-646, July 1, 1951.

it is a fairly good approximation to replace this angle-dependent contribution by the expression which corresponds to the interaction of two-point dipoles which are perfectly aligned. This allows us to write the following approximate angle-independent potential:

$$\varphi(r) = 4\epsilon\left[\left(\frac{\sigma}{r}\right)^{12} - \left(\frac{\sigma}{r}\right)^{6}\right] - \frac{2\mu^2}{r^3} \qquad (8.6\text{–}1)^2$$

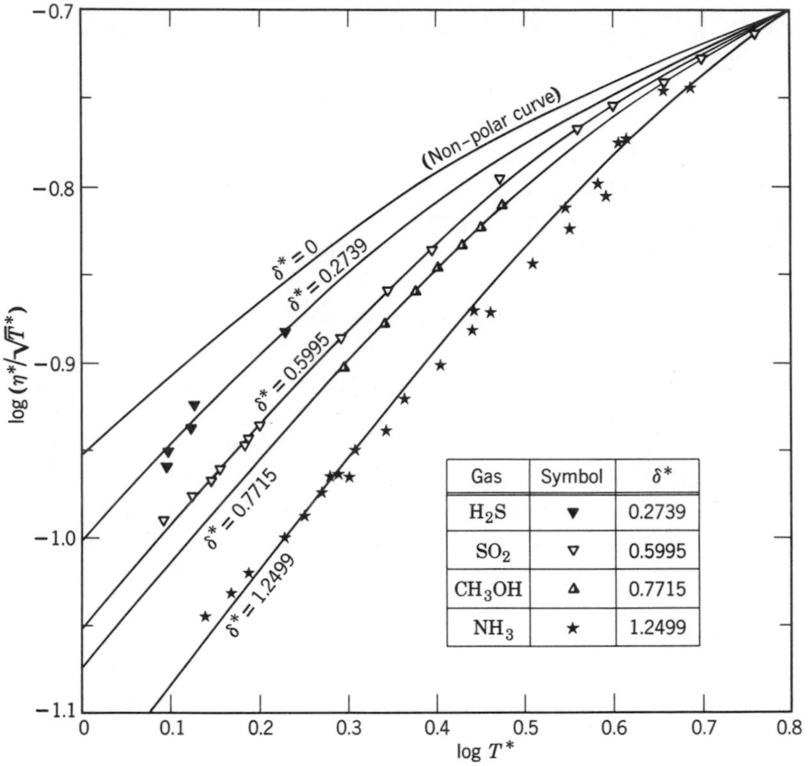

Gas	Symbol	δ^*
H_2S	▼	0.2739
SO_2	▽	0.5995
CH_3OH	▲	0.7715
NH_3	★	1.2499

Fig. 8.6–1. Comparison of experimental data with the calculated results based on the Krieger potential function given in Eq. 8.6–1. The deviations from non-polar behavior are greater for larger values of δ^* in keeping with the principle of corresponding states for polar molecules.

For low-energy collisions the attractive forces are generally quite important and this potential function is a poor approximation to the true interaction.

[2] It should be mentioned that it is not possible to evaluate the second virial coefficient for this potential since, without the angle-dependent factor, the integral for $B(T)$ does not converge. Accordingly the results of calculations based on this potential energy function cannot be compared with results for equilibrium statistical mechanics.

The transport coefficients may be calculated for this angle independent potential function, and they depend on the parameters σ and ϵ and also on a dimensionless quantity:

$$\delta^* = \tfrac{1}{2}\mu^{*2} = \tfrac{1}{2}\,\frac{\mu^2}{\epsilon\sigma^3} \tag{8.6–2}$$

This quantity (which is analogous to the t^* defined in connection with Stockmayer potential in § 3.10) is a measure of the extent to which a substance deviates from non-polar behavior.

The reduced collision cross-section $\Omega^{(2,2)\star}$ characteristic of viscosity and thermal conductivity has been evaluated[1] for the potential energy function given in Eq. 8.6–1. This function is tabulated in Table IX over a very large range of the reduced temperature T^*. By means of this table parameters in the potential function of Eq. 8.6–1 have been determined for a dozen gases. These parameters are given in Table 8.6–1.

TABLE 8.6–1

PARAMETERS FOR THE APPROXIMATE ANGLE-INDEPENDENT POTENTIAL FOR POLAR MOLECULES[a] (EQ. 8.6–1)

Gas	μ (debyes)[b]	ϵ/k (°K)	σ (Å)	δ^*
NO	0.0672	112.4	3.508	0.003371
CO	0.1172	109.9	3.585	0.009830
$CHCl_3$	1.05	415.2	5.117	0.07177
H_2S	0.931	221.1	3.733	0.2739
HCl	1.034	218.0	3.506	0.4123
SO_2	1.611	191.4	4.341	0.5995
NOCl	1.83	205.2	4.332	0.7272
CH_3Cl	1.861	243.6	4.076	0.7606
CH_3OH	1.680	194.9	4.082	0.7715
CH_3COCH_3	2.85	158.4	5.485	1.1253
NH_3	1.437	146.8	3.441	1.2499
H_2O	1.831	230.9	2.824	2.333

[a] The data which were analyzed for the force constants are summarized by Krieger, Ref. 1.

[b] 1 debye = 10^{-18} esu.

In Fig. 8.6–1 the calculated curve for the viscosity of non-polar gases is plotted in reduced units. In addition the calculated curves for several polar gases are shown. This indicates the direction and magnitude of the deviations from non-polar behavior. Also shown in the figure are the experimental points for these three gases. It can be seen that the calculated curves fit the experimental points quite nicely.

Illustrative Example

Problem. Calculate the viscosity of NH_3 at 800°K.

Solution. The force constants from Table 8.6–1 are

$$\epsilon/k = 146.8°\text{K}$$

$$\sigma = 3.441 \text{ Å}$$

$$\delta^* = 1.2499$$

Then $T^* = 5.4496$. From Table IX, $\Omega^{(2,2)*}(T^*, \delta^*) = 0.9388$. $M = 17.032$. From Eq. 8.2–18

$$[\eta]_1 \times 10^7 = 266.93 \frac{\sqrt{(17.032)(800)}}{(3.441)^2(0.9388)} = 2803 \text{ g/cm-sec.}$$

b. Viscosity and diffusion for mixtures containing one polar component

In § 3.10f a method for calculating the virial coefficients for mixtures containing polar and non-polar gases is described. The same method may be applied to the calculation of transport coefficients.

Let us first consider the diffusion of a polar gas into a non-polar gas. The only forces which we need to know are those between the unlike molecules in the gas, that is, the interaction between the polar and the non-polar molecules. In § 13.5 it is shown that the effective potential energy of interaction between a polar and a non-polar molecule has the same form as that between two non-polar molecules. Hence the Lennard-Jones potential may be used for this polar–non-polar interaction. It may be shown that the force constants describing this interaction may be obtained from the combining laws:

$$\sigma_{np} = \tfrac{1}{2}(\sigma_n + \sigma_p)\, \xi^{-1/6} \tag{8.6–3}$$

$$\epsilon_{np} = \sqrt{\epsilon_n \epsilon_p}\, \xi^2 \tag{8.6–4}$$

in which

$$\xi = \left[1 + \frac{1}{4} \alpha_n{}^* \mu_p{}^{*2} \sqrt{\frac{\epsilon_p}{\epsilon_n}}\right] = \left[1 + \frac{1}{2}\sqrt{2}\, \alpha_n{}^* t_p{}^* \sqrt{\frac{\epsilon_p}{\epsilon_n}}\right] \tag{8.6–5}$$

where σ_n, ϵ_n = Lennard-Jones potential parameters for the non-polar molecules (Table I–A),

σ_p, ϵ_p = Stockmayer potential parameters for the polar molecule (Table 3.10–1),

$\alpha_n{}^*$ = reduced polarizability of the non-polar molecule $= \alpha_n/\sigma_n{}^3$,

$\mu_p{}^*$ = reduced dipole moment of the polar molecule $= \mu_p/\sqrt{\epsilon_p \sigma_p{}^3}$,

$t_p{}^* = \mu_p{}^{*2}/\sqrt{8}$ (tabulated in Table 3.10–1).

Using these force constants, we may calculate the first approximation to the coefficient of diffusion using Eq. 8.2–44 and the table of $\Omega^{(1,1)\star}$ given in Table I–M. In Table 8.6–2 calculated and experimental results are compared for the diffusivity of water into several non-polar gases. The agreement is generally satisfactory.

TABLE 8.6–2

COEFFICIENT OF DIFFUSION FOR H_2O AND SOME NON-POLAR GASES

Gas Pair	T (°C)	($\mathscr{D}_{12}$) (cm^2 sec^{-1})		
		Exptl[a]	Exptl[b]	Calcd
H_2O-H_2	34.4	1.02	0.91	0.95
	55.5	1.12	0.99	1.07
	79.2	1.20	1.10	1.21
H_2O-CO_2	34.4	0.202	0.174	0.183
	55.5	0.211	0.192	0.208
	79.2	0.241	0.215	0.239
H_2O-He	34.0	0.90	...	0.95
	55.3	1.01	...	1.07
	79.3	1.12	...	1.21
H_2O-N_2	34.4	0.256	...	0.255
	55.4	0.303	...	0.289
	79.0	0.359	...	0.329

[a] F. A. Schwertz and J. E. Brow, *J. Chem. Phys.*, **19**, 640 (1951).
[b] A. Winkelman, *Wied. Ann.*, **22**, 152 (1884); **36**, 93 (1889).

Illustrative Example

Problem. Estimate the coefficient of diffusion for the gas pair NH_3-CH_4 at 5 atm pressure and 500°K.

Solution. The force constants are as follows:

CH_4: $\epsilon_n/k = 136.5°K$ $\sigma_n = 3.822$ Å (Table I–A)

NH_3: $\epsilon_p/k = 320°K$ $\sigma_p = 2.60$ Å (Table 3.10–1)

$$t_p^* = 1.0$$

$$\alpha_n \times 10^{24} = 2.61 \text{ cm}^3, \ \alpha_n^* = 0.04675 \qquad \text{(Eq. 8.6–5)}$$

$$\sigma_{np} = 3.184 \text{ Å} \qquad \text{(Eq. 8.6–3)}$$

$$\epsilon_{np}/k = 229.7°K \qquad \text{(Eq. 8.6–4)}$$

With these force constants, $T_{np}^* = kT/\epsilon_{np} = 2.177$. From Table I–M for the Lennard-Jones potential:

$$\Omega^{(1,1)*}(T_{np}^*) = 1.045$$

Equation 8.2–44 may then be used to obtain

$$[\mathscr{D}_{np}]_1 = 0.137 \text{ cm}^2 \text{ sec}^{-1}$$

This same method may be used for the calculation of the viscosity of a mixture of gases containing one polar component. For this calculation Eq. 8.2–22 or Eq. 8.2–25 may be used. First of all, we have to compute the quantities $[\eta_n]_1$, $[\eta_{np}]_1$, $[\eta_p]_1$, and $A_{np}^\star$. The first of the quantities, the viscosity of the pure non-polar component, may be calculated from Eq. 8.2–18 by means of the force constants determined from viscosity. The viscosity of the pure polar component may be calculated according to the methods outlined in § 8.6a, or the experimental values may be used. The quantities $[\eta_{np}]_1$ and $A_{np}^\star$ which involve the polar–non-polar interaction may be computed using the Lennard-Jones (6-12) tables and the combining laws in Eqs. 8.6–3, 4, 5. A numerical example is given to indicate the details of the calculation.

Illustrative Example

Problem. Compute the coefficient of viscosity of the ternary mixture 50 per cent CH_4, 35 per cent N_2, and 15 per cent NH_3 at one atmosphere pressure and $T = 380°K$. Use Eq. 8.2–25 and also Eq. 8.2–30 and compare the results obtained by the two methods.

Solution. (a) The coefficient of viscosity of a three-component mixture may be calculated from Eq. 8.2–25. The elements of the determinants H_{ij} must first be calculated. This is done by considering the six types of interactions which take place between the three chemical species. The force constants for the interactions, the tabulated functions needed in the calculation, and some of the intermediate results of the calculations are shown in Table 8.6–3. After the H_{ij} have been calculated the evaluation of the determinants in Eq. 8.2–25 gives for the final result:

$$[\eta_{\text{mix}}]_1 \times 10^7 = 1689 \text{ g/cm-sec}$$

(b) The intermediate results in Table 8.6–3 can be used to calculate the viscosity according to Eq. 8.2–30, in the form given in the illustrative example in connection with Table 8.4–8. Here the use of this equation gives the same result to four significant figures as Eq. 8.2–25. Usually the results from these two methods do not differ by more than 2 per cent.

The viscosities of moist air, calculated according to the method described above, are shown in Table 8.6–4. Air was assumed to be a pure gas with the force constants given in Table I–A. It is interesting to note that these calculations suggest that between 100 and 500°K the viscosity decreases with increasing moisture content whereas above 800°K the reverse is true. There are as yet no experimental data to substantiate this.

TABLE 8.6–3. CALCULATION OF THE VISCOSITY OF A TERNARY MIXTURE CONTAINING ONE POLAR COMPONENT

Components	*Mole Fractions*	*Molecular Weights*	*Polarizabilities*
1: CH_4 (non-polar)	$x_1 = 0.50$	$M_1 = 16.04$	$\alpha_1 = 2.61$ Å^3
2: N_2 (non-polar)	$x_2 = 0.35$	$M_2 = 28.02$	$\alpha_2 = 1.76$ Å^3
3: NH_3 (polar)	$x_3 = 0.15$	$M_3 = 17.03$	

i	j	σ_{ij} (Å)	ϵ_{ij}/k (°K)	Polar Parameters	$T_{ij}^* = \frac{kT}{\epsilon_{ij}}$	$\Omega_{ij}^{(2,2)\star}$	$\frac{2M_iM_j}{(M_i+M_j)}$ [h]	$\sqrt{\frac{2M_iM_jT}{(M_i+M_j)}}$ [i]	$[\eta_{ij}]_1 \times 10^7$ (gm/cm sec)	$A_{ij}^\star$ [l]	$\frac{M_j}{M_i}$	$\frac{M_iM_j}{(M_i+M_j)^2}$	H_{ij}
1	1	3.822[a]	136.5[a]	—	2.784	1.060[f]	16.04	78.07	1346[j]	—	—	—	+4040[m]
1	2	3.752[b]	111.7[b]	—	3.402	1.007[f]	20.40	88.05	1658[k]	1.096	1.747	0.2315	−254[n]
1	3	3.184[c]	229.7[c]	—	1.654	1.263[f]	16.52	79.23	1652[k]	1.096	1.062	0.2498	−118[n]
2	2	3.681[a]	91.46[a]	—	4.155	0.9622[f]	28.02	103.2	2113[j]	—	—	—	+1872[m]
2	3	3.117[c]	187.5[c]	—	2.027	1.170[f]	21.18	89.71	2107[k]	1.094	0.608	0.2351	−61[n]
3	3	3.441[d]	146.8[d]	$\delta^* = 1.25$[d]	2.589	1.357[g]	17.03	80.45	1337[j]	—	—	—	+1122[m]
(3)	(3)	2.60[e]	320[e]	$t^* = 1.0$[e]	—	—	—	—	—	—	—	—	—

[a] From Table I–A: Force constants for the Lennard-Jones (6-12) potential.
[b] Use empirical combining laws in Eqs. 8.4–8 and 9 for non-polar—non-polar interaction.
[c] Use empirical combining laws in Eqs. 8.6–3 and 4 for polar—non-polar interaction; use *Stockmayer* force constants for the polar component.
[d] From Table 8.6–1: Force constants for the *Krieger* potential (Eq. 8.6–1).
[e] From Table 3.10–1: Force constants for the *Stockmayer* potential (Eq. 1.3–33).
[f] From Table I–M: Table for L.J. (6-12) potential.
[g] From Table IX: Table for Krieger potential.
[h] This equals M_i for $i = j$. [i] This equals $\sqrt{M_iT}$ for $i = j$.
[j] From Eq. 8.2–18. [k] From Eq. 8.2–21.
[l] From Table I–N: Table for L.J. (6-12) potential.
[m] From Eq. 8.2–26.
[n] From Eq. 8.2–27.

TABLE 8.6–4

VISCOSITY OF MOIST AIR

$[\eta]_1 \times 10^7$ g cm^{-1} sec^{-1}

Temperature (°K)	Per Cent Moisture			
	0.0[a]	0.5	1.0	5.0
100	702 (703)	701	700	688
150	1038 (1036)	1035	1033	1016
200	1337 (1335)	1335	1333	1315
273.16	1724 (1717)	1722	1720	1704
300	1851 (1843)	1849	1847	1832
400	2290 (2276)	2289	2288	2278
500	2678 (2659)	2678	2677	2671
600	3034	3034	3035	3033
800	3680	3680	3681	3687
1000	4257	4260	4263	4274
1200	4761	4765	4768	4786
1400	5251	5253	5257	5280
1600	5735	5739	5744	5770
2000	6680	6685	6690	6720
3000	8685	8689	8691	8730
5000	12070	12090	12100	12160

[a] Values of the viscosity of dry air given in parenthesis were calculated by considering air to be a multicomponent mixture.

APPENDIX A. FORMULAE FOR THE HIGHER APPROXIMATIONS TO THE TRANSPORT COEFFICIENTS

There are two schemes for obtaining the higher approximations to the transport coefficients. The Chapman and Cowling method discussed in § 7.3 and a new method developed by Kihara.[1] The Chapman and Cowling method gives the following results:

(1) *The Coefficient of Viscosity of Pure Gases* (see Eq. 8.2–19)

$$f_\eta^{(3)} = 1 + \frac{b_{12}^2}{b_{11}b_{22} - b_{12}^2} + \frac{b_{11}(b_{12}b_{23} - b_{22}b_{13})^2}{(b_{11}b_{22} - b_{12}^2)(b_{11}b_{22}b_{33} + 2b_{12}b_{13}b_{23} - b_{12}^2b_{33} - b_{23}^2b_{11} - b_{13}^2b_{22})} \tag{8.A–1}$$

[1] T. Kihara, *Imperfect Gases.* Originally published in Japanese [Asakura Bookstore, Tokyo, (1949)] and translated into English by the United States Office of Air Research, Wright-Patterson Air Force Base.

in which

$$b_{11} = 4\Omega^{(2,2)\star}$$

$$b_{12} = 7\Omega^{(2,2)\star} - 8\Omega^{(2,3)\star}$$

$$b_{22} = \frac{301}{12}\Omega^{(2,2)\star} - 28\Omega^{(2,3)\star} + 20\Omega^{(2,4)\star}$$

$$b_{13} = \frac{63}{8}\Omega^{(2,2)\star} - 18\Omega^{(2,3)\star} + 10\Omega^{(2,4)\star}$$

$$b_{23} = \frac{1365}{32}\Omega^{(2,2)\star} - \frac{321}{4}\Omega^{(2,3)\star} + \frac{125}{2}\Omega^{(2,4)\star} - 30\Omega^{(2,5)\star}$$

$$b_{33} = \frac{25137}{256}\Omega^{(2,2)\star} - \frac{1755}{8}\Omega^{(2,3)\star} + \frac{1905}{8}\Omega^{(2,4)\star} - 135\Omega^{(2,5)\star} + \frac{105}{2}\Omega^{(2,6)\star} + 12\Omega^{(4,4)\star}$$

(2) *The Coefficient of Thermal Conductivity of Pure Gases* (see Eq. 8.2–32)

$$f_\lambda^{(3)} = 1 + \frac{a_{12}^2}{a_{11}a_{22} - a_{12}^2} + \frac{a_{11}(a_{12}a_{23} - a_{22}a_{13})^2}{(a_{11}a_{22} - a_{12}^2)(a_{11}a_{22}a_{33} + 2a_{12}a_{13}a_{23} - a_{11}a_{23}^2 - a_{22}a_{13}^2 - a_{33}a_{12}^2)} \tag{8.A–2}$$

in which

$$a_{11} = b_{11} \quad a_{12} = b_{12} \quad a_{13} = b_{13}$$

$$a_{22} = \frac{77}{4}\Omega^{(2,2)\star} - 28\Omega^{(2,3)\star} + 20\Omega^{(2,4)\star}$$

$$a_{23} = \frac{945}{32}\Omega^{(2,2)\star} - \frac{261}{4}\Omega^{(2,3)\star} + \frac{125}{2}\Omega^{(2,4)\star} - 30\Omega^{(2,5)\star}$$

$$a_{33} = \frac{14553}{256}\Omega^{(2,2)\star} - \frac{1215}{8}\Omega^{(2,3)\star} + \frac{1565}{8}\Omega^{(2,4)\star} - 135\Omega^{(2,5)\star} + \frac{105}{2}\Omega^{(2,6)\star} + 4\Omega^{(4,4)\star}$$

(3) *The Coefficient of Self-diffusion* (see Eq. 8.2–47)

$$f_{\mathscr{D}}^{(2)} = \frac{1}{1 - \Delta} \tag{8.A–3}$$

where

$$\Delta = \frac{(6\text{C}^\star - 5)^2}{(55 - 12\text{B}^\star + 16\text{A}^\star)}$$

in which A★, B★, C★ are the functions defined in Eqs. 8.2–15, 16, 17.

(4) *The Coefficient of Binary Diffusion* (see Eq. 8.2–45)

$$f^{(2)}_{\mathscr{D}_{12}} = \frac{1}{1 - \Delta_{12}} \tag{8.A–4}$$

where

$$\Delta_{12} = \frac{(6\text{C}_{12}{}^\star - 5)^2}{60(X_\lambda + Y_\lambda)} W$$

C★ is defined in Eq. 8.2–17, X_λ and Y_λ are defined in Eq. 8.2–36, and W is given by

$$W = \frac{x_1{}^2}{[\lambda_1]_1}\left(\frac{M_1}{M_2}\right) + \frac{2x_1x_2}{[\lambda_{12}]_1}\left(1 + \frac{15}{8\text{A}_{12}{}^\star}\frac{(M_1 - M_2)^2}{M_1M_2}\right) + \frac{x_2{}^2}{[\lambda_2]_1}\left(\frac{M_2}{M_1}\right)$$

in which the x_i and M_i are mole fractions and molecular weights, A★ is the function defined in Eq. 8.2–15, $[\lambda_i]_1$ is the thermal conductivity given in Eq. 8.2–31, and $[\lambda_{12}]_1$ is the quantity defined in Eq. 8.2–35.

(5) *The Thermal Diffusion Ratio of a Binary Mixture*[2]

$$[k_T]_2 = \frac{5}{2S_{00}}\left[x_1\left(\frac{M_1 + M_2}{2M_1}\right)^{1/2} S_{01} + x_2\left(\frac{M_1 + M_2}{2M_2}\right)^{1/2} S_{0-1}\right] \tag{8.A–5}$$

where the S_{00}, S_{01}, and S_{0-1} are the determinants,

$$S_{00} = \begin{vmatrix} s_{-2-2} & s_{-2-1} & s_{-21} & s_{-22} \\ s_{-1-2} & s_{-1-1} & s_{-11} & s_{-12} \\ s_{1-2} & s_{1-1} & s_{11} & s_{12} \\ s_{2-2} & s_{2-1} & s_{21} & s_{22} \end{vmatrix}$$

$$S_{01} = \begin{vmatrix} s_{-2-2} & s_{-2-1} & s_{-20} & s_{-22} \\ s_{-1-2} & s_{-1-1} & s_{-10} & s_{-12} \\ s_{1-2} & s_{1-1} & s_{10} & s_{12} \\ s_{2-2} & s_{2-1} & s_{20} & s_{22} \end{vmatrix}$$

$$S_{0-1} = \begin{vmatrix} s_{-2-2} & s_{-20} & s_{-21} & s_{-22} \\ s_{-1-2} & s_{-10} & s_{-11} & s_{-12} \\ s_{1-2} & s_{10} & s_{11} & s_{12} \\ s_{2-2} & s_{20} & s_{21} & s_{22} \end{vmatrix}$$

[2] E. A. Mason, *J. Chem. Phys.*, **22** (1954).

and the elements of the determinants are:

$$s_{00} = 8\,\frac{M_1 M_2}{(M_1 + M_2)^2}\,\Omega_{12}^{(1,1)\star}$$

$$s_{10} = s_{01} = 8\,\frac{(2M_1)^{1/2} M_2^{\,2}}{(M_1 + M_2)^{5/2}}\left[\frac{5}{4}\,\Omega_{12}^{(1,1)\star} - \frac{3}{2}\,\Omega_{12}^{(1,2)\star}\right]$$

$$s_{20} = s_{02} = 4\,\frac{(2M_1)^{1/2} M_2^{\,3}}{(M_1 + M_2)^{7/2}}\left[\frac{35}{8}\,\Omega_{12}^{(1,1)\star} - \frac{21}{2}\,\Omega_{12}^{(1,2)\star} + 6\Omega_{12}^{(1,3)\star}\right]$$

$$s_{-10} = s_{0-1} = -\left(\frac{M_1}{M_2}\right)^{3/2} s_{01} \qquad s_{-20} = s_{0-2} = -\left(\frac{M_1}{M_2}\right)^{5/2} s_{02}$$

$$\begin{aligned} s_{11} = \frac{8M_2}{(M_1 + M_2)^3}&\left[\frac{5}{8}\,(6M_1^{\,2} + 5M_2^{\,2})\Omega_{12}^{(1,1)\star} - \frac{15}{2}\,M_2^{\,2}\,\Omega_{12}^{(1,2)\star} \right.\\ &\left.\quad + 6M_2^{\,2}\,\Omega_{12}^{(1,3)\star} + 2M_1 M_2\,\Omega_{12}^{(2,2)\star}\right]\\ &+ 4\Omega_{11}^{(2,2)\star}\left(\frac{2M_2}{M_1 + M_2}\right)^{1/2}\left[\frac{\sigma_{11}}{\sigma_{12}}\right]^2 \frac{x_1}{x_2} \end{aligned}$$

$$\begin{aligned} s_{21} = s_{12} = \frac{8M_2^{\,2}}{(M_1 + M_2)^4}&\left[\frac{35}{32}\,(12M_1^{\,2} + 5M_2^{\,2})\Omega_{12}^{(1,1)\star} - \frac{63}{16}\,(4M_1^{\,2} \right.\\ &\quad + 5M_2^{\,2})\Omega_{12}^{(1,2)\star} + \frac{57}{2} M_2^{\,2}\Omega_{12}^{(1,3)\star} - 15M_2^{\,2}\Omega_{12}^{(1,4)\star}\\ &\left.\quad + 7M_1 M_2\,\Omega_{12}^{(2,2)\star} - 8M_1 M_2\,\Omega_{12}^{(2,3)\star}\right]\\ &+ \left(\frac{2M_2}{M_1 + M_2}\right)^{1/2}[7\Omega_{11}^{(2,2)\star} - 8\Omega_{11}^{(2,3)\star}]\left[\frac{\sigma_{11}}{\sigma_{12}}\right]^2 \frac{x_1}{x_2} \end{aligned}$$

$$\begin{aligned} s_{1-1} = s_{-11} = -\frac{8(M_1 M_2)^{3/2}}{(M_1 + M_2)^3}&\left[\frac{55}{8}\,\Omega_{12}^{(1,1)\star} - \frac{15}{2}\,\Omega_{12}^{(1,2)\star}\right.\\ &\left.\quad + 6\Omega_{12}^{(1,3)\star} - 2\Omega_{12}^{(2,2)\star}\right] \end{aligned}$$

$$\begin{aligned} s_{1-2} = s_{-21} = -\frac{8M_1^{\,5/2} M_2^{\,3/2}}{(M_1 + M_2)^4}&\left[\frac{595}{32}\,\Omega_{12}^{(1,1)\star} - \frac{567}{16}\,\Omega_{12}^{(1,2)\star} + \frac{57}{2}\,\Omega_{12}^{(1,3)\star}\right.\\ &\left.\quad - 15\Omega_{12}^{(1,4)\star} - 7\Omega_{12}^{(2,2)\star} + 8\Omega_{12}^{(2,3)\star}\right] \end{aligned}$$

$$s_{22} = \frac{8M_2}{(M_1+M_2)^5}\Bigg[\frac{35}{128}(40M_1^4 + 168M_1^2M_2^2 + 35M_2^4)\Omega_{12}^{(1,1)\star} - \frac{21M_2^2}{16}(84M_1^2 + 35M_2^2)\Omega_{12}^{(1,2)\star} + \frac{3}{4}M_2^2(108M_1^2 + 133M_2^2)\Omega_{12}^{(1,3)\star} - 105M_2^4\Omega_{12}^{(1,4)\star} + 45M_2^4\Omega_{12}^{(1,5)\star} + \frac{7}{2}M_1M_2(4M_1^2 + 7M_2^2)\Omega_{12}^{(2,2)\star} - 56M_1M_2^3\Omega_{12}^{(2,3)\star} + 40M_1M_2^3\Omega_{12}^{(2,4)\star} + 12M_1^2M_2^2\Omega_{12}^{(3,3)\star}\Bigg]$$

$$+ \left(\frac{2M_2}{M_1+M_2}\right)^{1/2}\left[\frac{77}{4}\Omega_{11}^{(2,2)\star} - 28\Omega_{11}^{(2,3)\star} + 20\Omega_{11}^{(2,4)\star}\right]\left[\frac{\sigma_{11}}{\sigma_{12}}\right]^2\frac{x_1}{x_2}$$

$$s_{2-2} = s_{-22} = -\frac{8(M_1M_2)^{5/2}}{(M_1+M_2)^5}\Bigg[\frac{8505}{128}\Omega_{12}^{(1,1)\star} - \frac{2499}{16}\Omega_{12}^{(1,2)\star} + \frac{723}{4}\Omega_{12}^{(1,3)\star} - 105\Omega_{12}^{(1,4)\star} + 45\Omega_{12}^{(1,5)\star} - \frac{77}{2}\Omega_{12}^{(2,2)\star} + 56\Omega_{12}^{(2,3)\star} - 40\Omega_{12}^{(2,4)\star} + 12\Omega_{12}^{(3,3)\star}\Bigg]$$

The other elements are obtained by noting that s_{ij} equals s_{-i-j} except that the roles of the two molecules are interchanged (this rule does not apply if either i or j is zero). The quantity σ which appears in these equations is the characteristic length which is used in the definition of the reduced collision integrals $\Omega^{(l,s)\star}$.

Kihara[1] obtained somewhat simpler expressions for the higher approximations to the transport coefficients in the following manner. According to Chapman and Cowling[3] the transport coefficients can be expressed as ratios of infinite determinants. The various orders of the Chapman and Cowling approximations correspond to replacing the infinite determinants by finite determinants of successively larger size. Kihara noted that the off-diagonal elements are small compared to the diagonal elements.

[3] S. Chapman and T. G. Cowling, *Mathematical Theory of Non-uniform Gases*, Cambridge Press (1952), p. 149 and 150.

His approximation consists of expanding the infinite determinants in powers of the off-diagonal elements. Expanding through the second power of the off-diagonal elements leads to results which are considerably simpler than Chapman and Cowling's second order approximation for viscosity, thermal conductivity, and diffusion and their first approximation to thermal diffusion. Kihara's approximation is exact in either the case of a Lorentzian ($M_1 \ll M_2$ and $x_1 \ll x_2$) or a Maxwellian ($\varphi = dr^{-4}$) gas. Kihara obtained the following results:

For pure gases:

$$f_\eta^{(\text{Kihara})} = 1 + \frac{3}{49}\left[\frac{4\Omega^{(2,3)\star}}{\Omega^{(2,2)\star}} - \frac{7}{2}\right]^2 \tag{8.A-6}$$

$$f_\lambda^{(\text{Kihara})} = 1 + \frac{2}{21}\left[\frac{4\Omega^{(2,3)\star}}{\Omega^{(2,2)\star}} - \frac{7}{2}\right]^2 \tag{8.A-7}$$

$$f_{\mathscr{D}}^{(\text{Kihara})} = 1 + \frac{(6\text{C}^\star - 5)^2}{16\text{A}^\star + 40} \tag{8.A-8}$$

For binary mixtures:

$$k_T^{(\text{Kihara})} = \frac{(6\text{C}_{12}{}^\star - 5)x_1x_2[S_1x_1 - S_2x_2]}{Q_1x_1{}^2 + Q_2x_2{}^2 + Q_{12}x_1x_2} \tag{8.A-9}$$

in which

$$S_1 = \frac{2}{5}\left(\frac{M_1}{M_2}\right)\left(\frac{2M_2}{M_1 + M_2}\right)^{1/2}\left(\frac{\Omega_1^{(2,2)\star}}{\Omega_{12}^{(1,1)\star}}\right)\left(\frac{\sigma_1{}^2}{\sigma_{12}{}^2}\right) - \frac{8}{5}\frac{M_1M_2}{(M_1 + M_2)^2}\text{A}_{12}{}^\star - \frac{3M_2(M_2 - M_1)}{(M_1 + M_2)^2}$$

S_2 is the same as S_1 after an interchange of roles of molecules 1 and 2.

$$Q_1 = \left(\frac{2}{5}\right)\frac{2}{(M_1 + M_2)M_2}\left(\frac{2M_2}{M_1 + M_2}\right)^{1/2}\left(\frac{\Omega_1^{(2,2)\star}}{\Omega_{12}^{(1,1)\star}}\right)\left(\frac{\sigma_1{}^2}{\sigma_{12}{}^2}\right) \cdot \left[3M_2{}^2 + M_1{}^2 + \frac{8}{5}M_1M_2\text{A}_{12}{}^\star\right]$$

Q_2 is same as Q_1 after an interchange of roles of molecules 1 and 2.

$$Q_{12} = \left(\frac{2}{5}\right)\left[\frac{15(M_1 - M_2)^2}{(M_1 + M_2)^2} + \frac{32M_1M_2}{(M_1 + M_2)^2}\text{A}_{12}{}^\star + \frac{8}{5}\frac{(M_1 + M_2)}{(M_1M_2)^{1/2}}\left(\frac{\Omega_1^{(2,2)\star}}{\Omega_{12}^{(1,1)\star}}\right)\left(\frac{\Omega_2^{(2,2)\star}}{\Omega_{12}^{(1,1)\star}}\right)\left(\frac{\sigma_1{}^2\sigma_2{}^2}{\sigma_{12}{}^4}\right)\right]$$

$k_T^{(\text{Kihara})}$ is much easier to compute than the $[k_T]_2$ since it involves fewer integrals. For a binary mixture of heavy isotopes, in place of Eq. 8.2–52, Kihara obtains the result.

$$k_T^{\star(\text{Kihara})} = \frac{59}{56}\left(\frac{6C^\star - 5}{A^\star}\right) \tag{8.A-10}$$

PROBLEMS

1. Show that for the Lennard-Jones (6-12) potential the product $B\eta^{3/2}T^{-3/4}$ is a universal function of $T^* = kT/\epsilon$. (B = second virial coefficient, η = coefficient of viscosity, T = absolute temperature).

2. By means of the tabulated functions for the Lennard-Jones (6-12) potential, calculate the following:
(a) The coefficient of viscosity of SF_6 at 500°K and 2 atm pressure.
(b) The coefficient of viscosity of a 1 to 1 mixture of Cl_2 and Br_2 at 450°K and 1 atm pressure.
(c) The coefficient of diffusion of the gas pair H_2O-CH_4 at 5 atm pressure and 500°K.
(d) The dimensionless ratio $\rho\mathscr{D}/\eta$ for Ne at 250°K.
(e) The quantity $k_T{}^\star$ for the isotopic thermal diffusion of Cl_2 at room temperature and pressure, for example, the diffusion of $Cl^{35}Cl^{35}$ into $Cl^{37}Cl^{37}$.

3. Estimate the following:
(a) The coefficient of thermal conductivity of CH_3COCH_3 at 450°K.
(b) The thermal diffusion ratio of a mixture of 85 per cent CH_4 and 15 per cent NH_3 at 500°K.
(c) The coefficient of viscosity of a mixture of 80 per cent N_2, 15 per cent O_2, and 5 per cent CH_3OH, at 800°K and 5 atm pressure.

4. Obtain the force constants for the Lennard-Jones (6-12) potential for N_2 and A from the experimental self-diffusion coefficients given in Table 8.4–13. Compare the results with the parameters obtained from the analysis of viscosity and compressibility data.

5. Use the results of this chapter to investigate the relative importance of the attractive and repulsive components of the intermolecular potential on the coefficient of viscosity of a pure gas. Calculate $\Omega^{(2,2)\star}$ for $\varphi_{\text{L.J.}} = 4\epsilon[(\sigma/r)^{12} - (\sigma/r)^6]$ and also for $\varphi_{\text{Inv.12}} = 4\epsilon(\sigma/r)^{12}$ at $T^* = kT/\epsilon = 1, 10, 100, 400$. Show that above $T^* = 10$ the contribution to $\eta(T)$ or $\Omega^{(2,2)\star}$ due to the attractive forces is less than 10 per cent. Use the results of Chapter 3 to make a similar analysis of the second virial coefficient, for which the attractive forces play an extremely important role at $T^* = 10$.

· 9 ·

The Transport Properties of Dense Gases and Liquids

The preceding two chapters deal with the kinetic theory of dilute gases and the use of this theory to calculate the transport coefficients. The entire development is based upon the Boltzmann integro-differential equation for the distribution function $f(\boldsymbol{r}, \boldsymbol{v}, t)$. This equation takes into account two-body collisions only and also assumes that the molecular dimensions are small in comparison with the mean distance between the molecules. Hence the results of this kinetic theory are not applicable to dense gases and liquids. In this chapter we turn our attention to four different approaches to the study of transport phenomena in dense systems. They are discussed in increasing order of mathematical complexity and rigor.

In the first section we consider the possibilities of correlating the pressure and temperature dependence of the transport properties by means of the principle of corresponding states in its various forms. On the basis of this principle, generalized charts have been prepared for the coefficient of viscosity. These charts provide the best means at the present time for estimating the viscosity of dense gases. It is unfortunate that sufficient experimental data are not available for the construction of corresponding states graphs for the other transport coefficients.

In the second section we discuss Eyring's application of the theory of absolute reaction rates to the various transport phenomena.[1] The energies and entropies of activation which appear in the general formulation of the various transport coefficients are evaluated by comparison with experimental data. These constants are then interpreted in terms of a simple model of the liquid or dense gas. The Eyring theory has been particularly successful in applications to plastic flow. It seems well adapted to transport properties in liquids, but is not suitable for gaseous systems.

The third section is devoted to a description of the Enskog theory of

[1] The basic theory of absolute reaction rates is discussed in Appendix A.

dense gases. This development, which preceded Eyring's work, is an extension of the low-density gas theory of Chapter 7, but has been developed only for gases composed of rigid spheres. The restriction to rigid spheres is made because multibody collisions need not be considered. The extension of the dilute gas kinetic theory involves then the introduction of the corrections necessary to account for the fact that the molecular diameter is not small in comparison with the average intermolecular distance in dense gases and liquids. Because of this fact it is necessary to take into account the transport of momentum and kinetic energy which takes place instantaneously between the centers of two rigid spherical molecules at a collision. This "collisional transfer" is indeed the principal mechanism for transport at high densities.[2]

Although the Enskog theory was derived for rigid spheres, the results can be applied to real gases. The transport properties of dense gases can be estimated in this manner from a knowledge of the transport coefficients in the dilute gas, the compressibility data for the dense gas, and an effective collision diameter for the molecules. When the effective collision diameter is adjusted so as to make a calculated value of a high density transport coefficient agree with an experimental value, excellent empirical agreement is obtained over a wide range of densities.

The final section is a summary of the rigorous kinetic theory of dense gases, with which the names of Kirkwood, Born, and Green have become associated. By means of statistical mechanics it is shown that we may begin with the Liouville equation and obtain exact expressions for the flux vectors in terms of the non-equilibrium radial distribution function. It is the evaluation of the non-equilibrium radial distribution function which is then the primary problem in this approach. Several approximate methods of accomplishing this have been suggested, but at present no completely satisfactory technique has been evolved. This statistical mechanical approach will ultimately lead to a kinetic theory of dense gases of accuracy comparable to that of dilute gases discussed

[2] The inclusion of the collisional mechanism for transfer of momentum enables us to explain a point in the theory of dilute gases which otherwise seems puzzling. In equilibrium statistical mechanics the admission of two-body collisions leads to the second virial coefficient as a correction to the ideal gas law. In non-equilibrium statistical mechanics (kinetic theory) the Boltzmann integro-differential equation, which allows for two-body collisions, leads to a pressure tensor which reduces in the equilibrium case to the ideal gas law. This apparent disagreement between two theories, each based on two-body collisions, results from the fact that in the kinetic theory of dilute gases the two-body collisions have really not been considered completely. When the collisional transfer terms are added to the Boltzmann equation, the subsequent analysis leads quite naturally to a pressure tensor which contains a second virial coefficient.

in Chapter 7. At the present, however, the theory has not yet attained the same degree of maturity, and only meager numerical results are available.

1. The Principle of Corresponding States

The pressure dependence of the transport properties has received very little attention from the experimentalists, and consequently only a limited amount of empirical information is available.[1] This information may be summarized and correlated by means of the principle ofcorresponding states. The application of this principle to the equation of state of dense gases and liquids is discussed in § 4.1. It is shown there that corresponding states arguments provide a practical method for making use of measured properties of one substance to predict the properties of other substances under conditions where no data exist and no satisfactory theoretical treatments may be applied. Similar techniques may be applied in the theory of transport phenomena.

a. Experimental observation of the transport properties at high densities

We begin this section by summarizing some of the experimental results in the field of high-density transport phenomena. This brief discussion should serve to give a rough quantitative idea of the effect of pressure on the transport coefficients and to indicate their behavior as the gas is compressed until it finally reaches the liquid state.

i. *Viscosity*[2–5]

The experimental isotherms for the coefficient of viscosity of CO_2 as a function of pressure[6] are given in Fig. 9.1–1. For this gas measurements

[1] J. R. Partington, *Advanced Treatise on Physical Chemistry*, Longmans (1950).

[2] An extensive survey of the high-pressure viscosity measurements up to 1944 is given by E. W. Comings, B. J. Mayland, and R. S. Egly, *The Viscosity of Gases at High Pressures*, Engineering Experimental Station Bulletin Series 354, Vol. 42, No. 15, University of Illinois, November 28, 1944. A complete review of the bulk (or second) coefficient of viscosity in gases and liquids is given by S. M. Karim and L. Rosenhead, *Rev. Mod. Phys.*, **24**, 108 (1952). Experimental measurements of this coefficient have been made by F. Liebermann, *Phys. Rev.*, **73**, 537(A) (1948); *J. Accoust. Soc. Am.*, **20**, 868 (1948); and *Phys. Rev.*, **75**, 1415 (1949).

[3] D. M. Newitt, *The Design of High Pressure Plant and the Properties of Fluids at High Pressures*, Oxford University Press (1940), p. 404 *et seq.*

[4] O. A. Hougen and K. M. Watson, *Chemical Process Principles*, Wiley (1947), Part III, pp. 869 et seq. A recent treatise, J. B. Maxwell's *Data Book on Hydrocarbons*, Van Nostrand (1951), gives corresponding states charts similar to those of Hougen and Watson for the coefficient of viscosity, the compressibility factor, and all of the thermodynamical properties of light, medium, and heavy molecular weight hydrocarbons treated separately.

[5] Measurements of the viscosity of N_2 have been made with great accuracy by A. Michels and A. O. Gibson, *Proc. Roy. Soc.* (*London*), **A134**, 288 (1931).

[6] P. Phillips, *Proc. Roy. Soc.* (*London*), **A87**, 48 (1912).

have been made which extend into the critical region, and thus a good idea of the behavior of the viscosity in both the gaseous and liquid phase is obtained. Below the critical temperature there are discontinuities in the viscosity isotherms. By analogy with the p-V isotherms we may draw S-shaped curves to connect the points of discontinuity (this is shown as a

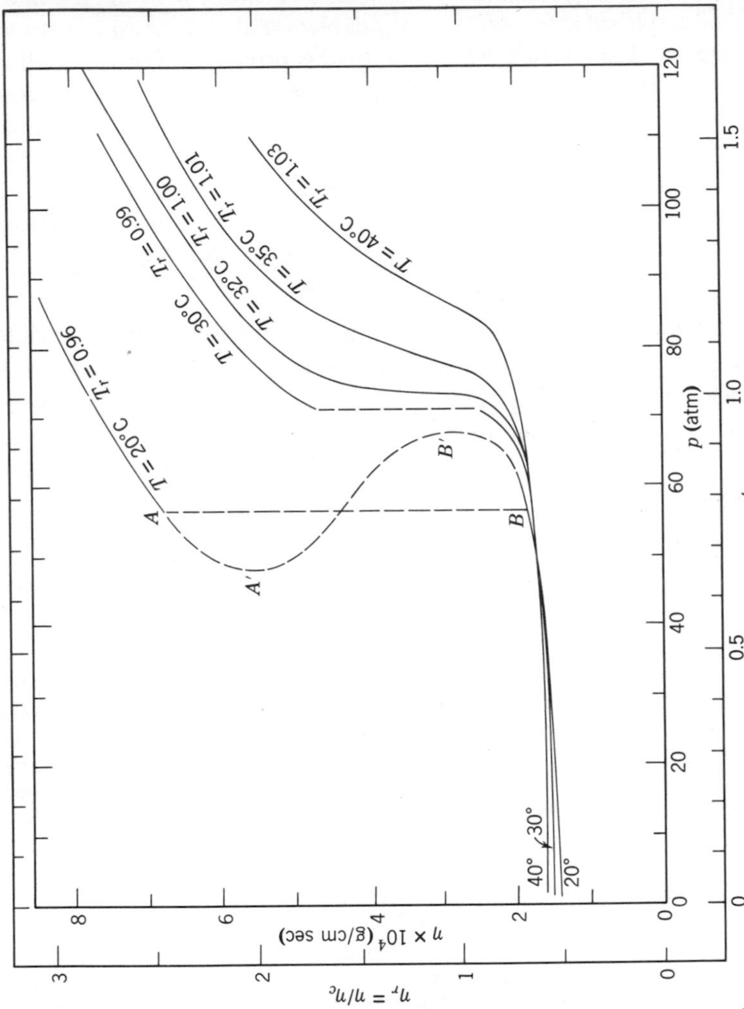

Fig. 9.1–1. The viscosity of CO_2 as a function of pressure at several temperatures. [From D. M. Newitt, *The Design of High Pressure Plant and the Properties of Fluids at High Pressures*, Oxford University Press (1940), p. 409.]

dotted line in Fig. 9.1–1). The portion AA' of this curve may be interpreted as the viscosity of the superheated liquid, and the portion BB' as the viscosity of the supercooled vapor. Note that there is a crossing of the isotherms as the system goes from the gas phase to the liquid phase, since with increasing temperature the viscosity of a liquid decreases and that of a gas increases. The crossing actually takes place before the gas is liquefied.

ii. *Thermal Conductivity*

Few measurements have been made of thermal conductivity of gases at high pressures.[7] In Fig. 9.1–2 is shown the coefficient of thermal conductivity for argon[8] in the vicinity of the critical region. Some experimental measurements have also been made for N_2 and CO_2 in this region.[8] Measurements have been made on air, carbon dioxide, and some organic vapors[9] at pressures ranging from 50 to 760 mm Hg. In this pressure region there is little effect on the thermal conductivity of gases made up of ordinary molecules. However, for those substances which tend to form hydrogen bonded dimers the thermal conductivity has been found to increase rapidly with pressure in this region.

iii. *Diffusion*

According to the kinetic theory of dilute gases the diffusion coefficient is inversely proportional to the overall density. Hence in studying the effect of pressure on the diffusion coefficient the product $\rho\mathscr{D}_{12}$ should be studied. Unfortunately, there are practically no data on the pressure dependence of $\rho\mathscr{D}_{12}$ except some recent measurements[10] of the self-diffusion coefficient of CO_2, CS_2, CH_4, and ordinary diffusion in some liquid mixtures. For the self-diffusion of CO_2 at 42°C the product $\rho\mathscr{D}$ is reduced to about half its low-pressure value at densities around $\rho = 0.7$ gram per cc.

iv. *Thermal Diffusion*

Because of the importance of thermal diffusion as a separation process,

[7] A summary of the experimental measurements of thermal conductivity has been given by E. U. Franck, *Chemie-Ingenieur Technik*, **25**, 238 (1953).

[8] E. Borovik, *J. Phys. USSR*, **11**, 149 (1947)—N_2. Sellschopp, *Forsch. Gebiete Ingenieurw.*, **5**, 162 (1934)—CO_2. A. Uhlir, Jr., *J. Chem. Phys.*, **20**, 463 (1952)—A, N_2.

[9] J. D. Lambert, E. N. Staines, and S. D. Woods, *Proc. Roy. Soc.* (*London*), **A200**, 262 (1950).

[10] Self-diffusion CO_2: K. D. Timmerhaus and H. G. Drickamer, *J. Chem. Phys.*, **19**, 1242 (1951); **20**, 981 (1952); W. L. Robb and H. G. Drickamer, *ibid.*, **19**, 1504 (1951).

Self-diffusion CS_2: R. C. Koeller and H. G. Drickamer, *ibid.*, **21**, 267 (1953).

Self-diffusion CH_4: Q. R. Jeffries and H. G. Drickamer, *ibid.* (forthcoming publication).

Liquid I_2-Sulfur: D. R. Cova and H. G. Drickamer, *ibid.* (forthcoming publication).

Liquid SnI_4-CCl_4: E. P. Doane and H. G. Drickamer, *ibid.* (forthcoming publication).

Liquid CS_2-Organic Mixtures: R. C. Koeller and H. G. Drickamer, *ibid.*, **21**, 575 (1953).

Water and Sulfate Solutions: R. B. Cuddeback, R. C. Koeller, and H. G. Drickamer, *ibid.*, **21**, 589 (1953).

Water and Alcohol Solutions: R. B. Cuddeback and H. G. Drickamer, *ibid.*, **21**, 597 (1953).

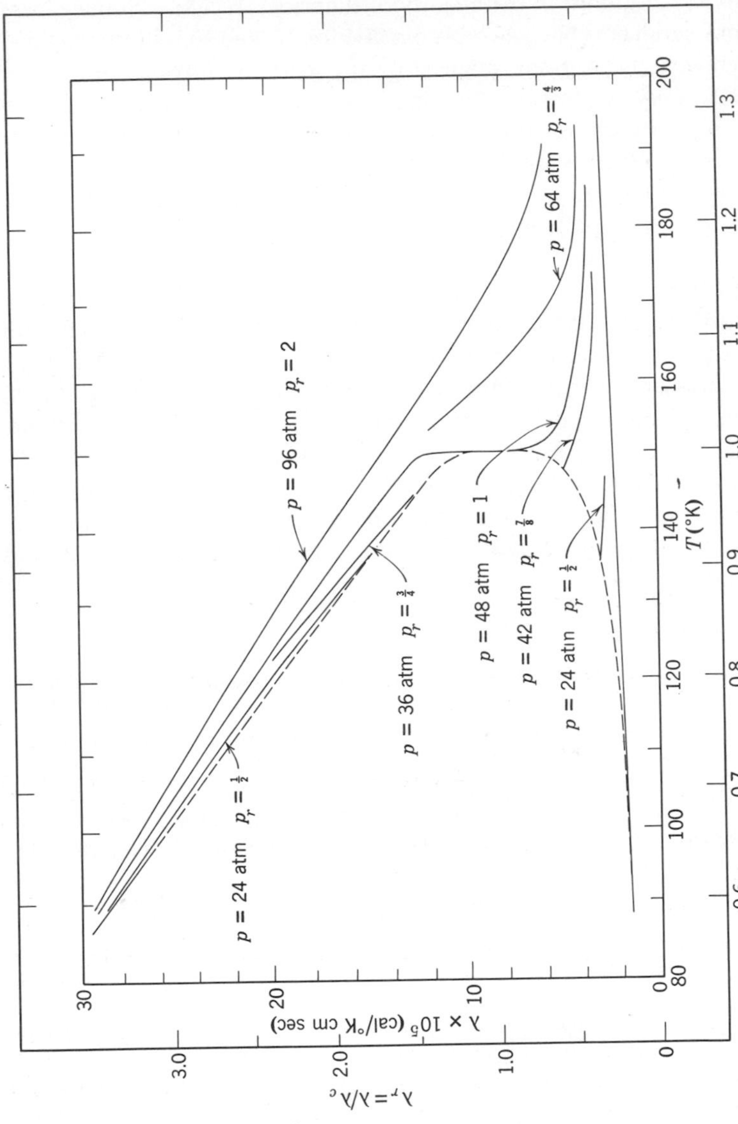

Fig. 9.1–2. The thermal conductivity of argon as a function temperature at several pressures. [From A. Uhlir, Jr., *J. Chem. Phys.*, **20**, 463 (1952).]

a considerable amount of attention has recently been devoted to the experimental study of this phenomenon.[11,12] To illustrate the effect of pressure on the thermal diffusion ratio the experimental results for several gas pairs are summarized in Fig. 9.1–3. It is clear that for some gas systems a considerably greater separation can be achieved at high pressures.

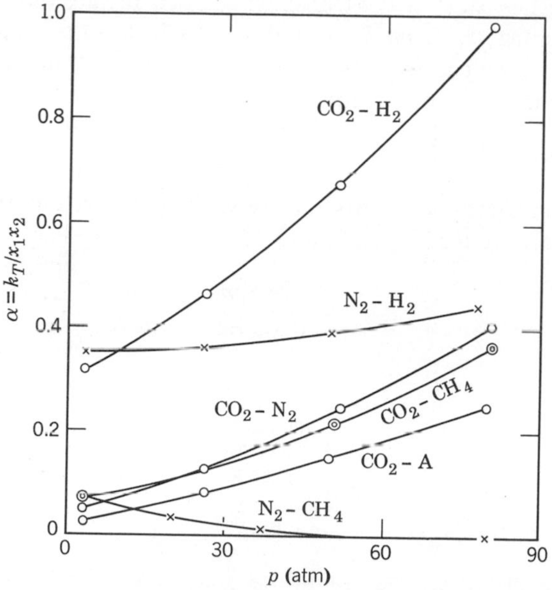

Fig. 9.1–3. Pressure dependence of the thermal diffusion factor $\alpha = k_T/x_1x_2$ at $T = 427°K$. The average mole fraction of the components is about 0.5. [From E. W. Becker, *J. Chem. Phys.*, **19**, 131 (1951).]

b. Development of a principle of corresponding states for spherical non-polar molecules

A principle of corresponding states may be derived by means of dimensional analysis. Let us consider a gas made up of spherical non-polar molecules and let us assume that the intermolecular potential

[11] E. W. Becker, *J. Chem. Phys.*, **19**, 131 (1951), *Zeit. f. Naturforschung*, **5a**, 457 (1950), has studied the systems CO_2-H_2, H_2-N_2, CO_2-N_2, CO_2-CH_4, CO_2-A, and N_2-CH_4 by means of a two-bulb system.

[12] A separation column has been used by Drickamer and his co-workers for the study of the effect of pressure on thermal diffusion: (a) H. G. Drickamer, V. J. O'Brien, J. C. Bresee, and C. E. Ockert, *J. Chem. Phys.*, **16**, 122 (1948)—CO_2-C_3H_8. (b) H. G. Drickamer, E. W. Mellow, and L. H. Tung, *J. Chem. Phys.*, **18**, 945 (1950)—A-Ne. (c) L. H. Tung and H. G. Drickamer, *J. Chem. Phys.*, **18**, 1031 (1950)—Xe-CH_4. (d) N. C. Pierce, R. B. Duffield, and H. G. Drickamer, *J. Chem. Phys.*, **18**, 950 (1950); E. B. Giller, R. B. Duffield, and H. G. Drickamer, *J. Chem. Phys.*, **18**, 1027 (1950)—Xe-C_2H_6.

energy may be characterized by two parameters—a characteristic length σ and a characteristic energy ϵ. This is true, for example, if the forces between molecules are two-body forces and if the potential of interaction is of the Lennard-Jones type. The properties of the molecules in a substance are then specified by the mass m and the two constants σ and ϵ. The bulk properties, such as the transport coefficients, are then functions of the six quantities, v, T, m, k, σ, and ϵ. As in the discussion of the equation of state, we can express the temperature and volume in terms of the dimensionless groups T^* and v^*:

$$T^* = kT/\epsilon \qquad v^* = v/\sigma^3 = \tilde{V}/\tilde{N}\sigma^3 \tag{9.1-1}$$

Similarly the transport coefficients themselves may be written in terms of the dimensionless groups $\mathscr{D}^*$, η^*, and λ^*.

$$\begin{aligned} \mathscr{D}^* &= \frac{\mathscr{D}\sigma^2}{\sqrt{m\epsilon}}\frac{m}{\sigma^3} \\ \eta^* &= \frac{\eta\sigma^2}{\sqrt{m\epsilon}} \\ \lambda^* &= \frac{\lambda\sigma^2}{\sqrt{m\epsilon}}\frac{m}{k} \end{aligned} \tag{9.1-2}$$

That these are dimensionless quantities may easily be seen from the formulae for the low-density transport coefficients given in Eqs. 8.2–9, 10, 11. The dimensionless groups $\mathscr{D}^*$, η^*, and λ^* are then functions of T^*, v^*, k, m, σ, and ϵ. The first two variables are dimensionless whereas the last four are not. Clearly any dimensionless function can be written in terms of dimensionless arguments. Therefore, since no dimensionless combinations of k, m, σ, and ϵ exist, it follows the $\mathscr{D}^*$, η^*, and λ^* are independent of these parameters.[13] Thus:

$$\begin{aligned} \mathscr{D}^* &= \mathscr{D}^*(v^*, T^*) \\ \eta^* &= \eta^*(v^*, T^*) \\ \lambda^* &= \lambda^*(v^*, T^*) \end{aligned} \tag{9.1-3}$$

The functional form of these reduced transport coefficients depends only on the form assumed for the intermolecular potential energy function.

[13] For a discussion of dimensional analysis see P. W. Bridgman, *Dimensional Analysis*, Yale University Press, 2nd Ed. (1931); also J. H. Perry, *Chemical Engineers' Handbook*, McGraw-Hill, 3rd Ed. (1950), pp. 93 et seq.

From the formulae given in § 8.2 it is clear that in the low-density limit the reduced transport coefficients have the form indicated in Eqs. 9.1–3:

$$\mathscr{D}^*(v^*, T^*) = \frac{3}{8\sqrt{\pi}} \frac{\sqrt{T^*}}{\Omega^{(1,1)\star}(T^*)} v^*$$

$$\eta^*(v^*, T^*) = \frac{5}{16\sqrt{\pi}} \frac{\sqrt{T^*}}{\Omega^{(2,2)\star}(T^*)} \tag{9.1–4}$$

$$\lambda^*(v^*, T^*) = \frac{75}{64\sqrt{\pi}} \frac{\sqrt{T^*}}{\Omega^{(2,2)\star}(T^*)}$$

At finite pressures the functional form is more complicated and has not yet been successfully obtained from theoretical developments. In view of this fact, the principle of corresponding states may be of considerable value for predicting the transport coefficients at high densities.

c. Applications of the principle of corresponding states

The coefficient of viscosity is the only one of the transport coefficients which has been studied to any extent by means of the principle of corresponding states. The principle may be applied in several different ways, which we describe briefly.

i. *Reduction with Molecular Parameters*

It would be possible to apply Eqs. 9.1–3 directly to a study of the transport properties at high pressures. This method has not been used, however, and is the least practical inasmuch as it applies well only to those gases which satisfy the basic assumptions of the method, that is, spherical non-polar molecules. The noble gases can be studied by means of this relation and also any other group of molecules which are chemically similar.

ii. *Reduction with Critical Constants, p_c and T_c*

According to the principle of corresponding states as applied to the equation of state, ϵ is a universal constant multiplied by T_c, and σ is proportional to $\tilde{V}_c^{1/3}$. Hence the transport coefficients reduced by various combinations of $\tilde{V}_c$ and T_c are functions of the reduced temperature $T_r = T/T_c$ and the reduced volume $V_r = V/V_c$. This method of reduction of the viscosity was first suggested and applied by Kamerlingh Onnes.[14]

[14] H. Kamerlingh Onnes, *Verhand. Akad. Amsterdam*, **21**, 2de Stuk, 8 (1881).

Inasmuch as it is usually difficult to measure the critical volume accurately, it is more convenient to perform the indicated reductions with the critical pressure. Then we may write

$$\begin{aligned} \mathscr{D}_R &= \mathscr{D} M^{1/2} p_c^{1/3} (RT_c)^{-5/6} = \mathscr{D}_R(p_r, T_r) \\ \eta_R &= \eta M^{-1/2} p_c^{-2/3} (RT_c)^{1/6} = \eta_R(p_r, T_r) \\ \lambda_R &= \lambda M^{1/2} p_c^{-2/3} (RT_c)^{1/6} = \lambda_R(p_r, T_r) \end{aligned} \tag{9.1-5}$$

These relations should be generally more applicable than those given in Eq. 9.1-3.

iii. *Reduction with Critical Values of the Transport Coefficients*

The transport coefficients may also be reduced by dividing them by their values at the critical point. Then we obtain the universal relations

$$\begin{aligned} \mathscr{D}_r &= \mathscr{D}/\mathscr{D}_c = \mathscr{D}_r(p_r, T_r) \\ \eta_r &= \eta/\eta_c = \eta_r(p_r, T_r) \\ \lambda_r &= \lambda/\lambda_c = \lambda_r(p_r, T_r) \end{aligned} \tag{9.1-6}$$

in which $T_r = T/T_c$ and $p_r = p/p_c$. It is clear that the $\mathscr{D}_r$, η_r, λ_r are constant multiples of $\mathscr{D}_R$, η_R, λ_R, respectively. The $\eta_r(p_r, T_r)$ forms the basis of the plot of "generalized viscosities" given in Hougen and Watson[4] and shown in Fig. 9.1-4. Of course the transport coefficients cannot easily be measured at the critical point. However, these critical values may be obtained by curve-fitting experimental data in any particular region to the generalized curve. This method is thus one which provides a method of extrapolation of measured values and of necessity fits the measured region accurately. In this respect this method is preferable to the preceding one. It has, however, the disadvantage that experimental values of the transport coefficients must be available. However, it is possible to estimate the critical value of the viscosity by means of the relation[3]

$$\eta_c \times 10^7 = 616 \frac{\sqrt{MT_c}}{\tilde{V}_c^{2/3}} \tag{9.1-7}$$

This is consistent with the concepts discussed in the previous paragraph, and similar expressions could be derived for the other transport properties. It is clear that if such expressions are used for the coefficients at the critical point this application reduces to the same method as that discussed in the preceding paragraph.

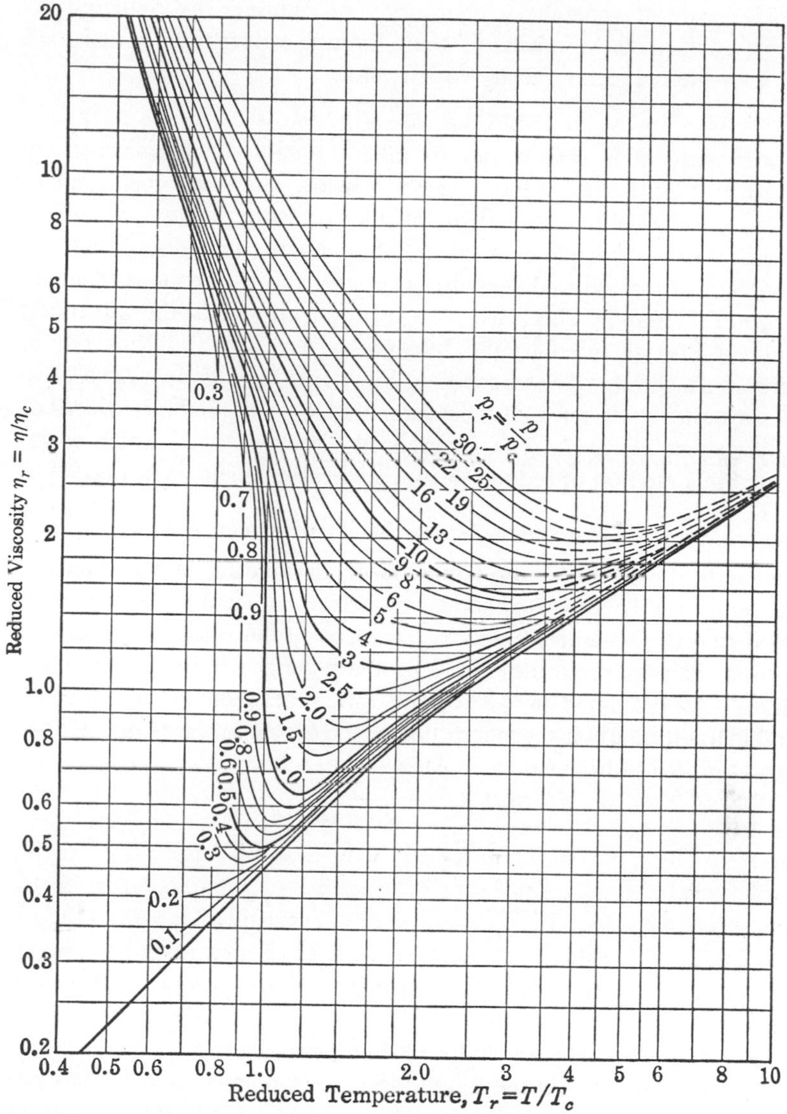

Fig. 9.1–4. The reduced viscosity $\eta_r = \eta/\eta_c$ as a function of the reduced temperature $T_r = T/T_c$ at various values of the reduced pressure $p_r = p/p_c$. [From O. A. Hougen and K. M. Watson, *Chemical Process Principles*, Wiley (1947). Graph originally prepared by O. A. Uyehara and K. M. Watson, *National Petroleum News*, Technical Section, **36**, 764 (Oct. 4, 1944).]

iv. *Reduction with Zero-Pressure Properties*[1]

Another type of generalized chart may be obtained by reducing the transport coefficients by means of their limiting values at low densities. In this case the reduced viscosity is defined as

$$\eta^{\#} = \eta(T, p)/\eta(T, p = 0) \qquad (9.1\text{–}8)$$

(For most gases it is satisfactory to take the value of the viscosity at 1 atm to be the limiting value at zero pressure, since the coefficient of viscosity is relatively independent of the pressure at low densities.) According to the principle of corresponding states this reduced viscosity is a function of the reduced pressure $p_r = p/p_c$ and the reduced temperature $T_r = T/T_c$ only. This form of the application has the advantage that the results are fitted to the zero-pressure values and thus reduce properly in this limit. The viscosity at low densities is known for a great many substances. It may also be estimated by the methods described in the preceding chapter. The generalized viscosity chart[1] which corresponds to this method of reduction of the variables is shown in Fig. 9.1–5.

d. The principle of corresponding states for polar molecules[15]

The applications of the principle of corresponding states discussed above apply strictly only to spherical non-polar molecules. It was there assumed that the potential function representing the interaction between the various pairs of molecules could be characterized by two parameters, σ and ϵ. As discussed in § 3.10, the forces between polar molecules depend in addition upon the magnitude of the dipole moment, μ. Consequently, Eqs. 9.1–3 become, for polar gases:

$$\begin{aligned} \mathscr{D}^* &= \frac{\mathscr{D}\sigma^2}{\sqrt{m\epsilon}}\frac{m}{\sigma^3} &&= \mathscr{D}^*(T^*, v^*; \mu^*) \\ \eta^* &= \frac{\eta\sigma^2}{\sqrt{m\epsilon}} &&= \eta^*(T^*, v^*; \mu^*) \qquad (9.1\text{–}9) \\ \lambda^* &= \frac{\lambda\sigma^2}{\sqrt{m\epsilon}}\frac{m}{k} &&= \lambda^*(T^*, v^*; \mu^*) \end{aligned}$$

in which $\mu^* = \mu/\sqrt{\epsilon\sigma^3}$ is the reduced dipole moment.

As pointed out in § 8.6 the kinetic theory of polar molecules has not yet been developed to the point that the function $\eta^*(T^*, v^*; \mu^*)$ may be rigorously predicted even in the low-density limit. Let us, however, consider those few polar molecules for which both the viscosity and the second virial coefficient have been measured. As discussed in § 3.10, the second virial coefficient measurements may be used to estimate the

[15] J. S. Rowlinson and J. R. Townley, *Trans. Faraday*, **49**, 1 (1953).

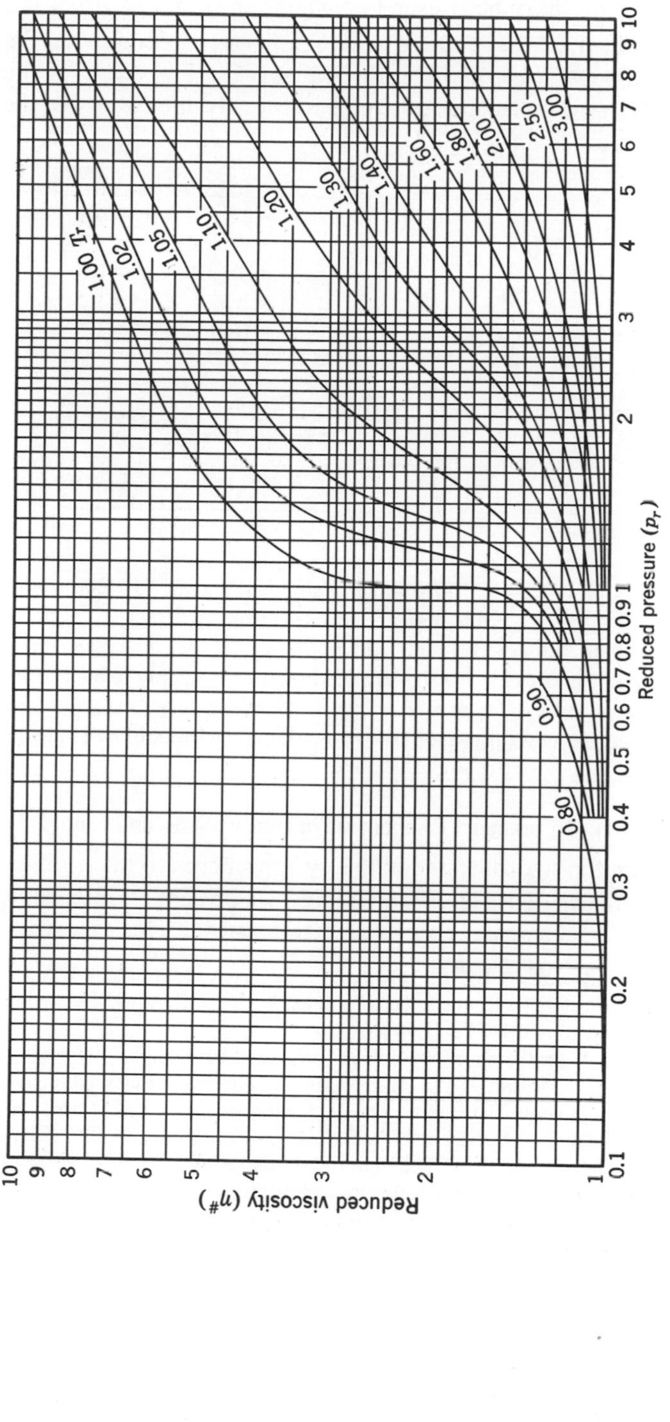

Fig. 9.1–5. The viscosity reduced by the zero pressure value as a function of the reduced pressure and temperature. [From E. W. Comings, B. J. Mayland, and R. S. Egly, *The Viscosity of Gases at High Pressures*, Engineering Experiment Station Bulletin Series 354, Vol. 42, No. 15, University of Illinois, November 28, 1944.]

molecular force constants and also μ^*. These constants along with the zero pressure viscosities have been used to compute the reduced viscosities $\eta^* = \eta\sigma^2/\sqrt{m\epsilon}$. In Fig. 9.1–6 these curves are given along with the theoretical curve for $\mu^* = 0$, as given by Eq. 9.1–4. The effect of the polar terms in the intermolecular potential is roughly indicated by the dependence of the curves on μ^*.

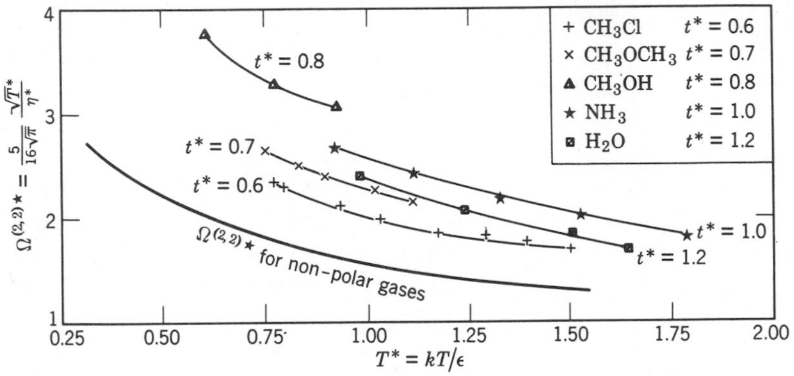

Fig. 9.1–6. Experimental $\Omega^{(2,2)\star}$ for some polar gases. Plotted are the experimental values of $\Omega^{(2,2)\star}$ for several polar gases calculated from $[\Omega^{(2,2)}]_{\text{exptl}} = 266.93 [\sqrt{MT}/\sigma^2(\eta \times 10^7)]$. The values of σ and ϵ used are those calculated by Rowlinson from second virial coefficients (see § 3.10). The parameter t^* is simply related to the reduced dipole moment μ^* by $t = \mu^{*2}/\sqrt{8} = \mu^2/\sqrt{8}\epsilon\sigma^3$. According to the principle of corresponding states, the deviations from the non-polar curve should be the greater for larger t^* values.

2. The Eyring Theory of Transport Phenomena in Dense Gases and Liquids[1, 2]

Before discussing the rigorous kinetic theory approaches to the problem of transport processes in dense gases and liquids, we present an interesting approach based on the theory of absolute reaction rates. This theory has

[1] A very brief derivation of the Eyring rate equation is given in Appendix 9.A. A more complete discussion may be found in S. Glasstone, K. J. Laidler, and H. Eyring, *Theory of Rate Processes*, McGraw-Hill (1941).

[2] The first application of the theory of absolute reaction rates to transport phenomena was given by H. Eyring, *J. Chem. Phys.*, **4**, 283 (1936). Review articles have been prepared by R. E. Powell, W. E. Roseveare, and H. Eyring, *Ind. and Eng. Chem.*, **33**, 430 (1941), and J. F. Kincaid, H. Eyring, and A. E. Stearn, *Chem. Revs.*, **28**, 301 (1941). The former is very concise. Both articles summarize the applications to viscosity (including the effects of temperature and pressure), diffusion, ionic conductance, and thermal conductivity. The latter article also considers the special problems arising from the motion of large molecules which is of interest in plastic flows. Another summary of the applications to transport phenomena is given in Glasstone, Laidler, and Eyring, *loc. cit.*, Ch. IX.

been moderately successful in predicting the transport coefficients in the liquid phase and explaining them on a simple pictorial basis. The fundamental equation for the specific rate constant k' is the Eyring equation (Eq. 9A–11):

$$k' = \kappa(kT/h)e^{-\Delta\tilde{G}^{\ddagger}/RT} = \kappa(kT/h)e^{\Delta\tilde{S}^{\ddagger}/R}\, e^{-\Delta\tilde{H}^{\ddagger}/RT} \qquad (9.2\text{–}1)$$

Here $\Delta\tilde{G}^{\ddagger}$, $\Delta\tilde{H}^{\ddagger}$, and $\Delta\tilde{S}^{\ddagger}$ are the Gibbs free energy, enthalpy, and entropy of activation, respectively. The factor κ is the *transmission coefficient*, that is, the probability that a process actually takes place once the system is in the *activated state*. In most well-behaved rate processes, κ varies between $\frac{1}{2}$ and 1, and in this discussion it is assumed to be unity.

Clearly, in order to apply this theory to the study of diffusion, viscosity, and thermal conductivity it is necessary to assume that there is some one type of mechanism which is responsible for the flow of molecules, and in which there is one slow step which can be identified with the "activated state." It is necessary to know the number of molecules involved in an elementary flow process, but it is not necessary that the mechanism be specified. However, it is impossible to ascertain *a priori* whether one, two, or a large number of molecules cooperate in the elementary flow process. Eyring has proposed that the flow ordinarily involves only one molecule at a time so that the rate processes are unimolecular. The results give good empirical agreement, and energies and entropies of activation are obtained which are of a magnitude which may be explained on the basis of a simple unimolecular model.

a. The coefficient of viscosity

In order to describe the process of viscous flow let us consider the model of a liquid shown in Fig. 9.2–1 with n molecules per unit volume. As in the discussion of the high density equation of state in § 4.4, we imagine that a liquid has a lattice-like structure and that the molecules are confined to their individual cells by their neighbors. Let the distance between lattice sites be a, and the distance between adjacent planes of molecules be δ. The fundamental rate process which we consider is the movement of a molecule to a vacant site near by. In order to squeeze through the "bottleneck" formed by its nearest neighbors, the wandering molecule must pass through a region of high potential energy. This is indicated in Fig. 9.2–1. The potential curve is symmetrical about the "bottleneck" if there are no external forces on the system. If there is an external force per unit area F tending to displace one layer of molecules with respect to another layer, the potential energy curve becomes distorted so that the molecule goes "downhill" if it jumps in the same direction as the impressed force and goes "uphill" if it goes in the opposite direction.

Let us define as the forward process the movement of a molecule into a hole in the direction of the applied force; the reverse process is then defined as the movement of a molecule into a hole in the direction opposite

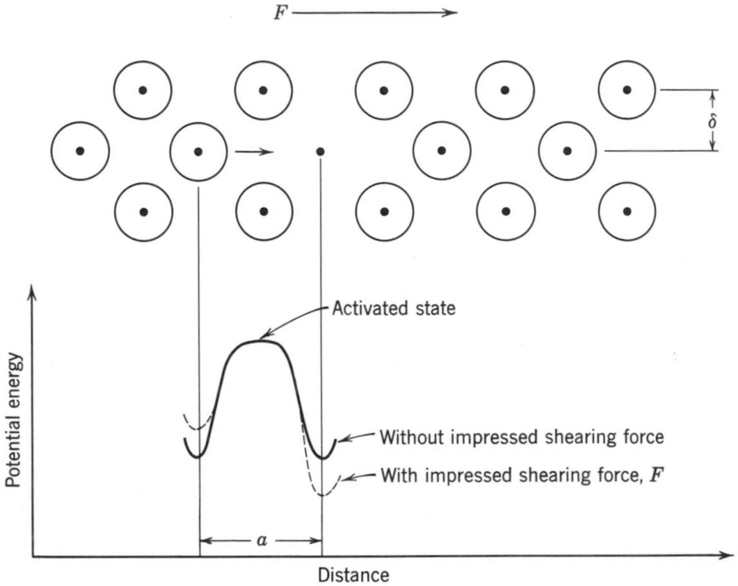

Fig. 9.2–1. Cross-section of an idealized liquid illustrating the fundamental rate process involved in viscous flow. A molecule must pass through a bottleneck in order to move into an unoccupied site.

to that of the applied force. Let k_f' and k_r' be the frequencies of the forward and the reverse processes. Then the net velocity of flow of fluid with respect to the lattice sites in the direction of the applied force is $v_0 = a(k_f' - k_r')$.

The frequencies k_f' and k_r' are given by Eq. 9.2–1, but the free energy of activation for the two processes is different, since the forward process is easier than the reverse process. The force acting on a particular molecule and tending to move it forward is the force per unit area, F, multiplied by the area associated with one molecule, $1/n\delta$. This force, $F/n\delta$, acts to lessen the free energy of activation for a jump in the direction of the force and to increase the free energy of activation for a jump in the opposite direction. If the activated state is midway between the two lattice sites, the work done by the external force in moving the molecule a distance $\frac{1}{2}a$

into the activated state is $\frac{1}{2}aF/n\delta$. This work is the amount by which the free energy of activation in the two directions is changed. Thus the frequencies k_f' and k_r' may be written as

$$k_f' = k_0' e^{+aF/2\delta nkT} \tag{9.2–2}$$

$$k_r' = k_0' e^{-aF/2\delta nkT} \tag{9.2–3}$$

in which k_0' is the value of k_f' and k_r' in the absence of an external force F. The net velocity of flow of one layer with respect to the one next to it is then

$$v_0 = a(k_f' - k_r') = 2ak_0' \sinh (aF/2\delta nkT) \tag{9.2–4}$$

From this result and the definition of the coefficient of viscosity given in Eq. 8.1–22 we get

$$\eta = \frac{F}{v_0/\delta} = \frac{F\delta}{2ak_0' \sinh (aF/2n\delta kT)} \tag{9.2–5}$$

This equation predicts that the viscosity is dependent on the external force—that is, the flow is *non-Newtonian.*[3] It should be noted that the Eyring theory is the only existing molecular treatment of transport phenomena which explains such behavior. For ordinary liquids and reasonably small external forces, $aF/2\delta nkT$ is very small compared to unity. Hence $\sinh (aF/2\delta nkT)$ can be replaced by the first term in its Taylor expansion, which is $aF/2\delta nkT$, and the expression for the coefficient of viscosity becomes

$$\eta = \left(\frac{\delta}{a}\right)^2 \frac{nkT}{k_0'} = \left(\frac{\delta}{a}\right)^2 nhe^{+\Delta\tilde{G}^{\ddagger}/RT} \tag{9.2–6}$$

In this case the flow is *Newtonian* in the sense that the viscosity is independent of the applied force. Often it is assumed for the sake of simplicity that the distance between molecular layers, δ, is the same as the distance between the lattice points, a, so that the factor $(\delta/a)^2$ is unity. In plastic flow the applied forces are sufficiently large that the argument of the hyperbolic sine is large compared to unity and the viscosity depends upon the magnitude of the applied forces.

Equations 9.2–5, 6 serve to express the viscosity in terms of the free energy of activation, $\Delta\tilde{G}^{\ddagger}$, which quantity is obtained empirically. Since the bonds between neighboring molecules, which must be broken in order to make a hole, are the same as those which are broken in the process of vaporization, it follows that the energy required to form a hole (the size of the specific volume of a molecule) is the energy of vaporization, $\Delta\tilde{U}_{\text{vap}}$.

[3] For discussions of non-Newtonian flow, see: M. Reiner, *Deformation and Flow*, H. K. Lewis and Co., London (1949), and W. Philippoff, *Viskosität der Kolloide*, Steinkopff (1942) [lithoprinted by Edwards Brothers (1944)].

We might, therefore, suppose that the free energy of activation is proportional to the energy of vaporization.

The enthalpy of vaporization, $\Delta H_{\text{vap}} = \Delta U_{\text{vap}} + RT$ is a somewhat more familiar quantity than ΔU_{vap}. Empirically it is found that

$$\Delta \tilde{G}^{\ddagger} = \Delta \tilde{U}_{\text{vap}}/2.45 \tag{9.2-7}$$

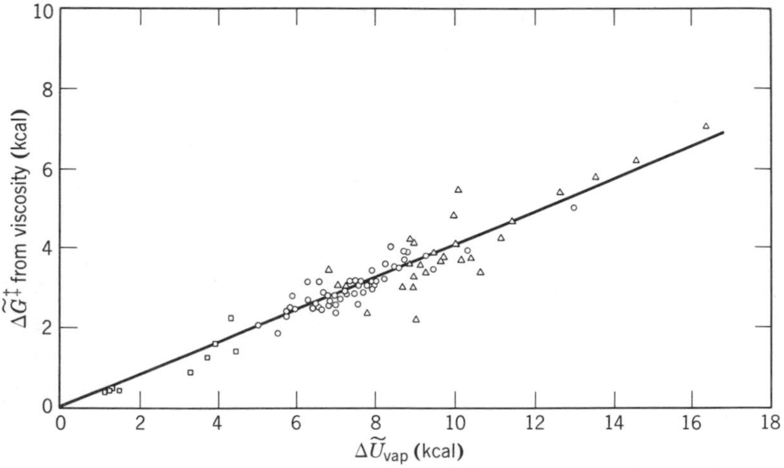

Fig. 9.2-2. Graphical demonstration of the validity of Eq. 9.2-7. The squares represent "permanent gases," the triangles represent hydrogen-bonded liquids, and the circles represent other liquids. [From J. F. Kincaid, H. Eyring, and A. E. Stearn, *Chem. Rev.*, **28**, 301 (1941).]

The general validity of this relation is shown in Fig. 9.2-2, where the free energies of activation obtained empirically from the observed viscosities of a large number of molecules (using Eq. 9.2-6) are compared with the observed energies of vaporization.

The fact that $\Delta \tilde{G}^{\ddagger} = \Delta \tilde{U}_{\text{vap}}/2.45$ seems to indicate that the size of the hole required to explain the viscous flow process is only a fraction of the specific volume of a molecule. A possible mechanism[4] of viscous flow consistent with this result is shown in Fig. 9.2-3. Here a pair of molecules squeeze together, rotate through approximately 90°, then separate. The extra volume required would be of the order of one-third the volume of a molecule.

The energy of vaporization can be estimated by Trouton's rule:

$$\Delta \tilde{U}_{\text{vap}} = \Delta \tilde{H}_{\text{vap}} - RT_b = 9.4RT_b \tag{9.2-8}$$

[4] J. O. Hirschfelder, D. Stevenson, and H. Eyring, *J. Chem. Phys.*, **5**, 896 (1937).

where T_b is the boiling point at 1 atm. The use of this relation enables us to write for the viscosity of the liquid:

$$\eta = hne^{3.8T_b/T} \tag{9.2–9}$$

This equation is useful for rough estimates.

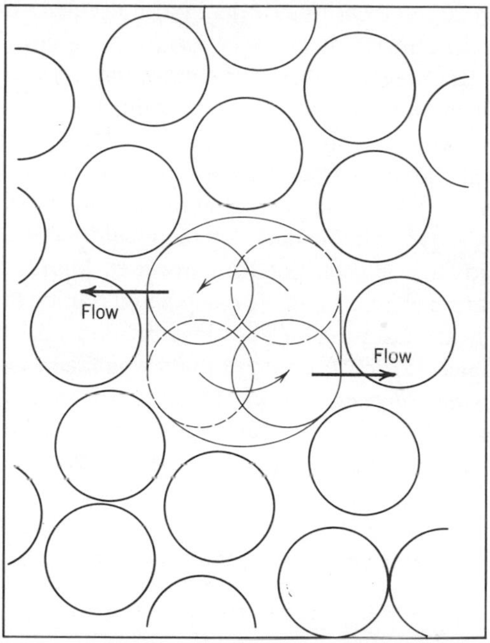

Fig. 9.2–3. Viscous flow by means of the rotation of double molecules. Two molecules collide to form a double molecule instantaneously. If there is sufficient space available, this double molecule can rotate and then dissociate. One layer of liquid can flow past another layer by a succession of these processes.

From the principle of corresponding states all substances at their melting points T_m should have the same value of $\Delta\tilde{U}_{\text{vap}}/RT_m$. Thus $\Delta\tilde{G}^{\ddagger}/RT_m$ and η/n should be the same for all substances at their melting points. For medium-sized molecules n does not vary much for different liquids, and it is found that at the melting point the viscosity is approximately 0.02 poise.

Let us now see what information can be obtained from experimental measurements of viscosity. From the *temperature dependence of viscosity at constant pressure* we can obtain the enthalpy of activation. For most substances it varies from one-third to one-fourth the energy of vaporization. For associated liquids it is much larger than for normal liquids. For liquid metals the heat of vaporization is very small and has a value consistent with the notion that the metallic ion is the unit of flow and the outer shell of conducting electrons is not involved. For long polymer molecules, the heat of activation is found to be around 10 kcal per mole independent of the chain length. This corresponds to a flow unit between 20 to 40 carbon atoms in a molecule. In other words, the long molecules seem to move snake fashion, one coil at a time.

By measuring the *temperature dependence of viscosity at constant volume* some information can be obtained about the role of holes in the flow process. We would think that the number of holes in a liquid would be almost independent of temperature at constant volume. If the heat of activation were due solely to the formation of holes, the temperature variation of the viscosity at constant volume would indeed be very small. For normal liquids this is true, but for associated liquids there is a considerable temperature effect. Thus for associated liquids there is evidence that part of the heat of activation goes into breaking the bonds between the associated molecules to make small units which can flow easier.

From the *pressure dependence of viscosity at constant temperature* can be determined the volume of activation or the additional volume required for the activated state.[5] For normal liquids this turns out to be approximately one-sixth of the volume per molecule.

The best empirical relationship which Eyring and his co-workers were able to find for the variation of the viscosity with composition is

$$\log \eta = x_1 \log \eta_1 + x_2 \log \eta_2 \tag{9.2-10}$$

Here η_1 and η_2 are the viscosities of the two pure components, and x_1 and x_2 are their mole fractions.

Recently Moore, Gibbs, and Eyring[6] extended the theory to hydrocarbons. They find sharp transition points where new types of motions set in. At low temperatures, the motion of the molecules is largely translational. At intermediate temperatures rocking or libration becomes important. Finally, at high temperatures, the molecules have free rotation about their long axes. At low temperatures flow takes place through the cooperation of two or more molecules. At high temperatures the flow is a unimolecular process. At the boiling point, for most aliphatic and aromatic hydrocarbons (in place of Eq. 9.2–7), it is found that $\Delta\tilde{G}^{\ddagger} = -450 + (\Delta\tilde{U}_{\text{vap}}/1.87)$ where the 450 is in cal/mole. The

[5] D. Frisch, H. Eyring, and J. Kincaid, *J. Appl. Phys.*, **11**, 75 (1940), showed that as the pressure is increased, the energy of activation for viscous flow is increased by pv'. From the experimental data, it is found that v' is usually around one-sixth the volume per molecule of the liquid.

[6] R. J. Moore, P. Gibbs, and H. Eyring, *J. Phys. Chem.*, **57**, 172 (1953).

viscosity of lubricating oils can be interpreted on the basis of the present theory, but it is an exceedingly complex problem.

b. The coefficient of diffusion

The theory of diffusion follows easily from the theory of viscosity. Let us first consider the self-diffusion in a system where the number density n is a function of the coordinate x. Then if the concentration in a layer of molecules is n, the concentration in the neighboring layer separated by the distance δ is $n + \delta(dn/dx)$. The number of molecules which pass from a square centimeter of the first layer to the second layer in unit time is $\delta n\, k_0'$, and the number which pass in the opposite direction is $\delta k_0'(n + \delta(dn/dx))$. The excess in rate of flow in the negative direction is equal to the coefficient of self-diffusion, $\mathscr{D}$, times the concentration gradient. Hence the self-diffusion coefficient is given by

$$\mathscr{D} = \delta^2 k_0' \tag{9.2–11}$$

Here k_0' is the frequency of jumps in the absence of external forces. This quantity may be expressed in terms of the coefficient of viscosity by means of Eq. 9.2–6, so that

$$\mathscr{D} = \delta^2 \left(\frac{\delta}{a}\right)^2 \frac{nkT}{\eta} \tag{9.2–12}$$

This expression can be further simplified if we make the approximation that $\delta = a = n^{-1/3}$,

$$\eta\mathscr{D} = \frac{kT}{\delta} = n^{1/3}kT \tag{9.2–13}$$

When diffusion takes place in mixtures, it is the gradient of the activity and not the concentration which is the driving force. Equation 9.2–11 may be corrected to take into account the gradient of the activity a_1 rather than that of the concentration n_1. This results in the formula

$$\eta\mathscr{D}_{12} = \frac{kT}{\delta}\left(\frac{d \log a_1}{d \log n_1}\right) \tag{9.2–14}$$

The factor $\left(\dfrac{d \log a_1}{d \log n_1}\right)$ can be calculated from vapor-pressure data. A rule for estimating the concentration dependence of the coefficient of diffusion may be based upon the empirical observation that the ratio $\eta\mathscr{D}_{12}\Big/\left(\dfrac{d \log a_1}{d \log n_1}\right)$ varies linearly with concentration. This behavior is illustrated in Fig. 9.2–4.

The agreement between the calculated and the observed coefficients of diffusion is very poor. For a number of liquid pairs the calculated values

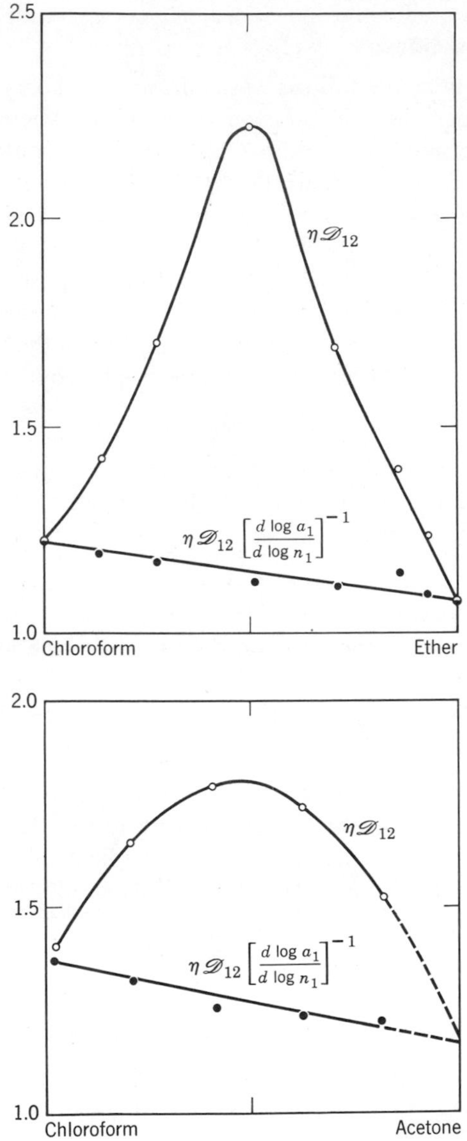

Fig. 9.2–4. Effect of activity on the product of the coefficient of diffusion and viscosity. [From R. E. Powell, W. E. Roseveare, and Henry Eyring, *Ind. and Eng. Chem.*, **33**, 430 (1941).]

are either too large or too small by factors of the order of four. Perhaps the mechanism of diffusion is somewhat different from that for viscous flow. For example, diffusion might occur by a bimolecular mechanism as is suggested by the flow mechanism of Fig. 9.2–3.

c. The coefficient of thermal conductivity

The thermal conductivity of a dense gas or liquid depends upon the very rapid transmission of the energy through the molecules themselves.[7] This mechanism is best understood by a consideration of the speed of sound in liquids. It is found that the speed of sound in a liquid is from five to ten times larger than the kinetic theory speed of the molecules themselves. The speed of sound $c^{(\text{liq})}$ in liquids can be understood by supposing that, when two molecules collide, energy is transferred instantaneously from the center of the one molecule to the center of the other. On this basis

$$c^{(\text{liq})} = \left(\frac{v}{v_f}\right)^{1/3} c^{(\text{gas})} \tag{9.2–15}$$

Here $v = n^{-1}$ is the volume per molecule in the liquid, and v_f is its "free volume" (see § 4.4). The free volume of liquids can be calculated from the vapor pressure or the equation of state, and it is found that Eq. 9.2–15 gives excellent agreement with the observed speed of sound for a large number of liquids. As a matter of fact, Eyring and his co-workers are so convinced of the validity of Eq. 9.2–15 that they use this relation to estimate the free volumes of liquids from the observed speed of sound.

According to crude kinetic theory arguments, the thermal conductivity of a monatomic gas is given by Eq. 1.2–14:

$$\lambda^{(\text{gas})} = \tfrac{1}{3} n c_v \Omega l \tag{9.2–16}$$

Here $\Omega = \sqrt{8kT/\pi m}$ is the average kinetic theory velocity of the molecules, l is the mean free path, and c_v is the specific heat per molecule at constant volume. For a liquid this expression must be modified in the following manner. The specific heat c_v for a liquid is very nearly equal to $3k$ (rather than $3k/2$ for the gas) since the potential that the molecules move in may be approximated by a simple three-dimensional harmonic potential. The mean free path is replaced by $v^{1/3}$, the distance that energy is transferred per single collision. In accord with the speed of sound arguments, the speed that the energy travels should now be $(v/v_f)^{1/3}$ times the speed that it travels in the gas. Thus the crude kinetic theory arguments lead to the following expression for the thermal

[7] This is known as the "collisional transfer" of energy. It is discussed in considerably more detail in §§ 9.3 and 9.4.

conductivity of a monatomic liquid:

$$\lambda^{(\text{liq})} = n^{2/3}k\sqrt{\frac{8kT}{\pi m}}\left(\frac{v}{v_f}\right)^{1/3} \tag{9.2–17}$$

Equation 9.2–15 may now be used to eliminate the free volume. Letting $c^{(\text{gas})} = \sqrt{\gamma kT/m}$, we get

$$\lambda^{(\text{liq})} = n^{2/3}k\sqrt{8/\pi\gamma}\, c^{(\text{liq})} \tag{9.2–18}$$

in which $\gamma = c_p/c_v$. The thermal conductivity for polyatomic molecules can be obtained by multiplying the previous result by $(9\gamma - 5)/4$ to correct both for the internal degrees of freedom and for the error in λ due to the mean-free-path approximations. In order to make the resulting relation agree with a very satisfactory empirical relation of Bridgman,[8] Eyring supposes that only the rotational and translational degrees of freedom are effective in transferring energy so that the proper value to use for γ in $(9\gamma - 5)/4$ is usually 4/3. Accordingly, we write for *polyatomic* substances:

$$\lambda^{(\text{liq})} = 2.80kn^{2/3}\gamma^{-1/2}c^{(\text{liq})} \tag{9.2–19}$$

Here the ratio of specific heats, γ, should be taken to be the values which are measured in speed of sound measurements (presumably it is different from the factor 4/3 used in the Eucken correction). This formulae applies extremely well (a mean deviation of around 10 per cent) for a large number of liquids. Bridgman has pointed out that Eq. 9.2–19 gives the correct temperature dependence of the thermal conductivity of liquids at one atmosphere. However, for most liquids the thermal conductivity increases by a factor of two when the pressure is raised to 12,000 atm, whereas Eq. 9.2–19 indicates that the thermal conductivity should increase by a factor of four.

3. The Enskog Theory of Transport Phenomena in Dense Gases and Liquids[1, 2, 3]

The rigorous kinetic theory of dilute gases, which is discussed in Chapter 7, is based on the Boltzmann equation (Eq. 7.1–25). In the derivation of this equation (§ 7.1) it is assumed that there are two-body collisions only

[8] P. W. Bridgman, *Proc. Am. Acad. Arts Sci.*, **59**, 109 (1923); *The Physics of High Pressures*, G. Bell, London (1931).

[1] D. Enskog, *Kungliga Svenska Vetenskapsakademiens Handlingar*, **63**, No. 4 (1922). In German.

[2] A summary of Enskog's work is given in S. Chapman and T. G. Cowling, *The Mathematical Theory of Non-uniform Gases*, Cambridge University Press (1939). See Chapter 16.

[3] Recently C. F. Curtiss, University Wisconsin Naval Research Laboratory Report, OOR-3 (1953), has extended the Enskog theory for use in real gases.

and that the molecules have no finite extension in space (or, more exactly, that the molecular diameter σ is small compared with the average distance between the molecules.) Both these assumptions are certainly valid in dilute gases. In dense gases, however, these two assumptions must be reconsidered.

Enskog was the first to make an advance in this direction, by developing a kinetic theory of dense gases made up of rigid spherical molecules of diameter σ. For this special model there are essentially no three-body and higher-order collisions. By considering only two-body collisions and by taking into account the finite size of the molecules he was able to graft a theory of dense gases onto the dilute gas theory developed earlier. As a gas is compressed there are two effects which become important because molecules have volume: (i) "*Collisional transfer*" *of momentum and energy*—when two rigid-sphere molecules undergo a collision, there is an instantaneous transport of energy and momentum from the center of one molecule to the center of the other. (ii) *Change in the number of collisions per second*—the frequency of collisions is increased because σ is not negligibly small compared with the average distance between the molecules, and the frequency of collisions is decreased because the molecules are close enough to shield one another from oncoming molecules. Thus the frequency of collisions in a gas made up of rigid spheres differs by a factor Y from that in a gas made up of point particles.[4] The factor Y is intimately related to the equation of state. As is shown later (Eq. 9.3–32), the equation of state for rigid spheres in terms of Y is

$$\frac{p\tilde{V}}{RT} = 1 + \frac{b_0}{\tilde{V}} Y \tag{9.3–1}$$

where $b_0 = \frac{2}{3}\pi\tilde{N}\sigma^3$ is the second virial coefficient. The quantity Y has already been obtained in Eq. 3.5–1 as

$$Y = 1 + 0.6250(b_0/\tilde{V}) + 0.2869(b_0/\tilde{V})^2 + 0.115(b_0/\tilde{V})^3 \cdots \tag{9.3–2}$$

in connection with the virial expansion of the equation of state.

The derivation given in this section (for *pure gases* only) follows closely the presentation given in Chapter 7, and the same notation is used throughout. After the theory is described, we summarize the results which are obtained for rigid spherical molecules. We then discuss how Enskog used these results to correlate high-pressure transport property data with equation of state data. This is accomplished by evaluating the factor Y from equation of state measurements by replacing the external pressure, p, in Eq. 9.3–1 by the sum of the external and the internal pressures.

[4] Enskog calls this quantity χ. We use the symbol Y, since χ is used for the angle of deflection.

This sum is equal to the "thermal pressure,"[5]

$$T\left(\frac{\partial p}{\partial T}\right)_{\tilde{V}} = \frac{RT}{\tilde{V}}\left(1 + \frac{b_0}{\tilde{V}}\,Y\right) \tag{9.3–3}$$

It is shown that this method of choosing Y is physically sensible and is consistent with the viewpoints adopted by Eyring and Hildebrand in their studies of the liquid phase.

a. The Boltzmann equation as modified for a dense gas

In § 7.1b the Boltzmann equation for the distribution function $f(\boldsymbol{r}, \boldsymbol{v}, t)$ is obtained by means of physical and geometrical arguments. A similar analysis may be used to derive an integro-differential equation for the distribution function in a dense gas. It is clear that the left side ("streaming terms") of the Boltzmann equation remains unchanged in dense gases, but the integral on the right side of the equation is modified because of the finite size of the molecules.

It is shown in § 7.1b that the frequency of collisions in the volume element $d\boldsymbol{r}$ about $\boldsymbol{r}$ in which the velocities of the molecules are in the range $d\boldsymbol{v}$ about $\boldsymbol{v}$ and $d\boldsymbol{v}_1$ about $\boldsymbol{v}_1$ and in which the collision parameters are in the range db about b and $d\epsilon$ about ϵ, is[6, 7]

$$f(\boldsymbol{r},\boldsymbol{v})\, f_1(\boldsymbol{r}, \boldsymbol{v}_1) g b\, db\, d\epsilon\, d\boldsymbol{v}\, d\boldsymbol{v}_1\, d\boldsymbol{r} \tag{9.3–4}$$

Two modifications must be made in this expression in order to describe the frequency of collisions in a dense gas of rigid spheres: (i) Because of the finite size of the colliding molecules the centers of the two molecules are not at the same point. If one molecule is at $\boldsymbol{r}$, the center of the second molecule is at $(\boldsymbol{r} - \sigma\boldsymbol{k})$, where $\boldsymbol{k}$ is the unit vector in the direction from the center of the second molecule to the center of the first molecule at the instant of contact during a collision. Accordingly, the distribution function $f_1(\boldsymbol{r}, \boldsymbol{v}_1)$ should really be evaluated at the point $(\boldsymbol{r} - \sigma\boldsymbol{k})$. (ii) In a dense gas the volume per molecule, v, is of the same order as the volume of a molecule, $\frac{4}{3}\pi(\frac{1}{2}\sigma)^2$. Therefore, the volume in which the center of any one molecule can lie is reduced, and the probability of a collision is increased. Thus the frequency of collisions (Eq. 9.3–4) is

[5] For rigid spheres the thermal pressure is equal to the external pressure so that Eqs. 9.3–1 and 3 are identical.

[6] In Chapter 7, where multicomponent gases are considered, the collisions between different chemical species were considered. Consequently the two colliding molecules were specified by subscripts i and j, which designated the types of molecules. For a pure component it is necessary to make a distinction between the two molecules in the collision; this is done by the dummy index "1."

[7] The angle ϵ is not needed in the discussion of dilute gases, because of the cylindrical symmetry involved. This angle, which goes from 0 to 2π, is defined in Fig. 7.1–1.

increased by a factor Y which for rigid spheres depends only on the number density, $n(\boldsymbol{r}, t)$. The function Y is evaluated at the point of contact of the two colliding spherical molecules, that is, at $(\boldsymbol{r} - \frac{1}{2}\sigma\boldsymbol{k})$. Consequently, the expression

$$Y(\boldsymbol{r} - \tfrac{1}{2}\sigma\boldsymbol{k}, t)\, f(\boldsymbol{r}, \boldsymbol{v}, t) f_1(\boldsymbol{r} - \sigma\boldsymbol{k}, \boldsymbol{v}_1, t) gb\, db\, d\epsilon\, d\boldsymbol{v}\, d\boldsymbol{v}_1\, d\boldsymbol{r} \qquad (9.3\text{–}5)$$

should be used in place of that given in Eq. 9.3–4 when dense gases are considered.

With this modification in the frequency of collisions, the differential equation for the distribution function may be obtained by arguments similar to those used in § 7.1b for the derivation of the Boltzmann equation. The resulting equation is

$$\frac{\partial f}{\partial t} + \left(\boldsymbol{v} \cdot \frac{\partial f}{\partial \boldsymbol{r}}\right) + \left(\frac{\boldsymbol{X}}{m} \cdot \frac{\partial f}{\partial \boldsymbol{v}}\right) =$$

$$\iiint \begin{bmatrix} Y(\boldsymbol{r} + \frac{1}{2}\sigma\boldsymbol{k}) f(\boldsymbol{r}, \boldsymbol{v}') f_1(\boldsymbol{r} + \sigma\boldsymbol{k}, \boldsymbol{v}_1') \\ - Y(\boldsymbol{r} - \frac{1}{2}\sigma\boldsymbol{k}) f(\boldsymbol{r}, \boldsymbol{v}) f_1(\boldsymbol{r} - \sigma\boldsymbol{k}, \boldsymbol{v}_1) \end{bmatrix} gb\, db\, d\epsilon\, d\boldsymbol{v}_1 \qquad (9.3\text{–}6)$$

The conditions in the gas are assumed to be slowly varying in space. Hence the functions $f(\boldsymbol{r} + \sigma\boldsymbol{k}, \boldsymbol{v}, t)$ and $Y(\boldsymbol{r} + \frac{1}{2}\sigma\boldsymbol{k}, t)$ may be expanded in a Taylor series. Then Eq. 9.3–6 may be rewritten in the form:

$$\frac{\partial f}{\partial t} + \left(\boldsymbol{v} \cdot \frac{\partial f}{\partial \boldsymbol{r}}\right) + \left(\frac{\boldsymbol{X}}{m} \cdot \frac{\partial f}{\partial \boldsymbol{v}}\right) = J_1 + J_2 + J_3 + J_4 + J_5 + J_6 + \cdots \qquad (9.3\text{–}7)$$

where

$$J_1 = Y \iiint \{f' f_1' - f f_1\}\, gb\, db\, d\epsilon\, d\boldsymbol{v}_1$$

$$J_2 = \sigma Y \iiint \left(\boldsymbol{k} \cdot \left\{f' \frac{\partial f_1'}{\partial \boldsymbol{r}} + f \frac{\partial f_1}{\partial \boldsymbol{r}}\right\}\right) gb\, db\, d\epsilon\, d\boldsymbol{v}_1$$

$$J_3 = \tfrac{1}{2}\sigma \iiint \left(\boldsymbol{k} \cdot \frac{\partial Y}{\partial \boldsymbol{r}}\right) \{f' f_1' + f f_1\}\, gb\, db\, d\epsilon\, d\boldsymbol{v}_1$$

$$J_4 = \tfrac{1}{2}\sigma^2 Y \iiint \left(\boldsymbol{k}\boldsymbol{k} : \left\{f' \frac{\partial}{\partial \boldsymbol{r}} \frac{\partial f_1'}{\partial \boldsymbol{r}} - f \frac{\partial}{\partial \boldsymbol{r}} \frac{\partial f_1}{\partial \boldsymbol{r}}\right\}\right) gb\, db\, d\epsilon\, d\boldsymbol{v}_1$$

$$J_5 = \tfrac{1}{2}\sigma^2 \iiint \left(\boldsymbol{k} \cdot \frac{\partial Y}{\partial \boldsymbol{r}}\right) \left(\boldsymbol{k} \cdot \left\{f' \frac{\partial f_1'}{\partial \boldsymbol{r}} - f \frac{\partial f_1}{\partial \boldsymbol{r}}\right\}\right) gb\, db\, d\epsilon\, d\boldsymbol{v}_1$$

$$J_6 = \tfrac{1}{8}\sigma^2 \iiint \left(\boldsymbol{k}\boldsymbol{k} : \frac{\partial}{\partial \boldsymbol{r}} \frac{\partial Y}{\partial \boldsymbol{r}}\right) \{f' f_1' - f f_1\}\, gb\, db\, d\epsilon\, d\boldsymbol{v}_1$$

It is this equation which determines the distribution function in a dense gas composed of rigid spherical molecules. Before discussing the solution, however, we examine the flux vectors and the equations of change.

b. The flux vectors

In § 7.2b the flux of various molecular properties—mass, momentum, kinetic energy—across an element of surface in a dilute gas was considered. Since in that discussion the molecules are considered to be point particles, the general expression for a flux vector in Eq. 7.2–18 represents the transport of molecular properties due to the flow of molecules across the element of surface. We now consider the additional transport of molecular properties which occurs due to collisions in which the centers of the molecules are on opposite sides of the element of surface. In such collisions there is an instantaneous transfer of momentum and energy from the center of one molecule to the center of the other molecule, the so-called collisional transfer which we have already mentioned.

Let us now consider the mechanism of collisional transfer by using Fig. 7.2–1. The vector $\boldsymbol{n}$ is a unit vector, normal to the element of surface dS, which goes from the negative side to the positive side. In a collision between two molecules in which the first lies on the positive side and the second lies on the negative side of the surface, the product $(\boldsymbol{k} \cdot \boldsymbol{n})$ is positive (since $\boldsymbol{k}$ is the unit vector in the direction of the first molecule from the second). In these collisions the line joining the centers of the molecules crosses the element of surface dS at the instant of the collision. Therefore, the center of the first molecule lies in a cylinder built on dS with generators parallel to $\boldsymbol{k}$ of length σ. The volume of this cylinder is $\sigma(\boldsymbol{k} \cdot \boldsymbol{n})dS$. The mean positions of the centers of the two molecules at the instant of the collisions are $(\boldsymbol{r} + \frac{1}{2}\sigma\boldsymbol{k})$ and $(\boldsymbol{r} - \frac{1}{2}\sigma\boldsymbol{k})$, and the mean position of the point of contact is $\boldsymbol{r}$. Hence by analogy with Eq. 9.3–5 the probable number of such collisions in unit time, in which the velocities lie in ranges $d\boldsymbol{v}$ and $d\boldsymbol{v}_1$ about $\boldsymbol{v}$ and $\boldsymbol{v}_1$ and the collision parameters lie within ranges db about b and $d\epsilon$ about ϵ, is

$$Y(\boldsymbol{r})f(\boldsymbol{r} + \tfrac{1}{2}\sigma\boldsymbol{k}, \boldsymbol{v}, t)f(\boldsymbol{r} - \tfrac{1}{2}\sigma\boldsymbol{k}, \boldsymbol{v}, t)gb\, db\, d\epsilon\, d\boldsymbol{v}\, d\boldsymbol{v}_1\, \sigma(\boldsymbol{k} \cdot \boldsymbol{n})\, dS \qquad (9.3\text{–}8)$$

Since a quantity $(\psi' - \psi)$ of a property ψ is transferred across the surface on each collision of this sort, the total rate of transfer of property ψ by collisions per unit time and per unit area is

$$(\boldsymbol{n} \cdot \boldsymbol{\Psi}_\Phi) = \sigma Y(\boldsymbol{r}) \iiiint (\psi' - \psi) f(\boldsymbol{r} + \tfrac{1}{2}\sigma\boldsymbol{k}, \boldsymbol{v}, t) f_1(\boldsymbol{r} - \tfrac{1}{2}\sigma\boldsymbol{k}, \boldsymbol{v}_1, t) \times (\boldsymbol{k} \cdot \boldsymbol{n})\, gb\, db\, d\epsilon\, d\boldsymbol{v}\, d\boldsymbol{v}_1 \qquad (9.3\text{–}9)$$

The integration is over all variables such that $(\boldsymbol{k} \cdot \boldsymbol{n})$ is positive.

The restriction of the region of integration is inconvenient, but the difficulty may be circumvented in the following way. Let us first interchange the roles of the two colliding molecules, that is, let us interchange the labels on the integration variables in Eq. 9.3–9. Then $\boldsymbol{k}$ is replaced by $-\boldsymbol{k}$ and $(\psi' - \psi)$ by $(\psi_1' - \psi_1)$. Since ψ is a *summational invariant*, $(\psi_1' - \psi_1) = -(\psi' - \psi)$. Consequently, the integrand of Eq. 9.3–9 is unchanged by this interchange of the integration variables. The only difference is, in fact, that the integration is over all variables such that $(\boldsymbol{k} \cdot \boldsymbol{n})$ is negative. Hence Eq. 9.3–9 may be rewritten as

$$(\boldsymbol{n} \cdot \boldsymbol{\Psi}_\Phi) = \boldsymbol{n} \cdot \tfrac{1}{2}\sigma Y(\boldsymbol{r}) \iiiint (\psi' - \psi) f(\boldsymbol{r} + \tfrac{1}{2}\sigma\boldsymbol{k}, \boldsymbol{v}, t) f_1(\boldsymbol{r} - \tfrac{1}{2}\sigma\boldsymbol{k}, \boldsymbol{v}_1, t) \times \boldsymbol{k} g b \, db \, d\epsilon \, d\boldsymbol{v} \, d\boldsymbol{v}_1 \tag{9.3–10}$$

in which the integration is over all values of the variables.

We have thus shown that the contribution of the "collisional transfer" to the flux of property ψ is

$$\boldsymbol{\Psi}_\Phi = \tfrac{1}{2}\sigma Y(\boldsymbol{r}) \iiiint (\psi' - \psi) f(\boldsymbol{r} + \tfrac{1}{2}\sigma\boldsymbol{k}, \boldsymbol{v}, t) f_1(\boldsymbol{r} - \tfrac{1}{2}\sigma\boldsymbol{k}, \boldsymbol{v}_1, t) \times \boldsymbol{k} g b \, db \, d\epsilon \, d\boldsymbol{v} \, d\boldsymbol{v}_1 \tag{9.3–11}$$

As in the derivation of Eq. 9.3–7, the distribution functions may be expanded in Taylor series, with the result that $\boldsymbol{\Psi}_\Phi$ may be rewritten as

$$\boldsymbol{\Psi}_\Phi = \tfrac{1}{2}\sigma Y(\boldsymbol{r}) \iiiint (\psi' - \psi) f f_1 \boldsymbol{k} g b \, db \, d\epsilon \, d\boldsymbol{v} \, d\boldsymbol{v}_1 + \tfrac{1}{4}\sigma^2 Y(\boldsymbol{r}) \iiiint (\psi' - \psi) \left(\boldsymbol{k} \cdot f f_1 \frac{\partial}{\partial \boldsymbol{r}} \ln \frac{f}{f_1}\right) \boldsymbol{k} g b \, db \, d\epsilon \, d\boldsymbol{v} \, d\boldsymbol{v}_1 + \cdots \tag{9.3–12}$$

In addition to the collisional transfer of ψ, there is also the contribution to the flux due to the flow of molecules across the surface as given by Eq. 7.2–18:

$$\boldsymbol{\Psi}_K = \int \psi f \boldsymbol{V} \, d\boldsymbol{v} \tag{9.3–13}$$

The total flux of the property ψ is then the sum of the two contributions

$$\boldsymbol{\Psi} = \boldsymbol{\Psi}_K + \boldsymbol{\Psi}_\Phi \tag{9.3–14}$$

The subscripts K and Φ indicate the contributions due to the kinetic energy (flow of molecules) and the potential energy (collisional transfer due to the finite size of the molecules). The kinetic energy term is the predominant contribution at low densities, and the potential energy term is the primary term at high densities.

c. The equations of change

The equations of change may be derived in much the same manner as in the theory of dilute gases. When the modified Boltzmann equation (Eq. 9.3–7) is multiplied by a summational invariant and integrated over $\boldsymbol{v}$, the result is

$$\int \psi \left\{ \frac{\partial f}{\partial t} + \left(\boldsymbol{v} \cdot \frac{\partial f}{\partial \boldsymbol{r}} \right) + \left(\frac{\boldsymbol{X}}{m} \cdot \frac{\partial f}{\partial \boldsymbol{v}} \right) \right\} d\boldsymbol{v} = I_1 + I_2 + I_3 + I_4 + I_5 + I_6 + \cdots \tag{9.3–15}$$

in which

$$I_i = \int \psi J_i \, d\boldsymbol{v} \tag{9.3–15a}$$

After lengthy manipulations[8] the integrals I_i may be shown to assume

[8] The vanishing of I_1 is described in § 7.2d. The same arguments apply to I_6. The manipulations for I_2 are as follows. I_2 is defined by Eq. 9.3–15a as

$$I_2 = \sigma Y \iiiint \psi \left(\boldsymbol{k} \cdot \left\{ f' \frac{\partial f_1'}{\partial \boldsymbol{r}} + f \frac{\partial f_1}{\partial \boldsymbol{r}} \right\} \right) gb \, db \, d\epsilon \, d\boldsymbol{v} \, d\boldsymbol{v}_1 \tag{a}$$

According to arguments presented in § 7.2d:

$$I_2 = -\sigma Y \iiiint \psi' \left(\boldsymbol{k} \cdot \left\{ f' \frac{\partial f_1'}{\partial \boldsymbol{r}} + f \frac{\partial f_1}{\partial \boldsymbol{r}} \right\} \right) gb \, db \, d\epsilon \, d\boldsymbol{v} \, d\boldsymbol{v}_1 \tag{b}$$

Hence

$$I_2 = \tfrac{1}{2}\sigma Y \iiiint \{\psi - \psi'\} \left(\boldsymbol{k} \cdot \left\{ f' \frac{\partial f_1'}{\partial \boldsymbol{r}} + f \frac{\partial f_1}{\partial \boldsymbol{r}} \right\} \right) gb \, db \, d\epsilon \, d\boldsymbol{v} \, d\boldsymbol{v}_1 \tag{c}$$

By similar arguments it can be shown that

$$\tfrac{1}{2}\sigma Y \iiiint (\psi - \psi') \left(\boldsymbol{k} \cdot f' \frac{\partial f_1'}{\partial \boldsymbol{r}} \right) gb \, db \, d\epsilon \, d\boldsymbol{v} \, d\boldsymbol{v}_1 = \tfrac{1}{2}\sigma Y \iiiint (\psi - \psi') \left(\boldsymbol{k} \cdot f \frac{\partial f_1}{\partial \boldsymbol{r}} \right) gb \, db \, d\epsilon \, d\boldsymbol{v} \, d\boldsymbol{v}_1 \tag{d}$$

From this it follows that

$$I_2 = \sigma Y \iiiint (\psi - \psi') \left(\boldsymbol{k} \cdot f \frac{\partial f_1}{\partial \boldsymbol{r}} \right) gb \, db \, d\epsilon \, d\boldsymbol{v} \, d\boldsymbol{v}_1 \tag{e}$$

Now let us interchange the roles of the two molecules. Then

$$\boldsymbol{k} \rightarrow -\boldsymbol{k} \text{ and } (\psi - \psi') \rightarrow -(\psi - \psi')$$

(as described in connection with Eqs. 9.3–9 and 10). Consequently,

$$I_2 = \sigma Y \iiiint (\psi - \psi') \left(\boldsymbol{k} \cdot f_1 \frac{\partial f}{\partial \boldsymbol{r}} \right) gb \, db \, d\epsilon \, d\boldsymbol{v} \, d\boldsymbol{v}_1 \tag{f}$$

Combining these last two expressions, we get the expression given in Eq. 9.3–16 for I_2. The expressions given there for the other I_i are obtained by similar manipulations.

the form:

$$I_1 = 0$$

$$I_2 = \tfrac{1}{2}\sigma Y \iiiint \{\psi - \psi'\} \left(\boldsymbol{k} \cdot \frac{\partial}{\partial \boldsymbol{r}} ff_1\right) gb\, db\, d\epsilon\, d\boldsymbol{v}\, d\boldsymbol{v}_1$$

$$I_3 = \tfrac{1}{2}\sigma \iiiint \{\psi - \psi'\} \left(\boldsymbol{k} \cdot \frac{\partial Y}{\partial \boldsymbol{r}}\right) ff_1 gb\, db\, d\epsilon\, d\boldsymbol{v}\, d\boldsymbol{v}_1$$

$$I_4 = \tfrac{1}{4}\sigma^2 Y \iiiint \{\psi - \psi'\} \left(\boldsymbol{kk} : \frac{\partial}{\partial \boldsymbol{r}}\left\{ff_1 \frac{\partial}{\partial \boldsymbol{r}} \ln \frac{f}{f_1}\right\}\right) gb\, db\, d\epsilon\, d\boldsymbol{v}\, d\boldsymbol{v}_1$$

$$I_5 = \tfrac{1}{4}\sigma^2 \iiiint \{\psi - \psi'\} \left(\boldsymbol{k} \cdot \frac{\partial Y}{\partial \boldsymbol{r}}\right)\left(\boldsymbol{k} \cdot ff_1 \frac{\partial}{\partial \boldsymbol{r}} \ln \frac{f}{f_1}\right) gb\, db\, d\epsilon\, d\boldsymbol{v}\, d\boldsymbol{v}_1$$

$$I_6 = 0 \tag{9.3–16}$$

From these expressions it is easy to see that

$$I_2 + I_3 = -\left(\frac{\partial}{\partial \boldsymbol{r}} \cdot \left\{\tfrac{1}{2}\sigma Y \iiiint (\psi' - \psi) ff_1 \boldsymbol{k}\, gb\, db\, d\epsilon\, d\boldsymbol{v}\, d\boldsymbol{v}_1\right\}\right) \tag{9.3–17}$$

$$I_4 + I_5 = -\left(\frac{\partial}{\partial \boldsymbol{r}} \cdot \left\{\tfrac{1}{4}\sigma^2 Y \iiiint (\psi' - \psi) \times \left(\boldsymbol{k} \cdot ff_1 \frac{\partial}{\partial \boldsymbol{r}} \ln \frac{f}{f_1}\right) \boldsymbol{k} gb\, db\, d\epsilon\, d\boldsymbol{v}\, d\boldsymbol{v}_1\right\}\right) \tag{9.3–18}$$

A comparison of these results with Eq. 9.3–12 indicates that $\sum_{i=1}^{6} I_i$ is just exactly equal to $-\left(\frac{\partial}{\partial \boldsymbol{r}} \cdot \boldsymbol{\Psi}_\Phi\right)$ so that Eq. 9.3–15 may be rewritten as

$$\int \psi \left\{\frac{\partial f}{\partial t} + \left(\boldsymbol{v} \cdot \frac{\partial f}{\partial \boldsymbol{r}}\right) + \left(\frac{\boldsymbol{X}}{m} \cdot \frac{\partial f}{\partial \boldsymbol{v}}\right)\right\} d\boldsymbol{v} = -\left(\frac{\partial}{\partial \boldsymbol{r}} \cdot \boldsymbol{\Psi}_\Phi\right) \tag{9.3–19}$$

This is the general equation of change.

When we let ψ be, in turn, m, $m\boldsymbol{V}$, and $\tfrac{1}{2}mV^2$ (as was done in § 7.2e), we obtain the usual equation of continuity, the equation of motion, and the equation of energy balance. The only difference in the final result is that the pressure tensor, $\mathsf{p} = \mathsf{p}_k + \mathsf{p}_\Phi$, and the heat flux vector, $\boldsymbol{q} = \boldsymbol{q}_k + \boldsymbol{q}_\Phi$, are made up of two contributions (kinetic and potential) as indicated in Eq. 9.3–14.

d. The solution of the modified Boltzmann equation

The Boltzmann equation as modified for high densities (Eq. 9.3–7) may be solved by a method quite analogous to that used for the solution of the ordinary (low-density) Boltzmann equation as described in § 7.3. The distribution function may be expanded in a series as indicated in Eq. 7.3–11. We consider, however, only the first-order perturbation and write simply

$$f(\boldsymbol{r}, \boldsymbol{v}, t) = f^{[0]}(\boldsymbol{v})\,[1 + \phi(\boldsymbol{r}, \boldsymbol{v}, t)] \tag{9.3–20}$$

in which $f^{[0]}$ is the unperturbed distribution function

$$f^{[0]}(\boldsymbol{v}) = n\left(\frac{m}{2\pi kT}\right)^{3/2} e^{-m(\boldsymbol{v}-\boldsymbol{v}_0)^2/2kT} \tag{9.3–21}$$

Throughout the treatment the perturbation function ϕ and the derivatives of n, $\boldsymbol{v}_0$, and T are considered to be small quantities.

When the above expression for $f(\boldsymbol{r}, \boldsymbol{v}, t)$ is substituted into Eq. 9.3–7, we obtain an integro-differential equation for the perturbation function ϕ. The ("streaming") terms on the left and the first term on the right, J_1, are the same as those which we obtain in the theory of dilute gases. The perturbation function does not appear in the integrals J_2 and J_3 to the approximation we are considering, inasmuch as these terms already involve derivatives of the macroscopic variables. Similarly, J_4, J_5, J_6 are all zero in this approximation since they involve second derivatives of the macroscopic variables or squares of first derivatives. The integration of the terms J_2 and J_3 may be performed[9] and we obtain the following results:

$$J_2 = -\tfrac{2}{3}\pi n\sigma^3 Y f^{[0]} \left[\begin{aligned} &2\left(\boldsymbol{V}\cdot\frac{\partial \ln n}{\partial \boldsymbol{r}}\right) + (\tfrac{3}{5}W^2 - \tfrac{1}{2})\left(\boldsymbol{V}\cdot\frac{\partial \ln T}{\partial \boldsymbol{r}}\right) \\ &+ \tfrac{4}{5}\left(\boldsymbol{W}\boldsymbol{W} : \frac{\partial}{\partial \boldsymbol{r}}\boldsymbol{v}_0\right) + (\tfrac{2}{5}W^2 - 1)\left(\frac{\partial}{\partial \boldsymbol{r}}\cdot\boldsymbol{v}_0\right) \end{aligned} \right]$$

$$J_3 = -\tfrac{2}{3}\pi n\sigma^3 f^{[0]}\left(\boldsymbol{V}\cdot\frac{\partial Y}{\partial \boldsymbol{r}}\right) \tag{9.3–22}$$

where, as in Chapter 7, the dimensionless velocity $\boldsymbol{W}$ is defined as $\boldsymbol{W} = \sqrt{m/2kT}\,\boldsymbol{V}$.

[9] For the details of the algebraic manipulations involved in these integrations and in the remainder of this analysis, see Chapman and Cowling, *loc. cit.*, pp. 278 et seq.

When these results are used along with the results in § 7.3c the following equation is obtained for the perturbation function ϕ:

$$\frac{1}{Y} f^{[0]} \left[\left(1 + \frac{4}{15}\pi n \sigma^3 Y\right)\left(\mathsf{b} : \frac{\partial}{\partial \boldsymbol{r}} \boldsymbol{v}_0\right) - \left(1 + \frac{2}{5}\pi n \sigma^3 Y\right)\left(\frac{5}{2} - W^2\right)\left(\boldsymbol{V} \cdot \frac{\partial \ln T}{\partial \boldsymbol{r}}\right)\right]$$

$$= \iiint f_1^{[0]} f^{[0]} (\phi' + \phi_1' - \phi - \phi_1) g b \, db \, d\epsilon \, d\boldsymbol{v}_1 \qquad (9.3\text{–}23)$$

in which, as in Chapter 7, $\mathsf{b} = 2(\boldsymbol{W}\boldsymbol{W} - \frac{1}{3}W^2\mathsf{U})$. In obtaining this expression the equations of change have been used to eliminate the time derivatives of the macroscopic variables. Equation 9.3–23 for dense gases is analogous to Eq. 7.3–26 for dilute gases. In fact, the two equations are exactly the same except that in the dense gas equation the coefficient of $\frac{\partial}{\partial \boldsymbol{r}} \boldsymbol{v}_0$ is multiplied by $\frac{1}{Y}\left(1 + \frac{4}{15}\pi n \sigma^3 Y\right)$ and the coefficient of $\frac{\partial \ln T}{\partial \boldsymbol{r}}$ is multiplied by $\frac{1}{Y}\left(1 + \frac{2}{5}\pi n \sigma^3 Y\right)$. The solution to Eq. 9.3–23 is thus:

$$\phi = -\frac{1}{Y}\left(1 + \frac{2}{5}\pi n \sigma^3 Y\right)\left(\boldsymbol{A} \cdot \frac{\partial \ln T}{\partial \boldsymbol{r}}\right) - \frac{1}{Y}\left(1 + \frac{4}{15}\pi n \sigma^3 Y\right)\left(\mathsf{B} : \frac{\partial}{\partial \boldsymbol{r}} \boldsymbol{v}_0\right) \qquad (9.3\text{–}24)$$

where functions $\boldsymbol{A}$ and B are the functions defined and calculated in § 7.3.

e. The transport coefficients

We now have everything we need for the evaluation of the transport coefficients: expressions for the fluxes as integrals over the distribution function f (Eqs. 9.3–12, 13, 14), the distribution function f in terms of a perturbation function (Eq. 9.3–20), and finally an expression for the perturbation function itself (Eq. 9.3–24). Let us first examine the kinetic contributions to the pressure tensor and the heat flux vector, p_K and $\boldsymbol{q}_K$. Then we obtain expressions for the collisional transfer contributions to the pressure tensor and the heat flux vector, p_Φ and $\boldsymbol{q}_\Phi$, and obtain explicit expressions for the bulk and shear coefficients of viscosity and the coefficient of thermal conductivity.

The kinetic contributions to the pressure tensor and the heat flux vector may be obtained from Eq. 9.3–13. This expression is formally the same as that used in the kinetic theory of dilute gases. The expression for ϕ which is now used, however, differs from that in Chapter 7 in the coefficients of $\boldsymbol{A}$ and B, as described in connection with Eqs. 9.3–23, 24.

Accordingly, we may write down at once the following results:[10]

$$\mathsf{p}_K = nkT\mathsf{U} - \frac{2}{Y}(1 + \tfrac{4}{15}\pi n\sigma^3 Y)\,\eta^0\mathsf{S} \tag{9.3–25}$$

$$\boldsymbol{q}_K = -\frac{1}{Y}(1 + \tfrac{2}{5}\pi n\sigma^3 Y)\,\lambda^0\,\frac{\partial T}{\partial \boldsymbol{r}} \tag{9.3–26}$$

Here η^0 and λ^0 are the coefficients of viscosity and thermal conductivity in the dilute gas limit, and S is the *rate of shear tensor* defined in Eq. 7.4–16.

i. *The Coefficients of Shear Viscosity and Bulk Viscosity*

The contribution to the pressure tensor due to collisional transfer may be obtained from Eq. 9.3–12 by setting ψ equal to $m\boldsymbol{v}$. The first integral in this expression may be evaluated and is

$$\begin{aligned}
&\tfrac{4}{15}\,\pi n\sigma^3(nmY)\,(\overline{\boldsymbol{V}\boldsymbol{V}} + \tfrac{1}{2}\overline{V^2}\mathsf{U})\\
&\quad = \tfrac{4}{15}\,\pi n\sigma^3\,Y(\mathsf{p}_K + \tfrac{3}{2}nkT\mathsf{U})\\
&\quad = nkT(\tfrac{2}{3}\pi n\sigma^3 Y)\mathsf{U} - \tfrac{8}{15}\,\pi n\sigma^3(1 + \tfrac{4}{15}\pi n\sigma^3 Y)\,\eta^0\mathsf{S}
\end{aligned} \tag{9.3–27}$$

The second form given here is obtained by using Eq. 9.3–13 for p_K and the kinetic theory definition of temperature. The third form is obtained by using Eq. 9.3–25.

The second integral in Eq. 9.3–12 involves derivatives of the distribution function and hence does not contain the perturbation function in the approximation which we are considering. Consequently, the integral may be evaluated directly, and the result is

$$-\kappa\left\{\tfrac{6}{5}\mathsf{S} + \left(\frac{\partial}{\partial \boldsymbol{r}}\cdot\boldsymbol{v}_0\right)\mathsf{U}\right\} \tag{9.3–28}$$

in which

$$\kappa = \tfrac{4}{9}n^2\sigma^4 Y\sqrt{\pi mkT} \tag{9.3–29}$$

The quantity κ, which is presently identified as the coefficient of bulk viscosity, may be written in terms of the zero-pressure coefficient of shear viscosity (Eq. 8.2–10), thus[11]

$$\kappa = 1.002\,(\tfrac{2}{3}\pi n\sigma^3)^2\,Y\eta^0 \tag{9.3–30}$$

[10] Equation 9.3–25 differs from Eq. 7.4–17 not only in the inclusion of the additional factors introduced in Eq. 9.3–24 but also in the fact that we write nkT in place of p, the static pressure. This is done, of course, since there is an additional term in p_Φ which adds to this, giving the true equation of state.

[11] The numerical factor 1.002 is $16(0.984)/5\pi$. The quantity 0.984 is the correction to the zero-pressure viscosity for the higher approximation in the series of Sonine polynomials (see Table 8.3–2).

The total contribution to the momentum flux due to collisional transfer is the sum of the expressions in Eq. 9.3–27 and 28. When the kinetic contribution is added to this, we get for the total pressure tensor:

$$\mathsf{p} = \left\{nkT(1 + \tfrac{2}{3}\pi n\sigma^3 Y) - \kappa\left(\frac{\partial}{\partial \boldsymbol{r}} \cdot \boldsymbol{v}_0\right)\right\}\mathsf{U}$$

$$- \left\{\frac{2}{Y}(1 + \tfrac{4}{15}\,\pi n\sigma^3 Y)^2\,\eta^0 + \tfrac{6}{5}\kappa\right\}\mathsf{S} \qquad (9.3\text{–}31)$$

Comparison of this expression with Eq. 7.6–29 indicates that κ is the coefficient of bulk viscosity. From Eq. 9.3–31 it follows that the kinetic theory gives for the static pressure

$$p = nkT(1 + \tfrac{2}{3}\pi n\sigma^3 Y) \qquad (9.3\text{–}32)$$

Since we know the static pressure from the equation of state for rigid spheres, Eq. 9.3–32 provides a means for evaluating the quantity Y. When Eq. 9.3–31 is compared with the defining equation for the coefficient of shear viscosity η (Eq. 7.6–29) it is seen that

$$\eta = \frac{1}{Y}(1 + \tfrac{4}{15}\,\pi n\sigma^3 Y)^2\eta^0 + \tfrac{3}{5}\kappa$$

$$= \frac{1}{Y}(1 + \tfrac{8}{15}\,\pi n\sigma^3 Y + 0.761(\tfrac{2}{3}\pi n\sigma^3 Y)^2)\eta^0 \qquad (9.3\text{–}33)$$

This expression is discussed further in § 9.3f.

ii. *The Coefficient of Thermal Conductivity*

The contribution to the heat flux vector due to collisional transfer may be obtained from Eq. 9.3–12 by letting ψ equal $\frac{1}{2}mv^2$. The first integral in this expression is

$$\tfrac{1}{5}\pi n\sigma^3 Y(nm\overline{V^2\boldsymbol{V}}) = -\tfrac{2}{5}\pi n\sigma^3(1 + \tfrac{2}{5}\pi n\sigma^3 Y)\lambda^0\frac{\partial T}{\partial \boldsymbol{r}} \qquad (9.3\text{–}34)$$

The second integral becomes

$$-\frac{3k}{2m}\kappa\frac{\partial T}{\partial \boldsymbol{r}} \qquad (9.3\text{–}35)$$

in which κ is the coefficient of bulk viscosity given previously. When these two terms are added to the kinetic contribution to the heat flux vector given in Eq. 9.3–26, we get for the total heat flux vector:

$$\boldsymbol{q} = -\left\{\frac{1}{Y}(1 + \tfrac{2}{5}\pi n\sigma^3 Y)^2\lambda^0 + \frac{3k}{2m}\kappa\right\}\frac{\partial T}{\partial \boldsymbol{r}} \qquad (9.3\text{–}36)$$

Hence the coefficient of thermal conductivity is[12]

$$\lambda = \frac{1}{Y}(1 + \tfrac{2}{5}\pi n\sigma^3 Y)^2\lambda^0 + \frac{3k}{2m}\kappa$$

$$= \frac{1}{Y}(1 + \tfrac{4}{5}\pi n\sigma^3 Y + 0.755\,(\tfrac{2}{3}\pi n\sigma^3 Y)^2)\lambda^0 \qquad (9.3\text{–}37)$$

This formula receives further attention in § 9.3f.

Equation 9.3–37 is valid only for monatomic molecules, of course. For a dense polyatomic gas, this equation may be modified by introducing the basic notions which led to the Eucken correction in the dilute gas (§ 7.6b). The resulting equation is

$$\lambda^{\text{Eucken}} = \frac{1}{Y}\left(\frac{c_v}{k} + \frac{9}{4}\right)\frac{k}{m}\eta^0 + \tfrac{5}{2}\pi n\sigma^3[\tfrac{6}{5} + 0.755(\tfrac{2}{3}\pi n\sigma^3)\,Y]\,\frac{k}{m}\eta^0 \qquad (9.3\text{–}37a)$$

Because the rotations of polyatomic molecules are hindered at high densities, however, it is not expected that this relation is applicable beyond the range of moderate densities.

iii. *The Coefficient of Diffusion*

The theory and applications discussed thus far have been restricted to pure gases. The Enskog theory of dense gases has been extended to include binary mixtures.[13] The results for viscosity, thermal conductivity, and thermal diffusion are quite complicated and are not given here. The coefficient of diffusion for a dense gas, however, is simply related to the low-density value by [14]

$$n\,D_{12} = \frac{(n\,D_{12})^0}{Y_{12}} \qquad (9.3\text{–}38)$$

The quantity Y_{12} is a generalization of the function Y introduced earlier and depends on the diameters of both molecules, σ_1 and σ_2:

$$Y_{12} = 1 + \tfrac{2}{3}\pi n_1\sigma_1{}^3\left(\frac{\sigma_1 + 4\sigma_2}{4\sigma_1 + 4\sigma_2}\right) + \tfrac{2}{3}\pi n_2\sigma_2{}^3\left(\frac{4\sigma_1 + \sigma_2}{4\sigma_1 + 4\sigma_2}\right) + \cdots \qquad (9.3\text{–}39)$$

We have seen in this section that the momentum flux (pressure tensor) and the energy flux (heat flux vector) are made up of two parts, one due

[12] The numerical constant, 0.755 involves the corrections for the higher approximations (see Table 8.3–2).

[13] This generalization was carried out by H. H. Thorne of the University of Sydney in Australia. See Chapman and Cowling, *loc. cit.*, pp. 292 et seq.

[14] The $(nD_{12})^0$ is the quantity calculated on the basis of the low-density kinetic theory for a gas of the same temperature.

to the flux of molecules and the other due to collisional transfer. The mass flux vector $\boldsymbol{j}$, which is related to the coefficient of diffusion, is different from the other two flux vectors in that it clearly has no contribution due to collisional transfer.

f. Summary of results for rigid spheres

We now summarize the results of the Enskog theory of the transport coefficients of a dense gas made up of rigid spherical molecules. The transport coefficients divided by their zero-pressure values (indicated by superscripts 0) and multiplied by the reduced volume may be written in terms of a dimensionless quantity y defined by

$$y = (b_0/\tilde{V})Y = (\tfrac{2}{3}\pi n\sigma^3)Y \tag{9.3–40}$$

In terms of y, the transport coefficients are

$$\begin{aligned}
&\text{Shear viscosity} && \frac{\eta}{\eta^0}\frac{\tilde{V}}{b_0} = \frac{1}{y} + 0.8 + 0.761y \\
&\text{Bulk viscosity} && \frac{\kappa}{\eta^0}\frac{\tilde{V}}{b_0} = 1.002y \\
&\text{Thermal conductivity}^{15} && \frac{\lambda}{\lambda^0}\frac{\tilde{V}}{b_0} = \frac{1}{y} + 1.2 + 0.755y \\
&\text{Self-diffusion}^{16} && \frac{pD}{(pD)^0}\frac{\tilde{V}}{b_0} = \frac{1}{y} + 1
\end{aligned} \tag{9.3–41}$$

The reduced shear viscosity times the reduced volume as a function of the parameter y exhibits a minimum. The same is true for the reduced thermal conductivity times the reduced volume. These minima are given by

$$\begin{aligned}
\left[\frac{\eta}{\eta^0}\frac{\tilde{V}}{b_0}\right]_{\min} &= 2.545, \quad \text{where } y = 1.146 \\
\left[\frac{\lambda}{\lambda^0}\frac{\tilde{V}}{b_0}\right]_{\min} &= 2.938, \quad \text{where } y = 1.151
\end{aligned} \tag{9.3–42}$$

The variation of the various transport coefficients with y is shown graphically in Fig. 9.3–1.

For rigid spherical molecules the parameter y is equal to the compressibility factor minus one:

$$y = (p\tilde{V}/RT) - 1 \tag{9.3–43}$$

[15] This is for monatomic gases. For polyatomic molecules Eq. 9.3–37a applies.

[16] $(pD)^0$ is the self-diffusion coefficient at 1 atm as calculated by the methods of Chapter 8.

In the region of low and moderate densities y may be written in the virial form:

$$y = \left(\frac{b_0}{\tilde{V}}\right) + 0.6250\left(\frac{b_0}{\tilde{V}}\right)^2 + 0.2869\left(\frac{b_0}{\tilde{V}}\right)^3 + 0.115\left(\frac{b_0}{\tilde{V}}\right)^4 + \cdots \quad (9.3\text{–}44)$$

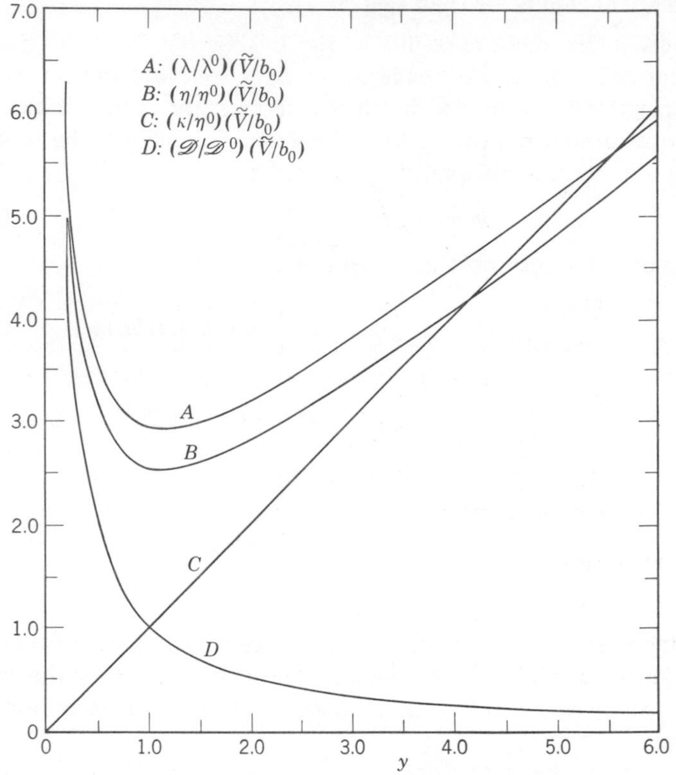

Fig. 9.3–1. The transport coefficients of a gas composed of rigid spherical molecules according to the Enskog theory.

In the high-density region probably the best equation of state for rigid spheres is obtained from the radial distribution function by Kirkwood, Maun, and Alder[17] (see § 4.9). Their results are given in Table 9.3–1.

[17] J. G. Kirkwood, E. K. Maun, and B. J. Alder, *J. Chem. Phys.*, **18**, 1040 (1950); see also § 4.9. The values which Kirkwood, Maun, and Alder obtained for densities greater than $b_0/\tilde{V} = 1.6$ are smaller than would be obtained by the Eyring equation of state (Eq. 4.5–3, using the constant 0.6962) by the factor $\tilde{V}/0.6962b_0$. The results of Kirkwood, Maun, and Alder have recently been verified and extended by A. G. McLellan, *Proc. Roy. Soc.* (*London*), **A210**, 509 (1952). Recent unpublished calculations of the equation of state (using Monte Carlo methods) by M. Rosenbluth, however, indicate that the Eyring free volume equation may be preferable.

TABLE 9.3–1

THE QUANTITY y AS A FUNCTION OF $(b_0/\tilde{V})$ FOR A VERY DENSE GAS COMPOSED OF RIGID SPHERES[17]

$$y = (p\tilde{V}/RT) - 1$$

$b_0/\tilde{V}$	y	$b_0/\tilde{V}$	y	$b_0/\tilde{V}$	y
0.3535	0.44	1.377	2.91	2.058	5.46
0.6250	0.91	1.527	3.43	2.160	5.99
0.8511	1.39	1.664	3.93	2.278	6.50
1.047	1.89	1.805	4.44	2.387	6.93
1.224	2.40	1.934	4.95	2.962	∞

The dependence of y on $b_0/\tilde{V}$ for rigid spheres is given in Fig. 9.3–2. This graph and those given in the previous figure summarize completely the results of the Enskog theory of the transport phenomena of dense gases and liquids which are made up of rigid spherical molecules.

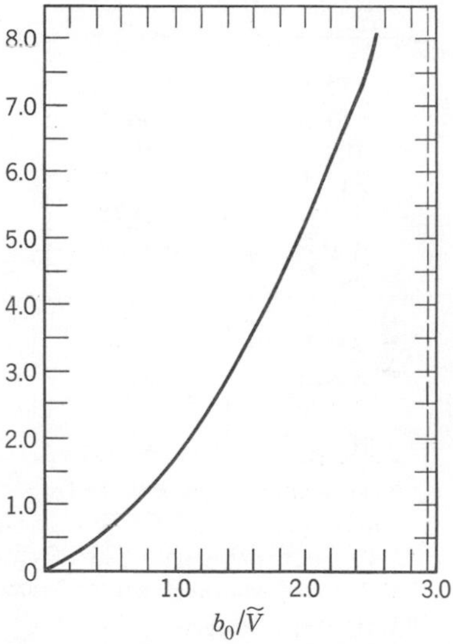

Fig. 9.3–2. The quantity $y - (p\tilde{V}/RT) - 1$ as a function of $b_0/\tilde{V}$ for rigid spheres (as calculated by Kirkwood, Maun, and Alder[17]). The curve is asymptotic to the dashed vertical line.

g. Applications of results to real gases

Although the formulae for the transport coefficients given above in Eq. 9.3–41 were obtained for gases composed of rigid spherical molecules, Enskog[1, 2] showed that these results can be applied to real gases with reasonable success. In order to use the above formulae, it is necessary to specify b_0 and y. Enskog suggested that the pressure in Eq. 9.3–43 be replaced by the "thermal pressure," $T(\partial p/\partial T)_{\tilde{V}}$, so that y may be determined from the experimental p-$\tilde{V}$-T data by using the relation

$$y = \frac{\tilde{V}}{RT}\left[T\left(\frac{\partial p}{\partial T}\right)_{\tilde{V}}\right] - 1 \qquad (9.3\text{–}45)$$

For rigid spheres this equation and Eq. 9.3–43 may easily be shown to be identical, but such is not the case for real gases. Enskog also suggested that b_0 be evaluated by fitting the minimum in the curve of $(\eta/\eta^0)\tilde{V}$ as a function of y.[18, 19]

A justification for Enskog's method may be obtained by the following considerations. The pressure experienced by a single molecule is made up of two components: the external pressure, p, due to the containing walls of the vessel, and the "internal pressure" $(\partial\tilde{U}/\partial\tilde{V})_T$, which represents the force of cohesion of the molecules. The sum of the external and internal pressures is called the "thermal pressure", and is thermodynamically equal to $T(\partial p/\partial T)_{\tilde{V}}$. When Enskog suggested that the

TABLE 9.3–2

THE VISCOSITY OF NITROGEN AT 50°C AS A FUNCTION OF PRESSURE[a]

p (atm)	ρ (g/cm³)[b]	$\left(\frac{\eta}{\rho}\right)_{\text{exptl}} \times 10^7$ (cm²/sec)	$\eta \times 10^7$ (g cm^{-1} sec^{-1}) Experimental[c]	$\eta \times 10^7$ (g cm^{-1} sec^{-1}) Calculated
15.37	0.01623	117900	1913	1810
57.60	0.06049	32740	1981	1900
104.5	0.1083	19280	2088	2050
212.4	0.2067	11480	2373	2240
320.4	0.2875	9520	2737	2660
430.2	0.3528	8870	3129	3080
541.7	0.4053	8660	3509	3480
630.4	0.4409	8590	3786	3800
742.1	0.4786	8700	4163	4180
854.1	0.5117	8890	4550	4550
965.8	0.5404	9090	4913	4920

[a] This comparison is taken from Chapman and Cowling, *The Mathematical Theory of Non-uniform Gases*, Cambridge University Press (1939), p. 289.

[b] Compressibility data taken from Deming and Shupe, *Phys. Rev.*, **37**, 638 (1931).

[c] Viscosity data taken from Michels and Gibson, *Proc. Roy. Soc.*, (*London*), **A134**, 288 (1931).

[18] The values of b_0 obtained in this way are of the same order of magnitude as those obtained from the coefficient of viscosity of dilute gases for the rigid sphere model. However, the agreement is not particularly good. Other methods of determining b_0 will present themselves after more experimental data become available.

[19] Actually the value of b_0 cannot be assigned arbitrarily. In order that η^0, λ^0, and $\mathscr{D}^0$ be the low-pressure limits of the respective transport coefficients, it is necessary that $y\tilde{V} \to b_0$ as $\rho \to 0$. If y is defined by Eq. 9.3–45 it follows that $b_0 = B + T\dfrac{dB}{dT}$, where B is the second virial coefficient.

quantity y be determined from the experimental compressibility data by means of Eq. 9.3–45, he supposed that a real gas is equivalent to a rigid-sphere gas in which the external pressure has been replaced by the thermal pressure. This notion forms the basis of Hildebrand's treatment of the solubility of non-electrolytes in liquids, and it forms the basis for Eyring's equation of state of liquids (see § 4.5). From the empirical success of the theories of Hildebrand and Eyring, we can conclude that this model is satisfactory for liquids and very dense gases. It should not, however, be good for dilute gases and becomes progressively poorer as the temperature decreases. Under such conditions real gas molecules have a tendency to form small clusters, a phenomenon which does not occur with rigid spherical molecules.

An illustration of the application of Enskog's semi-empirical extension of his rigid-sphere theory is given in Table 9.3–2. A comparison is given there between the calculated and experimental viscosities of N_2 at 50°C up to 1000 atm. It is evident that an excellent correlation is obtained. In Table 9.3–3 a similar comparison is given for CO_2. The two numerical

TABLE 9.3–3[a]

THE VISCOSITY[b] OF CARBON DIOXIDE AT 40.3°C AS A FUNCTION OF PRESSURE

p (atm)	ρ (g/cm³)	$\left(\frac{\eta}{\rho}\right)_{\text{exptl}} \times 10^7$ (cm²/sec)	$\eta \times 10^7$ (g cm⁻¹ sec⁻¹) Experimental	$\eta \times 10^7$ (g cm⁻¹ sec⁻¹) Calculated
45.3	0.100	18000	1800	1910
64.3	0.170	11500	1960	1990
75.9	0.240	9080	2180	2160
82.7	0.310	7840	2430	2400
86.8	0.380	7240	2750	2730
89.2	0.450	7020	3160	3150
91.7	0.520	7040	3660	3670
94.9	0.590	7220	4260	4270
101.6	0.660	7560	4990	4980
114.6	0.730	7950	5800	5780

[a] This table is taken from D. Enskog, *Kungliga Svenska Vetenskaps-akademiens Handlingar*, **63**, No. 4 (1922).

[b] The experimental compressibility and viscosity data are those of E. Warburg and L. v. Babo, *Wied. Ann.*, **17**, 390 (1882).

comparisons given here are a rather convincing proof that Enskog's method of applying the rigid-sphere results to real gases has in some way taken into account the primary features in the transport phenomena of dense gases.

4. The Transport Properties of Dense Gases and Liquids from Non-equilibrium Statistical Mechanics[1]

In Chapter 7 the theory of transport phenomena in dilute gases is developed from the principles of non-equilibrium statistical mechanics. An explicit formulation of the transport coefficients in terms of intermolecular forces is obtained by solving the Boltzmann equation for the distribution function $f^{(1)}(\boldsymbol{r}, \boldsymbol{p}, t)$. In this section a rigorous kinetic theory of dense gases is developed on the basis of the Liouville equation. If it is assumed that the forces are two-body forces, the flux vectors may be expressed in terms of the non-equilibrium pair distribution function. Thus the principal problem in the kinetic theory of dense gases and liquids is the evaluation of this non-equilibrium pair distribution function. (In § 4.9 it is shown that the problem of computing the equilibrium pair distribution function is the key to understanding the equation of state of dense gases and liquids.) Certainly this approach to the study of transport phenomena is more satisfying from a theoretical viewpoint than the developments given in §§ 9.2 and 9.3. At the present time, however, only very limited calculations have been carried out, so that the method may not yet be used for practical work. We present the salient features of this frontier field, since the statistical mechanical approach shows great promise and since some of the elements of the theory enable us to understand better the meaning of the Eyring and Enskog theories.

The discussion given here is based on classical statistical mechanics, and the system under consideration is taken to consist of N identical molecules.[2] For simplicity it is assumed that these molecules are point particles with no internal degrees of freedom, although many of the results are, in fact, more general. It is further assumed that the forces between the molecules are two-body forces, so that the potential energy of the system $\Phi(\boldsymbol{r}^N)$ may be written in the form

$$\Phi(\boldsymbol{r}^N) = \tfrac{1}{2} \sum_{i=1}^{N} \sum_{j=1}^{N} \varphi(r_{ij})$$

in which $\varphi(r_{ij})$ is the potential energy of interaction between molecules i and j which are a distance r_{ij} apart.

[1] J. H. Irving and J. G. Kirkwood, *J. Chem. Phys.*, **18**, 817 (1950).

[2] Irving and Kirkwood (Ref. 1) have given the theory for mixtures of several chemical species.

a. The Liouville equation and the general equation of change[3]

The system of N molecules which we are considering may be represented by an ensemble of dynamically similar systems, as is described in § 7.1. The state of a single system in the ensemble may be described by one point in a $6N$-dimensional phase space (γ-space), and the state of the representative ensemble is then described by a collection of points in the same phase space. The distribution function $f^{(N)}$ representing the distribution of this cloud of points in phase space satisfies the Liouville equation:

$$\frac{\partial f^{(N)}}{\partial t} = -\frac{1}{m}\left(\boldsymbol{p}^N \cdot \frac{\partial f^{(N)}}{\partial \boldsymbol{r}^N}\right) + \left(\frac{\partial \Phi}{\partial \boldsymbol{r}^N} \cdot \frac{\partial f^{(N)}}{\partial \boldsymbol{p}^N}\right) \tag{9.4-1}$$

As described in § 2.1, the distribution function is normalized to $N!$:

$$\iint f^{(N)}\, d\boldsymbol{r}^N\, d\boldsymbol{p}^N = N! \tag{9.4-2}$$

Let $\alpha(\boldsymbol{r}^N, \boldsymbol{p}^N)$ be any dynamical variable which is not explicitly dependent on time. According to the basic principles of non-equilibrium statistical mechanics (§ 7.1), the expectation value of α is the average value

$$\bar{\alpha} = \frac{1}{N!}\iint \alpha(\boldsymbol{r}^N, \boldsymbol{p}^N) f^{(N)}(\boldsymbol{r}^N, \boldsymbol{p}^N, t)\, d\boldsymbol{r}^N\, d\boldsymbol{p}^N \tag{9.4-3}$$

This is the value of α which one would expect to measure. From this definition and the Liouville equation the rate of change of the expectation value of $\bar{\alpha}$ is found to be

$$\begin{aligned}
\frac{d\bar{\alpha}}{dt} &= \frac{1}{N!}\iint \alpha \frac{\partial f^{(N)}}{\partial t}\, d\boldsymbol{r}^N\, d\boldsymbol{p}^N \\
&= \frac{1}{N!}\iint \alpha\left[-\frac{1}{m}\left(\boldsymbol{p}^N \cdot \frac{\partial f^{(N)}}{\partial \boldsymbol{r}^N}\right) + \left(\frac{\partial \Phi}{\partial \boldsymbol{r}^N} \cdot \frac{\partial f^{(N)}}{\partial \boldsymbol{p}^N}\right)\right] d\boldsymbol{r}^N\, d\boldsymbol{p}^N \\
&= \frac{1}{N!}\iint f^{(N)}\left[\frac{1}{m}\left(\boldsymbol{p}^N \cdot \frac{\partial \alpha}{\partial \boldsymbol{r}^N}\right) - \left(\frac{\partial \Phi}{\partial \boldsymbol{r}^N} \cdot \frac{\partial \alpha}{\partial \boldsymbol{p}^N}\right)\right] d\boldsymbol{r}^N\, d\boldsymbol{p}^N \\
&= \overline{\frac{1}{m}\left(\boldsymbol{p}^N \cdot \frac{\partial \alpha}{\partial \boldsymbol{r}^N}\right) - \left(\frac{\partial \Phi}{\partial \boldsymbol{r}^N} \cdot \frac{\partial \alpha}{\partial \boldsymbol{p}^N}\right)}
\end{aligned} \tag{9.4-4}$$

[3] The distribution functions in classical statistical mechanics are used throughout this section. A complete summary of these functions, their definitions, and interrelations is given in § 2.1.

The transition from the second to the third step is made by means of Green's theorem and the assumption that $f^{(N)}$ decreases sufficiently rapidly as $\boldsymbol{r}^N \to \infty$ and $\boldsymbol{p}^N \to \infty$. This result is known as the "general equation of change."

b. The macroscopic variables

The three basic equations of change may be obtained from the general equation of change by considering in turn three dynamical variables related to the densities (in ordinary three-dimensional space) of mass, momentum and energy.

The probability per unit volume that molecule k is at the point $\boldsymbol{r}$ is

$$\overline{\delta(\boldsymbol{r}_k - \boldsymbol{r})} = \frac{1}{N!}\iint \delta(\boldsymbol{r}_k - \boldsymbol{r}) f^{(N)}\, d\boldsymbol{r}^N\, d\boldsymbol{p}^N \tag{9.4–5}$$

in which $\delta(\boldsymbol{r}_k - \boldsymbol{r})$ is a Dirac δ-function. Consequently the (probable) *total number density* at $\boldsymbol{r}$ is

$$n(\boldsymbol{r}, t) = \sum_{k=1}^{N} \overline{\delta(\boldsymbol{r}_k - \boldsymbol{r})} \tag{9.4–6}$$

and the *total mass density* is

$$\rho(\boldsymbol{r}, t) = \sum_{k=1}^{N} \overline{m\delta(\boldsymbol{r}_k - \boldsymbol{r})} \tag{9.4–7}$$

Similarly, the contribution of molecule k to the momentum per unit volume at $\boldsymbol{r}$ is

$$\overline{\boldsymbol{p}_k\delta(\boldsymbol{r}_k - \boldsymbol{r})} = \frac{1}{N!}\iint \boldsymbol{p}_k\delta(\boldsymbol{r}_k - \boldsymbol{r}) f^{(N)}\, d\boldsymbol{r}^N\, d\boldsymbol{p}^N \tag{9.4–8}$$

Accordingly, the *total momentum density* is

$$\rho(\boldsymbol{r}, t)\boldsymbol{v}_0(\boldsymbol{r}, t) = \sum_{k=1}^{N} \overline{\boldsymbol{p}_k\delta(\boldsymbol{r}_k - \boldsymbol{r})} \tag{9.4–9}$$

The quantity $\boldsymbol{v}_0(\boldsymbol{r}, t)$ is the mass average velocity of the molecules, that is, the macroscopic velocity of the fluid.

The internal energy of a gas is made up of the kinetic energy of the random motion of the molecules (that is, the motion relative to $\boldsymbol{v}_0$) and the potential energy associated with the intermolecular forces.[4] The kinetic energy per unit volume at $\boldsymbol{r}$ is:

$$\sum_{k=1}^{N} \overline{(p_k^2/2m)\delta(\boldsymbol{r}_k - \boldsymbol{r})} = \frac{1}{N!}\sum_{k=1}^{N}\iint \frac{p_k^2}{2m}\,\delta(\boldsymbol{r}_k - \boldsymbol{r}) f^{(N)}\, d\boldsymbol{r}^N\, d\boldsymbol{p}^N \tag{9.4–10}$$

[4] Irving and Kirkwood[1] define the internal energy as the sum of the total kinetic energy, the potential of the intermolecular forces, and the potential energy related to the external forces. That is, they include, in addition to the terms included here, the potential energy of the system due to the external forces and the kinetic energy associated with the macroscopic flow. The difference in the definitions causes small changes in the energy balance equation, but of course does not affect the definitions of the flux vectors.

This quantity, however, includes the kinetic energy $\frac{1}{2}\rho v_0^2$ which is contributed by the macroscopic motion of the fluid. Hence the *kinetic energy density* associated with the random motion of the molecules is

$$n(\boldsymbol{r}, t)u_K(\boldsymbol{r}, t) = \overline{\sum_{k=1}^{N} \left(\frac{p_k^2}{2m}\right) \delta(\boldsymbol{r}_k - \boldsymbol{r})} - \tfrac{1}{2}\rho v_0^2 \qquad (9.4\text{–}11)$$

where $u_K(\boldsymbol{r}, t)$ is the kinetic contribution to the internal energy per molecule.

The densities of mass, momentum, and kinetic energy may be defined in a straightforward manner since the mass, momentum, and kinetic energy of a molecule may be considered as localized at the molecule. In contrast to this, the potential energy $\varphi(r_{ij})$, associated with the mutual force between molecules i and j, depends on the location of both molecules and hence is not so naturally localizable. Since the forces between molecules are of short range compared with macroscopic dimensions, this problem presents no difficulties from a macroscopic view. A very reasonable artifice is to assume formally that one-half of the potential energy $\varphi(r_{ij})$ is localized at each molecule. Such a definition maintains the natural symmetry and enables us to write for the *total potential energy density*:

$$n(\boldsymbol{r}, t)u_\Phi(\boldsymbol{r}, t) = \tfrac{1}{2} \overline{\sum_{i=1}^{N} \sum_{j=1}^{N} \varphi_{ij}\delta(\boldsymbol{r}_j - \boldsymbol{r})} \qquad (9.4\text{–}12)$$

Here $u_\Phi(\boldsymbol{r}, t)$ is the potential contribution to the internal energy per molecule. The *total internal energy* per molecule is then

$$u(\boldsymbol{r}, t) = u_K(\boldsymbol{r}, t) + u_\Phi(\boldsymbol{r}, t) \qquad (9.4\text{–}13)$$

We have thus succeeded in writing the densities of mass, momentum, and internal energy in terms of averages or integrals over $f^{(N)}(\boldsymbol{r}, \boldsymbol{p}, t)$.

c. The macroscopic variables in terms of the lower-order distribution functions

Let us now rewrite the results which we have obtained in terms of integrals over low-order distribution functions. The distribution function $f^{(1)}$ in the phase space of a single molecule is the integral of $f^{(N)}$ over the position and momentum coordinates of all the molecules save one. To avoid singling out any one particular molecule in the integration process, we may write the function $f^{(1)}$ in the following symmetric form:

$$f^{(1)}(\boldsymbol{r}, \boldsymbol{p}, t) = \overline{\sum_{k=1}^{N} \delta(\boldsymbol{r}_k - \boldsymbol{r})\delta(\boldsymbol{p}_k - \boldsymbol{p})} \qquad (9.4\text{–}14)$$

And, similarly, we may write

$$f^{(2)}(\boldsymbol{r}, \boldsymbol{r}', \boldsymbol{p}, \boldsymbol{p}', t) = \overline{\sum_{j=1}^{N} \sum_{\substack{k=1 \\ k \neq j}}^{N} \delta(\boldsymbol{r}_j - \boldsymbol{r})\delta(\boldsymbol{r}_k - \boldsymbol{r}')\delta(\boldsymbol{p}_j - \boldsymbol{p})\delta(\boldsymbol{p}_k - \boldsymbol{p}')} \tag{9.4–15}$$

for the distribution function in the phase space of pairs. In terms of these functions the number density, mass average velocity, and kinetic and potential energy per molecule may be written as

$$n(\boldsymbol{r}, t) = \int f^{(1)}(\boldsymbol{r}, \boldsymbol{p}, t)\, d\boldsymbol{p} \tag{9.4–16}$$

$$\boldsymbol{v}_0(\boldsymbol{r}, t) = \frac{1}{n} \int \left(\frac{\boldsymbol{p}}{m}\right) f^{(1)}(\boldsymbol{r}, \boldsymbol{p}, t)\, d\boldsymbol{p} \tag{9.4–17}$$

$$u_K(\boldsymbol{r}, t) = \frac{m}{2n} \int \left[\frac{p^2}{m^2} - v_0^{\,2}\right] f^{(1)}(\boldsymbol{r}, \boldsymbol{p}, t)\, d\boldsymbol{p} \tag{9.4–18}$$

$$u_\Phi(\boldsymbol{r}, t) = \frac{1}{2n} \iiint \varphi(|\boldsymbol{r} - \boldsymbol{r}'|) f^{(2)}(\boldsymbol{r}, \boldsymbol{r}', \boldsymbol{p}, \boldsymbol{p}', t)\, d\boldsymbol{r}'\, d\boldsymbol{p}\, d\boldsymbol{p}' \tag{9.4–19}$$

The first three of these relations correspond to the definitions given in § 7.2a.

There are several other distribution functions which are useful in the development that follows. The function $n^{(2)}(\boldsymbol{r}, \boldsymbol{r}', t)$ gives the probability that one molecule is at $\boldsymbol{r}$ and another is at $\boldsymbol{r}'$. It is defined according to Eq. 2.1–8 as

$$n^{(2)}(\boldsymbol{r}, \boldsymbol{r}', t) = \iint f^{(2)}(\boldsymbol{r}, \boldsymbol{r}', \boldsymbol{p}, \boldsymbol{p}', t)\, d\boldsymbol{p}\, d\boldsymbol{p}' \tag{9.4–20}$$

It is convenient to express the function $n^{(2)}$ in terms of the ordinary number density and a "non-equilibrium radial distribution function," $g(\boldsymbol{r}, \boldsymbol{R}, t)$, thus

$$n^{(2)}(\boldsymbol{r}, \boldsymbol{r} + \boldsymbol{R}, t) = n(\boldsymbol{r}, t)n(\boldsymbol{r} + \boldsymbol{R}, t)g(\boldsymbol{r}, \boldsymbol{R}, t) \tag{9.4–21}$$

in which we have chosen to write $(\boldsymbol{r}' - \boldsymbol{r})$ as $\boldsymbol{R}$. This radial distribution function depends macroscopically on $\boldsymbol{r}$ and microscopically on $\boldsymbol{R}$. For values of $\boldsymbol{R}$ large compared to the range of the intermolecular forces $g(\boldsymbol{r}, \boldsymbol{R}, t)$ approaches unity. In equilibrium statistical mechanics the radial distribution function is independent of $\boldsymbol{r}$ and t and becomes simply $g(R)$.

The expression for $\boldsymbol{u}_\Phi(\boldsymbol{r}, t)$ given in Eq. 9.4–19 may now be rewritten in terms of the non-equilibrium radial distribution function:

$$u_\Phi(\boldsymbol{r}, t) = \tfrac{1}{2} \int \varphi(R) n(\boldsymbol{r} + \boldsymbol{R}, t) g(\boldsymbol{r}, \boldsymbol{R}, t)\, d\boldsymbol{R} \tag{9.4–22}$$

Inasmuch as the number density $n(\boldsymbol{r}, t)$ has only macroscopic dependence on $\boldsymbol{r}$ and the intermolecular forces are short range, this expression can be written with little error thus:

$$u_\Phi(\boldsymbol{r}, t) = \tfrac{1}{2} n(\boldsymbol{r}, t) \int \varphi(R) g(\boldsymbol{r}, \boldsymbol{R}, t)\, d\boldsymbol{R} \tag{9.4–23}$$

Another distribution function which finds use later in the discussion is the function $\boldsymbol{j}^{(2)}$, defined thus:

$$\boldsymbol{j}^{(2)}(\boldsymbol{r}, \boldsymbol{r}', t) = \iint (\boldsymbol{p} \oplus \boldsymbol{p}') f^{(2)}(\boldsymbol{r}, \boldsymbol{r}', \boldsymbol{p}, \boldsymbol{p}', t)\, d\boldsymbol{p}\, d\boldsymbol{p}' \tag{9.4–24}$$

This is the probability momentum density in the configuration space of a pair of molecules, and $(\boldsymbol{p} \oplus \boldsymbol{p}')$ is a six-component vector, the first three components of which are $\boldsymbol{p}$ and the second three components are $\boldsymbol{p}'$.

d. The flux vectors and the equations of change

In § 7.2e the three equations of change were derived for dilute gases. The same equations may be derived for dense gases by substituting various dynamical variables for α into Eq. 9.4–4. The only difference in the results is that more general expressions are obtained for the flux vectors. The derivations of these expressions are quite lengthy[1] and only the results are presented here.

The *equation of continuity* may be derived by setting α in Eq. 9.4–4 equal to:

$$\alpha = m \sum_{k=1}^{N} \delta(\boldsymbol{r}_k - \boldsymbol{r}) \tag{9.4–25}$$

Inasmuch as the rate of change of the expectation value of α is the expectation value of the dynamical variable,

$$\begin{aligned} \frac{1}{m}\left(\boldsymbol{p}^N \cdot \frac{\partial \alpha}{\partial \boldsymbol{r}^N}\right) - \left(\frac{\partial \Phi}{\partial \boldsymbol{r}^N} \cdot \frac{\partial \alpha}{\partial \boldsymbol{p}^N}\right) &= \left(\boldsymbol{p}^N \cdot \frac{\partial}{\partial \boldsymbol{r}^N} \sum_{k=1}^{N} \delta(\boldsymbol{r}_k - \boldsymbol{r})\right) \\ &= -\left(\frac{\partial}{\partial \boldsymbol{r}} \cdot \sum_{k=1}^{N} \boldsymbol{p}_k \delta(\boldsymbol{r}_k - \boldsymbol{r})\right) \end{aligned} \tag{9.4–26}$$

it follows from the definitions of the density and the mass-average velocity (given in Eqs. 9.4–7 and 9) that:

$$\frac{\partial \rho}{\partial t} + \left(\frac{\partial}{\partial \boldsymbol{r}} \cdot \rho \boldsymbol{v}_0\right) = 0 \tag{9.4–27}$$

This is identical with the equation of continuity obtained in § 7.2e.

The *equation of motion* is derived in a similar manner. It is obtained by writing the general equation of change with the dynamical variable, $\boldsymbol{\alpha}$, given by

$$\boldsymbol{\alpha} = \sum_{k=1}^{N} \boldsymbol{p}_k \delta(\boldsymbol{r}_k - \boldsymbol{r}) \tag{9.4–28}$$

After considerable manipulation[1] we obtain the same equation of motion which we obtain for the dilute gas:

$$\rho \frac{\partial \boldsymbol{v}_0}{\partial t} + \rho \left(\boldsymbol{v}_0 \cdot \frac{\partial}{\partial \boldsymbol{r}} \boldsymbol{v}_0\right) = -\left(\frac{\partial}{\partial \boldsymbol{r}} \cdot \mathsf{p}\right) + n\boldsymbol{X} \tag{9.4–29}$$

It is found, however, that the pressure tensor is made up of two terms:

$$\mathsf{p} = \mathsf{p}_K + \mathsf{p}_\Phi \tag{9.4–30}$$

where

$$\mathsf{p}_K(\boldsymbol{r}, t) = m \int \left(\frac{\boldsymbol{p}}{m} - \boldsymbol{v}_0\right)\left(\frac{\boldsymbol{p}}{m} - \boldsymbol{v}_0\right) f^{(1)}(\boldsymbol{r}, \boldsymbol{p})\, d\boldsymbol{p} \tag{9.4–31}$$

$$\mathsf{p}_\Phi(\boldsymbol{r}, t) = -\tfrac{1}{2}[n(\boldsymbol{r}, t)]^2 \int \frac{d\varphi(R)}{dR} g(\boldsymbol{r}, \boldsymbol{R}, t) \frac{\boldsymbol{R}\boldsymbol{R}}{R}\, d\boldsymbol{R} \tag{9.4–32}$$

The first term, p_K, is the kinetic contribution and is the dominant term in gases.[5] The second term, p_Φ, is the potential contribution and is the dominant term in liquids. This term represents the "collisional transfer" of momentum, or the transfer of momentum between the centers of the colliding molecules which takes place almost instantaneously during a molecular encounter.[6] Under equilibrium conditions the pressure tensor p becomes diagonal, with each of the diagonal elements equal to

$$p = nkT - \tfrac{1}{6}n^2 \int \frac{d\varphi(R)}{dR} g(R) 4\pi R^3\, dR \tag{9.4–33}$$

[5] p_K is identical with the expression for the pressure tensor in dilute gases given by Eq. (7.2–23). The term $\left(\frac{\boldsymbol{p}}{m} - \boldsymbol{v}_0\right)$ is the "peculiar velocity" defined in Eq. 7.2–5.

[6] Although the similarity is not apparent, this term and the corresponding term in the energy flux are generalizations of the corresponding terms introduced in the Enskog theory of § 9.3.

This is the equation of state derived from the virial theorem as described in § 3.1.

The *equation of energy balance* may be obtained from the general equation of change in a similar manner. The result is

$$\frac{\partial}{\partial t}(nu) + \left(\frac{\partial}{\partial \boldsymbol{r}} \cdot nu\boldsymbol{v}_0\right) + \left(\frac{\partial}{\partial \boldsymbol{r}} \cdot \boldsymbol{q}\right) + \left(\mathsf{p} : \frac{\partial}{\partial \boldsymbol{r}} \boldsymbol{v}_0\right) = 0 \qquad (9.4\text{–}34)$$

This is the same as the equation found for dilute gases, except that the heat flux vector, $\boldsymbol{q}$, has the more general form

$$\boldsymbol{q} = \boldsymbol{q}_K + \boldsymbol{q}_\Phi \qquad (9.4\text{–}35)$$

where

$$\boldsymbol{q}_K(\boldsymbol{r}, t) = \tfrac{1}{2}m \int \left|\frac{\boldsymbol{p}}{m} - \boldsymbol{v}_0\right|^2 \left(\frac{\boldsymbol{p}}{m} - \boldsymbol{v}_0\right) f^{(1)}(\boldsymbol{r}, \boldsymbol{p}, t)\, d\boldsymbol{p} \qquad (9.4\text{–}36)$$

$$\boldsymbol{q}_\Phi(\boldsymbol{r}, t) = \frac{1}{2m} \int \left[\varphi(R)\mathsf{U} - \frac{\partial \varphi}{\partial R}\frac{\boldsymbol{R}\boldsymbol{R}}{R}\right] \cdot \left[\boldsymbol{j}_1^{(2)}(\boldsymbol{r}, \boldsymbol{r} + \boldsymbol{R}, t) - m\boldsymbol{v}_0(\boldsymbol{r}, t) n^{(2)}(\boldsymbol{r}, \boldsymbol{r} + \boldsymbol{R}, t)\right] d\boldsymbol{R} \qquad (9.4\text{–}37)$$

Here U is the unit tensor, and $\boldsymbol{j}_1^{(2)}$ represents the first three components of $\boldsymbol{j}^{(2)}$. The first term $\boldsymbol{q}_K$ is the kinetic contribution and is the dominant term in gases.[7] The second term, $\boldsymbol{q}_\Phi$, is the potential contributons which arises because of the "collisional transfer" of energy and is the dominant term in liquids.

e. The calculation of the transport coefficients

In this manner we see that the ordinary equations of change apply to a dense gas or liquid, and we have obtained expressions for the flux vectors in terms of the pair distribution function and its integrals. These are the basic expressions which must be evaluated in order to extend the theory of transport phenomena into the dense gas and liquid region.

The pair distribution function can be obtained rigorously either through the solution of the Liouville equation or the equivalent set of coupled equations for the lower-order distribution functions (Eqs. 4.9–15). However, this is completely impossible in practice, and it is necessary to make use of some approximate method which acts to terminate the

[7] $\boldsymbol{q}_K$ is identical with the expression given in Eq. 7.2–26.

sequence of equations. These approximate methods involve some form of the superposition approximation discussed in § 4.9.

Born and Green[8] have introduced one form of the superposition approximation to obtain an integral equation for the radial distribution function. This equation has been solved by a perturbation method valid under conditions only slightly removed from equilibrium. The resulting solution is then used to obtain the flux vectors and values of the transport coefficients for dense gases and liquids. Although a formal solution has been obtained, the transport coefficients have not yet been completely evaluated numerically. According to Born and Green, a comparison with experimental data indicates that their calculated results are of the correct order of magnitude and have qualitatively the right density and temperature dependence.

The validity of the superposition principle has been examined by Klein and Prigogine[9] by considering a hypothetical one-dimensional gas. They find that the equations based on the approximation cannot describe the dissipative effects.

Kirkwood[10] has developed a general statistical mechanical theory of transport phenomena. This development leads to a theory of the friction factor similar to that which Chandrasekhar[11] developed on the basis of the phenomenological theory of Brownian motion. Particles moving through a fluid are subject to viscous resistance. If the particles are large spheres of radius r, the fluid acts as a continuous medium and the friction constant has the Stokes' value $6\pi\eta r$. Kirkwood generalized the concept of the friction coefficient to apply to small particles or molecules. The ratios of the two coefficients of viscosity to the friction factor were obtained in terms of integrals of the intermolecular potential and the equilibrium distribution function. Kirkwood, Buff, and Green[12] used these results to evaluate the ratio of the coefficient of shear viscosity to the friction constant for liquid argon at 89°K, using the Lennard-Jones potential and the experimental radial distribution function of Eisenstein and Gingrich.[13] Although the theory of the friction constant is complete, it is not yet possible to evaluate the constant accurately. A crude estimate of the friction constant leads to a value of the shear viscosity of argon in reasonable agreement with experiment.

[8] M. Born and H. S. Green, *A General Kinetic Theory of Liquids*, Cambridge University Press (1949); H. S. Green, *Molecular Theory of Fluids*, Interscience Press (1952).

[9] G. Klein and I. Prigogine, *Physica*, **19** (1953).

[10] J. G. Kirkwood, *J. Chem. Phys.*, **14**, 180 (1946).

[11] S. Chandrasekhar, *Revs. Mod. Phys.*, **15**, 1 (1945).

[12] J. G. Kirkwood, F. P. Buff, and M. S. Green, *J. Chem. Phys.*, **17**, 988 (1949).

[13] A. Eisenstein and N. S. Gingrich, *Phys. Rev.*, **62**, 261 (1942).

APPENDIX A. THE EYRING THEORY OF REACTION RATES [1–5]

The theory of absolute reaction rates was originally devised by Eyring[1] to explain the rates of chemical reactions. It was soon realized, however, that this theory could be satisfactorily applied to a great many other rate processes. The application to the theory of transport phenomena in liquids and dense gases is discussed in § 9.2. In this appendix we present the basic notions of the theory of absolute reaction rates in terms of a particular chemical reaction.

Let us consider a hypothetical reaction of the form:

$$A + BC \xrightarrow{k'} AB + C \tag{9.A–1}$$

According to the principles of chemical kinetics, the rate R of the reaction is proportional to the concentrations n_A and n_{BC}:

$$R = k' n_A n_{BC} \tag{9.A–2}$$

The quantity k' is referred to as the "specific reaction rate."

In the older chemical kinetics it was customary to express the specific reaction rate in the Arrhenius form,

$$k' = s\Gamma e^{-E^{\ddagger}/kT} \tag{9.A–3}$$

Here $E^{\ddagger}$ is the energy of activation, Γ is the number of collisions per unit volume per unit time between molecules of the type A and molecules of the type BC, and $s\Gamma$ is known as the "frequency factor." The product $\Gamma \exp(-E^{\ddagger}/kT)$ is the rate of collisions between A and BC molecules in which the kinetic energy associated with the component of the relative velocity along the lines of centers in the collision is greater than the activation energy. The number s should then be the probability that the geometrical and the internal relations are favorable for the reaction. The disadvantage of the Arrhenius equation is that s cannot be predicted. Sometimes s is very small compared to unity, and sometimes it is very large compared to unity. When s is larger than unity or the specific rate decreases with temperature, the simple collisional explanation of reaction rates breaks down, and it is necessary to make a more careful formulation based on statistical mechanics.

[1] H. Eyring, *J. Chem. Phys.*, **3**, 107 (1935).

[2] H. Eyring, *J. Chem. Phys.*, **4**, 283 (1936).

[3] J. F. Kincaid, H. Eyring, and A. E. Stearn, *Chem. Revs.*, **28**, 301 (1941).

[4] S. Glasstone, K. J. Laidler, and H. Eyring, *Theory of Rate Processes*, McGraw-Hill (1941).

[5] H. Eyring, J. Walter, and G. E. Kimball, *Quantum Chemistry*, Wiley (1944), Ch. XVI.

Let us now examine the reaction given in Eq. 9.A–1 from a detailed microscopic viewpoint. If it is assumed that this reaction of an atom with a diatomic molecule takes place in such a way that A, B, and C always remain in a straight line,[6] the course of the reaction may be followed by noting the values of the two interatomic distances r_{AB} and r_{BC}. Before a collision takes place between A and BC, r_{AB} is large and r_{BC} is small. If during the course of the collision a chemical reaction takes place, then after the products have separated from one another r_{AB} is small and r_{BC} is large. If such a chemical reaction does occur, there is one stage during the collision in which all three atoms are very close to one another. It is customary to speak of this combined molecule as the "collision complex." We may give it a chemical symbol $(ABC)^{\ddagger}$ and rewrite Eq. 9.A–1 as

$$A + BC \rightleftharpoons (ABC)^{\ddagger} \rightarrow AB + C \tag{9.A–4}$$

We write the first stage of this process as reversible, thus indicating that, once a collision complex has been formed, the atoms may separate in such a way as to give either the components A and BC or the components AB and C.

The course of the reaction may be followed on a potential energy surface of the form shown[7] in Fig. 9.A–1. The configuration space may be divided into three regions: the upper left triangle corresponds to the initial state $A + BC$; the lower right triangle corresponds to the final state, $AB + C$; the swath across the middle represents the "activated state" in which the collision complex is formed. The dotted line indicates the trajectory which a ball-bearing would follow if placed at the minimum of the saddle and allowed to roll down either side of the energy hill. This path is known as the "reaction coordinate." A cross-section through the energy surface along the reaction coordinate is shown in Fig. 9.A–2.

[6] The purpose of keeping the three atoms in a line is to simplify the discussion given here by eliminating the necessity for introducing a third dynamical variable, the angle between A, B, and C. In a real chemical reaction, the path of lowest energy often corresponds to the three atoms in a line. Deviations from this line are taken into account by introducing bending vibrations in the partition function for the activated complex.

[7] It will be noted that potential energy surfaces of the kind shown in Fig. 9.A–1 have their coordinates skewed, and the scale of distances is not always the same for the ordinates as for the abscissas. This is done so as to simplify the dynamics of the collision process. In the skewed coordinate system, the gradient of the energy surface at any point is proportional to the force acting on the system, and the kinetic energy is proportional to the sum of the squares of the rates of change of these new coordinates. The trajectory on the energy surface corresponding to a collision will then be the same as would be obtained by the motion of a mass point on this energy surface. (See S. Glasstone, K. Laidler, and H. Eyring, *Rate Processes*, McGraw-Hill (1941), p. 100.)

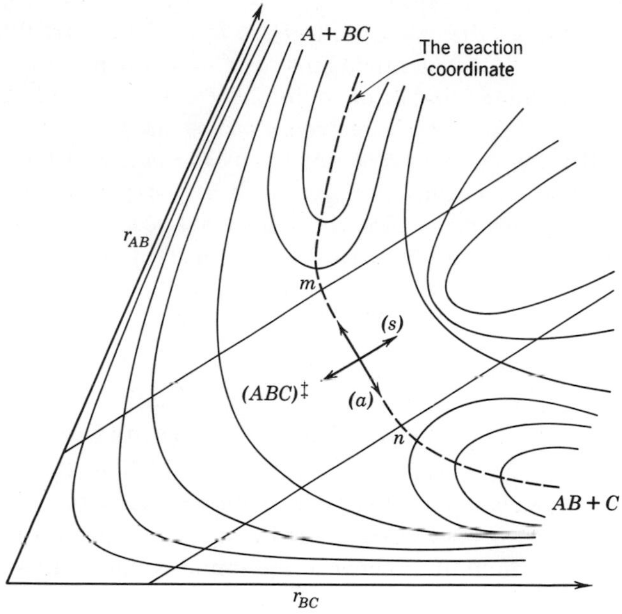

Fig. 9.A–1. Potential energy surface for the reaction of A with BC in one dimension. Dotted line is the "reaction coordinate." (s) and (a) illustrate the symmetric and anti-symmetric normal modes of vibration of the activated complex.

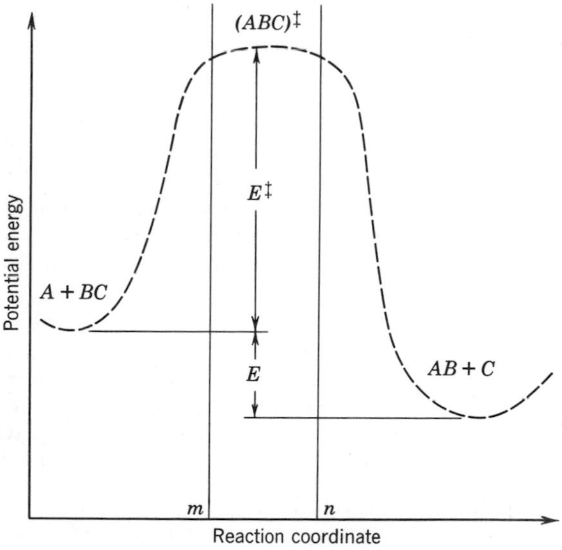

Fig. 9.A–2. Potential energy as a function of distance along the "reaction coordinate." The top of this curve corresponds to a saddle point in Fig. 9.A–1.

Let us now consider the calculation of the rate of reaction R and the specific reaction rate k'. The rate of the reaction is the product of three factors: (i) the average number of molecules in the activated state, $n^{\ddagger}$; (ii) the frequency with which a molecule passes through the activated state, that is, the average velocity $\bar{v}$ divided by the barrier width w; and (iii) the "transmission coefficient," κ, which is the probability that a chemical reaction takes place after the system has reached the activated state. Accordingly, we may write for the rate of reaction:

$$R = \kappa n^{\ddagger}(\bar{v}/w) \tag{9.A–5}$$

The transmission coefficient is not known but is usually assumed to be unity.[8] The width of the activated state region is rather ill defined, but this quantity cancels out presently. The average velocity $\bar{v}$ with which the system crosses the activated state[9] is $\sqrt{kT/2\pi m^{\ddagger}}$ in which $m^{\ddagger}$ is the effective mass of the activated complex along the reaction coordinate.

The quantity $n^{\ddagger}$ can be written in terms of an equilibrium constant, $K^{\ddagger}$, describing the equilibrium between the initial component A and BC and the activated complex $(ABC)^{\ddagger}$:

$$K^{\ddagger} = n^{\ddagger}/n_A n_{BC} = z^{\ddagger}/z_A z_{BC} \tag{9.A–6}$$

Here z_A and z_{BC} are the partition functions for atom A and molecule BC; $z^{\ddagger}$ is the partition function for the activated complex. In order to examine $z^{\ddagger}$ we must first study the behavior of the collision complex $(ABC)^{\ddagger}$. When the system is in the state $A + BC$ there are two translational degrees of freedom and one degree of vibrational freedom; the same is true when the system is in state $AB + C$. When the system is in the form of a complex $(ABC)^{\ddagger}$, there are one degree of translational freedom and two vibrational degrees of freedom. The normal modes of vibration are indicated in Fig. 9.A–1. There is a symmetric vibration (s) perpendicular to the reaction coordinate and an antisymmetric vibration (a) along the reaction coordinate. These vibrations are illustrated in Fig. 9.A–3.

[8] Extensive calculations for a large number of hypothetical cases [J. O. Hirschfelder and E. Wigner, *J. Chem. Phys.*, **7**, 616 (1939); H. M. Hulburt and J. O. Hirschfelder, *J. Chem. Phys.*, **11**, 276 (1943)] have shown that the transmission coefficient is of the order of unity or lies between $\frac{1}{2}$ and 1 for those reactions which behave classically. However, if the reaction entails the quantum mechanical crossing of two potential energy surfaces, the transmission coefficient can be extremely small (of the order of 10^{-5}).

[9] The velocity $\bar{v}$ is given by

$$\bar{v} = \int_0^{\infty} v e^{-mv^2/2kT}\, dv \Big/ \int_0^{\infty} e^{-mv^2/2kT}\, dv = \sqrt{kT/2\pi m}$$

The symmetric mode is an honest vibration, but the antisymmetric mode is not a true vibration because the potential surface is very nearly constant in the direction of the "vibration." In view of this fact, it is assumed that this "vibrational" mode may be replaced by a translational mode and that the collision complex is confined to move in a one-dimensional box of length w. This corresponds physically to the assumption that the top of the barrier is very nearly flat.[10]

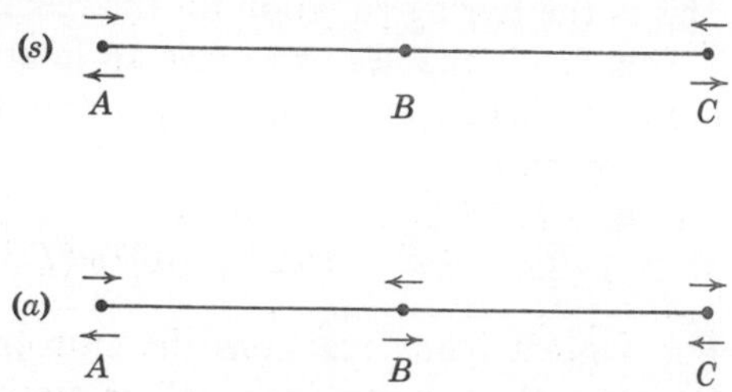

Fig. 9.A–3. The symmetric and antisymmetric modes of vibration of the activated complex.

When this assumption is made the partition function $z^{\ddagger}$ for the activated complex may be written as

$$z^{\ddagger} = z^{\ddagger\prime} \sqrt{\frac{2\pi m^{\ddagger} kT}{h^2}}\, w \tag{9.A–7}$$

Here $z^{\ddagger\prime}$ is the partition function of the idealized activated complex in which the antisymmetrical vibrational degree of freedom has been omitted; and $\sqrt{2\pi m^{\ddagger} kT/h^2}\; w$ is the partition function corresponding to the restricted translational motion along the reaction path at the top of the barrier. We may then define an "equilibrium" constant K in the following way:

$$K^{\ddagger} = K \sqrt{\frac{2\pi m^{\ddagger} kT}{h^2}}\, w = \frac{n^{\ddagger}}{n_A n_{BC}} = \frac{z^{\ddagger\prime}}{z_A z_{BC}} \sqrt{\frac{2\pi m^{\ddagger} kT}{h^2}}\, w \tag{9.A–8}$$

This allows us to write Eq. 9.A–5 as

$$R = \kappa K (kT/h)\, n_A n_{BC} \tag{9.A–9}$$

The specific reaction rate constant is then obtained as

$$k' = \kappa\, (kT/h) K \tag{9.A–10}$$

The universal factor kT/h is equal to $6.25 \times 10^{12}\ (T/300)\ \text{sec}^{-1}$. Usually

[10] Wigner has obtained corrections to the reaction rate for the curvature of the energy surface in the vicinity of the activated state. [E. P. Wigner, *Z. phys. Chem.*, **1319**, 903 (1932); see also Glasstone, Laidler, and Eyring, *The Theory of Rate Processes*, McGraw-Hill (1941), p. 191.]

it is convenient to write K in terms of a free energy of activation, $\Delta\tilde{G}^{\ddagger}$, so that Eq. 9.A–10 becomes

$$k' = \kappa\left(\frac{kT}{h}\right)e^{-\Delta\tilde{G}^{\ddagger}/RT} = \kappa\left(\frac{kT}{h}\right)e^{-[\Delta\tilde{H}^{\ddagger} - T\Delta\tilde{S}^{\ddagger}]/RT} \tag{9.A–11}$$

This is the Eyring equation for the reaction rate constant.[11]

This result enables us to give an interpretation to the frequency factor in the Arrhenius equation. According to Eqs. 9.A–3 and 11 this factor, $s\Gamma$, is given by

$$s\Gamma = (6.25 \times 10^{12})\kappa(T/300)e^{+\Delta\tilde{S}^{\ddagger}/R}\ \text{sec}^{-1} \tag{9.A–12}$$

For a great many reactions the entropy of activation can be estimated from simple thermodynamical or statistical mechanical considerations. For unimolecular reactions we would expect $\Delta\tilde{S}^{\ddagger}$ to be small so that the frequency factor would have a value of the order of 10^{13}. For bimolecular reactions we expect the entropy of activation to be negative because of the three degrees of translational freedom which are lost when the two reacting molecules collide to form a single activated complex. This is borne out quantitatively by experiment. In some activated complexes, rotational degrees of freedom which are present in the initial molecules are lacking. This would tend to make the reaction rate unusually slow. In other activated states, rotations are permitted which are impossible in the initial state, and this gives rise to the unusually rapid reactions. The combination of $(C_2H_5)_2S$ and C_2H_5Br,

$$(C_2H_5)_2S + C_2H_5Br \rightarrow (C_2H_5)_3SBr$$

occurs 100 times more frequently than the kinetic frequency of collisions between such molecules. This can be explained on the basis of rotational freedom in the activated state. The oxidation of nitric oxide has a

[11] In well-behaved rate processes (where quantum effects are not important) κ varies between $\frac{1}{2}$ and 1. It is, however, difficult to distinguish experimentally between κ and $\Delta\tilde{S}^{\ddagger}$. Hence for some purposes it is convenient to define an effective entropy of activation $\Delta\tilde{S}^{\ddagger}_{\text{eff}}$, which includes the effect of κ, and to rewrite Eq. 9.A–11 as

$$k' = \left(\frac{kT}{h}\right)e^{-\Delta\tilde{G}^{\ddagger}_{\text{eff}}/RT} = \left(\frac{kT}{h}\right)e^{-[\Delta\tilde{H}^{\ddagger} - T\Delta\tilde{S}^{\ddagger}_{\text{eff}}]/RT}$$

where

$$\Delta\tilde{G}^{\ddagger}_{\text{eff}} = \Delta\tilde{H}^{\ddagger} - T\Delta\tilde{S}^{\ddagger}_{\text{eff}}$$
$$\Delta\tilde{S}^{\ddagger}_{\text{eff}} = \Delta\tilde{S}^{\ddagger} + R\ln\kappa$$

negative temperature coefficient because there is no activation energy and the rotations are restricted in the activated state. This explanation accounts quantitatively for the observed anomalous results.[12]

The theory of absolute reaction rates can be applied to chemical reactions in the liquid phase[13] as well as to gas phase reactions. In these applications the number densities are replaced by activities. The Eyring rate equation reduces to the Brønsted equation, and the various activity coefficients allow for the influence of the environment upon the specific reaction rate. For a general chemical reaction having the stoichimetrical form:

$$aA + bB + \cdots \rightleftharpoons (aA - bB - \cdots)^{\ddagger} \rightarrow \text{products} \qquad (9.A\text{–}13)$$

the reaction rate in a dense gas or liquid phase is given by

$$R = (\alpha_A{}^a \alpha_B{}^b \cdots / \alpha^{\ddagger})\, k'_{\text{gas}}\, n_A{}^a n_B{}^b \cdots \qquad (9.A\text{–}14)$$

Here the activity coefficients, $\alpha_A{}^a$, $\alpha_B{}^b$, . . . and $\alpha^{\ddagger}$ of the initial molecules and of the activated complex, are defined with respect to the dilute gas in which the activity coefficients are unity. The specific reaction rate, k'(gas), applies to a reaction taking place in a dilute gas. Regardless of the order of the reaction, the specific reaction rate in the dilute gas is given by Eq. 9.A–11.

Although Eq. 9.A–11 was derived for the special case of a chemical reaction, it is possible to apply the result to a number of different rate problems in which a system goes through some sort of an activated state. In § 9.2 we discuss the applications of this theory to the transport phenomena in dense gases and liquids.

PROBLEMS

1. Use Table 9.3–2 and the principle of corresponding states to estimate the viscosity of argon as a function of pressure at constant temperature.
2. Use the principle of corresponding states to estimate the viscosity and thermal conductivity of N_2 at 60 atm and 100°K.
3. Use the Eyring theory of transport phenomena to estimate the viscosity of liquid N_2 at the normal boiling point.
4. Explain why the viscosity of a gas increases with temperature whereas the viscosity of a liquid decreases with temperature.

[12] H. Gershinowitz and H. Eyring, *J. Am. Chem. Soc.*, **57**, 985 (1935).
[13] W. F. K. Wynne-Jones and H. Eyring, *J. Chem. Phys.*, **3**, 107 (1935).

· 10 ·

Quantum Theory and Transport Phenomena

by J. de Boer[1] and R. Byron Bird

The three preceding chapters deal with the classical theory of transport phenomena in dilute and dense gases. We now consider the modifications to the theory of transport phenomena due to the quantum theory.

In the first section the general formulation of the problem of the transport phenomena is presented in terms of the non-equilibrium quantum statistical mechanics. It is shown that the results are formally analogous to those obtained by classical theory. From this work we can obtain the Boltzmann equation appropriate for the quantum mechanical description of dilute gases. This relation differs from the corresponding classical equation in that it takes into account the quantum effects due to the wave nature of the molecules (*diffraction effects*) and also those effects which owe their existence to the statistics of the particles (*symmetry effects*). The diffraction effects are of importance when the de Broglie wavelength associated with the molecules is of the order of magnitude of the molecular dimensions. The symmetry effects become important when the associated de Broglie wavelength is of the order of magnitude of the average distance between the molecules in the gas.

The quantum theory of the transport phenomena of dilute gases may be developed along two different lines. At "very low" temperatures, where quantum effects are quite important, the transport coefficients may be expressed in terms of the "phase shifts." At "intermediate temperatures," where deviations from classical behavior are small, the phase shifts may be obtained by the WKB method, and then the transport coefficients are obtained as power series in Planck's constant. These two approaches, which are discussed in the second and third sections of this chapter, are analogous to the two quantum mechanical formulations of the second virial coefficient (see §§ 6.4 and 6.5).

[1] Director of the *Instituut voor Theoretische Physica*, University of Amsterdam, The Netherlands.

At the present time very little has been done in connection with the quantum corrections to the transport properties of dense gases and liquids. Some information may ultimately be obtained by analyzing experimental data in terms of the principle of corresponding states in quantum mechanics. This topic is dealt with briefly in the last section of the chapter.

1. Non-equilibrium Quantum Statistical Mechanics

In § 9.4 the statistical mechanics of dense gases and liquids according to classical theory is discussed. In the present section we indicate how this theory may be extended to apply to fluids in which quantum effects are important. It is shown that the usual equations of hydrodynamics may be obtained from the quantum mechanical Liouville equation. These results are valid for dense gases and liquids. In the low-density limit it is possible to obtain the quantum mechanical Boltzmann equation from this approach.

a. General statistical mechanical theory[2]

The classical statistical mechanics is based upon the concept of an ensemble and a distribution function[3] in phase space $f^{(N)}(\boldsymbol{r}^N, \boldsymbol{p}^N, t)$, as described in § 2.1. The time rate of change of this distribution function is given by the Liouville equation. Lower-order distribution functions may be defined as integrals over $f^{(N)}(\boldsymbol{r}^N, \boldsymbol{p}^N, t)$, and the time rate of change of these functions may be obtained by a corresponding integration of the Liouville equation. The average value of a physical property $X(\boldsymbol{r}^N, \boldsymbol{p}^N)$ is obtained by integrating over all of phase space the function $X(\boldsymbol{r}^N, \boldsymbol{p}^N)$ multiplied by the distribution function. These notions are used in the classical discussion of the transport phenomena in dense gases and liquids given in § 9.4.

In the formulation of quantum statistical mechanics the concept of a distribution function cannot be taken over immediately from the classical theory, inasmuch as the Heisenberg uncertainty principle does not allow a precise specification of the location of a system point in phase space. Two approaches have been suggested for defining distribution functions in quantum theory. One of these has been outlined in § 2.2, where it is

[2] J. H. Irving and R. W. Zwanzig, *J. Chem. Phys.*, **19**, 1173 (1951).

[3] The various distribution functions are given in Chapter 2. In discussions of equilibrium statistical mechanics it is customary to use the distribution function $P^{(N)}(\boldsymbol{r}^N, \boldsymbol{p}^N, t)$ defined in Eq. 2.1–1. In discussions of kinetic theory many workers prefer to use $f^{(N)}(\boldsymbol{r}^N, \boldsymbol{p}^N, t)$, which is defined in Eq. 2.1–5. The latter has the advantage that the lowest-order function $f^{(1)}(\boldsymbol{r}, \boldsymbol{p}, t)$, is just the ordinary (singlet) distribution function used in the kinetic theory of dilute gases.

shown that in the matrix formulation of quantum mechanics it is possible to construct a "probability density matrix" which may be interpreted as the analog of the classical distribution function in phase space. The time rate of change of this probability density matrix is given by the quantum mechanical analog of the Liouville equation. Lower-order density matrices may be defined as the integrals over the original density matrix. The average value of a physical property $X(\boldsymbol{r}^N, \boldsymbol{p}^N)$ is obtained by taking the trace of the matrix which is the product of the probability density matrix and the matrix which corresponds to the physical property $X(\boldsymbol{r}^N, \boldsymbol{p}^N)$. This formulation of quantum statistical mechanics is used in Chapter 6 in the discussion of the quantum mechanical description of the equation of state.

There is a second approach to the problem of formulating quantum statistical mechanics which has been proposed by Wigner.[4] In this method one constructs a "distribution function" $\mathscr{F}^{(N)}(\boldsymbol{r}^N, \boldsymbol{p}^N, t)$, which has no simple interpretation in terms of probability concepts but can be used directly for calculating average values in a manner precisely analogous to the classical formula for average values. It is this procedure which we use in the following discussion.

The Wigner distribution function may be defined in terms of probability density matrices in either coordinate language or momentum language:[5, 6]

$$\mathscr{F}^{(N)}(\boldsymbol{r}^N, \boldsymbol{p}^N, t) = \frac{1}{h^{3N}} \int e^{(i/\hbar)(\boldsymbol{p}^N \cdot \boldsymbol{r}'^N)} \mathscr{N}^{(N)}(\boldsymbol{r}^N - \tfrac{1}{2}\boldsymbol{r}'^N, \boldsymbol{r}^N + \tfrac{1}{2}\boldsymbol{r}'^N, t)\, d\boldsymbol{r}'^N \tag{10.1-1}$$

$$= \frac{1}{h^{3N}} \int e^{-(i/\hbar)(\boldsymbol{p}'^N \cdot \boldsymbol{r}^N)} \mathscr{N}^{(N)}(\boldsymbol{p}^N - \tfrac{1}{2}\boldsymbol{p}'^N, \boldsymbol{p}^N + \tfrac{1}{2}\boldsymbol{p}'^N, t)\, d\boldsymbol{p}'^N$$

This distribution function $\mathscr{F}^{(N)}(\boldsymbol{r}^N, \boldsymbol{p}^N, t)$ is everywhere real although not necessarily positive. Integration of this function over all of momentum space gives the diagonal elements of the probability density matrix in configuration space. Similarly, integration over all of coordinate space

[4] E. P. Wigner, *Phys. Rev.*, **40**, 479 (1932).

[5] The density matrix $\mathscr{N}^{(N)}(\boldsymbol{r}^N, \boldsymbol{r}'^N, t)$ is defined by Eq. 2.2–24 and differs from the matrix $\mathscr{P}^{(N)}(\boldsymbol{r}^N, \boldsymbol{r}'^N, t)$ by a factor of $N!$, just as is true of $f^{(N)}(\boldsymbol{r}^N, \boldsymbol{p}^N, t)$ and $P^{(N)}(\boldsymbol{r}^N, \boldsymbol{p}^N, t)$ in classical statistical mechanics.

[6] The quantity $\mathscr{N}^{(N)}(\boldsymbol{p}^N, \boldsymbol{p}'^N, t)$ is the $\mathscr{N}$-matrix in momentum language. It is not independent of $\mathscr{N}^{(N)}(\boldsymbol{r}^N, \boldsymbol{r}'^N, t)$ because of the Fourier transform relation between coordinate and momentum representations of the wave function. This is a point of major difference between the quantum and classical formulations of statistical mechanics. In the latter case the probability densities in configuration and momentum spaces can be independently specified, which independence permits the factorization of the classical distribution function for a canonical ensemble:

$$P^{(N)}(\boldsymbol{r}^N, \boldsymbol{p}^N) = P^{(N)}(\boldsymbol{r}^N)\, P^{(N)}(\boldsymbol{p}^N)$$

gives the diagonal elements of the probability density matrix in the momentum representation:

$$\int \mathscr{F}^{(N)}(\mathbf{r}^N, \mathbf{p}^N, t)\, d\mathbf{p}^N = \mathscr{N}^{(N)}(\mathbf{r}^N, \mathbf{r}^N, t) \tag{10.1–2}$$

$$\int \mathscr{F}^{(N)}(\mathbf{r}^N, \mathbf{p}^N, t)\, d\mathbf{r}^N = \mathscr{N}^{(N)}(\mathbf{p}^N, \mathbf{p}^N, t) \tag{10.1–3}$$

The particular advantage of the Wigner distribution function is that the calculation of average values is performed exactly as in classical statistical mechanics, that is, by direct integration over all of phase space:

$$\bar{X} = \iint \mathscr{F}^{(N)}(\mathbf{r}^N, \mathbf{p}^N, t) X(\mathbf{r}^N, \mathbf{p}^N)\, d\mathbf{r}^N\, d\mathbf{p}^N \tag{10.1–4}$$

Thus the operator technique described in § 2.2 is avoided.

In view of the expression for average values given in Eq. 10.1–4 it is possible to transfer many of the results of classical statistical mechanics into quantum statistical mechanics simply by replacing $f^{(N)}(\mathbf{r}^N, \mathbf{p}^N, t)$ by $\mathscr{F}^{(N)}(\mathbf{r}^N, \mathbf{p}^N, t)$. In particular it is possible to carry over into quantum mechanics the expressions for the flux vectors and the equations of change given in § 9.4. In this way it is established that the usual equations of hydrodynamics are valid in quantum theory as well as in classical theory.[2]

b. The Boltzmann equation for dilute gas mixtures

In § 7.1c it is shown that the classical Boltzmann equation for dilute gases may be obtained from the Liouville equation for the distribution function $f^{(N)}(\mathbf{r}^N, \mathbf{p}^N, t)$. It has recently been shown[7] that it is possible to get the quantum mechanical Boltzmann equation for dilute gases from the differential equation for the Wigner distribution function $\mathscr{F}^{(N)}(\mathbf{r}^N, \mathbf{p}^N, t)$. It may thus be shown that the Boltzmann equation for the usual (singlet) distribution function $f_i(\mathbf{r}, \mathbf{v}_i, t)$ for the ith species of a ν-component gas mixture has the following form in quantum mechanics:[8]

$$\frac{\partial f_i}{\partial t} + \left(\mathbf{v}_i \cdot \frac{\partial}{\partial \mathbf{r}} f_i\right) + \left(\frac{\mathbf{X}_i}{m_i} \cdot \frac{\partial}{\partial \mathbf{v}_i} f_i\right)$$
$$= \sum_{j=1}^{\nu} \iiint [f_i' f_j' (1 + \theta_i f_i)(1 + \theta_j f_j) - f_i f_j (1 + \theta_i f_i')(1 + \theta_j f_j')]$$
$$\times\, \alpha(g_{ij}, \chi) \sin\chi\, d\chi\, d\epsilon\, d\mathbf{v}_j \tag{10.1–5}$$

[7] H. Mori and S. Ono, *Prog. Theo. Phys.*, **8**, 327 (1952).

[8] This form of the Boltzmann equation was given earlier by E. A. Uehling and G. E. Uhlenbeck, *Phys. Rev.*, **43**, 552 (1933), who gave the first complete treatment of the quantum theory of transport phenomena.

Here $\theta_i = (h/m_i)^3(\delta/G_i)$, where G_i is a statistical weight factor of the ith molecule and $\delta = -1, 0, 1$ for Fermi-Dirac, Boltzmann, and Einstein-Bose statistics, respectively. The quantities g_{ij} and χ are the initial relative speed and the angle of deflection of the trajectory of two interacting particles, and $\alpha(g_{ij}, \chi)$ is the scattering probability defined in § 1.7b. We see that the "streaming terms" on the left-hand side of the Boltzmann equation are the same as in classical theory[9] but that the collision integrals on the right-hand side differ from the corresponding classical quantities in two respects: (i) the replacement of $g_{ij}b\,db$ by $\alpha(g_{ij}, \chi)\sin\chi\,d\chi$ because of the "diffraction effects," and (ii) the introduction of the factors $(1 + \theta_i f_i)$ due to the "symmetry effects." Let us now discuss briefly these differences between the classical and quantum mechanical formulations of the Boltzmann equation.

The first difference arises because of the essential wave nature of the molecules. In classical collision theory it is possible to determine exactly (for any interaction law) the angle of deflection, χ. And for the number of collisions per unit volume and per unit length of time, in which $\mathbf{v}_i$, $\mathbf{v}_j$, and b lie in ranges $d\mathbf{v}_i$, $d\mathbf{v}_j$, and db, we may write

$$f_i f_j g_{ij}(2\pi b\,db)\,d\mathbf{v}_i\,d\mathbf{v}_j \tag{10.1–6}$$

In wave mechanics, on the other hand, the Heisenberg uncertainty principle forbids the simultaneous determination of the position and the velocity of a molecule. Hence it is impossible to determine exactly the angle of deflection χ after the collision of two molecules. Let us, however, consider a stream of molecules, with mass m_i, velocity $\mathbf{v}_i$, and number density n_i, which is interacting with a stream of molecules with mass m_j, velocity $\mathbf{v}_j$, and number density n_j. Then it is possible to determine the probable number of collisions per unit volume per unit length of time, such that the relative velocity after collision, $\mathbf{g}_{ij}'$, lies within a solid angle, $d\boldsymbol{\omega} = 2\pi \sin\chi\,d\chi$ about $\mathbf{g}_{ij}$ as polar axis. This probable number of collisions is clearly proportional to the number density of both streams, and the proportionality factor is dependent upon χ and g_{ij}. Hence the probable number of collisions is $n_i n_j \alpha(g_{ij}, \chi)\,d\boldsymbol{\omega}$. This defines the quantity $\alpha(g_{ij}, \chi)$. Now let one stream of gas be those molecules in the gas with velocity range $d\mathbf{v}_i$ about $\mathbf{v}_i$, and let the second stream be those with velocity $d\mathbf{v}_j$ about $\mathbf{v}_j$. Then

$$f_i f_j \alpha(g_{ij}, \chi)\,(2\pi \sin\chi\,d\chi)\,d\mathbf{v}_i\,d\mathbf{v}_j \tag{10.1–7}$$

is the number of collisions per unit volume per unit length of time according to quantum theory. Hence the classical development in Chapter 7

[9] A proof of this was given by Nordheim and Kikuchi, *Z. Physik*, **60**, 652 (1930).

may be altered to account for the wave nature of the molecules, by everywhere replacing $g_{ij}b\,db$ by $\alpha(g_{ij}, \chi) \sin \chi\, d\chi$. The quantum mechanical calculation of $\alpha(g_{ij}, \chi)$ is given in § 1.7b.

The second difference, that is, the introduction of the factors $(1 + \theta_i f_i)$, occurs solely because of the "statistics" of the molecules. Let us begin by considering a one-component gas in volume V, made up of molecules or particles which obey Fermi-Dirac statistics (the Pauli exclusion principle). Then we know that there may be no more than $VG(m/h)^3\, d\mathbf{v}$ such particles in the velocity range $d\mathbf{v}$. G is the "statistical weight" of the particle which is the number of independent quantum states in which the particle possesses the same internal energy. For an electron, for example, $G = 2$, since there are two accessible spin states. If $Vf(\mathbf{v})\, d\mathbf{v}$ molecules have velocities in the range $d\mathbf{v}$ about $\mathbf{v}$, the probability of a collision, which would result in an additional molecule entering this velocity range, is reduced in the ratio $[1 - f(\mathbf{v})\,(h/m)^3/G]$. This behavior is associated with the concept of the "apparent repulsion" between Fermi-Dirac particles, which is discussed in § 6.3a. This is equivalent to saying that, if there are already $VG(m/h)^3\, d\mathbf{v}$ particles in the velocity range $d\mathbf{v}$, and if the result of a collision would be that an additional particle would enter the same velocity range, the collision simply cannot take place. For Bose-Einstein particles, we must include factors like $[1 + f(\mathbf{v})\,(h/m)^3/G]$, which corresponds to the "apparent attraction" between the molecules. For Boltzmann statistics, all types of collisions are permitted, and then the θ_i are zero.

When the quantum corrections due to the statistics effects become important, a gas is spoken of as being "degenerate" or in a "state of congestion." The same terminology is used in the analogous discussion of the quantum theory of the equation of state. In order to determine the conditions under which these symmetry effects are of importance, we come back to the statement that the number of particles per unit volume in a velocity range $d\mathbf{v}$ may not exceed $G(m/h)^3\, d\mathbf{v}$. Under those conditions where the velocity distribution is Maxwellian, the number of particles per unit volume is

$$f\, d\mathbf{v} = n\left(\frac{m}{2\pi kT}\right)^{3/2} e^{-\frac{1}{2}mv^2/kT}\, d\mathbf{v} \tag{10.1–8}$$

and the largest density exists at $\mathbf{v} = 0$ where $f\, d\mathbf{v} = n(m/2\pi kT)^{3/2}\, d\mathbf{v}$. Now, under normal conditions,

$$n\left(\frac{m}{2\pi kT}\right)^{3/2} d\mathbf{v} \ll G\left(\frac{m}{h}\right)^3 d\mathbf{v} \tag{10.1–9}$$

and the occupation of the quantum levels is so dilute that no congestion or degeneration exists. In the other limit of high densities or low temperatures

$$n\left(\frac{m}{2\pi kT}\right)^{3/2} d\mathbf{v} \gg G\left(\frac{m}{h}\right)^{3} d\mathbf{v} \qquad (10.1\text{–}10)$$

and the density of particles is much higher than the density of states. In this case, however, the degeneracy according to Fermi-Dirac or Bose-Einstein statistics plays a role giving deviations from the Maxwell distribution. We may thus introduce with advantage Sommerfeld's "degeneracy parameter,"[10] $\lambda^3 n/G$, so that

if $\lambda^3 n/G \ll 1$, degeneracy is but slight.

if $\lambda^3 n/G \gg 1$, degeneracy is very great.

Here $\lambda^2 = h^2/2\pi mkT$. From this it is clear that degeneracy is greatest for light particles or molecules at high densities and low temperatures. This effect would then be quite prominent in an electron gas. For even the lightest atomic and molecular gases, however, this effect is almost entirely negligible except at extremely low temperatures (for example, for He, about 1°K). We can draw the conclusion, then, that the most important quantum effects are those due to the wave nature of the molecules—that is, the diffraction effects.

Before proceeding to discuss these two effects in detail, let us summarize the important differences between them. Diffraction effects become important when the temperature is sufficiently low that the de Broglie wavelength is about as large as the dimensions of the molecules. For symmetry effects to become important, however, it is necessary that the temperature be so low *and* the density so high that the de Broglie wavelength is of the order of magnitude of the average distance between the molecules in the gas. Consequently the magnitude of the symmetry effects is mainly density dependent, whereas the diffraction effects are density independent.

2. Transport Phenomena at Very Low Temperatures

The quantum mechanical version of the Boltzmann equation given in Eq. 10.1–5 may be handled in very much the same way as the classical Boltzmann equation in Chapter 7. Without solving the Boltzmann equation, we may proceed to show that the hydrodynamical equations of change are obtained from Eq. 10.1–5. The actual solutions of the equation to obtain the explicit expressions for the flux vectors and the

[10] A. Sommerfeld, *Z. Physik*, **47**, 1 and 43 (1928); see also §2.5b.

transport properties proceeds along the same lines as outlined in Chapter 7 for the classical theory. Hence only the results are presented here. First we discuss the results obtained by considering diffraction effects only. Then we show that these results are modified when the symmetry effects are also considered. The section is concluded with a summary of the various quantum mechanical calculations which have been made at low temperatures.

a. The diffraction effects

We have pointed out that the diffraction effects may be taken into account by replacing $gb\,db$ in the classical expressions by $\alpha(g, \chi) \sin \chi\, d\chi$. Accordingly, the expressions for the cross-sections $Q^{(n)}(g)$ given in Eq. 8.2–2 for classical theory become, in quantum mechanics,

$$Q^{(n)}(g) = \frac{2\pi}{g} \int_0^\pi (1 - \cos^n \chi)\alpha(g, \chi) \sin \chi\, d\chi \qquad (10.2\text{–}1)$$

The quantity $\alpha(g, \chi)$ gives the probability of an angle of deflection χ. Explicit formulae have been obtained from this quantity for Boltzmann, Bose-Einstein, and Fermi-Dirac statistics (see Eqs. 1.7–26, 27, 28) from the quantum theory of collisions.

Let us now examine the expressions for $Q^{(1)}$ and $Q^{(2)}$ for Boltzmann statistics. When the expression for $\alpha(g, \chi)$ for Boltzmann statistics is substituted into Eq. 10.2–1, we obtain after lengthy algebraic manipulation the following expressions for the quantum mechanical cross-sections:[1]

$$Q^{(1)} = 2\left(\frac{2\pi}{\kappa^2}\right) \sum_{l=0,1,2,\cdots}^{\infty} (l+1) \sin^2(\eta_{l+1} - \eta_l)$$

$$Q^{(2)} = \left(\frac{2\pi}{\kappa^2}\right) \sum_{l=0,1,2,\cdots}^{\infty} \frac{(l+1)(l+2)}{(l+\frac{3}{2})} \sin^2(\eta_{l+2} - \eta_l) \qquad (10.2\text{–}2)$$

Here l and κ are quantum numbers characteristic of the angular momentum and the relative kinetic energy of a two-molecule collision, and the $\eta_l(\kappa)$ are the phase shifts in the radial wave function for a binary

[1] These are the same formulae which are given in standard references on the quantum theory of transport phenomena, except that they are usually written in a more complicated form. The more compact form presented here was first suggested by Professor H. Kramers of the University of Leiden. These formulae are easier to use from a computational standpoint and bring out nicely the analogy with the classical formulae.

collision (see § 1.7a). It is interesting to compare these results with the analogous formulae in classical kinetic theory, which are

$$Q^{(1)} = 2 \int_0^\infty \sin^2 \tfrac{1}{2}\chi \quad 2\pi b\, db$$

$$Q^{(2)} = \int_0^\infty \sin^2 \chi \quad 2\pi b\, db \tag{10.2–3}$$

At high temperatures where the deviations from classical theory are negligible the quantum mechanical expressions approach the classical expressions in accordance with the correspondence:

$$l \to \frac{bg\mu}{\hbar} = b\kappa \qquad [\eta_{l+2}(\kappa) - \eta_l(\kappa)] \to \chi(b, g) \tag{10.2–4}$$

where μ is the reduced mass of the colliding pair of molecules. This correspondence is discussed in more detail in § 10.3.

It was pointed out in Chapter 8 that the primary problem encountered in the calculation of the transport phenomena is the evaluation of the angle of deflection $\chi(b, g)$ for many values of the collision parameter b and the initial relative velocity g. Or, more fundamentally, we have to know the angle of deflection as a function of the angular momentum μbg and the relative kinetic energy $\frac{1}{2}\mu g^2$. Similarly, in quantum mechanical calculations of the transport phenomena, the major problem is the evaluation of the phase shifts, $\eta_l(\kappa)$, which are obtained by solving the radial wave equation for a collision for many values of the quantum numbers l and κ, or, for many values of the angular momentum $\hbar\sqrt{l(l+1)}$ and the relative kinetic energy $\hbar^2\kappa^2/2\mu$. In the classical theory the cross-sections are obtained by an integration over b, and in the analogous quantum formulae a summation over l is performed. In both classical and quantum theory the $\Omega^{(n,t)}$ integrals are obtained from the expression

$$\sqrt{2\pi\mu/kT}\,\Omega^{(n,t)} = \int_0^\infty e^{-\gamma^2}\gamma^{2t+3}Q^{(n)}\, d\gamma \tag{10.2–5}$$

In the classical theory $\gamma^2 = \mu g^2/2kT$, and in quantum theory $\gamma^2 = \hbar^2\kappa^2/2\mu kT$. Once the $\Omega^{(n,t)}$ have been calculated, either from the classical cross-sections or from the quantum mechanical cross-sections, the transport coefficients may be computed according to the formulae given in § 8.2.

We have thus succeeded in expressing the transport cross-sections, and hence the transport properties themselves, in terms of the phase shifts, $\eta_l(\kappa)$. The calculations of the phase shifts have been described in §§ 6.4b and c, in connection with the calculation of the second virial coefficient at very low temperatures. The actual calculation of the transport coefficients at low temperatures is discussed in § 10.2c.

b. The symmetry effects

Thus far the discussion has been limited to Boltzmann statistics. When the particles are considered to be indistinguishable and the symmetry of the wave functions is taken into account, we must use the expressions for $\alpha(g, \chi)$ which are given in Eqs. 1.7–27 and 28 for Bose-Einstein and Fermi-Dirac statistics, respectively. Then the formulae for the cross-sections become, in Bose-Einstein statistics,

$$Q^{(1)}_{\text{B.E.}} = 4\left(\frac{2\pi}{\kappa^2}\right) \sum_{l=0,\,2,\,4,\,\cdots}^{\infty} (2l+1)\sin^2\eta_l$$

$$Q^{(2)}_{\text{B.E.}} = 2\left(\frac{2\pi}{\kappa^2}\right) \sum_{l=0,\,2,\,4,\,\cdots}^{\infty} \frac{(l+1)(l+2)}{(l+\frac{3}{2})}\sin^2(\eta_{l+2}-\eta_l) \qquad (10.2\text{–}6)$$

and, in Fermi-Dirac statistics,

$$Q^{(1)}_{\text{F.D.}} = 4\left(\frac{2\pi}{\kappa^2}\right) \sum_{l=1,\,3,\,5,\,\cdots}^{\infty} (2l+1)\sin^2\eta_l$$

$$Q^{(2)}_{\text{F.D.}} = 2\left(\frac{2\pi}{\kappa^2}\right) \sum_{l=1,\,3,\,5,\,\cdots}^{\infty} \frac{(l+1)(l+2)}{(l+\frac{3}{2})}\sin^2(\eta_{l+2}-\eta_l) \qquad (10.2\text{–}7)$$

These expressions are valid for particles with zero spin. For particles with spin $s \neq 0$, the cross-sections are given by

$$[Q^{(n)}_{\text{B.E.}}]^{(s)} = \left(\frac{s+1}{2s+1}\right) Q^{(n)}_{\text{B.E.}} + \left(\frac{s}{2s+1}\right) Q^{(n)}_{\text{F.D.}} \qquad (10.2\text{–}8)$$

$$[Q^{(n)}_{\text{F.D.}}]^{(s)} = \left(\frac{s+1}{2s+1}\right) Q^{(n)}_{\text{F.D.}} + \left(\frac{s}{2s+1}\right) Q^{(n)}_{\text{B.E.}} \qquad (10.2\text{–}9)$$

The $Q^{(n)}_{\text{B.E.}}$ and $Q^{(n)}_{\text{F.D.}}$ without a superscript are those calculated by Eqs. 10.2–6 and 7 for particles with zero spin. Equation 10.2–9 is used for calculating the cross-sections and transport coefficients for He^3, which contains an odd number of particles and has spin $s = \frac{1}{2}$. For the calculation of the transport coefficients the expressions given in Eqs. 10.2–6, 7, 8 and 9 may be substituted directly into Eq. 10.2–5 in order to obtain the integrals $\Omega^{(n,\,t)}$.

A second effect, which should be considered when the symmetrization of the wave functions is taken into account, is the correction of the transport coefficients resulting from the inclusion of the terms θf in the quantum mechanical Boltzmann integro-differential equation. This correction, which is often referred to as the "symmetry effect" proper, is considered next.

In Chapter 7 it is shown that the main problem in the development of the theory of transport phenomena is the solution of a set of integral equations for functions $A_i(W_i)$, $\mathsf{B}_i(W_i)$, and $C_i^k(W_i)$, which give, respectively, the coefficients of thermal conductivity, viscosity, and diffusion. We have just seen that, by simply changing $gb\,db$ into $\alpha(g, \chi) \sin \chi\, d\chi$, we get immediately the correct quantum mechanical expression for the transport properties which include the diffraction effects (and the first "statistics" effect mentioned above). To get the transport properties in quantum mechanics including both "diffraction" and "symmetry" effects, it becomes necessary to re-solve the set of integral equations just mentioned with the factors $(1 + \theta_i f_i)$ included. This has been accomplished, and the formal results have been given elsewhere for both pure gases[2] and gaseous mixtures.[3]

For viscosity and thermal conductivity of pure gases the following explicit formulae have been given[2] (good to the second approximation in the solution of the integral equations):

$$[\eta]_2 = \frac{5kT}{8\Omega^{(2,2)}} f_\eta^{(2)} \left[1 \pm n \frac{h^3}{(2\pi mkT)^{3/2}} (\delta_\eta^{(1)} + \delta_\eta^{(2)})\right] \qquad (10.2\text{–}10)$$

$$[\lambda]_2 = \frac{25c_v kT}{16\Omega^{(2,2)}} f_\lambda^{(2)} \left[1 \pm n \frac{h^3}{(2\pi mkT)^{3/2}} (\delta_\lambda^{(1)} + \delta_\lambda^{(2)})\right] \qquad (10.2\text{–}11)$$

The plus sign is for Bose-Einstein, the minus sign for Fermi-Dirac statistics. The quantities $\Omega^{(2,2)}$, $f_\eta^{(2)}$, and $f_\lambda^{(2)}$ must be calculated quantum mechanically by means of the cross-sections given in Eqs. 10.2–6, 7, 8 and 9. The $f_\eta^{(2)}$ and $f_\lambda^{(2)}$ are factors very close to unity[4, 5] and represent the inclusion of the next higher terms in the Sonine polynomial expansion in

[2] E. A. Uehling and G. E. Uhlenbeck, *Phys. Rev.*, **43**, 552 (1933). E. A. Uehling, *Phys. Rev.*, **46**, 917 (1934).

[3] E. J. Hellund and E. A. Uehling, *Phys. Rev.*, **56**, 818 (1939).

[4] For an inverse twelfth power repulsive potential $f_\eta^{(2)}$ and $f_\lambda^{(2)}$ approach 1.016 and 1.025, respectively, as T approaches absolute zero. Calculation of these quantities for the Lennard-Jones (6-12) potential indicates that the correction is appreciable only at very low temperatures. (See footnote 6.)

[5] These factors are defined in classical theory in Eqs. 8.2–19, 32.

Chapter 7 (but *not* the higher terms in the Enskog expansion solution of the Boltzmann equation, which include higher-order derivatives of the gradients of the temperature, concentration, and pressure).

Equations 10.2–10, 11 without the brackets are the quantum mechanical expressions for the transport coefficients, including of course the symmetrization of the cross-sections as indicated above in Eqs. 10.2–6 and 7. The brackets account for the so-called "symmetry-effect" due to the θf-corrections considered here. The functions $\delta_\eta^{(1)}$ and $\delta_\lambda^{(1)}$, which result from the first approximation, are given by

$$\delta_\eta^{(1)} = 2^{-7/2}\left[4 - \frac{128}{3^{3/2}}\frac{\Upsilon^{(2,2)}}{\Omega^{(2,2)}}\right] \tag{10.2–12}$$

$$\delta_\lambda^{(1)} = 2^{-7/2}\left[7 - \frac{128}{3^{3/2}}\frac{\Upsilon^{(2,3)} + 6\Upsilon^{(2,2)}}{9\Omega^{(2,2)}}\right] \tag{10.2–13}$$

The quantities $\Upsilon^{(n,t)}$ are integrals like the $\Omega^{(n,t)}$ defined in Eq. 10.2–5 except that the $\exp(-\gamma^2)$ is replaced by $\exp(-\frac{4}{3}\gamma^2)$. The terms $\delta_\eta^{(2)}$ and $\delta_\lambda^{(2)}$, which occur in the second-order approximation, contain the $\Omega^{(n,t)}$ and $\Upsilon^{(n,t)}$ with $n = 2, 4$ and $t = 2, 3, 4, 5$. These terms are small in comparison with $\delta_\eta^{(1)}$ and $\delta_\lambda^{(1)}$ and are not considered further here.

Hence we see that the inclusion of the factors $(1 + \theta_i f_i)$ in the Boltzmann equation leads to a density-dependent contribution which is directly due to symmetry effects. An actual evaluation[6] of this symmetry correction for He^4 gas at temperatures around 1°K indicates that it is of the same order of magnitude as the Enskog correction term for dense gases,[7] which accounts approximately for the change in the transport coefficients with density in the classical theory. A change of this order of magnitude has been observed by Ubbink[8] in the thermal conductivity. It is not possible to analyze these data at the present time, however, because of our lack of knowledge of the effect of multiple collisions on the density dependence of the transport properties.

Because we consider in this section only the density-independent part of the transport coefficients, this second symmetry effect will not be considered further. The reader is reminded, however, that the statistics effects which enter into the cross-sections are important at moderately low temperatures and therefore must be taken into account.

[6] J. de Boer, *Physica*, **10**, 348 (1943).

[7] The Enskog theory of the density dependence of the transport coefficients of a gas composed of rigid spherical molecules is discussed in § 9.3.

[8] J. B. Ubbink, Doctoral Dissertation, Leiden (1945).

c. Calculations at very low temperatures

The viscosities of helium and hydrogen have been calculated from Eq. 10.2–6 for the rigid-sphere model,[9, 10] for which an analytic evaluation of all the phase shifts is possible (see § 6.4b–i). For this simple potential field it was found that the quantum mechanical results showed considerably better agreement with the experimental data than calculations based on the classical theory.

The viscosity of He^4 has also been calculated,[11] using Slater's[12] interatomic potential function. The agreement between calculated and experimental results is not exceptionally good, although the shape of the viscosity versus temperature curve appears to be about right. It must be remembered, however, that Slater's potential function was derived from quantum mechanics alone and contains no constants which are adjusted to the experimental data. In view of this fact the calculations based on this potential must not be regarded as too unsatisfactory. The calculated results based on Slater's potential and on the rigid-sphere model are compared with the available experimental data in Fig. 10.2–1.

The most extensive low-temperature transport property calculations have been made using the Lennard-Jones (6-12) potential. The computations of the phase shifts for this potential are described in § 6.4c, and from the tables of phase shifts the viscosities of the isotopes of helium[11, 13] and the isotopes of hydrogen[14] have been calculated. As an illustration we consider here the results for He^3 and He^4. Very recently the coefficient of self-diffusion has been calculated for the isotopes of helium.[15]

The starting point for the calculation of the transport properties of dilute gases in quantum mechanics is the solution of the radial wave equation for a pair of interacting molecules. This equation may be written in reduced form by using the parameters in the Lennard-Jones (6-12) potential as a basis for the reduction of the variables. The radial wave equation then assumes the form

$$\frac{d^2}{dr^{*2}}(r^*\psi) + \left[\kappa^{*2} - \frac{l(l+1)}{r^{*2}} - \frac{16\pi^2}{\Lambda^{*2}}\left(\frac{1}{r^{*12}} - \frac{1}{r^{*6}}\right)\right](r^*\psi) = 0 \quad (10.2\text{–}14)$$

in which $r^* = r/\sigma$ and $\kappa^* = \kappa\sigma$. We see thus that for various substances a different value of the quantum mechanical parameter $\Lambda^* = h/(\sigma\sqrt{m\epsilon})$

[9] H. S. W. Massey and C. B. O. Mohr, *Proc. Roy. Soc.* (*London*), **A141**, 434 (1933).
[10] E. A. Uehling, *Phys. Rev.*, **46**, 917 (1934).
[11] H. S. W. Massey and C. B. O. Mohr, *Proc. Roy. Soc.* (*London*), **A144**, 188 (1934).
[12] See Equation 14.2–13 and J. C. Slater, *Phys. Rev.*, **32**, 349 (1928).
[13] J. de Boer and E. G. D. Cohen, *Physica*, **17**, 993 (1951).
[14] R. Miyako, *Proc. Physico-Mathematical Society of Japan* (Ser. 3), **24**, 852 (1942).
[15] E. G. D. Cohen, M. J. Offerhaus, and J. de Boer, *Physica* (in preparation).

has to be inserted into the differential equation. The method of obtaining the phase shifts from this equation is discussed in § 6.4c, and the numerical results are given there. Values of the quantum mechanical parameter Λ^* for various substances are given in Table 6.5–2.

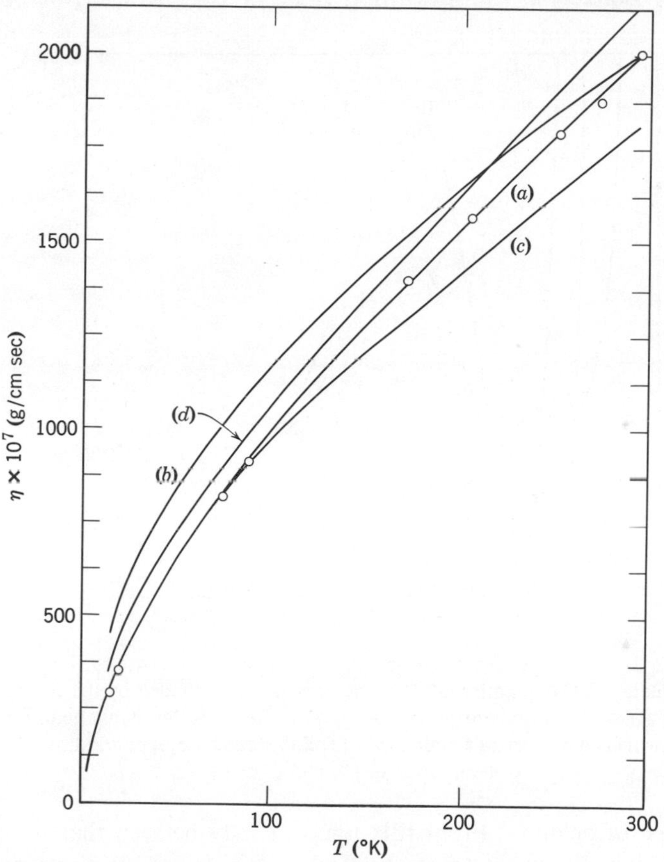

Fig. 10.2–1. Comparison of the calculated and experimental values of the viscosity of He^4. (a) Experimental. (b) Calculated for rigid spheres in classical theory. (c) Calculated for rigid spheres in quantum theory (Uehling). (d) Calculated for Slater potential in quantum theory. [Material for graph was taken from S. Chapman and T. G. Cowling, *The Mathematical Theory of Non-uniform Gases*, Cambridge University Press, 1939—Table 30, p. 303.]

After the phase shifts have been computed from the radial wave equation, the cross-sections $Q^{(1)}$ (for diffusion) and $Q^{(2)}$ (for viscosity and thermal conductivity) may be determined. For He^4, which has zero spin, it is necessary to calculate $Q^{(n)}_{\text{B.E.}}$ from Eq. 10.2–6. For He^3, which has spin $\frac{1}{2}$, we have to calculate both $Q^{(n)}_{\text{F.D.}}$ and $Q^{(n)}_{\text{B.E.}}$ and use Eq. 10.2–9 to compute the cross-sections. The calculated values of the cross-sections for the isotopes of helium are shown[13] in Fig. 10.2–2. This graph illustrates nicely the diffraction effects encountered in transport phenomena. In Fig. 10.2–3 we compare the classical curves for $Q^{(1)}$ and $Q^{(2)}$ with the analogous quantum mechanical curves calculated on the basis of Boltzmann statistics for a value of Λ^* characteristic of the

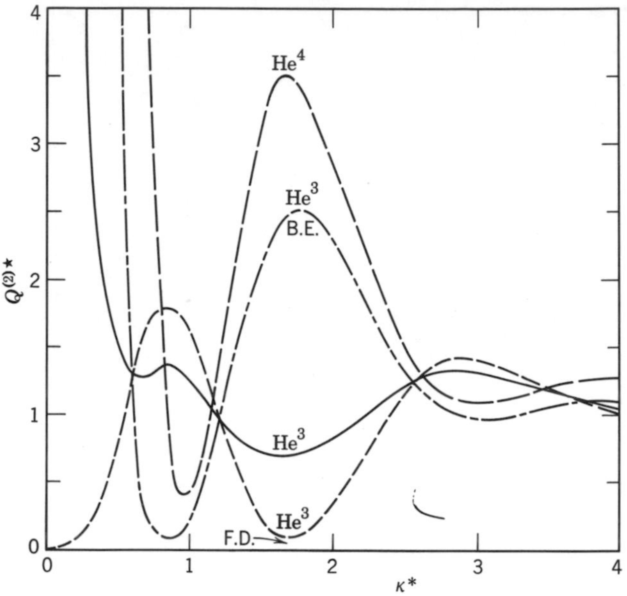

Fig. 10.2–2. The dependence of the quantum mechanical cross-section $Q^{(2)}$ on the energy. The quantity $Q^{(2)\star}$ is the cross-section divided by the corresponding classical rigid sphere value. $\kappa^* = \kappa\sigma$, where κ is the energy quantum number which characterizes a collision. [Taken from J. de Boer and E. G. D. Cohen, *Physica*, **17**, 993 (1951).]

light isotope of helium. From this figure it may be seen that for low-energy collisions the quantum mechanical cross-sections are considerably smaller than the corresponding classical quantities.

The values of the viscosity calculated from the cross-sections shown in Fig. 10.2–2 are given in Table 10.2–1 and graphically in Fig. 10.2–4. It may be seen that the viscosity of He^3 is considerably greater than that of He^4. Furthermore, at very low temperatures the viscosity of the heavier isotope is proportional to the 3/2 power of the temperature, whereas that for the lighter isotope is proportional to the square root of the temperature. This difference in temperature dependence stems from the fact that there are no stationary states for a pair of He^3 atoms whereas for He^4 there is either a real or a virtual level at the top of the energy well.

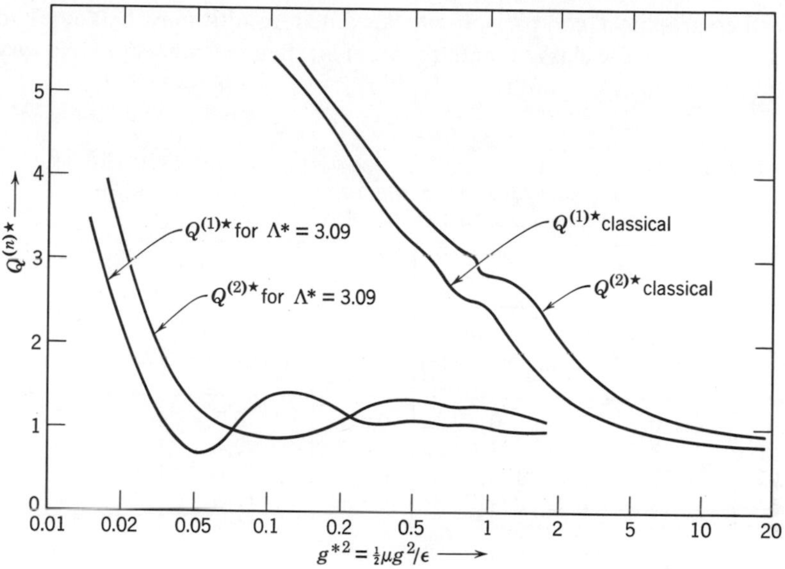

Fig. 10.2–3. A comparison of the cross-sections $Q^{(1)\star}$ and $Q^{(2)\star}$ as given by the classical and quantum theories. The quantum mechanical curves are for Boltzmann statistics.

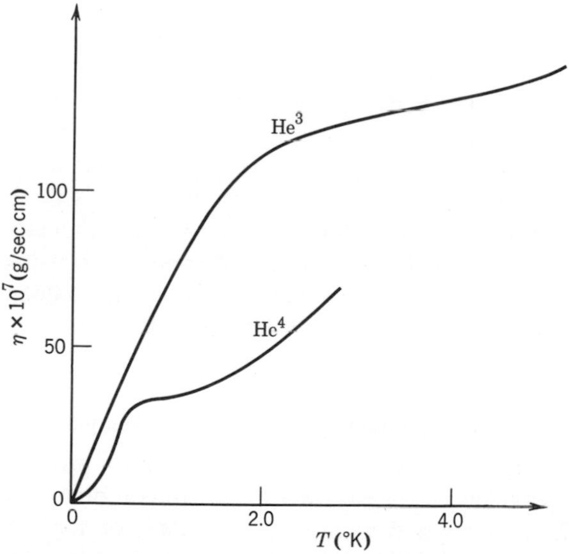

Fig. 10.2–4. The viscosity of He^3 and He^4 as a function of temperature, according to quantum mechanical calculations based on the Lennard-Jones potential. [Taken from J. de Boer and E. G. D. Cohen, *Physica*, **17**, 993 (1951).]

A further graphical comparison of calculated results may be found in Fig. 8.4–6, where the classical and quantum mechanical curves for viscosity are given on the same graph.

TABLE 10.2–1

THE VISCOSITY AND THERMAL CONDUCTIVITY OF He^3 and He^4 AS CALCULATED FROM QUANTUM MECHANICAL THEORY FOR THE LENNARD-JONES (6-12) POTENTIAL[6, 13]

He^3			He^4		
T(°K)	$\eta \times 10^7$ (g/cm-sec)	$\lambda \times 10^7$ (cal/cm-sec-°K)	T(°K)	$\eta \times 10^7$ (g/cm-sec)	$\lambda \times 10^7$ (cal/cm-sec-°K)
0.	0.	0.	0.091	0.7	1.3
0.51	37.7	93.1	0.183	2.4	4.6
1.02	72.0	178.	0.303	8.0	14.9
2.04	113.	279.	0.366	12.6	23.6
3.07	124.	306.	0.457	20.1	37.8
4.09	131.	324.	0.640	30.9	57.9
5.11	140.	346.	0.915	33.8	63.4
			1.280	36.1	67.6
			1.634	41.2	77.2
			1.828	44.6	83.7
			2.285	55.6	104.1
			2.740	67.3	127.1

As was mentioned in connection with the calculation of second virial coefficients, the calculation of the properties of gases from phase shifts is fairly well limited to the very low temperature region, since for higher temperatures it is necessary to calculate the phase shifts for many more values of the quantum numbers l and κ. For higher temperatures, where the deviations from classical behavior are not great, it is possible to obtain a series development in powers of Planck's constant analogous to that obtained for the second virial coefficient in § 6.5. This approach is discussed in the following section.

3. Transport Phenomena at Intermediate Temperatures

In the last section it is shown that the transport properties can be calculated at *very low temperatures* by the use of quantum statistical mechanics. In Chapter 8 the classical formulae for the transport coefficients are given, whereby the properties of gases may be calculated at *high temperatures*. In this section we wish to discuss the description of the transport phenomena in the "*intermediate temperature*" region, in which the quantum deviations from classical behavior are small.

In § 6.5 the calculation of the second virial coefficient in this intermediate temperature region is discussed. It is found there that the quantum correction to the second virial coefficient may be written as a power series in $\hbar^2$. This series expansion has been developed by two methods. One method involves the solution of the Bloch differential equation (this is the method used in § 6.5). In the other method the phase shifts are expanded by the WKB method. This latter technique, which was developed by Kahn,[1] may also be applied to the calculation of the transport coefficients. It is found that the quantum corrections to the transport coefficients may also be written as power series $\hbar^2$.

a. The WKB development of the phase shifts[2, 3]

The phase shifts for a binary collision are obtained by solving the radial wave equations given by Eqs. 1.7–3 and 4. The first of these is the differential equation for $(r\psi_{\kappa l})$, which describes the relative radial motion of two particles that interact according to an interaction potential energy function $\varphi(r)$. The second is a differential equation for $(r\psi^0_{\kappa l})$, which describes the relative motion of two non-interacting particles. The solution to the first of these equations may be written in the form

$$(r\psi_{\kappa l}) = \exp\,[iu_{\kappa l}(r)/\hbar] \tag{10.3–1}$$

According to the WKB method, the function $u_{\kappa l}(r)$ may then be developed in the series

$$u_{\kappa l}(r) = u^{(0)}_{\kappa l} + \left(\frac{\hbar}{i}\right) u^{(1)}_{\kappa l} + \left(\frac{\hbar}{i}\right)^2 u^{(2)}_{\kappa l} + \cdots \tag{10.3–2}$$

The $u^{(i)}_{\kappa l}(r)$ are determined by substituting Eqs. 10.3–1 and 2 into Eq. 1.7–3 and equating equal powers of Planck's constant.[4] Then the solution takes the form

$$(r\psi_{\kappa l}) = \left(\frac{\hbar^2}{2\mu}(\kappa^2 - f_l)\right)^{-1/4} \exp \pm i \left[\int_{r_m}^{r} (\kappa^2 - f_l)^{1/2}\, dr + \frac{1}{32}\int_{r_m}^{r} \frac{4f_l''(\kappa^2 - f_l) + 5f_l'^2}{(\kappa^2 - f_l)^{5/2}}\, dr + \cdots\right] \tag{10.3–3}$$

[1] B. Kahn, Dissertation, Utrecht (1938).

[2] A brief description of the WKB method is given in § 1.6e. A somewhat more extensive explanation is given in L. I. Schiff, *Quantum Mechanics*, McGraw-Hill (1949), and a detailed discussion may be found in E. C. Kemble, *Fundamental Principles of Quantum Mechanics*, McGraw-Hill (1937).

[3] The quantum dynamics of binary collisions is discussed in § 1.7. The results of that section are used in this discussion of the phase shifts.

[4] In performing this operation we disregard the fact that $\hbar$ appears also in the quantum mechanical centrifugal potential $[\hbar^2 l(l + 1)/2\mu r^2]$.

The index l is the angular momentum quantum number, and κ is the quantum number which indicates the total relative kinetic energy of the colliding pair of molecules. The quantity $f_l(r)$ is $[l(l+1)/r^2] + [2\mu\varphi(r)/\hbar^2]$ and r_m is a limit point of classical motion, that is, a point at which $f_l(r) = \kappa^2$. We restrict the discussion which follows to interaction potentials for which there is but *one* such classical limiting point, namely, the distance of closest approach of the two molecules.

Two linear combinations of the two solutions in Eq. 10.3–3 must be found: one for the "classical region," where $f_l < \kappa^2$, and another for the "non-classical region," for which $f_l > \kappa^2$. To join these two solutions at the classical limiting point, we use the Kramers' connection formulae.[2] When in this way the WKB solution for $(r\psi_{\kappa l})$ has been determined, it is easy to find the phase shifts. The phase shifts may be developed in an expansion:

$$\eta_l(\kappa) = \eta_l^{[1]}(\kappa) + \eta_l^{[2]}(\kappa) + \eta_l^{[3]}(\kappa) + \cdots \tag{10.3–4}$$

the successive terms arising from the various terms in the exponent of Eq. 10.3–3. This discussion is confined to the first two WKB approximations. The first approximation gives the correct classical formulae for the transport properties, and the second approximation gives rise to the first quantum correction, that is, the correction proportional to $\hbar^2$.

The use of the connection formulae yields for the first WKB approximation to the wave function in the "classical region":

$$(r\psi_{\kappa l}) = \left(\frac{\hbar^2}{2\mu}(\kappa^2 - f_l)\right)^{-1/4} \cos\left(-\frac{\pi}{4} + \int_{r_m}^{r} \sqrt{\kappa^2 - f_l(r)}\, dr\right) \tag{10.3–5}$$

For large r this simplifies to

$$(r\psi_{\kappa l}) \sim \cos\left[\kappa r - \kappa r_m - \frac{\pi}{4} + \int_{r_m}^{r} [\sqrt{\kappa^2 - f_l(r)} - \kappa]\, dr\right] \quad \textit{large } r \tag{10.3–6}$$

This then is the solution of Eq. 1.7–3, the radial wave equation with an interaction potential $\varphi(r)$, according to the first WKB approximation. To obtain the solution of Eq. 1.7–4 to the same approximation, we set $f_l(r)$ equal to $l(l+1)/r^2$ in Eq. 10.3–6 and perform the indicated integration. This gives then for the radial wave function for two non-interacting particles at large r:

$$(r\psi_{\kappa l}{}^0) \sim \cos\left[\kappa r - \frac{\pi}{4} - \frac{\pi}{2}\sqrt{l(l+1)}\right] \quad \textit{large } r \tag{10.3–7}$$

The phase shift is defined as the difference, at large *r*, in the phase between the radial wave functions, with and without the interaction $\varphi(r)$. From Eqs. 10.3–6 and 7 the phase shift may be found to be

$$\eta_l^{[1]}(\kappa) = \frac{\pi}{2}\sqrt{l(l+1)} - \kappa r_m + \int_{r_m}^{\infty} \left(\sqrt{\kappa^2 - f_l(r)} - \kappa\right) dr \qquad (10.3\text{–}8)$$

according to the first WKB approximation.

In a similar way we find for the second WKB approximation:

$$\eta_l^{[2]}(\kappa) = \frac{\pi}{16\sqrt{l(l+1)}} - \frac{1}{32}\int_{r_m}^{\infty} \frac{4f_l''\,(\kappa^2 - f_l) + 5f_l'^2}{(\kappa^2 - f_l)^{5/2}}\, dr \qquad (10.3\text{–}9)$$

The integral in this expression does not converge. An examination of Kramers' connection formulae reveals,[1] however, that the integral must be interpreted as half the integral over the contour in the complex *r*-plane shown in Fig. 10.3–1. It has been shown by Hadamard[5] that this integral in the complex *r*-plane may be rewritten as the principal part of the integral along the real *r*-axis. This means that we must integrate partially the integral in Eq. 10.3–9 a sufficient number of times until a convergent integral appears, and all infinite terms of the integrated parts must be discarded. Doing this, we finally obtain

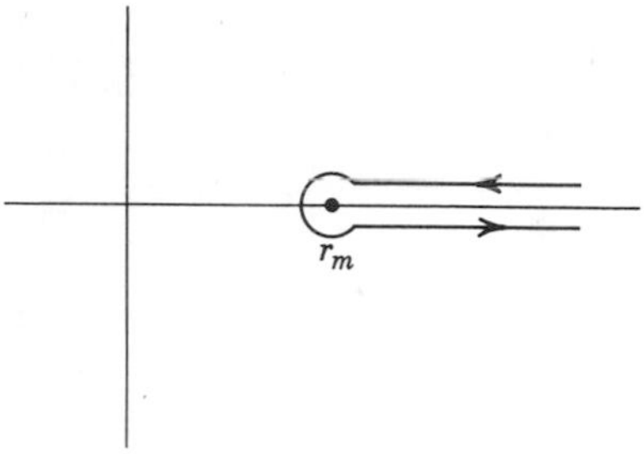

Fig. 10.3–1. The path of integration in the complex *r*-plane used in the evaluation of the integral in Eq. 10.3–9. [From B. Kahn, Doctoral Dissertation, Utrecht (1938).]

$$\eta_l^{[2]}(\kappa) = \frac{\pi}{16\sqrt{l(l+1)}} - \frac{1}{24}\int_{r_m}^{\infty} \frac{(f_l'''/f_l') - (f_l''/f_l')^2}{\sqrt{\kappa^2 - f_l(r)}}\, dr \qquad (10.3\text{–}10)$$

This is the second term in the expansion of the phase shifts by the WKB method.

b. The cross-sections as power series in Planck's constant[6]

In Eqs. 10.2–2 are given the formulae in Boltzmann statistics for the cross-sections in terms of the phase shifts. The substitution of the expressions for $\eta_l^{[1]}(\kappa)$ and $\eta_l^{[2]}(\kappa)$ into the expressions for the cross-sections

[5] J. Hadamard, *Le problème de Cauchy*, Paris (1932), p. 184.

[6] J. de Boer and R. B. Bird, *Physica*, **20**, 185 (1954).

leads to a development in a series, the various terms of which are proportional to successive powers of $\hbar$.

The differences in the phase shifts, $[\eta_{l+n} - \eta_l]$, occurring in Eq. 10.2–2 may be written in terms of derivatives according to a Taylor expansion of η_{l+n} as a function of l:

$$[\eta_{l+n} - \eta_l] = \sum_j \frac{n^j}{j!} \frac{\partial^j \eta_l}{\partial l^j} \tag{10.3–11}$$

It turns out, however, to be more convenient to introduce a variable, b, defined by $\hbar\sqrt{l(l+1)} = \mu g b$, and to express the phase shift differences in terms of derivatives with respect to b. We also replace κ by its equivalent $\mu g/\hbar$. When the WKB expressions for $\eta_l^{[1]}(\kappa)$ and $\eta_l^{[2]}(\kappa)$ are used, we obtain:

$$[\eta_{l+1} - \eta_l] = \tfrac{1}{2}\chi + \tfrac{1}{4}b \frac{\partial \chi}{\partial b}\left(\frac{\hbar}{\mu g b}\right) + \frac{1}{16}\left[\chi - \psi + b\frac{\partial \psi}{\partial b} + \frac{4}{3}b^2 \frac{\partial^2 \chi}{\partial b^2}\right]\left(\frac{\hbar}{\mu g b}\right)^2 + O(\hbar^3) \tag{10.3–12}$$

$$[\eta_{l+2} - \eta_l] = \chi + b \frac{\partial \chi}{\partial b}\left(\frac{\hbar}{\mu g b}\right) + \frac{1}{8}\left[\chi - \psi + b\frac{\partial \psi}{\partial b} + \frac{16}{3}b^2 \frac{\partial^2 \chi}{\partial b^2}\right]\left(\frac{\hbar}{\mu g b}\right)^2 + O(\hbar^3) \tag{10.3–13}$$

The quantities χ and ψ are defined in terms of the first and second approximation to the phase shifts, thus:

$$\chi = \frac{2}{\kappa}\frac{\partial \eta^{[1]}}{\partial b} \tag{10.3–14}$$

$$\psi = 16 b \kappa \eta^{[2]} \tag{10.3–15}$$

By means of the explicit expressions for the first and second WKB approximations to the phase shifts given in Eqs. 10.3–8, 10, we obtain the following integral expressions for χ and ψ:

$$\chi(b, g) = \pi - 2b \int_{r_m}^{\infty} [1 - F]^{-1/2} r^{-2}\, dr \tag{10.3–16}$$

$$\psi(b, g) = \pi - \tfrac{2}{3}b \int_{r_m}^{\infty} [(F'''/F') - (F''/F')^2]\,[1 - F]^{-1/2}\, dr \tag{10.3–17}$$

In these expressions the quantity $F(r)$ is the "effective potential" in units of the initial relative kinetic energy $\frac{1}{2}\mu g^2$:

$$F(r) = \frac{\varphi(r)}{\frac{1}{2}\mu g^2} + \frac{b^2}{r^2} \tag{10.3–18}$$

and the primes on $F(r)$ indicate differentiation with respect to r. The quantity $\chi(b,g)$ is the classical angle of deflection given in Eq. 1.5–26, and consequently the variable b which we introduced is the impact parameter defined in § 1.5. From Eq. 10.3–13 it is clear that

$$[\eta_{l+2}(\kappa) - \eta_l(\kappa)] \xrightarrow[\text{limit}]{\text{classical}} \chi(b, g) \tag{10.3–19}$$

This is then the correspondence relation[7] between the phase shifts and the angle of deflection.

The cross-sections may now be obtained by substituting Eqs. 10.3–12 and 13 into the formulae for $Q^{(1)}$ and $Q^{(2)}$, which are given in Eq. 10.2–2 for Boltzmann statistics. The quantities, $\sin(\eta_{l+n} - \eta_l)$, may be developed in a power series in $\hbar/\mu g b$, and the summations over l may be transformed into an integration over the variable b by means of the expression

$$dl = \left(\frac{\mu g}{\hbar}\right)\left(1 - \frac{1}{8}\left(\frac{\hbar}{\mu g b}\right)^2 + \cdots\right) db \tag{10.3–20}$$

By this means the cross-sections are obtained as a series, the terms of which contain successively higher powers of Planck's constant. The first term, proportional to $\hbar^0$, is just the classical cross-section $Q_{\text{cl}}^{(1)}$ or $Q_{\text{cl}}^{(2)}$ given in Eq. 10.2–3. The terms proportional to odd powers of $\hbar$ may be shown to vanish by partial integrations. Hence the final expressions have the form

$$Q^{(n)} = Q_{\text{cl}}^{(n)} + \left(\frac{\hbar}{\mu g}\right)^2 Q_{\text{I}}^{(n)} + \left(\frac{\hbar}{\mu g}\right)^4 Q_{\text{II}}^{(n)} + \cdots \tag{10.3–21}$$

The $Q_{\text{I}}^{(n)}$ are the first quantum corrections to the cross-sections and have been found to be

$$\begin{aligned}
Q_{\text{I}}^{(1)} &= 2\pi\left[\frac{1}{8}\int_0^\infty (\sin\chi)(\chi - \psi)\frac{db}{b}\right.\\
&\qquad \left. - \frac{1}{8}\int_0^\infty (\cos\chi)\left(\psi + \frac{1}{3}b\frac{\partial\chi}{\partial b}\right)\frac{\partial\chi}{\partial b}\,db + \frac{1}{6}\right]\\
Q_{\text{I}}^{(2)} &= 2\pi\left[\frac{1}{8}\int_0^\infty (\sin 2\chi)(\chi - \psi)\frac{db}{b}\right.\\
&\qquad \left. - \frac{1}{4}\int_0^\infty (\cos 2\chi)\left(\psi + \frac{4}{3}b\frac{\partial\chi}{\partial b}\right)\frac{\partial\chi}{\partial b}\,db - \frac{1}{4}\int_0^\infty (\sin^2\chi)\frac{db}{b}\right]
\end{aligned} \tag{10.3–22}$$

Explicit expressions for the $Q_{\text{II}}^{(n)}$ have not yet been obtained.

[7] This correspondence has been obtained by another method as outlined in N. F. Mott and H. S. W. Massey, *The Theory of Atomic Collisions*, Oxford University Press (1949), pp. 120 et seq. The method given there does not provide directly a means for obtaining the quantum corrections to the classical value.

Substitution of these expressions into the formula for $\Omega^{(n,t)}$ given in Eq. 10.2–5 leads to

$$\Omega^{(n,t)} = \Omega_{\text{cl}}^{(n,t)} + \left(\frac{\hbar}{\mu}\right)^2 \Omega_{\text{I}}^{(n,t)} + \left(\frac{\hbar}{\mu}\right)^4 \Omega_{\text{II}}^{(n,t)} + \cdots \tag{10.3–23}$$

in which

$$\begin{aligned} \sqrt{2\pi\mu/kT}\,\Omega_{\text{cl}}^{(n,t)} &= \int_0^\infty e^{-\gamma^2}\gamma^{2t+3}Q_{\text{cl}}^{(n)}\,d\gamma \\ \sqrt{2\pi\mu/kT}\,\Omega_{\text{I}}^{(n,t)} &= \int_0^\infty e^{-\gamma^2}\gamma^{2t+3}Q_{\text{I}}^{(n)}g^{-2}\,d\gamma \\ \sqrt{2\pi\mu/kT}\,\Omega_{\text{II}}^{(n,t)} &= \int_0^\infty e^{-\gamma^2}\gamma^{2t+3}Q_{\text{II}}^{(n)}g^{-4}\,d\gamma \end{aligned} \tag{10.3–24}$$

The variable γ is defined as $\gamma^2 = \frac{1}{2}\mu g^2/kT$. Thus we have succeeded in obtaining expressions for the quantum deviations from the classical values of the $\Omega^{(n,t)}$ and hence also for the transport coefficients themselves.

c. Calculations for an inverse twelfth-power repulsive potential

Calculations of the quantum deviations of transport properties according to the formulae above cannot be performed for rigid spheres easily, since derivatives of the potential functions occur in the formulae for χ and ψ. The simplest model for which the calculations may be made is one which represents the molecules as point centers of repulsion. We consider here the special case of the potential function:

$$\varphi(r) = 4\epsilon(\sigma/r)^{12} \tag{10.3–25}$$

which is just the repulsive component of the Lennard-Jones (6-12) potential. Classical transport property calculations for potentials of this type have been discussed in § 8.3b. The particular advantage of this model is that the quantities χ and ψ may be written as a function of a single variable, y_0, and furthermore the integrations over γ in Eq. 10.3–24 may be performed analytically.

It is convenient to introduce the quantities y, y_m, y_0, and z, which are defined by:

$$y = b/r \qquad y_m = b/r_m \qquad z = y/y_m$$

$$y_0 = b\left(\frac{\frac{1}{2}\mu g^2}{12\cdot 4\epsilon\sigma^{12}}\right)^{1/12} = \left(\frac{b}{\sigma}\right)\left(\frac{\frac{1}{2}\mu g^2}{48\epsilon}\right)^{1/12} \tag{10.3–26}$$

The length r_m is the classical distance of closest approach in a collision (defined in connection with Eq. 1.5–26), and y_m which is a function of y_0, is determined as the positive root of the equation:

$$1 - y_m{}^2 - \frac{1}{12}\left(\frac{y_m}{y_0}\right)^{12} = 0 \tag{10.3–27}$$

In terms of these quantities the integrals χ and ψ may be written in a form convenient for purposes of calculation:

$$\chi(y_0) = \pi - 2y_m \int_0^1 \frac{dz}{\sqrt{1 - F^{(0)}(z)}} \tag{10.3–28}$$

$$\psi(y_0) = \pi - \tfrac{2}{3}y_m \int_0^1 \frac{F^{(3)}F^{(1)} - F^{(2)2} + 2F^{(1)2} + 2F^{(1)}F^{(2)}}{F^{(1)2}\sqrt{1 - F^{(0)}}}\, dz \tag{10.3–29}$$

in which

$$F^{(0)}(z) = y_m{}^2 z^2 + \frac{1}{12}\left(\frac{y_m z}{y_0}\right)^{12} \tag{10.3–30}$$

$$F^{(k)}(z) = \tfrac{1}{2}z^k \left(\frac{d^k}{dz^k} F^{(0)}\right) \tag{10.3–31}$$

In Table III we give the calculated values of y_m, χ, ψ, and $\chi' = d\chi/dy_0$ as functions of y_0.

From the table of χ and ψ, the classical cross-sections (Eq. 10.2–3) and the first quantum corrections (Eq. 10.3–22) may be calculated. The results may be expressed in the form

$$Q_{\text{cl}}^{(n)} = 2\pi \left(\frac{12 \cdot 4\epsilon\sigma^{12}}{\frac{1}{2}\mu g^2}\right)^{1/6} A^{(n)} \;;\; Q_{\text{I}}^{(n)} = 2\pi B^{(n)} \tag{10.3–32}$$

The quantities $A^{(n)}$ and $B^{(n)}$ are integrals over y_0 and do not depend on g. Their numerical values are given by

$$A^{(1)} = +0.3458 \qquad B^{(1)} = +0.0653$$

$$A^{(2)} = +0.2787 \qquad B^{(2)} = +0.5251$$

The integrals $\Omega^{(n,t)}$ may then be written as

$$\Omega^{(n,t)} = A^{(n)} \sqrt{\frac{\pi kT}{\mu}} \left(\frac{6}{T^*}\right)^{1/6} \sigma^2 \, \Gamma(t + \tfrac{11}{6}) \left[1 + K_{\text{I}}(n, t) \frac{\Lambda^{*2}}{T^{*5/6}} + \cdots\right] \tag{10.3-33}$$

in which

$$\Lambda^* = \frac{h}{\sigma\sqrt{2\mu\epsilon}} \qquad T^* = kT/\epsilon$$

$$K_{\text{I}}(n, 1) = [B^{(n)}/A^{(n)}] \, (7.706 \times 10^{-3}) \tag{10.3-34}$$

$$K_{\text{I}}(n, 2) = [B^{(n)}/A^{(n)}] \, (5.439 \times 10^{-3})$$

According to the calculations of the first quantum correction to the transport coefficients, the quantum deviations of the viscosity, thermal conductivity, and self-diffusion of He and H_2 are less than 0.5 per cent at room temperature. The magnitude of the second quantum correction has not yet been estimated. The experimental data are not sufficiently good at the present time to warrant a comparison of experimental and calculated results.

4. The Principle of Corresponding States in Quantum Mechanics[1]

The discussion in the two preceding sections is applicable only to dilute gases in which three-body collisions are negligible. It is possible, however, to formulate for the transport coefficients a principle of corresponding states, the validity of which is not limited to this region of low densities, but which is valid for all densities and, in particular, also in the liquid state.

This principle of corresponding states may be established by means of dimensional arguments presented in § 9.1b. Let the interaction potential between a pair of molecules be characterized by two parameters, a characteristic length σ and a characteristic energy ϵ. Then in quantum theory the bulk properties, such as the transport coefficients, are functions of the seven quantities, v, T, m, k, σ, ϵ, and h. Dimensional analysis then indicates that the reduced transport coefficients (defined in Eq. 9.1-2) may be written in the form

$$\begin{aligned} \mathscr{D}^* &= \mathscr{D}^*(v^*, T^*; \Lambda^*) \\ \eta^* &= \eta^*(v^*, T^*; \Lambda^*) \\ \lambda^* &= \lambda^*(v^*, T^*; \Lambda^*) \end{aligned} \tag{10.4-1}$$

[1] Other discussions of the principle of corresponding states may be found elsewhere in this volume. § 4.1: Classical principle applied to equation of state. § 6.6: Quantum principle applied to equation of state. § 9.1: Classical principle applied to transport properties.

The variables v^* and T^* are the reduced volume and temperature defined in Eq. 9.1–1, and Λ^* is the quantum mechanical parameter defined by

$$\Lambda^* = \frac{h}{\sigma\sqrt{m\epsilon}} \qquad (10.4\text{–}2)$$

The meaning and interpretation of this parameter have been discussed in § 6.6, where the principle of corresponding states is applied to equilibrium properties. The values of Λ^* for various substances are given in Table 6.5–2.

The principle of corresponding states may also be formulated in terms of reduction with the critical constants. For example, we may write

$$\begin{aligned} \mathscr{D}_r &= \mathscr{D}_r(p_r, T_r; \Lambda_r) \\ \eta_r &= \eta_r(p_r, T_r; \Lambda_r) \\ \lambda_r &= \lambda_r(p_r, T_r; \Lambda_r) \end{aligned} \qquad (10.4\text{–}3)$$

in which the reduced transport coefficients, the reduced pressure, and the reduced temperature are those defined in connection with Eq. 9.1–6. The quantity Λ_r is the dimensionless combination:

$$\Lambda_r = \frac{h}{v_c^{1/3}(mkT_c)^{1/2}} \qquad (10.4\text{–}4)$$

which was used in the earliest studies of the quantum deviations from the classical equation of state.[2] However, as pointed out in § 6.6a, this quantity Λ_r is not completely satisfactory, since it is dependent upon quantum effects through v_c and T_c. The parameter Λ^* does not suffer from this objection.

At the present time there are not sufficient viscosity, thermal conductivity, or diffusion data to make it possible to apply the principle of corresponding states in quantum mechanics. When such data become available, this principle should provide a means of correlating the experimental facts and predicting the quantum properties of fluids.

PROBLEMS

1. Estimate the quantum correction to the viscosity of neon at 300°K.
2. Is the relation $[\lambda]_1 = \frac{15}{4}\frac{k}{m}[\eta]_1$ (see Eq. 8.2–31) valid in quantum mechanics?

[2] A. Byk, *Ann. Physik*, **66**, 157 (1921); **69**, 161 (1922). See also § 6.6a.

· 11 ·

Hydrodynamic Applications of the Equations of Change Ⓝ

In Chapters 2 through 6 the equilibrium properties of gases and liquids are studied; in Chapters 7 through 10 the non-equilibrium properties are examined. In this chapter we consider the application of these results to the study of the hydrodynamics of fluids. The solution of any hydrodynamical problem requires the following fundamental equations:

(i) The thermal equation of state, $p = p(V, T)$.
(ii) The caloric equation of state, $U = U(V, T)$.
(iii) The equation of continuity.
(iv) The equation of motion.
(v) The equation of energy balance.

These five equations, along with equations describing the temperature and density dependence of the transport coefficients, form the starting point for the solution of problems of fluid flow. The solution to practical hydrodynamical problems requires the solution of these equations for specific initial and boundary conditions. Many various types of phenomena can be described by means of this set of equations and the associated boundary conditions. In this chapter we illustrate the application of these equations to the description of the propagation of waves of infinitesimal amplitude (sound waves), waves of finite amplitude, and shock waves. We also show how the explicit inclusion of chemical reactions enables us to describe flames and detonations. Finally we discuss the flow of fluids through nozzles as applied to rocket propulsion. For simplicity, the discussions in this chapter are limited to laminar flow.

The equations of change (Eqs. iii, iv, and v) contain, the mass fluxes $\boldsymbol{j}_i$, the momentum flux p, and the heat flux $\boldsymbol{q}$. In order to apply the equations of change to hydrodynamical problems it is necessary to express the fluxes in terms of the gradients of the physical properties and the transport coefficients. Relations between the flux vectors may be obtained by means of the thermodynamics of irreversible processes and the Onsager relations. In this chapter we indicate how the energy transfer by radiation can be included in the energy flux vector.

1. The Hydrodynamic Equations

The dynamics of a fluid may be expressed compactly in terms of the equations of change. They describe the changes in the macroscopic properties of the fluid (that is, the local number density, stream velocity, and temperature) in terms of the flux of mass (the diffusion velocities), the flux of momentum (the pressure tensor), the flux of energy, and the chemical kinetics. The equations of change have been derived for very general conditions both classically (see § 9.4) and quantum mechanically (see § 10.1). In this section we summarize the results and discuss the limit of applicability of these equations. We also give a derivation of the equation of change of entropy, which is used later in the chapter in connection with the theory of propagation of sound waves, waves of finite amplitude, detonations, and flow through nozzles.

a. Applicability of the equations of change

Although the equations of change are general and apply to any fluid, they are clearly useful only under conditions that make it physically meaningful to discuss point properties. The local density, velocity, and temperature have been defined formally, but these definitions are reasonable only under those conditions where the fluid behaves as a continuum. When there are large differences in the macroscopic properties over distances of the order of a mean free path, the distribution of the velocities of the molecules deviates considerably from a Maxwellian distribution. Under these conditions, the flux vectors can no longer be expressed in terms of the local density, flow velocity, and temperature and their first derivatives. Two well known examples of a fluid under such a condition are: (i) an *extremely dilute gas*[1,2] (or "Knudsen gas"), in which the dimensions of the containing vessel or an object immersed in the gas are of the same order of magnitude as the mean free path, and (ii) a *shock wave*,[3] in which the macroscopic properties as a function of distance undergo an abrupt change within a distance of a few mean free paths. In both these cases it is meaningless to speak of point values of the macroscopic variables.

We might well question the applicability of the equations of change

[1] M. Knudsen, *Kinetic Theory of Gases*, Methuen (London) and Wiley (New York), 1950.

[2] See §§ 1.2b and 7.5.

[3] See §§ 11.5c and 11.8.

to the description of turbulent motion. It is well known that fluid flow in pipes may be either laminar or turbulent. Laminar flow, which occurs in slowly moving fluids,[4] is characterized by smoothly varying streamlines. As the rate of flow is increased, however, the flow becomes turbulent; small eddies appear, and there is superimposed on the overall flow a complex pattern of more or less random motions. The dimensions of these eddies are always large compared to the mean free path, so that the turbulent motion is macroscopic rather than molecular. Accordingly, the concept of the fluid as a continuum remains valid, and the ordinary equations of change may be used. In these equations the variables refer to instantaneous values at a point. For most practical purposes, however, we are interested in the values of these quantities averaged over a time long compared with the period of fluctuations. Hence, in turbulent flow, the equations of change are modified by time averaging to obtain relations among the average macroscopic variables. The equations presented in this chapter form the basis of the theory of turbulence, but this subject is not discussed further here.[5]

Let us now consider in somewhat more detail the energy balance equation. Energy transfer in practical problems[6] may take place by one or several of four mechanisms: conduction,[7] diffusion, convection, and radiation. Up to this point we have considered only the first two of these mechanisms. Let us now examine briefly the phenomenon of energy transfer by the two types of convection—forced and natural. In forced convection the flow pattern is prescribed directly by the hydrodynamics and boundary conditions of the problem. In natural convection, the

[4] The nature of the flow in circular pipes is determined by the Reynolds number, $D\rho v/\eta$. Here D is the diameter of the pipe, ρ is the density, v is the velocity, and η is the coefficient of viscosity. For small Reynolds number the flow is laminar; for high Reynolds number the flow is usually turbulent.

[5] For a discussion of the theory of turbulence, see: (a) S. Goldstein, *Modern Developments in Fluid Dynamics*, Vols. 1 and 2, Oxford University Press (1938). (b) H. L. Dryden, Sr., *Quart. Appl. Math.*, **1**, 7 (1943). (c) G. K. Batchelor, *The Theory of Homogeneous Turbulence*, Cambridge University Press (1953). (d) S. Goldstein, *Statistical Theory of Turbulence*, Lecture Series No. 6, Institute for Fluid Dynamics and Applied Mathematics, University of Maryland (1950). (e) F. N. Frenkiel, *Introduction to Some Topics in Turbulence*, Lecture Series No. 3, Institute for Fluid Dynamics and Applied Mathematics, University of Maryland (1950). (f) H. Schlichting, *Boundary-Layer Theory*, Pergamon Press, New York (1955).

[6] For general treatments of practical heat-transfer problems in gases and liquids, see: (a) W. H. McAdams, *Heat Transmission*, McGraw-Hill (3rd Ed., 1954). (b) M. Jakob, *Heat Transfer*, John Wiley, Vol. I (1949) and Vol. II (1957). (c) J. H. Perry, *Chemical Engineers' Handbook*, McGraw-Hill, 3rd Ed. (1950), Section 6.

[7] For mathematical treatment of conduction in solids (no flow), see: (a) H. S. Carslaw and J. C. Jaeger, *Conduction of Heat in Solids*, Oxford University Press (2nd Ed., 1959). (b) L. R. Ingersoll, O. J. Zobel, A. C. Ingersoll, *Heat Conduction*, McGraw-Hill (1948).

flow is established by density gradients developed by the heat transfer and the gravitational acceleration. Of all the possible flow patterns, the steady-state flow realized in nature is the most stable with respect to perturbations. Although natural convection represents an exceedingly difficult type of hydrodynamical boundary-value problem, there are a few special examples where satisfactory theoretical treatments have been developed. The most notable of these are: (i) the convection currents in a Clusius-Dickel thermal diffusion column[8] (a gas or liquid constrained to the annular region between two concentric vertical tubes maintained at different temperatures), and (ii) the cellular convection of a gas or liquid constrained between two large horizontal flat plates which are kept at different temperatures.[9] Convection plays a very important rôle in diffusion methods of separating mixtures.[10] Natural convection, like turbulence, is beyond the scope of this book.

When energy is transferred by radiation,[11] it is necessary to replace the energy flux $\boldsymbol{q}$ in the equations of change by $(\boldsymbol{q} + \boldsymbol{q}_R)$, the sum of the flux due to conduction and diffusion and that due to radiation. The nature and magnitude of this radiation flux is considered in detail in § 11.3. In flames or other systems involving high temperatures, radiation can be an important mechanism for transferring energy. In principle, radiation pressure p_R should be added to the hydrodynamic pressure tensor, and the density of radiation energy $\hat{U}_R$ should be added to the internal energy of the system. It is, however, only under astronomical or atomic-bomb conditions that the radiation energy[12] or the radiation

[8] R. C. Jones and W. H. Furry, *Revs. Mod. Phys.*, **18**, 151 (1946).

[9] Lord Rayleigh, *Phil. Mag.*, **32**, 529 (1916). H. Jeffreys, *Phil. Mag.*, **2**, 833 (1926); *Proc. Roy. Soc. (London)*, **A118**, 195 (1928); *Quart. J. Mech. Appl. Math.*, IV (3), September 1951. Experimental confirmations of the theory are given by K. Chandra, *Proc. Roy. Soc. (London)*, **A164**, 231 (1938). S. Chandrasekhar, *Proc. Roy. Soc. (London)*, **A210**, 26 (1951).

[10] (a) M. Benedict and A. Boas, *Chem. Eng. Prog.*, **47**, 51 (1951). (b) M. Benedict, *Diffusion Separation Methods*, *Encyclopedia Chem. Tech.*, **5**, 76 (1950). (c) M. Ruhemann, *Separation of Gases*, Oxford University Press (1949), 2nd Ed.

[11] For further discussions of radiative transfer, see: (a) S. Chandrasekhar, *Radiative Transfer*, Oxford University Press (1950). (b) S. Chandrasekhar, *An Introduction to Stellar Structure*, Chicago University Press (1939). (c) S. Rosseland, *Theoretical Astrophysics*, Oxford University Press (1936).

[12] The fact that radiation energy is usually negligible with respect to the material internal energy may be seen in the following manner. The radiation energy of a black body at temperature T is

$$\hat{U}_R = \rho a T^4 = 1.833 \times 10^{-22} \rho T^4 \text{ cal/g}$$

Here a is the Stefan-Boltzmann radiation constant. If the matter density, ρ, is unity and $T = 100{,}000°\text{K}$, $\hat{U}_R$ is only 0.02 cal/g.

pressure[13] becomes appreciable. Hence these two effects of radiation are not considered here.

b. Summary of the equations of change

The macroscopic variables describing the state of a system are the number densities of the various chemical species n_i, the mass average (or stream) velocity[14] $\boldsymbol{v}$, and the temperature T. These quantities are related to the quantities conserved in a molecular collision: the masses of the individual molecules, the momenta of the colliding molecules, and the energies of the colliding molecules. Corresponding to each of these "summational invariants" there is an equation of change: the equations of continuity of the individual species, the equation of motion, and the equation of energy balance.[15] These equations are:

1. (a) The equations of continuity of the individual species:

$$\frac{Dn_i}{Dt} = \frac{\partial n_i}{\partial t} + \left(\boldsymbol{v} \cdot \frac{\partial}{\partial \boldsymbol{r}} n_i\right) = -n_i \left(\frac{\partial}{\partial \boldsymbol{r}} \cdot \boldsymbol{v}\right) - \left(\frac{\partial}{\partial \boldsymbol{r}} \cdot n_i \overline{\boldsymbol{V}}_i\right) + K_i \qquad (11.1\text{–}1)$$

(b) The overall equation of continuity:

$$\frac{D\rho}{Dt} = \frac{\partial \rho}{\partial t} + \left(\boldsymbol{v} \cdot \frac{\partial}{\partial \boldsymbol{r}} \rho\right) = -\rho \left(\frac{\partial}{\partial \boldsymbol{r}} \cdot \boldsymbol{v}\right) \qquad (11.1\text{–}2)$$

2. The equation of motion:

$$\frac{D\boldsymbol{v}}{Dt} = \frac{\partial \boldsymbol{v}}{\partial t} + \left(\boldsymbol{v} \cdot \frac{\partial}{\partial \boldsymbol{r}} \boldsymbol{v}\right) = -\frac{1}{\rho}\left(\frac{\partial}{\partial \boldsymbol{r}} \cdot \mathsf{p}\right) + \frac{1}{\rho} \sum_i n_i \boldsymbol{X}_i \qquad (11.1\text{–}3)$$

3. The equation of energy balance:

$$\frac{D\hat{U}}{Dt} = \frac{\partial \hat{U}}{\partial t} + \left(\boldsymbol{v} \cdot \frac{\partial}{\partial \boldsymbol{r}} \hat{U}\right) = -\frac{1}{\rho}\left(\frac{\partial}{\partial \boldsymbol{r}} \cdot \{\boldsymbol{q} + \boldsymbol{q}_R\}\right) - \frac{1}{\rho}\left(\mathsf{p} : \frac{\partial}{\partial \boldsymbol{r}} \boldsymbol{v}\right) + \frac{1}{\rho} \sum_i n_i (\overline{\boldsymbol{V}}_i \cdot \boldsymbol{X}_i) \qquad (11.1\text{–}4)$$

[13] Under equilibrium conditions the radiation pressure is given by

$$p_R = aT^4 = 2.523 \times 10^{-21} T^4 \text{ atm}$$

If $T = 10{,}000°$K, $p_R = 2.5 \times 10^{-5}$ atm. If $T = 100{,}000°$K, $p_R = 0.25$ atm. Thus, for all ordinary applications, radiation pressure is negligible.

[14] In Chapters 7 to 10 the symbol $\boldsymbol{v}_0$ is used for the mass-average velocity. In the hydrodynamic applications discussed later in this chapter, it is cumbersome to carry the subscript 0. Hence it is omitted in all of Chapter 11.

[15] The conservation of angular momentum in collisions leads to another equation of change. This equation describes the coupling of the angular momentum associated with the macroscopic motion of the gas and that associated with the rotation of the molecules. This equation, which is not generally recognized, is discussed in § 7.6d.

Here ρ is the density of the fluid, and $\hat{U}$ is the internal energy per gram. The quantities leading to the irreversibility of the flow are: K_i, the rate of formation of the ith chemical species per unit volume per unit time; $\overline{\boldsymbol{V}}_i$, the diffusion velocity of the ith species; p, the pressure tensor; and $\boldsymbol{q} + \boldsymbol{q}_R$, the energy flux vector. Expressions for these quantities which apply to a dilute gas in the absence of radiation are discussed in § 8.1. In § 11.2 the thermodynamics of irreversible processes is used to develop expressions for the flux vectors which apply under more general conditions. In § 11.3 the radiation contribution $\boldsymbol{q}_R$ to the energy flux vector is considered.

The substantial derivative D/Dt appearing in Eqs. 11.1-1, 2, 3, and 4, represents the time rate of change following a fluid element which moves with velocity $\boldsymbol{v}$. According to Eq. 11.1-1, the number density of species i changes for three reasons: the first term on the right indicates the change due to expansion of the fluid, the second term accounts for the change due to diffusion processes, and the third term represents the change due to the production of the ith component by chemical reaction. According to Eq. 11.1-2, the density of the fluid changes only because of the expansion of the fluid represented by the term on the right. According to Eq. 11.1-3, the velocity of the fluid element changes because of the gradient of the pressure tensor and also because of the external forces acting upon the various species present. The pressure tensor may be written as the sum of two terms:

$$\mathsf{p} = p\mathsf{U} + \mathsf{P} \qquad (11.1\text{-}5)$$

the first term representing static pressure and the second term representing the viscous effects. According to Eq. 11.1-4, the internal energy changes for the following reasons: the first term on the right represents the change due to the energy flux including the radiation effects, the second term represents the change due to the pV-work and the viscous effects, and the third term describes the change due to the work which the diffusing molecules do in overcoming the external forces.

For some purposes it is convenient to have equations of change of the variables T and p. For a one-component system these relations, which are contained in those above, are

$$\frac{DT}{Dt} = \frac{\partial T}{\partial t} + \left(\boldsymbol{v} \cdot \frac{\partial T}{\partial \boldsymbol{r}}\right) = -\frac{1}{\rho \hat{C}_v}\left(\frac{\partial}{\partial \boldsymbol{r}} \cdot \{\boldsymbol{q} + \boldsymbol{q}_R\}\right) - \frac{1}{\rho \hat{C}_v}\left(\mathsf{P} : \frac{\partial}{\partial \boldsymbol{r}} \boldsymbol{v}\right)$$
$$+ \frac{1}{\rho \hat{C}_v}\left(p - T\left(\frac{\partial p}{\partial T}\right)_\rho\right)\left(\frac{\partial}{\partial \boldsymbol{r}} \cdot \boldsymbol{v}\right) \qquad (11.1\text{-}6)$$

and

$$\frac{Dp}{Dt} = \frac{\partial p}{\partial t} + \left(\boldsymbol{v} \cdot \frac{\partial p}{\partial \boldsymbol{r}}\right) = -\frac{1}{\rho \hat{C}_v}\left(\frac{\partial p}{\partial T}\right)_\rho \left(\frac{\partial}{\partial \boldsymbol{r}} \cdot \{\boldsymbol{q} + \boldsymbol{q}_R\}\right)$$
$$-\frac{1}{\rho \hat{C}_v}\left(\frac{\partial p}{\partial T}\right)_\rho \left(\mathsf{p} : \frac{\partial}{\partial \boldsymbol{r}} \boldsymbol{v}\right)$$
$$+\frac{1}{\rho \hat{C}_v}\left(\frac{\partial p}{\partial T}\right)_\rho \left(p - T\left(\frac{\partial p}{\partial T}\right)_\rho\right)\left(\frac{\partial}{\partial \boldsymbol{r}} \cdot \boldsymbol{v}\right)$$
$$-\rho\left(\frac{\partial p}{\partial \rho}\right)_T \left(\frac{\partial}{\partial \boldsymbol{r}} \cdot \boldsymbol{v}\right) \qquad (11.1\text{–}7)$$

The analogous equations for general multicomponent fluids are complicated by the fact that the partial molar internal energies are functions of the density and chemical composition as well as the temperature.

c. The equation of change of entropy

The equations of change described above provide a complete description of the hydrodynamics of a fluid. Nevertheless, another equation which describes the rate of change of the entropy in a flow process is very useful, particularly under adiabatic conditions. This equation is written in such a form as to exhibit the rate of irreversible production of entropy due to each of the various processes going on within the fluid; the principles of the thermodynamics of irreversible processes may be applied to obtain information as to the form of the flux vectors. This information is particularly valuable in the case of a liquid where the form of the flux vectors would otherwise be unknown.

Let us consider the rate of change of entropy within a finite region of space, Δ. The region is defined by a surface, each portion of which moves with the local flow velocity of the fluid, $\boldsymbol{v}$. The entropy of the fluid within the region changes for two reasons: (i) because of the reversible flow of entropy through the bounding surface and (ii) because of the irreversible production of entropy. Let $\hat{S}$ be the entropy per unit mass, $\boldsymbol{\sigma}$ be the flux vector representing the reversible flow of entropy, and g be the rate of irreversible entropy production. Then, in terms of these quantities,

$$\frac{d}{dt}\int_\Delta \rho \hat{S}\, d\boldsymbol{r} = -\int_\Delta (\boldsymbol{\sigma} \cdot d\boldsymbol{S}) + \int_\Delta g\, d\boldsymbol{r} \qquad (11.1\text{–}8)$$

Here $\int_\Delta d\boldsymbol{S}$ indicates an integration over the surface of the region Δ under consideration. This is the equation of change of the entropy in integral form.

From the meaning of the differentiation, it is clear that this equation can be rewritten in the form

$$\int_\Delta \frac{\partial}{\partial t}(\rho\hat{S})\, d\boldsymbol{r} + \int_\Delta \rho\hat{S}\,(\boldsymbol{v}\cdot d\boldsymbol{S}) = -\int_\Delta (\boldsymbol{\sigma}\cdot d\boldsymbol{S}) + \int_\Delta g\, d\boldsymbol{r} \qquad (11.1\text{–}9)$$

Then, using Gauss's theorem, we obtain the relation

$$\int_\Delta \left[\frac{\partial}{\partial t}(\rho\hat{S}) + \left(\frac{\partial}{\partial \boldsymbol{r}}\cdot(\rho\hat{S}\boldsymbol{v})\right) + \left(\frac{\partial}{\partial \boldsymbol{r}}\cdot\boldsymbol{\sigma}\right) - g\right] d\boldsymbol{r} = 0 \qquad (11.1\text{–}10)$$

Since this expression is true for any region in space, it follows that

$$\frac{\partial}{\partial t}(\rho\hat{S}) + \frac{\partial}{\partial \boldsymbol{r}}\cdot(\rho\hat{S}\boldsymbol{v}) = -\left(\frac{\partial}{\partial \boldsymbol{r}}\cdot\boldsymbol{\sigma}\right) + g \qquad (11.1\text{–}11)$$

and, using the equation of continuity (Eq. 11.1–2), one finds that

$$\rho\frac{\partial \hat{S}}{\partial t} + \left(\rho\boldsymbol{v}\cdot\frac{\partial \hat{S}}{\partial \boldsymbol{r}}\right) = -\left(\frac{\partial}{\partial \boldsymbol{r}}\cdot\boldsymbol{\sigma}\right) + g \qquad (11.1\text{–}12)$$

This is the *equation of change of entropy* in the differential form.

It is convenient to write the equation of change in terms of the substantial derivative, D/Dt. In terms of this operator, Eq. 11.1–12 is[16]

$$\rho\frac{D\hat{S}}{Dt} = -\left(\frac{\partial}{\partial \boldsymbol{r}}\cdot\boldsymbol{\sigma}\right) + g \qquad (11.1\text{–}13)$$

An equation of change of entropy of this form may also be obtained from the equations of change of § 11.1b. A comparison of the two equations then gives an explicit expression for the rate of irreversible production of entropy, g.

Under equilibrium conditions the entropy is a quantity which depends only on the state of the system. Under non-equilibrium conditions the entropy per gram $\hat{S}$, at a point, is taken to be the same function of the local temperature, density, and composition. The differential of the entropy is

$$T\,d\hat{S} = d\hat{U} + p\,d(1/\rho) - \Sigma_i \mu_i d(n_i/\rho) \qquad (11.1\text{–}14)$$

Here μ_i is the chemical potential (or partial molar Gibbs free energy). In an equilibrium system p is the pressure exerted by the fluid. In a

[16] It should be noted that the derivation of this equation does not make use of the specific properties of the entropy, $\hat{S}$, and hence a similar equation applies to any extensive property of the gas.

non-equilibrium system p is taken to be the same function of the local temperature, density, and composition. As discussed in § 11.2e only under special conditions is one-third the sum of the diagonal elements of the pressure tensor equal to p.

From Eq. 11.1–14 it follows immediately that

$$T\frac{D\hat{S}}{Dt} = \frac{D\hat{U}}{Dt} + p\frac{D(1/\rho)}{Dt} - \Sigma_i \mu_i \frac{D(n_i/\rho)}{Dt} \tag{11.1–15}$$

The equations of change of § 11.1b may be used to eliminate the time derivatives on the right of this equation. The result is an equation of the same form as Eq. 11.1–13, with $\boldsymbol{\sigma}$ and g given by

$$\boldsymbol{\sigma} = \frac{1}{T}[\{\boldsymbol{q} + \boldsymbol{q}_R\} - \Sigma_i n_i \mu_i \overline{\boldsymbol{V}}_i] \tag{11.1–16}$$

$$g = -\frac{1}{T^2}\left((\boldsymbol{q} + \boldsymbol{q}_R)\cdot\frac{\partial T}{\partial \boldsymbol{r}}\right) - \frac{1}{T}\left((\mathsf{p} - p\mathsf{U}):\frac{\partial}{\partial \boldsymbol{r}}\boldsymbol{v}\right)$$
$$- \Sigma_i n_i\left(\overline{\boldsymbol{V}}_i\cdot\left\{\frac{\partial}{\partial \boldsymbol{r}}\left(\frac{\mu_i}{T}\right) - \frac{1}{T}\boldsymbol{X}_i\right\}\right) - \frac{1}{T}\Sigma_i \mu_i K_i \tag{11.1–17}$$

Let us now rewrite the quantities $\boldsymbol{\sigma}$ and g in a somewhat more convenient form.

The vector $\boldsymbol{\sigma}$ represents the reversible flow of entropy. That this is reasonable may be seen from the following arguments. The total energy flux, $\boldsymbol{q} + \boldsymbol{q}_R$, may be written as the sum of two terms:

$$\boldsymbol{q} + \boldsymbol{q}_R = \boldsymbol{\epsilon} + \Sigma_i n_i \overline{H}_i \overline{\boldsymbol{V}}_i \tag{11.1–18}$$

where $\overline{H}_i$ is the partial molal enthalpy. The second term is the flux of energy incidental to the diffusion processes, whereas $\boldsymbol{\epsilon}$ (which is defined by this equation) is the flux of thermal energy. It follows from Eqs. 11.1–16 and 18 that

$$\boldsymbol{\sigma} = \frac{1}{T}\boldsymbol{\epsilon} + \Sigma_i n_i \overline{S}_i \overline{\boldsymbol{V}}_i \tag{11.1–19}$$

where $\overline{S}_i$ is the partial molal entropy. In this form it is seen that $\boldsymbol{\sigma}$ is the sum of two terms. The first term is the reversible flow of entropy due to the heat flow; the second term is the flow incidental to the diffusion processes.

The quantity g may be rewritten by introducing the expression for the rates of formation, K_i, of the various types of molecules. The chemical kinetics of a reacting mixture may be described in terms of a set of chemical reactions, which we write symbolically as

$$\beta_{1j}[1] + \beta_{2j}[2] + \cdots \rightleftharpoons \eta_{1j}[1] + \eta_{2j}[2] + \cdots \qquad (11.1\text{–}20)$$

the β_{ij} and the η_{ij} being integers and the $[i]$ indicating the ith species. Let the rate constant for the jth forward reaction be k_j and that for the jth backward reaction be k_j', so that the rate of the forward reaction is

$$k_j f_1^{\beta_{1j}} f_2^{\beta_{2j}} \cdots \qquad (11.1\text{–}21)$$

where f_i is the fugacity of component i. A similar expression applies to the backward reaction. Then the total rate of formation of molecules of i by all the chemical reactions is

$$K_i = \Sigma_j(\eta_{ij} - \beta_{ij})\,[(k_j f_1^{\beta_{1j}} f_2^{\beta_{2j}} \cdots) - (k_j' f_1^{\eta_{1j}} f_2^{\eta_{2j}} \cdots)] \qquad (11.1\text{–}22)$$

Let us now define the *chemical affinity* Y_j and the *net rate* r_j of the jth reaction by

$$Y_j = -\Sigma_i(\eta_{ij} - \beta_{ij})\mu_i \qquad (11.1\text{–}23)$$

$$r_j = (k_j f_1^{\beta_{1j}} f_2^{\beta_{2j}} \cdots) - (k_j' f_1^{\eta_{1j}} f_2^{\eta_{2j}} \cdots) \qquad (11.1\text{–}24)$$

Then, according to Eq. 11.1–17, the contribution of the chemical reactions to the rate of production of entropy is

$$-\frac{1}{T}\Sigma_i \mu_i K_i = \frac{1}{T}\Sigma_i r_i Y_i \qquad (11.1\text{–}25)$$

When this expression and that given in Eq. 11.1–18 for the energy flux are substituted into Eq. 11.1–17 for the quantity g, we obtain the result

$$g = -\frac{1}{T}\Sigma_i(\boldsymbol{j}_i \cdot \boldsymbol{\Lambda}_i) - \frac{1}{T}\left((\mathsf{p} - p\mathsf{U}) : \frac{\partial}{\partial \boldsymbol{r}}\boldsymbol{v}\right) - \frac{1}{T^2}\left(\boldsymbol{\epsilon} \cdot \frac{\partial T}{\partial \boldsymbol{r}}\right) + \frac{1}{T}\Sigma_i\, r_i Y_i \qquad (11.1\text{–}26)$$

in which $\boldsymbol{j}_i = n_i m_i \overline{\boldsymbol{V}}_i$ is the flux of mass of species i defined in Eq. 7.2–19 and $\boldsymbol{\Lambda}_i$ is[17]

$$\boldsymbol{\Lambda}_i = \frac{1}{m_i}\frac{\partial \mu_i}{\partial \boldsymbol{r}} + \frac{\bar{S}_i}{m_i}\frac{\partial T}{\partial \boldsymbol{r}} - \frac{1}{m_i}\boldsymbol{X}_i$$

$$= \frac{1}{m_i}\sum_{\substack{j=1\\ j\neq i}}^{\nu}\left(\frac{\partial \mu_i}{\partial x_j}\right)_{\substack{T,p,x_k\\ k\neq i,j}}\frac{\partial x_j}{\partial \boldsymbol{r}} + \frac{\bar{V}_i}{m_i}\frac{\partial p}{\partial \boldsymbol{r}} - \frac{1}{m_i}\boldsymbol{X}_i \qquad (11.1\text{–}27)$$

[17] The second form of this equation is obtained by making use of the fact that the chemical potential μ_i depends on the state of the system and, in particular, may be considered as a function of T, p, and the x_j $(j \neq i)$. The partial derivatives with respect to T and p are eliminated by the thermodynamic relations,

$$\left(\frac{\partial \mu_i}{\partial T}\right)_{p,\,x_j} = -\bar{S}_i \quad \text{and} \quad \left(\frac{\partial \mu_i}{\partial p}\right)_{T,\,x_j} = \bar{V}_i$$

Note that $\bar{V}_i$ (light face) is the partial molal volume, not to be confused with $\overline{\boldsymbol{V}}_i$ (bold face) which is a diffusion velocity.

Equation 11.1–26 then gives the rate of irreversible entropy production. The first term is the contribution due to diffusion, the second term that due to momentum transfer, the third term the contribution due to energy transfer, and the last term is due to chemical reactions. This equation is of such a form that we may apply the principles of the thermodynamics of irreversible processes to obtain expressions for the fluxes. However, before considering the implications of this equation, let us discuss briefly the principles of the thermodynamics of irreversible processes.

2. The Thermodynamics of Irreversible Processes[1]

Up to this point the transport phenomena have been studied from the standpoint of non-equilibrium statistical mechanics or kinetic theory. The equations of change have been expressed in terms of the flux vectors, which, in turn, are given in terms of integrals of the distribution functions. Ultimately we would like to express the flux vectors in terms of the properties of the individual molecules. On the basis of such a molecular theory it is possible to predict transport properties under conditions where no experimental data exist. Such a molecular theory has been developed only for certain special types of molecules and for certain limited conditions. For a *dilute monatomic gas* the flux vectors and the transport coefficients are derived classically[2] in Chapter 7 and quantum mechanically in Chapter 10. This theory has been extended to a *dilute polyatomic gas* (see § 7.6c), but no numerical results have thus far been obtained. The transport phenomena of a *dense monatomic gas* are discussed in Chapter 9 in terms of the recent developments of non-equilibrium statistical mechanics. Here again, although formal results have been obtained, much numerical work needs to be done in order to make the results of practical value.

For a fluid made up of any kind of molecules and under any arbitrary conditions of temperature and pressure, it is not possible at the present time to use statistical mechanics to obtain the form of the flux vectors and to derive expressions for the transport properties in terms of intermolecular forces. For such a "general" fluid, a certain amount of information may be obtained from the thermodynamics of irreversible processes. It is possible to derive the form of the flux vectors and by means of the "reciprocal relations" of Onsager to obtain certain relationships between the transport coefficients. A purely thermodynamic

[1] S. R. De Groot, *Thermodynamics of Irreversible Processes*, North-Holland Publishing Co., Amsterdam (1951). I. Prigogine, "Étude Thermodynamique des Processus Irréversibles" (Dissertation, University of Liège), Dunod (Paris, 1947).

[2] A convenient summary of these results is given in § 8.1.

approach, however, cannot lead to expressions for the transport coefficients in terms of the molecular properties.

a. The Onsager reciprocal relations

We have seen in previous chapters that the fluxes, which lead to the occurrence of the irreversible phenomena, depend upon a number of quantities such as the gradients in the temperature or concentration or the external forces. These causes are usually referred to as *generalized forces* or *affinities*, designated by X_i. With each of the affinities is associated a *flux*, designated by J_i. The generalized forces and fluxes can be scalar, vector, or tensor quantities. However, for the abstract treatment it is convenient to consider them all as scalar components. In general, any affinity can give rise to any flux. For example, if there is in a system both a mass gradient and a temperature gradient, the following fluxes are observed: (i) mass flux due to the mass gradient (ordinary diffusion); (ii) energy flux due to the temperature gradient (thermal conductivity); (iii) mass flux due to the temperature gradient (thermal diffusion or the "Soret effect"); and (iv) energy flux due to the mass gradient (the "Dufour effect"). We see thus that there are two types of effects—*direct effects*, such as (i) and (ii), and *coupled effects*, such as (iii) and (iv).

It is assumed as a *postulate* of the thermodynamics of irreversible processes that, *for situations not too far removed from equilibrium*, the fluxes may be written in the form

$$J_i = \Sigma_j \alpha_{ij} X_j \tag{11.2-1}$$

which states that the fluxes are linear functions of the generalized forces. The α_{ij} are referred to as the *phenomenological coefficients*. The diagonal coefficients α_{ii} are the coefficients which represent the direct effects; the off-diagonal coefficients α_{ij} $(i \neq j)$ are the phenomenological coefficients for the coupled effects. The expressions for the fluxes obtained by the various treatments of transport phenomena in the preceding four chapters are of this same general form. Such "linear" relations are also found in connection with other types of physical and chemical phenomena, for example, in thermomagnetic effects, thermogalvanic effects, electrokinetic effects, etc.[1] Linear relations should always apply sufficiently close to equilibrium; the postulate of Eq. 11.2-1 then defines the range of applicability of the thermodynamics of irreversible processes.

The *fundamental theorem* of the thermodynamics of irreversible processes is due to Onsager.[3] This theorem, the proof of which is discussed later,

[3] L. Onsager, *Phys. Rev.*, **37**, 405 (1931); **38**, 2265 (1931).

states that if a "proper choice" of the fluxes and the affinities has been made, the phenomenological coefficients α_{ij} are symmetric:

$$\alpha_{ij} = \alpha_{ji} \tag{11.2–2}$$

These equations are commonly referred to as the "reciprocal relations." The "proper choice" of the fluxes and affinities may be explained in the following manner. Let us consider an isolated system. The state of the system may be described by a set of variables, $w_1, w_2, w_3, \ldots$. These variables may be, for example, the local values of the temperature, density, and concentrations. In this case, because of the continuous variation of the properties, the variables form an infinite set. For convenience the variables are chosen in such a manner that at thermodynamic equilibrium all the variables are zero. Then, since at equilibrium the entropy of the system is a maximum, we may write as a first approximation for the deviation, ΔS, of the entropy from the maximum value, a quadratic form in the variables[4]

$$\Delta S = -\tfrac{1}{2}\,\Sigma_i\Sigma_j g_{ij} w_i w_j \tag{11.2–3}$$

The "proper choice" of the fluxes and affinities may now be given in terms of the state variables and their time derivatives:[5]

$$J_i = \dot{w}_i \tag{11.2–4}$$

$$X_i = T\frac{\partial}{\partial w_i}\,\Delta S = -T\,\Sigma_j g_{ij} w_j \tag{11.2–5}$$

With these definitions the fundamental theorem of Onsager given in Eq. 11.2–2 is valid.

Onsager's proof of the reciprocal relations is based on very general statistical mechanical arguments and is founded basically on the concept of microscopic reversibility. The principle of microscopic reversibility refers to the symmetry of the mechanical equations of motion with respect to the time variable, or, in other words, to the invariance under the transformation $t \to -t$. The proof depends on a formal treatment of the kinetics of irreversible processes and does not depend upon the detailed nature of the process under consideration.

It is assumed that the rate of a macroscopic irreversible process is the same as the average rate of regression of statistical fluctuations in the state of the system. Let us consider a system in a particular non-equilibrium state. We wish to determine the rate of approach to equilibrium. To accomplish this, let us consider the same system in the

[4] The coefficients g_{ij} (which are essentially the mixed second derivatives appearing in a Taylor series) are clearly symmetric.

[5] The T is introduced in the definition of X_i for convenience. This is in accord with the usual convention.

corresponding equilibrium state. Because of statistical fluctuations, there is a small but finite probability of finding this system in any microscopic state. Let us wait until a fluctuation occurs which brings the system into a state corresponding to the particular non-equilibrium state which we are studying. Again after a time t the system may be found in any one of the microscopic states of the system. However, one class of these states is much more probable than any other, and this corresponds to a new non-equilibrium state of the system. In this manner on the basis of the theory of fluctuations we can trace out the approach of the system to equilibrium.

Because of the large number of degrees of freedom of the macroscopic system, the probability of a fluctuation is small, and the system is much more likely to be found in a microscopic state corresponding directly to the equilibrium state than in any other. This is the basis of the usefulness of the statistical method. For a similar reason the path of the regression of a fluctuation is well defined, with the probability of a deviation from this path being of a still smaller order of magnitude. Physically this corresponds to the fact that the irreversible process is well specified.

By these arguments Onsager developed a formal theory of the rates of irreversible processes. Then, assuming the linear law, he obtained expressions for the coefficients. The principle of microscopic reversibility then implies the reciprocal relations.

When Eq. 11.2–3 is differentiated with respect to time, we obtain an expression which contains the J_i and the X_i, as defined in the last two equations:

$$\frac{d}{dt}(\Delta S) = -\Sigma_i \Sigma_j g_{ij} \dot{w}_i w_j = \frac{1}{T} \Sigma_i X_i J_i \tag{11.2–6}$$

This expression represents the rate of irreversible production of entropy. In Eq. 11.1–26 we obtained an expression for a quantity g. This quantity is the rate of irreversible production of entropy in a small element in a fluid moving with the stream velocity $\boldsymbol{v}$. (The actual change of entropy of a fluid element, which is clearly not an isolated system, DS/Dt, is the sum of g and a term $\left(\frac{\partial}{\partial \boldsymbol{r}} \cdot \boldsymbol{\sigma}\right)$, the latter being a measure of the reversible entropy change due to the flow of thermal energy.) We see that the expression for g (Eq. 11.1–26) is of the same form as the expression of the equation above. Intuitively we may compare these two equations to obtain expressions for the J_i and the X_i. There is a lack of uniqueness due to trivial constant factors and a further lack of uniqueness since any set of linearly independent combinations of a particular set of J_i may be used. Nevertheless, the reciprocity relations apply to any choice so long as the rate of irreversible production of entropy is of the form given in Eq. 11.2–6. It should, however, be noted that the fluxes J_i obtained by this method from Eq. 11.1–26 are not the quantities appearing in the basic theorem of Onsager defined by Eq. 11.2–4. For example, the flux of thermal energy $\boldsymbol{\epsilon}$ is clearly not the time derivative of any macroscopic state variable. The application of the reciprocal relations to the fluxes and the affinities, as they are usually defined, requires further justification. The proof of the applicability of the Onsager reciprocal relations in various specific cases has been given.[6]

The macroscopic state variables of a system are defined in terms of the microscopic state, that is, in terms of the position and momenta of all the particles. The definition is usually in the form of an average value or an integral. In the derivation of the reciprocal relations Onsager tacitly assumed that the state variables w_i are even functions of the particle velocity (so that they are unchanged by the time inversion). Casimir and Tellegen[7] considered the more general situation in which some of the state variables are odd functions. They showed that the α_{ij} are symmetric if both i and j refer to even variables or if both i and j refer to odd variables, but the α_{ij} are antisymmetric if one index refers to an even variable and the other to an odd variable.

In the applications of the reciprocal relations discussed in this section the only state variables considered are the concentrations n_i, the mass average velocity $\mathbf{v}$, and the temperature T. These quantities are defined in terms of the microscopic variables by Eq. 7.3–15, 16, and 17. For situations near equilibrium the distribution function is symmetric in the velocities. Thus n_i and T are even functions of the molecular velocities, whereas $\mathbf{v}$ is an odd function. Hence the α_{ij} which couple the diffusion and thermal conductivity processes are symmetric, whereas the coefficients which couple viscous effects with either other process would be antisymmetric. However, as is discussed in § 11.2b, in an isotropic medium coupling cannot occur between the viscous effects and thermal conductivity or diffusion.

b. Application to the transport phenomena[8]

Let us now consider the application of the Onsager reciprocal relations to the study of transport phenomena of fluids in which the transport of energy by radiation is negligible. The rate of irreversible production of entropy in a flow process is given by Eq. 11.1–26. A comparison of this

[6] S. R. de Groot, *Thermodynamics of Irreversible Processes*, North-Holland Publishing Co., Amsterdam (1951), pp. 41 et seq., pp. 218 et seq.

[7] *Ibid.*, Ch. XI.

[8] L. Onsager, *Annals N.Y. Acad. Sci.*, **46**, 241 (1945).

expression with the form of Eq. 11.2–6 indicates a proper choice of the fluxes and affinities. These quantities are tabulated in Table 11.2–1, where for convenience we have introduced the tensor P defined as the pressure tensor less the hydrostatic contribution,

$$\mathsf{P} = \mathsf{p} - p\mathsf{U} \tag{11.2–7}$$

If it is assumed that the system is not too far removed from equilibrium, the linear law may be applied to this expression. This leads to expressions for the flux vectors equivalent to the first approximation of Enskog. That is, the expressions for the flux vectors are linear in the first derivatives of the macroscopic variables and do not contain higher derivatives or powers of the first derivatives. The linear law may also be used to obtain limiting forms of the expressions for the rates of the chemical reactions applicable to systems near chemical equilibrium. However, since these latter results are of limited applicability only, they will not be discussed here.

TABLE 11.2–1

Fluxes and Affinities in a Flowing Fluid

Flux, J_i	*Affinity* (*Generalized Force*), X_i
$\boldsymbol{j}_i = n_i m_i \overline{\boldsymbol{V}}_i$	$-\boldsymbol{\Lambda}_i$ (defined by Eq. 11.1–27)
$\mathsf{P} = \mathsf{p} - p\mathsf{U}$	$-\dfrac{\partial}{\partial \boldsymbol{r}} \boldsymbol{v}$
$\boldsymbol{\epsilon} = \boldsymbol{q} - \Sigma_i n_i \overline{H}_i \overline{\boldsymbol{V}}_i$	$-\dfrac{1}{T}\dfrac{\partial T}{\partial \boldsymbol{r}}$
r_i (defined by Eq. 11.1–24)	Y_i (defined by Eq. 11.1–23)

If the system under consideration is in a state not too far removed from equilibrium, the linear law given in Eq. 11.2–1 indicates that each of the components of the fluxes above may be written as a linear combination of all the components of all the affinities. However, if the system is isotropic, it may be shown that those terms which correspond to a coupling of tensors whose orders differ by an odd number do not occur. Thus no coupling occurs between $\boldsymbol{j}_i$ or $\boldsymbol{\epsilon}$ (first-order tensors) and P (second-order tensor) or r_i (zeroth-order tensor). Coupling does occur between the energy flux $\boldsymbol{\epsilon}$ and the mass flux $\boldsymbol{j}_i$, resulting in the Soret effect and the Dufour effect. Coupling also occurs between the momentum flux and the chemical reaction rates, since there is a difference of two in the order of the tensors. This coupling is proportional to the trace of the affinity, $-\frac{\partial}{\partial \boldsymbol{r}}\boldsymbol{v}$. Such an effect has not been studied experimentally and is not further discussed here.

In the next subsection we show how the thermodynamics of irreversible processes may be used to study the momentum flux in a fluid in which there are no chemical reactions taking place. It is shown how the form of the pressure tensor may be deduced and how we may calculate the contributions of the viscous effects to the rate of production of entropy. In the following subsection the fluxes of mass and energy are studied, and it is shown how the diffusion and heat conduction processes contribute to the rate of production of entropy.

c. Application to momentum transport

The application of the linear law (Eq. 11.2–1) to the components of the flux P and the affinity $-\frac{\partial}{\partial \boldsymbol{r}}\boldsymbol{v}$ gives

$$P_{ij} = -\sum_k \sum_l \alpha_{ij}{}^{kl} \frac{\partial v_l}{\partial x_k} \qquad (11.2\text{–}8)$$

Here v_1, v_2, and v_3 are respectively the x, y, and z components of $\boldsymbol{v}$. The set of phenomenological coefficients $\alpha_{ij}{}^{kl}$ is a matrix of eighty-one elements. However, not all these elements are independent. For example, from Onsager's reciprocal relations it is clear that

$$\alpha_{ij}{}^{kl} = \alpha_{kl}{}^{ij} \qquad (11.2\text{–}9)$$

Furthermore in the statistical mechanical derivations of the equations of change, the pressure tensor is defined in such a way that it is symmetric. Such a definition is necessary, for otherwise each small element of volume would be subject to a torque. Accordingly the $\alpha_{ij}{}^{kl}$ must be such that

$$\alpha_{ij}{}^{kl} = \alpha_{ji}{}^{kl} \qquad (11.2\text{–}10)$$

Combining the last two results, we find that

$$\alpha_{ij}{}^{kl} = \alpha_{ij}{}^{lk} \qquad (11.2\text{–}11)$$

and Eq. 11.2–8 may be written in the simpler form:

$$P_{ij} = -\tfrac{1}{2} \sum_k \sum_l \alpha_{ij}{}^{kl} \left(\frac{\partial v_l}{\partial x_k} + \frac{\partial v_k}{\partial x_l} \right) \qquad (11.2\text{–}12)$$

Because of the above symmetry relations there are only twenty-one independent coefficients $\alpha_{ij}{}^{kl}$. These are the "elastic constants" of the medium.

The same symmetry requirements may be obtained by assuming that P is identically zero for motions corresponding to rigid-body translations and rotations. Hence, in this case, Onsager's reciprocal relations have a simple physical interpretation.

If the medium has any natural symmetry, the number of independent elastic constants is considerably less than twenty-one. In particular, if the medium is isotropic, the relation between P and $\left[\left(\frac{\partial}{\partial \mathbf{r}} \mathbf{v}\right) + \left(\frac{\partial}{\partial \mathbf{r}} \mathbf{v}\right)^\dagger\right]$ is independent of a rotation of the coordinate frame. Then it can be shown that the $\alpha_{ij}{}^{kl}$ are of such form that[9]

$$\mathsf{P} = \mathsf{p} - p\mathsf{U} = -\eta \left[\left(\frac{\partial}{\partial \mathbf{r}} \mathbf{v}\right) + \left(\frac{\partial}{\partial \mathbf{r}} \mathbf{v}\right)^\dagger\right] + (\tfrac{2}{3}\eta - \kappa)\left(\frac{\partial}{\partial \mathbf{r}} \cdot \mathbf{v}\right)\mathsf{U} \tag{11.2–13}$$

where η and κ are two independent coefficients, which are known as the coefficients of shear and bulk viscosity.[10] This form follows immediately from the condition of isotropy since the only tensors upon which P may depend are the U, $\frac{\partial}{\partial \mathbf{r}} \mathbf{v}$, and the transpose $\left(\frac{\partial}{\partial \mathbf{r}} \mathbf{v}\right)^\dagger$. Hence P must be a linear combination of these three tensors. However, the antisymmetric combination of $\frac{\partial}{\partial \mathbf{r}} \mathbf{v}$ and its transpose are eliminated by the symmetry arguments of the preceding paragraph. Hence the form given by Eq. 11.2–13 follows. Thus in an isotropic medium there are in general two coefficients of viscosity. The *shear viscosity* η is important in flows in which successive plane layers of the fluid move with different velocities. The coefficient of *bulk viscosity* κ is important in the pure expansion of a fluid.[11]

From Eqs. 11.1–26 and 11.2–13, it follows that the contribution of the viscous effects to the rate of production of entropy is

$$g_v = \frac{1}{T}\left[2\eta\mathsf{S} + \kappa\left(\frac{\partial}{\partial \mathbf{r}} \cdot \mathbf{v}\right)\mathsf{U}\right] : \left(\frac{\partial}{\partial \mathbf{r}} \mathbf{v}\right) \tag{11.2–14}$$

[9] This treatment is essentially that of B. de St. Venant., *Compt. rend.*, **17**, 1240 (1843), and G. C. Stokes, *Trans. Cambridge Phil. Soc.*, **8** (1845). It is interesting to note that the only assumptions made are that the normal and shear stresses are linear functions of the deformation velocities.

[10] The coefficient of bulk viscosity is discussed in § 7.6c in connection with the kinetic theory of polyatomic molecules and in § 9.3 in connection with the theory of dense gases.

[11] S. M. Karim and L. Rosenhead, *Revs. Mod. Phys.*, **24**, 108 (1952).

where S is the "rate of shear tensor" defined by Eq. 7.4–16. This expression may be rearranged into the form

$$g_v = \frac{2\eta}{T}(\mathsf{S} : \mathsf{S}) + \frac{\kappa}{T}\left(\frac{\partial}{\partial \boldsymbol{r}} \cdot \boldsymbol{v}\right)^2 \tag{11.2–15}$$

The factors multiplying both η and κ are sums of squares, and hence both are positive. According to the second law,

$$g_v \geq 0 \tag{11.2–16}$$

for all $\frac{\partial}{\partial \boldsymbol{r}} \boldsymbol{v}$. Since either factor may be zero while the other factor is not, it follows that

$$\eta \geq 0 \quad \text{and} \quad \kappa \geq 0 \tag{11.2–17}$$

The kinetic theory of dilute gases in the Navier-Stokes approximation (as given in Chapter 7) leads to an expression for the pressure tensor in complete agreement with the form of Eq. 11.2–13. In this limit, however, the coefficient of bulk viscosity κ is zero. The integral expressions given in Chapter 7 for the coefficient of shear viscosity of ideal gases are such as to lead to positive values in accordance with Eq. 11.2–17.

d. Application to mass and energy transport

Let us now consider the application of the linear law and the Onsager reciprocal relations to the processes of diffusion and thermal conduction in a fluid containing ν chemical species. When only these terms are considered, the rate of entropy production is (according to Eq. 11.1–26):

$$g = \frac{1}{T}\left[-\frac{1}{T}\left(\frac{\partial T}{\partial \boldsymbol{r}} \cdot \boldsymbol{\epsilon}\right) - \sum_{i=1}^{\nu} (\boldsymbol{\Lambda}_i \cdot \boldsymbol{j}_i)\right] \tag{11.2–18}$$

The situation is somewhat complicated because all the fluxes $\boldsymbol{j}_i$ are not independent. Because of the definition of the diffusion velocity,[12] $\sum_{i=1}^{\nu} \boldsymbol{j}_i = 0$. Hence one of the $\boldsymbol{j}_i$ may be eliminated from Eq. 11.2–18. In particular, we choose to eliminate the mass flux vector for the kth component, $\boldsymbol{j}_k$. Then the expression for g may be rewritten in the form

$$g = \frac{1}{T}\left[-\frac{1}{T}\left(\frac{\partial T}{\partial \boldsymbol{r}} \cdot \boldsymbol{\epsilon}\right) - \sum_{i=1}^{\nu} (\{\boldsymbol{\Lambda}_i - \boldsymbol{\Lambda}_k\} \cdot \boldsymbol{j}_i)\right] \tag{11.2–19}$$

[12] The diffusion velocity is defined in § 7.2a.

The application of the linear law then gives the following expressions for the fluxes $\boldsymbol{\epsilon}$ and $\boldsymbol{j}_i$:

$$\boldsymbol{\epsilon} = -\frac{\alpha_{00}}{T}\frac{\partial T}{\partial \boldsymbol{r}} - \sum_{\substack{j=1\\j\neq k}}^{\nu} \alpha_{0j}(\boldsymbol{\Lambda}_j - \boldsymbol{\Lambda}_k) \tag{11.2-20}$$

$$\boldsymbol{j}_i = -\frac{\alpha_{i0}}{T}\frac{\partial T}{\partial \boldsymbol{r}} - \sum_{\substack{j=1\\j\neq k}}^{\nu} \alpha_{ij}(\boldsymbol{\Lambda}_j - \boldsymbol{\Lambda}_k) \qquad (i \neq k) \tag{11.2-21}$$

The constants α_{ij} are the phenomenological coefficients of Onsager which satisfy the reciprocal relations.[13] The index 0 refers to the temperature variable; the other indices refer to the components in the mixture. For the present, the phenomenological coefficients with either index k are not defined.

The above expressions for $\boldsymbol{\epsilon}$ and $\boldsymbol{j}_i$ may be written in another form so that the kth component no longer plays a special role. From Eq. 11.2-21 and the fact that $\sum_{i=1}^{\nu} \boldsymbol{j}_i = 0$ it follows that

$$\boldsymbol{j}_k = \frac{1}{T}\frac{\partial T}{\partial \boldsymbol{r}} \sum_{\substack{i=1\\i\neq k}}^{\nu} \alpha_{i0} + \sum_{\substack{j=1\\j\neq k}}^{\nu} \sum_{\substack{i=1\\i\neq k}}^{\nu} \alpha_{ij}(\boldsymbol{\Lambda}_j - \boldsymbol{\Lambda}_k) \tag{11.2-22}$$

Equation 11.2-21 may then be made correct formally for $i = k$ by defining

$$\alpha_{kj} = -\sum_{\substack{i=1\\i\neq k}}^{\nu} \alpha_{ij} \qquad j = 0, 1, 2, 3, \cdots, \nu \tag{11.2-23}$$

Let us define the α_{jk} so as to extend the reciprocal relations correspondingly:

$$\alpha_{jk} = \alpha_{kj} = -\sum_{\substack{i=1\\i\neq k}}^{\nu} \alpha_{ji} \qquad j = 0, 1, 2, 3, \cdots, \nu \tag{11.2-24}$$

In terms of these quantities Eqs. 11.2-20 and 21 may now be written in the simpler form:

$$\boldsymbol{\epsilon} = -\frac{\alpha_{00}}{T}\frac{\partial T}{\partial \boldsymbol{r}} - \sum_{j=1}^{\nu} \alpha_{0j}\boldsymbol{\Lambda}_j \tag{11.2-25}$$

$$\boldsymbol{j}_i = -\frac{\alpha_{i0}}{T}\frac{\partial T}{\partial \boldsymbol{r}} - \sum_{j=1}^{\nu} \alpha_{ij}\boldsymbol{\Lambda}_j \tag{11.2-26}$$

[13] For a completely general system the phenomenological coefficients are tensors. The reciprocal relations of Onsager then imply that

$$\alpha_{ij} = \alpha_{ji}^{\dagger}$$

where † indicates the transpose. In an isotropic system it is clear that the coefficients are scalar multiples of the unit tensor. It is only this case which we shall consider here.

The α_{ij} are symmetric and satisfy the linear relations (Eqs. 11.2–23 and 24), which may be written in the form

$$\sum_{i=1}^{\nu} \alpha_{ij} = \sum_{i=1}^{\nu} \alpha_{ji} = 0 \tag{11.2–27}$$

It is convenient to write the expressions for $\boldsymbol{\epsilon}$ and $\boldsymbol{j}_i$ in terms of a set of quantities $\boldsymbol{d}_i$ which are closely related to the $\boldsymbol{\Lambda}_i$. These $\boldsymbol{d}_i$ are generalizations of the $\boldsymbol{d}_i$ which were defined in Eq. 7.3–27 in the discussion of the kinetic theory of dilute gases. We define the generalized $\boldsymbol{d}_i$ by

$$\boldsymbol{d}_i = \frac{n_i m_i}{nkT}\left[\boldsymbol{\Lambda}_i - \frac{1}{\rho}\frac{\partial p}{\partial \boldsymbol{r}} + \frac{1}{\rho}\sum_{j=1}^{\nu} n_j \boldsymbol{X}_j\right] \tag{11.2–28}$$

Insertion of the expression for $\boldsymbol{\Lambda}_i$ (given in Eq. 11.1–27) into this equation gives[14]

$$\boldsymbol{d}_i = \frac{n_i}{nkT}\left[\sum_{\substack{j=1\\ j\neq i}}^{\nu} \left(\frac{\partial \mu_i}{\partial x_j}\right)_{\substack{T,p,x_k\\ k\neq i,j}} \frac{\partial x_j}{\partial \boldsymbol{r}} + \left(\overline{V}_i - \frac{m_i}{\rho}\right)\frac{\partial p}{\partial \boldsymbol{r}} - \left(\boldsymbol{X}_i - \frac{m_i}{\rho}\sum_{j=1}^{\nu} n_j \boldsymbol{X}_j\right)\right] \tag{11.2–29}$$

It is easy to show that $\Sigma_i \boldsymbol{d}_i = 0$ by making use of the properties of partial molal quantities and the Gibbs-Duhem relation. Now using the above expression for $\boldsymbol{d}_i$ and the relations given in Eq. 11.2–27, we obtain the following expressions for the fluxes:

$$\boldsymbol{\epsilon} = -\frac{\alpha_{00}}{T}\frac{\partial T}{\partial \boldsymbol{r}} - nkT\sum_{j=1}^{\nu} \frac{\alpha_{0j}}{n_j m_j}\boldsymbol{d}_j \tag{11.2–30}$$

$$\boldsymbol{j}_i = -\frac{\alpha_{i0}}{T}\frac{\partial T}{\partial \boldsymbol{r}} - nkT\sum_{j=1}^{\nu} \frac{\alpha_{ij}}{n_j m_j}\boldsymbol{d}_j \tag{11.2–31}$$

These expressions are equivalent to those given above but have a formal resemblance to those obtained by the kinetic theory treatment of a perfect gas.

[14] In the special case of a mixture of perfect gases,

$$\overline{V}_i = \frac{1}{n} \quad \text{and} \quad \left(\frac{\partial \mu_i}{\partial x_j}\right)_{\substack{T,p,x_k\\ k\neq i,j}} = -\frac{kT}{x_i}$$

Substitution of these values into Eq. 11.2–29 gives exactly the expression for $\boldsymbol{d}_i$ given in Eq. 7.3–27.

The kinetic theory of dilute gases as discussed in Chapter 7 gives expressions for the flux vectors for energy and diffusion which may be written in the form

$$\boldsymbol{\epsilon} = -\lambda' \frac{\partial T}{\partial \boldsymbol{r}} - nkT \sum_{j=1}^{\nu} \frac{D_j^T}{n_j m_j} \boldsymbol{d}_j \qquad (11.2\text{–}32)$$

$$\boldsymbol{j}_i = -\frac{D_i^T}{T}\frac{\partial T}{\partial \boldsymbol{r}} + \frac{n^2}{\rho} \sum_{j=1}^{\nu} m_i m_j D_{ij} \boldsymbol{d}_j \qquad (11.2\text{–}33)$$

The quantity λ' is closely related to the coefficient of thermal conductivity (see Eq. 7.4–65). The D_{ij} are generalized diffusion coefficients, and the D_i^T are generalized thermal diffusion coefficients (these quantities are defined in § 7.4a). Inasmuch as the $\boldsymbol{d}_j$ are not linearly independent, the D_{ij} are not simply related to the α_{ij}. In Chapter 7, the D_{ij} were fixed by defining

$$D_{ii} = 0 \qquad (11.2\text{–}34)$$

In the case of the α_{ij} the uniqueness is imposed in an entirely different manner by the reciprocal relations.

Let us now examine the consistency of the results of the kinetic theory of dilute gases with those from the thermodynamics of irreversible processes. It is at once clear that one set of the reciprocal relations is valid, namely,

$$\alpha_{i0} = \alpha_{0i} = D_i^T \qquad (11.2\text{–}35)$$

It is not so clear, however, that the remaining reciprocal relations are satisfied. Making use of the fact that $\Sigma_i \boldsymbol{d}_i = 0$ to eliminate the "diagonal" elements from Eq. 11.2–31, we see by comparison with Eq. 11.2–33 that the D_{ij} are related to the α_{ij} in the following manner:

$$D_{ij} = -\frac{\rho kT}{n m_i m_j}\left(\frac{\alpha_{ij}}{n_j m_j} + \frac{1}{n_i m_i}\sum_{\substack{k=1\\k\neq i}}^{\nu} \alpha_{ik}\right) \qquad (11.2\text{–}36)$$

This equation may be solved for the α_{ij} to obtain the relation

$$\alpha_{ij} = \frac{n n_j m_j m_i}{\rho^2 kT}\left[-\rho m_j D_{ij} + \sum_{\substack{k=1\\k\neq i}}^{\nu} n_k m_k^2 D_{ik}\right] \qquad (11.2\text{–}37)$$

Thus the D_{ij} must be such that this linear combination is symmetric.[15]

[15] For a ν-component mixture there are $\frac{1}{2}\nu(\nu - 1)$ reciprocal relations, and hence the $\nu(\nu - 1)$ values of D_{ij} may be expressed in terms of $\frac{1}{2}\nu(\nu - 1)$ quantities. For example, the dilute gas kinetic theory expressions for the D_{ij} have been expressed in terms of the $\frac{1}{2}\nu(\nu - 1)$ values of the binary diffusion constants $\mathscr{D}_{ij}$ for the various pairs of components. [See Eq. 7.4–44.]

For a two-component mixture, Eq. 11.2–37 reduces to

$$\alpha_{ij} = -\frac{n}{\rho^2 kT} n_i n_j m_i^2 m_j^2 D_{ij} \tag{11.2–38}$$

and hence the symmetry relations imply that

$$D_{ij} = D_{ji} \tag{11.2–39}$$

In this simple case the result is trivial in that we can obtain it directly from Eq. 11.2–33, making use of the fact that $\Sigma \boldsymbol{d}_i = 0$. In general, however, the reciprocal relations impose important restrictions.

For a three-component mixture, Eq. 11.2–37 reduces to

$$\alpha_{12} = \frac{n n_2 m_1 m_2}{\rho^2 kT} [-m_2(\rho - n_2 m_2) D_{12} + n_3 m_3^2 D_{13}] \tag{11.2–40}$$

The kinetic theory results of Chapter 7 give the following relation for D_{12} in terms of the binary diffusion constants, $\mathscr{D}_{ij}$:

$$D_{12} = \mathscr{D}_{12} \left[1 + \frac{n_3 \left(\dfrac{m_3}{m_2} \mathscr{D}_{13} - \mathscr{D}_{12} \right)}{n_1 \mathscr{D}_{23} + n_2 \mathscr{D}_{13} + n_3 \mathscr{D}_{12}} \right] \tag{11.2–41}$$

and similar expressions for the other D_{ij}. Thus for a dilute gas

$$\alpha_{12} = \frac{n n_1 n_2 m_1 m_2 \begin{bmatrix} n_3 m_3^2 \mathscr{D}_{13} \mathscr{D}_{23} - m_2(\rho - n_2 m_2) \mathscr{D}_{12} \mathscr{D}_{23} \\ - m_1(\rho - n_1 m_1) \mathscr{D}_{12} \mathscr{D}_{13} \end{bmatrix}}{\rho^2 kT (n_1 \mathscr{D}_{23} + n_2 \mathscr{D}_{13} + n_3 \mathscr{D}_{12})} \tag{11.2–42}$$

This expression is symmetric in "1" and "2", and hence in this case the kinetic theory result is consistent with the reciprocity relations. It should be possible to show that the result for a general multicomponent mixture is consistent.

The rate of production of entropy due to thermal conductivity and diffusion processes is given by Eq. 11.2–18. Introducing the $\boldsymbol{d}_i$ defined by Eq. 11.2–28 and making use of the fact that $\Sigma_i \boldsymbol{d}_i = 0$, we obtain the relation

$$g = -\frac{1}{T^2} \left(\frac{\partial T}{\partial \boldsymbol{r}} \cdot \boldsymbol{\epsilon} \right) - nk\, \Sigma_i (\overline{\boldsymbol{V}}_i \cdot \boldsymbol{d}_i) \tag{11.2–43}$$

Then from Eqs. 11.2–32 and 7.4–48 and 65 it follows that, for a perfect gas,

$$g = \frac{\lambda}{T^2} \left(\frac{\partial T}{\partial \boldsymbol{r}} \cdot \frac{\partial T}{\partial \boldsymbol{r}} \right) + \frac{k}{2} \Sigma_{i,j} \frac{n_i n_j}{n \mathscr{D}_{ij}} (\overline{\boldsymbol{V}}_j - \overline{\boldsymbol{V}}_i)^2 \tag{11.2–44}$$

Since each term in this expression can separately be zero, it follows that the second law, which states that

$$g \geq 0 \tag{11.2–45}$$

implies that

$$\lambda \geq 0 \quad \text{and} \quad \mathscr{D}_{ij} \geq 0 \tag{11.2–46}$$

e. Summary of results

The expressions for the flux vectors applying to a fluid under general conditions have been developed above. The results may be summarized in the following manner.

(a) *The pressure tensor* is given by Eq. 11.2–13 as

$$\mathsf{p} = p\mathsf{U} - \eta\left[\left(\frac{\partial}{\partial \boldsymbol{r}}\boldsymbol{v}\right) + \left(\frac{\partial}{\partial \boldsymbol{r}}\boldsymbol{v}\right)^{\dagger} - \frac{2}{3}\left(\frac{\partial}{\partial \boldsymbol{r}}\cdot\boldsymbol{v}\right)\mathsf{U}\right] - \kappa\left(\frac{\partial}{\partial \boldsymbol{r}}\cdot\boldsymbol{v}\right)\mathsf{U} \tag{11.2–47}$$

The coefficients η and κ are the coefficients of shear and bulk viscosity, respectively. In a dilute gas made up of molecules without internal degrees of freedom, the coefficient of bulk viscosity κ is zero and the static pressure is one-third the trace of the pressure tensor. In § 7.6c it is shown that the presence of internal degrees of freedom introduces a finite bulk viscosity, and in Chapter 9 it is shown that the bulk viscosity is not zero in a dense gas or liquid. Nevertheless, this effect is generally small, and it is often sufficiently accurate to neglect these terms.

(b) *The energy flux*, $\boldsymbol{q}$, is given by Eqs. 11.1–18 and 11.2–32. For a fluid made up of single component $\boldsymbol{q}$ is of the form

$$\boldsymbol{q} = -\lambda\frac{\partial T}{\partial \boldsymbol{r}} \tag{11.2–48}$$

where λ is the coefficient of thermal conductivity. In a mixture it is often sufficiently accurate to write $\boldsymbol{q}$ in the form

$$\boldsymbol{q} = -\lambda\frac{\partial T}{\partial \boldsymbol{r}} + \textstyle\sum_i n_i \overline{H}_i \overline{\boldsymbol{V}}_i \tag{11.2–49}$$

where $\overline{\boldsymbol{V}}_i$ is the diffusion velocity of component i. The added terms represent the flow of energy incidental to the diffusion processes. This expression for $\boldsymbol{q}$ is approximate in that the terms representing the Dufour effect, the direct effect of concentration and pressure gradients on the energy flow, have been omitted. The Dufour effect which is the reciprocal process to thermal diffusion is generally small and can usually be neglected.

(c) *The diffusion velocity* of component i is given by Eq. 11.2–33 in terms of the $\boldsymbol{d}_i$ given by Eq. 11.2–29. This expression is

$$\overline{\boldsymbol{V}}_i = \frac{n^2}{n_i\rho} \Sigma_j m_j D_{ij} \boldsymbol{d}_j - \frac{D_i^T}{n_i m_i} \frac{\partial \ln T}{\partial \boldsymbol{r}} \tag{11.2–50}$$

The last term in this expression represents the direct effect of a temperature gradient. This contribution is referred to as the thermal diffusion effect or in liquids as the Sorét effect. This contribution is usually small and can often be neglected. The remaining terms depend on the $\boldsymbol{d}_j$ as defined by Eq. 11.2–29. The first term in $\boldsymbol{d}_j$ represents the direct effect of a concentration gradient. In a dilute gas this term is simply the gradient of the mole fraction of species j. The added terms represent the effect of a pressure gradient (pressure diffusion) and external forces.

The D_{ij} of Eq. 11.2–50, which are defined in such a manner that $D_{ii} = 0$, are known as the multicomponent diffusion coefficients. These coefficients depend on the entire composition of the gas or liquid. In the special case of a binary mixture it is convenient to use $\mathscr{D}_{12}$ to refer to D_{12} and to define

$$k_T = \frac{\rho}{n^2 m_1 m_2} \frac{D_1^T}{\mathscr{D}_{12}} \tag{11.2–51}$$

If these definitions are used, the expression for the diffusion velocity, Eq. 11.2–50, in the special case of a binary mixture becomes

$$\overline{\boldsymbol{V}}_1 = \frac{n^2}{n_1\rho} m_2 \mathscr{D}_{12} \left[\boldsymbol{d}_2 - k_T \frac{\partial \ln T}{\partial \boldsymbol{r}}\right] \tag{11.2–52}$$

Then, since the binary diffusion coefficients are symmetric, $\mathscr{D}_{12} = \mathscr{D}_{21}$, and the diffusion velocities are defined so that $\Sigma_i n_i m_i \overline{\boldsymbol{V}}_i = 0$, it follows that

$$\overline{\boldsymbol{V}}_2 - \overline{\boldsymbol{V}}_1 = \frac{n^2}{n_1 n_2} \mathscr{D}_{12} \left[\boldsymbol{d}_1 + k_T \frac{\partial \ln T}{\partial \boldsymbol{r}}\right] \tag{11.2–53}$$

For a dilute gas, this result has been generalized to give the result given by Eq. 7.4–48. This result is

$$\Sigma_j \frac{n_i n_j}{n^2 \mathscr{D}_{ij}} (\overline{\boldsymbol{V}}_j - \overline{\boldsymbol{V}}_i) = \boldsymbol{d}_i - \frac{\partial \ln T}{\partial \boldsymbol{r}} \Sigma_j \frac{n_i n_j}{n^2 \mathscr{D}_{ij}} \left(\frac{D_j^T}{n_j m_j} - \frac{D_i^T}{n_i m_i}\right) \tag{11.2–54}$$

for the diffusion velocities in a multicomponent mixture. There is empirical evidence that this result also applies quite well in dense gases and liquids.

The *Navier-Stokes equations* of hydrodynamics (generalized to include more than one component and chemical kinetics) are given by Eqs. 11.1–1,

2, 3, and 4, when the pressure tensor is given by Eq. 11.2–47, the energy flux is given by Eq. 11.2–49, and the diffusion velocities are given by Eq. 11.2–50. These expressions for the fluxes, and hence the Navier-Stokes equations, should apply quite well to dense gases and liquids, as well as to dilute gases, as long as the gradients of velocity, concentration, temperature, and pressure are moderately small.

In the solution of diffusion problems[16] it is often convenient to express the equations of continuity with respect to the number average velocity,

$$\boldsymbol{\omega} = \boldsymbol{v} + \frac{1}{n} \Sigma_j n_j \overline{\boldsymbol{V}}_j \tag{11.2–55}$$

Using this equation to replace $\boldsymbol{v}$ in Eq. 11.1–1, we obtain the equations of continuity:

$$\frac{\partial n_i}{\partial t} + \left(\frac{\partial}{\partial \boldsymbol{r}} \cdot n_i \boldsymbol{\omega}\right) + \left(\frac{\partial}{\partial \boldsymbol{r}} \cdot n_i \left[\overline{\boldsymbol{V}}_i - \frac{1}{n} \Sigma_j n_j \overline{\boldsymbol{V}}_j\right]\right) = K_i \tag{11.2–56}$$

If these equations are added up for all components of a ν-component fluid, we obtain the equation

$$\frac{\partial n}{\partial t} + \left(\frac{\partial}{\partial \boldsymbol{r}} \cdot n \boldsymbol{\omega}\right) = \Sigma_j K_j \tag{11.2–57}$$

From Eq. 11.2–57 we see that $\boldsymbol{\omega}$ is a constant (independent of position and time) and easily determined from the boundary conditions if the following conditions apply: (1) the chemical reactions do not either increase or decrease the number of molecules, that is, $\Sigma_j K_j = 0$; (2) the temperature and pressure are constant so that n is constant; and (3) the flow is irrotational, that is, $[(\partial/\partial \boldsymbol{r}) \times \boldsymbol{\omega}] = 0$. In the case of a dilute gas containing two components, substituting the explicit expressions for the diffusion velocities as given by Eqs. 11.2–52 and 8.1–2 into Eq. 11.2–56, we find that

$$K_1 = \frac{\partial n_1}{\partial t} + \left(\frac{\partial}{\partial \boldsymbol{r}} \cdot n_1 \boldsymbol{\omega}\right) - \left(\frac{\partial}{\partial \boldsymbol{r}} \cdot n \mathscr{D}_{12} \left\{ \frac{\partial}{\partial \boldsymbol{r}}\left(\frac{n_1}{n}\right) + \frac{n_1 n_2 (m_2 - m_1)}{n\rho} \frac{\partial \ln p}{\partial \boldsymbol{r}} + \frac{n_1 n_2}{p\rho}(m_1 \boldsymbol{X}_2 - m_2 \boldsymbol{X}_1) + k_T \frac{\partial \ln T}{\partial \boldsymbol{r}} \right\}\right) \tag{11.2–58}$$

[16] For the solution of many types of diffusion problems see W. Jost's *Diffusion in Solids, Liquids, Gases* (Academic Press, 1952). For solutions to some special cases where the coefficient of diffusion depends on concentration, see J. L. Hwang, *J. Chem. Phys.*, **20**, 1320 (1952), and R. H. Stokes, *Trans. Faraday Soc.*, **48**, 887 (1952).

It is easy to see that Eq. 11.2–58 reduces to the usual *Fick's law* equation for diffusion, Eq. 8.1–12, of a two-component dilute gas in a closed vessel at constant temperature and pressure with no chemical reactions.

3. Energy Transfer by Radiation[1–3]

Energy transfer by radiation is often important in problems involving systems at high temperatures. If the fluid is sufficiently transparent, radiation provides a means for transporting energy for large distances; the radiant heating of rooms by radiators or by electric heating units is an example. If the fluid is opaque, the radiation travels in small random jumps from a point of emission to one of absorption. The average distance between these jumps is known as the "radiation mean free path," and the transfer of energy by radiation in an opaque medium closely parallels the kinetic theory notion of diffusion. The radiation in molten iron in a smelter is of this nature. The radiation in the hot gases in a diesel engine is another example.

In § 12.6 the theory of the absorption and emission of radiation is developed. In the presence of radiation a molecule has a certain probability of either absorbing or emitting light of a frequency characteristic of some transition from one quantum state to another. Or a molecule in an excited state has a certain probability of spontaneously emitting light of such a characteristic frequency.[4] Each substance therefore has an absorption spectrum which can be expressed in terms of the coefficient of absorption, μ_ν, which is a function of the frequency. Since the absorption spectrum depends upon the distribution of the molecules in their various quantum states, μ_ν depends upon the temperature of the substance. In § 13.7 it is shown that the spectral lines for isolated molecules have a natural width (due to the spontaneous emission of light), and as the molecules are brought together these lines become broader (due to pressure broadening) and become displaced (due to distortions of the molecules themselves). Thus the coefficient of absorption depends upon the density of the system or its state of aggregation.

[1] Most of the material in this section is from J. L. Magee, "The Effect of Radiation in Flames," CM-627, University of Wisconsin Naval Research Laboratory (August 1950).

[2] S. Chandrasekhar, *Radiative Transfer*, Oxford University Press (1950); *An Introduction to Stellar Structure*, Chicago University Press (1939).

[3] S. Rosseland, *Theoretical Astrophysics*, Oxford University Press (1936).

[4] A detailed treatment of the spontaneous emission of light is not given in Chapter 12 because it is readily available in many standard references such as A. E. Ruark and H. C. Urey, *Atoms, Molecules, and Quanta*, McGraw-Hill (1930), p. 60; H. Eyring, J. Walter, and G. E. Kimball, *Quantum Chemistry*, John Wiley (1944), p. 114.

The theory of the function $\mu_\nu(T, \rho)$ is described in Chapters 12 and 13. The calculations, however, are very difficult,[5] and up to the present time, except for a few astronomical cases,[3] the best values of this function are obtained empirically. After radiation has been absorbed and re-emitted a large number of times, the intensity of the radiation as a function of frequency becomes characteristic of the temperature rather than of the substance itself. This thermal radiation is called black-body radiation.[6] Thus it is possible to measure temperatures on the basis of radiation intensities. The more opaque the substance, the smaller is the length of the optical path required to establish this type of radiation.

From very simple considerations it is clear that the flux of radiation at any point $\boldsymbol{r}_1$ can be expressed as an integral over all space. Radiation which reaches this point must have been emitted by the matter at some other point $\boldsymbol{r}_2$. The ray could have come directly from the point of emission or it could have been scattered once or more along the way.[7] Fortunately, scattering does not play an important role in most problems of interest, and therefore we neglect it in this treatment.

If A is the rate of radiation energy absorption per unit volume, and R is the rate of radiation energy emission per unit volume, the divergence of the radiation flux, $\boldsymbol{q}_R$, is given by

$$\left(\frac{\partial}{\partial \boldsymbol{r}} \cdot \boldsymbol{q}_R\right) = R - A \tag{11.3–1}$$

Let us suppose that the material has a coefficient of absorption, $\mu_\nu(\text{cm}^2/g)$, for light of frequency ν. Also let $R_\nu(\boldsymbol{r})$ be the energy emitted

[5] Approximate calculations have been made by S. S. Penner on the radiation emitted from the diatomic gases, CO, HI, HBr, HCl, and HF. [*J. Appl. Phys.*, **21**, 685 (1950), and GALCIT (Guggenheim Aeronautical Laboratory, California Institute of Technology) Progress Report 9–38 (1949).]

[6] Black-body radiation is treated in considerable detail in a number of standard references. For example, A. E. Ruark and H. C. Urey, *Atoms, Molecules, and Quanta*, McGraw-Hill (1930), p. 53; L. Brillouin, *Die Quantenstatistik*, Julius Springer (1931), Ch. I.

[7] A great deal of complication in radiative transfer problems comes from scattering. In reference 2 it is shown that the total cross-section σ_s for light scattering by a molecule is $\sigma_s = \dfrac{512\pi^7\alpha^2}{3\lambda^4}$ cm², where α is the polarizability of a molecule in cubic centimeters and λ is the wavelength in centimeters. For visible light λ is of the order of 10^{-4} cm; for an average molecule α is of the order of 10^{-23} cm³. Thus σ_s is of the order of 5×10^{-25} cm². The mean free path for scattering is $1/n\sigma_s$. Scattering is negligible if its mean free path is long compared to either the dimensions of the system or else long compared to the mean free path for absorption. For a gas containing $n = 10^{19}$ molecules/cm³, the mean free path for scattering is 2×10^5 cm or one mile. Scattering can be important in fluids which are turbid due to fluctuations (see § 12.7) or in fluids containing smoke, dust, or other suspended small solid particles.

per cm³ per second in unit frequency range about ν, and $\boldsymbol{q}_\nu(\boldsymbol{r})$ be the radiation energy flux in this frequency range. Then the total rate of energy emission R and the total radiation energy flux $\boldsymbol{q}_R$ are given by the equations:

$$R(\boldsymbol{r}) = \int_0^\infty R_\nu(\boldsymbol{r})\, d\nu \tag{11.3–2}$$

$$\boldsymbol{q}_R(\boldsymbol{r}) = \int_0^\infty \boldsymbol{q}_\nu(\boldsymbol{r})\, d\nu \tag{11.3–3}$$

From geometrical considerations it may be shown that $\boldsymbol{q}_\nu$ can be expressed in terms of R_ν and μ_ν by the integral

$$\boldsymbol{q}_\nu(\boldsymbol{r}_1) = -\int R_\nu(\boldsymbol{r}_2)\left(\frac{\boldsymbol{r}_2 - \boldsymbol{r}_1}{r_{12}}\right)\frac{1}{4\pi r_{12}^2}\exp\left(-\int_0^{r_{12}} \rho\mu_\nu\, dl\right) d\boldsymbol{r}_2 \tag{11.3–4}$$

Here $r_{12} = |\boldsymbol{r}_1 - \boldsymbol{r}_2|$, the integral, $\int_0^{r_{12}} \mu_\nu\, dl$, is to be taken along the line connecting these two points, and ρ is the matter density.

If the problem is one dimensional in the sense that R_ν and μ_ν vary only in the x-direction, the y- and z-components of the radiation flux vanish, and the x-component $q_{\nu x}$ is given by the one-dimensional integral,[8]

$$q_{\nu x}(x_1) = \int_{-\infty}^{x} J_\nu(x_2)\, dx_2 - \int_x^\infty J_\nu(x_2)\, dx_2 \tag{11.3–5}$$

where

$$J_\nu(x_2) = \tfrac{1}{2}R_\nu(x_2)\begin{bmatrix}\exp(-\tau_\nu(x_2, x_1)) \\ +\tau_\nu(x_2, x_1)\,\mathrm{Ei}(-\tau_\nu(x_2, x_1))\end{bmatrix} \tag{11.3–6}$$

and

$$\tau_\nu(x_2, x_1) = \left|\int_{x_1}^{x_2} \rho\mu_\nu(x')\, dx'\right| \tag{11.3–7}$$

The symbol $\mathrm{Ei}(-\tau_\nu(x_2, x_1))$ is the exponential integral.

[8] The cartesian coordinates in Eq. 11.3–4 are replaced by cylindrical coordinates (ϕ_2, ρ_2, x_2). The integration over ϕ_2 can be carried out immediately to give a factor of 2π. Now eliminating ρ_2 in terms of a new variable $s = (x_2^2 + \rho_2^2)^{1/2}$ leads to the double integral

$$q_{\nu x}(x_1) = -\tfrac{1}{2}\int_{-\infty}^{\infty} dx_2 \int_0^\infty R_\nu(x_2)\frac{x_2}{s^2}\exp\left(-\tau_\nu(x_2, x_1)\frac{s}{x_2}\right) ds$$

Integration over s gives Eq. 11.3–5.

a. Radiation flux for two special cases

There are two special cases for which the radiation flux can be treated with facility: (i) opaque materials, in which the absorption of radiation is so intense that the radiation is in local thermodynamic equilibrium with the matter, and (ii) transparent materials, in which there is little self-absorption of the radiated energy.

i. *Intense Absorbtion of Radiation and the Method of Rosseland*

If the medium were of infinite size and at constant temperature, the energy density, e_ν, of the radiation (in unit frequency range) would be characteristic of a black body at the temperature, T, of the matter with which it is in equilibrium:

$$e_\nu = \frac{8\pi h\nu^3}{c^3} \frac{1}{(e^{h\nu/kT} - 1)} \qquad (11.3\text{–}8)$$

Since light travels with the velocity c, and the material has an absorption coefficient μ_ν, the energy absorbed in this frequency range is $ce_\nu\rho\mu_\nu$ (per cm^3 per sec). Since a radiative equilibrium exists, the radiation emitted is equal to the radiation absorbed so that

$$R_\nu = ce_\nu\rho\mu_\nu \qquad (11.3\text{–}9)$$

Thus Eq. 11.3–4 becomes

$$\boldsymbol{q}_\nu = -\frac{\rho c\mu_\nu}{4\pi} \int \frac{(\boldsymbol{r}_2 - \boldsymbol{r}_1)}{{r_{12}}^3} e_\nu(\boldsymbol{r}_2) \exp(-\rho\mu_\nu r_{12})\, d\boldsymbol{r}_2 \qquad (11.3\text{–}10)$$

Now consider a situation in which the temperature varies very slowly in a distance of $(\rho\mu_\nu)^{-1}$ (for any frequency). Then, to a first approximation, R_ν is given by Eq. 11.3–9, and $e_\nu(\boldsymbol{r}_2)$ is characteristic of the local temperature $T(\boldsymbol{r}_2)$. Then for a point $\boldsymbol{r}_2$ in the vicinity of $\boldsymbol{r}_1$, e_ν can be approximated by the first terms in a Taylor's series expansion:

$$e_\nu(\boldsymbol{r}_2) = e_\nu(\boldsymbol{r}_1) + \left(\frac{\partial e_\nu}{\partial \boldsymbol{r}_1} \cdot (\boldsymbol{r}_2 - \boldsymbol{r}_1)\right) \qquad (11.3\text{–}11)$$

The coefficient of absorption varies sufficiently slowly that it may be taken locally to be constant. Integration of the term involving $e_\nu(\boldsymbol{r}_1)$ in Eq. 11.3–10 then gives zero; the remaining terms may be integrated to give[9]

$$\boldsymbol{q}_\nu = -\frac{c}{3\rho\mu_\nu} \frac{\partial e_\nu}{\partial \boldsymbol{r}} \qquad (11.3\text{–}12)$$

[9] This integration can easily be carried out using spherical coordinates.

Or, since e_ν is a function of the local temperature only, we can express this relation in the form

$$\mathbf{q}_\nu = -\frac{c}{3\rho\mu_\nu}\frac{de_\nu}{dT}\frac{\partial T}{\partial \mathbf{r}} \tag{11.3–13}$$

Then, according to Eq. 11.3–3, the total flux is given by the integral of the $\mathbf{q}_\nu$ over the frequency so that

$$\mathbf{q}_R = -\frac{c}{3}\left[\int_0^\infty \frac{1}{\rho\mu_\nu}\frac{de_\nu}{dT}\,d\nu\right]\frac{\partial T}{\partial \mathbf{r}} \tag{11.3–14}$$

Rosseland[3] defined a mean free path, λ_R, for the thermal radiation such that

$$\mathbf{q}_R = -\frac{c\lambda_R}{3}\frac{d(aT^4)}{dT}\frac{\partial T}{\partial \mathbf{r}} \tag{11.3–15}$$

Here a is the Stefan-Boltzmann constant (7.67×10^{-15} ergs cm^{-3} deg^{-4}), and aT^4 is the energy of the black-body radiation contained in one cubic centimeter of volume,

$$aT^4 = \int_0^\infty e_\nu\,d\nu \tag{11.3–16}$$

A comparison of Eqs. 11.3–14 and 15 shows that[10]

$$\lambda_R = \frac{\displaystyle\int_0^\infty \frac{1}{\mu_\nu}\frac{de_\nu}{dT}\,d\nu}{\displaystyle\rho\int_0^\infty \frac{de_\nu}{dT}\,d\nu} \tag{11.3–17}$$

The Rosseland definition of the mean free path corresponds to photons traveling with the velocity of light in random directions in jumps of an average length λ_R. From this viewpoint, Eq. 11.3–15 is the simple kinetic theory expression for the diffusion of photons.

ii. *Weak Absorbtion of Radiation* (*Non-luminous Flames, etc.*)

There are a great many examples, such as non-luminous flames,[11] where the rate of energy absorption A is small compared to the rate of energy

[10] Discussion of induced emission has been neglected in this treatment. The only result of the inclusion of this effect is to multiply the absorption coefficient in Eq. 11.3–17 by the factor $[1 - \exp(-h\nu/kT)]$. See § 11.1, ref. 11.

[11] R. T. Haslam, W. G. Lovell, and R. D. Hunneman, *Ind. Eng. Chem.*, **17**, 272 (1925).

emitted R. Under these conditions A can be neglected, and Eq. 11.3–1 becomes

$$\left(\frac{\partial}{\partial \boldsymbol{r}} \cdot \boldsymbol{q}_\nu(\boldsymbol{r})\right) = R_\nu(\boldsymbol{r}) \tag{11.3–18}$$

and Eq. 11.3–4 becomes

$$\boldsymbol{q}_\nu(\boldsymbol{r}_1) = -\frac{1}{4\pi}\int \frac{(\boldsymbol{r}_2 - \boldsymbol{r}_1)}{r_{12}{}^3} R_\nu(\boldsymbol{r}_2)\, d\boldsymbol{r}_2 \tag{11.3–19}$$

There are two kinds of radiation emission processes, thermal radiation and chemiluminescence. The rate of emission of thermal radiation, R_ν, is given by Eq. 11.3–9 in terms of $\mu_\nu\rho$ and the black-body radiation density, e_ν. The emission of chemiluminescence depends upon the chemical kinetics of photochemical reactions, and each special case must be treated separately. Experimental evidence indicates that the radiation in flames is a combination of chemiluminescence and thermal radiation, with the chemiluminescence being the more important.[12] Time lags in the specific heat, corresponding to a relaxation time for the transfer of energy between translational and internal degrees of freedom within a molecule,[12, 13] lead to non-thermal radiation which might be classed with chemiluminescence.

For thermal radiation, the radiation flux can be determined from the absorption coefficient $\mu(T)$. However, engineers present their radiation data in terms of an effective emissivity, ϵ, which is a function of the size of the experimental apparatus and the density (or pressure) of the matter. They consider the radiation emitted by a hemisphere of fluid of radius L kept at a constant temperature and density. As far as the radiation is concerned, the material outside the hemisphere might be absent. Under these conditions Eq. 11.3–4 may be integrated (in spherical coordinates) to give the axial component of the flux at the center of the hemisphere,

$$q_\nu = \frac{1}{4}\frac{R_\nu}{\rho\mu_\nu}(1 - e^{-\rho\mu_\nu L}) \tag{11.3–20}$$

Since the radiation is thermal, R_ν is given by Eq. 11.3–9 so that

$$q_\nu = \tfrac{1}{4}\, c e_\nu (1 - e^{-\rho\mu_\nu L}) \tag{11.3–21}$$

[12] A. G. Gaydon, *Spectroscopy and Combustion Theory*, Chapman and Hall (1948), 2nd Ed. This book furnishes the most complete account available of the various radiation mechanisms involved in flames. Many references are cited.

[13] Theoretical research on these molecular relaxation times are given in: (a) L. Landau and E. Teller, *Physik Z. Sowjet Union*, **10**, 34 (1936). (b) H. Bethe and E. Teller (informal report, unpublished). (c) R. N. Schwartz, Z. I. Slawsky, and K. F. Herzfeld, *J. Chem. Phys.*, **20**, 1591 (1952). Experimental results are given in: (d) I. M. Metter, *Physik Z. Sowjet Union*, **12**, 232 (1937). (e) A. Kantrowitz, *J. Chem. Phys.*, **14**, 150 (1946). (f) P. W. Haber and A. Kantrowitz, *J. Chem. Phys.*, **15**, 275 (1947).

and the total axial component of the radiation flux at this point is

$$q_R = \int_0^\infty q_\nu \, d\nu = \frac{c}{4} aT^4 \left[1 - \frac{1}{(aT^4)} \int_0^\infty e_\nu \exp(-\rho\mu_\nu L) \, d\nu \right] \tag{11.3–22}$$

The factor $caT^4/4$ is the radiation flux which would be emitted from a black body at the temperature T. The second factor can, therefore, be interpreted as the effective emissivity,

$$\epsilon(T, \rho L) = 1 - \frac{1}{aT^4} \int_0^\infty e_\nu \exp(-\rho L \mu_\nu) \, d\nu \tag{11.3–23}$$

Tables of $\epsilon(T, \rho L)$ are available for quite a few materials.[14] These emissivities correspond to an effective coefficient of absorption, $\mu(T, \rho L)$, defined by the relation

$$\exp(-\rho L \mu) = \frac{\displaystyle\int_0^\infty e_\nu \exp(-\rho L \mu_\nu) \, d\nu}{\displaystyle\int_0^\infty e_\nu \, d\nu} \tag{11.3–24}$$

The effective coefficient of absorption can then be expressed in terms of the emissivity by the relation

$$\mu = -\frac{1}{\rho L} \ln(1 - \epsilon(T, \rho L)) \tag{11.3–25}$$

In determining the radiation flux, $\mu(T, \rho L)$ is used in place of μ_ν in all the previous formulae. It is clear, however, that considerable error is made both by not taking into account the frequency dependence of the coefficient of absorption and also by not knowing, for any actual problem with complicated geometry, what value to use for ρL.

b. Stationary radiation front

If a moving body is maintained at a high temperature, the surrounding fluid is heated up and the temperature distribution eventually reaches a steady state. Let us consider the simplest example of a steady-state radiation front. Suppose that an infinitely large flat plate, moving with the velocity v perpendicular to its face, is maintained at the temperature, T_0, and surrounded by a homogeneous fluid of constant specific heat $\hat{C}_v$.

[14] (a) See § 11.1, reference 11. Also (b) H. C. Hottel, "Radiant Heat from Water Vapor," *Trans. Am. Inst. Chem. Eng.*, **38**, 531 (1942). (c) A. Schack, "Strahlung der Feuergase," *Arch. für Eisenhüttenw.*, **19**, 11 (1948) (CO_2, H_2O up to 2000°C).

If we neglect the kinetic energy and thermal conductivity of the fluid and set the external forces equal to zero, the equation of energy balance (Eq. 11.1–4) for a steady state $\left(\frac{\partial \hat{U}}{\partial t} = 0\right)$ becomes

$$\rho v \hat{C}_v \frac{dT}{dx} = -\frac{dq_{Rx}}{dx} \tag{11.3–26}$$

Here x is the distance from the moving wall and q_{Rx} is the component of radiation flux perpendicular to the wall. Equation 11.3–26 may be integrated immediately to give

$$\rho v \hat{C}_v (T - T_\infty) = -q_{Rx} + (q_{Rx})_\infty \tag{11.3–27}$$

The subscripts ∞ refer to $x = \infty$. Let us assume that T_∞ and $(q_{Rx})_\infty$ are negligible. If the absorption is intense so that the radiation flux can be expressed in terms of the Rosseland mean free path, Eq. 11.3–27 becomes

$$\rho v C_v T - \frac{c\lambda_R}{3} \frac{d(aT^4)}{dT} \frac{dT}{dx} = 0 \tag{11.3–28}$$

If the mean free path varies as the s power of the temperature,

$$\lambda_R = \lambda_0 T^s \tag{11.3–29}$$

where λ_0 is a constant independent of temperature, Eq. 11.3–28 can be integrated to give

$$(T^{s+3} - T_0^{s+3}) - \frac{3(s+3)}{4} \frac{\rho \hat{C}_v v}{\lambda_0 ca} x = 0 \tag{11.3–30}$$

If we let

$$x_0 = -\frac{4\lambda_0 ca T_0^{s+3}}{3(s+3)\rho \hat{C}_v v} \tag{11.3–31}$$

Eq. 11.3–30 can be written in either the form

$$\frac{x}{x_0} = 1 - \left(\frac{T}{T_0}\right)^{s+3} \tag{11.3–32}$$

or else

$$T = T_0 \left(1 - \frac{x}{x_0}\right)^{1/(s+3)} \tag{11.3–33}$$

The constant x_0 then is the distance from the place, $x = 0$, where the temperature is maintained at the temperature T_0 to the place where the temperature has dropped to zero. The radiation preceding a shock or detonation wave has very much the structure considered in this example.

4. The Theory of Sound Propagation

In the remainder of this chapter we discuss a number of non-equilibrium flow processes. The equations of change (given in §§ 11.1b and 11.2e) form the starting point for the development of these theories. In this section we consider the propagation of sound waves (waves of infinitesimal amplitude) through a fluid. If the perturbations are taken to be infinitesimal, it is possible to simplify the equations of change by discarding squares and higher powers of small quantities so that the equations of change become linear differential equations.

We begin by neglecting the "dissipative terms"—those containing the diffusion, viscosity, thermal conductivity, and chemical kinetics. The linearized differential equations obtained in this case lead to solutions representing waves which travel without absorption; the results apply to any fluid. When the dissipative terms are included the linearized differential equations lead to solutions representing traveling waves which are absorbed. The absorption coefficient depends upon the transport coefficients, the chemical kinetics, and any relaxation phenomena, and our results are applicable strictly to dilute gases only.

a. Propagation without absorption

In the study of the propagation of sound waves it is convenient to consider the entropy equation rather than the equation of energy balance as one of the equations of change. When we neglect the dissipative terms which lead to absorption, the *entropy equation* (Eq. 11.1–11) is

$$\frac{\partial \hat{S}}{\partial t} + \left(\boldsymbol{v} \cdot \frac{\partial \hat{S}}{\partial \boldsymbol{r}}\right) = 0 \tag{11.4–1}$$

That is, to this approximation the entropy of an element of gas moving with the stream velocity $\boldsymbol{v}$ remains constant. Although it is clearly not necessary for the treatment, for simplicity we assume that the unperturbed system is in a uniform state at rest; that is, except for the perturbations induced by the passage of the sound wave, the stream velocity is everywhere zero, and the pressure and density have everywhere the constant values p_0 and ρ_0 respectively.

When the dissipative terms are neglected, the equation of motion (11.1–3) is

$$\rho \frac{\partial \boldsymbol{v}}{\partial t} + \left(\rho \boldsymbol{v} \cdot \frac{\partial}{\partial \boldsymbol{r}} \boldsymbol{v}\right) = -\frac{\partial p}{\partial \boldsymbol{r}} \tag{11.4–2}$$

This equation may be linearized by the following arguments. First, the mass velocity, $\mathbf{v}$, associated with the passage of the sound wave is infinitesimal. Therefore, the term $\left(\rho\mathbf{v}\cdot\frac{\partial\mathbf{v}}{\partial\mathbf{r}}\right)$ involves the square of a small quantity and can be dropped. Furthermore, in the term $\rho\frac{\partial\mathbf{v}}{\partial t}$ the density ρ may be replaced by the equilibrium value ρ_0 since the derivative $\partial\mathbf{v}/\partial t$ is itself a small quantity. Thus the *linearized equation of motion* is

$$\rho_0\frac{\partial\mathbf{v}}{\partial t}+\frac{\partial p}{\partial\mathbf{r}}=0 \tag{11.4–3}$$

We rewrite this equation in terms of ρ rather than p. The pressure may be considered a function of $\hat{S}$ and ρ; but because of the conservation of entropy during the passage of a sound wave (Eq. 11.4–1), p is a function of ρ alone, and we may write

$$\frac{\partial p}{\partial\mathbf{r}}=c_0^{\,2}\frac{\partial\rho}{\partial\mathbf{r}} \tag{11.4–4}$$

Here c_0 is the value of[1]

$$c=\sqrt{\left(\frac{\partial p}{\partial\rho}\right)_{\hat{S}}}=\sqrt{\gamma\left(\frac{\partial p}{\partial\rho}\right)_T} \tag{11.4–5}$$

under the equilibrium conditions.[2] (The quantity c is a thermodynamic property of the system. It will shortly become evident that c_0 is the speed of propagation of thc sound wave.) Thus the equation of motion becomes

$$\frac{\partial\mathbf{v}}{\partial t}+\frac{c_0^{\,2}}{\rho_0}\frac{\partial\rho}{\partial\mathbf{r}}=0 \tag{11.4–6}$$

Let us now consider the equation of continuity (11.1–2). The term $\left(\mathbf{v}\cdot\frac{\partial\rho}{\partial\mathbf{r}}\right)$ is a small quantity of the second order, and therefore we obtain

$$\frac{\partial\rho}{\partial t}+\rho_0\left(\frac{\partial}{\partial\mathbf{r}}\cdot\mathbf{v}\right)=0 \tag{11.4–7}$$

for the *linearized equation of continuity.*

[1] For a perfect gas $p=\rho kT/m$ and $c=\sqrt{\gamma\frac{p}{\rho}}=\sqrt{\gamma kT/m}$, where $\gamma=\frac{\tilde{C}_p}{\tilde{C}_v}=1+\frac{R}{\tilde{C}_v}$. For real fluids c depends weakly on the density.

[2] The second form of Eq. 11.4–5 follows from straightforward thermodynamical arguments.

Equations 11.4–1, 6, and 7 form the basis for the theory of sound propagation without absorption. From these three equations we can obtain a second-order partial differential equation for the density, the solutions of which give a description of the wave motion. If the equation of continuity (11.4–7) is differentiated with respect to time, we obtain

$$\frac{\partial^2 \rho}{\partial t^2} + \rho_0 \left(\frac{\partial}{\partial \boldsymbol{r}} \cdot \frac{\partial \boldsymbol{v}}{\partial t}\right) = 0 \tag{11.4–8}$$

The equation of motion (11.4–6) may be used to eliminate the quantity $\boldsymbol{v}$ from Eq. 11.4–8, thus:

$$\frac{\partial^2 \rho}{\partial t^2} = c_0^2 \left(\frac{\partial}{\partial \boldsymbol{r}} \cdot \frac{\partial \rho}{\partial \boldsymbol{r}}\right) \tag{11.4–9}$$

A solution of this equation is

$$\rho = \rho_0 \left[1 + \phi_0 \sin \frac{2\pi}{\lambda} (z - c_0 t)\right] \tag{11.4–10}$$

This solution represents a harmonic wave of wavelength λ and amplitude $\rho_0\phi_0$, traveling in the positive z direction with speed c_0. An arbitrary solution can be written as the sum of such solutions, each representing a sound wave of a particular wavelength, traveling in a particular direction.

This last result may be combined with the equation of motion (11.4–6) to obtain the components of the velocity, thus:

$$\frac{\partial v_z}{\partial t} = -\frac{2\pi}{\lambda} c_0^2 \phi_0 \cos \frac{2\pi}{\lambda} (z - c_0 t); \qquad \frac{\partial v_x}{\partial t} = \frac{\partial v_y}{\partial t} = 0 \tag{11.4–11}$$

Integration with respect to t gives at once[3]

$$v_z = c_0 \phi_0 \sin \frac{2\pi}{\lambda} (z - c_0 t); \qquad v_x = v_y = 0 \tag{11.4–12}$$

Hence the velocity wave, of amplitude $\phi_0 c_0$, is in phase with the density wave. Inasmuch as the pressure and density are related by the adiabatic relation (Eq. 11.4–4), the pressure and density waves are in phase, and the amplitude of the pressure wave is $\rho_0 c_0^2 \phi_0$.

b. Propagation with absorption[4]

Let us now consider the effect of the dissipative terms in the equations of change. At any particular point in space, the gas is alternately compressed and expanded. The irreversibility of this cycle leads to an absorption of energy. This irreversibility and consequent absorption

[3] The additive constants are taken to be zero since it is assumed that except for the passage of the sound wave, the fluid is at rest.

[4] J. J. Markham, R. T. Beyer, and R. B. Lindsay, *Revs. Mod. Phys.*, **23**, 353 (1951). Also L. Bergmann, *Der Ultraschall* [S. Hirzel, Zürich, 1949].

and dispersion are due to : (i) viscosity, (ii) thermal conductivity, (iii) diffusion, (iv) chemical reactions, and (v) the time lag in the transfer of energy among the various degrees of freedom of the molecules. The transfer of energy may be treated mathematically as a special type of chemical reaction.

A set of linear differential equations describing the propagation of a sound wave (with absorption) may be obtained from the usual equations of change in the following manner. The effects of the sound waves are considered to be small perturbations. Accordingly, the expressions for each of the macroscopic variables are written as the sum of two terms, one representing the unperturbed value and the other representing the perturbation. For example, the density may be written as

$$\rho = \rho_0[1 + \phi] \tag{11.4–13}$$

If expressions of this form are substituted into the equations of change, the terms involving products of perturbations may be dropped (since they represent squares of small quantities) and the terms containing only the unperturbed values of the variables may also be dropped (since these quantities themselves satisfy the equations of change). The result is a set of homogeneous linear differential equations in the perturbation functions.

A solution of such a set of linear homogeneous differential equations consists of a superposition of harmonic waves of different frequencies ν. For example, the perturbation in the density is of the form

$$\phi = \phi_0 e^{i(\alpha z - 2\pi\nu t)}; \; \alpha = \frac{2\pi}{\lambda} + i\kappa \tag{11.4–14}$$

The perturbations in the other quantities are of the same form. The quantity ϕ_0 is an amplitude factor, and α is a complex wave number. The real part of α is the reciprocal of the wavelength λ multiplied by 2π and the imaginary part is the absorption coefficient κ.

If expressions for each of the variables, similar to that given in Eq. 11.4–14, are used as trial solutions in the linearized equations of change, we obtain a set of homogeneous linear algebraic equations for the amplitude factors. This set of equations possesses a non-trivial solution if and only if the determinant of the coefficients is zero. This provides an implicit equation for α as a function of ν. If the terms representing the dissipative mechanisms are omitted from this equation, the resulting value of α is real. That is, there is no absorption and the solution is identical to that obtained in § 11.4a. The inclusion of the dissipative terms leads to a complex value of α. Its real part, $2\pi/\lambda$, is simply related to the velocity of propagation, and its imaginary part, κ, to the absorption coefficient.

Since the absorption of sound due to the transport processes (that is, in the absence of chemical reactions and relaxation phenomena) is generally small, it is convenient to expand the expression for κ and keep only terms of the first order. In this approximation, κ is the sum:

$$\kappa = \kappa_\eta + \kappa_\lambda + \kappa_D \tag{11.4–15}$$

Each term represents the effect of one of the transport processes. The contributions due to viscosity, thermal conductivity, and diffusion in a multicomponent mixture are

$$\kappa_\eta = \frac{8\pi^2\nu^2}{3c^2}\frac{\eta}{\rho} \tag{11.4–16}$$

$$\kappa_\lambda = \frac{4\pi^2(\gamma-1)^2}{2\gamma}\frac{\nu^2}{c^3}\frac{\lambda}{nk} \tag{11.4–17}$$

$$\kappa_D = \frac{2\pi^2\nu^2}{nc^3}\sum_k\left[\gamma\frac{n^2}{\rho}\sum_j m_j D_{kj}\left(\frac{n_j m_j}{\rho}-\frac{n_j}{n}\right)+(\gamma-1)\frac{D_k^T}{m_k}\right]$$
$$\times\left[1-\frac{(\gamma-1)}{\gamma n}\sum_j\frac{n_j}{\mathscr{D}_{jk}}\left(\frac{D_j^T}{n_j m_j}-\frac{D_k^T}{n_k m_k}\right)\right] \tag{11.4–18}$$

The predominant term in the last expression may be rearranged into the form

$$\frac{\pi^2\gamma\nu^2}{c^3\rho^2}\sum_{i,j,k} n_j n_k(m_j-m_k)(m_j D_{ij}-m_k D_{ik}) \tag{11.4–19}$$

and represents the effect of the diffusion resulting from the pressure gradient. For a binary mixture[5] κ_D may be written more simply in terms of the thermal diffusion ratio [defined by Eq. 8.1–10]

$$\kappa_D = \frac{2\gamma\pi^2\nu^2}{c^3\rho^2}n_1 n_2\mathscr{D}_{12}\left[(m_2-m_1)+\frac{(\gamma-1)}{\gamma}\frac{n\rho}{n_1 n_2}k_T\right]^2 \tag{11.4–20}$$

It is clear from the forms of the above expressions for κ_η and κ_λ that these quantities are positive. Furthermore, it can be seen from the last equation that for a binary mixture κ_D is positive. This is probably true in general, so that κ is always positive.

[5] The expressions for a binary mixture were obtained by M. Kohler, *Ann. Physik*, **39**, 209 (1941).

To the linear approximation discussed thus far, the velocity of propagation of the sound wave is c_0. The transport processes do not appreciably affect the velocity of the sound wave (only quadratic and higher terms in the transport coefficients appear).

Having considered the effect of transport phenomena on the process of absorption, let us now turn our attention to the effect of chemical reactions. It often happens that chemical reactions give rise to considerable absorption and dispersion. The expression for κ under these conditions is quite complicated.[6] [7] However, under conditions such that the absorption of sound due to the chemical reactions is small, the expression for κ can be expanded to obtain a term linear in the reaction constants. This chemical contribution to the absorption coefficient is

$$\kappa_c = \frac{(\gamma - 1)^2}{2\gamma c n (kT)^2} \sum_j [(\Delta u)_j - (\eta_j - \beta_j) c_v T]^2 \, k_j n_1^{\beta_{1j}} n_2^{\beta_{2j}} \cdots \tag{11.4-21}$$

Here, $(\Delta u)_j$ is the internal energy change of the jth reaction, c_v is the heat capacity per molecule of the mixture, the β_{ij} are the number of molecules of i entering into the jth reaction, and $(\eta_j - \beta_j)$ is the increase in the number of molecules due to the reaction.

The transfer of translational energy to the internal degrees of freedom of the molecule may be considered as a special case of a reaction rate. The gas is assumed to consist of two types of molecules: the unexcited molecules, A, and molecules A^*, which possess an additional amount of energy, ϵ, in an internal degree of freedom. The "chemical" reaction is then of the form

$$M + A \rightleftharpoons M + A^* \tag{11.4-22}$$

where M may be a molecule of A or A^*. This type of chemical reaction has been studied by Kneser.[8] The rate of the reaction is characterized by a relaxation time τ defined by

$$\tau = [n(k_a + k_a')]^{-1} \tag{11.4-23}$$

where k_a and k_a' are the rate constants of the forward and backward reactions. Let c_a be that part of the heat capacity per molecule at constant volume due to the degrees of freedom other than that under consideration (or that of the unreacting mixture). (See § 2.5d.) The increase in heat capacity per molecule at constant volume due to the extra degree of freedom

[6] G. Damköhler, *Z. Electrochem.*, **48**, No. 2 and 3 (1942). (Translated by the National Advisory Committee for Aeronautics as T.M. 1268 and 1269.)

[7] K. Herzfeld, *J. Chem. Phys.*, **9**, 513 (1941).

[8] M. O. Kneser, *Ann. Physik*, II, 761 (1931).

or due to the reaction (under conditions of complete equilibrium) is

$$c_1 = k\left(\frac{\epsilon}{kT}\right)^2 e^{\epsilon/kT}\,(1 + e^{\epsilon/kT})^{-2} \tag{11.4–24}$$

Let

$$c_v = c_a + c_1 \tag{11.4–25}$$

be the specific heat of the mixture under conditions of complete equilibrium. Kneser showed that for such a gas the velocity of sound is

$$c = \left[\frac{kT}{m}\left(1 + \frac{k[c_v + c_a(2\pi\nu\tau)^2]}{c_v^{\,2} + c_a^{\,2}(2\pi\nu\tau)^2}\right)\right]^{1/2} \tag{11.4–26}$$

and the absorption coefficient is

$$\kappa = \frac{kc_1 2\pi^2\nu^2\tau}{c[c_v(c_v + k) + c_a(c_a + k)\,(2\pi\nu\tau)^2]} \tag{11.4–27}$$

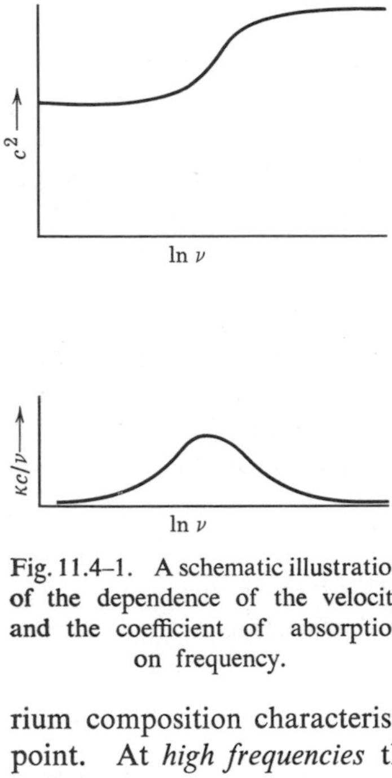

Fig. 11.4–1. A schematic illustration of the dependence of the velocity and the coefficient of absorption on frequency.

The velocity of sound as a function of frequency as given by Eq. 11.4–26 is a step function of the form indicated in Fig. 11.4–1. It is clear from the expression that at *low frequencies* (that is, low compared to the characteristic frequency, τ^{-1}) the velocity of sound is given by the usual expression $c = \sqrt{\gamma kT/m}$, in which the γ is the ratio of the heat capacities of the reacting mixture. Under these conditions the composition of the mixture changes and adjusts itself so that the composition at any point and any time is the equilibrium composition characteristic of the density and temperature at that point. At *high frequencies* the expression gives a velocity of sound in which the value of γ is that characteristic of the non-reacting mixture, since in this case the composition remains constant and does not follow the oscillations. The point of inflection of c^2 as a function of ln ν is at the frequency

$$\nu = \frac{1}{2\pi\tau}\frac{c_v}{c_a} \tag{11.4–28}$$

The absorption coefficient per wavelength is $\kappa c/\nu$. As would be expected, this quantity is small for both high and low frequencies. This curve is illustrated in Fig. 11.4–1. The maximum in this curve occurs at the point

$$\nu = \frac{1}{2\pi\tau}\sqrt{\frac{c_v(c_v + k)}{c_a(c_a + k)}} \qquad (11.4\text{–}29)$$

which is approximately the same frequency as that at which the change in velocity occurs. For c_a of the same order as c_v the half width of the absorption curve is approximately 3.8 octaves.

Interesting complications occur in the study of the absorption of sound of high frequency. When the wavelength of the sound approaches the mean free path in magnitude, the gas no longer behaves as a continuum, and the Navier-Stokes equations are no longer applicable. As discussed in § 7.3b, the Enskog series solution of the Boltzmann equation is an expansion in powers of a quantity which is essentially the ratio of the mean free path to a characteristic distance in which the macroscopic properties change appreciably. The Navier-Stokes equations are the equations resulting from the first approximation of Enskog. The results of the second approximation are referred to as the Burnett equations. In order to study the absorption of sound of short wavelengths it is necessary to make use of the higher approximations.

Primakoff[9] and later Tsein and Schamberg[10] used the second approximation or the Burnett equations to obtain corrections to the absorption coefficient due to the approach of the wavelength to the mean free path. Wang Chang and Uhlenbeck[11] have applied these results to the calculation of the dispersion of sound in helium. The corrections to the absorption coefficient obtained by the use of higher approximation is appreciable in the range of short wavelengths. The difficulties involved in the application of the higher approximations are sufficiently great that it is probably impractical to go beyond the stage reached by Wang Chang and Uhlenbeck. Furthermore, it is probable that the Enskog series is only asymptotically convergent. Hence it is necessary to make use of other methods to obtain information as to behavior of gases under the influence of large gradients in the macroscopic properties.

Mott-Smith[12] has obtained expressions for the absorption of sound of short wavelengths by making use of the Boltzmann equation without

[9] H. Primakoff, *J. Acoust. Soc. Am.*, **13**, 14 (1942).

[10] H. S. Tsien and R. Schamberg, *J. Acoust. Soc. Am.*, **18**, 334 (1946).

[11] C. S. Wang Chang, "On the Dispersion of Sound in Helium," University of Michigan, Department of Engineering Research Report UMH-3-F, APL/JHU CM-467 (1 May 1948). See also C. S. Wang Chang and G. E. Uhlenbeck, "On the Propagation of Sound in Monatomic Gases," University of Michigan, Department of Engineering research report to ONR (October, 1952).

[12] H. M. Mott-Smith, Private Communication, 1952.

the introduction of the equations of change. If we assume that the distribution of molecular velocities is only slightly different from Maxwellian, we may obtain directly from the Boltzmann equation a linear equation describing the propagation of sound waves. This approach avoids the difficulties inherent in the previous methods and is valid for any ratio of the mean free path to the wavelength. It is found that the absorption coefficient at high frequencies is less than that predicted by the Navier-Stokes equations, but that the Burnett equations overcorrect the result.

5. The Propagation of Finite Waves in One Dimension[1]

We now turn our attention from the infinitesimal sound waves considered in the last section to waves of finite amplitude. We consider here the propagation of finite waves in one dimension in terms of the *Riemann method of characteristics*. The effects of viscosity, thermal conductivity, and diffusion are neglected.[2] As a consequence of this the flow is taken to be isentropic. We will not, however, discard the second order terms in the equations of change.

The speed of sound c is defined by Eq. 11.4–5 as a thermodynamic quantity. It may be shown that for any real fluid the velocity of sound increases with pressure along an adiabat. The fact that the speed of sound is greater in the high-pressure part of a wave explains the formation of shock waves. Consider the sinusoidal wave traveling in the positive x-direction shown in Fig. 11.5–1a. According to the theory of the preceding section any small disturbance is propagated with the local velocity of sound. Thus the crest of the wave travels faster than the trough, and after some time the wave assumes the shape shown in Fig. 11.5–1b. Finally after a long time the crest overtakes the trough, and the waves have the sawtooth appearance of Fig. 11.5–1c. The abrupt discontinuity at the front of the sawtooth is called a shock wave. The behavior of shock waves is discussed in § 11.8.

a. The Riemann method of characteristics

As in the last section the starting point for the discussion is the equations of change. Once again it is convenient to use the entropy equation (11.1–11) in place of the energy equation (11.1–4). If the approximation

[1] R. Courant and K. O. Friederichs, *Supersonic Flow and Shock Waves*, Interscience (1948).

[2] The original method is restricted to one-dimensional problems and to the isentropic approximation. As will be mentioned later, however, with only slight modification the method can be adapted to the numerical solution of three-dimensional problems and take into account the effects of transport processes.

is made that the effect of the transport processes may be neglected, then we have the entropy equation, the equation of continuity, and the equation of motion in the following form:[3]

$$\frac{\partial \hat{S}}{\partial t} + v\frac{\partial \hat{S}}{\partial z} = 0 \tag{11.5–1}$$

$$\frac{\partial \rho}{\partial t} + v\frac{\partial \rho}{\partial z} = -\rho\frac{\partial v}{\partial z} \tag{11.5–2}$$

$$\frac{\partial v}{\partial t} + v\frac{\partial v}{\partial z} = -\frac{c^2}{\rho}\frac{\partial \rho}{\partial z} \tag{11.5–3}$$

These equations form the basis for the discussion presented in this section.

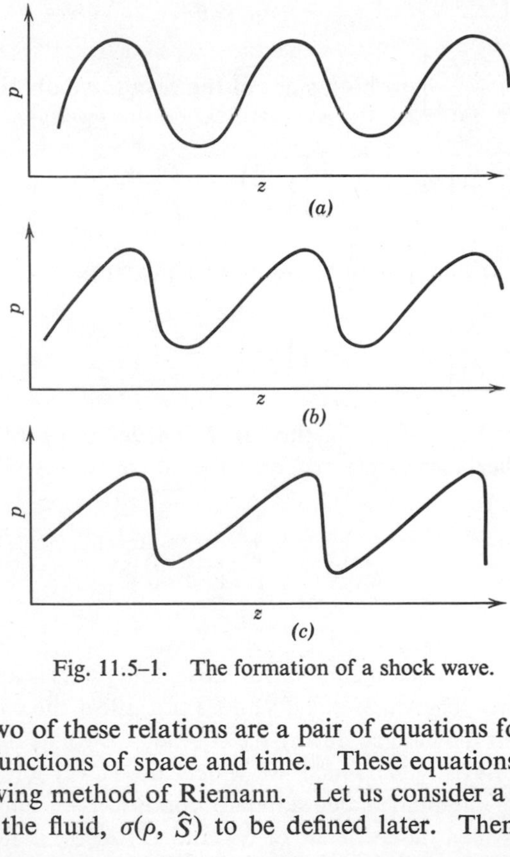

Fig. 11.5–1. The formation of a shock wave.

The last two of these relations are a pair of equations for the quantities ρ and v, as functions of space and time. These equations may be solved by the following method of Riemann. Let us consider a thermodynamic property of the fluid, $\sigma(\rho, \hat{S})$ to be defined later. Then application of

[3] The equation of motion (11.5–3) in this form is obtained by combining Eq. 11.4–2, written for one dimension, and Eq. 11.5–1. The quantity c is defined thermodynamically in Eq. 11.4–5.

the operator $\left(\frac{\partial}{\partial t} + v\frac{\partial}{\partial z}\right)$ to $\sigma(\rho, \hat{S})$ and use of the equation of continuity (11.5–2) gives

$$\left(\frac{\partial}{\partial t} + v\frac{\partial}{\partial z}\right)\sigma = \left(\frac{\partial \sigma}{\partial \rho}\right)_{\hat{S}}\left[\frac{\partial \rho}{\partial t} + v\frac{\partial \rho}{\partial z}\right] = -\rho\left(\frac{\partial \sigma}{\partial \rho}\right)_{\hat{S}}\frac{\partial v}{\partial z} \qquad (11.5\text{–}4)$$

since, according to the entropy equation (11.5–1), the entropy of a fluid element moving with velocity v is constant. Now adding the equation of motion (11.5–3) to this equation, we obtain

$$\left(\frac{\partial}{\partial t} + v\frac{\partial}{\partial z}\right)(v + \sigma) = -\frac{c^2}{\rho}\frac{\partial \rho}{\partial z} - \rho\left(\frac{\partial \sigma}{\partial \rho}\right)_{\hat{S}}\frac{\partial v}{\partial z} \qquad (11.5\text{–}5)$$

By adding $c\left[\frac{\partial v}{\partial z} + \frac{\partial \sigma}{\partial z}\right]$ to both sides of the result, we obtain

$$\left[\frac{\partial}{\partial t} + (v + c)\frac{\partial}{\partial z}\right](v + \sigma) = \left[\left(\frac{\partial \sigma}{\partial \rho}\right)_{\hat{S}} - \frac{c}{\rho}\right]\left(c\frac{\partial \rho}{\partial z} - \rho\frac{\partial v}{\partial z}\right) \qquad (11.5\text{–}6)$$

By a similar set of manipulations, we obtain the equation

$$\left[\frac{\partial}{\partial t} + (v - c)\frac{\partial}{\partial z}\right](v - \sigma) = \left[\left(\frac{\partial \sigma}{\partial \rho}\right)_{\hat{S}} - \frac{c}{\rho}\right]\left(c\frac{\partial \rho}{\partial z} + \rho\frac{\partial v}{\partial z}\right) \qquad (11.5\text{–}7)$$

The important trick of the method is in the definition of the quantity $\sigma(\rho, \hat{S})$. This thermodynamic property, the so-called *Riemann characteristic*, is defined by

$$\sigma(\rho, \hat{S}) = \int_{\rho_0(\hat{S})}^{\rho}\left(\frac{c}{\rho}\right)d\rho \qquad (11.5\text{–}8)$$

Here the integration is taken along an adiabat, and $\rho_0(\hat{S})$ is any convenient reference density. The value of $\rho_0(\hat{S})$ does not affect the calculations, as long as it remains unchanged during the course of the calculation. There are two definitions of $\rho_0(\hat{S})$ which are widely used: (1) $\rho_0(\hat{S})$ is taken to be the density of the fluid under standard conditions of temperature and pressure (and is then independent of $\hat{S}$), and (2) $\rho_0(\hat{S})$ is taken to be the density which the fluid with specific entropy $\hat{S}$ has at the standard pressure. The choice of definition of $\rho_0(\hat{S})$ usually depends on the particular application under consideration.

As a consequence of the above definition of $\sigma(\rho, \hat{S})$, its derivative with respect to the density is

$$\left(\frac{\partial \sigma}{\partial \rho}\right)_{\hat{S}} = \frac{c}{\rho} \tag{11.5–9}$$

Hence Eqs. 11.5–6, 7 simplify to

$$\left[\frac{\partial}{\partial t} + (v + c)\frac{\partial}{\partial z}\right] f = 0 \qquad f = v + \sigma \tag{11.5–10}$$

$$\left[\frac{\partial}{\partial t} + (v - c)\frac{\partial}{\partial z}\right] g = 0 \qquad g = v - \sigma \tag{11.5–11}$$

The first of these equations states that the property $f = v + \sigma$ remains unchanged in the neighborhood of a point moving with the velocity $(v + c)$. Similarly, the second equation states that the quantity $g = v - \sigma$ remains unchanged in the region of a point moving with the velocity $(v - c)$. These equations, along with the entropy equation (11.5–1), determine the complete hydrodynamic behavior of the gas. The entropy equation states that the entropy, in the neighborhood of a point moving with the gas at the velocity v, remains unchanged in time.

It is assumed that at some initial time t_0 the velocity $v(z)$, the density $\rho(z)$, and the specific entropy $\hat{S}(z)$ are known as functions of position. From the thermodynamic properties of the system we can then calculate the values of $c(z)$ and $\sigma(z)$, and consequently also $f(z)$ and $g(z)$. Then, making use of the concepts of the preceding paragraph, we can calculate the values of $f(z)$, $g(z)$, and $\hat{S}(z)$ at a somewhat later time, $t_0 + \Delta t$. Having these values, we can easily calculate v and σ from

$$v(z) = \tfrac{1}{2}[f(z) + g(z)] \tag{11.5–12}$$

$$\sigma(z) = \tfrac{1}{2}[f(z) - g(z)] \tag{11.5–13}$$

Then from a knowledge of the thermodynamics of the system we can find $c(z)$ [and, if desired, $\rho(z)$, $p(z)$, and $T(z)$]. The process may then be repeated to generate the complete solution to the hydrodynamical problem.

The Riemann method is applicable as long as the "characteristics" $f(z) = (v + \sigma)$ and $g(z) = (v - \sigma)$ remain single valued. However, as we shall see later in this section, it is altogether possible for two different characteristics f_1 and f_2 (which start at the initial time at two different points z_1 and z_2) to intersect. Under these conditions the velocity, density, and other hydrodynamical variables are no longer uniquely specified at the point of intersection, and a shock wave has set in. Of course, this situation cannot actually take place. As a point of intersection of the characteristics is approached the gradients in density, temperature, pressure, and velocity become large. Somewhere before the point of intersection the gradients become sufficiently large that one is no longer justified in neglecting the terms involving the viscosity and thermal conductivity. Nevertheless, the crossing of the characteristics serves as a useful method of predicting the time and place of the formation of a shock wave.

This "method of characteristics" can be used for the solution of three-dimensional problems and for problems involving viscosity, thermal conductivity, diffusion, and external forces. In such problems the basic equations for the method, that is, the equation of entropy and the differential equations for f and g, do not have zero on the right-hand side. Consequently f, g, and $\hat{S}$ vary slowly instead of remaining constant along their respective curves. This, however, does not seriously impede the numerical calculations.

b. Application of the method of characteristics to a perfect gas

A certain amount of qualitative information about the propagation of finite waves may be obtained by considering the simple case of a perfect gas with constant specific heat. Such a gas has the following properties:

Equation of state: $$p = (\rho/m)kT \tag{11.5–14}$$

Equation of an adiabat: $$(p/p_0) = (\rho/\rho_0)^\gamma \tag{11.5–15}$$

Speed of sound: $$c = \sqrt{\frac{\gamma kT}{m}} = \sqrt{\frac{\gamma p}{\rho}} = c_0\left(\frac{\rho}{\rho_0}\right)^{\frac{\gamma-1}{2}} \tag{11.5–16}$$

Riemann characteristic: $$\sigma = \frac{2}{\gamma - 1}c \tag{11.5–17}$$

In the definition of the Riemann characteristic, the reference density is taken to be zero. We discuss now solutions for the perfect gas with $\gamma = 3$ and with $\gamma = \dfrac{2m+1}{2m-1}$ (m, an integer).

i. $\gamma = 3$ *or* $m = 1$

The solution to the hydrodynamical equations is particularly easy in the special case of $\gamma = 3$. These solutions describe roughly the propagation of finite waves through a solid since most solids follow approximately the ideal gas adiabat with $\gamma = 3$, that is, $(p/p_0) = (\rho/\rho_0)^3$. (This value of γ is not to be confused with the true ratio of specific heats which lies between 1 and $\frac{5}{3}$.) In this case the velocity of sound is proportional to the density, and the Riemann characteristic is just equal to the velocity of sound:

$$\sigma = c = c_0\left(\frac{\rho}{\rho_0}\right) \tag{11.5–18}$$

Hence $f = (v + c)$ is constant along the curve of $z = z(t)$ whose slope is $(v + c)$; and $g = (v - c)$ is constant along the curve whose slope is $(v - c)$. Therefore, f is constant along the line

$$z = a(f) + ft \tag{11.5–19}$$

and g is constant along the line

$$z = b(g) + gt \tag{11.5–20}$$

The quantities $a(f)$ and $b(g)$ are functions determined by the initial conditions. These equations may be solved simultaneously to obtain

$$t = \frac{b(g) - a(f)}{f - g} \tag{11.5–21}$$

$$z = \frac{fb(g) - ga(f)}{f - g} \tag{11.5–22}$$

Also, from the definition of f and g, it follows that

$$v(z, t) = \tfrac{1}{2}(f + g) \tag{11.5–23}$$

$$c(z, t) = \tfrac{1}{2}(f - g) \tag{11.5–24}$$

The last four equations give a complete solution to the hydrodynamic equations in parametric form. From a knowledge of the velocity and density as functions of position at the initial time, we can calculate the velocity of sound, $c(z, 0)$, and the values of $f(z, 0)$ and $g(z, 0)$. The latter functions determine the functions $a(f)$ and $b(g)$. A knowledge of $a(f)$ and $b(g)$ enables us to use Eqs. 11.5–21 and 22 to determine the values of z and t for any desired value of f and g. Equations 11.5–23 and 24 are used to compute $v(z, t)$ and $c(z, t)$. Then, since $c = c_0(\rho/\rho_0)$, all the properties of the fluid motion are known.

ii. $\gamma = \dfrac{2m + 1}{2m - 1}$; (*m, integer*)

Darboux[4] obtained analytical solutions to the hydrodynamical equations for all values of γ such that $\gamma = \dfrac{2m + 1}{2m - 1}$, where m is an integer.

[4] J. Hadamard, *Leçons sur la propagation des ondes*, Paris (1902).

The case where $\gamma = 3$ ($m = 1$) has already been considered. Two other cases are of particular interest: $m = 2$, which corresponds to a perfect monatomic gas ($\gamma = 1.677$), and $m = 3$, which corresponds to air ($\gamma = 1.400$). The equations of Darboux amount to the solution of the following parametric equations:

$$f = v + \sigma, \qquad g = v - \sigma \tag{11.5–25}$$

$$Z = \left(\frac{1}{\sigma}\right)^{m-1}\left[\frac{\partial^{(m-1)}}{\partial\sigma^{(m-1)}}\left(\frac{a(f) + b(g)}{\sigma}\right)\right]_v \tag{11.5–26}$$

$$t = \left(\frac{\partial Z}{\partial v}\right)_\sigma, \qquad z = -\sigma\left(\frac{\partial Z}{\partial \sigma}\right)_v \tag{11.5–27}$$

Here $a(f)$, $b(g)$, and Z are parameters. The hydrodynamical equations are then solved in much the same manner as when $\gamma = 3$.

c. The formation of shock waves in a perfect gas

As discussed above, the formation of a shock wave occurs at the intersection of characteristics having different values. The following example shows how such a condition might arise. Consider a perfect gas at time $t = 0$, in a condition defined by

$0 < z < \infty$	The gas is at rest with uniform temperature, pressure, and density.
$-\infty < z < 0$	The gas is non-uniform in an arbitrary fashion.

The characteristics f and g are shown schematically in Fig. 11.5–2 as a function of time. There are three regions shown in this figure:

(I) The gas remains undisturbed. Here all the characteristics are constant. This region is bounded by the straight line with slope $(dz/dt) = c_0$, the velocity of sound under the uniform condition.

(II) The gas remains arbitrarily non-uniform. This region is bounded by the wavy line with slope $(dz/dt) = -c$, the (negative) velocity of sound under the local conditions.

(III) Between regions I and II, the characteristics $f = v + \sigma$ follow straight lines since all the characteristics $g = v - \sigma$ with which they intersect arise in region I and therefore all have the same value $g = -2c_0/(\gamma - 1)$. The slope of the f line is $(v + c)$, given by the relation:

$$\begin{aligned} v + c &= \tfrac{1}{2}(f + g) + \left(\frac{\gamma - 1}{2}\right)\tfrac{1}{2}(f - g) \\ &= \left(\frac{\gamma + 1}{4}\right)f + \frac{(\gamma - 3)c_0}{2(\gamma - 1)} \end{aligned} \tag{11.5–28}$$

and hence the slope of f is constant for each value of f.

Since the f characteristics in region III are straight lines having slopes which are linear functions of the value of f itself, it is quite possible for two different f characteristics to intersect at a point S, as shown in Fig. 11.5–2. A shock wave forms at such a point.

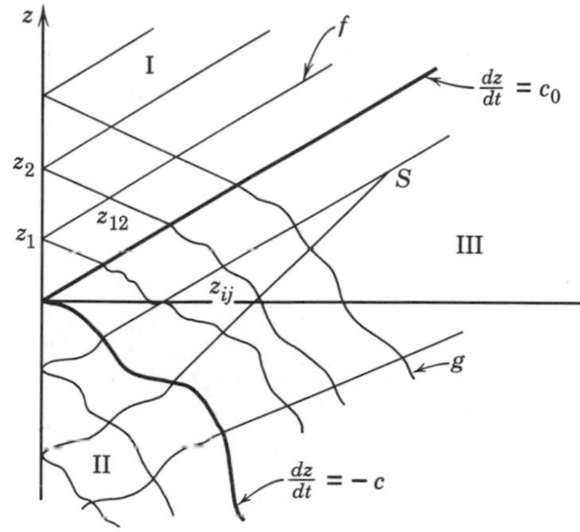

Fig. 11.5–2. Schematic illustration of the general behavior of the characteristics f and g.

To illustrate the formation of a shock wave let us consider a gas in a cylinder fitted with a piston, which can be set into motion in an arbitrary manner. The position of the piston at any time is taken to be

$$\begin{aligned} z &= 0 \qquad t < 0 \\ z &= W(t) \qquad t \geq 0 \end{aligned} \tag{11.5–29}$$

Let the motion of the piston be restricted to subsonic velocities.

In Fig. 11.5–3 the lines of constant f with slope $(v + c)$ are shown drawn from the face of the piston. We suppose that the gas satisfies the ideal gas adiabat so that $\sigma = 2c/(\gamma - 1)$. Again, as in the previous problem, we can construct the line with $dz/dt = c_0$. To the left of this line, the gas remains undisturbed. At any point on the face of the piston, $(v - \sigma) = -2c_0/(\gamma - 1)$ [since the lines of constant $(v - \sigma)$ arise in the undisturbed part of the fluid as in the previous problem]. Thus since on the face of the piston, $v = dW/dt$ it follows that at this point,

$$\sigma = \frac{2c_0}{\gamma - 1} + \frac{dW}{dt} \tag{11.5-30}$$

Then, since $c = \frac{\gamma - 1}{2}\sigma$ and $v = \frac{dW}{dt}$, we have

$$c = c_0 + \frac{\gamma - 1}{2}\frac{dW}{dt} \tag{11.5–31}$$

$$v + c = c_0 + \frac{\gamma + 1}{2}\frac{dW}{dt} \tag{11.5–32}$$

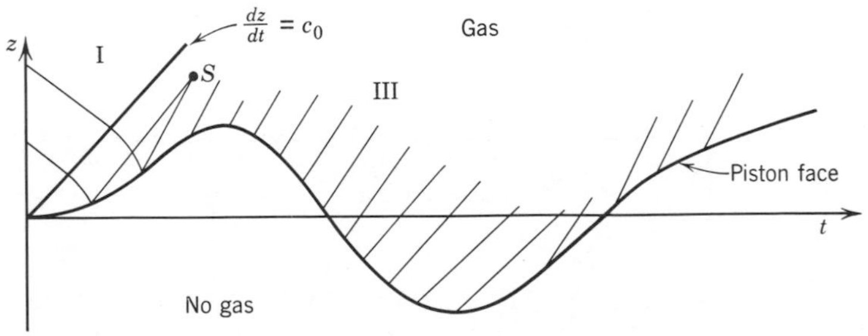

Fig. 11.5–3. Schematic illustration of formation of a shock wave.

From Eq. 11.5–31 it can be seen that whenever dW/dt is positive, $c > c_0$, and the density of the gas in the neighborhood of the piston face is increased. If dW/dt is negative, the gas in the neighborhood of the face is expanded. A line starting from a point (z_1, t_1), where dW/dt is positive but small, will have a slope less than the line starting from point (z_2, t_2), where dW/dt is larger. Thus, if $z_2 > z_1$ these lines meet at some point. It is clear that the less the piston face is accelerated, the smaller will be the differences in the slopes of the lines of constant $(v + \sigma)$, and a longer time will be required before the characteristic lines cross and a shock wave forms. That is:

1. Whenever the piston is accelerating, the lines of constant $(v + \sigma)$ tend to come together to form shock waves.
2. Whenever the piston is decelerating, the lines of constant $(v + \sigma)$ tend to go apart and not to form shock waves.

These are special cases of the more general theorem that shock waves always will be formed, if given sufficient time, when a gas is compressed but will not be formed when a gas is expanded. A few examples are illustrated in Fig. 11.5–4.

The transformation of a sinusoidal wave into one of a sawtooth form was mentioned earlier in this section. The distance at which this complete transformation takes place can be determined in the following manner.

Let us consider once again a gas contained in a cylinder fitted with a piston. Suppose that the piston moves with sinusoidal motion of small amplitude and with frequency ν, in such a way that sound waves are generated. At a sufficient distance from the piston the shape of the

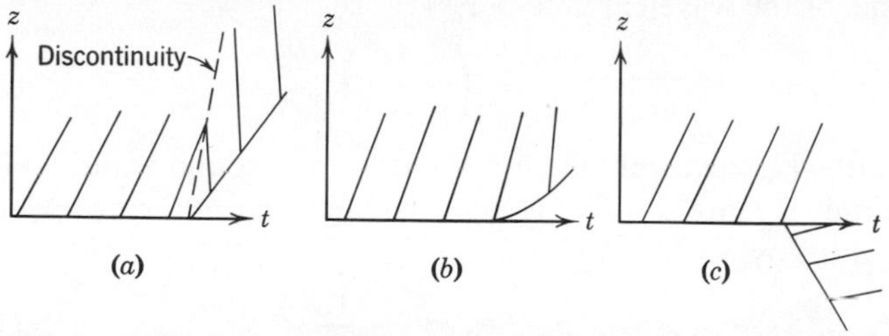

Fig. 11.5–4. Several illustrations of wave formation. (a) The piston is pushed suddenly into the gas. A shock wave develops immediately at the wall. (b) The piston is pushed gradually into the gas. Shock wave develops later. (c) The piston is withdrawn suddenly from the gas. No shock wave forms.

sound wave is transformed into a sawtooth form. To determine the distance required for the transformation to occur, we determine the point of intersection of two adjacent characteristic lines. Consider two lines of constant $f = (v + \sigma)$ emanating from the piston as shown in Fig. 11.5–5. The points (z_1, t_1) and (z_2, t_2) are considered arbitrarily close together. The slope, m, of the constant f lines is, according to Eq. 11.5–32,

$$m = (v + c) = c_0 + \frac{\gamma + 1}{2} V \qquad (11.5\text{–}33)$$

where V is the velocity of the piston. Thus, the slope of the line emanating from (z_2, t_2) is,

$$m + \frac{dm}{dt}(t_2 - t_1) = c_0 + \frac{\gamma + 1}{2}\left\{V + \frac{dV}{dt}(t_2 - t_1)\right\} \qquad (11.5\text{–}34)$$

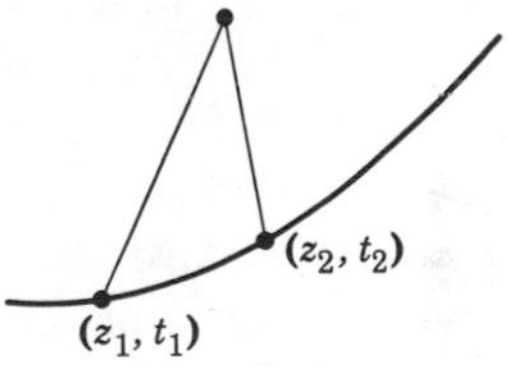

Fig. 11.5–5. An illustration of the crossing of two characteristic lines.

From these considerations it can be shown that the distance to the point of intersection of neighboring lines is

$$\Delta z = \frac{m(m - \gamma)}{\dfrac{dm}{dt}} = \frac{\left(c_0 + \dfrac{\gamma + 1}{2} V\right)\left(c_0 + \dfrac{\gamma - 1}{2} V\right)}{\dfrac{\gamma + 1}{2}\dfrac{dV}{dt}} \qquad (11.5\text{–}35)$$

Now we assume that the piston is moving with sinusoidal variation:

$$V = V_0 \sin 2\pi\nu t \qquad V_0 \ll c_0 \qquad (11.5\text{–}36)$$

Then the closest point of intersection is at

$$\Delta z = \left(\frac{2}{\gamma + 1}\right) \frac{c_0^2}{2\pi\nu V_0} \tag{11.5–37}$$

or in terms of the wavelength $\lambda = c_0/\nu$:

$$\frac{\Delta z}{\lambda} = \left(\frac{2}{\gamma + 1}\right) \frac{c_0}{2\pi V_0} \tag{11.5–38}$$

The quantity V_0 represents the amplitude of the sound wave. However, the amplitude is more commonly described in terms of the "overpressure," which is given by

$$p - p_0 = \gamma p_0 \frac{V_0}{c_0} \tag{11.5–39}$$

Thus in terms of the amplitude in the pressure wave a shock wave forms after a number of wavelengths given by

$$\frac{\Delta z}{\lambda} = \left(\frac{2\gamma}{\gamma + 1}\right) \left(\frac{p_0}{p - p_0}\right) \left(\frac{1}{2\pi}\right) \tag{11.5–40}$$

As an example suppose that we have a wave in air ($\gamma = 1.4$) at 1 atm pressure with an overpressure, $p - p_0 = 0.001$ atm. Then the wave would change into sawtooth form in $\Delta z/\lambda = 186$ wavelengths. This indicates that all sound waves degenerate into small periodic shock waves and that the simple theory of sound propagation does not apply at large distances. However, the present discussion is based on the neglect of such complicating factors as viscosity and thermal conductivity. These factors lead to an absorption of the sound wave. They also tend to destroy the abrupt discontinuous nature of the shock front and hence apparently retard the formation. The actual changes occurring in the wave form are a balance between the tendency to change into a sawtooth form and the absorption processes.

6. One-Dimensional Steady-State Equations of Change

The three sections following this section deal with the theoretical treatment of flames, shock waves, and detonations, all three of which may be described in terms of a steady-state formulation. Accordingly, the mathematical descriptions of these three phenomena have a great deal in common. It is, therefore, the purpose of this section to discuss some of the general principles of steady-state phenomena and to present the basic equations which form the starting point for each of the discussions given in the next three sections. We also present the limiting linear forms of the equations, which describe the behavior of a system which is in a state only slightly removed from chemical and thermal equilibrium.

For simplicity the discussion is limited to one-dimensional steady-state systems—that is, systems in which the properties of the fluid are uniform over parallel planes, and the properties are functions of a single-space coordinate z. In the theory of flames the coordinate system is fixed with respect to the flameholder. In the theory of shock waves and detonations, the coordinate system moves with the wave. A particular value of z then corresponds to a particular position within the wave, and the properties at this point are independent of time. Large positive values of z correspond to points where the gas has already passed through the wave, and chemical and thermal equilibrium has been attained. The properties of the fluid at $z = \infty$ are indicated by a subscript ∞. Most of the equations given in this section are applicable to fluids of any sort and under any conditions of density and temperature. At a number of points special formulae are given which are, strictly speaking, valid only for a dilute gas, that is, one which obeys the ideal gas law ($p = nkT$) and for which the transport phenomena are described by the Chapman-Enskog theory of Chapter 7. In the text it is clearly indicated which equations belong to this latter category and to what extent they may be applied outside the dilute gas range. It is assumed that the fluid is a reacting multicomponent mixture. External forces and radiation flux are not considered inasmuch as their inclusion would complicate the development. They usually do not play an important role in determining the hydrodynamical behavior of a fluid.

a. The basic equations for a system under general conditions

The fundamental hydrodynamic equations of change are summarized in § 11.1b. There the equations of continuity, motion, and energy balance are given in terms of the fluxes: the diffusion velocities $\overline{\boldsymbol{V}}_i$ (or the mass fluxes $\boldsymbol{j}_i$), the pressure tensor p, and the heat flux vector $\boldsymbol{q}$. These fluxes may be written in terms of the transport coefficients and the derivatives of the variables as described in § 11.2. Hence it is possible to rewrite the equations of change in terms of the transport coefficients. In the discussions in the next three sections, however, it turns out to be more convenient to do the following: We write the equation of motion in terms of the coefficient of viscosity, and the equation of energy balance in terms of the coefficient of thermal conductivity. The equations of continuity, however, we leave in their original form—in terms of the diffusion velocities. Then we include, in addition to the equations of change, the relations which give the diffusion velocities in terms of the diffusion coefficients. We call these relations the "diffusion equations." Finally, in order to describe the behavior of a fluid system, it is necessary to specify the equation of state. Hence the basic equations which we consider are: (i) the equations of continuity, (ii) the equation of motion, (iii) the equation of energy balance, (iv) the diffusion equations, and (v) the equation of state.

i. *The Equations of Continuity*

The overall equation of continuity of a one-dimensional system in a steady state is obtained from Eq. 11.1–2 by setting the time derivative equal to zero. Since none of the properties of the gas depend on either x or y, we obtain

$$\frac{d}{dz}\rho v = 0 \tag{11.6–1}$$

This equation may be integrated immediately to give

$$M = \rho v \tag{11.6–2}$$

The constant of integration, M, is identified as the *mass rate of flow* (per unit cross-section in the xy-plane) and is independent of the coordinate z.

Similarly the equations of continuity for the individual chemical components (Eq. 11.1–1) become

$$\frac{d}{dz}[n_i(v + \overline{V}_i)] = K_i \tag{11.6–3}$$

It is convenient to introduce as a new dependent variable the quantity G_i, which is the *fraction of the mass rate of flow* contributed by the ith chemical component:

$$G_i = \frac{m_i n_i(v + \overline{V}_i)}{M} \tag{11.6–4}$$

In terms of G_i the equations of continuity become

$$M\frac{dG_i}{dz} = m_i K_i \tag{11.6–5}$$

Let us now discuss the number of linearly independent G_i for a system which consists of s chemical species reacting according to a set of l' chemical reactions (indicated by the subscript j) which have the stoichiometrical form

$$\beta_{1j}[1] + \beta_{2j}[2] + \cdots \rightleftharpoons \eta_{1j}[1] + \eta_{2j}[2] + \cdots \tag{11.6–6}$$

If k_j and k_j' are the rate constants for the forward and reverse reactions, respectively, the net rate of the jth reaction is

$$r_j = k_j(T)n_1^{\beta_{1j}}n_2^{\beta_{2j}}\cdots - k_j'(T)n_1^{\eta_{1j}}n_2^{\eta_{2j}}\cdots \tag{11.6–7a}$$

$$= k_j(T)\left(\frac{p}{kT}\right)^{\Sigma_i\beta_{ij}} x_1^{\beta_{1j}}x_2^{\beta_{2j}}\cdots - k'(T)\left(\frac{p}{kT}\right)^{\Sigma_i\eta_{ij}} x_1^{\eta_{1j}}x_2^{\eta_{2j}}\cdots \tag{11.6–7b}$$

Then the values of K_i are given by:

$$K_i = \sum_{j=1}^{l'} (\eta_{ij} - \beta_{ij}) r_j \tag{11.6–8}$$

Since the η_{ij} and β_{ij} are constants, it follows that there can be at most only l' linearly independent K_i corresponding to the l' functions r_j. In some cases not all the r_j are linearly independent, and hence the number of linearly independent K_i may be less than l'. For example, if there are a different kinds of atoms present, and ν_{ik} is the number of atoms of the kth kind in a molecule of the ith kind, there are surely a relations of the form

$$\Sigma_i \nu_{ik} K_i = 0 \qquad k = 1, 2, \cdots, a \tag{11.6–9}$$

Equation 11.6–9 expresses the fact that chemical reactions neither destroy nor create atoms. However, not all the a equations of Eq. 11.6–9 are really linearly independent if certain groups go through all the chemical reactions intact. In this case, the number of independent relations expressed by Eq. 11.6–9 is equal to the number of independent components in the sense of the phase rule, $a' \leq a$. Thus the number l of linearly independent K_i is either $(s - a')$ or else l', whichever is the smaller. From Eq. 11.6–5 it is clear that the number of linearly independent G_i is the same as the number of linearly independent K_i.

ii. *The Equation of Motion*

The equation of motion is given in Eq. 11.1–3 in terms of the pressure tensor. In § 11.2 it is pointed out that the form of the pressure tensor may be obtained quite generally by means of the thermodynamics of irreversible processes. For one-dimensional flow the zz-component of the pressure is

$$p_{zz} = p - (\tfrac{4}{3}\eta + \kappa)\frac{dv}{dz} \tag{11.6–10}$$

Substitution of this expression into the equation of motion written for a steady state in one dimension gives

$$\rho v \frac{dv}{dz} + \frac{dp}{dz} - \frac{d}{dz}\left((\tfrac{4}{3}\eta + \kappa)\frac{dv}{dz}\right) = 0 \tag{11.6–11}$$

Inasmuch as $\rho v = M$ is a constant, this equation may be integrated immediately to give

$$Mv + p - (\tfrac{4}{3}\eta + \kappa)\frac{dv}{dz} = B \tag{11.6–12}$$

Here B is a constant of integration which depends upon the boundary conditions. If complete chemical and thermal equilibrium is attained at the point $z = \infty$, it follows that $(dv/dz)_\infty = 0$ and $B = Mv_\infty + p_\infty$.

Hence we obtain finally

$$(\tfrac{4}{3}\eta + \kappa)\frac{dv}{dz} = (p - p_\infty) + M(v - v_\infty) \tag{11.6–13}$$

for the equation of motion.

iii. *The Equation of Energy Balance*

The equation of energy balance is given in Eq. 11.1–4 in terms of the heat flux vector. If external forces and radiation flux are neglected, Eqs. 11.1–4 and 11.6–11 give for one-dimensional steady-state flow

$$\rho v \frac{d\hat{U}}{dz} + \frac{d}{dz} pv + \rho v^2 \frac{dv}{dz} + \frac{dq}{dz} - \frac{d}{dz}\left[(\tfrac{4}{3}\eta + \kappa)\, v \frac{dv}{dz}\right] = 0 \tag{11.6–14}$$

This equation may be integrated immediately to give

$$M(\hat{U} + \frac{p}{\rho} + \tfrac{1}{2}v^2) + q - \left[(\tfrac{4}{3}\eta + \kappa)\, v \frac{dv}{dz}\right] = L \tag{11.6–15}$$

in which L is a constant of integration. If there is complete chemical and thermal equilibrium at the point $z = \infty$, then $L = M(\hat{U} + (p/\rho) + \tfrac{1}{2}v^2)_\infty$. The quantity $(\hat{U} + (p/\rho))$ is the enthalpy per unit mass of the gas:

$$\hat{U} + \frac{p}{\rho} = \hat{H} = \frac{n}{\rho} \textstyle\sum_i x_i m_i \hat{H}_i \tag{11.6–16}$$

The quantity $\hat{H}_i(T)$ is the enthalpy per gram of pure component i.

An expression for the heat flux vector in terms of the transport coefficients has been obtained from the kinetic theory of dilute gases given in Chapter 7 (see Eq. 7.4–64). This expression is

$$q = -\lambda \frac{dT}{dz} + \textstyle\sum_i n_i m_i \hat{H}_i \bar{V}_i - p \sum_j \sum_k \dfrac{n_k D_j^T}{n^2 m_j \mathscr{D}_{jk}} (\bar{V}_k - \bar{V}_j) \tag{11.6–17}$$

This result applies strictly only to a dilute gas. However, according to the discussion of § 11.2, the same form applies to a liquid except that in the latter case the enthalpies in the second term are to be interpreted as partial molar quantities and the thermal diffusion term, which is usually small, must be somewhat modified. Substituting the expression for the heat flux vector into Eq. 11.6–14 and using the equation of motion (11.6–13), we finally obtain

$$\frac{\lambda}{M}\frac{dT}{dz} = \textstyle\sum_i G_i \hat{H}_i - (\sum_i G_i \hat{H}_i)_\infty + \dfrac{p_\infty - p}{\rho}$$

$$- \frac{p}{n^2} \sum_{i,j} \frac{D_i^T[x_i m_i G_j - x_j m_j G_i]}{x_i m_i^2 m_j \mathscr{D}_{ij}} - \tfrac{1}{2}(v - v_\infty)^2 \tag{11.6–18}$$

iv. *The Diffusion Equations*

The kinetic theory of dilute gases gives expressions relating the mass flux vectors (or the diffusion velocities) to the coefficients of diffusion and thermal diffusion (see Eq. 7.4–48). These equations may be written for the one-dimensional problem in terms of the quantities G_i, thus:

$$\frac{dx_i}{dz} = \frac{M}{n} \sum_j \frac{(x_i m_i G_j - x_j m_j G_i)}{m_i m_j \mathscr{D}_{ij}} - x_i \left(1 - \frac{n m_i}{\rho}\right) \frac{d \ln p}{dz} + \frac{1}{n} \frac{d \ln T}{dz} \sum_j \frac{x_i m_i D_j^T - x_j m_j D_i^T}{m_i m_j \mathscr{D}_{ij}} \tag{11.6–19}$$

As discussed in § 11.2, although this result applies strictly only to a dilute gas, there is empirical evidence that the same form applies to a liquid.

v. *The Equation of State*

For the sake of simplicity we often assume that the equation of state may be described by the ideal gas law:

$$p = nkT \tag{11.6–20}$$

The pressure p is that measured with respect to the moving gas stream.

These five sets of equations determine the variables p, x_i, G_i, v, and T as a function of the coordinate z, once the boundary conditions have been specified. At the point $z = \infty$, where complete chemical and thermal equilibrium has been obtained, the derivatives of each of these dependent variables with respect to z is zero. From the diffusion equations and from the condition that all the $(dx_i/dz)_\infty$ vanish, it follows that

$$G_{i\infty} = \frac{n_\infty m_i}{\rho_\infty} x_{i\infty} \tag{11.6–21}$$

From the equations of continuity, the requirement that the $(dG_i/dz)_\infty$ vanish implies that

$$K_i(x_{j\infty}, T_\infty) = 0 \tag{11.6–22}$$

The determination of the temperature at $z = \infty$ requires the knowledge of some additional boundary conditions, for example, those at $z = 0$ or $z = -\infty$.

b. The basic equations for a system near equilibrium[1]

Let us now consider the form assumed by the basic steady-state equations when the system is only slightly removed from chemical and thermal equilibrium. As z approaches ∞, the basic equations become linear in the difference between the values of the variables and their limiting values at $z = \infty$. These linear relations are readily solved and provide asymptotic solutions to the general equations of change. In the equations given

[1] This discussion applies only to a dilute gas.

here, the symbol δ indicates the difference between the variable and its limiting values; for example, $\delta T = T - T_\infty$. It is also understood that all the quantities appearing in the equations are evaluated at $z = \infty$. If there are l independent G_i and s chemical components, there are altogether $(l + s + 2)$ linearly independent functions. We take as the independent functions the first l of the G_i, the first $(s - 1)$ of the x_i, and the variables $T, v,$ and p. The remaining G_i are expressed as linear combinations of the first l,

$$G_i = \sum_{j=1}^{l} a_{ij}G_j + b_i \qquad i = (l + 1), (l + 2), \cdots, s \tag{11.6–23}$$

The constants a_{ij} are determined by the relations between the K_i, and the constants b_i are adjusted to give G_i the correct limiting value given by Eq. 11.6–21. Similarly, x_s is given in terms of the first $(s - 1)$ of the x_i by the relation:

$$x_s = 1 - \sum_{j=1}^{s-1} x_j \tag{11.6–24}$$

We now make Taylor expansions of various parts of the equations of change and retain terms through the first powers of δT, δv, δp, δG_i, and δx_i. To this degree of approximation the equations of change become:

(1) *The Equation of Continuity*

(a) *Overall conservation of mass*

$$0 = \frac{\delta v}{v} + \frac{\delta p}{p} - \frac{\delta T}{T} + \frac{\sum_{i=1}^{s-1} (m_i - m_s)\,\delta x_i}{\sum_{i=1}^{s} m_i x_i} \tag{11.6–25}$$

(b) *Continuity of individual components*

$$\frac{d(\delta G_i)}{dz} = A_{G_iT}\,\delta T + A_{G_ip}\,\delta p + \sum_{j=1}^{s-1} A_{G_ix_j}\,\delta x_j \qquad i = 1, 2, 3, \cdots, l \tag{11.6–26}$$

(2) *The Equation of Motion*

$$(\tfrac{4}{3}\eta + \kappa)\frac{d(\delta v)}{dz} = \delta p + M\,\delta v \tag{11.6–27}$$

(3) *The Equation of Energy Balance*

$$\frac{d(\delta T)}{dz} = A_{TT}\,\delta T + A_{Tp}\,\delta p + \sum_{j=1}^{s-1} A_{Tx_j}\,\delta x_j + \sum_{j=1}^{l} A_{TG_j}\,\delta G_j \tag{11.6–28}$$

(4) *The Diffusion Equations*

$$\frac{d(\delta x_i)}{dz} + B_{ip}\frac{d(\delta p)}{dz} + B_{iT}\frac{d(\delta T)}{dz} = \sum_{j=1}^{s-1} A_{x_ix_j}\,\delta x_j + \sum_{j=1}^{l} A_{x_iG_j}\,\delta G_j \tag{11.6–29}$$

$$i = 1, 2, 3, \cdots, s - 1$$

The coefficients A and B are given by

$$A_{G_iT} = \frac{m_i}{M}\frac{\partial K_i}{\partial T} \tag{11.6–30}$$

$$A_{G_ip} = \frac{m_i}{M}\frac{\partial K_i}{\partial p} \tag{11.6–31}$$

$$A_{G_ix_j} = \frac{m_i}{M}\left[\frac{\partial K_i}{\partial x_j} - \frac{\partial K_i}{\partial x_s}\right] \tag{11.6–32}$$ [2]

$$B_{ip} = \frac{x_i}{p}\left(1 - \frac{nm_i}{\rho}\right) \tag{11.6–33}$$

$$B_{iT} = -\frac{1}{nT}\sum_{j=1}^{s}\frac{x_i m_i D_j^T - x_j m_j D_i^T}{m_i m_j \mathscr{D}_{ij}} \tag{11.6–34}$$

$$A_{x_ix_j} = \frac{M}{\rho}\left[-\frac{x_i}{\mathscr{D}_{ij}} + \frac{x_i}{\mathscr{D}_{is}} + \delta_{ij}\sum_{k=1}^{s}\frac{x_k}{\mathscr{D}_{ik}}\right] \tag{11.6–35}$$

$$A_{x_iG_j} = \frac{M}{n}\left[\frac{x_i}{m_j\mathscr{D}_{ij}} + \sum_{k=l+1}^{s}\frac{x_i a_{kj}}{m_k\mathscr{D}_{ik}} - \delta_{ij}\sum_{k=1}^{s}\frac{x_k}{m_i\mathscr{D}_{ik}}\right] \quad i \leq l \tag{11.6–36a}$$

$$= \frac{M}{n}\left[\frac{x_i}{m_j\mathscr{D}_{ij}} + \sum_{k=l+1}^{s}\frac{x_i a_{kj}}{m_k\mathscr{D}_{ik}} - a_{ij}\sum_{k=1}^{s}\frac{x_k}{m_i\mathscr{D}_{ik}}\right] \quad i > l \tag{11.6–36b}$$

$$A_{TT} = \frac{Mn}{\lambda\rho}\sum_{j=1}^{s} m_j x_j \hat{C}_{pj} \tag{11.6–37}$$

$$A_{Tp} = -\frac{M}{\lambda\rho} \tag{11.6–38}$$

$$A_{Tx_j} = \frac{M}{\lambda}\frac{kT}{\rho}\sum_{i=1}^{s}\left[\frac{D_i^T}{\mathscr{D}_{ij}} - \frac{D_i^T}{\mathscr{D}_{is}} - \frac{x_i}{x_j}\frac{D_j^T}{\mathscr{D}_{ij}} + \frac{x_i}{x_s}\frac{D_s^T}{\mathscr{D}_{is}}\right] \tag{11.6–39}$$

$$A_{TG_j} = \frac{M}{\lambda}\left[\hat{H}_j + \sum_{i=l+1}^{s}\hat{H}_i a_{ij}\right] - \frac{M}{\lambda}\frac{kT}{n}\left[\sum_{i=1}^{s}\left(\frac{D_i^T}{m_j\mathscr{D}_{ij}} - \frac{D_j^T x_i}{x_j m_j \mathscr{D}_{ij}}\right) \right.$$
$$\left. \sum_{k=l+1}^{s} a_{kj}\left[\sum_{i=1}^{s}\left(\frac{D_i^T}{m_k\mathscr{D}_{ik}} - \frac{x_i D_k^T}{x_k m_k \mathscr{D}_{ki}}\right)\right]\right] \tag{11.6–40}$$

[2] The partial derivatives of K_i with respect to the mole fractions are the expressions which would be obtained from Eqs. 11.6–7b and 11.6–8 if all the s mole fractions were linearly independent.

Equations 11.6–25 through 29 then form a set of $(l + s + 1)$ linear first-order differential equations and one linear algebraic equation for the same number of dependent variables. The solutions to these equations have the form

$$\begin{aligned} \delta T &= \Sigma_k t^{(k)} \exp(\alpha^{(k)} z) \\ \delta x_i &= \Sigma_k t^{(k)} [x_i]^{(k)} \exp(\alpha^{(k)} z) \\ \delta G_i &= \Sigma_k t^{(k)} [G_i]^{(k)} \exp(\alpha^{(k)} z) \\ \delta p &= \Sigma_k t^{(k)} [p]^{(k)} \exp(\alpha^{(k)} z) \\ \delta v &= \Sigma_k t^{(k)} [v]^{(k)} \exp(\alpha^{(k)} z) \end{aligned} \tag{11.6–41}$$

Here the $t^{(k)}$ are constants specified by the boundary conditions. If all the $t^{(k)}$ except one are set equal to zero and the resulting expressions substituted into the above equations, we obtain a set of linear algebraic equations for the $\alpha^{(k)}$ and the constants $[x_i]^{(k)}$, $[G_i]^{(k)}$, $[p]^{(k)}$, and $[v]^{(k)}$. These equations are

$$-\frac{1}{T} + \frac{[p]^{(k)}}{p} + \frac{[v]^{(k)}}{v} + \frac{\sum_{i=1}^{s-1} (m_i - m_s)\,[x_i]^{(k)}}{\sum_{i=1}^{s} m_i x_i} = 0 \tag{11.6–42}$$

$$A_{G_jT} + A_{G_jp}[p]^{(k)} + \sum_{i=1}^{s-1} A_{G_jx_i}[x_i]^{(k)} - \alpha^{(k)}[G_j]^{(k)} = 0 \quad j = 1, 2, \cdots, l \tag{11.6–43}$$

$$[p]^{(k)} + (M - (\tfrac{4}{3}\eta + \kappa)\alpha^{(k)})\,[v]^{(k)} = 0 \tag{11.6–44}$$

$$-\alpha^{(k)}B_{jT} - \alpha^{(k)}B_{jp}[p]^{(k)} + \sum_{i=1}^{s-1} (A_{x_jx_i} - \alpha^{(k)}\delta_{ij})[x_i]^{(k)} + \sum_{i=1}^{l} A_{x_jG_i}[G_i]^{(k)} = 0$$
$$j = 1, 2, \cdots, s - 1 \tag{11.6–45}$$

$$(A_{TT} - \alpha^{(k)}) + A_{Tp}[p]^{(k)} + \sum_{i=1}^{s-1} A_{Tx_i}[x_i]^{(k)} + \sum_{i=1}^{l} A_{TG_i}[G_i]^{(k)} = 0 \tag{11.6–46}$$

These linear equations can be solved with the usual algebraic methods with or without the use of determinants.

The $\alpha^{(k)}$ are then given by the roots of the secular equation:[3]

[3] In the secular equation, for convenience of notation, $m = \sum_{i=1}^{s} m_i x_i$.

$$\begin{vmatrix}
-\dfrac{1}{T} & \dfrac{1}{p} & \dfrac{1}{v} & \left(\dfrac{m_1 - m_s}{m}\right) & \cdots & \left(\dfrac{m_{s-1} - m_s}{m}\right) & 0 & \cdots & 0 \\
0 & 1 & M - (\frac{4}{3}\eta + \kappa)\alpha^{(k)} & 0 & \cdots & 0 & 0 & \cdots & 0 \\
A_{TT} - \alpha^{(k)} & A_{Tp} & 0 & A_{Tx_1} & \cdots & A_{Tx_{s-1}} & A_{TG_1} & \cdots & A_{TG_l} \\
-\alpha^{(k)}B_{1T} & -\alpha^{(k)}B_{1p} & 0 & (A_{x_1x_1} - \alpha^{(k)}) & \cdots & A_{x_1x_{s-1}} & A_{x_1G_1} & \cdots & A_{x_1G_l} \\
\cdot & \cdot & \cdot & \cdot & \cdots & \cdot & \cdot & \cdots & \cdot \\
\cdot & \cdot & \cdot & \cdot & \cdots & \cdot & \cdot & \cdots & \cdot \\
\cdot & \cdot & \cdot & \cdot & \cdots & \cdot & \cdot & \cdots & \cdot \\
-\alpha^{(k)}B_{s-1,\,T} & -\alpha^{(k)}B_{s-1,\,p} & 0 & A_{x_{s-1}x_1} & \cdots & A_{x_{s-1}x_{s-1}} - \alpha^{(k)} & A_{x_{s-1}G_1} & \cdots & A_{x_{s-1}G_l} \\
A_{G_1T} & A_{G_1p} & 0 & A_{G_1x_1} & \cdots & A_{G_1x_{s-1}} & -\alpha^{(k)} & \cdots & 0 \\
\cdot & \cdot & \cdot & \cdot & \cdots & \cdot & \cdot & \cdots & \cdot \\
\cdot & \cdot & \cdot & \cdot & \cdots & \cdot & \cdot & \cdots & \cdot \\
\cdot & \cdot & \cdot & \cdot & \cdots & \cdot & \cdot & \cdots & \cdot \\
A_{G_lT} & A_{G_lp} & 0 & A_{G_lx_1} & \cdots & A_{G_lx_{s-}} & 0 & \cdots & -\alpha^{(k)}
\end{vmatrix} = 0 \qquad (11.6\text{–}47)$$

There are altogether $(l + s + 1)$ roots $\alpha^{(k)}$. If complete chemical and thermal equilibrium is attained as z approaches infinity, only the negative values of $\alpha^{(k)}$ can be physically significant (have values of $t^{(k)}$ different from zero).

7. The Theory of Flame Propagation[1]

A flame is a thermal wave accompanied by exothermic chemical reactions which travels with subsonic velocities. A detonation, as distinguished from a flame, travels with velocities supersonic with respect to the material in front of the wave, that is, on the cold side. The velocity of detonation is determined by the equations of conservation of mass, momentum, and energy (along with the Chapman-Jouguet condition), whereas the velocity of flame propagation depends upon the detailed chemical kinetics and the coefficients of diffusion and thermal conductivity. In this section we consider the theory of one-dimensional steady-state laminar flames in homogeneous gas mixtures. In most flames the pressure drop through the flame front is small. It is therefore possible to ignore the effects of viscosity. Furthermore, the kinetic energy associated with the motion of the gases is small compared to the energy released by the reaction. We first consider the boundary conditions and general equations describing the propagation of a flame. Then, as an example, we consider in detail the nature of a hypothetical flame in which the chemical kinetics consists of a single unimolecular rearrangement.

A steady-state flame must be stabilized by the presence of a flame holder.[2] A flame traveling down a large diameter tube does not travel with a plane front, is usually turbulent, and does not approach a steady state.[3] The velocity of travel of such a flame depends on the nature

[1] J. O. Hirschfelder and C. F. Curtiss, *J. Chem. Phys.*, **17**, 1076 (1949), and *J. Phys. and Colloid Chem.*, **55**, 744 (1951); C. F. Curtiss, J. O. Hirschfelder, and D. E. Campbell, "Theory of Flame Propagation and Detonation, III," University of Wisconsin Naval Research Laboratory CM-690 (1952) and *Fourth International Symposium on Flames and Combustion*, Williams and Wilkins (1953); J. O. Hirschfelder, C. F. Curtiss, and D. E. Campbell, *J. Phys. Chem.*, **57**, 403 (1953); and J. O. Hirschfelder and E. S. Campbell, "Analytical (Power Series) Solutions to the Flame Equations," University of Wisconsin Naval Research Laboratory CM-784 (1953).

[2] Although the flame holder is required from mathematical considerations there is some question as to its physical necessity. G. H. Markstein, *J. Aeronaut. Sci.*, **18**, 199 (1951), succeeded in establishing a steady-state flat flame in a pyrex cylinder 10 cm in diameter. The geometry in these experiments was the same as Fig. 11.7–3 except that a flameholder was lacking. In this case the heat transfer to the walls was sufficient to stabilize the position of the flame.

[3] Complete descriptions of experimental flame phenomena are given in the treatises: B. Lewis and G. Von Elbe, *Combustion, Flames and Explosions*, Academic Press (1951), and W. Jost, *Explosion and Combustion Processes in Gases* (translated

and diameter of the tube, and if the tube is sufficiently long the flame either goes out or changes into a detonation.[4]

a. Qualitative discussion of the Bunsen burner flame

A Bunsen flame provides an excellent example of a steady-state system. In a Bunsen burner, as illustrated in Fig. 11.7–1, the fuel and oxidizer are introduced separately at the bottom of a mixing chamber. The mixing chamber is made long enough to insure a homogeneous mixture by the time the gases reach the top of the tube. The flame zone is a right circular cone[5] separated from the mouth of the tube by a quenching zone.[6] The angle of the cone depends on the nature and the rate of flow of the gases.

Let ρ_0 be the density of the cold gases, v_0 be the component of the velocity[7] of the cold gases normal to the flame front, and ρ_∞ and v_∞ be the corresponding quantities on the hot side of the front. The quantity v_0, which is referred to as the flame velocity, is characteristic of the gas mixture and is independent of the details of the burner or rate of flow of the gases. The flame velocity v_0 is determined theoretically by the solution of the equations of change.

Experimentally the flame velocity may be determined from the angle of the cone on a Bunsen burner. Let us consider in detail the flow of gases

---

by H. O. Croft), McGraw-Hill (1946). An excellent discussion of the earlier theories of flame propagation is given by M. W. Evans, "Theoretical Concepts of Flame Propagation," *Chem. Revs.*, **53**, 363 (1952). Another excellent survey has been given by F. T. McClure and W. G. Berl, *Ind. and Eng. Chem.*, **45**, 1415 (1953).

[4] A thorough discussion of traveling flames is given by W. Jost, *Explosion and Combustion Processes in Gases* (translated by H. O. Croft), McGraw-Hill (1946), p. 91, and by B. Lewis and G. Von Elbe, *Combustion, Flames and Explosions*, Academic Press (1951), p. 317. Because of surface drag and the heat transfer to the walls the flame front is curved. Because of the increased surface due to the curvature the apparent flame velocity of traveling waves in large diameter tubes is usually more than twice the Bunsen flame velocity. The hydrodynamical stability of flame fronts is considered theoretically by H. Einbinder, *J. Chem. Phys.*, **21**, 480 (1953).

[5] The flame zone (except for the very tip and near the edges) is a true right circular cone if the velocity of the gases in the tube is independent of the distance from the center of the tube. The constant velocity profile can be attained by properly shaping the tube near the mouth. See H. Mache and A. Hebra, *Akad. Wiss. Abteilung Wien* (IIa), **150**, 157 (1941), and J. W. Andersen, *Rev. Sci. Instr.*, **19**, 822 (1948).

[6] The length of the quenching zone is determined by the heat transfer from the flame to the mouth of the tube. See R. Friedman, *Third Symposium on Combustion, Flames and Explosion Phenomena*, Williams and Wilkins (1948).

[7] In this chapter the symbol $\boldsymbol{v}$ stands for the mass average velocity, which is called $\boldsymbol{v}_0$ in Chapters 7–10. The latter should not be confused with the quantity v_0 defined here.

through the flame zone. Because of the cylindrical symmetry it is necessary to consider only the two-dimensional situation represented by the flow in a plane containing the axis of the tube. Let θ be the angle between the cone and the axis of the tube as illustrated in Fig. 11.7–1. Then the components of the velocity of the cold gases, $\boldsymbol{v}^{(0)}$, perpendicular and parallel to the burning surface, are

$$v_{\perp}^{(0)} = v^{(0)} \sin \theta = v_0 \tag{11.7–1}$$

$$v_{\parallel}^{(0)} = v^{(0)} \cos \theta \tag{11.7–2}$$

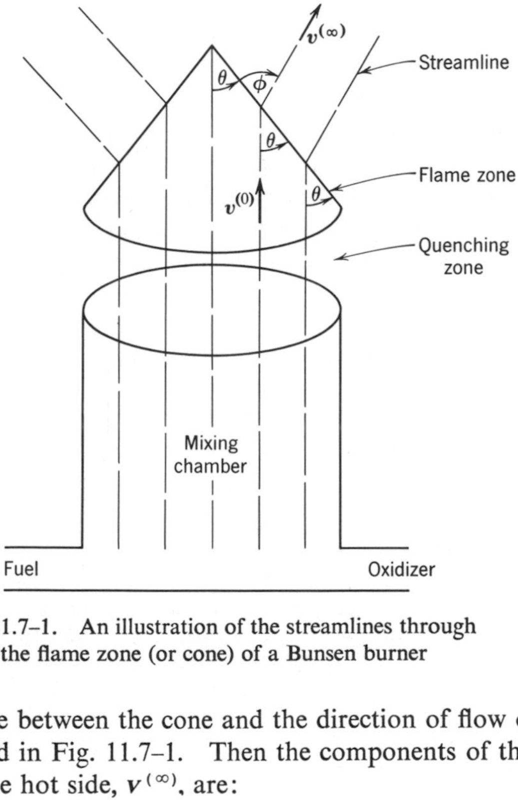

Fig. 11.7–1. An illustration of the streamlines through the flame zone (or cone) of a Bunsen burner

Let ϕ be the angle between the cone and the direction of flow of the hot gases as illustrated in Fig. 11.7–1. Then the components of the velocity of the gases on the hot side, $\boldsymbol{v}^{(\infty)}$, are:

$$v_{\perp}^{(\infty)} = v^{(\infty)} \sin \phi = v_\infty \tag{11.7–3}$$

$$v_{\parallel}^{(\infty)} = v^{(\infty)} \cos \phi \tag{11.7–4}$$

The components of the velocity parallel to the flame front are unchanged by passage of the gas through the flame:

$$v^{(0)} \cos \theta = v^{(\infty)} \cos \phi \tag{11.7–5}$$

In terms of v_0 and v_∞, as given by the equations above, this equation becomes

$$\frac{v_0}{v_\infty} = \frac{\tan\theta}{\tan\phi} \tag{11.7–6}$$

Since the equation of continuity states that $\rho_0 v_0 = \rho_\infty v_\infty$, this result implies that

$$\frac{\rho_\infty}{\rho_0} = \frac{\tan\theta}{\tan\phi} \tag{11.7–7}$$

Figure 11.7–2 shows the actual streamlines in a Bunsen flame. In accordance with Eq. 11.7–1, a knowledge of $v^{(0)}$ and a measurement of the angle θ that the flame zone makes with the vertical, leads to a determination of the flame velocity. In accordance with Eq. 11.7–7, measurements of the angles of deflection of the streamlines determine the ratio of density of the hot to the cold gases. Observations of this kind can be used to indicate the degree to which the gases burn towards complete chemical equilibrium. This method of analysis in conjunction with microscopic examination of films, such as Fig. 11.7–2, has been used as the basis for an experimental determination of the temperature as a function of distance throughout the combustion zone.[8]

Usually the flame velocity and other characteristics of the combustion do not vary appreciably from streamline to streamline (except near the tip and near the edges), although there is a considerable variation in the curvature of the conical flame front. This is because the radius of curvature is ordinarily very large compared to the thickness of the burning zone, which is usually of the order of a millimeter. Since the flame characteristics are not sensitive to the radius of curvature, we consider the limit of a large radius of curvature where the burning surface is plane. For such a flame the temperature and chemical composition depend only on the distance z perpendicular to this surface. The results of this one-dimensional theory may be applied to three-dimensional burners by assuming that the temperature, chemical composition, and component of velocity perpendicular to the flame surface vary with the distance from the flame surface in the same manner in a burner as in the hypothetical one-dimensional case, and that the component of velocity of the gases parallel to the flame surface remains unchanged in passing through the flame zone.

Though the flame zone is sufficiently thin that the one-dimensional theory can be used, it is nevertheless sufficiently thick that the concepts

[8] J. W. Andersen and R. S. Fein, *J. Chem. Phys.*, **17**, 1268 (1949).

of the macroscopic properties of a continuum are applicable. That is, since the burning zone is usually hundreds of mean free paths thick, it is possible to attach significance to the concepts of local temperature, pressure, density, and chemical composition and to use the usual equations of change to determine the variations in these quantities.

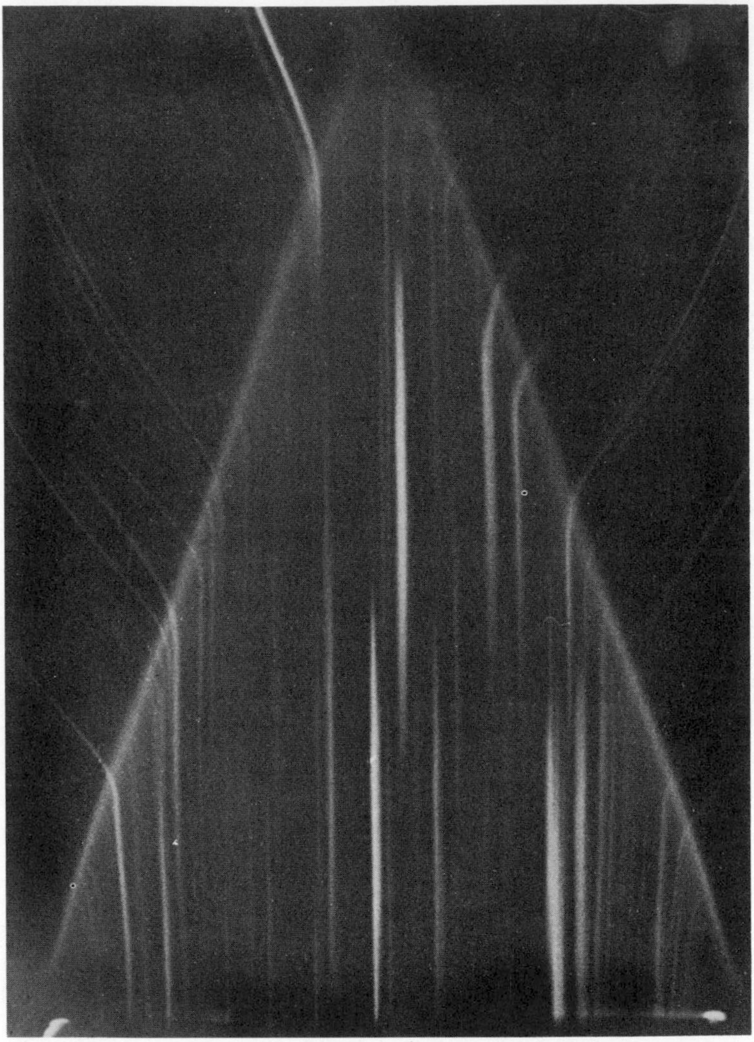

Fig. 11.7–2. A photograph showing the streamlines through a cone on a Bunsen burner. The exit of the tube was so designed as to obtain a constant-velocity profile. [From J. W. Andersen and R. S. Fein, *J. Chem. Phys.*, **17**, 1268 (1949).]

In some flames[9] the transfer of energy between vibrational and translational motion is so slow that it is significant to define a vibrational as well as a translational temperature. In other systems, there are metastable excited electronic states which should be considered as separate molecular species. These complications tend to destroy the notion of local temperature and make the chemical reaction rates in a flame somewhat different from those in a static system. However, in the present discussion this lack of thermal equilibrium is not considered explicitly since it would tend to confuse the basic principles of flame propagation.

Radiation plays an important role in flame propagation, but the specificity of the radiation and quenching processes makes it necessary to consider each example separately.[9] The development given in § 11.3 makes it possible to include radiation transfer in the theory of flames presented here.[10] Experimental results indicate that the radiation from a flame is a mixture of chemiluminescence and thermal radiation, with the chemiluminescence usually dominant. A very bright flame emits less than one-half per cent of its chemical energy in the form of visible light. Most of the radiation emitted is in the form of infrared radiation bands. All molecules which emerge from an exothermic chemical reaction are initially formed in either excited electronic or vibrational states. The molecules if left to themselves give off this energy in the form of radiation. However, in collisions they also transfer this energy to other molecules in the form of translational or thermal energy. Usually it requires a very large number of collisions to effect such an energy transfer. The number of collisions required varies a great deal with the molecular species. Some species are remarkably effective in bringing about the energy transfer and thereby quenching the radiation. For example, in a carbon monoxide-oxygen flame a small trace of water vapor[11] reduces the fraction of the chemical energy emitted in the form of radiation from 24 per cent to 3 per cent. In this case the flame velocity is greatly affected by the presence of the water vapor.

b. The theory of steady-state one-dimensional flame propagation

The concept of one-dimensional steady-state flame propagation is an idealization of the behavior of the gases in a small segment of a Bunsen burner flame zone. Figure 11.7 3 shows the hypothetical burner system which we assume. The lower portion resembles the Bunsen burner as

[9] A. G. Gaydon, *Spectroscopy and Combustion Theory*, Chapman-Hall, 2nd ed. (1948).

[10] J. L. Magee, "The Effect of Radiation in Flames," University of Wisconsin Naval Research Laboratory CM-627 (1950).

[11] D. A. Hall and K. Tawada, *Trans. Faraday Soc.*, **26**, 600 (1930).

far as the intakes and the mixing chamber are concerned. However, in place of the mouth of the tube there is a porous plug which serves as a "flameholder." Above the porous plug the straight sides of the burner are extended so as to prevent the streamlines from spreading. This burner is assumed to be sufficiently.large that there are no wall effects, and the flame zone is planar (at least away from the walls).

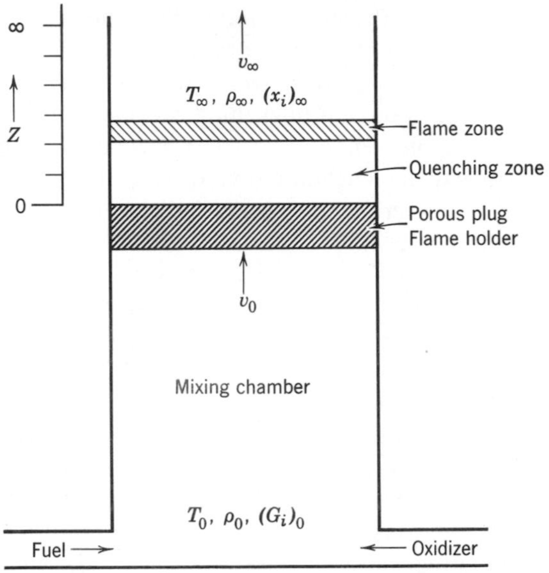

11.7–3. Burner system assumed as a model for one-dimensional flames.

The flameholder is necessary in order that the equations of change possess steady-state solutions. Without the flameholder two difficulties develop in the attempt to obtain a mathematical solution to the problems. First, the product molecules tend to diffuse backward through the flame zone into the unreacted gas, thereby preventing the establishment of a steady state. Secondly, the usual expressions for the rates of chemical reactions are such that there is a finite, although small, rate of reaction at the intake temperature. For these reasons[12] it is necessary that in the solution of the one-dimensional problem we introduce the concept of a flameholder which has two properties. (i) The flameholder is a semi-permeable porous plug through which the fuel and oxidizer molecules pass freely but through which the product molecules formed in the chemical reactions cannot pass. This prevents back diffusion into the mixing

[12] In the three-dimensional problem of burning in a Bunsen cone, the flame is stabilized by small effects due to the presence of the end of the tube.

chamber which would be incompatible with a steady state. (ii) The flameholder serves as a heat sink extracting an amount of heat from the flame (see Eq. 11.2–49),

$$q_0 = -\lambda_0 \left(\frac{dT}{dz}\right)_0 + (\sum_i n_i \bar{H}_i \bar{V}_i)_0 \tag{11.7–8}$$

Here z is the distance from the flameholder, and the subscript 0 is used to refer to quantities at the flameholder. This heat transfer lends stability to the position of the flame relative to the flameholder.

The temperature, density, and mass rates of flow of the various components are known in the mixing chamber and have the same values at the cold boundary, $z = 0$. The heat transfer to the flameholder is specified. At the hot boundary, $z = \infty$, there is complete thermal and chemical equilibrium so that T_∞, ρ_∞, and $(x_i)_\infty$ are known.

The equations describing the propagation of a flame are the one-dimensional steady-state equations of change and the diffusion equations, discussed in the preceding section. These equations along with the boundary conditions possess a solution for only one value of the mass rate of flow M. This solution describes the structure of the flame front. There are boundary conditions at both $z = \infty$ (the "hot boundary") and $z = 0$ (the "cold boundary") at the flameholder.

The boundary conditions at the hot boundary, where chemical and thermal equilibrium have been established, are discussed in § 11.6b. The boundary conditions at the cold boundary are related to the properties of the flameholder. Because of diffusion of the product molecules from the flame all the way back to the flameholder, the chemical composition of the gases at the flameholder, that is, the $(x_i)_0$ are not specified. However, the fractions of the mass rates of flow contributed by the various chemical species, $(G_i)_0$, are specified at the flameholder in terms of the chemical composition of the cold gases in the mixing chamber,

$$(G_i)_0 = \left(\frac{nm_i x_i}{\rho}\right)_{\substack{\text{mixing}\\\text{chamber}}} \tag{11.7–9}$$

Because the $(x_i)_0$ are not specified, it is not possible in a simple way to integrate the equations of change from the cold towards the hot boundary. The values of T_0 and q_0, which are the temperature and the strength of the heat sink at the flameholder, complete the specification of the cold boundary conditions.

Since the $(x_i)_0$ are not specified, numerical solutions[13] of the equations

[13] Difficulties in obtaining numerical solutions are often due to either "instability" or "overstability" of the family of solutions to the differential equations. A numerical procedure which has proved helpful in these cases is discussed by C. F. Curtiss and J. O. Hirschfelder, "Integration of Stiff Equations," *Proc. Natl. Acad. Sci*, **38**, 235 (1952).

of change are usually made from the flame temperature T_∞ towards the low temperatures. The starting conditions at the hot boundary are discussed in § 11.6b. If there is more than one linearly independent G_i there is usually more than one negative root $\alpha^{(k)}$ (see Eq. 11.6–47) so that the determination of the flame velocity becomes a multi-eigenvalue problem. For a fixed value of the flame temperature the equations may be integrated toward the cold boundary without reference to the values of either T_0 or q_0. The lowest possible temperature of the flameholder consistent with the conservation of energy is given the symbol T_0'. This temperature corresponds to $q_0 = 0$.

At the present time there are only three examples where it is possible to compare theoretical and experimental results.

(a) *Ethylene Oxide Decomposition.* This was treated as a unimolecular decomposition.

$$(v_0)_{\text{exptl}} = 12.5 \text{ cm/sec} \qquad \text{(ref. 14)}$$

$$(v_0)_{\text{calcd}} = 9.6 \text{ cm/sec} \qquad \text{(ref. 14)}$$

(b) *Hydrazine Decomposition.* This was treated as a unimolecular decomposition, using Szwarc's[15] experimental rate constant. Adams and Stocks[16] believe that better agreement between theory and experiment would be obtained if all the steps in the chain reaction were considered. For an initial temperature of 150°C and one atmosphere pressure,

$$(v_0)_{\text{exptl}} = 200 \text{ cm/sec} \qquad \text{(ref. 17)}$$

$$(v_0)_{\text{calcd}} = 294 \text{ cm/sec} \qquad \text{(ref. 18)}$$

(c) *Ozone Decomposition.* This is the first case where the flame theory has been carried out for a chain reacting system:

$$O_3 \rightleftharpoons O + O_2$$

$$O + O_3 \rightleftharpoons O_2 + O_2$$

[14] M. Gerstein, G. E. McDonald, and R. L. Schalla, *Fourth Symposium on Flames, Combustion and Detonations*, Boston (1952).

[15] M. Szwarc, *J. Chem. Phys.*, **17**, 505 (1949).

[16] G. K. Adams and G. W. Stocks, *Fourth Symposium on Flames, Combustion, and Detonations*, Boston (1952).

[17] R. C. Murray and A. R. Hall, *Trans. Faraday Soc.*, **47**, 743 (1951). Owing to a typographical error their value of λ is too small by a factor of 10.

[18] J. O. Hirschfelder, C. F. Curtiss, and D. E. Campbell, *J. Phys. Chem.*, **57**, 403 (1953). The value given above has been corrected for the error in ref. 17.

For a mixture of 25 per cent (molar) of ozone and 75 per cent of oxygen at an initial temperature of 300°K and a pressure of 624 mm Hg:

$(v_0)_{\text{exptl}}$ = 55 cm/sec (ref. 19)

$(v_0)_{\text{calcd.}}$ =
- 47 cm/sec (using best diffusion constants) (ref. 18)
- 51 cm/sec (using diffusion coefficients 20 per cent smaller) (ref. 18)
- 85 cm/sec (setting diffusion coefficients equal zero) (ref. 18)
- 255 cm/sec (setting diffusion coefficients equal to zero and assuming that the oxygen atom concentration corresponds to a pseudo-stationary equilibrium with the ozone) (ref. 20)

The effect of pressure on flame propagation may be seen from the pressure dependence of the various quantities. The coefficients of diffusion, $\mathscr{D}_{ij}$, vary inversely as the first power of the pressure; the thermal conductivity, λ, is independent of pressure; and the chemical reaction rates vary as p^β, where β is the order of the chemical reactions. For most ordinary flames we can neglect the kinetic energy of the gases, thermal diffusion, and radiation flux. If all the chemical reactions are of the same order β, and if all quantities evaluated for one atmosphere pressure are indicated by the subscript 1, the equations of change have the form

$$\frac{M}{p^\beta}\frac{dG_i}{dz} = [K_i]_1 \tag{11.7–10}$$

$$\frac{1}{M}\frac{dx_i}{dz} = kT \sum_j \frac{1}{[\mathscr{D}_{ij}]_1}\left(x_i \frac{G_j}{m_j} - x_j \frac{G_i}{m_i}\right) \tag{11.7–11}$$

$$\frac{1}{M}\frac{dT}{dz} = \frac{1}{\lambda_1}[\textstyle\sum_i \hat{H}_i G_i - (\sum_i \hat{H}_i G_i)_\infty] \tag{11.7–12}$$

Since the right-hand sides of these equations are independent of pressure, it is clear that all the equations and their boundary conditions remain invariant if

$$M = p^{\beta/2} M_1 \tag{11.7–13}$$

[19] B. Lewis and G. Von Elbe, *J. Chem. Phys.*, **2**, 283 (1934). The fact that the observations were made on spherically expanding flames should make $(v_0)_{\text{exptl}}$ somewhat smaller than would be observed for a plane flame front.

[20] B. Lewis and G. Von Elbe, *J. Chem. Phys.*, **2**, 537 (1934).

and if all distances z are $p^{-\beta/2}$ times the values they would have if the pressure were one atmosphere. Since the flame velocity is proportional to M/p, it follows that for unimolecular reactions $v_0 \sim p^{-1/2}$; for second-order reactions, v_0 is independent of p; and for third-order reactions, $v_0 \sim p^{1/2}$. In actual flames involving chain reactions the chain-starting mechanisms are either first or second order, the chain-carrying reactions are second order, and the chain-stopping mechanisms are either second or third order. At high pressures the chain-starting reactions therefore become less important, and the chain stoppers become more important. This leads to the conclusion (borne out by experimental observations) that the effective value of β is less than 2. However, since most of the chain starters are formed in the hot part of the flame and diffuse back, the kinetic mechanism of forming these chain starters is not important, so that in practice β is very close to 2.

c. Simple example of a flame (unimolecular reversible reaction)

The solution of the basic equations describing a real flame involves difficult numerical procedures. The difficulties occur primarily because of the complicated kinetics describing the reactions taking place and the large number of variables which must be considered. Hence in order to discuss the basic nature of the solutions, uncomplicated by the chemical kinetics, we discuss here a particularly simple case. We consider a flame in which the kinetics may be described by a single reversible unimolecular reaction. The reaction consists of fuel molecules A reacting to give product molecules B, with the liberation of Q calories per molecule:

$$A \rightleftharpoons B \tag{11.7–14}$$

This system is sufficiently simple that we can investigate the nature of the solutions of the equations of change, investigate the significance of the boundary conditions, and determine the dependence of the flame velocity and the structure of the flame zone upon the values of the various parameters.

Since one fuel molecule produces one product molecule, $m_A = m_B = m$. For simplicity we take the specific heat per gram at constant pressure to be independent of the temperature and to be the same for both species: $(\hat{C}_p)_A = (\hat{C}_p)_B = \hat{C}_p$. Furthermore, in this example there is only one independent mole fraction (since $x_A + x_B = 1$), and there is only one independent fraction of the mass rate of flow (since $G_A + G_B = 1$). To simplify the notation we let $x_A \equiv x$ and $G_A \equiv G$. The rate at which molecules of A are formed (in molecules cm^{-3} sec^{-1}) is

$$K = -nxk'e^{-E^\ddagger/kT} + n(1 - x)k'e^{-(E^\ddagger+Q)/kT} \tag{11.7–15}$$

The steric factor k' is assumed to be the same for both the forward and the reverse reactions, and $E^{\ddagger}$ is the activation energy per molecule for the forward reaction.

For this example it is convenient to rewrite the equations of change in terms of dimensionless quantities. We define the dimensionless variables —temperature, velocity, and distance—thus:

$$\tau = kT/E^{\ddagger} = \text{reduced temperature} \tag{11.7–16}$$

$$u = v/v_{\infty} = \text{reduced velocity} \tag{11.7–17}$$

$$\zeta = M\hat{C}_p \int_0^z \frac{dz}{\lambda} = \text{reduced distance (from flameholder)} \tag{11.7–18}$$

When the equations of change are written in terms of these quantities, we obtain equations for x, u, and τ in terms of ζ. Certain dimensionless groups appear when the equations are written in this way. These dimensionless groups are:

(i) The *reduced mass rate of flow*,

$$\mu = M\sqrt{\hat{C}_p/k'\lambda\rho} \tag{11.7–19}$$

which replaces the parameter M as the eigenvalue of the problem.

(ii) The *Mach number* at the hot boundary,

$$\kappa_{\infty} = (v/c)_{\infty} \tag{11.7–20}$$

in which $c = (\gamma' kT/m)^{1/2}$ is the velocity of sound, γ' being the specific heat ratio for the reacting gas mixture. The latter may be obtained from Eq. 11.4–26:

$$\gamma' = 1 + \cfrac{1}{(\gamma - 1)^{-1} + \left(\cfrac{Q}{kT}\right)^2 \cfrac{e^{+Q/kT}}{(1 + e^{+Q/kT})^2}} \tag{11.7–21}$$

Here γ is the specific heat ratio of the gas mixture if no chemical reactions were taking place. If the chemical reaction under consideration has no back reaction, then at the hot boundary the specific heat ratio γ' would equal γ.

(iii) The *reduced energy of reaction*,

$$\beta = Q/E^{\ddagger} \tag{11.7–22}$$

(iv) The *reduced coefficient of diffusion*,

$$\delta = \frac{\hat{C}_p \rho \mathscr{D}_{AB}}{\lambda} \tag{11.7–23}$$

which is the ratio of the Prandtl number to the Schmidt number (see § 1.2). This parameter usually has a value about $\delta = 4\gamma/(8\gamma - 5)$ or approximately unity.

(v) The *reduced coefficient of viscosity*,

$$\omega = \frac{4}{3}\frac{\hat{C}_p \eta}{\lambda} \tag{11.7–24}$$

which is the Prandtl number (see § 1.2) multiplied by a factor $\frac{4}{3}$. According to the Eucken correction (see §§ 7.6b and 8.4d) ω has the value $\frac{16}{3}\frac{\gamma}{(9\gamma - 5)}$ or approximately unity.

In terms of these dimensionless variables and parameters the flame equations are:

Equation of continuity: $$\frac{dG}{d\zeta} = \frac{1}{\mu^2} f(x, \tau) \tag{11.7–25}$$

Equation of motion: $$\frac{du}{d\zeta} = \frac{1}{\omega} h(u, \tau) \tag{11.7–26}$$

Equation of energy balance: $$\frac{d\tau}{d\zeta} = g(u, \tau, G) \tag{11.7–27}$$

Diffusion equation: $$\frac{dx}{d\zeta} = \frac{1}{\delta}(x - G) \tag{11.7–28}$$

In these equations the functions f, g, and h are given by:

$$f(x, \tau) = e^{-1/\tau}\,[-x + (1 - x)\,e^{-\beta/\tau}] \tag{11.7–29}$$

$$h(u, \tau) = (u - 1) + \frac{1}{\kappa_\infty^{\;2}\gamma'}\left(\frac{\tau}{u\tau_\infty} - 1\right) \tag{11.7–30}$$

$$g(u, \tau, G) = \left(\frac{\gamma - 1}{\gamma}\right)\beta\,(G - G_\infty) - (\tau_\infty - \tau) + \left(\frac{\gamma - 1}{\gamma}\right)\left[(u\tau_\infty - \tau) - \frac{\kappa_\infty^{\;2}}{2}\gamma'\tau_\infty\,(u - 1)^2\right] \tag{11.7–31}$$

The *boundary conditions at the hot boundary* are such that the derivatives in Eqs. 11.7–25 through 28 are zero for $\zeta = \infty$. That is, in terms of τ_∞:

$$x_\infty = \frac{e^{-\beta/\tau_\infty}}{1 + e^{-\beta/\tau_\infty}} \tag{11.7–32}$$

$$u_\infty = 1 \tag{11.7–33}$$

$$G_\infty = x_\infty \tag{11.7–34}$$

The relation of τ_∞ to τ_0 is discussed presently.

The *boundary conditions at the cold boundary* are specified by the properties of the flameholder and the fuel gas. For simplicity we assume that the fuel gas consists of pure A, so that

$$G_0 = 1 \tag{11.7–35}$$

Because of back diffusion right up to the flameholder the value of x_0 may not be specified. In terms of the strength q_0 of the heat sink at the flameholder, the value of g at the cold boundary is given by

$$\begin{aligned} -q_0 &= \lambda_0 \left(\frac{dT}{dz}\right)_0 - \frac{MQ}{m}(1 - x_0) \\ &= \left(\frac{E^{\ddagger} M \hat{C}_p}{k'}\right) g_0 - \frac{MQ}{m}(1 - x_0) \end{aligned} \tag{11.7–36}$$

Furthermore, at the flameholder $(dv/dz)_0 = 0$, so that

$$h_0 = h(u_0, \tau_0) = 0 \tag{11.7–37}$$

This completes the statement of the boundary conditions.

The boundary conditions may now be written in a somewhat more convenient form. Since $h = 0$ at the cold boundary, the defining equation for $h(u, \tau)$ (Eq. 11.7–30) provides a quadratic equation for u_0 in terms of τ_0. The solution of this equation is

$$u_0 = \tfrac{1}{2}\left[1 + \frac{1}{\kappa_\infty{}^2\gamma'} \pm \sqrt{\left(1 + \frac{1}{\kappa_\infty{}^2\gamma'}\right)^2 - \frac{4}{\kappa_\infty{}^2\gamma'}\frac{\tau_0}{\tau_\infty}}\right] \tag{11.7–38}$$

Using this solution and the defining equation for $g(u, \tau, G)$ (Eq. 11.7–31), we can obtain from Eq. 11.7–36 a relation between τ_0, τ_∞, q_0, and x_0. Physically the initial temperature τ_0 of the gas and the gradient in the temperature or g_0 are specified. Hence this result could be used as an equation for determining τ_∞ from τ_0. Actually, since the numerical integrations are usually carried out from the hot boundary to the cold boundary, it is frequently more convenient to specify τ_∞ and use the result described above as an equation for determining τ_0 from τ_∞. The result is an expression for τ_0 which depends on the strength of the heat sink q_0. The lowest possible value of τ_0 is that obtained by taking q_0 to be zero. This value is denoted by τ_0'.

In most flames the high-temperature Mach number, κ_∞, is small compared to unity. For such flames the lower sign in Eq. 11.7–38 applies. If the expression is expanded, we obtain a simple relation between u_0 and τ_0:

$$u_0 = \frac{\tau_0}{\tau_\infty}\left[1 - \kappa_\infty{}^2\gamma'\left(1 - \frac{\tau_0}{\tau_\infty}\right) + \cdots\right] \tag{11.7–39}$$

Since the mass rate of flow M is constant, we obtain from the definition of u and the ideal gas law:

$$u = \frac{v}{v_\infty} = \frac{\rho_\infty}{\rho} = \frac{p_\infty}{p}\frac{\tau}{\tau_\infty} \tag{11.7–40}$$

Hence Eq. 11.7–39 implies that the pressure ratio is

$$\frac{p_\infty}{p_0} = \frac{\tau_\infty}{\tau_0}u_0 = 1 - \kappa_\infty{}^2\gamma'\left(1 - \frac{\tau_0}{\tau_\infty}\right) + \cdots \tag{11.7–41}$$

When typical values of the parameter are substituted into this expression, it follows that for ordinary flames the pressure ratio p_∞/p_0 is about 0.998. For these ordinary flames the effects of viscosity may be neglected.

If the viscosity of the gas is neglected, the equation of motion (11.7–26) becomes simply: $h(u, \tau) = 0$. This is a quadratic equation for u as a function of τ, which may be solved to give the relation

$$u = \tfrac{1}{2}\left[1 + \frac{1}{\kappa_\infty{}^2\gamma'} \pm \sqrt{\left(1 + \frac{1}{\kappa_\infty{}^2\gamma'}\right)^2 - \frac{4}{\kappa_\infty{}^2\gamma'}\frac{\tau}{\tau_\infty}}\right] \tag{11.7–42}$$

This equation may be used to eliminate the variable u from the energy balance equation. The flame equations then consist of the remaining three equations, which define x, τ, and G as functions of ζ.

In the remaining portion of this section we discuss the solution of these equations, in which viscosity is neglected. As mentioned previously, the kinetic energy associated with the motion of the gases is usually negligible. We begin by considering the solution of the flame equations with this approximation—first without diffusion effects ($\delta = 0$) and then with diffusion. The section is concluded with a discussion of the effect of the kinetic energy terms, which become important in solving the flame equations for high-velocity flames.

d. Simple example of a flame: kinetic energy and diffusion neglected

The simplest example of a flame is obtained by neglecting the kinetic energy of the gases (an excellent approximation for ordinary flames) and setting the coefficient of diffusion equal to zero. In this case the diffusion equation (11.7–28) states that $G = x$. Actually diffusion has little effect on G but a large effect on x. Therefore the behavior of x in the following analysis is similar to the behavior of G in a flame with diffusion. Division of the equation of continuity (11.7–25) by the equation of energy balance (11.7–27) gives a differential equation for x as a function of temperature, thus:

$$\frac{dx}{d\tau} = \frac{1}{\mu^2}\frac{f(x, \tau)}{g(x, \tau)} \tag{11.7–43}$$

The function $f(x, \tau)$ is given by Eq. 11.7–29, and $g(x, \tau)$ is given by Eq. 11.7–31, in which the kinetic energy term (that is, the last term) is neglected:

$$g(x, \tau) = \left(\frac{\gamma - 1}{\gamma}\right)\beta(x - x_\infty) - (\tau_\infty - \tau) \qquad (11.7\text{–}44)$$

Hence for this case the behavior of the flame is described by a single ordinary differential equation.

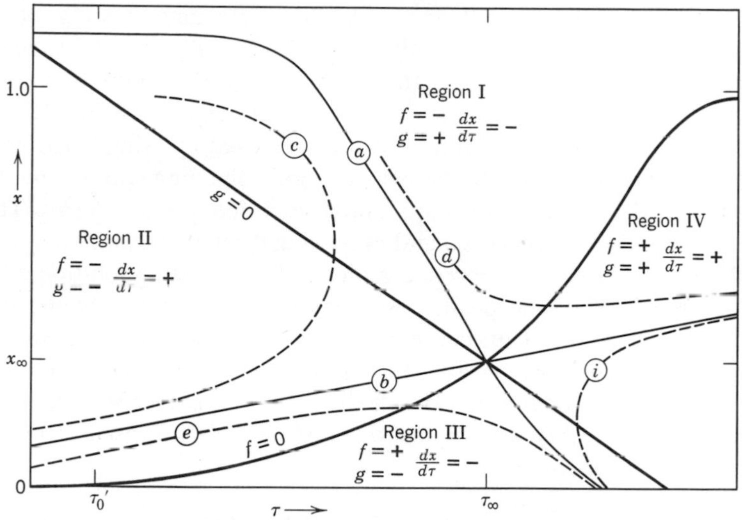

Fig. 11.7–4. Schematic illustration of the behavior of solutions for simple flames (diffusion and kinetic energy neglected).

Physical considerations impose two boundary conditions on the differential equation given above. At the hot boundary $\tau = \tau_\infty$, and x is given by Eq. 11.7–32. At the cold boundary x is equal to unity, and $\tau = \tau_0$. The value of τ_0 is obtained from Eq. 11.7–36. In terms of τ_0' defined by

$$\tau_0' = \tau_\infty - \left(\frac{\gamma - 1}{\gamma}\right)\beta(1 - x_\infty) \qquad (11.7\text{–}45)$$

the value of τ_0 is

$$\tau_0 = \tau_0' - q_0\left(\frac{k}{E^{\ddagger}M\hat{C}_p}\right) \qquad (11.7\text{–}46)$$

Inasmuch as the boundary conditions are overspecified, a satisfactory solution to Eq. 11.7–43 can be obtained for only one value (or possibly a small number of values) of the dimensionless mass rate of flow μ. The allowed value of μ determines the observed flame velocity.

The nature of the solutions of Eq. 11.7–43 is illustrated schematically in Fig. 11.7–4. At (x_∞, τ_∞) the system is at complete chemical and thermal equilibrium so that both $f = 0$ and $g = 0$. The value of x_∞ is the point of crossing of the two curves $f = 0$ and $g = 0$. As a matter of fact, the crossing of these two curves divides the $x\tau$-plane into four regions, each having different signs of f and g so that each is characterized by a particular sign for $dx/d\tau$. Physically significant solutions are found only in Region I. From the differential equation in Eq. 11.7–43 it is clear that any solution which crosses the curve $f = 0$ does so with a zero slope [this is illustrated by the curves (*d*) and (*e*)]. Similarly any crossing of the $g = 0$ curve occurs with an infinite slope [this is illustrated by curves (*c*) and (*i*)]. The exceptions to this behavior are the solutions passing through the singular point, (x_∞, τ_∞). Here the expression for $dx/d\tau$ is indeterminate. This indeterminacy can be removed by using l'Hospital's procedure of taking the derivatives of both the numerator and the denominator. This leads to a quadratic equation for $(dx/d\tau)_\infty$. Thus there are two solutions (curves *a* and *b*) passing through the point (x_∞, τ_∞). Clearly the curve *b* cannot represent a physically interesting solution, since its slope must always be positive so that it could not satisfy the cold boundary conditions. Thus curve *a* is the only solution satisfying the hot boundary conditions, which, for the proper value of μ, may also satisfy the cold boundary condition. Hence this solution is the only one representing physical reality and is the only one which we discuss further. The initial slope of curve *a* is

$$\left(\frac{dx}{d\tau}\right)_\infty = -\frac{\gamma}{2\beta(\gamma-1)}\left[1 + B + \sqrt{(1+B)^2 + 4A}\right] \tag{11.7–47}$$

where

$$A = \frac{\beta^2(\gamma-1)}{\mu^2\gamma}\,\frac{x_\infty}{\tau_\infty{}^2}\,e^{-1/\tau_\infty}\,; \quad B = \frac{e^{-1/\tau_\infty}}{\mu^2(1-x_\infty)}$$

The greater the assumed values of μ (or M) the smaller is the initial slope. The effect on the singular solution *a* of varying μ (or M) is shown in Fig. 11.7–5. Clearly curve 1 corresponds to too small a value of μ to satisfy the cold boundary conditions. Curves 3 and 4, on the other hand, have too large a value of μ. Curve 2 is correct provided that τ_0 is sufficiently larger than τ_0'.

The singular solution for any value of μ may be considered as a true solution for some value of q_0. The temperature τ_0, for which the solution is a valid solution, is the value at which the solution curve crosses the line $x = 1$. The value of τ_0 as a function of μ is shown schematically in Fig. 11.7–6. If τ_0 is but slightly larger than τ_0', μ is almost independent of τ_0. Actually, T_0 can increase by the order of a thousand degrees before the value of μ is appreciably changed, if reasonable values are assumed for the flame parameters.

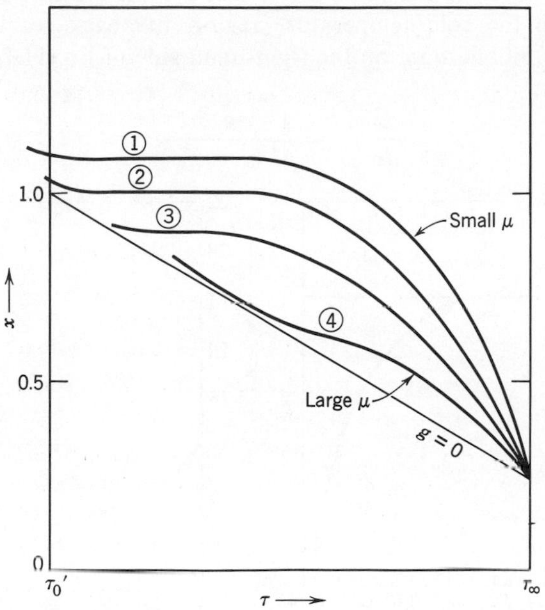

Fig. 11.7–5. Effect on the singular solution of varying μ (or M).

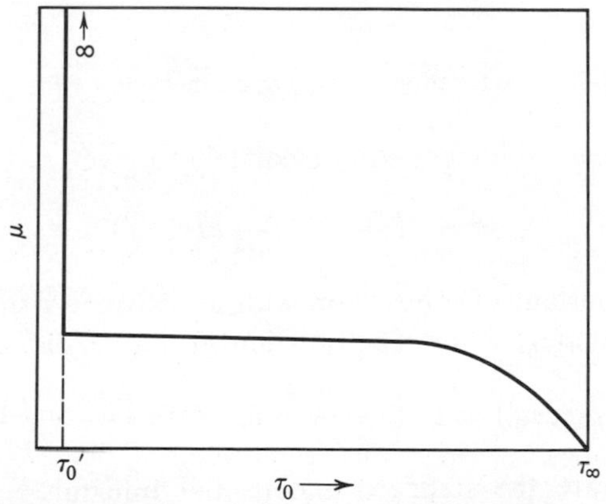

Fig. 11.7–6. Schematic illustration of μ as a function of τ_0. This illustrates the dependence of the flame velocity on the strength of the heat sink.

The nature of the plateau in the μ versus τ curve may be examined by studying the nature of the solutions to Eq. 11.7–43 in the neighborhood of $x = 1$. In the cold temperature region the back reaction can be neglected. If, in addition, on the right-hand side of Eq. 11.7–43, x is set equal to unity,

$$\frac{dx}{d\tau} = -\frac{1}{\mu^2}\frac{e^{-1/\tau}}{(\tau - \tau_0')} \tag{11.7–48}$$

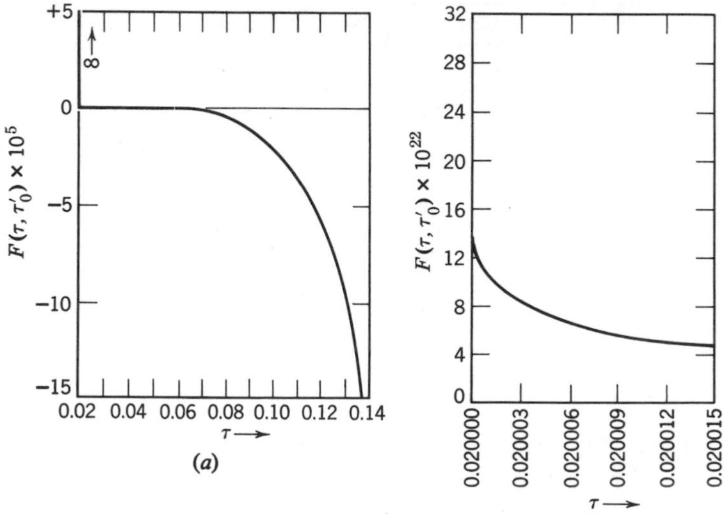

(a)

(b)

Fig. 11.7–7. The function $F(\tau, \tau_0')$ as a function of τ for $\tau_0' = 0.02$.

This equation can be integrated immediately to give

$$x = (1 + \epsilon) + \frac{1}{\mu^2}F(\tau, \tau_0') \tag{11.7–49}$$

where ϵ is a constant of integration with an extremely small value to be adjusted so that $x(\tau_0) = 1$. The function $F(\tau, \tau_0)$ is defined as

$$F(\tau, \tau_0') = \text{Ei}\left(-\frac{1}{\tau}\right) - e^{-1/\tau_0'}\text{Ei}\left(\frac{1}{\tau_0'} - \frac{1}{\tau}\right) \tag{11.7–50}$$

where the Ei are the standard exponential integrals.[21] The value of $F(\tau, \tau_0')$ as a function of τ is shown in Fig. 11.7–7 for $\tau_0' = 0.02$. This value of τ_0' corresponds to the reasonable values, $T_0' = 300°\text{K}$ and

[21] $\text{Ei}(-x) = -\int_x^\infty \frac{e^{-t}}{t}\,dt;\quad \text{Ei}(x) = \int_{-\infty}^x \frac{e^t}{t}\,dt.$

$E^{\ddagger} = 30{,}000$ cal per mole. It can be seen from Fig. 11.7–7a that the value of x remains practically constant up to $\tau = 0.08$ or $T = 1200°K$, at which point the reaction starts to set in. From this figure it is not at all apparent that $F(\tau, \tau_0')$ becomes positive and even infinite for very small values of $\tau - \tau_0'$. To illustrate this behavior, we present the same information in Fig. 11.7–7b, where the scales are greatly magnified. The nature of the solution in this region is somewhat affected by the approximations introduced in writing Eq. 11.7–48. However, certain results are apparent and still valid. The value of $F(\tau, \tau_0')$ goes from 10^{-21} to ∞ in the short space of $\tau - \tau_0' = 10^{-6}$ or $T - T_0' = 0.015°K$. Since $1/\mu^2$ is of the order of 1000, it appears that an extremely small heat sink $(-q_0)$, which makes T_0 as little as 0.015°K above T_0', suffices to make the calculated value of $x(T_0)$ practically independent of T_0 for a very large range of T_0. This explains the plateau in the μ versus τ curve. The value of μ is essentially independent of the strength of the heat sink, provided that it is such that τ_0 is greater than about $\tau_0' + 10^{-6}$ and less than about 0.08. In a flame involving diffusion, the exact value of τ_0 has little effect on G but has a considerable effect on x near the cold boundary.

e. Simple example of a flame: kinetic energy neglected, but not diffusion

Diffusion plays an important role in ordinary flames. When diffusion is not neglected the quantities x and G are no longer equal. The three equations which determine x, τ, and G as functions of ζ are the equation of continuity (11.7–25), the equation of energy balance (11.7–27), and the diffusion equation (11.7–28). The function $f(x, \tau)$ is given by Eq. 11.7–29, and the function $g(\tau, G)$ is given by Eq. 11.7–31, in which the kinetic energy term (that is, the last term) is neglected. We may obtain a pair of coupled differential equations for x and G as functions of τ by dividing the energy balance equation into the other two equations.

The point $(G_\infty, x_\infty, \tau_\infty)$ is a singular point for the flame equations, and therefore it is necessary to examine the nature of the solutions in its vicinity. If a Taylor series expansion of $f(x, \tau)$ is made about this point, it follows that near the hot boundary the flame equations become linear in the variables $(G - G_\infty)$, $(x - x_\infty)$, and $(\tau - \tau_\infty)$:

$$\frac{d(\tau - \tau_\infty)}{d\zeta} = \frac{\beta(\gamma - 1)}{\gamma}(G - G_\infty) + (\tau - \tau_\infty) \qquad (11.7\text{–}51)$$

$$\frac{d(G - G_\infty)}{d\zeta} = -B(x - x_\infty) + \frac{\gamma A}{\beta(\gamma - 1)}(\tau - \tau_\infty) \qquad (11.7\text{–}52)$$

$$\frac{d(x - x_\infty)}{d\zeta} = -\frac{1}{\delta}(G - G_\infty) + \frac{1}{\delta}(x - x_\infty) \qquad (11.7\text{–}53)$$

Here the parameters A and B are defined by Eq. 11.7–47. The most general solution to this set of equations has the form

$$G - G_\infty = b_1 w_1 e^{\alpha_1 \zeta} + b_2 w_2 e^{\alpha_2 \zeta} + b_3 w_3 e^{\alpha_3 \zeta} \tag{11.7–54}$$

$$x - x_\infty = b_1 s_1 e^{\alpha_1 \zeta} + b_2 s_2 e^{\alpha_2 \zeta} + b_3 s_3 e^{\alpha_3 \zeta} \tag{11.7–55}$$

$$\tau - \tau_\infty = b_1 e^{\alpha_1 \zeta} + b_2 e^{\alpha_2 \zeta} + b_3 e^{\alpha_3 \zeta} \tag{11.7–56}$$

An equation for the α_i is obtained by substituting these equations into Eqs. 11.7–51, 52, 53 and setting the determinant of the coefficient of the three algebraic equations equal to zero:

$$-\delta\alpha^3 + (\delta + 1)\alpha^2 - (-B + 1 - \delta A)\alpha - (A + B) = 0 \tag{11.7–57}$$

The solutions of the algebraic equations then give the following expressions for the w_i and s_i in terms of the roots α_i of the cubic equation:

$$w_i = \frac{\gamma}{\beta(\gamma - 1)} (\alpha_i - 1) \tag{11.7–58}$$

$$s_i = \frac{\gamma}{\beta(\gamma - 1)} \left(\frac{\alpha_i - 1}{1 - \alpha_i \delta}\right) \tag{11.7–59}$$

With physically reasonable choices of the parameters, there is one negative root of Eq. 11.7–57, which we denote by α_1. Since only negative α's have physical significance in a flame problem, this means that there is only one physically acceptable starting condition, and $b_2 = b_3 = 0$. To a good approximation the negative root is given by the relation

$$\alpha_1 = -\frac{B}{1 - \alpha_1 \delta} - \frac{A}{1 + A/(1 - \alpha_1 \delta)} \tag{11.7–60}$$

If there were no back reaction in the unimolecular rearrangement, the value of A would be zero. Since the value of A is usually very small, the sole effect of neglecting completely the back reactions would be to shift the value of the root slightly, and the nature of the solutions would remain unchanged.

Once the initial conditions at the hot boundary have been determined so that $(dG/d\tau)_\infty = w_1$ and $(dx/d\tau)_\infty = s_1$ are known, the integration of the flame equations would seem like a simple numerical problem. However, if the constant, δ, is small, the diffusion equation becomes "stiff" and special methods are required.[13] The effects of diffusion on μ,

x versus τ, G versus τ, and τ versus ζ are shown[22] in Figs. 11.7–8, 9, and 10. It will be noticed that diffusion has little effect on the G versus τ curve. To a surprisingly good approximation, G and x can be expressed in the forms:

$$x \doteq 1 - \left(\frac{\tau - \tau_0'}{\tau_\infty - \tau_0'}\right)^{1/\delta} \tag{11.7–61}$$

$$G \doteq 1 - \frac{a\tau^2 e^{-b/\tau}}{\tau - \tau_0'} \tag{11.7–62}$$

Here a and b are adjustable constants.

There are two approximate methods for determining the velocity and structure of flames which have been used quite extensively; one was developed by Boys and Corner[23] and the other by Adams.[24] The basic notion of these schemes is as follows. In the flame equation,

$$\frac{dG}{d\tau} = \frac{1}{\mu^2}\frac{f(x, \tau)}{g(G, \tau)} \tag{11.7–63}$$

the value of x and G in the right side of the equation are approximated by

$$x = x_\infty + s_1(\tau - \tau_\infty) \tag{11.7–64}$$

$$G = G_\infty + w_1(\tau - \tau_\infty) \tag{11.7–65}$$

Then the right side of Eq. 11.7–63 becomes a function of τ only, and the equation can be solved in terms of integrals. The validity of this type of approximation depends upon the fact that it is only in the vicinity of the point $(G_\infty, x_\infty, \tau_\infty)$ that the correct solution lies near the curve $g(G, \tau) = 0$. The flame equation is properly integrated in this region, and it is assumed that $f(x, \tau)$ and $g(G, \tau)$ are not very sensitive to the values of x and G elsewhere. This type of treatment does give the right order of magnitude to the flame velocity for simple cases such as the unimolecular rearrangements, provided that the coefficient of diffusion is not too small. For flames involving chain reactions it may be a very poor approximation.

[22] These curves and the numerical examples in the remainder of this section are based upon the following numerical values:

$T_\infty = 3000°K$	$T_0' = 300°K$
$E^\ddagger = 30{,}000$ cal/mole	$\gamma = 1.2$
$\beta = 1.0848$	$x_\infty = 0.00439$
$\tau_\infty = 0.2$	$\tau_0' = 0.02$

[23] S. F. Boys and J. Corner, *Proc. Roy. Soc.* (*London*), **A197**, 90 (1949); J. Corner, *Proc. Roy. Soc.* (*London*), **A198**, 388 (1949).

[24] See M. J. Henkel, W. P. Spaulding, and J. O. Hirschfelder, *Third Symposium on Combustion*, Williams and Wilkins (1949), 127.

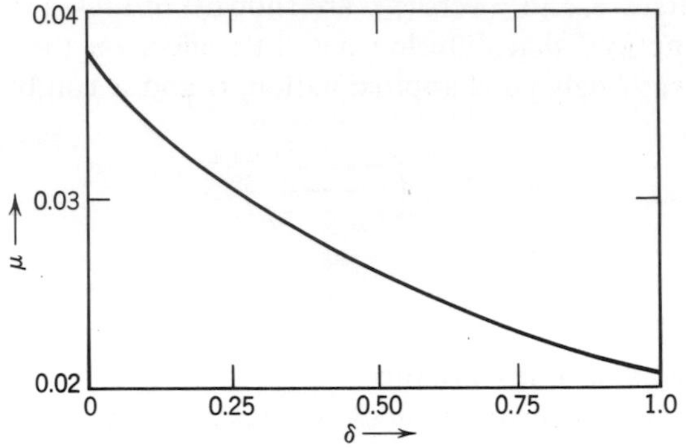

Fig. 11.7–8. The effect of diffusion on the dimensionless mass rate of flow, μ.

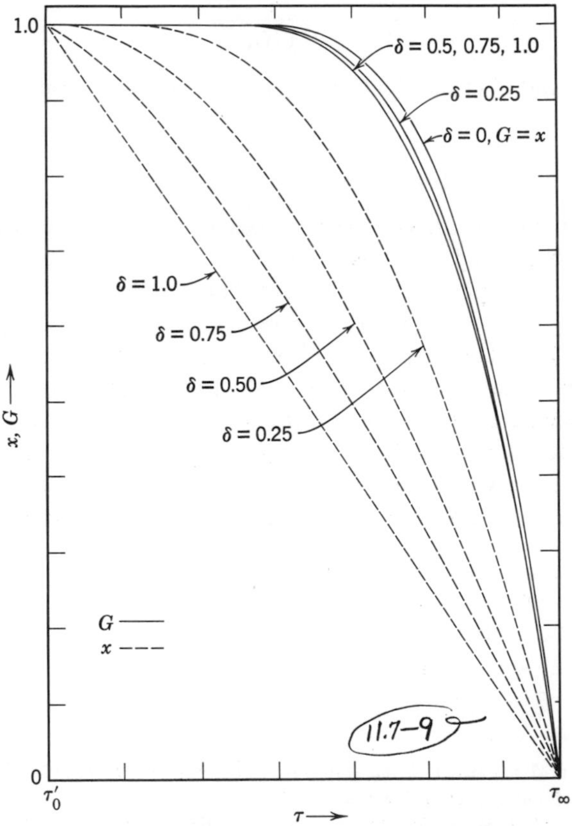

Fig. 11.7–9. The effect of diffusion on $x(\tau)$ and $G(\tau)$.

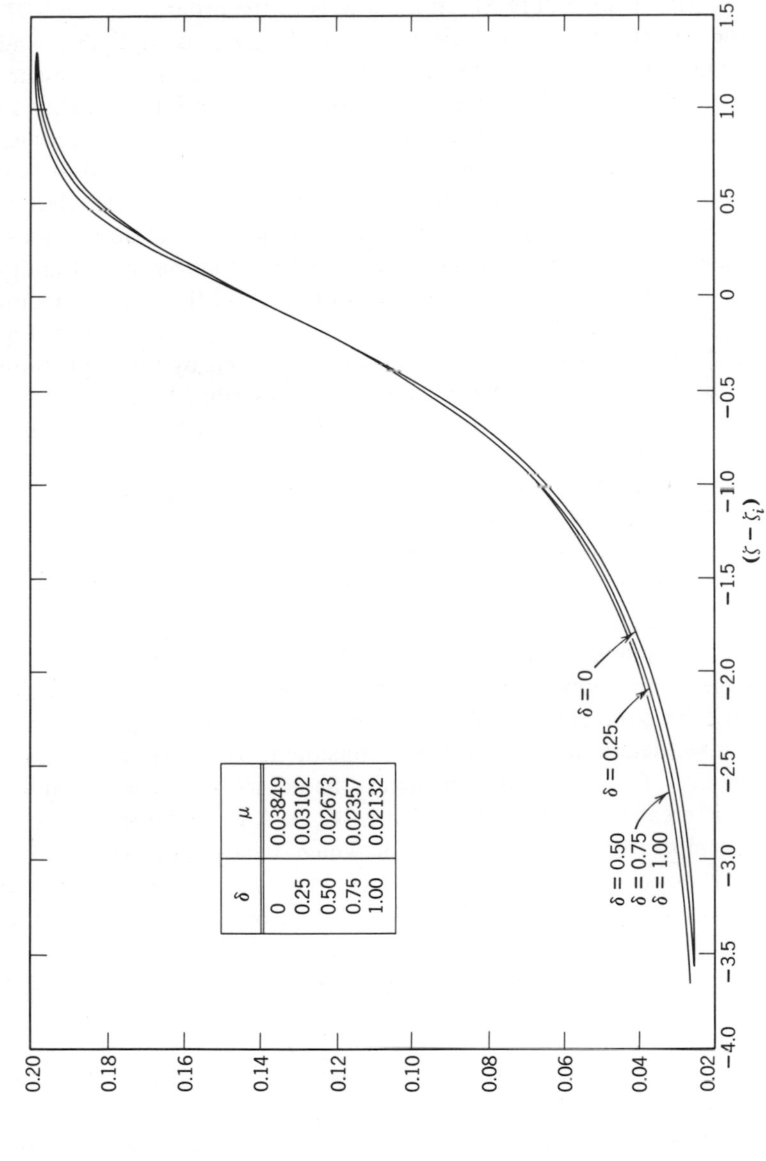

Fig. 11.7–10. An illustration of the dependence of temperature on distance. ζ_i is the value of ζ at the inflection point.

f. Simple example of a flame: diffusion neglected, but not kinetic energy

Ordinarily flame velocities are of the order of 100 cm per sec, and the velocity of the burned gases is of the order of 1000 cm per sec. The velocity of sound in the hot gases is of the order of 100,000 cm per sec, so that the high-temperature Mach number is of the order of $\kappa_\infty = 0.01$. Under these conditions the kinetic energy of the gases is negligible, and the previous approximations are satisfactory. However, as the pressure or the chemical kinetics is varied, it is possible for the flame velocity to increase to the point where the kinetic energy of the gases becomes important. For simplicity let us assume that the coefficients of diffusion and viscosity are zero. A more complete treatment, including the effect of viscosity, is discussed briefly in § 11.9, along with the theory of detonations.

The equations describing the flame are now the equation of continuity (11.7–25) and the energy balance equation (11.7–27). The function $f(x, \tau)$ is given by Eq. 11.7–29, and the function $g(x, \tau)$ is given by Eq. 11.7–31, in which G is replaced by x and u is replaced by the expression given in Eq. 11.7–42. Thus the function $x(\tau)$ is described by a differential equation of the form of Eq. 11.7–43, in which the function $g(x, \tau)$ now contains the kinetic energy terms.

The nature of the solutions to the differential equation may be described by means of a diagram similar to that given in Fig. 11.7–4. The first effect of the kinetic energy is to make the curves $g(x, \tau) = 0$ parabolas in the $x\tau$-plane instead of straight lines. Fig. 11.7–11 shows the curves for $g(x, \tau) = 0$ for different values of κ_∞. For $\kappa_\infty = 1/\sqrt{\gamma'}$ the slope at τ_∞ is infinite. For $\kappa_\infty = 1$ the slope at τ_∞ of the curve $g = 0$ is the same as the slope of the curve $f = 0$. For values of κ_∞ greater than unity the parabolas $g = 0$ cross the curve $f = 0$ at a point above τ_∞, which we denote by τ_∞'. Careful consideration shows that there is no possibility of a physically satisfactory flame solution starting at τ_∞ when κ_∞ is greater than unity.[25] That is, $\kappa_\infty = 1$ is the largest value of the high-temperature Mach number for which steady-state propagation of flames is possible. We shall see in § 11.9 that this corresponds to the "lower Chapman-Jouguet point" and could be predicted from considerations of conservation of mass, momentum, and energy.

When κ_∞ lies between $1/\sqrt{\gamma'}$ and unity, the temperature on the $g = 0$ curve reaches a maximum value:

$$\tau_s = \tau_\infty \frac{(1 + \kappa_\infty^2 \gamma')^2}{4\kappa_\infty^2 \gamma'} \qquad (11.7\text{–}66)$$

[25] The upper point of crossing, τ_∞', forms a good starting point for a flame calculation. With respect to this new temperature, however, there is a new high-temperature Mach number, κ_∞', which is less than unity.

At the same point, the velocity, pressure, and density are given by

$$u_s = \frac{1 + \kappa_\infty^2 \gamma'}{2\kappa_\infty^2 \gamma'} = \frac{\rho_\infty}{\rho_s} \tag{11.7–67}$$

$$\frac{p_s}{p_\infty} = \frac{1 + \kappa_\infty^2 \gamma'}{2} \tag{11.7–68}$$

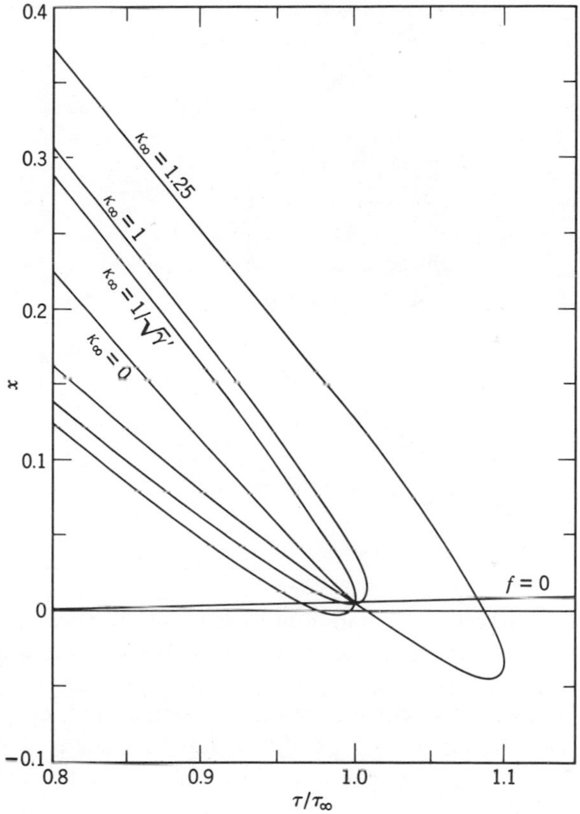

Fig. 11.7–11. Curves of $g(x, \tau) = 0$ for several values of κ_∞.

Figure 11.7–12 shows the nature of the solutions of the flame equation in the region between τ_s and τ_∞. Any physically acceptable solution of the equation must pass through the point (x_s, τ_s). However, regardless of the value of μ, there is a solution (*a*) which passes from the hot boundary (x_∞, τ_∞) to the point (x_s, τ_s). Furthermore, there is only one solution which passes through the point (x_s, τ_s). Therefore, a solution of the equation satisfying both the hot and the cold boundary conditions may be found by a numerical integration from the point (x_s, τ_s) to the flame-holder. The value of μ for a particular value of κ_∞ is fixed by the requirement that this solution satisfy the cold boundary condition.

One point to remember in considering fast flames is that either τ_0 or τ_∞ varies for different values of κ_∞. From a practical standpoint it is

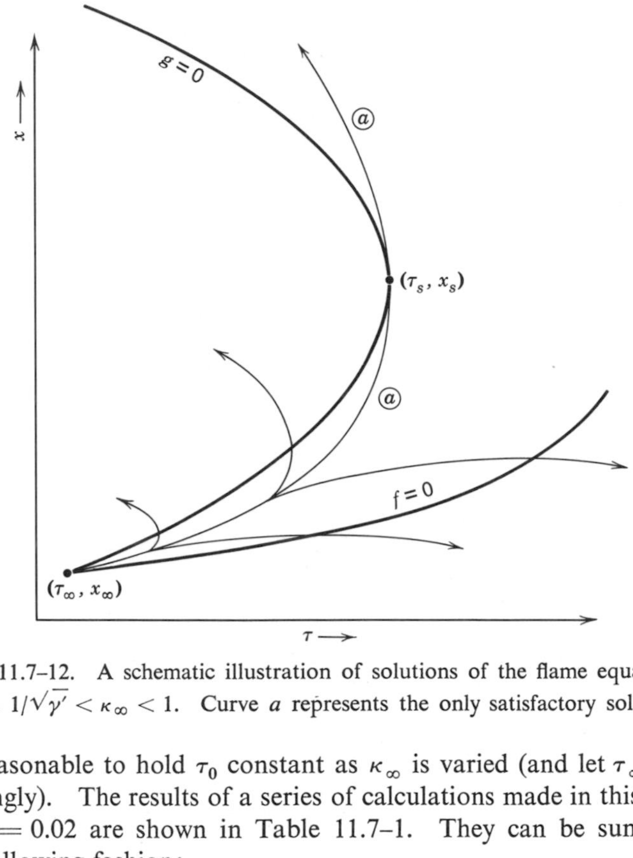

Fig. 11.7–12. A schematic illustration of solutions of the flame equations when $1/\sqrt{\gamma'} < \kappa_\infty < 1$. Curve *a* represents the only satisfactory solution.

more reasonable to hold τ_0 constant as κ_∞ is varied (and let τ_∞ change accordingly). The results of a series of calculations made in this manner with $\tau_0 = 0.02$ are shown in Table 11.7–1. They can be summarized in the following fashion:

(1) There is a critical pressure for the cold gases below which it is not possible to establish a steady-state flame. For the numerical example under consideration, this pressure is $p_0 = 0.02535\sqrt{k'\lambda n E^\ddagger/\hat{C}_p}$. For a bimolecular reaction (as contrasted to a unimolecular reaction) the criterion for the possibility of a steady-state flame does not involve the initial pressure; instead, there is a critical ambient temperature, τ_0, below which no flames occur.

(2) At very high initial pressure, the kinetic energy of the gases is

negligible; the parameter μ is constant, and the flame velocity varies as $p_0^{-1/2}$.

(3) As the initial pressure becomes smaller the flame velocity becomes larger and larger until finally, at the critical initial pressure, the Mach number of the hot gases is unity.

(4) The mass rate of flow remains surprisingly constant as the pressure is varied. At the critical initial pressure, μ is equal to 0.7887 times its value at very high initial pressures.

TABLE 11.7–1

EFFECT OF VARYING THE KINETIC ENERGY OF THE GASES

κ_∞	τ_∞/τ_0	p_0/p_∞	$u_0 = v_0/v_\infty$	$p_0\sqrt{\hat{C}_p/(\lambda k' nE^\ddagger)}$	$\mu = M\sqrt{\hat{C}_p/(\lambda k' mn)}$	$v_0\sqrt{mE^\ddagger}/(kT_0)$
0	10.000	1.0000	0.1000	∞	0.03858	0.0000
0.527	9.738	1.3064	0.0786	0.03525	0.03525	1.0000
0.907	9.257	1.9295	0.0560	0.02576	0.03079	1.195
0.922	9.173	1.9621	0.0556	0.02537	0.03043	1.200
1.000	9.110	2.1349	0.0514	0.02535	0.03043	1.200

8. The Theory of Shock Wave Propagation

A shock wave is a wave in which the properties of a gas change sharply within a short distance in space. The tendency of any compressional wave in a gas to transform into a shock wave is discussed in § 11.5. If we neglect the terms in the hydrodynamic equations involving viscosity, thermal conductivity, and diffusion, the shock wave manifests itself as a mathematical discontinuity in the solutions. When these dissipative mechanisms are included, the net effect is to change the discontinuity into a slightly more gradual transition, which takes place within a distance of a few mean free paths (for example, approximately 10^{-5} cm in a gas at one atmosphere and room temperature). Because of the extremely sharp gradients in the macroscopic properties of the gas which occur in a shock wave, the Navier-Stokes equations are often not sufficiently accurate to describe the structure and thickness of the wave. Attempts at a more accurate analysis of the structure of shock waves are discussed at the conclusion of this section.

Figure 11.8–1 illustrates the shock wave produced by a piston moving with a uniform velocity, $(v_0 - v_\infty)$. In this case a steady state is set up with a pressure p_0 on one side of the shock and p_∞ on the other side. This situation is quite different from shock waves produced by an explosion or a shock tube, which do not represent true steady states. In an explosion or shock tube after the shock wave has passed a point, the pressure decreases (sometimes it passes through a suction phase where p_∞ is less than p_0 or oscillates) and eventually returns to p_0. However, even in such transient shocks the behavior and structure of the shock front can be described accurately at any instant by the steady-state theory, since the thickness of the shock front (the distance in which the pressure rise takes place, approximately 10^{-5} cm) is very small compared to the length of the overall wave.

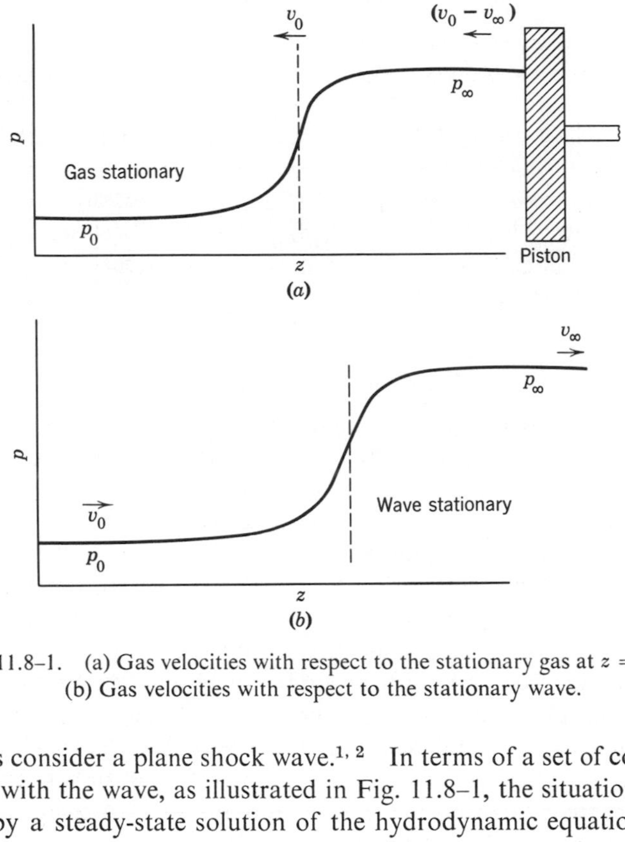

Fig. 11.8–1. (a) Gas velocities with respect to the stationary gas at $z = -\infty$. (b) Gas velocities with respect to the stationary wave.

Let us consider a plane shock wave.[1, 2] In terms of a set of coordinates moving with the wave, as illustrated in Fig. 11.8–1, the situation is represented by a steady-state solution of the hydrodynamic equations. (The actual formation of such a wave, that is, the transformation of a time-dependent solution into the steady-state solution, is discussed in § 11.5.) The conditions relating the properties of the gas on the two sides of the shock can easily be obtained from the equations of change of § 11.6.

[1] R. Courant and K. O. Friedrichs, *Supersonic Flows and Shock Waves*, Interscience Press (1948).

[2] R. H. Cole, *Underwater Explosions*, Princeton University Press (1948).

It is assumed that not only in the limit that $x \to \infty$ (indicated by a subscript ∞) but also in the limit that $x \to -\infty$ (indicated by a subscript 0) all the derivatives are zero. The velocity of the shock wave with respect to the gas at $-\infty$ is then v_0. The equations of change then provide relations between the properties on the two sides of the shock. For the present it is assumed that solutions of the differential equations exist which satisfy these conditions. That this is always true is indicated later in this section and also in the succeeding section in connection with the discussion of detonations.

We first consider the equations relating the properties on the two sides of the shock wave. Although these relations are valid, even when the transport phenomena are included, they give no indication whatsoever as to the detailed structure of the shock wave. The detailed structure of the shock wave, which is described by the equations of change, is discussed in the last part of this section. It is shown that the thickness of the shock wave depends upon the magnitude of the transport coefficients. The solutions of the equations of change become discontinuous in the limit as both η and λ approach zero.

a. The Hugoniot relations

The equations of change for a steady-state one-dimensional problem are given in § 11.6a. If it is assumed that the derivatives at $x = -\infty$ are zero, these equations (11.6–2, 13, 15) give the following relations between the variables on the two sides of the shock wave:

$$M = \rho_0 v_0 = \rho_\infty v_\infty \tag{11.8–1}$$

$$M v_0 + p_0 = M v_\infty + p_\infty \tag{11.8–2}$$

$$\hat{H}_0 + \tfrac{1}{2} v_0^2 = \hat{H}_\infty + \tfrac{1}{2} v_\infty^2 \tag{11.8–3}$$

These relations, which are known as the *Hugoniot relations*, are relations among the eight quantities, ρ_0, v_0, p_0, $\hat{H}_0$, ρ_∞, v_∞, p_∞, and $\hat{H}_\infty$. However, if we make use of the thermodynamic dependence of $\hat{H}$ on ρ and p, the number of variables can be reduced to six. Hence the equations are sufficient to specify three of the variables in terms of the remaining three. It is usual to specify the density and pressure on the low-pressure side of the shock wave, ρ_0 and p_0, and also an additional parameter which indicates the strength of the shock, such as the pressure on the high side, p_∞. The Hugoniot relations are then solved to obtain the values of the remaining quantities v_0, v_∞, and ρ_∞. The value of v_0 is the velocity of the cold gas into the shock or the velocity of propagation of the shock wave into stationary gas on the low-pressure side. The value of v_∞ is the velocity of the hot gases away from the front.

It is convenient to rearrange the Hugoniot relations into a somewhat different form. From the equations of continuity and motion (11.8–1 and 2), it may be shown that

$$M = \left[\rho_0\rho_\infty \frac{p_\infty - p_0}{\rho_\infty - \rho_0}\right]^{1/2} \tag{11.8–4}$$

Also, since $\frac{1}{2}(v_\infty{}^2 - v_0{}^2) = \frac{1}{2}(v_\infty - v_0)(v_\infty + v_0)$, it follows from the same pair of equations that

$$\tfrac{1}{2}(v_\infty{}^2 - v_0{}^2) = -\frac{(p_\infty - p_0)(\rho_\infty + \rho_0)}{2\rho_0\rho_\infty} \tag{11.8–5}$$

Then, when this result is combined with the equation of conservation of energy (11.8–3) and the relation $\hat{H} = \hat{U} + (p/\rho)$, we obtain the relation

$$(\hat{U}_\infty - \hat{U}_0) = \frac{(p_\infty + p_0)(\rho_\infty - \rho_0)}{2\rho_0\rho_\infty} \tag{11.8–6}$$

The last three equations are simply the Hugoniot relations in somewhat more convenient form. The equations cannot be solved explicitly without specifying the equation of state and thermodynamic properties of the gas. In a real gas the calculations may be somewhat cumbersome. However, a qualitative description of the phenomena may be obtained by considering the propagation of a shock wave through a perfect gas with constant specific heat.

b. Application of the Hugoniot relations to a perfect gas

For a perfect gas with constant specific heat, the internal energy per gram above that at 0°K is

$$\hat{U} = \hat{C}_v T = \frac{p}{(\gamma - 1)\rho} \tag{11.8–7}$$

Using this expression for the internal energy, we may solve the equation of conservation of energy (11.8–6) to obtain the density, ρ_∞, on the high-pressure side, in terms of ρ_0, p_0, and p_∞,

$$\rho_\infty = \rho_0 \frac{(\gamma + 1)p_\infty + (\gamma - 1)p_0}{(\gamma - 1)p_\infty + (\gamma + 1)p_0} \tag{11.8–8}$$

This relation may conveniently be written in terms of the density ratio u_0 and the pressure ratio ξ, defined by

$$u_0 = \rho_\infty/\rho_0 = v_0/v_\infty; \quad \xi = p_\infty/p_0 \tag{11.8–9}$$

The result is

$$u_0 = \frac{(\gamma - 1) + (\gamma + 1)\xi}{(\gamma + 1) + (\gamma - 1)\xi} \tag{11.8–10}$$

This relation is often referred to as the *Hugoniot shock adiabat*,[3] although this is a misnomer since the entropy of a gas does change in passing through a shock.

If the shock wave is weak, ξ is close to unity, and the expansion of the Hugoniot shock adiabat, Eq. 11.8–10, is

$$u_0 = 1 + \frac{1}{\gamma}(\xi - 1) - \frac{1}{2\gamma^2}(\gamma - 1)(\xi - 1)^2 + \frac{1}{4\gamma^3}(\gamma - 1)^2(\xi - 1)^3 + \cdots \tag{11.8–11}$$

This expansion may be compared to the expansion of the relation describing the isentropic compression of a gas,

$$u_0 = \xi^{1/\gamma} = 1 + \frac{1}{\gamma}(\xi - 1) - \frac{1}{2\gamma^2}(\gamma - 1)(\xi - 1)^2 + \frac{1}{6\gamma^3}(\gamma - 1)(2\gamma - 1)(\xi - 1)^3 + \cdots \tag{11.8–12}$$

It is interesting to note that the first three terms in the expansions of the Hugoniot shock adiabat and the isentropic relation are the same. This is related to the fact that very little entropy change takes place in a mild shock.

For strong shocks ξ is large, and the Hugoniot shock adiabat (Eq. 11.8–10) shows that the density ratio, u_0, approaches a limiting value,

$$\lim_{\xi \to \infty} u_0 = \frac{\gamma + 1}{\gamma - 1} \tag{11.8–13}$$

For example, for air $\gamma = 1.4$, and the limiting value of u_0 is 6.

From the perfect gas equation of state,

$$\frac{T_\infty}{T_0} = \frac{p_\infty \rho_0}{p_0 \rho_\infty} = \frac{\xi}{u_0} \tag{11.8–14}$$

In a strong shock ξ is large whereas u_0 approaches a limit. Hence in strong shocks T_∞ is large, and the shock wave may even be incandescent.

The Hugoniot shock adiabat (Eq. 11.8–10) may be rearranged into a form known as the *Rankine-Hugoniot relation*,

$$\frac{p_\infty - p_0}{\rho_\infty - \rho_0} = \gamma \frac{p_\infty + p_0}{\rho_\infty + \rho_0} \tag{11.8–15}$$

[3] This relation of course does not apply to the variation of pressure with density within the shock wave. See Eq. 11.8–43.

This form of the equation is interesting, particularly in view of the analogy with

$$\left(\frac{\partial p}{\partial \rho}\right)_{\hat{S}} = \gamma \frac{p}{\rho} \tag{11.8–16}$$

which describes the slope of a perfect gas adiabat.

Expressions for the velocities v_0 and v_∞ of the gas on the two sides of the wave may be obtained from Eqs. 11.8–1 and 4:

$$v_0 = \sqrt{\frac{\rho_\infty}{\rho_0}\frac{(p_\infty - p_0)}{(\rho_\infty - \rho_0)}} \tag{11.8–17}$$

$$v_\infty = \sqrt{\frac{\rho_0}{\rho_\infty}\frac{(p_\infty - p_0)}{(\rho_\infty - \rho_0)}} \tag{11.8–18}$$

From these equations and the Rankine-Hugoniot relation (Eq. 11.8–15) we may obtain the Mach numbers on the two sides of the shock front in terms of u_0 and ξ and the velocity of sound defined in Eq. 11.4–5:

$$\kappa_0 = \frac{v_0}{c_0} = \sqrt{u_0 \frac{(1+\xi)}{(1+u_0)}} \tag{11.8–19}$$

$$\kappa_\infty = \frac{v_\infty}{c_\infty} = \sqrt{\frac{1}{\xi}\frac{(1+\xi)}{(1+u_0)}} \tag{11.8–20}$$

It is shown below that the only physically realizable situations are those with $u_0 \geqslant 1$. From the Hugoniot shock adiabat (Eq. 11.8–10) it is clear that if $u_0 \geqslant 1$, then $\xi \geqslant u_0$. Thus, from the last two equations, it follows that

$$\kappa_0 \geqslant 1 \quad \text{or} \quad v_0 \geqslant c_0 \tag{11.8–21}$$

$$\kappa_\infty \leqslant 1 \quad \text{or} \quad v_\infty \leqslant c_\infty \tag{11.8–22}$$

These results state that the gas on the low-pressure side of a shock front travels with supersonic velocity with respect to the front and that the velocity of the heated, compressed gas is subsonic with respect to the front. If the shock wave moves into still gas on the low-pressure side, the wave overtakes the still gas with the supersonic velocity v_0.

It is clear from Eqs. 11.8–19 and 20 that in the limit of weak shocks, in which u_0 and ξ are unity and the properties of the gas on the two sides of the shock are the same, the velocity of propagation of the wave is the velocity of sound. Actually, in the limit there is no distinction between a weak shock wave and a sound wave.

The only physically realizable situations are those with $u_0 \geqslant 1$, since this condition is necessary in order that the change of entropy of the gas in passing through the shock wave be positive. The entropy of a gram of an ideal gas with constant specific heat is

$$\hat{S} = \hat{C}_p \ln T - \frac{k}{m} \ln p + \text{a constant}$$

$$= \hat{C}_v \ln (p\rho^{-\gamma}) - \hat{C}_p \ln \left(\frac{k}{m}\right) + \text{a constant} \quad (11.8\text{–}23)$$

Thus the difference in entropy of the gas on the two sides of the front is

$$\hat{S}_\infty - \hat{S}_0 = \hat{C}_v \ln \left(\frac{p_\infty \rho_0^{\gamma}}{p_0 \rho_\infty^{\gamma}}\right) = \hat{C}_v \ln (\xi u_0^{-\gamma}) \quad (11.8\text{–}24)$$

Since we define the positive z direction such that the gas flows from the region 0 to the region ∞, the second law of thermodynamics implies that

$$\xi u_0^{-\gamma} \geqslant 1 \quad (11.8\text{–}25)$$

But, combining this inequality with the Hugoniot shock adiabat, Eq. 11.8–10, we may show that the second law implies that $\xi \geqslant 1$ and $u_0 \geqslant 1$. That is, in a shock wave, the gas flows from the low-pressure side to the high-pressure side (or from the low-density to the high-density). The opposite flow would violate the second law of thermodynamics.

The use of the integrated equations of change, the Hugoniot relations, rather than the differential equations of change including the terms representing the dissipative mechanisms, makes necessary the introduction of the extraneous arguments based on the second law. The actual equations of change include the entropy equation of change and the second law, and hence no further information is required. It may be shown that no solutions of the differential equations representing the thermodynamically impossible shock waves of rarefaction exist. The nonexistence of shock waves of rarefaction was also indicated in the discussion of the formation of shock waves in § 11.4.

The change in entropy of a gram of gas in flowing through a shock wave in terms of the pressure ratio may be obtained by combining the Hugoniot shock adiabat (Eq. 11.8–10) with Eq. 11.8–24. If this result is expanded, we obtain an expression applicable to weak shock waves:

$$\hat{S}_\infty - \hat{S}_0 = \frac{\hat{C}_v}{12\gamma^2} (\gamma^2 - 1)(\xi - 1)^3 + \cdots \quad (11.8\text{–}26)$$

Since the first term in this expansion is the cubic term, this result further substantiates the fact that there is little change in entropy in a weak shock.

After a shock wave from an explosion or shock tube has passed a point the gas expands adiabatically to its original pressure p_0. Because of the increase in entropy of the gas, after the gas has expanded to the original pressure p_0, the residual temperature T_∞' is somewhat higher than the original temperature. This increase in temperature is related to the increase in entropy by the relation,

$$\hat{S}_\infty - \hat{S}_0 = \hat{C}_p \ln \frac{T_\infty'}{T_0} \tag{11.8–27}$$

This relation may be combined with the previous relations to obtain a general expression for the temperature increase. For weak shocks this expression becomes, on expansion,

$$T_\infty' - T_0 = T_0 \left(\frac{\gamma^2 - 1}{12\gamma^3}\right) (\xi - 1)^3 + \cdots \tag{11.8–28}$$

As an example of the exact results, let us consider the passage of a shock wave into air, for which $\gamma = 1.4$, at temperature, $T_0 = 273$°K. The dependence of the temperature increase on the strength of the shock (as indicated by the pressure ratio) is shown in Table 11.8–1. The table indicates that the energy dissipated is small if p_∞/p_0 is less than 2 or 3, but becomes large for stronger shocks. In contrast to gases the heating effect is negligible for shocks passing through liquids. For example, for a shock wave of approximately 1000 atm passing through water, $T_\infty' - T_0 = 0.025$°K.

TABLE 11.8–1

TEMPERATURE INCREASE DUE TO A SHOCK WAVE IN AIR

p_∞/p_0	2	3	5	10	50	100	500
$(T_\infty' - T_0)$ (°K)	2.5	10.3	31	97	579	1065	1417

Besides the pressure ratio p_∞/p_0, there are two other important measures for the strength of a shock wave.

(i) The positive impulse, I, is defined as

$$I = \int (p - p_0)\, dt \tag{11.8–29}$$

Here the integration is carried out from the time that the shock wave arrives to the time that the pressure first returns to p_0.

(ii) The energy of the shock wave (per unit area of shock front), E, is given by

$$E = \int_0^\infty (p - p_0)\, v\, dt \tag{11.8–30}$$

For a weak shock $v \doteq (p - p_0)/\rho_0 c_0$ so that

$$E = \frac{1}{\rho_0 c_0} \int_0^\infty (p - p_0)^2\, dt \tag{11.8–31}$$

Because of the energy dissipated through heating the shocked gas, the total energy of the shock wave decays according to the relation

$$\frac{dE}{dz} = \rho_0 \hat{C}_v (T_\infty{}' - T_0) \tag{11.8–32}$$

At very large distances the shock pressure decreases as $z^{-1/2}$. Three-dimensional spherical shock waves at a distance R from their source have a shock pressure which decreases as $R^{-1}(\ln R)^{-1/2}$.

c. The structure and thickness of a shock wave in a perfect gas[4–7]

The structure of a shock wave is described by a solution of the one-dimensional steady-state equations of change. As an example, let us consider the propagation of a shock wave through a perfect gas, with constant specific heat containing only a single chemical component.[8] For such a gas the one-dimensional steady-state equations of change are those given in § 11.6, written here for a one-component system:

$$\rho v = \rho_\infty v_\infty = M \tag{11.8–33}$$

$$Mv + p - \frac{4}{3}\eta \frac{dv}{dz} = Mv_\infty + p_\infty \tag{11.8–34}$$

$$\left(\frac{\gamma}{\gamma - 1}\right) M \frac{p}{\rho} + \frac{1}{2} Mv^2 - \lambda \frac{dT}{dz} - \frac{4}{3}\eta v \frac{dv}{dz} = \frac{\gamma}{(\gamma - 1)} M \frac{p_\infty}{\rho_\infty} + \frac{1}{2} Mv_\infty{}^2 \tag{11.8–35}$$

[4] G. I. Taylor and J. W. Maccoll, "The Mechanics of Compressible Fluids" in *Aerodynamic Theory*, edited by W. F. Durand (California Institute of Technology, Pasedena, 1943).

[5] R. Becker, *Z. Physik*, **8**, 321 (1922).

[6] M. Morduchow and P. A. Libby: *J. Aeronautical Sci.*, **16**, 674 (1949).

[7] H. Grad, *Comm. Pure and Applied Maths.*, **5**, 257 (1952).

[8] T. G. Cowling, *Phil. Mag.*, **33**, 61 (1942), has considered the effect of diffusion on the structure of a shock wave. He has shown that diffusion has essentially the same effect as viscosity and thermal conductivity. The diffusion velocities are often an appreciable fraction of the velocity of sound.

The perfect gas equation of state may be used to eliminate T from the equations of change. The equations may then be combined to obtain a second-order differential equation for v as a function of z:

$$\frac{4\lambda m}{3Mk}\frac{d}{dz}\left[\eta v\frac{dv}{dz}\right]-\frac{dv}{dz}\left[\left\{\frac{2\lambda m}{k}+\frac{4\eta}{3(\gamma-1)}\right\}v-\frac{\lambda m}{Mk}\{Mv_\infty+p_\infty\}\right]$$
$$-\frac{\gamma+1}{2(\gamma-1)}M(v-v_\infty)(v_0-v)=0 \qquad (11.8\text{–}36)$$

where v_0 is defined by

$$v_0=\frac{\gamma-1}{\gamma+1}v_\infty\left\{1+\frac{2\gamma}{\gamma-1}\frac{p_\infty}{\rho_\infty v_\infty{}^2}\right\} \qquad (11.8\text{–}37)$$

This symbol is chosen since, as will be shown presently, v_0 is velocity in the limit as $z \to -\infty$. This relation is, of course, contained in the Hugoniot relations of the previous paragraph. The differential equation may conveniently be written in a dimensionless form by using the dimensionless quantities, u, ζ, and ω, defined in Eqs. 11.7–17, 18, 24:

$$\frac{d}{d\zeta}\left[\omega u\frac{du}{d\zeta}\right]+\frac{\gamma+1}{2\gamma}\frac{du}{d\zeta}\left[1+u_0-\frac{4\gamma}{\gamma+1}\left(1+\frac{1}{2\gamma}\omega\right)u\right]$$
$$-\frac{(\gamma+1)}{2\gamma}(u-1)(u_0-u)=0 \qquad (11.8\text{–}38)$$

The solution of this second-order differential equation for $u(\zeta)$, for arbitrary values of the parameters, is difficult. However, when the quantity ω (which is $\frac{4}{3}$ times the Prandtl number) is equal to unity, the solution may be written in a simple form.[5, 6, 7] According to Table 1.2–2, where the experimental Prandtl numbers are given for a number of gases, the value of $\frac{3}{4}$ for the Prandtl number (or $\omega = 1$) is a very reasonable value. Hence we consider only the case $\omega = 1$ in the following discussion of the structure of shock waves.

For $\omega = 1$, the general solution of Eq. 11.8–38 is

$$u\frac{du}{d\zeta}+\frac{\gamma+1}{2\gamma}(u-1)(u_0-u)=Ce^{\zeta} \qquad (11.8\text{–}39)$$

where C is an arbitrary constant. Since it is assumed that in the limit as $z \to \infty$, both v and dv/dz remain finite, the constant C is taken to be zero. Thus the physically interesting solution (which is a singular solution) is

$$u\frac{du}{d\zeta}=-\frac{\gamma+1}{2\gamma}(u-1)(u_0-u) \qquad (11.8\text{–}40)$$

The general solution of this equation is

$$\zeta + \zeta_0 = \frac{2\gamma}{\gamma + 1} \frac{u_0 \ln |u_0 - u| - \ln |u - 1|}{u_0 - 1} \qquad (11.8\text{–}41)$$

where ζ_0 is an arbitrary constant. This equation gives implicitly the velocity as a function of position. Typical curves are illustrated in Fig. 11.8–2. The solution of the entire problem, that is, the evaluation of the

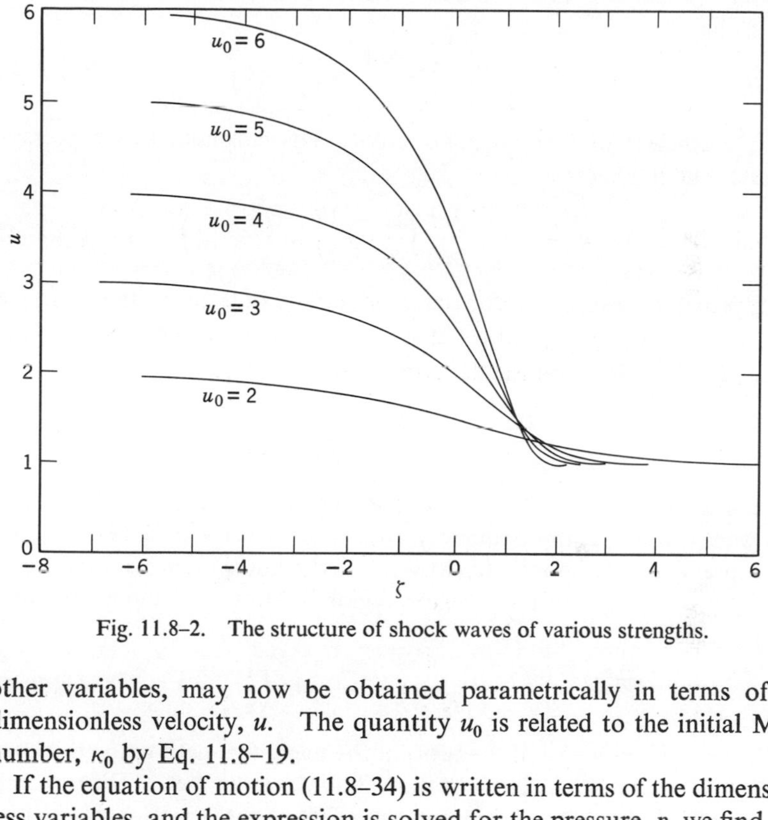

Fig. 11.8–2. The structure of shock waves of various strengths.

other variables, may now be obtained parametrically in terms of the dimensionless velocity, u. The quantity u_0 is related to the initial Mach number, κ_0 by Eq. 11.8–19.

If the equation of motion (11.8–34) is written in terms of the dimensionless variables, and the expression is solved for the pressure, p, we find that

$$\frac{\gamma p}{\rho_\infty {v_\infty}^2} = \frac{\gamma + 1}{2} + \frac{\gamma + 1}{2} u_0 - \gamma u + \gamma \omega \frac{du}{d\zeta} \qquad (11.8\text{–}42)$$

For $\omega = 1$, a parametric equation for the pressure may be obtained by replacing the derivative in this equation by the expression in Eq. 11.8–40. Then, if we use Eq. 11.8–37,

$$\frac{p}{p_\infty} = \left(\frac{\gamma + 1}{\gamma - 1} \frac{u_0}{u} - u\right) \Big/ \left(\frac{\gamma + 1}{\gamma - 1} u_0 - 1\right) \qquad (11.8\text{–}43)$$

It is clear that in order that the pressure be positive at $u = u_0$ ($z \to -\infty$), the value of u_0 must be less than $(\gamma + 1)/(\gamma - 1)$. This is the result (Eq. 11.8–13) obtained directly from the Hugoniot relations.

The thickness of a shock wave may be defined as the distance in which some particular fraction of the velocity change occurs. Let us define the thickness as the distance from the point at which $u = u_0 - \epsilon(u_0 - 1)$ to the point at which $u = 1 + \epsilon(u_0 - 1)$, where ϵ is an arbitrary small number. From Eq. 11.8–41, this distance in the dimensionless units is seen to be

$$\Delta\zeta = \frac{2\gamma}{\gamma + 1}\frac{u_0 + 1}{u_0 - 1}\ln\left(\frac{1}{\epsilon} - 1\right) \tag{11.8–44}$$

If the coefficient of thermal conductivity λ is constant, this expression gives for the thickness

$$\Delta z = \frac{2(\gamma - 1)}{\gamma + 1}\frac{\lambda m}{Mk}\left(\frac{u_0 + 1}{u_0 - 1}\right)\ln\left(\frac{1}{\epsilon} - 1\right) \tag{11.8–45}$$

An approximate expression for the conductivity in terms of the mean free path, l, is given in Eq. 1.2–14. If $c = \sqrt{\gamma kT/m}$ is the velocity of sound, then from the expression for the conductivity we find that

$$\frac{\lambda m}{\rho ck} = \frac{2}{3(\gamma - 1)}\sqrt{\frac{2}{\gamma\pi}}\,l \tag{11.8–46}$$

As seen from Eqs. 11.8–21 and 22, the velocity of the gas in the interior of a shock wave is approximately the local velocity of sound. Hence this expression may be used to express the thickness in terms of the mean free path in the gas in the interior region. Thus the number of mean free paths is

$$\frac{\Delta z}{l} = \frac{4}{3(\gamma + 1)}\sqrt{\frac{2}{\gamma\pi}}\frac{u_0 + 1}{u_0 - 1}\ln\left(\frac{1}{\epsilon} - 1\right) \tag{11.8–47}$$

Figure 11.8–3 is a plot of the ratio of the mean free path to the thickness of the shock wave as a function of the initial Mach number. The top curve is due to Thomas,[9] who considered the effect of the variation of the conductivity and viscosity with temperature. It is seen that a reasonably strong shock occurs in a distance involving only a few mean free paths. That is, the gradients in the macroscopic variables are sufficiently large that we are not justified in using the Navier-Stokes equations. These equations are based on the first approximation of Enskog. It was pointed out in § 7.3 that the first approximation is valid only if the variation in the macroscopic variables over a mean free path is not appreciable.

[9] L. H. Thomas, *J. Chem. Phys.*, **12**, 449 (1944).

Wang Chang[10] has made a thorough study of the structure of shock waves based on the Enskog series solution of the Boltzmann equation. She has considered the effect of the next two approximations beyond that of the Navier-Stokes equations. The results indicate that the series converges only very slowly if the initial Mach number is appreciably greater than unity. This indicates that, under the conditions of large

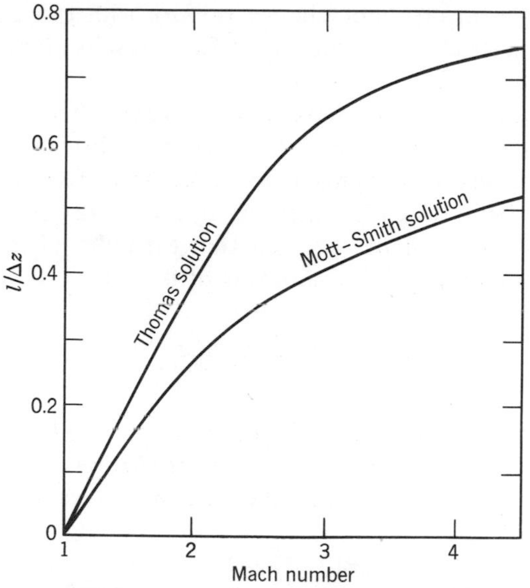

Fig. 11.8–3. The thickness of a shock wave as predicted by the solutions of Thomas and Mott-Smith. [From H. M. Mott-Smith, *Phys. Rev.*, **82**, 885 (1951).]

gradients such as occur in a strong shock, the concepts of local values of the macroscopic variables and the concepts of a continuum break down. In order to study the structure of strong shocks, it is necessary to reconsider the Boltzmann equation and consider other types of approximate solutions.

More recently Mott-Smith[11] has discussed an approach to the problem which is based directly on the Boltzmann equation and avoids any use of the hydrodynamic equations or the concept of flux vectors. He obtained an approximate solution of the Boltzmann equation describing the structure of the shock wave. In the usual treatment the function

[10] C. S. Wang Chang, "On the Theory of Thickness of Weak Shocks," University of Michigan Department of Engineering Report UMH-3-F (APL/JHU CM-503), Aug. 19, 1948.

[11] H. M. Mott-Smith, *Phys. Rev.*, **82**, 885 (1951).

describing the distribution of molecular velocities is assumed to be almost Maxwellian. Mott-Smith assumed that the distribution function was the sum of two exactly Maxwellian terms. Physically, the picture is that of a mixture of two gases of different temperatures and mass motion. The Boltzmann equation is used as an equation for the parameters appearing in the assumed distribution function. The theory is approximate in that the functional form of the distribution is assumed. However, it is shown that the assumed form does not change rapidly with time, so that the solution is nearly a steady-state solution. These results along with those of Thomas are illustrated in Fig. 11.8–3.

Hornig, Cowan, and Greene[12] have used optical methods to determine the thickness of shock waves in nitrogen, argon, hydrogen, and oxygen. The methods are based on the change in the reflectivity of the wave with the wavelength of the light, which is a measure of the density profile through the shock. The Thomas theory predicts that the index of refraction, as a function of position through the shock, is of the form

$$\eta(z) = 1 + \frac{\eta_\infty - \eta_0}{1 + e^{-4z/L}} \tag{11.8–48}$$

Here, the parameter L may be taken as a measure of the thickness. The experimental results are compared with the predictions of the Thomas theory in Table 11.8–2. It is seen that the experimental values are roughly

TABLE 11.8–2[11]

COMPARISON OF EXPERIMENTAL AND THEORETICAL SHOCK WAVE THICKNESS OF N_2 AT 25°C

p/p_0	p_0	$L \times 10^5$ (cm)	
		Experimental	Theory
1.71	42	3.2	2.0
1.71	68	2.0	1.3
1.71	85	1.8	1.0

[12] G. R. Cowan and D. F. Hornig, *J. Chem. Phys.*, **18**, 1008 (1950). See also E. F. Greene, G. R. Cowan, and D. F. Hornig, *J. Chem. Phys.*, **19**, 427 (1951), and E. F. Greene and D. F. Hornig, Technical Report No. 4, Office of Naval Research Contract N7onr-358, Brown University, August 1, 1952. E. F. Greene and D. F. Hornig, *J. Chem. Phys.*, **21**, 617 (1953).

twice those predicted by the Thomas theory. A comparison with Fig. 11.8–3 indicates that the results are much more in line with those predicted by Mott-Smith.

From the shock wave studies[12] it is found that 150 collisions are required to effect equilibrium between rotational and translational energy in hydrogen; for nitrogen and oxygen the equilibration occurs more rapidly.

9. Theory of Detonations

A detonation is a steady-state wave in which an exothermic chemical reaction supplies the energy to maintain the stationary conditions. The wave may be described as a flame preceded by a shock wave which preheats the material. A detonation differs from an ordinary flame in that the velocity of propagation is supersonic.

As in the theory of shock waves, discussed in the preceding section, the ultimate increases in the pressure, density, and temperature in a detonation are determined by the equations describing the overall conservation of mass, momentum, and energy. The velocity of propagation of steady-state detonation is determined by the Chapman-Jouguet condition. This condition, which is discussed presently, chooses the most stable solution from all the possible solutions of the equations of change. This solution is the one with the lowest possible velocity. Thus the overall characteristics of a detonation are completely determined by the equation of state and the calorific equation and do not depend on the chemical kinetics or the transport phenomena. However, the structure of the detonation wave does depend on these phenomena. The structure is determined by the solution of the differential equations of change. These are the same equations as are used in the two previous sections to describe the structure of flames and shock waves. The detonation solution near the cold boundary is similar to a shock solution, and near the hot boundary it is similar to a flame solution.

a. The Hugoniot relations and the Chapman-Jouguet condition

As in the discussion of flames and shock waves we use a coordinate system which moves with the wave. In this coordinate system the situation is a steady state. The cold boundary is at $z = -\infty$, and the hot boundary is at $z = \infty$. Conditions at the cold boundary are indicated by the subscript 0; conditions at the hot boundary by the subscript ∞. The material moves in the positive direction, and the velocity at $z = -\infty$, which is designated as v_0, is the velocity with which the detonation wave moves into the unreacted material. Hence v_0 is called the *detonation velocity*.

The relations between the variables on the two sides of a detonation wave are the same as those applying to a shock wave (Eqs. 11.8–1, 2, and 3). Again it is convenient to rearrange these equations to obtain the relations (Eqs. 11.8–4, 5, and 6). These relations are

$$M = \sqrt{\frac{p_\infty - p_0}{(1/\rho_0) - (1/\rho_\infty)}} \tag{11.9–1}$$

$$v_\infty^{\,2} - v_0^{\,2} = -(p_\infty - p_0)\left[\frac{1}{\rho_0} + \frac{1}{\rho_\infty}\right] \tag{11.9–2}$$

$$\hat{U}_\infty - \hat{U}_0 = \tfrac{1}{2}(p_\infty + p_0)\left[\frac{1}{\rho_0} - \frac{1}{\rho_\infty}\right] \tag{11.9–3}$$

Although these are valid relations between the values of the variables on the two sides of the detonation, the occurrence of a detonation depends on the existence and the stability of solutions of the differential equations describing the structure of the detonation.

The initial composition variables x_{i0}, the temperature T_0, the pressure p_0, and the density ρ_0 are assumed to be known so that

$$\hat{U}_0 = \sum_{i=1}^{s} x_{i0}\overline{U}_i(T_0, p_0, x_{j0}) / \sum_{i=1}^{s} x_{i0} M_i \tag{11.9–4}$$

is known. The difference between the detonation and the shock equations is in the form of $\hat{U}_\infty$. In a shock the chemical composition remains unchanged, whereas in a detonation the chemical composition changes so that energy is released and chemical equilibrium is attained after the gas passes through the wave.

The requirement of chemical equilibrium at $z = \infty$ implies that each of the reaction rates of Eqs. 11.6–8 are zero:

$$K_i(x_{j\infty}, T_\infty, p_\infty) = 0 \qquad i = 1, 2, \cdots, s \tag{11.9–5}$$

From these equations it is possible to determine the equilibrium chemical compositions as functions of the temperature and pressure, $x_{j\infty}(T_\infty\ p_\infty)$. The equation of state can be used to express the temperature in terms of the pressure, density, and chemical composition:

$$T_\infty = f(p_\infty, \rho_\infty, x_{j\infty}) \tag{11.9–6}$$

Making use of this form of the equation of state, we can determine the equilibrium chemical compositions as functions of pressure and density, $x_{j\infty}(p_\infty, \rho_\infty)$. Then, if the partial molal internal energies $\overline{U}_i(T_\infty, p_\infty, x_{j\infty})$ are known, the internal energy per gram, $\hat{U}_\infty$, is known as a function of p_∞ and ρ_∞:

$$\hat{U}_\infty(p_\infty, \rho_\infty) = \sum_{i=1}^{s} x_{i\infty}\overline{U}_i(T_\infty, p_\infty, x_{j\infty}) / \sum_{i=1}^{s} x_{i\infty} M_i \tag{11.9–7}$$

If this expression is used in Eq. 11.9–3 we obtain a relation between p_∞ and ρ_∞.

Figure 11.9–1 illustrates a Hugoniot curve, *DBCB′*, obtained in this manner. The lower curve, *ANA′O*, illustrates a Hugoniot curve which would apply to a shock wave with the same initial conditions as the detonation and in which the composition remains unchanged at its initial

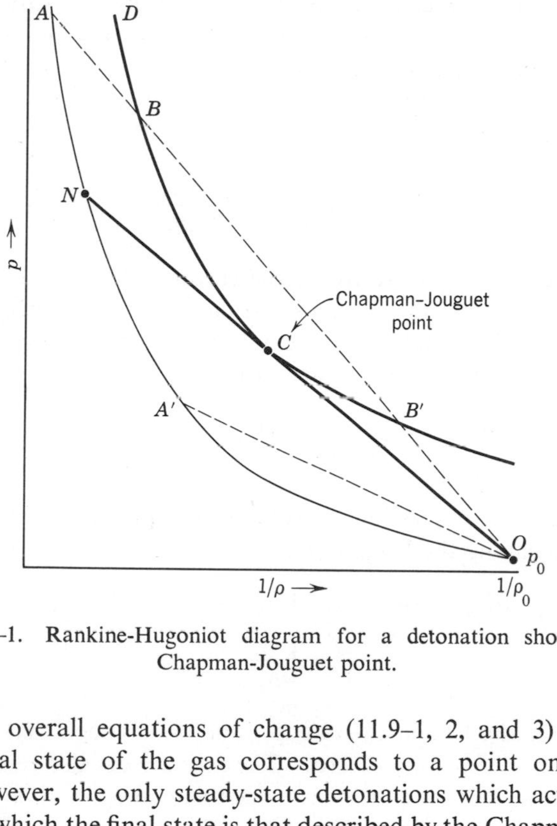

Fig. 11.9–1. Rankine-Hugoniot diagram for a detonation showing the Chapman-Jouguet point.

value. The overall equations of change (11.9–1, 2, and 3) imply only that the final state of the gas corresponds to a point on the upper curve. However, the only steady-state detonations which actually occur are those in which the final state is that described by the Chapman-Jouguet point, *C*. This point is characterized by the fact that the straight line from the initial point, *O*, to *C* is tangent to the Hugoniot curve, at a pressure higher[1] than p_0. The choice of the single point is a result of the Chapman-Jouguet condition, an additional condition not included in the conservation conditions. A justification of the Chapman-Jouguet

[1] There is another line on which a point of tangency occurs at a pressure less than p_0. This "lower Chapman-Jouguet point" represents the largest possible flame velocity (see § 11.7). This point is not considered in this section.

condition is considered presently, but first let us consider some of the properties of this particular solution.

According to Eq. 11.9–1 the negative of the slope of the line in Fig. 11.9–1 joining the initial point O with the final point—a point on the Hugoniot curve $DBCB'$—is the square of the mass rate of flow M. The Chapman-Jouguet condition thus chooses from all possible solutions the one which propagates with the lowest velocity.

The Chapman-Jouguet solution is such that the velocity of the hot gases with respect to the front, v_∞, is the local velocity of sound. This can be seen from the following arguments. Since the points along the Hugoniot curve represent states of thermodynamic equilibrium, the derivative of the internal energy $\hat{U}_\infty$ along the curve is

$$\frac{d\hat{U}_\infty}{d\rho_\infty} = \frac{p_\infty}{\rho_\infty{}^2} + T_\infty \frac{d\hat{S}_\infty}{d\rho_\infty} \tag{11.9–8}$$

where $d\hat{S}_\infty/d\rho_\infty$ is the derivative of the entropy along the curve. (This follows directly from the thermodynamic relations: $(\partial\hat{U}/\partial\rho)_{\hat{S}} = p/\rho^2$ and $(\partial\hat{U}/\partial S)_\rho = T$.) But since the internal energy along the curve is given directly by Eq. 11.9–3, the derivative is

$$\frac{d\hat{U}_\infty}{d\rho_\infty} = \frac{p_0 + p_\infty}{2\rho_\infty{}^2} + \frac{(\rho_\infty - \rho_0)}{2\rho_0\rho_\infty} \frac{dp_\infty}{d\rho_\infty} \tag{11.9–9}$$

If we equate the two expressions, we obtain an expression for the derivative of the entropy along the Hugoniot curve,

$$T_\infty \frac{d\hat{S}_\infty}{d\rho_\infty} = \frac{(\rho_\infty - \rho_0)}{2\rho_0\rho_\infty{}^3} \left[\frac{p_\infty - p_0}{\dfrac{1}{\rho_\infty} - \dfrac{1}{\rho_0}} - \frac{dp_\infty}{d(1/\rho_\infty)} \right] \tag{11.9–10}$$

Thus it is clear the Chapman-Jouguet condition is such that the point C is a point at which $d\hat{S}_\infty/d\rho_\infty$ is zero. The derivative is also zero at $\rho_\infty = \rho_0$. It can be shown[2] that the entropy is a maximum at ρ_0 and is a minimum at the Chapman-Jouguet point, C. Since the entropy at the Chapman-Jouguet point is stationary with respect to variations along the Hugoniot curve, the slope at this point is

$$\frac{dp_\infty}{d(1/\rho_\infty)} = -\rho_\infty{}^2 \left(\frac{\partial p_\infty}{\partial \rho_\infty}\right)_{\hat{S}_\infty} = \frac{p_\infty - p_0}{\dfrac{1}{\rho_\infty} - \dfrac{1}{\rho_0}} \tag{11.9–11}$$

[2] R. Courant and K. O. Friedrichs, *Supersonic Flow and Shock Waves*, Interscience Press (1948), p. 214.

But $(\partial p_\infty/\partial \rho_\infty)_{\hat{S}}$ is the square of the velocity of sound, so that from Eq. 11.9–1 it follows that

$$v_\infty = c_\infty \tag{11.9–12}$$

That is, the velocity of the hot gases with respect to the front is the local velocity of sound.

The Chapman-Jouguet condition leads to the lowest detonation velocity possible if the chemical reactions go to completion. A lower detonation velocity would correspond to a line on the Rankine-Hugoniot diagram, Fig. 11.9–1 (such as the line OA'), which does not intersect the final Hugoniot curve. Clearly in an actual detonation it is possible for the chemical reactions to proceed only part way to completion, but because the reaction rates are always finite this situation could not represent a true mathematical steady state with the hot boundary an infinite distance behind the wave front. If the velocity were higher than the Chapman-Jouguet velocity, the final state would be represented by a point such as B or B'. Let us consider these possibilties in detail.

Von Neumann,[3] Döring,[4] and Zeldovich[5] independently reached the conclusion that a detonation is a combustion process initiated by a shock wave. They assume that the time required for reactions to take place is long compared to the time involved in the passage of the shock wave. Thus a detonation may be represented on the Rankine-Hugoniot diagram, such as Fig. 11.9–1, by a shock wave in which the state changes from O to a point such as N or A followed by combustion process or flame in which the conditions change to those represented by a point on the final Hugoniot curve. It follows from Eq. 11.9–1 that if the shock wave and the chemical reactions actually occur separately, the three points lie on a straight line.

Let us consider a wave in which the final point is a point such as B above the Chapman-Jouguet point, C, on the final Hugoniot. The gas flow behind such a detonation front would be subsonic with respect to the front. Thus a wave of rarefaction may overtake the detonation and weaken it so that the end point moves down the Hugoniot curve. As the point C is reached the gas flow on the hot side approaches the velocity of sound, and it is no longer possible for waves to overtake the detonation.

The possibility of detonation in which the shock is followed by expansion to a point such as B' below the Chapman-Jouguet point C may easily be ruled out. Such a wave would consist of a shock wave to the point A,

[3] J. von Neumann, O.S.R.D., Rep. No. 549 (1942); Ball. Res. Lab. File No. X-122.

[4] W. Döring, *Ann. Physik*, **43**, 421 (1943).

[5] Y. B. Zeldovich, *J. Exp. Theoret. Phys.* (USSR), **10**, 542 (1940); translated in National Adv. Comm. for Aeronautics Tech. Memo. 1261 (1950).

followed by a flame to the point B and a "rarefaction shock" to B'. However, rarefaction shocks are unstable and break up into a number of smaller shocks. (In fact, no steady-state solutions of the equations of change representing rarefaction shocks exist, see § 11.8.) For example, the rarefaction shock could break into two shocks, one from B to C and one from C to B'. The second travels with a lower velocity and is left behind. The first travels faster than the original wave and, as shown in the previous discussion, overtakes the detonation and weakens it so that the final point approaches C.

The possibility of a solution in which the change takes place directly from O to a point below the Chapman-Jouguet point, such as point B', cannot be ruled out on a purely hydrodynamical basis. In such a wave the chemical reactions would take place at an appreciable rate in the gas under conditions close to the initial conditions, without the benefit of the shock heating and compression.

Eyring, Powell, Duffey, and Parlin[6] have extended the von Neumann-Döring-Zeldovich theory to problems involving curved detonation fronts and non-steady states.

The qualitative features of a detonation (according to the von Neumann-Döring-Zeldovich theory) are shown in Fig. 11.9–2. The first part of the detonation wave (known as the von Neumann spike) is an almost ideal shock wave in which very little chemical reaction takes place. The pressure at the spike (point N in Fig. 11.9–1) is approximately twice p_∞ whereas the temperature is approximately one-half T_∞. This initial pressure and temperature rise occurs in a normal shock thickness of approximately 10^{-5} cm. The second phase of the detonation wave is a gradual decrease in the pressure and an increase in the temperature concurrent with the completion of the chemical reactions. This second phase occurs in a distance of the order of one centimeter. The length of

TABLE 11.9–1

EXPERIMENTALLY DETERMINED LENGTHS OF REACTION ZONES FOR VARIOUS EXPLOSIVES[6]

Explosive	l (cm)
TNT	0.076
RDX	0.083
Picric acid	0.22
60-40 Amatol	0.398
Minol-2	0.538
Nitroguanidine	0.88
$2CO + O_2$ (gas)	1.1

[6] H. Eyring, R. Powell, G. Duffey, and R. Parlin, *Chem. Revs.*, **45**, 69 (1949).

this reaction zone, l, the distance from O to C, can be determined experimentally from the minimum diameter of a rod of explosive which propagates a steady-state detonation, from the changes in the detonation velocity when the rod of explosive is surrounded by an inert casing

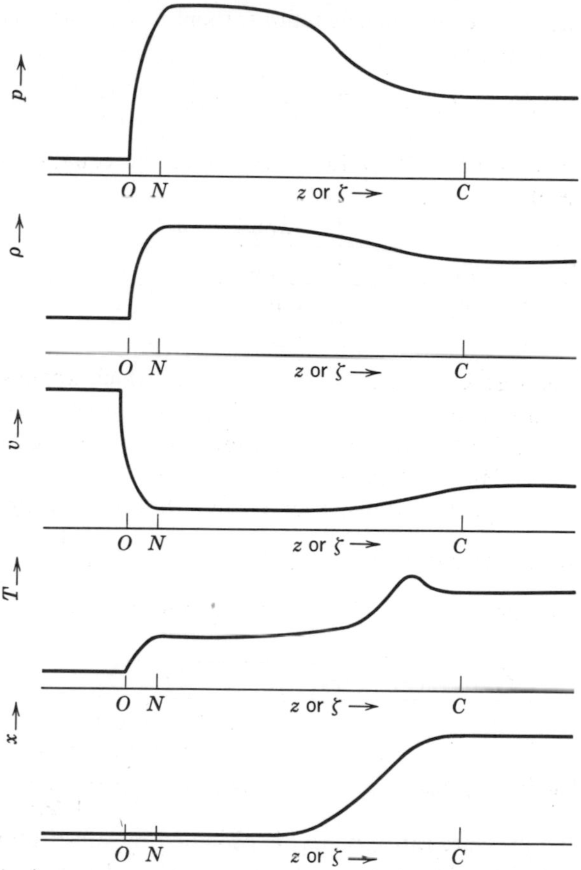

Fig. 11.9–2. Schematic representation of a detonation wave.

material of various thickness, or from the decrease in the detonation velocity when the detonation wave is made to go around a bend of known radius of curvature. Table 11.9–1 gives experimental values of the length of the reaction zone in detonations in a number of explosives.[6]

b. Applications of the theory of detonations to perfect gases

The properties of a detonation wave depend on the equation of state and the calorific equation. A detonation in a solid is very much influenced by the equation of state of the solid. However, in order to illustrate the nature of the solutions let us consider a detonation in which the system satisfies the perfect gas equation of state with a constant specific heat ratio, γ.

If $\hat{Q}$ represents the amount of energy released by one gram of the fluid during the course of the chemical reactions, then, if the system is a perfect gas with constant specific heat:

$$\hat{U}_\infty - \hat{U}_0 = -\hat{Q} + \frac{1}{\gamma - 1}\left(\frac{p_\infty}{\rho_\infty} - \frac{p_0}{\rho_0}\right) \tag{11.9–13}$$

This expression may be used in Eq. 11.9–3 and the equation solved for p_∞/p_0. The result is

$$\frac{p_\infty}{p_0} = \frac{\dfrac{\gamma+1}{\gamma-1} + \dfrac{2\hat{Q}\rho_0}{p_0} - \dfrac{\rho_0}{\rho_\infty}}{\dfrac{\gamma+1}{\gamma-1}\dfrac{\rho_0}{\rho_\infty} - 1} \tag{11.9–14}$$

This equation is a generalization of Eq. 11.8–10, which applies to shock waves. This equation describes the final Hugoniot curve (such as curve *DBCB′* of Fig. 11.9–1). The same equation with $\hat{Q}$ set equal to zero describes the initial Hugoniot curve, *ANA′O*.

The Chapman-Jouguet condition requires that the derivative $dp_\infty/d(1/\rho_\infty)$ defined by the last equation be equal to $(p_\infty - p_0)\Big/\left[\dfrac{1}{\rho_\infty} - \dfrac{1}{\rho_0}\right]$. The negative of this slope is then M^2. Carrying out the manipulations, we find that

$$\frac{\rho_0}{\rho_\infty} = 1 + \frac{\gamma-1}{\gamma}\frac{\hat{Q}\rho_0}{p_0} \mp \frac{\gamma-1}{\gamma}\frac{\hat{Q}\rho_0}{p_0}\sqrt{1 + \frac{2\gamma}{\gamma^2-1}\frac{p_0}{\hat{Q}\rho_0}} \tag{11.9–15}$$

$$M^2 = (\gamma^2-1)\rho_0{}^2\hat{Q} + \gamma p_0\rho_0 \pm (\gamma^2-1)\rho_0{}^2\hat{Q}\sqrt{1 + \frac{2\gamma}{\gamma^2-1}\frac{p_0}{\hat{Q}\rho_0}} \tag{11.9–16}$$

The value of the pressure ratio, p_∞/p_0, is obtained by substituting the last result in Eq. 11.9–14. The upper sign applies to the detonation solution. The lower root gives the largest possible flame velocity, and will not be considered here. With these results it is easy to verify that in a perfect gas the velocity of the hot gases with respect to the front is the local velocity of sound:

$$v_\infty = \sqrt{\gamma\frac{p_\infty}{\rho_\infty}} = c_\infty \tag{11.9–17}$$

This result was shown above to be true in general.

In many detonations, the initial pressure is of the order of 1 atm whereas the final pressure is of the order of 200,000 atm. Hence it is interesting to consider the limiting form of the results discussed above which apply if $p_0 \ll p_\infty$. The velocity of propagation of the detonation into still gas is

$$v_0 = \sqrt{2(\gamma^2 - 1)\hat{Q}} \tag{11.9–18}$$

The remaining quantities are given by the following simple expressions:

$$\frac{\rho_\infty}{\rho_0} = \frac{\gamma + 1}{\gamma} \tag{11.9–19}$$

$$\frac{p_\infty}{p_0} = 2(\gamma - 1)\frac{\hat{Q}\rho_0}{p_0} \tag{11.9–20}$$

These results describe completely the overall effect of a detonation.

Table 11.9–2 compares calculated and experimental detonation velocities[7] for mixtures of hydrogen and oxygen with and without additives. The value of $\hat{Q}$ was computed on the basis of complete thermal equilibrium

TABLE 11.9–2

COMPARISON OF EXPERIMENTAL AND THEORETICAL DETONATION VELOCITIES FOR EXPLOSIONS IN GASES[a, b]

$p_0 = 1$ atm $T_0 = 291°K$

Explosive Mixture	p_∞ (atm)	T (°K)	Detonation Velocity (m/sec)	
			Calculated	Experimental
$(2H_2 + O_2)$	18.05	3583	2806	2819
$(2H_2 + O_2) + 5O_2$	14.13	2620	1732	1700
$(2H_2 + O_2) + 5N_2$	14.39	2685	1850	1822
$(2H_2 + O_2) + 4H_2$	15.97	2976	3627	3527
$(2H_2 + O_2) + 5He$	16.32	3097	3613	3160
$(2H_2 + O_2) + 5A$	16.32	3097	1762	1700

[a] B. Lewis and J. Friauf, *J. Am. Chem. Soc.*, **52**, 3905 (1930).

[b] D. J. Berets, E. F. Greene, and G. B. Kistiakowsky, *J. Am. Chem. Soc.*, **72**, 1080 (1950), repeated the experiments of Lewis and Friauf and made the calculations with improved thermochemical data. Their results agree well with those of Lewis and Friauf, and their accuracy is sufficient to make the difference between experiment and theory significant.

[7] Excellent discussions of detonations in gases are given in the following: (a) W. Jost, *Explosions- und Verbrennungsvorgänge in Gasen*, Julius Springer (1939), reprinted by Edward Bros. (1943), pp. 161–207. (b) B. Lewis and G. Von Elbe, *Combustions, Flames, and Detonations*, Academic Press (1951), pp. 590–627.

at the Chapman-Jouguet point (equilibrium mixture of H_2O, H_2O_2, H, O, and OH) so that $\hat{Q}$ has a slightly different value for each experiment.[8] The value of gamma is that for the reacting gas mixture (see Eq. 11.7–21). The agreement between theory and experiment is excellent

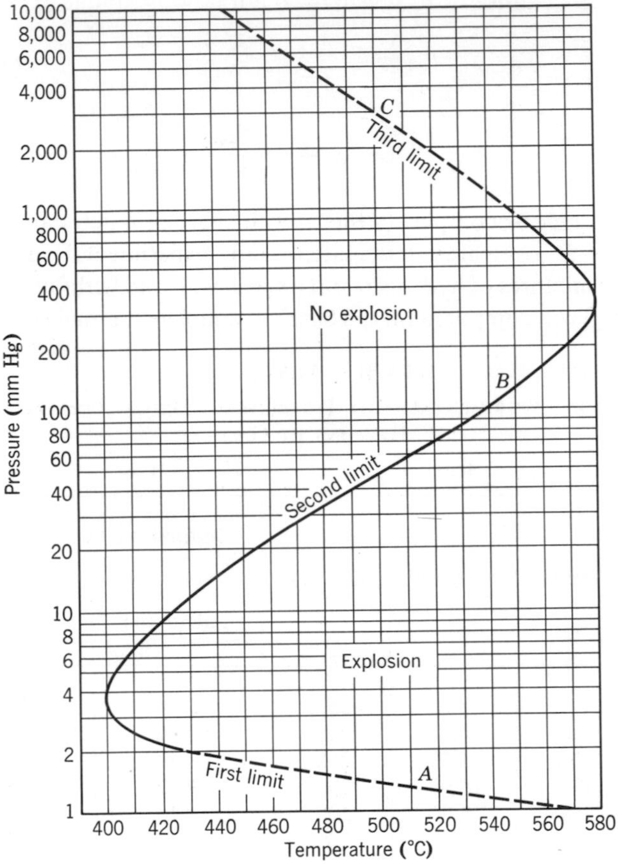

Fig. 11.9–3. Explosion limits for a stoichiometric mixture of hydrogen and oxygen. [From B. Lewis and G. von Elbe, *Combustions, Flames, and Detonations*, Academic Press (1951).]

except for systems near the explosion limits where there are real discrepancies.

The existence of explosion limits depends both on the size of the container (and the nature of its surface) and on the chemical kinetics of the

[8] Details of the calculations are given by B. Lewis and G. Von Elbe, *Phil. Mag.* (7), **20**, 44 (1935).

system. In those gases where the chemical reactions involve a branched or a thermal chain, there are always two and sometimes three explosion limits. Figure 11.9–3 shows the explosion limits for a stoichiometric mixture of hydrogen and oxygen.[7b] The curve A is the curve of lower explosion limits; B is the curve of upper explosion limits; and C is the third explosion limit. Steady-state detonations can occur only in the "tongue-shaped explosion peninsula" bounded by A and B or in the high-pressure region above C. In the very low-pressure region below the lower explosion limit, no detonations can occur because too large a fraction of the free radicals are absorbed and destroyed at the surface of the container or bomb. The upper explosion limit results from the homogeneous recombination of the free radicals in the gas phase by three-body collisions. In a hydroxen-oxygen mixture the upper limit is due to the reaction: $H + O_2 +$ any third molecule $\rightarrow HO_2 +$ the third molecule. The HO_2 is relatively inert and usually diffuses to the wall where it is destroyed. The third explosion limit seems peculiar to the $H_2 + O_2$ system, since it depends upon the pressure in the system getting sufficiently high that the HO_2 decomposes in the gas phase to restore the H atom more often than it diffuses to the wall.

c. The structure of a detonation wave

The structure of a detonation wave is described by a solution of the one-dimensional steady equations of change. These are the equations which are used in the study of flame propagation in § 11.7. The essential difference is that in the study of detonations we seek solutions in which the velocity of the wave relative to the cold gas is supersonic rather than subsonic.

As in the discussion of flame propagation let us consider as an example a one-dimensional steady-state detonation in a gas in which the energy is released by a single unimolecular reaction,

$$A \rightarrow B \tag{11.9–21}$$

In the discussion of detonations, however, a considerable simplification of the presentation is effected by neglecting the back reaction. The back reaction plays a very minor role and does not materially change the nature of the solutions. Further simplification can be obtained by neglecting the diffusion effects (that is, taking the diffusion constant to be zero). However, viscosity does play an important role in determining the structure of a detonation as well as a shock. Thus it is not possible to neglect viscous effects as in the study of flame propagation, but a real simplification occurs if the coefficient of viscosity is such that the constant ω (defined by Eq. 11.7–24) is unity. As explained in § 11.8, this choice of ω is reasonable, physically, and makes possible the analytic solution of the equations describing the structure of a pure shock wave.

The equations of change describing the structure of such a detonation are Eqs. 11.7–25, 26, and 27. But, because of the neglect of the back reaction, γ' is equal to γ, and the second term is dropped from the expression for the function $f(x, \tau)$. As discussed above, we neglect diffusion so that $G = x$. In the discussion of detonations, however, it is more common to consider p/p_∞, $u = \rho_\infty/\rho$, and x, the mole fraction of A, as the primary variables rather than to consider τ, u, and x as in the discussion of flame propagation. Since, according to the equation of state,

$$\frac{\tau}{\tau_\infty} = \frac{p}{p_\infty}\frac{\rho_\infty}{\rho} = u\frac{p}{p_\infty} \tag{11.9–22}$$

it is easy to transform variables. Thus the equations of change describing the structure of a detonation are

$$\frac{dx}{d\zeta} = \frac{1}{\mu^2} f(x, u, p/p_\infty) \tag{11.9–23}$$

$$\frac{du}{d\zeta} = \frac{1}{\omega} h(u, p/p_\infty) \tag{11.9–24}$$

$$\frac{d(p/p_\infty)}{d\zeta} = j(x, u, p/p_\infty) \tag{11.9–25}$$

where ζ is the reduced distance coordinate defined by Eq. 11.7–18,

$$j(x, u, p/p_\infty) = \frac{1}{u\tau_\infty} g - \frac{1}{\omega u}\frac{p}{p_\infty} h \tag{11.9–26}$$

and f, g, and h are functions defined by Eqs. 11.7–29, 30, and 31.

Since the detonation satisfies the Chapman-Jouguet condition, $\kappa_\infty = 1$. The equations of § 11.9b then determine M, ρ_∞/ρ_0, and p_∞/p_0 (as well as τ_∞/τ_0). The explicit forms of the functions f, h, and j applying to a detonation in which $\kappa_\infty = 1$ and $\omega = 1$ are

$$f(x, u, p/p_\infty) = -xe^{-1/\tau} \tag{11.9–27}$$

$$h(u, p/p_\infty) = u - 1 + \frac{1}{\gamma}\left(\frac{p}{p_\infty} - 1\right) \tag{11.9–28}$$

$$j(x, u, p/p_\infty) = \frac{\gamma - 1}{2u}\left[\frac{2Q}{\gamma k T_\infty} x - \left\{u - \frac{\gamma + 1}{\gamma} + \frac{p}{\gamma p_\infty}\right\}^2 - \frac{1}{\gamma^2}\left(\frac{\gamma + 1}{\gamma - 1}\right)\left(1 - \frac{p}{p_\infty}\right)^2\right] \tag{11.9–29}$$

The constant μ, defined by Eq. 11.7–19, is

$$\mu = M\sqrt{\hat{C}_p/k'\lambda\rho} \tag{11.9–30}$$

where k' is the steric factor in the chemical reaction rate (see Eq. 11.7–15). Whereas in the theory of flames the value of μ is an eigenvalue determined by detailed solutions of the equation of change, in the theory of detonations the value of μ is known a priori because of the Chapman-Jouguet condition.

The nature of the solutions of these equations may be described by means of a Rankine-Hugoniot diagram such as Fig. 11.9–1. Figure 11.9–4 is such a plot.[9] First, Eq. 11.9–14 is used to draw the final Hugoniot curve. The Chapman-Jouguet point, C, is then determined either from Eq. 11.9–15 or by drawing a line from the initial point, O, tangent to the final Hugoniot curve. Next, Eq. 11.9–14 with Q set equal to zero is used to draw the shock or initial Hugoniot curve. The line passing through O and the Chapman-Jouguet point C intersects the shock Hugoniot at the point, N, known as the "von Neumann spike." The von Neumann spike represents the final pressure and density of a shock wave of sufficient strength to travel with the detonation velocity. However, if the gas is subject to a shock from the initial condition, O, to the final state, N, the pressure as a function of density within the shock would not be represented by the shock Hugoniot, but rather by the solution of the equations of change as given by Eq. 11.8–43. Such a solution curve is drawn in Fig. 11.9–4. Figure 11.9–5 shows T/T_0 as a function of ρ_0/ρ along the shock solution curve and along the straight line OCN. In this figure it is seen that the temperature of the von Neumann spike, N, is somewhat less than half the final temperature at the Chapman-Jouguet point, C. Since the temperature is so low between O and N we would not expect the chemical reactions to occur to any appreciable extent in the short time required for the gas to pass through the initial shock. Actually the temperature at N is so low that in many practical cases we would expect a time lag or a quenching zone before the reactions set in.

A number of qualitative properties of the solutions may be obtained by considering the nature of the singularity at C and by considering the surfaces on which the derivatives are zero. In Fig. 11.9–4 the straight line OCN is the relation between pressure and density obtained by setting $h = 0$. (This relation is independent of x.) From Eq. 11.9–24 it is clear that the solutions are vertical, $d(p/p_0)/d(\rho_0/\rho) = \infty$, when they cross this line. The curves of constant x (curves $x = x_j$) are the contours defined by $j = 0$.

[9] The constants used in the examples of this section are the same as those used in the discussion of flames. See footnote 22 of § 11.7.

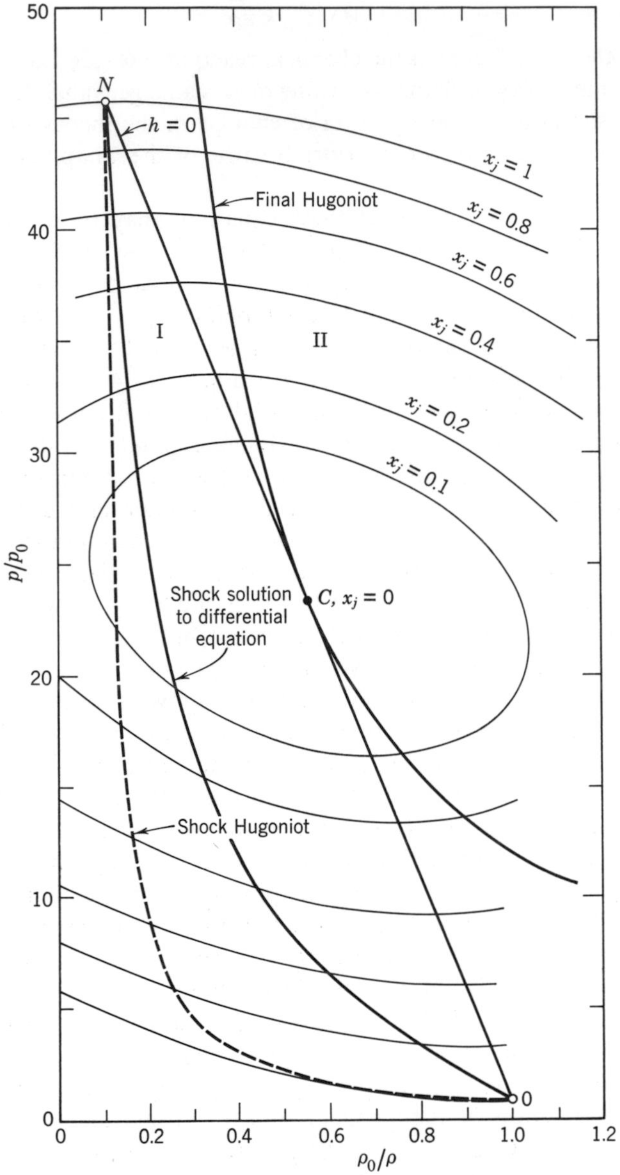

Fig. 11.9–4. A Rankine-Hugoniot diagram showing the shock solution of the differential equation, the initial and final Hugoniot curves, the line of $h = 0$, and the lines of $j = 0$.

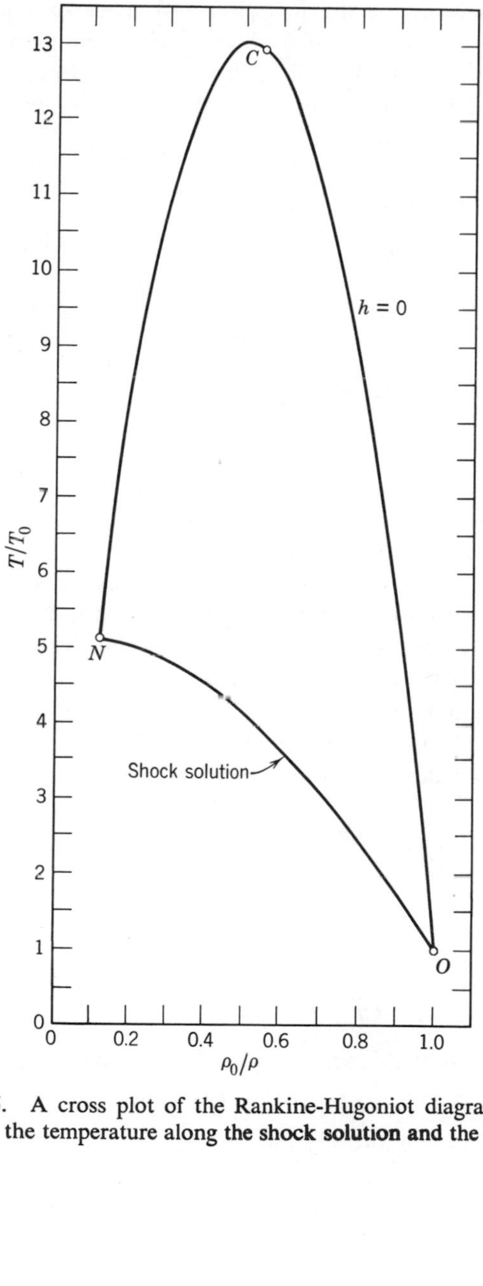

Fig. 11.9–5. A cross plot of the Rankine-Hugoniot diagram, Fig. 11.9–4, showing the temperature along the shock solution and the $h = 0$ curve.

From Eq. 11.9–25 it follows that the solution is horizontal, $\dfrac{d(p/p_0)}{d(\rho_0/\rho)} = 0$, when it crosses $j = 0$, that is, when the value of x on the solution curve is equal to x_j.

It is convenient to divide the $[(p/p_0), (\rho_0/\rho)]$ space of Fig. 11.9–4 into two regions: region I to the left of the line, $h = 0$, and region II to the right of this line. From Eq. 11.9–28 it is clear that h and hence $d(\rho_0/\rho)/d\zeta$ is negative in region I and positive in region II. Similarly, from Eq. 11.9–29 the value of j, and hence $\dfrac{d(p/p_0)}{d\zeta}$, is positive when x is greater than x_j and negative when x is less than x_j. Thus:

$$\text{Region I:} \qquad \frac{d(p/p_0)}{d(\rho_0/\rho)} < 0 \quad \text{if} \quad x > x_j \qquad\qquad (11.9\text{–}31a)$$
$$> 0 \quad \text{if} \quad x < x_j$$

$$\text{Region II:} \qquad \frac{d(p/p_0)}{d(\rho_0/\rho)} > 0 \quad \text{if} \quad x > x_j \qquad\qquad (11.9\text{–}31b)$$
$$< 0 \quad \text{if} \quad x < x_j$$

The hot boundary, the point C, is a singular point of the set of differential equations. Let us consider the nature of this singularity. For reasons which become apparent presently, we include κ_∞ as a parameter and consider detonations which do not necessarily satisfy the Chapman-Jouguet condition. That is, we consider detonations in which the final point lies on the Hugoniot curve of Fig. 11.9–4 above the point C. In the region near the hot boundary the functions on the right of the equations of change (11.9–23, 24, and 25) are linear in the deviations of the variables from their limiting values. These "linearized" equations are

$$\frac{dx}{d\zeta} = -\frac{1}{\mu^2} x e^{-1/\tau_\infty} \qquad (11.9\text{–}32)$$

$$\frac{du}{d\zeta} = (u - 1) + \frac{1}{\gamma \kappa_\infty^{\ 2}} \left(\frac{p}{p_\infty} - 1 \right) \qquad (11.9\text{–}33)$$

$$\frac{d(p/p_\infty)}{d\zeta} = \frac{(\gamma - 1)}{\gamma} \frac{Q}{kT_\infty} x - \frac{1}{\gamma \kappa_\infty^{\ 2}} (1 - \kappa_\infty^{\ 2}) \left(\frac{p}{p_\infty} - 1 \right) \qquad (11.9\text{–}34)$$

A general solution of this set of equations may be written in the form:

$$x = t_1 [x]_1 e^{\alpha_1 \zeta} + t_2 [x]_2 e^{\alpha_2 \zeta} + t_3 [x]_3 e^{\alpha_3 \zeta} \qquad (11.9\text{–}35)$$

$$u - 1 = t_1 e^{\alpha_1 \zeta} + t_2 e^{\alpha_2 \zeta} + t_3 e^{\alpha_3 \zeta} \qquad (11.9\text{–}36)$$

$$p/p_\infty = t_1 [p/p_\infty]_1 e^{\alpha_1 \zeta} + t_2 [p/p_\infty]_2 e^{\alpha_2 \zeta} + t_3 [p/p_\infty]_3 e^{\alpha_3 \zeta} \qquad (11.9\text{–}37)$$

The constants t_1, t_2, and t_3 are arbitrary and are determined by the boundary conditions on the problem. The quantities α_i, $[x]_i$, and $[p/p_\infty]_i$ are determined by substituting these expressions into the differential equations (11.9–32, 33, and 34). It is easily shown that

$$\alpha_1 = -\frac{1}{\gamma\kappa_\infty^2}(1-\kappa_\infty^2) \tag{11.9–38}$$

$$[x]_1 = 0 \tag{11.9–39}$$

$$[p/p_\infty]_1 = -\gamma + (\gamma-1)(1-\kappa_\infty^2) \tag{11.9–40}$$

$$\alpha_2 = -\frac{1}{\mu_2} e^{-1/\tau_\infty} \tag{11.9–41}$$

$$[x]_2 = \frac{\gamma}{\gamma-1}\frac{kT_\infty}{Q}\left[\frac{\gamma\kappa_\infty^2}{\mu^2}e^{-1/\tau_\infty} - (1-\kappa_\infty^2)\right]\left[1+\frac{1}{\mu^2}e^{-1/\tau_\infty}\right] \tag{11.9–42}$$

$$[p/p_\infty]_2 = -\gamma\kappa_\infty^2\left[1+\frac{1}{\mu^2}e^{-1/\tau_\infty}\right] \tag{11.9–43}$$

$$\alpha_3 = 1 \tag{11.9–44}$$

$$[x]_3 = 0 \tag{11.9–45}$$

$$[p/p_\infty]_3 = 0 \tag{11.9–46}$$

In a detonation solution, the variables approach finite limits as ζ approaches infinity. Thus, since α_3 is positive, t_3 must be taken to be zero, and the asymptotic solution is of the form

$$x = t_2[x]_2 e^{\alpha_2\zeta} \tag{11.9–47}$$

$$u = \rho_\infty/\rho = 1 + t_1 e^{\alpha_1\zeta} + t_2 e^{\alpha_2\zeta} \tag{11.9–48}$$

$$p/p_\infty = 1 + t_1[p/p_\infty]_1 e^{\alpha_1\zeta} + t_2[p/p_\infty]_2 e^{\alpha_2\zeta} \tag{11.9–49}$$

where the constants t_1 and t_2 are determined by the cold boundary conditions. The mole fraction, x, must be everywhere positive. Thus, since $[x]_2$ is positive, it is clear that t_2 must be chosen positive. The constant t_1 may be negative, zero, or positive. Solutions of the three types are indicated, schematically, in Fig. 11.9–6 and labeled *NDZ*, (2), and (3), respectively. There are one-parameter manifolds of solutions of the types *NDZ* and (3) due to various possible values of the ratio t_1/t_2.

The curve labeled *NDZ* represents the type of solution expected on the basis of the von Neumann-Döring-Zeldovich theory. This solution starts out along the pure shock solution to the differential equations.

Then, as the temperature rises and the chemical reactions set in, the solution deviates from this curve. A point of maximum pressure is reached when $x = x_j$. The *NDZ* solution then falls approaching *C* along the curve labeled "flame." This curve represents a normal flame solution to the equations in which the initial conditions are those labeled *N* and the final conditions are represented by *C*.

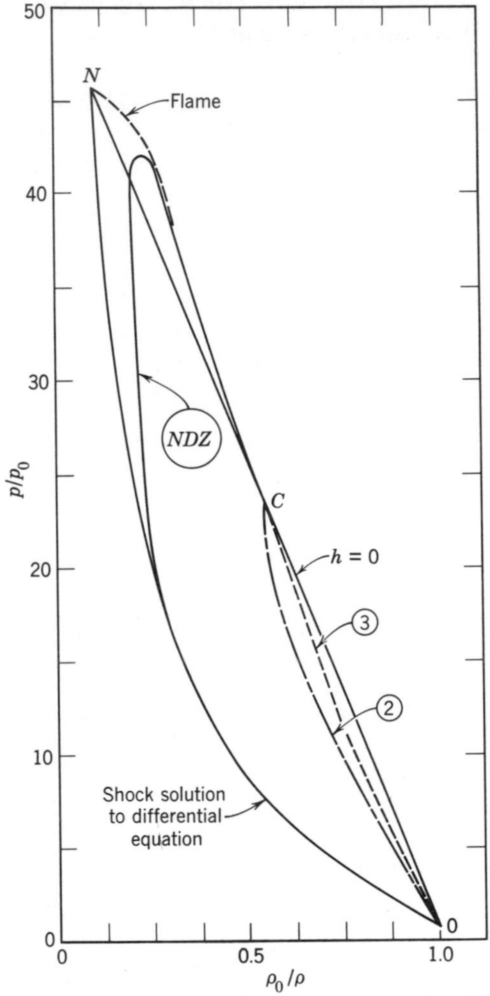

Fig. 11.9–6. A schematic illustration of the three possible types of solutions of the detonation equations.

The other two conceivable types of solutions to the detonation equations are illustrated by curves (2) and (3). These solutions proceed from *O* to *C* without a maximum in the pressure. The solution (2) approaches *C* along the singular solution, with $t_1 = 0$, $t_2 \neq 0$, while (3) approaches *C* along the other singular solution. The possibility and physical reality of these types of solutions are interesting questions.

10. The Flow of Propellant Gases in Rockets[1]

The flow of propellant gases in a rocket and through a nozzle may be considered as another example of the applications of the hydrodynamic equations of change. The interior ballistics of a rocket depend on the rate of production of the propellant gases and on the flow of these gases through the nozzle. In solid propellant rockets, the rate of production of propellant

[1] H. W. Liepmann and A. E. Puckett, *Introduction to Aerodynamics of a Compressible Fluid*, Wiley (1947).

gases depends upon the rate of burning of the solid charge. In order to maintain constant combustion chamber pressure throughout most of the burning time it is necessary to control the burning rate. The burning rate can be controlled by adjusting the composition of the solid components and the geometrical configurations. Ideally, during the major portion of the burning of a solid charge a steady state is maintained. In a liquid propellant rocket motor, the rate of production of gases is controlled by adjusting the rates of propellant flow.

In this section we are concerned with the steady-state solutions, assuming that the velocity of flow is uniform across any cross-section and neglecting heat transfer and drag at the walls. To take these factors into consideration would require a lengthy treatment of boundary layer theory, aerodynamics, and turbulence. In many practical cases the idealizations considered here are good approximations and are experimentally justified. The existence of a steady state makes the problem of calculating the conditions in the exit of the rocket amenable to a simple theoretical treatment. The pressure, temperature, and velocity of the gases may be computed at any part of the nozzle, and the resulting thrust which accelerates the rocket can be calculated from its geometry.

a. The equations of change

The flow of gas through a nozzle is described by the equations of change discussed in § 11.1. In this section it is convenient to use the equation of continuity, the equation of energy balance, and the equation of change of entropy as the independent equations. We shall assume that a steady state has been set up and discuss the solutions of the time-independent equations. The time-independent equations describing flow through a system of varying cross-section may be reduced to one-dimensional equations in the following manner.

Let z be the direction of the axis of the rocket (see Fig. 11.10–1) and let $f(x, y) = z$ be the equation of the bounding surface, that is, the inside surface of the containing vessel. Usually this surface has cylindrical symmetry about the z-axis. Now consider a plane normal to the z-axis and let S be the portion of the plane bounded by the intersection with the surface $f(x, y) = z$. The derivation of the one-dimensional equations applying to the present problem is based on a simple theorem. If $\boldsymbol{F}(\boldsymbol{r})$ is a vector field which on the surface $f(x, y) = z$ is tangent to the surface, then

$$\iint_S \left(\frac{\partial}{\partial \boldsymbol{r}} \cdot \boldsymbol{F}\right) dx\, dy = \frac{d}{dz} \iint_S F_z\, dx\, dy \qquad (11.10\text{–}1)$$

where F_z is the z component of $\boldsymbol{F}$.

The three-dimensional *equation of continuity* describing a steady state is given by Eq. 11.1–2 as

$$\left(\frac{\partial}{\partial \mathbf{r}} \cdot \rho \mathbf{v}\right) = 0 \tag{11.10–2}$$

Since the velocity of the gas at the surfaces of the containing vessel is either zero or tangent to the wall, we may apply the theorem of Eq. 11.10–1. Thus we find that

$$\frac{d}{dz}\iint \rho v_z \, dx \, dy = 0 \tag{11.10–3}$$

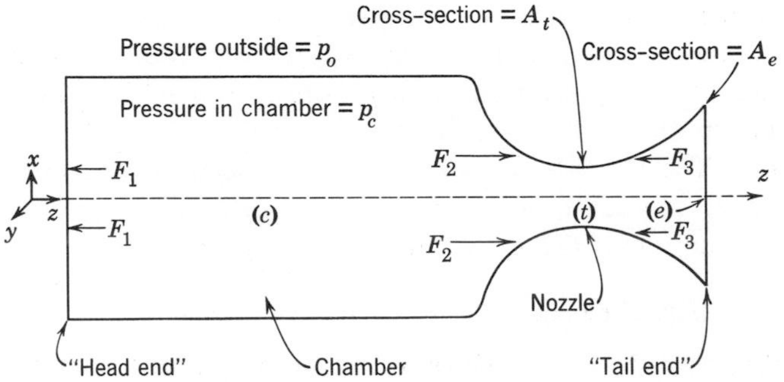

Fig. 11.10–1. Schematic representation of a rocket, showing the combustion chamber and the nozzle.

Then, integrating with respect to z, we get

$$\iint \rho v_z \, dx \, dy = M \tag{11.10–4}$$

where M is a constant. It is clear that M is the mass rate of flow of matter across any cross-section.[2] The conditions in a nozzle are nearly uniform across a cross-section. Hence it is convenient to replace this equation by

$$\rho(z)v(z)A(z) = M \tag{11.10–5}$$

where $A(z)$ is the cross-section as a function of z and $\rho(z)$ and $v(z)$ are average values defined in such a manner that this equation is correct.

The *equation of conservation of energy* may be derived in a similar

[2] The symbol M was used in the previous sections to denote a somewhat different quantity—the mass rate of flow per unit cross-section.

manner. If Eq. (11.1–3) multiplied by $\rho\mathbf{v}$ is added to Eq. (11.1–4) multiplied by ρ, we get

$$\left(\rho\mathbf{v}\cdot\frac{\partial}{\partial \mathbf{r}}(\hat{U}+\tfrac{1}{2}v^2)\right)+\left(\frac{\partial}{\partial \mathbf{r}}\cdot(\mathsf{p}\cdot\mathbf{v})\right)+\left(\frac{\partial}{\partial \mathbf{r}}\cdot\mathbf{q}\right)=0 \qquad (11.10\text{–}6)$$

Then, in view of the equation of continuity, (11.10–2)

$$\left(\frac{\partial}{\partial \mathbf{r}}\cdot[(\hat{U}+\tfrac{1}{2}v^2)\rho\mathbf{v}]\right)+\left(\frac{\partial}{\partial \mathbf{r}}\cdot(\mathsf{p}\cdot\mathbf{v})\right)+\left(\frac{\partial}{\partial \mathbf{r}}\cdot\mathbf{q}\right)=0 \qquad (11.10\text{–}7)$$

This equation is to be integrated over a plane normal to the z-axis. If we assume that there is no drag on the walls of the containing vessel and no heat transfer to the walls, the theorem of Eq. 11.10–1 may be applied. The result is

$$\iint(\hat{U}+\tfrac{1}{2}v^2)\rho v_z\,dx\,dy+\iint(\mathsf{p}\cdot\mathbf{v})_z\,dx\,dy+\iint q_z\,dx\,dy=\text{constant} \qquad (11.10\text{–}8)$$

If the effects of thermal conductivity and viscosity are neglected, this equation may be approximated by the one-dimensional equation,

$$(\hat{U}+\tfrac{1}{2}v^2)\rho vA+pvA=\text{constant} \qquad (11.10\text{–}9)$$

When this is divided by the constant ρvA, we obtain for the energy balance equation

$$\hat{H}+\tfrac{1}{2}v^2=\text{constant} \qquad (11.10\text{–}10)$$

where $\hat{H}=\hat{U}+(p/\rho)$ is the enthalpy per unit mass. It is convenient to evaluate the constant in this equation in terms of the conditions in the chamber of the rocket, that is, at a point far removed (in the negative z direction) from the nozzle. Indicating this point by the subscript c, we have

$$\tfrac{1}{2}(v^2-v_c^2)=\hat{H}_c-\hat{H} \qquad (11.10\text{–}11)$$

If the point c is chosen at the head end of the chamber, the velocity v_c is zero. In actual practice the conditions within the chamber of a rocket are nearly uniform, and the kinetic energy associated with the flow at any point in the chamber may be neglected. Thus the energy balance equation is (see Eq. 11.10–40 for practical units)

$$v=\sqrt{2(\hat{H}_c-\hat{H})} \qquad (11.10\text{–}12)$$

According to the discussions in § 11.1c, if the effects of diffusion, viscosity, thermal conductivity, and deviations from chemical equilibrium are neglected, the flow is isentropic. This condition is used as the third equation of change. This equation, the equation of continuity (11.10–5), and the equation of energy balance (11.10–12) describe completely the flow through a nozzle or orifice.

The energy balance equation (11.10–12) gives the velocity of the gas as a function of the enthalpy. The interpretations of this equation depend on the nature of the equation of state and the thermochemistry of the gas under consideration. In actual practice, these considerations may be rather complicated. The necessary numerical procedures are discussed later in this section. However, as an indication of the qualitative behavior of the equations we consider first a perfect gas with constant specific heats.

b. Applications to a perfect gas

If the specific heat of the gas is constant, the energy balance equation (11.10–12) becomes

$$v = \sqrt{2\hat{C}_p(T_c - T)} = \sqrt{\frac{2\gamma}{(\gamma - 1)}\frac{k}{m}(T_c - T)} \qquad (11.10\text{–}13)$$

This is an expression for the velocity of flow as a function of the temperature of the gas. Because of the isentropic nature of the flow, the relation between temperature and pressure in the flowing gas is given by the adiabatic equation of state. For a perfect gas, this relation is, in terms of the conditions in the chamber,

$$\frac{p}{p_c} = \left(\frac{\rho}{\rho_c}\right)^{\gamma} \quad \text{or} \quad \frac{T}{T_c} = \left(\frac{p}{p_c}\right)^{(\gamma-1)/\gamma} \qquad (11.10\text{–}14)$$

Thus Eq. 11.10–13 becomes

$$v = \left\{\frac{2\gamma}{\gamma - 1}\frac{kT_c}{m}\left[1 - \left(\frac{p}{p_c}\right)^{(\gamma-1)/\gamma}\right]\right\}^{1/2} \qquad (11.10\text{–}15)$$

This result can be expressed in terms of the velocity of sound (defined in Eq. 11.4–5) of the gas in the chamber:

$$v = c_c\left\{\left(\frac{2}{\gamma - 1}\right)\left[1 - \left(\frac{p}{p_c}\right)^{(\gamma-1)/\gamma}\right]\right\}^{1/2} \qquad (11.10\text{–}16)$$

Clearly the maximum velocity of the gas is obtained at complete expansion where $p/p_c = 0$. This maximum velocity is

$$v_m = \sqrt{\frac{2}{\gamma - 1}}\, c_c = \left(\frac{2\gamma kT_c}{(\gamma - 1)m}\right)^{1/2} \qquad (11.10\text{–}17)$$

As an example of a typical rocket let us assume that the gases in the chamber are at a temperature of 3500°K, have an average molecular weight of 25, and a specific heat ratio, $\gamma = 1.20$ (so that $(v_m/c_c) = \sqrt{2/(\gamma - 1)} \doteq 3$). Since (kT_c/m) is 1.1×10^{10} cm² per sec², the maximum gas velocity attainable in a rocket using this fuel is about 3.6×10^5 cm per sec, or 12,000 ft per sec. Actually complete expansion is never realized, and the final velocity is nearer twice the velocity of sound in the chamber, that is, of the order of 2×10^5 cm per sec or 7,000 ft per sec.

The conditions within the rocket and nozzle as a function of the cross-section are obtained by using the equation of continuity (11.10–5).

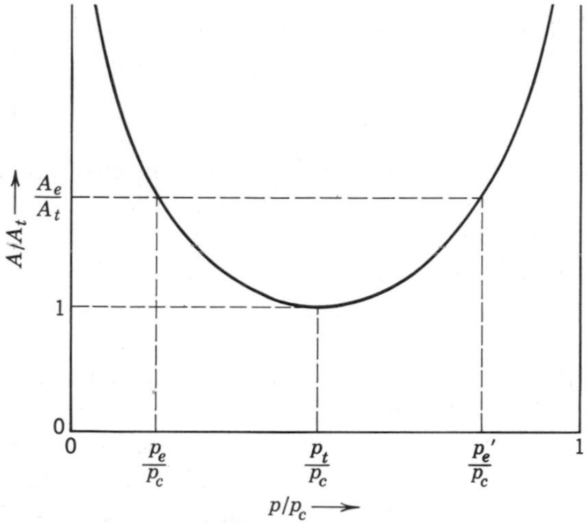

Fig. 11.10–2. A schematic illustration of the dependence of the pressure on the cross-sectional area.

Using the adiabatic equation of state (11.10–14) to eliminate the density, and Eq. 11.10–16 to eliminate the velocity, we obtain the relation,

$$A = \frac{M}{\rho v} = \left(\frac{\gamma - 1}{2}\right)^{1/2} \frac{M}{\rho_c c_c} \left(\frac{p_c}{p}\right)^{1/\gamma} \Big/ \left[1 - \left(\frac{p}{p_c}\right)^{(\gamma-1)/\gamma}\right]^{1/2} \tag{11.10–18}$$

This relation gives implicitly the pressure as a function of the cross-section, and is illustrated in Fig. 11.10–2.

There is a minimum value of A as a function of p. Let us indicate the values of the quantities at this point by a subscript t. Then by simple differentiation it is easy to show that p_t and A_t are given by

$$\frac{p_t}{p_c} = \left(\frac{2}{\gamma + 1}\right)^{\gamma/(\gamma-1)} \tag{11.10–19}$$

$$A_t = \frac{M}{\rho_c c_c} \left(\frac{\gamma + 1}{2}\right)^{\frac{(\gamma+1)}{2(\gamma-1)}} \tag{11.10–20}$$

Then from the adiabatic equation of state (11.10–14) and the equation of velocity (11.10–16), we may obtain expressions for ρ_t and v_t:

$$\rho_t = \rho_c \left(\frac{2}{\gamma + 1}\right)^{1/(\gamma-1)} \tag{11.10–21}$$

$$v_t = \sqrt{\frac{2}{\gamma + 1}}\, c_c \tag{11.10–22}$$

Combining the last relation with the definition of the velocity of sound (Eq. 11.4–5), the equation for the pressure ratio (Eq. 11.10–19), and the equation for the density ratio (Eq. 11.10–21), we find that

$$v_t = c_t \tag{11.10–23}$$

That is, the flow velocity at the point of minimum cross-section is the local velocity of sound.

For the typical propellant considered above with $T_c = 3500°K$, $\gamma = 1.2$, and molecular weight 25, we find that $p_t/p_c = 0.56$ and $v_t = 110{,}000$ cm sec^{-1}. If the chamber pressure, p_c, is 200 atm, $(M/A_t) = \rho_t v_t = 1{,}200$ gm per cm^2 sec.

Now let us consider the flow of gas from a chamber through a nozzle and out into the open. Let us assume that the pressure in the chamber is maintained at p_c and that the pressure in the surrounding external medium is maintained at p_0. Let A_t be the cross-sectional area at the orifice or nozzle and A_e be that at the end of the flange. From Fig. 11.10–2 it is clear that there are two possible pressures at the end of the flange, indicated by p_e and p_e'. There are three possible types of flow, which are the following:

(1) Ordinary *Bernoulli flow* occurs when

$$p_0 > p_e' \tag{11.10–24}$$

Under these conditions the pressure never reaches p_t, and the actual throat does not occur at the minimum in Fig. 11.10–2. The velocity of the gas remains subsonic throughout the flow. The velocity increases to a maximum, and the pressure decreases to a minimum at the throat.

(2) Usual *rocket flow* occurs when

$$p_0 < p_e \tag{11.10–25}$$

Under these conditions the actual throat corresponds to the point t. The velocity of the gas becomes sonic at the throat and continues to increase. The pressure decreases monotonically through the entire nozzle.

(3) Overexpanded nozzles result in *shock waves* when

$$p_e' > p_0 > p_e \tag{11.10–26}$$

Under these conditions the isentropic flow cannot be maintained, and shock waves form in the nozzle. Upstream from the shock waves, the flow occurs as under usual rocket conditions.

A net force or thrust on the rocket results from the unbalanced forces exerted by the gases in the chamber. If the chamber and nozzle are cylindrically symmetric this net thrust is in the direction counter to the nozzle. As indicated in Fig. 11.10–1, the thrust may be considered as the sum of four terms:

$$F = F_1 + F_2 + F_3 + F_4 \tag{11.10–27}$$

F_1 is the force exerted by the gases on the front of the chamber; F_2 is the force exerted on the rear of the chamber in the opposite direction; F_3 is the force exerted on the expanding portion of the nozzle; and F_4 is the unbalanced force resulting from the pressure p_0 of the external atmosphere acting on the entire chamber except for the area of the exit A_e. These forces are given by the expressions:

$$F_1 = p_c A_c \qquad F_4 = -p_0 A_e$$

$$F_2 = -\int_{A_t}^{A_c} p\, dA \qquad F_3 = \int_{A_t}^{A_e} p\, dA \tag{11.10–28}$$

The integrals are integrals of the pressure as a function of the area as given implicitly by Eq. 11.10–18 and illustrated in Fig. 11.10–2. In F_2 the integral is along the right branch of the curve, and in F_3 the integral is along the left branch.

The integration of the expressions for the thrust, F, is straightforward. The result may be written in terms of the velocity of the gas as given by Eq. 11.10–16 and the mass rate of discharge M to obtain the expression,

$$F = Mv_e + (p_e - p_0)A_e \tag{11.10–29}$$

That is, the total thrust on the rocket is the time rate of change of the momentum of the propellant gases up to the exit of the nozzle, plus the excess pressure of the gases on the exit area.

c. The thermochemistry of real gas mixtures

We have discussed the flow of an ideal gas through a rocket nozzle. The performance of a real rocket, however, depends on the properties of propellant gases, that is, hot chemically reacting mixtures. In general, the properties of the gas and the dynamics of the flow depend on the kinetics of the chemical reactions. At the high temperatures prevailing in a rocket chamber, however, the reaction rates are sufficiently fast that to a good approximation the composition of the gases is always that characteristic of thermodynamic equilibrium. If this condition is assumed, the properties of the mixture are described uniquely by the principles of thermodynamics.

At sufficiently high temperatures the assumption of thermodynamic equilibrium is good, since all the chemical reactions occur rapidly. As the gases expand and cool, however, the composition becomes "frozen." This occurs when the rate of the chemical reactions becomes slow compared to the rate of cooling. For example, consider the reaction of nitrogen with oxygen to form nitric oxide, which occurs when air is heated:

$$N_2 + O_2 \rightleftharpoons 2NO \qquad (11.10\text{–}30)$$

The time required for one-half the equilibrium concentration of nitric oxide to be formed is shown in Table 11.10–1. If the temperature is above 2300°K, the equilibrium is attained in a small fraction of a second, whereas at 1500°K it requires days.

TABLE 11.10–1[a]

TIME REQUIRED TO FORM ONE-HALF THE EQUILIBRIUM AMOUNT OF NITRIC OXIDE IN AIR AT ATMOSPHERIC PRESSURE

T (°K)	$t_{1/2}$ (sec)
1500	1.09×10^5
1700	3.54×10^3
1900	1.25×10^2
2100	5.06
2300	2.25×10^{-1}
2500	1.06×10^{-2}
2700	5.25×10^{-4}
2900	3.45×10^{-5}
3100	1.86×10^{-6}

[a] K. Jellinek, *Z. anorg. Chem.*, **49**, 229 (1906).

For a unimolecular reaction with activation energy $E^\ddagger$, the half-time[3] for the reaction is of the order of one second when $E^\ddagger/RT = 30$. If $E^\ddagger$ is 40,000 cal per mole, the half-time of the reaction is less than one second when the temperature is above 700°K. A reaction having an activation energy of 100,000 cal (corresponding to breaking a carbon-hydrogen bond) has a half-time of less than a second at temperatures above about 1700°K.

[3] With a normal value of the steric factor, the reaction rate is given by $k = 10^{13}e^{-E^\ddagger/RT}\text{sec}^{-1}$, $k = 1\ \text{sec}^{-1}$ when $E^\ddagger/RT = 30$.

Fortunately for the sake of computational work, the combustion in most guns and rockets occurs at such high temperatures that thermodynamic equilibrium is very nearly attained. At these temperatures, however, the molecules dissociate so that a large number of molecular species must be considered. Even a small trace of free radicals or atoms may have a large effect on the internal energy and other thermodynamic properties.

The equilibrium composition may be obtained by the simultaneous solution of the equations of conservation of mass and the equations of equality of the chemical potentials. Since chemical reactions neither create nor destroy atoms, the total number of atoms of each species remains constant. Thus if one gram of mixture contains altogether g_j atoms of the jth kind; if a molecule of the ith kind contains ν_{ji} atoms of the jth kind; and if $\hat{N}_i$ is the number of molecules of the ith chemical compound in one gram of mixture, then

$$\Sigma_i \nu_{ji} \hat{N}_i = g_j \qquad j = 1, 2, \cdots, s \tag{11.10–31}$$

There is one equation of the form of Eq. 11.10–31 for each of the s atomic species.

If there are l chemical reactions which can be written in the stoichiometrical form

$$\beta_{k1}[1] + \beta_{k2}[2] + \cdots \rightleftharpoons \eta_{k1}[1] + \eta_{k2}[2] + \cdots$$
$$k = 1, 2, \cdots, l \tag{11.10–32}$$

and if μ_i is the chemical potential of the ith species, then at chemical equilibrium:

$$\Sigma_i [\beta_{ki} - \eta_{ki}] \mu_i = 0; \quad k = 1, 2, \cdots, l \tag{11.10–33}$$

An expression for the chemical potentials μ_i in terms of properties of pure component, i, and the equation of state of the mixture is given by Eq. 5.3–4.

Equations 11.10–31 and 33, together with the equation of state, define the equilibrium composition. The exact method of solution depends a great deal on both the specific problem and the availability of high-speed computing machinery. Brinkley[4] recommends getting a first approximation to the composition by assuming a perfect gas law, then using the first approximation composition to obtain a first approximation to the equation of state and the integral in Eq. 5.3–4. In this way we may obtain the correct composition by successive approximations. Corner[5]

[4] S. R. Brinkley, *J. Chem. Phys.*, **14**, 563 (1946); **15**, 107 (1947).

[5] J. Corner, *Theory of the Interior Ballistics of Guns*, Wiley (1950), Ch. 3.

and Hirschfelder, McClure, Curtiss, and Osborne[6] have given detailed procedures for obtaining the composition of powder gases. At high temperatures (but below about 3000°K), the dissociative reactions are unimportant, so that only the water-gas reaction need be considered:

$$CO + H_2O \rightleftharpoons CO_2 + H_2 \tag{11.10–34}$$

In powder gases between 2000° and 2500°K, the equilibrium is usually such that there are approximately 77 moles of CO to every 23 moles of CO_2. Based on this fact, a simplified system of thermochemistry of powder gases may be developed[7] in which the flame temperature, specific heat, and number of moles of gas per gram are expressed additively in terms of the original powder composition, that is, the sums of mole fractions of chemical components in the powder, each multiplied by a characteristic constant.

The flame temperature of a fuel is determined by a simple energy balance. Let $\hat{U}_f$ be the energy released when one gram of the fuel is broken down into the elements in their standard states and the mixture is cooled to absolute zero. This energy is equal to that required to form the gases of the resulting mixture, heat the mixture to the flame temperature, and do any pressure-volume work. Thus the equation representing the energy balance is

$$\hat{U}_f = \hat{U} + \int p \, d\hat{V} \tag{11.10–35}$$

where $\hat{V} = 1/\rho$ is the volume per gram, and $\hat{U}$ is the internal energy per gram of the resulting gas mixture.

Let us consider the two special cases. In obtaining the isochoric flame temperature, we take $\hat{V}$ to be constant. Then, since the integral is zero,

$$\text{(Isochoric):} \quad \hat{U}_f = \hat{U} \tag{11.10–36}$$

In obtaining the isobaric flame temperature, we take p to be constant. Then

$$\int p \, d\hat{V} = p\hat{V} - p\hat{V}_f \tag{11.10–37}$$

[6] J. O. Hirschfelder, F. T. McClure, C. F. Curtiss, and D. W. Osborne, Nat. Def. Res. Com. Report A-116 (November 1942).

[7] J. O. Hirschfelder and J. Sherman, Nat. Def. Res. Com. Report A-101 (October 1942); Nat. Def. Res. Com. Armor and Ordnance Memoranda A-67M to A-70M (March 1943).

where $\hat{V}_f$ is the specific volume of the fuel. The energy balance equation then becomes

$$\hat{U}_f + p\hat{V}_f = \hat{U} + p\hat{V} \tag{11.10–38}$$

or

$$\text{(Isobaric):} \quad \hat{H}_f = \hat{H} \tag{11.10–39}$$

The calculation of the thermodynamic properties of the equilibrium mixture provides the information necessary for the application of the equations in § 11.10a to the flow of a real gas mixture through a nozzle.

d. The flow of a real gas through a nozzle

For the applications of the equations describing the flow of gas through a nozzle, the properties of the gas may be conveniently summarized by two figures. Two such figures are 11.10–3 and 11.10–4 which give the properties of the gas which results from the burning of a typical rocket solid propellant fuel. Figure 11.10–3 is a Mollier diagram of the pressure and temperature of the gas as functions of the specific enthalpy $\hat{H}$ and the specific entropy $\hat{S}$. The isobaric adiabatic flame temperature is indicated so that, knowing the pressure, p_c, in the chamber, we obtain from the intersection of this pressure line with the adiabatic flame-temperature line the initial enthalpy, $\hat{H}_c$, and the initial entropy, $\hat{S}_c$, of the powder gas. The other graph (Fig. 11.10–4) is a plot of $p/T\rho$ versus T at constant pressure, which gives the equation of state in its most useful form for the applications under discussion. From the pressure and temperature it is a simple matter to determine the corresponding value of the density ρ. (Diagrams of pressure versus density for different values of the temperature are not sufficiently accurate.)

According to the discussion of the equations of change in § 11.10a the flow of the gas through a nozzle is isentropic. Thus the conditions along the flow are those along a vertical line on the Mollier diagram (Fig. 11.10–3). Equation 11.10–12 states that the increase in the kinetic energy of the gas is equal to the decrease in the enthalpy. If the enthalpy is expressed in calories per gram, this relation is

$$v = 300.2\sqrt{\hat{H}_c - \hat{H}} \text{ ft/sec} = 9150\sqrt{\hat{H}_c - \hat{H}} \text{ cm/sec} \tag{11.10–40}$$

This expression along with the Mollier diagram may be used to obtain the velocity of the gas as a function of the chamber pressure and the pressure at an arbitrary point in the flow, that is, $v = v(p_c,p)$. In a similar manner, a combination of the Mollier diagram with the diagram giving the equation of state determines the density of the powder gas along the nozzle as a function of the initial pressure in the chamber and the pressure at any point in the nozzle, that is, $\rho = \rho(p_c,p)$.

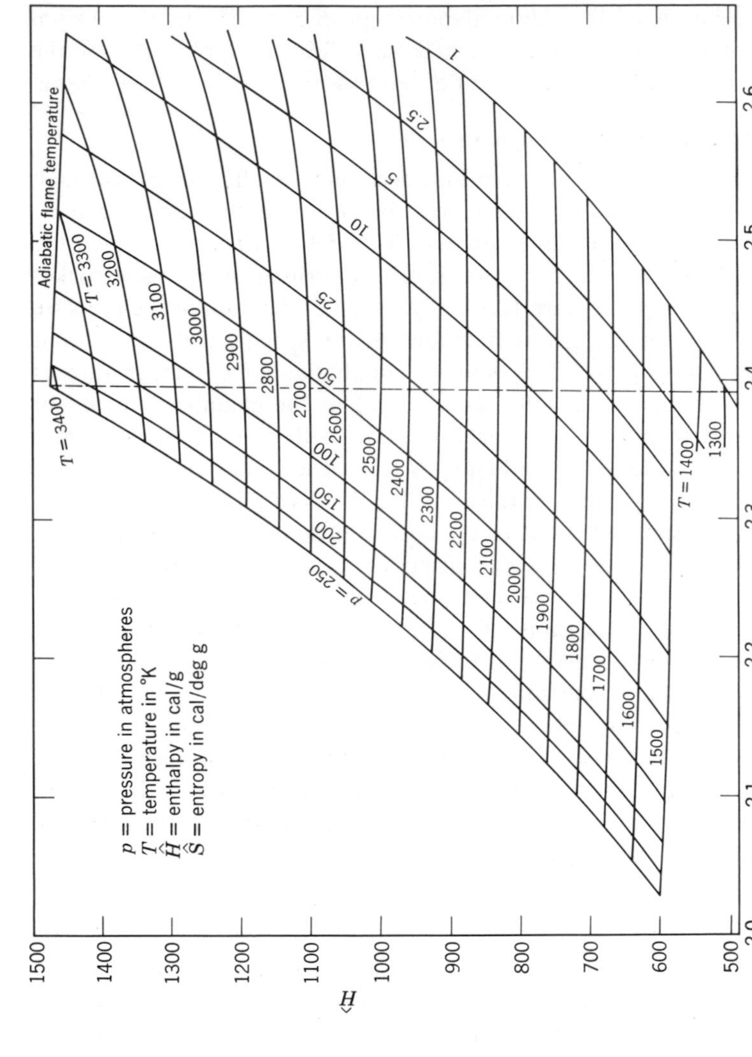

Fig. 11.10–3. Mollier diagram describing the thermochemistry of the gas resulting from a typical **rocket powder.**

The properties of the gas as a function of position along the nozzle may be obtained by making use of the equation of continuity (11.10–5), which states that $M = \rho v A$ is a constant. As the gas enters the nozzle, v is small and ρ is large. As the gas expands, ρ becomes small and v becomes large. A maximum occurs in the function ρv. This maximum is the value of M/A_t. Hence A/A_t at any point as a function of p is the maximum value of ρv divided by the value at the point. This plot may be obtained graphically from the functions described in the preceding paragraph. Then, by cross-plotting, ρ, v, or any of the other variables may be obtained as functions of A/A_t.

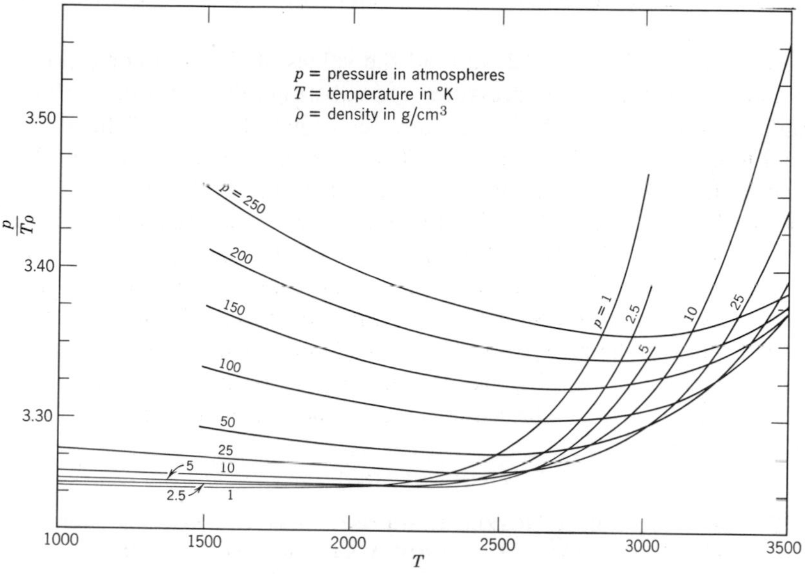

Fig. 11.10–4. The equation of state of a typical powder gas.

The actual performance of a rocket is determined by the thrust F exerted by the gases on the rocket. It may be shown[8] that the relation

$$F = Mv_e + (p_e - p_0)A_e \tag{11.10–41}$$

which was derived as Eq. 11.10–29 for the special case of a perfect gas, is valid in general. Since v_e and p_e may be calculated as functions of A_e/A_t by the methods just described, the thrust per unit area of throat, F/A_t, and hence the performance of a rocket, are determined by thermodynamic properties of the powder gas.

As an example of the procedure, let us consider a particular example. Suppose that the typical rocket powder mentioned above is placed in a rocket

[8] F. J. Malina, *J. Franklin Inst.*, **230**, 433 (1930).

chamber and that the ratio of the surface area of the powder to the cross-sectional area of the throat is adjusted so that the steady-state pressure in the chamber is 250 atm. This ratio is determined from the characteristic rate of burning of the powder rather than from thermodynamic considerations. From the Mollier diagram for this powder (Fig. 11.10–3) we see that when p_c is 250 atm, the isobaric adiabatic flame temperature is 3420°K. The specific enthalpy $\hat{H}_c$ under these conditions is 1476 cal per g, and the specific entropy $\hat{S}_c$ is 2.391 cal per g per °K. If the nozzle is well designed and if there is no heat loss, the gas expands in passing through the nozzle without change in entropy, so that the pressure and temperature during the expansion are given by the points along the dotted line.

To construct Table 11.10–2 we read the values of T and $\hat{H}$ corresponding to various values of the pressure, and substitute them in Eq. 11.10–40 to obtain the velocity v. We read the value of $p/T\rho$ for each of the points from Fig. 11.10–4 to determine ρ. Then we make use of Eq. 11.10–5 to find values of $\rho v = M/A$. Plotting the values of this ratio (Fig. 11.10–5) we see that a maximum value of 1513 g cm^{-2} sec^{-1} is reached at a pressure p of 137 atm. This means that $M/A_t = 1513$ g cm^{-2} sec^{-1} for a chamber pressure of 250 atm. (For each value of the chamber pressure there is a characteristic value of M/A_t.) To maintain the equilibrium pressure at 250 atm in the chamber, $1513A_t$ grams of powder must be burned per second. The values of A/A_t are obtained by dividing 1513 g cm^{-2} sec^{-1} by the values of M/A. The velocity as a function of A/A_t is illustrated in Fig. 11.10–6.

TABLE 11.10–2

THE CONDITIONS IN A NOZZLE RESULTING FROM THE EXPANSION OF A TYPICAL POWDER GAS FROM A CHAMBER AT 250 ATM

p/p_c	p (atm)	T (°K)	$\hat{H}_c - \hat{H}$ (cal/g)	v (cm/sec)	v (ft/sec)	$p/T\rho$ $\left(\frac{\text{atm cm}^3}{\text{g deg}}\right)$	ρ (g/cm³)	M/A $\left(\frac{\text{g}}{\text{cm}^2\ \text{sec}^1}\right)$	A/A_t
1.	250	3419	0	0	0	3.379	0.02164	0	∞
0.9	225	3373	26	46,800	1535	3.368	0.01981	927	1.632
0.8	200	3323	55	67,800	2224	3.357	0.1793	1216	1.244
0.6	150	3180	135	106,300	3488	3.335	0.01414	1503	1.007
0.4	100	2982	237	140,800	4619	3.307	0.01014	1428	1.060
0.2	50	2654	397	182,300	5981	3.278	0.005747	1048	1.444
0.1	25	2361	531	210,800	6916	3.263	0.003245	684.0	2.212
0.04	10	1986	688	239,900	7871	3.259	0.001545	370.6	4.082
0.02	5	1742	790	257,100	8435	3.257	0.0008813	226.6	6.677
0.01	2.5	1530	878	271,000	8891	3.255	0.0005020	136.0	11.12
0.004	1	1295	970	284,900	9347	3.254	0.0002373	67.6	22.38

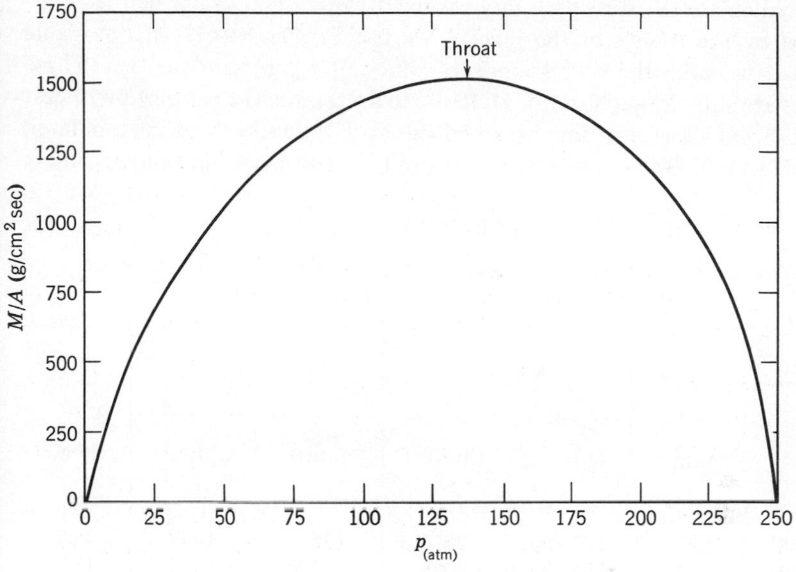

Fig. 11.10–5. Mass rate of flow of powder gas as a function of pressure for a chamber pressure of 250 atm.

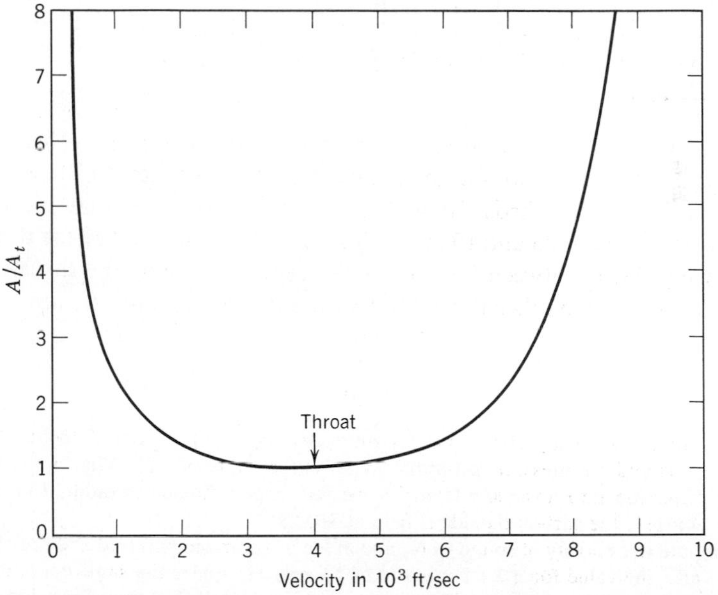

Fig. 11.10–6. Velocity of powder gas as a function of nozzle area for an initial pressure of 250 atm.

To calculate the thrust for any assumed value of A_e/A_t, which is determined by the design of the nozzle, we use Eq. 11.10–41. From Table 11.10–2 we take the corresponding values of v_e, p_e, and M/A_t. These values are substituted into Eq. 11.10–41 to determine the ratio of the thrust to the throat area for various assumed values of the ratio A_e/A_t, as tabulated in Table 11.10–3 for $p_0 = 1$ atm. It can be seen that if the exit pressure is

TABLE 11.10–3

THRUST ON THE ROCKET CHAMBER FOR VARIOUS VALUES OF A_e/A_t FOR THE EXPANSION OF A TYPICAL POWDER GAS

A_e/A_t	p_e	Mv_e/A_t		$A_e(p_e - p_o)/A_t$		F/A_t
	(atm)	(g/cm²)	(lb/in.²)	(atm)	(lb/in.²)	(lb/in.²)
1.000	137	177,700	2527	136	1999	4526
1.060	100	217,200	3089	104.9	1542	4631
1.444	50	281,300	4001	70.7	1039	5040
2.212	25	325,200	4625	53.1	780	5405
4.082	10	370,100	5264	36.7	539	5803
6.672	5	396,700	5642	26.7	392	6034
11.12	2.5	418,100	5947	16.7	245	6192
22.38	1.0	439,600	6253	0	0	6253

1 atm, the ratio of the exit area to the throat area is 22.38. This is a much larger ratio than would be feasible for most rockets. Usually the ratio of exit area to throat area is between 2 and 4, so that the exit pressure lies between 25 and 10 atm. Table 11.10–3 shows that the thrust for such nozzles is between 86 and 93 per cent as large as the thrust for nozzles with the same throat area but with an exit pressure of 1 atm.

PROBLEMS

1. In carbon dioxide at 3600°F the gas emissivity, $\epsilon(T, \rho L)$, is found[9] to be 0.085 when $L = 2$ ft and the pressure is 1 atm. What is the value of μ? What is the rate of energy emission into a vacuum from a sphere of carbon dioxide of radius 1 in. and pressure 24 atm if the carbon dioxide is held at 3600°F?

2. Compute the velocity of sound in N_2 and in He at room temperature and pressure. Compute also the value for a 1 : 1 mixture of N_2 and He under the same conditions. Perform the computations (a) assuming the gases to be ideal, (b) taking into account

[9] J. H. Perry, *Chemical Engineers' Handbook*, McGraw-Hill (1950), p. 490.

the second virial coefficients. Compare these velocities with the root mean square velocities of the molecules. What is the frequency at which the wavelength is equal to the mean free path?

3. Examine the behavior of a rarefaction wave by the method of the Riemann characteristics. Assume that the initial conditions are:

At $t = 0$:

$$v(z) = 0$$

$$T(z) = T_0, \text{ a constant}$$

$$\begin{cases} p(z) = p_0 - p_1 \cos \dfrac{\pi z}{L}; & \dfrac{-L}{2} \leqslant z \leqslant \dfrac{L}{2} \\ p(z) = p_0 & ; \quad |z| > \dfrac{L}{2} \end{cases}$$

Assume that the fluid obeys the perfect gas equation of state and that the specific heat ratio, γ, is constant.

4. Consider a shock wave in nitrogen at room temperature and atmospheric pressure. Assume that the pressure ratio $p_\infty/p_0 = 10$ and that the gas may be considered ideal. Calculate the density increase, the temperature increase, and the velocity of propagation of the wave. What is the increase in entropy of the gas due to the shock wave, and what is the final temperature if the gas is allowed to expand adiabatically to the initial pressure? Repeat the calculations for $p_\infty/p_0 = 2100$.

5. Use the thermodynamical data given in the U.S. Bureau of Standards Tables (Circular C461), "Selected Values of Properties of Hydrocarbons," or some other standard reference, to calculate the velocity of detonation and the Chapman-Jouguet pressure for the explosion of a stoichiometrical mixture of hydrogen and oxygen initially at 1 atm pressure and $T = 300°K$.

6. Calculate the isochoric and the isobaric flame temperatures for a stoichiometrical mixture of hydrogen and oxygen initially at 1 atm pressure and 300°K. (a) Assuming no hydroxyl concentration at the flame temperature. (b) Assuming thermal equilibrium of hydroxyl at the flame temperature.

7. Show that, when the mass average velocity $\boldsymbol{v}$ is dotted into the equation of motion (Eq. 11.1–3), one obtains an equation of change for the kinetic energy:

$$\frac{D}{Dt}(\tfrac{1}{2}v^2) = -\frac{1}{\rho}\left(\boldsymbol{v} \cdot \left(\frac{\partial}{\partial \boldsymbol{r}} \cdot \mathbf{p}\right)\right) + \frac{1}{\rho}\sum_i n_i(\boldsymbol{v} \cdot \boldsymbol{X}_i)$$

Show further that when the position vector $\boldsymbol{r}$ is crossed into the equation of motion and use is made of the symmetry of the pressure tensor, one obtains an equation of change for the angular momentum:

$$\frac{D}{Dt}[\boldsymbol{r} \times \boldsymbol{v}] = -\frac{1}{\rho}\left(\frac{\partial}{\partial \boldsymbol{r}} \cdot [\boldsymbol{r} \times \mathbf{p}]\right) + \frac{1}{\rho}\left[\boldsymbol{r} \times \sum_i n_i \boldsymbol{X}_i\right]$$

where $[\boldsymbol{r} \times \mathbf{p}]_{il} = \Sigma_j \Sigma_k \epsilon_{ijk} r_j p_{kl}$ and ϵ_{ijk} is the alternating unit tensor. Note that this equation contains no information about the possible interchange of angular momentum between the bulk flow and the "spin" of the molecules. The latter is associated with a non-symmetrical pressure tensor; for a discussion of this point see J. S. Dahler and L. E. Scriven [Nature, **192**, 36 (1961)] and J. S. Dahler [Phys. Rev. **129**, 1464 (1963)].

PART III

INTERMOLECULAR FORCES

· 12 ·

Electromagnetic Basis of Intermolecular Forces

It is the purpose of this chapter to provide the background of electromagnetic theory needed for a thorough study of intermolecular forces. The long-range intermolecular forces are electromagnetic in origin. There are three general types: those which are purely electrostatic in origin (such as interactions between dipoles or higher multipoles), induction forces, and the "dispersion" forces which are related to the electromagnetic phenomena of induced absorption and emission of light. We would also expect interactions between the magnetic moments of the molecules, but these forces are seldom important. The short-range forces, which result from the overlapping of the electron clouds of the molecules, must be considered on a purely quantum mechanical basis.

The first section is concerned with the electrostatic interaction between two general charge distributions. These interactions are expressed in terms of the multipole moments of the distributions. The recently developed "two-center" expansion of $1/r_{12}$ has made it possible to organize and simplify the study of the interaction of complex charge distributions even when they overlap. This type of mathematical approach is of great value in the evaluation of coulombic integrals in the quantum mechanical treatment of short-range intermolecular forces.

The second section deals with the relationship between the bulk electric properties and the properties of the individual molecules. For example, the dipole moment and polarizability of a molecule can be determined from the temperature dependence of the electric susceptibility. The dispersion forces can be expressed approximately in terms of the polarizabilities of the molecules. From the pressure dependence of the electric susceptibility can be obtained evidence of the formation of dimers or the alignment of neighboring molecules in a dense gas or liquid.

All the development up to this point is based on Coulomb's law. To understand the magnetic and the dispersion forces it is necessary to introduce the electromagnetic equations of Maxwell. These differential equations form the postulational basis of electromagnetic theory. From these equations we get the forces between two sets of moving charges.

The moving charges within the molecules produce magnetic fields and forces. If the molecules have permanent magnetic moments so that the substance is paramagnetic, the values of the magnetic moments are important in determining the intermolecular forces. For example, in § 13.6e the forces between two atoms, neither one of which is in an S-state, depend sensitively on their magnetic moments (or rotational quantum numbers).

The last two sections concern themselves with the theory of light emission and absorption. This phenomenon is closely related to the polarizability as a function of frequency. The polarizability can in turn be expressed in terms of the elements of the dipole moment matrix. These derivations then enable us to relate the bulk electromagnetic properties to the detailed internal properties of the individual molecules.

1. Electrostatics

From the basic expression for electrostatic interaction (Coulomb's law), we may obtain the electrostatic potential due to a charge distribution, $\mathscr{V}$, and the potential energy of interaction between two charge distributions, φ_{ab}. Both these problems are treated for continuous and discrete charge distributions. An expression for the potential $\mathscr{V}$ is obtained as a "one-center" (Neumann) expansion in terms of spherical harmonics. An analogous expression for the interaction potential φ_{ab} is obtained as a "two-center" expansion in terms of spherical harmonics. In both these expressions the quantities[1] Q_n^m, closely related to the multipole moments, appear in the expansion coefficients. This section is concluded with an application of these results to the special case of a dipole charge distribution. In the discussion which follows, both "discrete" and "continuous" charge distributions are considered. In the former case the charge distribution is considered to be made up of a set of discrete points, the charge at the ith point being e_i. In the latter case the total charge within a differential volume element $d\boldsymbol{r}_i$ about the point $\boldsymbol{r}_i$ is taken to be $\rho(\boldsymbol{r}_i)\, d\boldsymbol{r}_i$.

a. Coulombic interaction between charges and charge distributions

The potential energy of interaction between two discrete charges e_i and e_j or between two elements of continuous charge $\rho(\boldsymbol{r}_i)\, d\boldsymbol{r}_i$ and

[1] These Q_n^m are not to be confused with the associated Legendre functions of the second kind (which are never used in this book).

$\rho(\boldsymbol{r}_j)\, d\boldsymbol{r}_j$ is the coulombic energy:

$$\begin{cases} \varphi_{ij} = \dfrac{e_i e_j}{r_{ij}} & (12.1\text{–}1a) \\[2ex] \varphi_{ij} = \dfrac{\rho(\boldsymbol{r}_i)\rho(\boldsymbol{r}_j)}{r_{ij}}\, d\boldsymbol{r}_i\, d\boldsymbol{r}_j & (12.1\text{–}1b) \end{cases}$$

Associated with this potential is the force *on* the *i*th charge *due to* the *j*th charge:

$$\begin{cases} \boldsymbol{F}_{ij} = \dfrac{e_i e_j}{r_{ij}^3}\, \boldsymbol{r}_{ij} & (12.1\text{–}2a) \\[2ex] \boldsymbol{F}_{ij} = \dfrac{\rho(\boldsymbol{r}_i)\rho(\boldsymbol{r}_j)}{r_{ij}^3}\, \boldsymbol{r}_{ij}\, d\boldsymbol{r}_i\, d\boldsymbol{r}_j & (12.1\text{–}2b) \end{cases}$$

Here $\boldsymbol{r}_{ij}$ is the vector going *from* the *j*th charge *to* the *i*th charge so that $\boldsymbol{r}_{ij} = \boldsymbol{r}_i - \boldsymbol{r}_j$.

Let us now consider two complex charge distributions (which could, for example, be molecules) which we refer to as *a* and *b*. The total potential energy of interaction φ of this system is obtained by summing the potential energies of interaction between all possible pairs of charges in the two-molecules *a* and *b*. It is convenient to subdivide the total energy into three parts:

$$\varphi = \varphi_a + \varphi_b + \varphi_{ab} \qquad (12.1\text{–}3)$$

in which φ_a and φ_b are the self-energies of the charge distributions *a* and *b*, respectively, and φ_{ab} is the energy of interaction[2] between *a* and *b*. If the charges belonging to *a* are designated by the subscripts *i* and *i'* and those belonging to *b* by the subscripts *j* and *j'*, the various contributions to the total potential energy of the system of two interacting charge distributions are given by

$$\begin{cases} \varphi_a = \tfrac{1}{2} \sum_i \sum_{\substack{i' \\ i' \neq i}} \dfrac{e_i e_{i'}}{r_{ii'}} & (12.1\text{–}4a) \\[2ex] \varphi_a = \tfrac{1}{2} \displaystyle\iint \dfrac{\rho_a(\boldsymbol{r}_i)\rho_a(\boldsymbol{r}_{i'})}{r_{ii'}}\, d\boldsymbol{r}_i\, d\boldsymbol{r}_{i'} & (12.1\text{–}4b) \end{cases}$$

[2] If *a* and *b* are molecules φ_{ab} is the intermolecular potential except for terms which arise owing to the distortion of one charge distribution by the presence of the other distribution.

$$\varphi_b = \tfrac{1}{2} \textstyle\sum_j \sum_{j' \neq j} \dfrac{e_j e_{j'}}{r_{jj'}} \tag{12.1–5a}$$

$$\varphi_b = \tfrac{1}{2} \iint \frac{\rho_b(\boldsymbol{r}_j)\rho_b(\boldsymbol{r}_{j'})}{r_{jj'}}\, d\boldsymbol{r}_j\, d\boldsymbol{r}_j \tag{12.1–5b}$$

$$\varphi_{ab} = \textstyle\sum_i \sum_j \dfrac{e_i e_j}{r_{ij}} \tag{12.1–6a}$$

$$\varphi_{ab} = \iint \frac{\rho_a(\boldsymbol{r}_i)\rho_b(\boldsymbol{r}_j)}{r_{ij}}\, d\boldsymbol{r}_i\, d\boldsymbol{r}_j \tag{12.1–6b}$$

The total force on a due to the presence of b is associated with the potential energy φ_{ab}:

$$\boldsymbol{F}_{ab} = \textstyle\sum_i \sum_j \boldsymbol{F}_{ij} = \sum_i \sum_j \dfrac{e_i e_j}{r_{ij}^3}\, \boldsymbol{r}_{ij} \tag{12.1–7a}$$

$$\boldsymbol{F}_{ab} = \iint \boldsymbol{F}(\boldsymbol{r}_i, \boldsymbol{r}_j)\, d\boldsymbol{r}_i\, d\boldsymbol{r}_j = \iint \frac{\rho_a(\boldsymbol{r}_i)\rho_b(\boldsymbol{r}_j)}{r_{ij}^3}\, \boldsymbol{r}_{ij}\, d\boldsymbol{r}_i\, d\boldsymbol{r}_j \tag{12.1–7b}$$

In § 12.1e, an expression for the potential energy φ_{ab} is obtained as a two-center expansion in spherical harmonics.

b. The electrostatic potential and the electric field intensity

Let us consider a charge e_α at a position α near a discrete charge distribution. The force experienced by this charge due to the proximity of the charge distribution is

$$\boldsymbol{F}_\alpha = \textstyle\sum_i \boldsymbol{F}_{\alpha i} = \sum_i \dfrac{e_\alpha e_i}{r_{\alpha i}^3}\, \boldsymbol{r}_{\alpha i} \tag{12.1–8}$$

It is customary to define an *electric field intensity* $\mathscr{E}$ which is the *force per unit* charge due to a charge distribution:

$$\mathscr{E} = \frac{\boldsymbol{F}_\alpha}{e_\alpha} = \textstyle\sum_i \dfrac{e_i}{r_{\alpha i}^3}\, \boldsymbol{r}_{\alpha i} \tag{12.1–9}$$

There is associated with this quantity an *electrostatic potential* (*potential energy per unit charge*) $\mathscr{V}$ which is accordingly defined by:[3]

$$\mathscr{E} = -\frac{\partial \mathscr{V}}{\partial \boldsymbol{r}} \tag{12.1–10}$$

[3] $\mathscr{V}$ is φ_{ab}/e_α if the charge distribution b is just the charge e_α.

The electrostatic potential at position α due to a set of charges, e_i, is then

$$\mathscr{V} = \sum_i \frac{e_i}{r_{\alpha i}} \tag{12.1–11}$$

Both $\mathscr{E}$ and $\mathscr{V}$ are, of course, functions of the position of the point α.

The total force on charge distribution a due to distribution b may now be written in the form

$$\boldsymbol{F}_{ab} = \Sigma_i e_i \mathscr{E}_i \tag{12.2–12}$$

Here $\mathscr{E}_i$ is the electric field intensity at charge i in distribution a due to the charges in the distribution b. Since the sum of the forces exerted by the various members of a distribution on one another is zero, the $\mathscr{E}_i$ may be taken as the field due to all the charges in both distributions.

The above formulae for electric field intensity and electrostatic potential may also be written for continuous charge distributions. In § 12.1d an expression is derived for the electrostatic potential $\mathscr{V}$ in terms of a one-center (Neumann) expansion in spherical harmonics.

c. Multipole moments

With every charge distribution there is associated a set of quantities known as the multipole moments, which are of great importance in electrostatics. The first two moments are the total charge C and the dipole moment $\boldsymbol{\mu}$. These quantities are defined in the following way:

$$C = \Sigma_i e_i \tag{12.1–13}$$

$$\boldsymbol{\mu} = \Sigma_i e_i \boldsymbol{r}_i \tag{12.1–14}$$

In general all the multipole moments except the first non-zero moment depend on the position of the origin of coordinates. Usually the origin is chosen at either the center of gravity or the center of charge of the distribution.

There is a great deal of confusion as to the definition of the quadrupole moment. Formerly it was common practice to define the quadrupole moment in a form analogous to the above definitions of C and $\boldsymbol{\mu}$, thus:

$$\Theta = \Sigma_i e_i \boldsymbol{r}_i \boldsymbol{r}_i \tag{12.1–15}$$

However, for many purposes it is more convenient to define the quadrupole moment as the traceless tensor:

$$\mathsf{Q} = \Sigma_i e_i (3\boldsymbol{r}_i \boldsymbol{r}_i - r_i^2 \mathsf{U}) \tag{12.1–16}$$

This is the definition for the quadrupole moment tensor used throughout this book.

For a linear charge distribution along the z-axis or for a charge distribution cylindrically symmetric[4] about the z-axis, the off-diagonal elements of Q are zero, and Q_{xx} and Q_{yy} are each equal to $-\frac{1}{2}Q_{zz}$. Therefore, for such a distribution the quadrupole moment tensor is completely specified by one scalar quantity, for example, Q_{zz}. The scalar, $Q_{zz} \equiv Q$, is referred to as the quadrupole moment. In dealing with molecular problems it is convenient to define a quantity q, also referred to as the scalar value of the quadrupole moment, thus:[5]

$$q = Q_{zz}/e = Q/e \tag{12.1–17}$$

where e is the absolute value of the charge on an electron (q then has the dimensions of a cross-section). It should be pointed out that $\frac{1}{2}Q_{zz} = \Theta_{zz} - \Theta_{xx}$ is sometimes used as the scalar value of the quadrupole moment.[6] Some of the values of the quadrupole moments in the literature are for rotating molecules. These values are average values of the quadrupole moment in a space-fixed coordinate system. They depend upon the exact rotational state of the molecule, but usually they are about half the values for the non-rotating molecules.

When φ_{ab} and $\mathscr{V}$ are expanded in spherical harmonics, there occurs in the expansion coefficients a set of quantities, Q_n^m, which are related to the multipole moments just defined. These quantities are defined for a discrete or a continuous charge distribution in the following way:[7,8]

$$Q_n^m = \sum_i \{e_i r_i^n\} P_n^m(\cos\theta_i) e^{im\phi_i} \tag{12.1–18a}$$

$$Q_n^m = \iiint \{\rho(r, \theta, \phi) r^n\} P_n^m(\cos\theta) e^{im\phi} r^2\, dr \sin\theta\, d\theta\, d\phi \tag{12.1–18b}$$

The $P_n^m(\cos\theta)$ are the associated Legendre polynomials (see Appendix B of this chapter). Equation 12.1–18b may be written in simpler form if the charge distribution is expanded in an infinite series of spherical harmonics:

$$\rho(r, \theta, \phi) = \sum_{n=0}^{\infty} \sum_{m=-n}^{+n} \frac{(n-|m|)!}{(n+|m|)!} \left(\frac{2n+1}{4\pi}\right) \rho_{n,m}(r) P_n^m(\cos\theta) e^{-im\phi} \tag{12.1–19}$$

[4] A discrete charge distribution having an axis of symmetry which is at least threefold symmetric has similar properties.

[5] Norman F. Ramsey, *Phys. Rev.*, **78**, 221 (1950).

[6] C. Greenhow and W. V. Smith, *J. Chem. Phys.*, **19**, 1298 (1951); see also J. Slater and N. Frank, *Electromagnetism*, McGraw-Hill (1947), Appendix VI.

[7] The values of the Q_n^m depend upon the origin and orientation of the coordinate system. These are usually chosen so as to take advantage of whatever natural symmetry may exist in the problem.

[8] Throughout the book we adopt the convention $P_n^{-m}(\cos\theta) = P_n^m(\cos\theta)$.

The functions $\rho_{n,\,m}(r)$ are given in terms of the charge distribution by the relation

$$\rho_{n,\,m}(r) = \iint \rho(r, \theta, \phi) P_n^{\,m}(\cos\theta) e^{im\phi} \sin\theta \, d\theta \, d\phi \qquad (12.1\text{–}20)$$

Equation 12.1–18b then assumes the form

$$Q_n^{\,m} = \int_0^\infty \rho_{n,\,m}(r)\, r^{n+2}\, dr \qquad (12.1\text{–}21)$$

which is obtained by substituting Eq. 12.1–19 into Eq. 12.1–18b and making use of the orthogonality relations between the spherical harmonics (as given in Eq. 12.B–4).

The multipole moments defined in Eqs. 12.1–13, 14, 16 may be expressed in the following way in terms of the quantities, $Q_n^{\,m}$:

$$C = Q_0^{\,0} \qquad (12.1\text{–}22)$$

$$\mu_z - Q_1^{\,0}$$

$$\mu_x = \frac{1}{2}[Q_1^{\,1} + Q_1^{\,-1}]$$

$$\mu_y = \frac{1}{2i}[Q_1^{\,1} - Q_1^{\,-1}] \qquad (12.1\text{–}23)$$

$$Q_{zz} = 2Q_2^{\,0}$$

$$Q_{xx} = -\,Q_2^{\,0} + \frac{1}{4}[Q_2^{\,2} + Q_2^{\,-2}]$$

$$Q_{yy} = -\,Q_2^{\,0} - \frac{1}{4}[Q_2^{\,2} + Q_2^{\,-2}]$$

$$Q_{xz} = \frac{1}{2}[Q_2^{\,1} + Q_2^{\,-1}]$$

$$Q_{yz} = \frac{1}{2i}[Q_2^{\,1} - Q_2^{\,-1}] \qquad (12.1\text{–}24)$$

$$Q_{xy} = \frac{1}{4i}[Q_2^{\,2} - Q_2^{\,-2}]$$

d. The "one-center" expansion of the electrostatic potential due to a charge distribution

An expression for the electrostatic potential due to a discrete charge distribution is given in Eq. 12.1–11. In this expression and the analogous formula for a continuous charge distribution, there occurs the quantity $1/r_{i\alpha}$, in which $r_{i\alpha}$ is the distance from the ith charge, located at r_i, θ_i, ϕ_i, to the field point α, located at r, θ, ϕ (see Fig. 12.1–1). If the symbols $r_<$ and $r_>$ designate the lesser and greater of r_i and r, the quantity $1/r_{i\alpha}$ may be expanded in the "one-center" (or Neumann) expansion, [9–11] in the following way:

$$\frac{1}{r_{i\alpha}} = \sum_{n=0}^{\infty} \sum_{m=-n}^{+n} \frac{(n-|m|)!}{(n+|m|)!} \frac{r_<^n}{r_>^{n+1}} P_n^m(\cos\theta_i) P_n^m(\cos\theta) e^{im(\phi_i-\phi)} \quad (12.1\text{–}25)$$

Substitution of this expression for $1/r_{i\alpha}$ into the formulae for the electrostatic potential due to a discrete or continuous charge distribution gives

$$\mathscr{V}(r,\theta,\phi) = \sum_{n=0}^{\infty} \sum_{m=-n}^{+n} \frac{(n-|m|)!}{(n+|m|)!} P_n^m(\cos\theta) e^{-im\phi} \left[\frac{1}{r^{n+1}} \sum_{\substack{i \\ (r_i<r)}} e_i r_i^n P_n^m(\cos\theta_i) e^{im\phi_i} + r^n \sum_{\substack{i \\ (r_i>r)}} e_i \frac{1}{r_i^{n+1}} P_n^m(\cos\theta_i) e^{im\phi_i} \right] \quad (12.1\text{–}26a)$$

$$\mathscr{V}(r,\theta,\phi) = \sum_{n=0}^{\infty} \sum_{m=-n}^{+n} \frac{(n-|m|)!}{(n+|m|)!} P_n^m(\cos\theta) e^{-im\phi} \left[\frac{1}{r^{n+1}} \int_0^r r_i^n \rho_{n,m}(r_i) r_i^2\, dr_i + r^n \int_r^{\infty} \frac{1}{r_i^{n+1}} \rho_{n,m}(r_i) r_i^2\, dr_i \right] \quad (12.1\text{–}26b)$$

Here the $\rho_{n,m}(r)$ are the expansion coefficients defined in Eq. 12.1–20.

If the field point α lies completely outside the charge distribution, $r > r_i$ for all the charges and Eq. 12.1–26 simplifies to:

$$\mathscr{V}(r,\theta,\phi) = \sum_{n=0}^{\infty} \sum_{m=-n}^{+n} \frac{(n-|m|)!}{(n+|m|)!} \frac{Q_n^m}{r^{n+1}} P_n^m(\cos\theta) e^{-im\phi} \quad (12.1\text{–}27)$$

[9] H. Eyring, J. Walter, and G. E. Kimball, *Quantum Chemistry*, Wiley (1944), pp. 369 et seq.

[10] T. M. MacRobert, *Spherical Harmonics*, Dutton (1927), pp. 148 et seq.

[11] The quantity $1/r_{i\alpha}$ may also be expanded in terms of ellipsoidal coordinates; see K. Rüdenberg, *J. Chem. Phys.*, **19**, 1459 (1951).

The Q_n^m are the quantities defined in Eqs. 12.1–18 and 21 for discrete and continuous charge distributions. This expression for the electrostatic potential as an expansion in $1/r$ is particularly useful at large distances from the charge distribution.

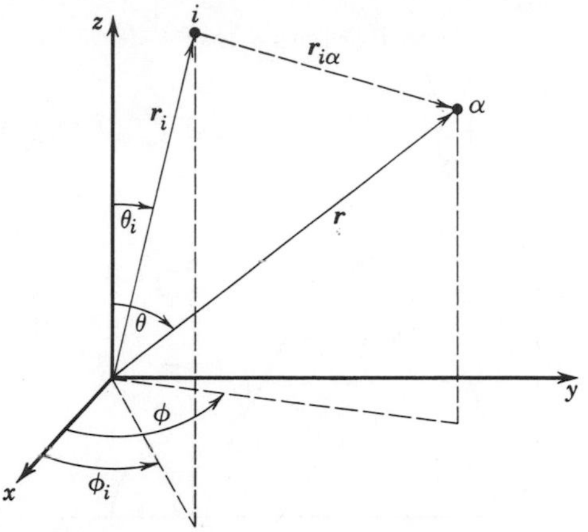

Fig. 12.1–1. Coordinates used in considering the contribution to the electrostatic potential $\mathscr{V}$ at point α due to a charge located at point *i*.

e. The "two-center" expansion of the potential energy of interaction of two charge distributions

In Eq. 12.1–6 are given expressions for the potential energy of interaction for two charge distributions, either discrete or continuous. In these expressions there is the quantity r_{ij} which is the distance between charge *i* in the first charge distribution and the charge *j* in the second. This distance is shown pictorially in Fig. 12.1–2, along with other coordinates which are used in this discussion. The reciprocal of r_{ij} may be expanded in a "two-center" expansion[12, 13] in the following manner:

$$\frac{1}{r_{ij}} = \sum_{n_a=0}^{\infty} \sum_{n_b=0}^{\infty} \sum_{m=-n_<}^{+n_<} B_{n_a, n_b}^{|m|}(r_i, r_j; r_{ab}) P_{n_a}^{m}(\cos\theta_i) P_{n_b}^{m}(\cos\theta_j) e^{im(\phi_j - \phi_i)} \tag{12.1–28}$$

Here we use the symbol $n_<$ to indicate the smaller of n_a and n_b. The coefficients $B_{n_a, n_b}^{|m|}$ are complicated functions of r_i, r_j, and r_{ab}. Formulae for these coefficients, as well as numerical values, are given at the end of this chapter in Appendix A. The angles θ_i and θ_j are defined with respect to the centers *a* and *b*, respectively, as shown in Fig. 12.1–2.

[12] R. J. Buehler and J. O. Hirschfelder, *Phys. Rev.*, **83**, 628 (1951); **85**, 149 (1952).

[13] Expressions for some of the simpler *B*'s were given somewhat earlier by B. C. Carlson and G. S. Rushbrooke, *Proc. Cambridge Phil. Soc.*, **46**, 626 (1950).

Substitution of this two-center expansion into the expressions in Eq. 12.1–6 gives for the interaction potential energy between two charge distributions:

$$\varphi_{ab} = \sum_{n_a=0}^{\infty} \sum_{n_b=0}^{\infty} \sum_{m=-n_<}^{+n_<} \Sigma_i \Sigma_j B^{|m|}_{n_a, n_b}(r_i, r_j; r_{ab})\, e_i e_j P_{n_a}{}^m(\cos\theta_i) \times P_{n_b}{}^m(\cos\theta_j) e^{im(\phi_j - \phi_i)} \quad (12.1\text{–}29a)$$

$$\varphi_{ab} = \sum_{n_a=0}^{\infty} \sum_{n_b=0}^{\infty} \sum_{m=-n_<}^{+n_<} \int_0^{\infty}\int_0^{\infty} B^{|m|}_{n_a, n_b}(r_i, r_j; r_{ab}) \rho^*_{n_a, m}(r_i) \rho_{n_b, m}(r_j) r_i^2\, dr_i\, r_j^2\, dr_j \quad (12.1\text{–}29b)$$

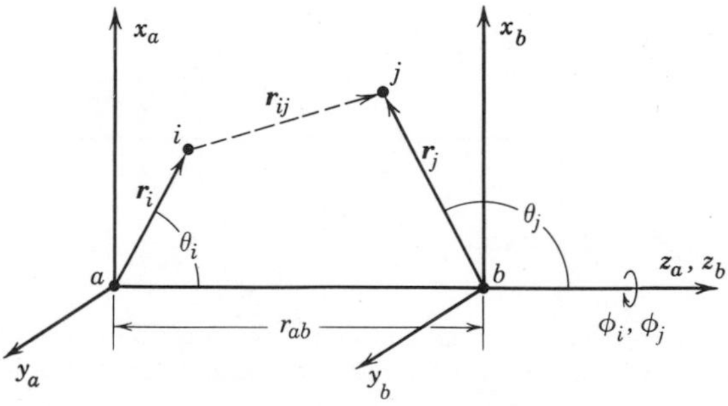

Fig. 12.1–2. The coordinates used in the discussion of the two-center expansion. Point a is the origin of a coordinate system in charge distribution a, and i is the location of a charge in this distribution. Point b is the origin of coordinates in charge distribution b, and j is the locetion of a charge in this distribution.

The asterisk on $\rho^*_{n_a, m}$ indicates the conjugate complex. These expressions are valid for any two charge distributions, whether they overlap or not. The functions $\rho_{n, m}(r)$ are defined in Eq. 12.1–20.

When the two charge distributions do not overlap, $r_{ab} > (r_i + r_j)$. For this case (designated as Region I in Appendix A to this chapter) the coefficients $B^{|m|}_{n_a n_b}$ have the form

$$B^{|m|}_{n_a, n_b}(r_i, r_j; r_{ab}) = \frac{(-1)^{n_b+m}(n_a + n_b)!}{(n_a + |m|)!(n_b + |m|)!} \frac{r_i^{n_a} r_j^{n_b}}{r_{ab}^{n_a+n_b+1}} \quad (12.1\text{–}30)$$

The potential energy of interaction between the two charge distributions is then

$$\varphi_{ab} = \sum_{n_a=0}^{\infty} \sum_{n_b=0}^{\infty} \sum_{m=-n_<}^{+n_<} \frac{(-1)^{n_b+m}(n_a + n_b)!}{(n_a + |m|)!(n_b + |m|)!} \frac{1}{r_{ab}^{n_a+n_b+1}} Q_{n_a}{}^{m*} Q_{n_b}{}^m \quad (12.1\text{–}31)$$

which is a power series in $1/r_{ab}$. The terms in the expansion represent the interaction of the various multipoles.

The expression for φ_{ab} given in this last equation is not in its most convenient form. The quantities $Q_{n_a}{}^m$ are those defined in Eq. 12.1–18 for either continuous or discrete charge distributions and apply to the distribution of charges about point a in the coordinate system pictured in Fig. 12.1–2; the quantities $Q_{n_b}{}^m$ are defined similarly for the distribution about b. The coordinate systems used for the calculation of $Q_{n_a}{}^m$ and $Q_{n_b}{}^m$ have the z-axis in the direction of the line between their centers.

It is usually more convenient to calculate the quantities $Q_n{}^m$ in a coordinate system fixed in some manner with respect to the charge distributions themselves. The coordinate axes fixed in the charge

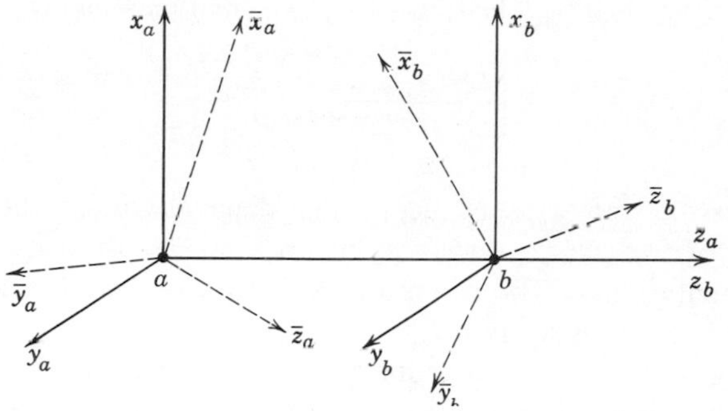

Fig. 12.1–3. Illustration of coordinate systems used in the calculation of the $Q_n{}^m$ and the $\bar{Q}_n{}^m$.

distributions are shown in Fig. 12.1–3. Quantities calculated in these rotated coordinate systems are denoted by bars placed over the symbols. When φ_{ab} is expressed in terms of the $\bar{Q}_n{}^m$ instead of the $Q_n{}^m$, the dependence of the energy of interaction on the relative orientation of the charge distributions becomes explicit.

In order to rewrite φ_{ab} in terms of the $\bar{Q}_n{}^m$ it is necessary to know the relationships between the latter quantities and the $Q_n{}^m$. Such a relation may be obtained from group theoretical arguments. It is clear from the definition of the quantities $Q_n{}^m$ that they transform under a rotation in a manner similar to the spherical harmonics of order n. The spherical harmonics form a basis of a representation of the three-dimension rotation group (see Appendix B at the end of this chapter). Let S_a be the rotation which transforms the coordinate system $x_a y_a z_a$ into the coordinate system $\bar{x}_a \bar{y}_a \bar{z}_a$, and S_b be the analogous rotation for the charge distribution about b. Then it may be shown that

$$Q_{n_a}{}^{m_a} = \sum_m i^{|m| - m - |m_a| + m_a} \left[\frac{(n_a + |m_a|)!(n_a - |m|)!}{(n_a - |m_a|)!(n_a + |m|)!}\right] D^{n_a}(S_a)_{m m_a} \bar{Q}_{n_a}{}^m \tag{12.1–32}$$

with a similar relation for charge distribution b. The coefficients $D^{n_a}(S_a)_{m_a m}$ are the representation coefficients of the three-dimensional rotation group. Formulae for these quantities are given and some of their properties are discussed in Appendix B at the end of this chapter.

The expression for the interaction of two charge distribution φ_{ab} in terms of the $\bar{Q}_n{}^m$, which are calculated with respect to coordinate systems imbedded in the distributions, is found from Eqs. 12.1–31 and 32 to be:

$$\varphi_{ab} = \sum_{\substack{n_a n_b \\ m_a m_b \\ m}} \frac{i^{m_a - |m_a| - m_b + |m_b|}(-1)^{n_b + m}[(n_a - |m_a|)!(n_b - |m_b|)!]^{1/2}(n_a + n_b)!\,\bar{Q}_{n_a}^{m_a *}\bar{Q}_{n_b}^{m_b}}{[(n_a + |m|)!(n_a - |m|)!(n_a + |m_a|)!(n_b + |m|)!(n_b - |m|)!(n_b + |m_b|)!]^{1/2}} \times \left[\frac{D^{n_a}(S_a)^*_{m_a m} D^{n_b}(S_b)_{m_b m}}{r_{ab}^{n_a + n_b + 1}}\right] \tag{12.1–33}$$

This expression indicates explicitly the dependence of the energy of interaction of two charge distributions on the separation r_{ab} and on the relative orientations. The orientations of the charge distributions are given by the rotations S_a and S_b.

From Eq. 12.1–33 and the properties of the representation coefficients it follows that, if φ_{ab} is averaged over all orientations of the two charge distributions a and b (rotated separately), all the terms with n_a and n_b different from zero vanish. Then this average value of φ_{ab} is equal to $\bar{Q}_{00}(a)\bar{Q}_{00}(b)/r_{ab}$. This is the interaction between two point charges, whose charges are equal to the net charges in the two distributions.

f. Behavior of electric dipoles

We now turn our attention to the simplest example of a discrete charge distribution, the dipole. A dipole consists of two equal and opposite charges, $-e$ and $+e$, separated by a distance l. According to Eq. 12.1–14 the dipole moment of this system is

$$\boldsymbol{\mu} = e\mathbf{l} \tag{12.1–34}$$

The vectors $\boldsymbol{\mu}$ and $\mathbf{l}$ go from the negative to the positive charge. In a *real dipole* the distance l is finite. However, at distances large compared to l, the electrical field depends principally on the size of the dipole moment and not on the values of e and l separately. On this account an *ideal dipole* (or *point dipole*) is defined as one in which l approaches zero as e approaches infinity, in such a manner that their product remains constant.

From the definitions of an ideal dipole and of an electric field it is easy to obtain the following formulae describing their interaction:

Potential energy of a dipole in an electric field:
$$\varphi = -(\boldsymbol{\mu} \cdot \mathscr{E}) \tag{12.1–35}$$

Force on a dipole in an electric field:
$$\boldsymbol{F} = \left(\boldsymbol{\mu} \cdot \frac{\partial}{\partial \boldsymbol{r}} \mathscr{E}\right) \tag{12.1–36}$$

Torque on a dipole in an electric field:
$$\boldsymbol{L} = [\boldsymbol{\mu} \times \mathscr{E}] \tag{12.1–37}$$

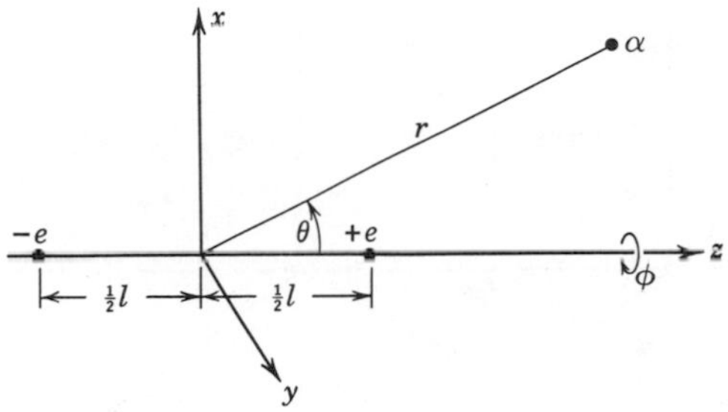

Fig. 12.1–4. Coordinate system and symbols used for deriving the electrostatic potential due to a dipole.

Note that the torque tends to rotate the dipole so that it is oriented in the direction of the field.

Let us now show how the results derived in the first part of this section may be applied to both real and ideal dipoles. First we discuss the electrostatic potential due to a single dipole in terms of the "one-center" expansion discussed in § 12.1d. Then we discuss the dipole-dipole interaction in terms of the results of the "two-center" expansion which was described in § 12.1e.

i. *Electrostatic Potential Due to a Dipole*

The electrostatic potential due to a real dipole may of course be written as the sum of the contributions due to each of the charges as in Eq. 12.1–11. However, it is often convenient to use the expansion given in Eq. 12.1–27. In terms of the coordinate system shown in Fig. 12.1–4 the quantities Q_n^m describing a real dipole are

$$Q_n^m = \delta_{m0}[1 - (-1)^n]\,(l/2)^n e \tag{12.1–38}$$

Q_1^0 is the dipole moment μ. The real dipole has non-zero values for alternate multipoles only. From this expression for the Q_n^m and the expression for the electrostatic potential due to a charge distribution given in Eq. 12.1–27, we get the following relation for the electrostatic potential (at point α in Fig. 12.1–4) due to a real dipole (for $r > \frac{1}{2}l$):

$$\mathscr{V}(r, \theta, \phi) = \frac{e}{r} \sum_{n=0}^{\infty} [1-(-1)^n] \left(\frac{l}{2r}\right)^n P_n(\cos\theta)$$

$$= \frac{\mu\cos\theta}{r^2}\left[1 + \frac{l^2}{8r^2}(5\cos^2\theta - 3) + \cdots\right] \qquad (12.1\text{–}39)$$

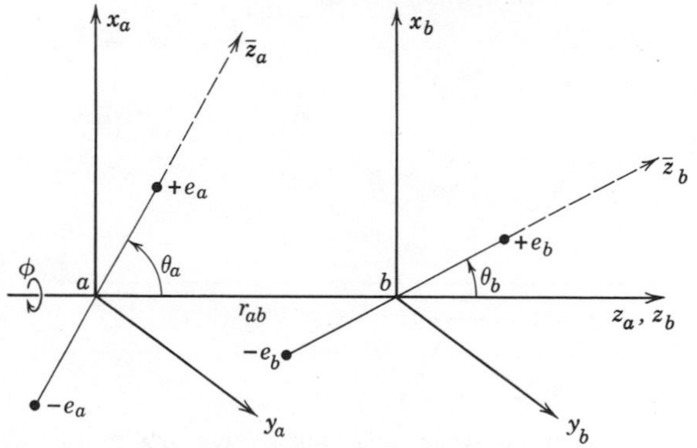

Fig. 12.1–5. Coordinate system and symbols used for discussing dipole-dipole interaction. Dipoles a and b have lengths l_a and l_b, respectively.

From this it is evident that for $r \gg l$ the real dipole acts like an ideal dipole and the only contribution to the potential is the "dipole term" of the general expression in Eq. 12.1–27.

Differentiation of Eq. 12.1–39 gives the electric field intensity due to a dipole:

$$\boldsymbol{\mathscr{E}} = -\frac{\partial\mathscr{V}}{\partial \boldsymbol{r}} = \boldsymbol{e}_r\mathscr{E}_r + \boldsymbol{e}_\theta\mathscr{E}_\theta \qquad (12.1\text{–}40)$$

in which

$$\mathscr{E}_r = -\frac{\partial\mathscr{V}}{\partial r} = \frac{2\mu\cos\theta}{r^3}\left[1 + \frac{l^2}{4r^2}(5\cos^2\theta - 3) + \cdots\right]$$

$$\mathscr{E}_\theta = -\frac{1}{r}\frac{\partial\mathscr{V}}{\partial\theta} = \frac{\mu\sin\theta}{r^3}\left[1 + \frac{3l^2}{8r^2}(5\cos^2\theta - 1) + \cdots\right] \qquad (12.1\text{–}41)$$

and $\boldsymbol{e}_r$ and $\boldsymbol{e}_\theta$ are unit vectors in the directions of increasing r and θ.

ii. *Potential Energy of Interaction of Two Dipoles*

The coordinate systems which may be used to describe the interaction of two dipoles are shown in Fig. 12.1–5. The general expression for the interaction of two discrete charge distributions, given in Eq. 12.1–29a, simplifies to the following for dipole-dipole interaction:

$$\varphi_{ab} = 4e_a e_b \sum_{n_a=0}^{\infty} \sum_{n_b=0}^{\infty} \sum_{m=-(2n_<+1)}^{m=(2n_<+1)} B^{|m|}_{(1+2n_a),(1+2n_b)}(\tfrac{1}{2}l_a, \tfrac{1}{2}l_b; r_{ab})$$
$$\times P^{|m|}_{1+2n_a}(\cos\theta_a) P^{|m|}_{1+2n_b}(\cos\theta_b) e^{im(\phi_b-\phi_a)} \quad (12.1\text{–}42)$$

This expression is valid for all separations and orientations of two dipoles.

When the distance between the centers of the dipoles, r_{ab}, is greater than $\frac{1}{2}(l_a + l_b)$, the charge distributions do not "overlap," and use may be made of Eq. 12.1–33. The $\bar{Q}_n^m$ to be used in this expression are to be calculated using the axes $\bar{z}_a$ and $\bar{z}_b$ in Fig. 12.1–5. These quantities are clearly the same as the Q_n^m of Eq. 12.1–38 and have non-zero values only when $m = 0$. The coefficients $D^n(S)_{0m}{}^*$ which are needed in Eq. 12.1–33 are simply related to the spherical harmonics:

$$D^n(S)_{0m}{}^* = i^{m-|m|}\sqrt{\frac{(n-|m|)!}{(n+|m|)!}}\, P_n^m(\cos\theta)e^{-im\phi} \quad (12.1\text{–}43)$$

The angles θ and ϕ refer to the orientation of the body-fixed $\bar{z}$-axis with respect to the xyz-coordinate frame with z-axis along the line of centers. Using these relations,[14] we find for the potential energy of interaction between two real dipoles:

$$\varphi_{ab} = e_a e_b \Sigma_{n_a}\Sigma_{n_b}\Sigma_m \frac{(-1)^{n_b+m}[1-(-1)^{n_a}][1-(-1)^{n_b}](n_a+n_b)!(\frac{1}{2}l_a)^{n_a}(\frac{1}{2}l_b)^{n_b}}{(n_a+|m|)!(n_b+|m|)!}$$
$$\times \frac{P_{n_a}{}^m(\cos\theta_a)P_{n_b}{}^m(\cos\theta_b)e^{im(\phi_b-\phi_a)}}{r_{ab}^{n_a+n_b+1}} \quad (12.1\text{–}44)$$

Inasmuch as the real dipole has only odd-numbered multipole moments, this expression for the interaction energy is a series containing terms in $1/r_{ab}{}^3$, $1/r_{ab}{}^5$, $1/r_{ab}{}^7$, $\cdots$.

The leading term in this expression for φ_{ab} is

$$\varphi_{ab} = \frac{\mu_a\mu_b}{r_{ab}{}^3}[-2\cos\theta_a\cos\theta_b + \sin\theta_a\sin\theta_b\cos(\phi_b-\phi_a)] \quad (12.1\text{–}45)$$

This represents the energy of interaction between two ideal dipoles. It is this function which appears in the Stockmayer potential (Eq. 1.3–33) for the interaction between polar molecules. When r_{ab} and l are comparable in size there is considerable distinction between real and ideal dipoles.

[14] We may alternatively use Eq. 12.1–31, which is given in terms of the Q_n^m rather than the $\bar{Q}_n^m$. The Q_n^m in the xyz-system of Fig. 12.1–5 are:

$$Q_n^m = [1-(-1)^n](\tfrac{1}{2}l)^n e P_n^m(\cos\theta)e^{im\phi}.$$

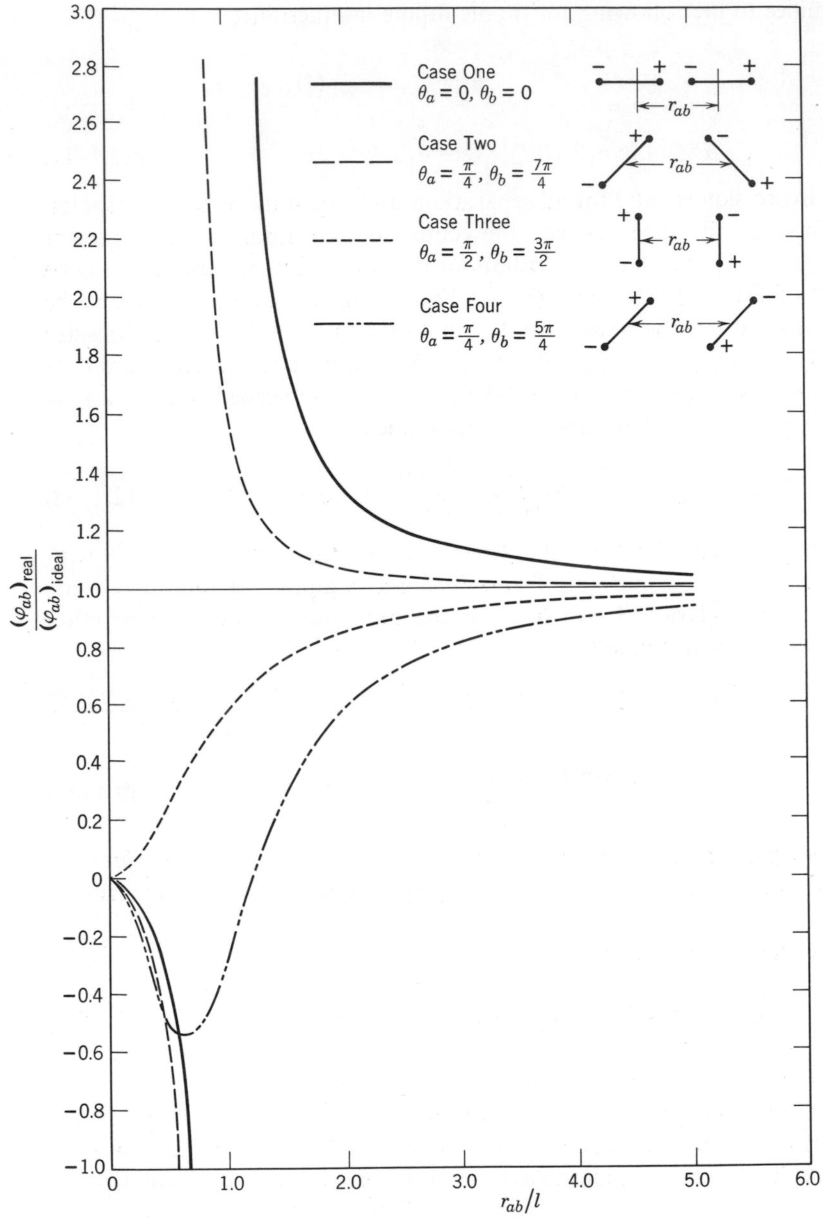

Fig. 12.1–6. The effect of the finite size on the energy of interaction of two real dipoles.

A comparison of the interaction potential energy φ_{ab} for real and ideal dipoles is given in Fig. 12.1–6 for four different relative orientations. When $(r_{ab}/l) < 2$, the deviation of the real dipoles from ideal behavior is appreciable.

Sometimes it is convenient to express the energy of two ideal dipoles in the vector form

$$\varphi_{ab} = \frac{1}{r_{ab}^3} [(\boldsymbol{\mu}_a \cdot \boldsymbol{\mu}_b) - 3(\boldsymbol{\mu}_a \cdot \boldsymbol{r}_{ab})(\boldsymbol{\mu}_b \cdot \boldsymbol{r}_{ab})/r_{ab}^2] \quad (12.1\text{–}46)$$

If (θ_a', ϕ_a'), (θ_b', ϕ_b'), and $(\theta_{ab}', \phi_{ab}')$ express the orientations of the three vectors $\boldsymbol{\mu}_a$, $\boldsymbol{\mu}_b$, and $\boldsymbol{r}_{ab}$ with respect to a common reference system, Eq. 12.1–46 becomes

$$\varphi_{ab} = \frac{\mu_a \mu_b}{r_{ab}^3} \left[\begin{aligned} &\cos\theta_a' \cos\theta_b' + \sin\theta_a' \sin\theta_b' \cos(\phi_b' - \phi_a') \\ &-3(\cos\theta_a' \cos\theta_{ab}' + \sin\theta_a' \sin\theta_{ab}' \cos(\phi_{ab}' - \phi_a')) \\ &\times(\cos\theta_b' \cos\theta_{ab}' + \sin\theta_b' \sin\theta_{ab}' \cos(\phi_{ab}' - \phi_b')) \end{aligned} \right] \quad (12.1\text{–}47)$$

These relations are useful in the discussion of the intermolecular forces resulting from the interaction of two polar molecules discussed in §§ 13.5 and 6 and the pressure broadening of microwaves arising from collisions of polar molecules discussed in § 13.7.

2. Polarization of Matter and the Electric Susceptibility[1]

Matter is made up of two kinds of charges, free and bound. Free charges can move through considerable distances, whereas bound charges, such as the electrons in atoms, can shift their average positions only by distances small compared to atomic dimensions, that is, by a small fraction of an angstrom. An electron in an atom maintains a stationary orbit by balancing the force of attraction towards the nucleus with centrifugal force generated by its motion. The internal electronic forces in atoms and molecules are very large compared to the forces produced by external electrical fields. In a *conductor* a fraction of the electrons are free to move from one place to another. These free electrons distribute themselves so as to make the electrical potential constant throughout the conductor. Any other distribution of free electrons would have a higher energy. In an *insulator* the electrons are firmly attached to individual atoms, molecules, or ions. When such an insulator is placed in an electric field, the electrons are pulled slightly in one direction while the nuclei are pulled in the opposite direction. This relative displacement of charges in matter is referred to as *polarization*.

[1] H. Fröhlich, *Theory of Dielectrics*, Oxford (1950).

When two molecules approach one another, a mutual polarization takes place. This polarization of the molecules may be an important contribution to the intermolecular potential. The extent to which the polarization takes place can be obtained from a study of the electric susceptibility of the bulk substance.

In the study of electrostatic phenomena in a dielectric, three fields are of importance, $\mathscr{E}$, $\mathscr{D}$, and $\mathscr{E}^{(\mathrm{loc})}$. The electric field, $\mathscr{E}$, measures the force on a macroscopic test charge in the dielectric. The electric displacement $\mathscr{D}$ is a field, the sources of which are the macroscopic charges. The difference between $\mathscr{E}$ and $\mathscr{D}$ is due to the polarization of the matter. The local field $\mathscr{E}^{(\mathrm{loc})}$ is a measure of the force on a molecule in the dielectric and is the field which acts to polarize the molecules and orient the permanent dipoles.

a. Polarizability and polarization

Let us consider a set of bound charges in an external field. As discussed above, the external field brings about a displacement of the charges. The differences between the multipole moments of the distorted charge distribution and those of the undistorted distribution are known as the induced multipole moments. For small external fields the induced dipole moment may be written in the following form:

$$\boldsymbol{\mu}^{(\mathrm{ind})} = \alpha \mathscr{E} \tag{12.2–1}$$

Here α is the *polarizability* of the object. The energy of the induced dipole in the electric field $\mathscr{E}$ is

$$\varphi = -\int_0^{\mathscr{E}} (\boldsymbol{\mu}^{(\mathrm{ind})} \cdot d\boldsymbol{\mathscr{E}}) = -\tfrac{1}{2}\alpha\mathscr{E}^2 \tag{12.2–2a}$$

In general the polarizability is a tensor $\boldsymbol{\alpha}$; that is, the induced dipole moment does not necessarily lie in the direction of the applied electric field. Then $\boldsymbol{\mu}^{(\mathrm{ind})} = (\boldsymbol{\alpha} \cdot \mathscr{E})$ and the energy of the induced dipole in the electric field $\mathscr{E}$ is

$$\varphi = -\tfrac{1}{2}(\mathscr{E} \cdot \boldsymbol{\alpha} \cdot \mathscr{E}) \tag{12.2–2b}$$

The meaning of polarizability may be illustrated by a simple example. Consider a conducting sphere of radius R placed in a homogeneous electric field of strength $\mathscr{E}$ in the z-direction. The electrostatic potential outside of the sphere is[2]

$$\mathscr{V} = -\mathscr{E} z\left(1 - \frac{R^3}{r^3}\right) \tag{12.2–3}$$

[2] L. Page, *Introduction to Theoretical Physics*, Van Nostrand (1935), p. 398.

But this is the same electrostatic potential as if a point dipole of strength $R^3\mathscr{E}$ were located at the center of the sphere and its potential superimposed on that of the external field. The polarizability of the conducting sphere is therefore

$$\alpha = R^3 \tag{12.2–4}$$

For a conducting ellipsoid the polarizability is a tensor with principal axes coinciding with the principal axes of the ellipsoid.

The polarization of matter due to the influence of an external electric field is due to two effects: (i) the polarizability of the individual molecules, and (ii) the partial orientation of permanent dipole moments of the molecules. The average dipole moment per unit volume due to these two effects is known as the *polarization* and is designated by the symbol $\mathscr{P}$.

b. The $\mathscr{D}$ and $\mathscr{E}$ fields

The electric field in a vacuum is due entirely to the presence of macroscopic charged bodies. If a dielectric (that is, an insulator) is placed in this field, the field within the dielectric is made up of the impressed field due to the macroscopic charged bodies and the field due to the polarization of each of the molecules and the permanent moments of each of the molecules of the dielectric. It is, however, rarely of interest to consider the field from such a detailed point of view. Instead we approach the problem from a statistical standpoint.

This is accomplished by introducing two vector fields, $\mathscr{D}$ and $\mathscr{E}$. The macroscopic charged bodies represent sources of the electric displacement vector, $\mathscr{D}$. Thus the integral of $\mathscr{D}$ over any closed surface is equal to 4π times the enclosed charge:

$$\int (\mathscr{D} \cdot \boldsymbol{dS}) = 4\pi \int \rho\, d\boldsymbol{r} \tag{12.2–5}$$

The electric field, $\mathscr{E}$, measures the force on a macroscopic charged body within the dielectric. Since this field is a conservative field, the net work done in carrying a test charge over a closed path is zero. Thus the line integral about any closed curve is

$$\oint (\mathscr{E} \cdot \boldsymbol{ds}) = 0 \tag{12.2–6}$$

These last two equations serve to define the vectors $\mathscr{D}$ and $\mathscr{E}$ and are used to obtain differential expression for the vector fields and the behavior of the fields at a boundary.

By the application of Green's theorem to Eq. 12.2–5 and Stokes' theorem to Eq. 12.2–6 we may obtain the following differential relations for the $\mathscr{D}$ and $\mathscr{E}$ fields:

$$\left(\frac{\partial}{\partial \boldsymbol{r}} \cdot \mathscr{D}\right) = 4\pi\rho \tag{12.2–7}$$

$$\left[\frac{\partial}{\partial \boldsymbol{r}} \times \mathscr{E}\right] = 0 \tag{12.2–8}$$

These equations apply in the interior of a dielectric.

At the boundary between two dielectrics 1 and 2 (or between a dielectric and a vacuum) there may be a surface density of real charges, $\rho^{(s)}$. From the foregoing integral definitions it may be shown that at the boundary the electric displacement $\mathscr{D}$ and the electric field $\mathscr{E}$ satisfy the following conditions:

$$(\boldsymbol{n} \cdot \{\mathscr{D}^{(2)} - \mathscr{D}^{(1)}\}) = 4\pi\rho^{(s)} \tag{12.2–9}$$

$$[\boldsymbol{n} \times \{\mathscr{E}^{(2)} - \mathscr{E}^{(1)}\}] = 0 \tag{12.2–10}$$

where $\boldsymbol{n}$ is a unit vector normal to the surface and in the direction from 1 to 2.

In order to determine the relation between $\mathscr{D}$ and $\mathscr{E}$ we consider the following experiment. First let us set up an electric field between two parallel condenser plates which produce a parallel electric field in the z-direction in a vacuum. The strength of this field can be called either $\mathscr{D}$ or $\mathscr{E}$ since in a vacuum the two are the same. Now let us replace the vacuum by an isotropic homogeneous dielectric medium. The $\mathscr{D}$ field remains the same, but the $\mathscr{E}$ field changes due to the polarization of the medium.

In the interior of the dielectric we remove a small element of volume of the matter having dimensions large compared to the distance between the molecules. We can then inquire as to the charges which would be required on the surfaces of the empty region to produce a force on a test charge in the cavity the same as the force which would exist if the test charge were embedded in the homogeneous medium. The dipole moment of these surface charges is equal to the total dipole moment of the matter which was removed.

For convenience we choose as the cavity a cylinder with ends parallel to the condenser plates. The radius, r, of the cylinder is taken large compared to the height so that the edge effects may be neglected. Let us consider the pair of end surfaces normal to the z-direction. From Eq. 12.2–9 it follows that

$$\{\mathscr{D}_z^{(o)} - \mathscr{D}_z^{(i)}\} = 4\pi\rho^{(s)} \tag{12.2–11}$$

in which $\rho^{(s)}$ is the charge density on a surface (which is equal and opposite on the two surfaces), and the superscripts o and i indicate positions outside and inside the cavity. Inasmuch as there is no matter inside the cavity,

$$\mathscr{D}^{(i)} = \mathscr{E}^{(i)} \tag{12.2–12}$$

and in order that the force on a test charge inside the cavity be the same as that before the removal of the small cylinder, $\mathscr{D}^{(i)}$ and $\mathscr{E}^{(i)}$ are both equal to $\mathscr{E}$, the field strength before the formation of the cavity. Because of the choice of the shape of the cavity, the displacement vector is unaffected by the presence of the cavity and

$$4\pi\rho^{(s)} = \mathscr{D}_z - \mathscr{E}_z \tag{12.2–13}$$

where $\mathscr{D}_z$ is the value before the formation of the cavity. We conclude then that the matter removed from the cavity had a dipole moment with a component in the z-direction of

$$(\pi r^2\rho^{(s)})l = \frac{r^2 l}{4}(\mathscr{D}_z - \mathscr{E}_z) \tag{12.2–14}$$

The polarization $\mathscr{P}$ is defined as the total dipole moment per unit volume of matter. Accordingly, the z-component of the polarization $\mathscr{P}$ is

$$\mathscr{P}_z = \frac{1}{4\pi}(\mathscr{D}_z - \mathscr{E}_z) \tag{12.2–15}$$

Then since the other components of $\mathscr{P}$, $\mathscr{D}$, and $\mathscr{E}$ are zero it follows that

$$\mathscr{E} = \mathscr{D} - 4\pi\mathscr{P} \tag{12.2–16}$$

It may be shown that this result applies to an anisotropic as well as an isotropic medium.

c. The local field, $\mathscr{E}^{(\mathrm{loc})}$

In the preceding discussion an expression was obtained for the $\mathscr{E}$ field in terms of the $\mathscr{D}$ field and the polarization $\mathscr{P}$. It should be kept in mind that this $\mathscr{E}$ field is the field associated with the force on the *macroscopic* test charge. Let us now inquire as to the field, $\mathscr{E}^{(\mathrm{loc})}$, which is experienced by one individual molecule. This field is made up of the sum of the $\mathscr{D}$ field due to the external charges and the field due to the polarization of all the other molecules (that is, excluding the particular molecule under consideration). Whereas the derivation of an expression for $\mathscr{E}$ was obtained by macroscopic arguments, the development of an expression for $\mathscr{E}^{(\mathrm{loc})}$ requires a microscopic point of view.

Let us consider a condenser with circular plates of radius R, the upper and lower plates being located at $+L$ and $-L$ on the z-axis and parallel to the xy-plane. R is taken to be large compared with L so that the field near the center of the cylindrical space between the condenser plates is essentially parallel to the z-axis. If there is a surface charge $\rho^{(s)}$ per unit area on the upper plate and an equivalent negative charge on the lower plate, the $\mathscr{D}$ field has only a z-component with magnitude $4\pi\rho^{(s)}$.

Now let there be placed between the condenser plates an isotropic dielectric containing n molecules per unit volume, each containing an ideal dipole of moment $\boldsymbol{\mu}$. The total dipole moment $\boldsymbol{\mu}^{(\mathrm{tot})}$ of a molecule is the sum of the permanent dipole moment $\boldsymbol{\mu}$ and the induced dipole moment $\boldsymbol{\mu}^{(\mathrm{ind})}$. The time average value of the total dipole moment $\bar{\boldsymbol{\mu}}^{(\mathrm{tot})}$ is a vector in the z-direction, that is, in the direction of the impressed electric field. The polarization vector $\mathscr{P}$ is then $n\bar{\boldsymbol{\mu}}^{(\mathrm{tot})}$.

We now inquire as to the field, $\mathscr{E}^{(\mathrm{loc})}$, experienced by a molecule located at the center of the cylindrical region. First, we note that the electric potential at this "central molecule" due to one dipole, $\bar{\boldsymbol{\mu}}^{(\mathrm{tot})}$, located at a position $\boldsymbol{r}$ is

$$\mathscr{V}^1 = \frac{(\bar{\boldsymbol{\mu}}^{(\mathrm{tot})} \cdot \boldsymbol{r})}{r^3} \tag{12.2–17}$$

and the z-component of the electric field intensity associated with this potential is

$$\mathscr{E}_z^{\,1} = -\frac{\partial}{\partial z}\left(\frac{\bar{\boldsymbol{\mu}}^{(\mathrm{tot})} \cdot \boldsymbol{r}}{r^3}\right) \tag{12.2–18}$$

The number density of molecules or dipoles in the vicinity of $\boldsymbol{r}$ is $ng(r)$, where $g(r)$ is the radial distribution function, discussed in detail in § 4.9a. Therefore the total field intensity which the central molecule experiences due to all the dipoles is in the z-direction and has a magnitude given by the integral over the cylindrical region weighted according to the radial distribution function. To this must be added the $\mathscr{D}$ field to obtain the expression for $\mathscr{E}^{(\mathrm{loc})}$:

$$\mathscr{E}_z^{(\mathrm{loc})} = \mathscr{D}_z + n\int_{\mathrm{cyl}} g(r)\mathscr{E}_z^{\,1} d\boldsymbol{r} \tag{12.2–19}$$

in which $\mathscr{E}_z^{\,1}$ is given by Eq. 12.2–18. This expression may also be written in terms of the derivative of the radial distribution function $g'(r) = dg/dr$:

$$\begin{aligned}\mathscr{E}_z^{(\mathrm{loc})} &= \mathscr{D}_z + n\int_{\mathrm{cyl}}\int_0^r g'(s)\mathscr{E}_z^{\,1}\, ds\, d\boldsymbol{r} \\ &= \mathscr{D}_z + n\int_0^\infty g'(s)\left[\int_{V(s)} \mathscr{E}_z^{\,1}\, d\boldsymbol{r}\right] ds\end{aligned} \tag{12.2–20}$$

To change the order of integration and obtain the second form of this equation it is necessary to assume that $g'(r)$ is different from zero only for values of s small with respect to the dimensions of the condenser. The volume $V(s)$ is the volume bounded on the outside by the cylinder and on the inside by a sphere of radius s.

The integral over $\boldsymbol{r}$ may be shown to be independent of s and to have the value[3]

$$\int_{V(s)} \mathscr{E}_z^{\,1}\, d\boldsymbol{r} = 4\pi\bar{\mu}^{(\text{tot})}\left[-\tfrac{2}{3} + \frac{L}{\sqrt{R^2+L^2}}\right]$$
$$\simeq -\frac{8\pi}{3}\bar{\mu}^{(\text{tot})} \quad \text{for} \quad R \gg L \tag{12.2-21}$$

The condition that R be very large compared to L corresponds physically to the requirement of a uniform field in the z-direction. Substituting this result into Eq. 12.2–20 and integrating over s [use must be made of the fact that $g(\infty) = 1$ and $g(0) = 0$], we obtain finally

$$\mathscr{E}^{(\text{loc})} = \mathscr{D} - \frac{8\pi}{3} n\,\bar{\boldsymbol{\mu}}^{(\text{tot})} = \mathscr{D} - \frac{8\pi}{3}\mathscr{P} \tag{12.2-22}$$

This result may also be written in terms of $\mathscr{E}$:

$$\mathscr{E}^{(\text{loc})} = \mathscr{E} + \tfrac{4}{3}\pi\mathscr{P} \tag{12.2-23}$$

This expression is independent of the details of the radial distribution function, but it does depend on the fact that the distribution function $g(r)$ is independent of angle. Thus the result would be somewhat different if the medium had local crystal structure. It is this field $\mathscr{E}^{(\text{loc})}$ which acts on an individual molecule and tends to polarize and align it in the direction of the field.

d. The electric susceptibility in terms of the dielectric constant

The polarization $\mathscr{P}$, the average dipole moment $\bar{\boldsymbol{\mu}}^{(\text{tot})}$, and the local electric field $\mathscr{E}^{(\text{loc})}$ may be related to one another by an equation of the same form as Eq. 12.2–1:

$$\mathscr{P} = n\bar{\boldsymbol{\mu}}^{(\text{tot})} = n\chi^{(e)}\mathscr{E}^{(\text{loc})} \tag{12.2-24}$$

The quantity $\chi^{(e)}$ is called the electric susceptibility per molecule. (The susceptibility per mole is $\tilde{N}\chi^{(e)}$.) It is analogous to the polarizability in Eq. 12.2–1. Indeed, if the molecules have no permanent dipoles, $\chi^{(e)}$ is identical with α. On the other hand, when the molecules have permanent dipoles, $\chi^{(e)}$ contains another term which is temperature dependent. This term is due to the alignment of the dipoles by the field.

[3] G. Jaffé, *J. Chem. Phys.*, **8**, 879 (1940).

The electric susceptibility may be related to the dielectric constant ϵ', defined by:

$$\mathscr{D} = \epsilon' \mathscr{E} \tag{12.2–25}$$

The dielectric constant is readily determined by experiment. In a non-isotropic medium ϵ' is a tensor since the $\mathscr{D}$ and $\mathscr{E}$ fields are not in the same direction. In terms of ϵ', Eqs. 12.2–16 and 23 may be rewritten as

$$\mathscr{P} = \frac{1}{4\pi}(\epsilon' - 1)\,\mathscr{E} \tag{12.2–26}$$

$$\mathscr{E}^{(\mathrm{loc})} = \tfrac{1}{3}(\epsilon' + 2)\,\mathscr{E} \tag{12.2–27}$$

From these relations and the defining equation for the susceptibility per molecule,

$$\chi^{(e)} = \frac{3}{4\pi n}\left(\frac{\epsilon' - 1}{\epsilon' + 2}\right) \tag{12.2–28}$$

Or, in terms of the density of the material, ρ, the molecular weight, M, and Avogadro's number, $\tilde{N}$:

$$\chi^{(e)} = \frac{3}{4\pi}\frac{M}{\tilde{N}\rho}\left(\frac{\epsilon' - 1}{\epsilon' + 2}\right) \tag{12.2–29}$$

This is known as the Clausius-Mosotti relation.[4] It can be shown that, except at high densities or high field intensities, the susceptibility of a mixture is additive:

$$\chi^{(e)} = \textstyle\sum_i x_i \chi_i^{(e)} \tag{12.2–30}$$

in which x_i is the mole fraction of component i and $\chi_i^{(e)}$ is the susceptibility of the pure ith component.

The Clausius-Mosotti relation can be used to measure the susceptibility $\chi^{(e)}$ and to predict the density dependence of the dielectric constant ϵ'. In the next subsection it is shown that $\chi^{(e)}$ is a function of the temperature

[4] The corrections to the Clausius-Mosotti relation for high density or high field strength are discussed by F. Booth, *J. Chem. Phys.*, **19**, 391 (1951); L. Onsager, *J. Am. Chem. Soc.*, **58**, 1486 (1936); J. Kirkwood, *J. Chem. Phys.*, **7**, 911 (1936); H. Fröhlich, *Theory of Dielectrics*, Oxford University Press (1949), Ch. II; A. Anselm, *J. Exp. Phys.*, Acad. Sci. USSR, **14**, 364 (1945). Booth showed that at high field strengths:

$$\epsilon' = \eta^2 + [\gamma\pi n(\eta^2 + 2)\mu/\mathscr{E}]\, L(\beta(\eta^2 + 2)\mu\mathscr{E}/kT)$$

where η is the optical refractive index, μ is the dipole moment of the molecule, $L(x)$ is the Langevin function discussed later in § 12.2, and γ and β are numerical constants which have been evaluated by two different methods. Onsager found that $\gamma = \frac{4}{3}$ and $\beta = \frac{1}{2}$. Kirkwood obtained $\gamma = (28/3\sqrt{73})$ and $\beta = (\sqrt{73}/6)$. As will be seen in Ch. 13, the quadrupole forces are exceedingly important in the interaction of two water molecules. Thus for water some modification of Booth's relation is required.

and depends parametrically on two properties of the molecules: polarizability and permanent dipole moment. Variations of $\chi^{(e)}$ with density can be used as an indication of changes in molecular structure such as the formation of dimers.

e. The electric susceptibility in terms of the molecular properties

In Eq. 12.2–24 the electric susceptibility is defined in terms of $\overline{\boldsymbol{\mu}}^{(\text{tot})}$ and $\mathscr{E}^{(\text{loc})}$. We now discuss the explicit evaluation of $\overline{\boldsymbol{\mu}}^{(\text{tot})}$, which is the average permanent plus induced dipole moment of a molecule in a dielectric which is placed in an electric field. This quantity can be written in terms of the polarizability and the permanent dipole moment of the molecules, with the result that the electric susceptibility may be expressed in terms of the molecular properties.

As an example of a dielectric let us consider an ideal polyatomic gas. In § 2.3d it is shown that the energy in such a system is partitioned among the molecules according to a Boltzmann distribution. The average value of any molecular property may accordingly be written as an average over a Boltzmann distribution of energy states. The molecular property of interest here is the dipole moment, which depends of course on the quantum state of the molecules. If we designate by $\boldsymbol{\mu}_j^{(\text{tot})}$ the quantum mechanical average of the total (permanent plus induced) dipole moment of a molecule in the jth quantum state, then:

$$\overline{\boldsymbol{\mu}}^{(\text{tot})} = \frac{\Sigma_j \boldsymbol{\mu}_j^{(\text{tot})} e^{-\epsilon_j/kT}}{\Sigma_j e^{-\epsilon_j/kT}} \tag{12.2–31}$$

Here the index j stands for the entire set of quantum numbers needed to describe the state of a molecule, and ϵ_j is the energy associated with that state.

This expression for $\overline{\boldsymbol{\mu}}^{(\text{tot})}$ may be simplified by making a few assumptions which are usually valid: (i) all molecules are in their ground electronic states, (ii) the rotational energy is independent of the vibrational quantum number, (iii) the dipole moment $\boldsymbol{\mu}_j^{(\text{tot})}$ is independent of the vibrational quantum number, and (iv) the separation between rotational energy levels is small compared with kT so that the rotational motion may be considered classically. When these assumptions are made, Eq. 12.2–31 may be shown to simplify to the classical average:[5]

$$\overline{\boldsymbol{\mu}}^{(\text{tot})} = \frac{\int \boldsymbol{\mu}^{(\text{tot})}(R) e^{-\varphi(R)/kT}\, dR}{\int e^{-\varphi(R)/kT}\, dR} \tag{12.2–32}$$

Here R represents the Euler angles[6] which specify the orientation of a

[5] G. S. Rushbrooke, *Introduction to Statistical Mechanics*, Oxford University Press (1949), p. 155.

[6] The Eulerian angles are defined in Appendix 12B.

molecule, $\varphi(R)$ is the potential energy of the molecule in a particular orientation, and $dR = \sin\theta\, d\theta\, d\phi\, d\psi$. Thus the average dipole moment is just the average value of $\boldsymbol{\mu}^{(\text{tot})}$ over all orientations, with the Boltzmann factor $\exp(-\varphi/kT)$ as a weighting factor.

To evaluate $\bar{\boldsymbol{\mu}}^{(\text{tot})}$, expressions for $\boldsymbol{\mu}^{(\text{tot})}$ and φ as functions of the angles must be inserted into the integrals in the preceding equation. Let the impressed electric field, $\mathscr{E}$, be in the z-direction of the space-fixed coordinates. For an isotropic substance $\mathscr{E}^{(\text{loc})}$ is in the same direction as $\mathscr{E}$. Then the total dipole moment and the potential of a molecule in a field $\mathscr{E}^{(\text{loc})}$ are given by the expressions:

$$\begin{cases} \mu_x^{(\text{tot})} = \mu \sin\theta \cos\phi \\ \mu_y^{(\text{tot})} = \mu \sin\theta \sin\phi \\ \mu_z^{(\text{tot})} = \mu \cos\theta + \alpha\mathscr{E}^{(\text{loc})} \end{cases} \tag{12.2-33}$$

$$\varphi = -\mu\mathscr{E}^{(\text{loc})}\cos\theta - \tfrac{1}{2}\alpha\mathscr{E}^{(\text{loc})2} \tag{12.2-34}$$

The integrals in Eq. 12.2–32 over the x- and y-components of $\boldsymbol{\mu}^{(\text{tot})}$ are zero. Hence $\bar{\boldsymbol{\mu}}^{(\text{tot})}$ is in the z-direction with the magnitude

$$\begin{aligned} \bar{\mu}^{(\text{tot})} &= \alpha\mathscr{E}^{(\text{loc})} + \frac{\displaystyle\int_0^\pi [\mu\cos\theta] e^{-\mu\mathscr{E}^{(\text{loc})}\cos\theta/kT}\sin\theta\, d\theta}{\displaystyle\int_0^\pi e^{-\mu\mathscr{E}^{(\text{loc})}\cos\theta/kT}\sin\theta\, d\theta} \\ &= \alpha\mathscr{E}^{(\text{loc})} + \mu L(\mu\mathscr{E}^{(\text{loc})}/kT) \end{aligned} \tag{12.2-35}$$

in which $L(x)$ is the Langevin function:[7]

$$L(x) = \frac{\displaystyle\int_{-x}^{+x} \xi e^{\xi}\, d\xi}{\displaystyle\int_{-x}^{+x} x e^{\xi}\, d\xi} = \coth x - \frac{1}{x} \cong \frac{1}{3}x - \frac{1}{45}x^3 + \cdots \tag{12.2-36}$$

Let us now consider two limiting cases of this equation. For *strong electric fields* or *low temperatures* (where $x = \mu\mathscr{E}^{(\text{loc})}/kT$ is large and $L(x)$ approaches unity), $\bar{\mu}^{(\text{tot})}$ approaches the value

$$\bar{\mu}^{(\text{tot})} = \alpha\mathscr{E}^{(\text{loc})} + \mu \tag{12.2-37}$$

[7] At low temperatures the Langevin function should be replaced by the Brillouin function to take into account the discrete nature of the rotational energy states. See J. H. Van Vleck, *Electric and Magnetic Susceptibilities*, Oxford University Press (1932), pp. 31 and 257.

This corresponds to "saturation," that is, perfect alignment of all the molecules. For *weak electric fields* or *high temperatures* $\bar{\mu}^{(\text{tot})}$ is given by the expansion

$$\bar{\mu}^{(\text{tot})} = \alpha\mathscr{E}^{(\text{loc})} + \frac{1}{3}\mu\left(\frac{\mu\mathscr{E}^{(\text{loc})}}{kT}\right) - \frac{1}{45}\mu\left(\frac{\mu\mathscr{E}^{(\text{loc})}}{kT}\right)^3 + \cdots \quad (12.2\text{–}38)$$

Here the Maclaurin type expansion of the Langevin function has been used.

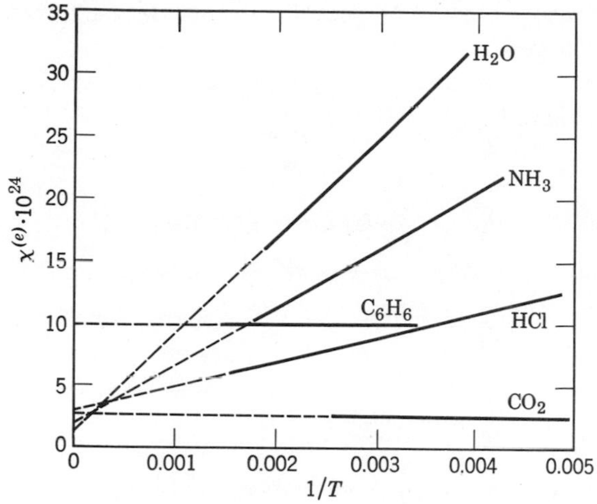

Fig. 12.2–1. Experimental curves showing the temperature dependence of the electric susceptibility. The slopes of the curves give the permanent dipole moments of the molecules, and the intercepts on the $\chi^{(e)}$-axis give their polarizabilities. R. J. W. Le Fèvrc, *Dipole Moments*, Methuen and Co., Ltd., London, 2d Ed., 1948.

Comparison of this last result with the definition of the electric susceptibility shows that for sufficiently low field strengths or high temperatures:

$$\chi^{(e)} = \alpha + \frac{\mu^2}{3kT} \quad (12.2\text{–}39)$$

This relation, together with the Clausius-Mosotti equation, enables us to find the permanent dipole moment and the polarizability of molecules from experimental measurements of the dielectric constant as a function of the temperature. A plot of the electric susceptibility against $1/T$ for several substances is shown in Fig. 12.2–1. Straight lines are obtained as predicted by Eq. 12.2–39. The slope gives a measure of the dipole moment, and the intercept is the polarizability. A knowledge of these molecular quantities is of great importance in the study of the interaction between pairs of polar molecules and between polar and non-polar molecules. This subject is given extensive treatment in the following chapter.

3. Maxwell's Equations of Electromagnetism

The discussions of the previous sections of this chapter deal with the behavior of stationary electric charges. In order to discuss the electrodynamics of moving charges, it is necessary to introduce several new quantities to describe the flow of electric currents and the forces associated with moving charges.

The *strength of an electric current*, i, is defined as the product of the charge per unit length σ, and its speed v:

$$i = \sigma v \tag{12.3–1}$$

Another quantity used is the *current density*, defined by

$$\boldsymbol{j} = \rho \boldsymbol{v} \tag{12.3–2}$$

This quantity is the flux of charge, that is, the charge which passes through a unit cross-section in a unit time. It satisfies the equation

$$\frac{\partial \rho}{\partial t} = -\left(\frac{\partial}{\partial \boldsymbol{r}} \cdot \rho \boldsymbol{v}\right) = -\left(\frac{\partial}{\partial \boldsymbol{r}} \cdot \boldsymbol{j}\right) \tag{12.3–3}$$

which describes the conservation of charge.

In § 12.1 it was shown how the force on a stationary charge could be described in terms of the electric field, $\mathscr{E}$. There are additional forces on charged particles in motion, and it is convenient to introduce the concept of a field in order to describe them. The *magnetic field* $\mathscr{B}$ at a point is defined in terms of the force $\boldsymbol{F}$ which acts on a charge e moving with a velocity $\boldsymbol{v}$ by the equation:

$$\boldsymbol{F} = e\mathscr{E} + \frac{e}{c} [\boldsymbol{v} \times \mathscr{B}] \tag{12.3–4}$$

Here c is the velocity of propagation of light in a vacuum.

Many experiments dealing with the electric and magnetic fields have led to a set of differential equations—Maxwell's equations—which determine the nature of the $\mathscr{E}$ and $\mathscr{B}$ fields due to sets of charges moving in a vacuum. These equations summarize the experimental results and now form the postulational basis of the theory of electrodynamics. No real "derivation" of these equations is possible, any more than one may derive the fundamental postulates of quantum mechanics. Accordingly, we begin this section by listing the four Maxwell equations and then proceed to indicate the origin of some of the terms appearing in them.

From Maxwell's equations may be derived the Coulombic law of interaction, which forms the basis for the discussion given in the previous two sections.

In § 12.2 it is shown that in a material medium we must consider two fields $\mathscr{E}$ and $\mathscr{D}$ which may be related to one another by means of the dielectric constant ϵ' or the electric susceptibility $\chi^{(e)}$. The analogous quantities for the magnetic field are the $\mathscr{B}$ and $\mathscr{H}$ fields, which are related to one another by means of the magnetic permeability μ' or the magnetic susceptibility $\chi^{(m)}$. We conclude this section with the set of Maxwell's equations written for a material medium.

a. Maxwell's equations in a vacuum

The following four differential equations describe the behavior of the electric and magnetic fields in a vacuum:

$$\left(\frac{\partial}{\partial \boldsymbol{r}} \cdot \mathscr{E}\right) = 4\pi\rho \tag{12.3–5}$$

$$\left(\frac{\partial}{\partial \boldsymbol{r}} \cdot \mathscr{B}\right) = 0 \tag{12.3–6}$$

$$\left[\frac{\partial}{\partial \boldsymbol{r}} \times \mathscr{E}\right] = -\frac{1}{c}\frac{\partial \mathscr{B}}{\partial t} \tag{12.3–7}$$

$$\left[\frac{\partial}{\partial \boldsymbol{r}} \times \mathscr{B}\right] = +\frac{1}{c}\left\{\frac{\partial \mathscr{E}}{\partial t} + 4\pi \boldsymbol{j}\right\} \tag{12.3–8}$$

These equations along with the boundary conditions serve to define uniquely the $\mathscr{E}$ and $\mathscr{B}$ fields.

The first two of these equations describe the "sources" of the fields. The relation between the divergence of $\mathscr{E}$ and the electric charge density is Coulomb's law used in § 12.1. It has been shown experimentally that the magnetic field, $\mathscr{B}$, satisfies the analogous relation given by Eq. 12.3–6. This relation may be interpreted as the statement that isolated magnetic poles (charges) do not exist.

The third relation given above is due to Faraday, who showed that a change in a magnetic field produces an electric field. It is this principle which is used in motors and generators.

The fourth relation comes originally from Ampère's law. If a current of strength i passes through a circular loop of wire of radius R, there is produced at the center, normal to the plane of the loop, a magnetic field of strength

$$\mathscr{B} = 2\pi i/cR \tag{12.3–9}$$

Ampère interpreted this and the results of the study of the general pattern of $\mathscr{B}$ as implying that each element, $\boldsymbol{ds}$, of the wire in the loop contributes a quantity

$$d\mathscr{B} = -\frac{i}{c}\frac{[\boldsymbol{r} \times \boldsymbol{ds}]}{r^3} \tag{12.3–10}$$

to the total magnetic field. Here $\boldsymbol{r}$ is the vector from the element of length $\boldsymbol{ds}$ to the field point. From this relation may be derived Ampère's law:

$$\left[\frac{\partial}{\partial \boldsymbol{r}} \times \mathscr{B}\right] = \frac{4\pi \boldsymbol{j}}{c} \tag{12.3–11}$$

which describes the magnetic fields due to steady currents.

Maxwell showed by the following arguments that, in the general case, this expression is inconsistent with the equation describing the conservation of charge (Eq. 12.3–3). Taking the divergence of both sides of Eq. 12.3–11, we obtain

$$\left(\frac{\partial}{\partial \boldsymbol{r}} \cdot \left[\frac{\partial}{\partial \boldsymbol{r}} \times \mathscr{B}\right]\right) = \frac{4\pi}{c}\left(\frac{\partial}{\partial \boldsymbol{r}} \cdot \boldsymbol{j}\right) \tag{12.3–12}$$

Inasmuch as the divergence of the curl of any vector is zero, it follows from this result and Eq. 12.3–3 that $(\partial\rho/\partial t) = 0$. This is true for steady-state conditions, but not in general. Hence Maxwell revised Ampère's law by adding a term called the "displacement current" $(1/c)$ $(\partial\mathscr{E}/\partial t)$ so that Eq. 12.3–11 is replaced by Eq. 12.3–8.

That Eq. 12.3–8 is consistent with the conservation of charge may be seen in the following manner. Taking the divergence of the equation, we obtain

$$\frac{4\pi}{c}\left(\frac{\partial}{\partial \boldsymbol{r}} \cdot \boldsymbol{j}\right) + \frac{1}{c}\left(\frac{\partial}{\partial \boldsymbol{r}} \cdot \frac{\partial \mathscr{E}}{\partial t}\right) = 0 \tag{12.3–13}$$

This result may be combined with the time derivative of Eq. 12.3–5:

$$\left(\frac{\partial}{\partial \boldsymbol{r}} \cdot \frac{\partial \mathscr{E}}{\partial t}\right) - 4\pi\left(\frac{\partial \rho}{\partial t}\right) = 0 \tag{12.3–14}$$

to give the equation for the conservation of charge. Maxwell's equation for $\left[\frac{\partial}{\partial \boldsymbol{r}} \times \mathscr{B}\right]$ containing the displacement current has been well substantiated by direct observation of the magnetic fields produced by moving charges. The displacement currents are particularly important in problems dealing with high-frequency alternating currents.

b. The scalar and vector potentials; magnetic multipoles

In § 12.1 it is pointed out that it is convenient to introduce the concept of the electrostatic potential, which is related to the electric field intensity. Maxwell's equations may be simplified by the introduction of two potentials, the scalar potential $\mathscr{V}$ and the vector potential $\mathscr{A}$. Since $\mathscr{B}$ is a vector with zero divergence it may be expressed as the curl of another vector. Hence the vector potential is defined so that

$$\mathscr{B} = \left[\frac{\partial}{\partial \boldsymbol{r}} \times \mathscr{A}\right] \tag{12.3–15}$$

It can be shown that in the general case $\mathscr{E}$ may be related to $\mathscr{A}$ and the scalar potential by

$$\mathscr{E} = -\frac{\partial}{\partial \boldsymbol{r}}\mathscr{V} - \frac{1}{c}\frac{\partial}{\partial t}\mathscr{A} \tag{12.3–16}$$

Obviously the definitions of $\mathscr{A}$ and $\mathscr{V}$ are not unique. The former can be changed by the addition of a gradient of a scalar function without changing the value of $\mathscr{B}$. Then if a corresponding change is made in $\mathscr{V}$, the value of $\mathscr{E}$ is also unaffected. It is convenient to remove most of the ambiguity in the $\mathscr{A}$ and $\mathscr{V}$ by requiring that they satisfy the relation

$$\frac{1}{c}\frac{\partial \mathscr{V}}{\partial t} + \left(\frac{\partial}{\partial \boldsymbol{r}} \cdot \mathscr{A}\right) = 0 \tag{12.3–17}$$

Then direct substitution of these expressions into Maxwell's equations gives

$$\left(\frac{\partial}{\partial \boldsymbol{r}} \cdot \frac{\partial}{\partial \boldsymbol{r}}\right) \mathscr{A} - \frac{1}{c^2}\frac{\partial^2}{\partial t^2}\mathscr{A} = -\frac{4\pi}{c}\rho \boldsymbol{v} \tag{12.3–18}$$

$$\left(\frac{\partial}{\partial \boldsymbol{r}} \cdot \frac{\partial}{\partial \boldsymbol{r}}\mathscr{V}\right) - \frac{1}{c^2}\frac{\partial^2}{\partial t^2}\mathscr{V} = -4\pi\rho \tag{12.3–19}$$

The solutions of the equations for $\mathscr{A}$ and $\mathscr{V}$ may be expressed in the form

$$\mathscr{A}(t = t_0) = \int \left(\frac{\rho(\boldsymbol{r}_i)\,\boldsymbol{v}}{c r_{i\alpha}}\right)_{t=t_0-\frac{r_{i\alpha}}{c}} d\boldsymbol{r}_i \tag{12.3–20}$$

$$\mathscr{V}(t = t_0) = \int \left(\frac{\rho(\boldsymbol{r}_i)}{r_{i\alpha}}\right)_{t=t_0-\frac{r_{i\alpha}}{c}} d\boldsymbol{r}_i \tag{12.3–21}$$

The integration is over the entire charge distribution; $\boldsymbol{r}_i$ is the location of the ith charge, and $\boldsymbol{r}_{i\alpha}$ is the vector to the ith charge from the field point.

Notice here the "retardation effects," that is the quantities which determine the potentials at time $t = t_0$ are the positions and velocities of the particles at time $t = t_0 - r_{i\alpha}/c$.

Because of the similarity in the expressions for $\mathscr{A}$ and $\mathscr{V}$ the two quantities may be handled in much the same manner.[1] Let us first consider the vector potential at some distance from a set of moving charges. This potential may be expanded in a manner similar to that used in § 12.1, thus:

$$\mathscr{A}(t = t_0) = \sum_i \left\{ \frac{e_i \boldsymbol{v}_i}{cr} + \frac{e_i \boldsymbol{v}_i (\boldsymbol{r}_i \cdot \boldsymbol{r})}{cr^3} + \cdots \right\}_{t=t_0-\frac{r_{i\alpha}}{c}} \tag{12.3–22}$$

Here $\boldsymbol{r}_i$ is the vector from the origin to the charge e_i, which is moving with a velocity $\boldsymbol{v}_i$, and $\boldsymbol{r}$ is the vector from the origin to the field point. The electrostatic expression is

$$\mathscr{V} = \frac{C}{r} + \frac{(\boldsymbol{\mu} \cdot \boldsymbol{r})}{r^3} + \frac{(\mathsf{Q} : \boldsymbol{rr})}{2r^5} + \cdots \tag{12.3–23}$$

in which the expressions for the multipole moments are modified by the retardation effects:

$$C = \Sigma e_i \tag{12.3–24}$$

$$\boldsymbol{\mu} = \Sigma(e_i \boldsymbol{r}_i)_{t=t_0-\frac{r_{i\alpha}}{c}} \tag{12.3–25}$$

$$\mathsf{Q} = \Sigma_i e_i (3\boldsymbol{r}_i \boldsymbol{r}_i - r_i^2 \mathsf{U})_{t=t_0-\frac{r_{i\alpha}}{c}}$$

$$= 3\Theta - \mathsf{U}\Sigma_i (e_i r_i^2)_{t=t_0-\frac{r_{i\alpha}}{c}} \tag{12.3–26}$$

These quantities are the total charge, the dipole moment, and the quadrupole moment of the charge distribution.

After considerable manipulations, which utilize the equation of conservation of charge, Eq. 12.3–22 can be rewritten in the form[2]

$$\mathscr{A} = \frac{1}{cr}\frac{\partial \boldsymbol{\mu}}{\partial t} + \frac{[\boldsymbol{m} \times \boldsymbol{r}]}{r^3} + \frac{1}{2cr^3}\left(\frac{\partial \Theta}{\partial t} \cdot \boldsymbol{r}\right) + \cdots \tag{12.3–27}$$

[1] $\mathscr{A}$ and $i\mathscr{V}$ are sometimes combined to form the four-potential, which is particularly convenient for treating the interactions of radiation and matter relativistically. See *Riemann-Webers Differentialgleichungen in der Physik*, by P. Frank and R. von Mises, Vieweg, Braunschweig (1927), 7th Ed., Vol. II, Section IV (by A. Sommerfeld).

[2] J. H. Van Vleck, *Electric and Magnetic Susceptibility*, Oxford University Press (1932), p. 10.

Here $\boldsymbol{m}$ is the *magnetic dipole moment* of the set of charges and is defined by

$$\boldsymbol{m} = \frac{1}{2c} \Sigma_i \{e_i[\boldsymbol{r}_i \times \boldsymbol{v}_i]\}_{t=t_0-\frac{r_{i\alpha}}{c}} \tag{12.3–28}$$

and $\boldsymbol{\mu}$ and Θ are the dipole and quadrupole moments of the distribution just defined. In the expansion for $\mathscr{A}$ there are of course higher magnetic multipoles analogous to the higher electric multipoles. Under steady-state conditions the first and third terms in Eq. 12.3–27 are zero, and the series for $\mathscr{A}$ becomes similar to that for the electrostatic potential.

The magnetic field due to a group of charges is given by the curl of the vector potential in Eq. 12.3–27. According to Eq. 12.3–27, the three most predominant contributions to the $\mathscr{B}$ field are: (i) the magnetic field due to an oscillating electric dipole, (ii) the field due to the magnetic dipole, and (iii) the field due to an oscillating electric quadrupole. When currents are steady, the retardation effect is zero. Then the time derivatives of the electric moments are zero, and the expression for $\mathscr{B}$ reduces to

$$\mathscr{B} = 3\frac{(\boldsymbol{m} \cdot \boldsymbol{r})}{r^5}\boldsymbol{r} - \frac{\boldsymbol{m}}{r^3} \qquad \textit{(steady current)} \tag{12.3–29}$$

The magnetic moment corresponding to this expression is a special case of Eq. 12.3–28. If the field is produced by the steady flow of a current of magnitude i, then

$$\boldsymbol{m} = \frac{i}{2c}\oint [\boldsymbol{r} \times d\boldsymbol{s}] \qquad \textit{(steady current)} \tag{12.3–30}$$

is the magnetic dipole moment.

Inasmuch as the angular momentum, $\boldsymbol{L}$, of a particle is $m[\boldsymbol{r} \times \boldsymbol{v}]$, the magnetic moment of the particle, as given by Eq. 12.3–28, may be expressed (neglecting retardation) in the form

$$\boldsymbol{m} = \frac{e}{2c}[\boldsymbol{r} \times \boldsymbol{v}] = \frac{e}{2mc}\boldsymbol{L} \tag{12.3–31}$$

The proportionality of $\boldsymbol{m}$ and $\boldsymbol{L}$ is useful in relating the magnetic moment to the dynamics of a molecule.

c. The magnetization of matter

Because of the polarization of matter (discussed in § 12.2) and the analogous effect—the magnetization of matter—the electric and magnetic fields in matter do not satisfy the Maxwell equations for a vacuum. The molecules in a substance consist of moving charged particles which interact with the impressed electric and magnetic fields. The forces exerted on the molecules by the impressed fields tend to orient and distort the molecules, and, because of the motion of the charged particles, the molecules produce additional electric and magnetic fields, which add to the external impressed fields.

Let us consider a magnetic field in a vacuum due to a permanent magnet or a current in a loop of wire. It is possible to measure the force on a moving charge or a small test circuit (small loop of wire carrying a current). It is observed that the force changes if the space is filled with matter and that the force depends upon the nature of the medium. This experiment is analogous to the electrostatic case in which it is observed that the force on a charge between condenser plates depends upon the nature of the dielectric. The magnetic field causes the medium itself to produce an additional field which adds to the field due to the external sources.

Let us designate the contribution to the total magnetic field due to the external permanent magnets and currents by $\mathscr{H}$, in analogy with $\mathscr{D}$. The force exerted on a test circuit is determined by a field which is the sum of $\mathscr{H}$ and the field due to the magnetization of matter. This magnetic field which determines the force on a macroscopic body is defined to be the $\mathscr{B}$ field (in analogy with $\mathscr{E}$). A quantity known as the *magnetization* may be defined by

$$-4\pi\mathscr{M} = \mathscr{H} - \mathscr{B} \tag{12.3–32}$$

The magnetization is shown in § 12.4a to be the magnetic moment per unit volume. This corresponds to the definition of the polarization $\mathscr{P}$:

$$+4\pi\mathscr{P} = \mathscr{D} - \mathscr{E} \tag{12.3–33}$$

The negative sign is somewhat surprising, but as described in the next section, it is important for the physical interpretation of the quantities $\mathscr{M}$ and $\mathscr{P}$.

We may also define a quantity, the *permeability* μ', by

$$\mathscr{B} = \mu'\mathscr{H} \tag{12.3–34}$$

This is analogous to the definition of the dielectric constant ϵ', which is defined as

$$\mathscr{D} = \epsilon'\mathscr{E} \tag{12.3–35}$$

Both μ' and ϵ' are really tensor quantities, but in an isotropic medium they may be considered scalar quantities. They are closely related to the quantities $\mathscr{M}$ and $\mathscr{P}$, and are properties of the material medium. Both μ' and ϵ' are unity in a vacuum.

The subjects of magnetization of matter and magnetic susceptibilities are discussed at considerable length in the next section. The primary reason for introducing the $\mathscr{H}$ and $\mathscr{B}$ fields at this point is so that we may write Maxwell's equations for a material medium.

d. Maxwell's equations for a material medium

Maxwell's equations described earlier in this section apply only to the fields in a vacuum. It may be shown by the methods discussed below that the fields in a material medium satisfy a similar set of equations:

$$\left(\frac{\partial}{\partial \mathbf{r}} \cdot \mathscr{D}\right) = 4\pi\rho \tag{12.3–36}$$

$$\left(\frac{\partial}{\partial \mathbf{r}} \cdot \mathscr{B}\right) = 0 \tag{12.3–37}$$

$$\left[\frac{\partial}{\partial \mathbf{r}} \times \mathscr{E}\right] = -\frac{1}{c}\frac{\partial \mathscr{B}}{\partial t} \tag{12.3–38}$$

$$\left[\frac{\partial}{\partial \mathbf{r}} \times \mathscr{H}\right] = +\frac{1}{c}\left\{\frac{\partial \mathscr{D}}{\partial t} + 4\pi \mathbf{j}\right\} \tag{12.3–39}$$

These equations, along with Eqs. 12.3–34 and 35 serve to specify the four vectors $\mathscr{D}$, $\mathscr{E}$, $\mathscr{H}$, and $\mathscr{B}$ uniquely if, in addition, it is required that ϵ' and μ' be independent of space and time, except at the boundaries between dielectrics.

We may now introduce the scalar and vector potentials defined by Eqs. 12.3–15 and 16. If $\mathscr{A}$ and $\mathscr{V}$ are related by the equation

$$\frac{\mu'\epsilon'}{c}\frac{\partial}{\partial t}\mathscr{V} + \left(\frac{\partial}{\partial \mathbf{r}} \cdot \mathscr{A}\right) = 0 \tag{12.3–40}$$

then direct substitution into Maxwell's equations for a material medium yields the following equations for the potentials:

$$\left(\frac{\partial}{\partial \mathbf{r}} \cdot \frac{\partial}{\partial \mathbf{r}}\right)\mathscr{A} - \frac{\mu'\epsilon'}{c^2}\frac{\partial^2}{\partial t^2}\mathscr{A} = -\frac{4\pi\mu'}{c}\rho\mathbf{v} \tag{12.3–41}$$

$$\left(\frac{\partial}{\partial \mathbf{r}} \cdot \frac{\partial}{\partial \mathbf{r}}\right)\mathscr{V} - \frac{\mu'\epsilon'}{c^2}\frac{\partial^2}{\partial t^2}\mathscr{V} = -\frac{4\pi\rho}{\epsilon'} \tag{12.3–42}$$

From the Maxwell equations the following relation may be developed for the conservation of electromagnetic energy:

$$\frac{\partial}{\partial t}I + \left(\frac{\partial}{\partial \mathbf{r}} \cdot \mathbf{S}\right) = -(\rho\mathbf{v} \cdot \mathscr{E}) \tag{12.3–43}$$

Here I is the *energy density* of the electromagnetic field and $\mathbf{S}$ is the *Poynting vector* or flux of *electromagnetic energy*, defined by

$$I = \frac{1}{8\pi}\{(\mathscr{B} \cdot \mathscr{H}) + (\mathscr{D} \cdot \mathscr{E})\} \tag{12.3–44}$$

$$\mathbf{S} = \frac{c}{4\pi}[\mathscr{E} \times \mathscr{H}] \tag{12.3–45}$$

The term $(\rho\mathbf{v} \cdot \mathscr{E})$ represents the work which the field does on the charges in a unit volume in a unit time. Equation 12.3–43 leads to the notion of electromagnetic momentum and radiation pressure.

In regions of space free from macroscopic charges and currents, Maxwell's equations can be rearranged into the form of the wave equations:

$$\left(\frac{\partial}{\partial \mathbf{r}} \cdot \frac{\partial}{\partial \mathbf{r}}\right) \mathscr{E} = \frac{\mu'\epsilon'}{c^2}\frac{\partial^2 \mathscr{E}}{\partial t^2} \tag{12.3–46}$$

$$\left(\frac{\partial}{\partial \mathbf{r}} \cdot \frac{\partial}{\partial \mathbf{r}}\right) \mathscr{B} = \frac{\mu'\epsilon'}{c^2}\frac{\partial^2 \mathscr{B}}{\partial t^2} \tag{12.3–47}$$

This form of the equations leads directly to the properties of electromagnetic waves. Since the index of refraction, η, is defined as the ratio of the velocity of light in a vacuum to the velocity of light in a medium, it follows directly from these two equations that

$$\eta = \sqrt{\mu'\epsilon'} \tag{12.3–48}$$

Usually μ' is very nearly unity so that η is approximately equal to $\sqrt{\epsilon'}$. The intensity of an electromagnetic wave is usually defined as the absolute value of the time average of the Poynting vector.

In order to study the behavior of the electric and magnetic fields in a material medium, it is possible to employ two approaches. In the *microscopic approach*, the Maxwell equations written for a vacuum are used, and the various charges making up the medium are considered individually. The polarization and magnetization of the matter are accounted for microscopically. If we knew the positions and velocities of all the elementary charges within a medium, this approach would yield the complete detailed structure of the electric and magnetic fields. Such fields would be rapidly fluctuating in space and time and would be of little value in most applications. In the *macroscopic approach*, on the other hand, the Maxwell equations written for a material medium are used, and the polarization and magnetization of the matter is taken into account on a bulk basis by means of the quantities μ' and ϵ'. When such an approach is used, we take into account only macroscopic charged bodies and currents, and the resulting description of the fields is also macroscopic.

Let us now consider the relation between the solutions which are obtained by the two approaches, and the interpretation of the quantities $\mathscr{M}$ and $\mathscr{P}$ introduced above. The solution to the two problems can be written in terms of the scalar and vector potentials. Let us first consider the solution to the microscopic problem. The potentials may be averaged over a small region of space, that is, small with respect to any macroscopic variations but large enough to contain many molecules. The result of this smoothing is a new function which now exhibits macroscopic variations only. It can be shown[3] that this new function is the same as we would obtain through the direct solution of the macroscopic Maxwell equations. Also, through this averaging process, the quantities $\mathscr{P}$ and $\mathscr{M}$ may be identified with the microscopic properties of the medium. It is shown that $\mathscr{P}$ is the total electric dipole moment of the molecules per unit volume and $\mathscr{M}$ is the total magnetic moment of the molecules per unit volume. As discussed in the next section, we may also relate $\mathscr{M}$ to the molecular magnetic moment by a method completely analogous to that used in § 12.2 in discussing the corresponding electrostatic problem. These results are a justification of the Maxwell equations for a material medium.

4. Magnetization of Matter and the Magnetic Susceptibility

In this section we consider the magnetic analogy of the discussion given in § 12.2 for electrostatics. We first discuss the behavior of the $\mathscr{H}$ and $\mathscr{B}$ fields at the boundary between two substances and show how these fields are related to the magnetization vector, $\mathscr{M}$. We then discuss the local field $\mathscr{B}^{(\mathrm{loc})}$ which is experienced by a single molecule in a medium. Finally a discussion of the magnetic susceptibility is given.

The magnetic susceptibility is useful in determining the magnetic moments of the individual molecules. These moments provide a key to the structure of the molecules. When the substance is paramagnetic, indicating that the molecules possess permanent magnetic moments, magnetic dipole-dipole forces may play an important role in the intermolecular forces.

a. The $\mathscr{H}$ and $\mathscr{B}$ fields

The differential relations for the $\mathscr{H}$ and $\mathscr{B}$ fields are the Maxwell equations for a material medium (Eqs. 12.3–37, 39). Under steady-state

[3] J. H. Van Vleck, *The Theory of Electric and Magnetic Susceptibilities*, Oxford University Press (1932), p. 10.

conditions, the "displacement current" may be neglected and the relations assume the form

$$\left(\frac{\partial}{\partial \boldsymbol{r}} \cdot \mathscr{B}\right) = 0 \tag{12.4–1}$$

$$\left[\frac{\partial}{\partial \boldsymbol{r}} \times \mathscr{H}\right] = \frac{4\pi}{c}\boldsymbol{j} \tag{12.4–2}$$

These relations apply in the interior of a material medium.

By the application of Green's theorem to the first of these relations and Stokes' theorem to the second, the following integral expressions may be obtained:

$$\int (\mathscr{B} \cdot d\boldsymbol{S}) = 0 \tag{12.4–3}$$

$$\oint (\mathscr{H} \cdot d\boldsymbol{s}) = \frac{4\pi}{c}\int (\boldsymbol{j} \cdot d\boldsymbol{S}) = \frac{4\pi}{c} i \tag{12.4–4}$$

in which i is the total current passing through a surface bounded by the contour over which the line integral is taken. At the boundary between two media 1 and 2 (or between a material medium and a vacuum), there may be a surface density of current (or current per unit length normal to the flow) $\boldsymbol{j}^{(s)}$. From the above integral expressions, it may be shown that at the boundary between the media, the following conditions are satisfied by the vectors $\mathscr{B}$ and $\mathscr{H}$:

$$(\boldsymbol{n} \cdot \{\mathscr{B}^{(2)} - \mathscr{B}^{(1)}\}) = 0 \tag{12.4–5}$$

$$(\boldsymbol{n} \times \{\mathscr{H}^{(2)} - \mathscr{H}^{(1)}\}) = \frac{4\pi}{c}\boldsymbol{j}^{(s)} \tag{12.4–6}$$

where $\boldsymbol{n}$ is a unit vector normal to the surface in the direction of 1 to 2. These equations are analogous to Eqs. 12.2–9, 10.

In order to obtain the relation between the $\mathscr{H}$ and $\mathscr{B}$ fields and the magnetization, $\mathscr{M}$, let us consider a simple experiment somewhat similar to that described in § 12.2b. Let us consider a long cylinder of dielectric surrounded by a coil of wire carrying a current (or more ideally, with a surface current on the outside surface). For simplicity let us consider an isotropic medium so that the $\mathscr{H}$ and $\mathscr{B}$ fields are parallel. Let us remove the material within a region of space bounded by a cylinder of length L and radius R within the dielectric with its axis parallel to the field. It is assumed that the dimensions of this cylinder are large compared to the molecular dimensions. The geometry is shown in Fig. 12.4–1. Then we inquire as to that nature of the surface currents which must be introduced in order that the force on a macroscopic test loop of current inside the cavity should be the same as before the material was removed.

The magnetic dipole moment of these currents is then the same as that of the removed material. The expressions given in Eqs. 12.4–5 and 6 may be applied to the cavity to obtain the relations:

$$\mathscr{B}^{(o)} - \mathscr{B}^{(i)} = 0 \qquad \textit{(end of cylinder)} \qquad (12.4\text{–}7)$$

$$\mathscr{H}^{(o)} - \mathscr{H}^{(i)} = \frac{4\pi}{c} j^{(s)} \qquad \textit{(sides of cylinder)} \qquad (12.4\text{–}8)$$

in which the superscripts i and o designate the quantities inside and outside the surface of the cavity, and $j^{(s)}$ represents the magnitude of a surface current circulating around the cylinder in the direction indicated in Fig. 12.4–1.

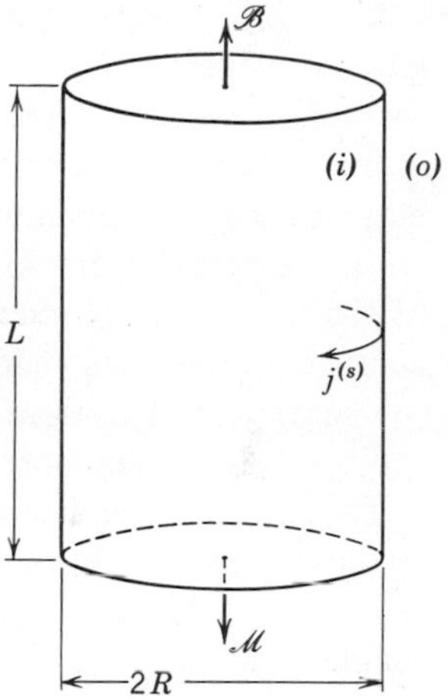

Fig. 12.4–1. A cavity in a material medium.

Since it is assumed that the force on a moving macroscopic charge inside the cylindrical cavity is the same as before the formation of the cavity and since there is no matter inside the cavity,

$$\mathscr{B}^{(i)} = \mathscr{H}^{(i)} - \mathscr{B} \qquad (12.4\text{–}9)$$

where $\mathscr{B}$ is the value before the formation of the cavity. Furthermore, because of the choice of the shape of the cavity,

$$\mathscr{H}^{(o)} = \mathscr{H} \qquad (12.4\text{–}10)$$

where $\mathscr{H}$ is the value before the formation of the cavity. Hence it is necessary to introduce a surface current of magnitude

$$j^{(s)} = \frac{c}{4\pi}(\mathscr{H} - \mathscr{B}) \qquad (12.4\text{–}11)$$

Since the total current i around the surface is $Lj^{(s)}$, according to Eq. 12.3–30 the magnetic moment associated with this current has the magnitude

$$m = \frac{\pi R^2 L}{c} j^{(s)} \qquad (12.4\text{–}12)$$

but in the direction opposite to that of the field. The magnetization vector $\mathscr{M}$, which is the magnetic moment per unit volume, is then obtained from the last two equations and is related to $\mathscr{H}$ and $\mathscr{B}$ by

$$-4\pi\mathscr{M} = \mathscr{H} - \mathscr{B} \qquad (12.4\text{–}13)$$

This expression is identical with Eq. 12.3–32 and indicates that the interpretation of $\mathscr{M}$ given in the last section is correct.

b. The local field, $\mathscr{B}^{(\mathrm{loc})}$

In the discussion just presented, a relation was found between the $\mathscr{H}$ and $\mathscr{B}$ fields and the magnetization $\mathscr{M}$. It should be kept in mind that the $\mathscr{B}$ field there described is associated with the force on a *macroscopic* test circuit. We now discuss the field which is experienced by an individual molecule.[1] We call this field $\mathscr{B}^{(\mathrm{loc})}$, by analogy with the corresponding electric field $\mathscr{E}^{(\mathrm{loc})}$.

In order to determine the magnetic field acting on a particular molecule, let us consider a long cylindrical coil of wire (of length L and radius R) carrying a current. The magnetic fields within the cylinder are parallel in the limit that $L \gg R$. Within this cylinder let there be placed a material with molecules containing permanent magnetic dipoles of moment $\boldsymbol{m}$. The total magnetic dipole moment of a molecule, $\boldsymbol{m}^{(\mathrm{tot})}$, is the sum of the permanent moment $\boldsymbol{m}$ and the induced moment $\boldsymbol{m}^{(\mathrm{ind})}$. The time average of the total magnetic dipole moment $\overline{\boldsymbol{m}}^{(\mathrm{tot})}$ is a vector in the z (or negative z) direction, that is in the direction of the impressed field (or the opposite). The magnetization $\mathscr{M}$ is equal to $n\overline{\boldsymbol{m}}^{(\mathrm{tot})}$.

The magnetic field on a molecule inside the coil is the sum of that due to the impressed field $\mathscr{H}$ and that due to the magnetization of the material within the cylinder. Again let us consider the isotropic case so that the magnetization of the matter is parallel to the field. The situation is very similar to the problem discussed in § 12.2c in connection with the analogous electrical problem. We determine the field at the origin due to magnetic dipoles placed at the center of each of the molecules in the material. The result is an expression very similar to Eq. 12.2–19:

$$\mathscr{B}_z^{(\mathrm{loc})} = \mathscr{H}_z + n\int_{\mathrm{cyl}} g(r)\, \mathscr{H}_z^{\,1}\, d\boldsymbol{r} \tag{12.4–14}$$

in which $g(r)$ is the radial distribution function, n is the number density and $\mathscr{H}_z^{\,1}$ is the field at the origin due to one magnetic dipole,

$$\mathscr{H}_z^{\,1} = -\frac{\partial}{\partial z}\left(\frac{\overline{\boldsymbol{m}}^{(\mathrm{tot})} \cdot \boldsymbol{r}}{r^3}\right) \tag{12.4–15}$$

The evaluation of this expression for $\mathscr{B}_z^{(\mathrm{loc})}$ may be performed in a manner similar to the evaluation of the corresponding integral for $\mathscr{E}_z^{(\mathrm{loc})}$. However, after the analog of Eq. 12.2–21 is obtained, a different limiting value must be selected. In order to obtain a parallel magnetic field within a coil and to eliminate edge effects, it is necessary to take $L \gg R$

[1] An alternative derivation and a good discussion of $\mathscr{B}^{(\mathrm{loc})}$ is given by J. Frenkel, *Lehrbuch der Elektrodynamik*, Julius Springer (1928), Vol. II, Section 4, p. 67.

(instead of $L \ll R$, as in the electrostatic case). This leads to a different result:

$$\int_{V(s)} \mathscr{H}_z^{\,1}\, d\boldsymbol{r} \cong +\frac{4\pi}{3}\,\overline{m}_z^{(\text{tot})} \tag{12.4–16}$$

so that the final expressions for $\mathscr{B}^{(\text{loc})}$ are

$$\mathscr{B}^{(\text{loc})} = \mathscr{H} + \frac{4\pi}{3}\, n\overline{\boldsymbol{m}}^{(\text{tot})} = \mathscr{H} + \frac{4\pi}{3}\,\mathscr{M} \tag{12.4–17}$$

$$\mathscr{B}^{(\text{loc})} = \mathscr{B} - \frac{8\pi}{3}\,\mathscr{M} \tag{12.4–18}$$

The derivation of Eq. 12.4–17 is analogous to Eq. 12.2–22; and Eq. 12.4–18 is analogous to Eq. 12.2–23. The origins of these two sets of equations are quite different because of the different boundary conditions that are applied in the two cases. Thus we come out with the surprising result that, as far as the local fields are concerned, $\mathscr{B}$ and $\mathscr{D}$ would seem to play a corresponding role. Whereas from the standpoint of the physical significance of the fields, $\mathscr{B}$ and $\mathscr{E}$ play corresponding roles.

c. The magnetic susceptibility in terms of the magnetic permeability

The magnetic susceptibility per molecule and the magnetic permeability are defined analogously to the electric susceptibility and the dielectric constant:

$$\overline{\boldsymbol{m}}^{(\text{tot})} = \chi^{(m)}\,\mathscr{B}^{(\text{loc})} \tag{12.4–19}$$

$$\mathscr{B} = \mu'\,\mathscr{H} \tag{12.4–20}$$

In a non-isotropic medium $\mathscr{B}$ and $\mathscr{H}$ are not in the same direction, and then μ' and $\chi^{(m)}$ are tensors. If n is the number density of molecules in the medium, the relation between the magnetic susceptibility per molecule and the magnetic permeability is

$$\chi^{(m)} = \frac{3}{4\pi n}\left(\frac{\mu' - 1}{\mu' + 2}\right) \tag{12.4–21}$$

This is the magnetic analog to the Clausius-Mosotti equation. The susceptibility per mole is $\tilde{N}\chi^{(m)}$.

There is an important difference between electric and magnetic susceptibility in that ϵ' is always greater than unity (and $\chi^{(e)}$ is always positive) whereas μ' may be either greater or less than unity (and $\chi^{(m)}$ may be positive or negative). Those substances for which μ' is less than unity are called *diamagnetic*. For such materials, μ' is so close to unity that

$\mathscr{B}^{(\text{loc})}$ is very nearly equal to $\mathscr{B}$, and the distinction scarcely needs to be made. In this case the susceptibility per molecule is given by

$$\chi^{(m)} \doteq \frac{1}{4\pi n}(\mu' - 1) \qquad \textit{(diamagnetic substances)} \qquad (12.4\text{–}22)$$

The negative susceptibility of diamagnetic substances occurs since, because of Larmor precession, a magnetic field induces a moment in the molecules in a direction opposite to that of the field.

If, on the other hand, the molecules possess permanent magnetic dipole moments, the field tends to align the molecules in the direction of the field, so that $\chi^{(m)}$ is positive and μ' is greater than unity. This case is referred to as *paramagnetism*.

The average magnetic dipole moment of the molecules and the magnetic susceptibility may be calculated in terms of molecular properties in much the same manner as that discussed in connection with the electrical case in § 12.2e. It is easily seen that in analogy with Eq. 12.2–35 the average magnetic dipole moment per molecule is in the z-direction and has the magnitude

$$\overline{m}^{(\text{tot})} = m^{(\text{ind})} + mL(m\mathscr{B}^{(\text{loc})}/kT) \qquad (12.4\text{–}23)$$

Here $L(x)$ is the Langevin function.[2] If the molecules possess no permanent magnetic dipole moments, the second term is zero, and the average moment is simply the induced moment. This leads to the negative susceptibility of diamagnetic substances since the induced moment is negative, that is, in the direction opposite to that of the field.

If the molecule possesses a permanent magnetic dipole, the first term is usually negligible, and the average moment depends essentially only on the alignment of the permanent dipoles. For small values of the argument, the Langevin function may be expanded and we obtain from Eq. 12.4–23 the result that for either a small field or a high temperature

$$\overline{m}^{(\text{tot})} = \frac{m^2}{3kT}\mathscr{B}^{(\text{loc})} \qquad (12.4\text{–}24)$$

$$\mathscr{M} = \frac{nm^2}{3kT}\mathscr{B}^{(\text{loc})} \qquad (12.4\text{–}25)$$

Thus for low field strength or high temperature the susceptibility is proportional to $1/T$, and the proportionality constant is a measure of the permanent magnetic dipole moment. Making use of the expression for

[2] At low temperatures the Langevin function has to be replaced by the Brillouin function to take into account the discrete nature of the rotational energy states. See Van Vleck, *Electric and Magnetic Susceptibilities*, Oxford University Press (1932), p. 257.

$\mathscr{B}^{(\mathrm{loc})}$, Eq. 12.4–17 and Eq. 12.4–25, we find that

$$\frac{\mathscr{M}}{\mathscr{H}} = \frac{3}{4\pi} \frac{\theta}{T - \theta} \tag{12.4–26}$$

where

$$\theta = \frac{4\pi}{9} \frac{nm^2}{k} \tag{12.4–27}$$

is known as the Curie temperature.

The Weiss theory[3] of *ferromagnetism* is based on Eq. 12.4–23. Above the Curie temperature, θ, a substance whose molecules have permanent magnetic moments, is paramagnetic. Below the Curie temperature there is spontaneous magnetization, that is, the magnetization is not zero in the absence of a field. This condition is referred to as ferromagnetism. If $\mathscr{H}$ is zero, Eq. 12.4–23 can be written in the form:

$$aT/\theta = 3L(a) \tag{12.4–28}$$

where

$$a = \left(\frac{3\theta}{T}\right) \frac{\overline{m}^{(\mathrm{tot})}}{m} \tag{12.4–29}$$

But $3L(a)/a$ decreases monotonically from unity when a is zero to zero when a is infinite. Therefore, when $T < \theta$, there exists a value of a, and hence a value of $\overline{m}^{(\mathrm{tot})}$, different from zero such that Eq. 12.4–28 is satisfied. However, when $T > \theta$, the only solution to Eq. 12.4–28 is $a = 0$ (hence, $\overline{m}^{(\mathrm{tot})} = 0$) and therefore, there is no possibility of spontaneous magnetization.

Although this classical theory gives a qualitative description of ferromagnetism, quantitative results depend upon the anomalous behavior of electron spins and their coupling. It is interesting to note that the existence of the Curie temperature depends on the sign of the term in Eq. 12.4–17 which is added to $\mathscr{H}$ to obtain $\mathscr{B}^{(\mathrm{loc})}$. The sign of the analogous term in the electric case is opposite, and hence no electrical analog of ferromagnetism exists.

5. Classical Theory of Light Absorption and the Index of Refraction

There are two types of long-range intermolecular forces: the electrostatic forces (such as dipole-dipole forces) and the "dispersion" or London forces (such as the inverse seventh-power attractive forces between nonpolar molecules). These dispersion forces are closely related to the emission and absorption of light by the molecules. In this and the following section, the classical and quantum theories of the polarizability and index of refraction are developed. The results are expressed in terms

[3] E. C. Stoner, *Magnetism*, Methuen (1946), p. 70.

of "oscillator strengths," f_i, and "characteristic frequencies," ν_i. In § 13.3 the dispersion forces are expressed in terms of these quantities. From a study of the index of refraction as a function of frequency, the f_i and ν_i can be determined. These quantities can, in turn, be used to predict forces between non-polar molecules. This section starts with a discussion of the electric and magnetic field produced by the Hertzian oscillator (or oscillating dipole), which represents an idealization of an antenna or source of light. We then discuss the motion of a charged particle in an electromagnetic field. These two topics provide the necessary background material for the classical and quantum mechanical treatments of the interaction of light and matter.

a. The oscillating dipole (the Hertzian oscillator)

Let us consider the radiation given off by a charge $+e$ which oscillates in a vacuum about another (fixed) charge $-e$. Let the oscillation take place along a line, with amplitude A and frequency $\nu = c/\lambda$. This "oscillating dipole" is the simplest example of an electromagnetic radiator and represents a radio antenna or source of light. The electromagnetic behavior of this system may be obtained by the solution of Eqs. 12.3–18, 19. We do not discuss the solutions of these equations here, but discuss briefly the results for the two limiting cases $r \ll \lambda$ and $r \gg \lambda$.

It may be shown[1] that in the neighborhood of the oscillator ($r \ll \lambda$) the $\mathscr{E}$ field is the same as the static field resulting from a dipole of strength $\mu = eA \cos(2\pi ct/\lambda)$. The corresponding $\mathscr{H}$ field is the same as the static magnetic field produced by a current element

$$i = \frac{d}{dt}\left[eA \cos(2\pi ct/\lambda)\right]$$

Far away from the oscillator ($r \gg \lambda$) the components of the $\mathscr{E}$ and $\mathscr{H}$ fields are

$$\begin{cases} \mathscr{E}_\theta = -\dfrac{\pi e A}{\lambda^2 r} \sin\theta \cos\dfrac{2\pi}{\lambda}(r - ct) \\ \mathscr{E}_r = 0 \qquad \mathscr{E}_\phi = 0 \end{cases} \tag{12.5–1a}$$

$$\begin{cases} \mathscr{H}_\phi = -\dfrac{\pi e A}{\lambda^2 r} \sin\theta \cos\dfrac{2\pi}{\lambda}(r - ct) \\ \mathscr{H}_r = 0 \qquad \mathscr{H}_\theta = 0 \end{cases} \tag{12.5–1b}$$

[1] See, for example, M. Abraham and R. Becker, *Electricity and Magnetism*, Blackie & Son, Ltd., London (1947), p. 223. G. Joos, *Theoretical Physics*, Hafner, New York (1934), p. 325. An excellent treatment of the electromagnetic theory of light and of optics is given by M. Born, *Optik*, Edwards (1943).

Inasmuch as $\mathscr{E}_\theta = \mathscr{H}_\phi$ and all of the other components of $\mathscr{E}$ and $\mathscr{H}$ are zero, the magnetic field intensity is perpendicular to the electric field intensity and equal to it in magnitude. Furthermore, there is no component of $\mathscr{E}$ or $\mathscr{H}$ in the direction of the propagation of the radiation, $\boldsymbol{r}$. At sufficiently large distances away from a Hertzian oscillator, therefore, $\mathscr{E}$ and $\mathscr{H}$ form a plane traveling electromagnetic wave.

It may be shown that the electromagnetic field at large distances from any set of moving charges (with no net charge) may be represented as due to a collection of Hertzian oscillators of different frequencies and oscillating in different directions. Therefore the electromagnetic radiation in field-free space consists of a set of superimposed waves of different frequencies traveling in different directions and with different polarizations. For each of these waves, the electric field $\mathscr{E}$ and the magnetic field $\mathscr{H}$ are equal in magnitude and normal to one another.

The polarization of light is defined, by convention, in terms of the plane containing $\mathscr{E}$ and $\boldsymbol{r}$. The light is *plane polarized* if this plane remains invariant. The light is *elliptically polarized* if $\mathscr{E}_x = \mathscr{E}_1 \sin \frac{2\pi}{\lambda}(z - ct)$ and $\mathscr{E}_y = \mathscr{E}_2 \cos \frac{2\pi}{\lambda}(z - ct)$. *Circular polarization* is the special case of elliptic polarization such that $\mathscr{E}_1 = \mathscr{E}_2$.

Later in this section and in several subsequent discussions, we describe the behavior of a molecule in an electromagnetic field. It is assumed that the wavelength of the light is large compared with the dimensions of the molecule and that the molecule is at a distance of many wavelengths from the source. Under these conditions, the electric intensity is, to a good approximation, uniform throughout the molecule. For light polarized in the x-direction and propagated in the z-direction, the only non-vanishing components of the vector fields are the x-component of $\mathscr{E}$ and the y-component of $\mathscr{H}$. The fields acting in the molecular domain are, then,

$$\mathscr{E}_x = \mathscr{E}_0 \sin 2\pi\nu t \qquad (12.5\text{–}2a)$$

$$\mathscr{H}_y = \mathscr{E}_0 \sin 2\pi\nu t \qquad (12.5\text{–}2b)$$

The energy density, I, of electromagnetic radiation is, according to Eq. 12.3–44, the mean value of

$$I = \frac{1}{8\pi}\{\mathscr{E}^2 + \mathscr{H}^2\} \qquad (12.5\text{–}3)$$

Since the mean value of $\mathscr{E}^2$ or $\mathscr{H}^2$ is

$$\lim_{\tau\to\infty} \mathscr{E}_0^2 \frac{1}{\tau}\int_0^\tau \sin^2(2\pi ct/\lambda)\,dt = \tfrac{1}{2}\mathscr{E}_0^2 \qquad (12.5\text{–}4)$$

where $\mathscr{E}_0$ is the amplitude of the oscillations in the electric or magnetic field. Thus the averaged energy density is:

$$\bar{I} = \frac{1}{8\pi} \mathscr{E}_0^2 \tag{12.5–5}$$

In this case the intensity of the electromagnetic wave or energy flux is *cI*.

b. The equation of motion of charged particles

Let us consider the molecules in a gas sufficiently dilute that the polarization can be neglected so that $\mathscr{E}^{(\text{loc})} = \mathscr{E} = \mathscr{D}$ and $\mathscr{B}^{(\text{loc})} = \mathscr{B} = \mathscr{H}$. The charged particles, electrons and nuclei, within the molecule are acted on by external fields and by the forces due to other particles within the molecule. Let $\mathscr{V}_i$ and $\mathscr{A}_i$ be the scalar and vector potentials evaluated at the position of the ith particle. Let us assume further that the force on a charged particle due to the other particles in the molecule results solely from the electrostatic (coulombic) interactions.[2] Hence this force is given by the negative of the gradient of Φ, the potential energy of the molecule. In terms of these quantities the force on the ith particle with charge e_i in a molecule is

$$\boldsymbol{F}_i = -\frac{\partial}{\partial \boldsymbol{r}_i}\Phi - e_i \frac{\partial}{\partial \boldsymbol{r}_i}\mathscr{V}_i - \frac{e_i}{c}\frac{\partial}{\partial t}\mathscr{A}_i + \frac{e_i}{c}\left[\boldsymbol{v}_i \times \left[\frac{\partial}{\partial \boldsymbol{r}} \times \mathscr{A}_i\right]\right] \tag{12.5–6}$$

Although this force field is not conservative, it is possible to construct a Lagrangian so that the equations of motion can be written in the form given in Eq. 1.4–4. This Lagrangian is[3]

$$L = \tfrac{1}{2}\textstyle\sum_i m v_i^2 - \Phi - \sum_i e_i \mathscr{V}_i + \sum_i \frac{e_i}{c}(\boldsymbol{v}_i \cdot \mathscr{A}_i) \tag{12.5–7}$$

and leads to generalized momenta (Eq. 1.4–5) which differ from the usual quantities. For example, in Cartesian coordinates

$$\boldsymbol{p}_i = m_i \boldsymbol{v}_i + \frac{e_i}{c}\mathscr{A}_i \tag{12.5–8}$$

From the Lagrangian, the Hamiltonian function may be formed according to Eq. 1.4–6. In Cartesian coordinates the function is

$$H = \textstyle\sum_i \frac{1}{2m_i}\left(\boldsymbol{p}_i - \frac{e_i}{c}\mathscr{A}_i\right)^2 + \Phi + \sum_i e_i \mathscr{V}_i \tag{12.5–9}$$

[2] The assumption of only coulombic interactions is equivalent to ignoring the small magnetic interactions between the electrons in the molecule due to their motions and spins.

[3] J. H. Van Vleck, *Electric and Magnetic Susceptibilities*, Oxford University Press (1932), pp. 19, et seq.

The Hamiltonian can be expressed in terms of $\mathscr{E}$ and $\mathscr{H}$ instead of $\mathscr{V}$ and $\mathscr{A}$. Then if the coordinates (not necessarily Cartesian) are defined independently of $\mathscr{E}$ and $\mathscr{H}$ and if both these vector fields are constant in both space and time, it can be shown[3] that the components of the dipole moments $\boldsymbol{\mu}$ and $\boldsymbol{m}$ in the direction of the applied fields are given by

$$\mu = -\frac{\partial H}{\partial \mathscr{E}} \qquad m = -\frac{\partial H}{\partial \mathscr{H}} \tag{12.5–10}$$

These relations are useful in determining the electric and magnetic moments of a molecule by calculating its energy in the presence of an external field.

Use may be made of the results of the Hertzian oscillator discussion to introduce a simplifying assumption in the expression given in Eq. 12.5–6 for the force on a charged particle. It was shown that at a large distance from a Hertzian oscillator the electric and magnetic field strengths have the same magnitude. It follows from this and from Eq. 12.3–4 that the magnetic force is smaller than the electrical force in the ratio v/c. In an atom or molecule the velocity of electrons in an atom or molecule is of the order of 1/137 times the velocity of light. Consequently, the effect of the $\mathscr{H}$ field can in such cases be neglected, and Eq. 12.5–6 may be replaced by

$$\boldsymbol{F}_i \doteq -\frac{\partial}{\partial \boldsymbol{r}_i}\Phi - e_i \frac{\partial}{\partial \boldsymbol{r}_i}\mathscr{V}_i \tag{12.5–11}$$

The examples we consider in this and the next section make use of this simplification.

c. The index of refraction (Drude's theory)[4]

A classical theory of the index of refraction of light was developed by Drude. This theory has been taken over into quantum mechanics with only minor changes, as discussed in the next section. The molecular model used in this theory is as follows. The molecule is regarded as a set of particles of charge e_i and mass m_i. Each of these particles is harmonically and isotropically bound to its individual equilibrium position. The force constant for the ith particle is k_i, its frequency of vibration is $\nu_i = (1/2\pi)\sqrt{k_i/m_i}$, and its displacement from the equilibrium position is $\delta \boldsymbol{r}_i = \boldsymbol{r}_i - \boldsymbol{r}_i^{(0)}$. The potential energy of the molecule is then $\Phi = \frac{1}{2}\sum_i k_i(\delta r_i)^2$.

Let us now imagine that the molecule is placed in a beam of light (an alternating electromagnetic field) of frequency ν_0 sufficiently low that the wavelength $\lambda_0 = c/\nu_0$ is large compared to the size of the molecule.

[4] P. K. L. Drude, *The Theory of Optics*, Longmans, Green, London (1933).

The external electric field is then essentially uniform throughout the molecule and has the intensity $\mathscr{E} = \mathscr{E}_0 \cos 2\pi\nu_0 t$. The force on the ith particle in the molecule is then given by Eq. 12.5–11:

$$\boldsymbol{F}_i = -k_i \boldsymbol{\delta r}_i + e_i \mathscr{E}_0 \cos 2\pi\nu_0 t \tag{12.5–12}$$

According to Newton's second law the equation of motion of the ith particle is, then,

$$m_i \frac{d^2}{dt^2} \boldsymbol{\delta r}_i + k_i\, \boldsymbol{\delta r}_i = e_i \mathscr{E}_0 \cos 2\pi\nu_0 t \tag{12.5–13}$$

After a sufficiently long time (so that the transients have decayed) the solution to this equation is independent of the initial conditions and is[5]

$$\boldsymbol{\delta r}_i = \left(\frac{e_i}{4\pi^2 m_i}\right) \frac{\mathscr{E}_0 \cos 2\pi\nu_0 t}{(\nu_i^2 - \nu_0^2)} \tag{12.5–14}$$

This gives the displacement of the ith particle in a molecule due to a varying impressed electric field.

From this last result may be obtained the induced electric dipole moment as a function of time:

$$\boldsymbol{\mu}^{(\text{ind})} = \textstyle\sum_i e_i\, \boldsymbol{\delta r}_i = \mathscr{E}_0 \cos 2\pi\nu_0 t \cdot \dfrac{1}{4\pi^2} \textstyle\sum_i \dfrac{e_i^2}{m_i(\nu_i^2 - \nu_0^2)} \tag{12.5–15}$$

Since the induced dipole moment is in the direction of the field, the polarizability, α, defined by Eq. 12.2–1, is a scalar equal to $\mu^{(\text{ind})}/\mathscr{E}$. Hence we obtain an expression for the polarizability of the molecule in terms of the properties of its constituent particles:

$$\alpha(\nu_0) = \frac{1}{4\pi^2} \sum_i \frac{e_i^2}{m_i(\nu_i^2 - \nu_0^2)} \tag{12.5–16a}$$

The polarizability is thus a function of the frequency, ν_0, of the incident radiation. The polarizability of a molecule in an electric field which does not vary with time is given by

$$\alpha(0) = \frac{1}{4\pi^2} \textstyle\sum_i e_i^2/(m_i \nu_i^2) \tag{12.5–16b}$$

The expression for the polarizability is often written in terms of *oscillator strengths*, f_i, which are defined as

$$f_i = \frac{e_i^2/m_i}{e^2/m} \tag{12.5–17}$$

in which e and m are the charge and mass of an electron. The classical interpretation of the f values is the effective number of electrons oscillating

[5] For a discussion of equations of this type, see, for example, G. Joos, *Theoretical Physics*, Hafner (1932).

with a characteristic frequency. In terms of these quantities

$$\alpha(\nu_0) = \frac{e^2}{4\pi^2 m} \sum_i \frac{f_i}{\nu_i^2 - \nu_0^2} \tag{12.5–18}$$

is the polarizability of a molecule.

If the molecules have no permanent dipole moment, the polarizability is identical with the electric susceptibility. The dielectric constant corresponding to zero frequency may then be obtained from the Clausius-Mosotti equation, Eq. 12.2–28, thus:

$$\frac{\epsilon' - 1}{\epsilon' + 2} = \frac{4\pi}{3} n\alpha(0) = \frac{ne^2}{3\pi m} \sum_i \frac{f_i}{\nu_i^2} \tag{12.5–19}$$

In connection with Eqs. 12.3–46 and 47 it was pointed out that the index of refraction, η, is very nearly $\sqrt{\epsilon'}$. Thus, the index of refraction for light of frequency ν_0 is given by

$$\frac{\eta^2 - 1}{\eta^2 + 2} = \frac{ne^2}{3\pi m} \sum_i \frac{f_i}{(\nu_i^2 - \nu_0^2)} \tag{12.5–20}$$

In many cases this simple expression reproduces the experimental dispersion curves quite well. As shown in the next section, the quantum mechanical derivation gives the same functional form for $\alpha(\nu_0)$, ϵ', and η. The "oscillator strengths" are found there to be certain matrix elements related to the dipole moments.

6. Quantum Theory of Light Absorption and the Index of Refraction

In this section we derive the quantum mechanical expressions for the polarizability and index of refraction. These expressions have the same general form as those derived in the previous section by classical arguments. We therefore obtain the quantum mechanical interpretation of the oscillator strengths in terms of the elements of the dipole moment matrix, and the characteristic frequencies in terms of the differences between pairs of energy levels in the molecule. The derivation is made in terms of the transition probabilities $|a_{lk}|^2$ for the induced absorption or emission of light. On this account this section begins with a simplified discussion of the quantum mechanical theory of light absorption.

a. Transition probabilities for a molecule in an electromagnetic field

Let us consider a molecule for which the unperturbed quantum mechanical Hamiltonian operator is $\mathscr{H}^{(0)}$. The corresponding unperturbed time-dependent wave functions satisfy the Schrödinger equation:

$$\mathscr{H}^{(0)}\Psi_l^{(0)} = E_l\Psi_l^{(0)} = -\frac{\hbar}{i}\frac{\partial \Psi_l^{(0)}}{\partial t} \tag{12.6–1}$$

where the E_l are the energy levels. The wave function may be factored thus:

$$\Psi_l^{(0)} = \psi_l^{(0)}\, e^{-iE_l t/\hbar} \tag{12.6–2}$$

where the $\psi_l^{(0)}$ are the time-independent wave functions for the unperturbed molecule.

We now consider the molecule in an electromagnetic radiation field of frequency $\nu_0 = c/\lambda_0$, traveling in the z-direction and polarized in the xz-plane, that is, with the $\mathscr{E}$ field in the x-direction. As in the previous section, the wavelength of the radiation is considered to be large compared with molecular dimensions, so that the electromagnetic field may be considered constant over the molecule. Also, since the velocity of the electrons is small compared to the velocity of light, the effect of the magnetic intensity of the light beam may be neglected. Hence, with these assumptions, the only component of the electromagnetic field which has to be considered is $\mathscr{E}_x = \mathscr{E}_0 \sin 2\pi\nu_0 t$, so that the total Hamiltonian operator for the molecule under the influence of the radiation is

$$\mathscr{H} = \mathscr{H}^{(0)} - (\mathscr{E}_0 \sin 2\pi\nu_0 t) \textstyle\sum_i e_i x_i \tag{12.6–3}$$

in which e_i and x_i are the charge and x-coordinate of the ith particle in the molecule.

The starting point for the quantum mechanical study of light absorption is then the Schrödinger equation written for the perturbed system:

$$\{\mathscr{H}^{(0)} - (\mathscr{E}_0 \sin 2\pi\nu_0 t) \textstyle\sum_i e_i x_i\}\Psi_l = -\dfrac{\hbar}{i}\dfrac{\partial \Psi_l}{\partial t} \tag{12.6–4}$$

All quantities associated with the unperturbed molecule are designated by the superscript 0. The wave function for the perturbed system in a state l may be expanded in terms of the unperturbed wave functions:

$$\Psi_l = \sum_{j=0}^{\infty} a_{lj}(t)\Psi_j^{(0)} \tag{12.6–5}$$

In general, the wave functions are complex, and an asterisk is used to indicate the complex conjugates. Substitution of this expression into the preceding equation, followed by multiplication by $\Psi_m^{(0)*}$ and integration over all space, gives the following differential equations for the expansion coefficients, a_{lm}:

$$\frac{\hbar}{i}\frac{da_{lm}(t)}{dt} = (\mathscr{E}_0 \sin 2\pi\nu_0 t) \sum_{j=0}^{\infty} a_{lj}(t)\,(\mu_x)_{mj} e^{i(E_m - E_j)t/\hbar} \tag{12.6–6}$$

Here $(\mu_x)_{mj}$ represents the integral:

$$(\mu_x)_{mj} = \int \psi_m^{(0)*}(\textstyle\sum_i e_i x_i)\psi_j^{(0)}\, d\mathbf{r}^n \tag{12.6–7}$$

These integrals are the matrix elements of the x-component of the dipole moment.

Let us suppose that at $t = 0$ the molecule is in the state l, so that $a_{ll}(0) = 1$, and all other $a_{lm}(0)$ are zero. Whether the state l is a high or a low energy state is not specified. We discuss the probability of transitions from this state to other states being brought about because of the electromagnetic perturbations. Let us investigate the behavior of the $a_{lm}(t)$ after a short time interval. During this short interval of time the probability of a transition having taken place is small so that the values of $a_{l1}, a_{l2}, a_{l3}, \ldots$ are all negligibly small compared with a_{ll}, and the latter is still approximately unity. Then Eq. 12.6–6 becomes

$$\begin{aligned}\frac{\hbar}{i}\frac{da_{lm}}{dt} &= (\mathscr{E}_0 \sin 2\pi\nu_0 t)\,(\mu_x)_{ml} e^{i(E_m - E_l)t/\hbar} \\ &= \mathscr{E}_0(\mu_x)_{ml}\,\frac{1}{2i}\,[e^{i(E_m - E_l + h\nu_0)t/\hbar} - e^{i(E_m - E_l - h\nu_0)t/\hbar}] \qquad (12.6\text{–}8)\end{aligned}$$

Direct integration of this equation gives

$$a_{lm} = \mathscr{E}_0(\mu_x)_{ml}\,\frac{1}{2i}\left[\frac{e^{i(E_m - E_l + h\nu_0)t/\hbar} - 1}{E_m - E_l + h\nu_0} - \frac{e^{i(E_m - E_l - h\nu_0)t/\hbar} - 1}{E_m - E_l - h\nu_0}\right] \qquad (12.6\text{–}9)$$

From this may be obtained the quantity $|a_{lm}|^2 = a_{lm}^* a_{lm}$:

$$|a_{lm}|^2 = +\frac{\mathscr{E}_0^2\,|(\mu_x)_{ml}|^2}{4}\left[\frac{2 - 2\cos[(E_l - E_m + h\nu_0)t/\hbar]}{(E_l - E_m + h\nu_0)^2} + \frac{2 - 2\cos[(E_l - E_m - h\nu_0)t/\hbar]}{(E_l - E_m - h\nu_0)^2} - \frac{\begin{array}{r}2 + 2\cos 4\pi\nu_0 t - 2\cos[(E_l - E_m + h\nu_0)t/\hbar] \\ -2\cos[(E_l - E_m - h\nu_0)t/\hbar]\end{array}}{(E_l - E_m)^2 - (h\nu_0)^2}\right]$$

(12.6–10)

This is the *transition probability* that the molecules go from state l to state m during a short time t under the influence of polarized light of frequency ν_0.

b. Induced absorption and emission of light

Let us suppose that $|E_l - E_m|$ is approximately equal to $h\nu_0$. Then the problem is one of resonance absorption or emission of light. If $E_l < E_m$, the transition leads to the absorption of light by the molecule; if $E_l > E_m$, then additional light of frequency ν_0 is emitted by the molecule. Equation 12.6–10 was derived on the basis that the light falling on the molecule is monochromatic. In actual practice this is never true and for the present purposes we assume that the frequency covers a narrow band ranging from ν_1 to ν_2 including the value $|E_l - E_m|/h$. In this case, we replace $\mathscr{E}_0^2$ in Eq. 12.6–10 by $8\pi I$ where I is the energy density of the radiation per unit frequency interval. Then the transition probability a'_{lm} is obtained by integrating Eq. 12.6–10 from ν_1 to ν_2, so that, neglecting the small terms:

$$|a'_{lm}|^2 = \int_{\nu_1}^{\nu_2} |a_{lm}|^2 \, d\nu = 4\pi I \, |(\mu_x)_{ml}|^2 \int_{\nu_1}^{\nu_2} \frac{1 - \cos[(|E_m - E_l| - h\nu)t/\hbar]}{(|E_m - E_l| - h\nu)^2} \, d\nu$$

$$= \frac{2I}{\hbar^2} |(\mu_x)_{ml}|^2 \, t \int_{\xi(\nu_1)}^{\xi(\nu_2)} \frac{1 - \cos\xi}{\xi^2} \, d\xi \tag{12.6–11}$$

in which the integration variable $\xi = (|E_m - E_l| - h\nu)t/\hbar$ has been used. If now the frequency band is wide compared to the natural width of the emission line,[1] there is little error in replacing $\xi(\nu_1)$ by $-\infty$ and $\xi(\nu_2)$ by $+\infty$. Integration then gives[2]

$$|a'_{lm}|^2 = \frac{2\pi I t}{\hbar^2} |(\mu_x)_{ml}|^2 \tag{12.6–12}$$

Thus the transition probability is proportional to the intensity of the light at the frequency $|E_l - E_m|/h$, to the square of the matrix component of the dipole moment, and to the time. In Appendix 12.C the values of these matrix components are given for many transitions of the hydrogen atom and for the excitation of other atoms from their ground (s-state) to the lowest P-state. For hydrogen it is seen that all the components of the dipole moment matrix vanish unless the azimuthal quantum number changes by ± 1 and the magnetic quantum number changes by 1, 0, or -1.

According to Eq. 12.6–12, transitions cannot occur when the matrix components for the dipole moment vanish. In actual practice such *forbidden transitions* do occur, but the intensity of such spectral lines is

[1] This emission line is never perfectly sharp. If the molecule is in a vacuum, there is a natural line width due to the reaction force of the emitted radiation on the emitting electron. At ordinary gas pressures the width of the line is due to the pressure broadening or the fact that the energy levels of the molecules are slightly shifted owing to van der Waals' interactions with other molecules. (See § 13.7.)

[2] This relation has been derived on the assumption that the light is polarized. In the case of isotropic radiation, the result may be shown to be

$$|a'_{lm}|^2 = \frac{2\pi I t}{3\hbar^2} |\mu_{ml}|^2$$

where

$$|\mu_{ml}|^2 = |(\mu_x)_{ml}|^2 + |(\mu_y)_{ml}|^2 + |(\mu_z)_{ml}|^2$$

weaker by a factor of 100 to 1000 than that of lines corresponding to *allowed transitions*. Metastable states are those from which the usual selection rules prohibit a transition to a lower energy state. Forbidden transitions are important in low-pressure systems where forbidden transitions with the emission of light occur more frequently than by conversion of electronic into translational energy in collisional processes. For example, the light in the night sky is largely made up of radiation resulting from such forbidden transitions.[3]

Another example of forbidden transitions is furnished by the infrared spectra of diatomic molecules. In elementary discussions it is generally stated that gases containing homonuclear, diatomic molecules can exhibit no rotational or vibrational spectra, because the molecules do not possess permanent dipole moments for any value of the internuclear separation. This rule arises from the vanishing of the quantum mechanical matrix elements of the dipole moment, and Eq. 12.6–12. These matrix elements are calculated by using the wave functions of an unperturbed molecule as described in Eq. 12.6–7. Small amounts of absorption in homonuclear diatomic gases, due to rotational and vibrational transitions, can nevertheless occur by means of other mechanisms:

(i) *Isotope Effect.* In ordinary gases there is always present in small amounts isotopes, such as HD or $O^{16}O^{18}$, which are not strictly homopolar.

(ii) *Electric Quadrupole Effect.* If the electric quadrupole moment of the free molecule changes with internuclear distance, a small amount of absorption takes place. This term is not present in Eq. 12.6–7, since it was assumed that the field was uniform over the molecule. This term depends on the first derivative of the field.

(iii) *Magnetic Dipole Effect.* If the free molecule possesses a magnetic dipole which changes with internuclear distance additional absorption may result. This term is lost by the neglect of the magnetic field terms in the perturbed Hamiltonian and the neglect of the variation of the field across the molecule.

(iv) *Electrical Distortion Effect.*[4] If the molecules are subjected to a homogeneous external field, the molecules are distorted and dipole moments are induced in the molecules so that absorption is possible.

(v) *Pressure Induced Effect.*[5] In compressed gases and liquids the molecular distortions during collisions make absorption possible.

[3] E. U. Condon and G. Shortley, *Atomic Spectra*, Cambridge University Press (1935), p. 282.

[4] E. U. Condon, *Phys. Rev.*, **41**, 759 (1932). M. F. Crawford and I. R. Dagg, *Phys. Rev.*, **91**, 1569 (1953).

[5] J. van Kranendonk and R. B. Bird, *Physica*, **17**, 953, 968 (1951). J. van Kranendonk, Doctoral Dissertation, Amsterdam (1952)—in English.

The first three effects take place in isolated molecules; the second and third effects may be obtained by removing the restrictions introduced at the beginning of this section.[6] The fourth and fifth effects listed above are due to distortions produced by external forces and are examples of "enforced dipole radiation." In the first four effects the absorption is proportional to the density of the absorbing medium; in pressure-induced absorption, however, the observed absorption is proportional to the square of the density.

c. The index of refraction

A formula for the index of refraction may be obtained quantum mechanically by a method quite similar to that described in § 12.5c in classical theory. If the molecules have no permanent dipole moment, the x-component of the electric dipole moment induced by the light beam is

$$(\mu_x^{(\mathrm{ind})})_{ll} = \int \Psi_l^*(\Sigma\, e_i x_i)\Psi_l \, d\boldsymbol{r}^n \qquad (12.6\text{–}13)$$

This integral differs from those in Eq. 12.6–7 in that now the perturbed wave functions Ψ_l are used. Substituting $\Psi_l = \Sigma_k a_{lk}\Psi_k^{(0)}$ into this equation, integrating, and remembering that $a_{ll} \doteq 1$ and all other a_{lk} are small, we obtain

$$\begin{aligned}(\mu_x^{(\mathrm{ind})})_{ll} &= \Sigma_j\Sigma_k a_{lj}^*(\mu_x)_{jk}a_{lk}e^{i(E_j-E_k)t/\hbar} \\ &\doteq \Sigma_k[(\mu_x)_{lk}a_{lk}e^{i(E_l-E_k)t/\hbar} + (\mu_x)_{lk}^* a_{lk}^* e^{-i(E_l-E_k)t/\hbar}] \qquad (12.6\text{–}14)\end{aligned}$$

Now, making use of the expression for the amplitudes given in Eq. 12.6–9, we find that

$$\begin{aligned}(\mu_x^{(\mathrm{ind})})_{ll} &= \mathscr{E}_0\Sigma_k \frac{2\,|(\mu_x)_{lk}|^2(E_k - E_l)}{(E_l - E_k)^2 - (h\nu_0)^2}\sin 2\pi\nu_0 t \\ &+ \mathscr{E}_0\Sigma_k \frac{2\,|(\mu_x)_{lk}|^2 h\nu_0 \sin[(E_l - E_k)t/\hbar]}{(E_l - E_k)^2 - (h\nu_0)^2} \qquad (12.6\text{–}15)\end{aligned}$$

The polarizability is defined in terms of the time average of the induced dipole moment. Thus the second term in this equation does not contribute to the polarizability since half of the time it is in phase with the applied electric field and half of the time it is in the opposite direction.

[6] See, for example, H. Eyring, J. Walter, and G. E. Kimball, *Quantum Chemistry*, Wiley (1944), pp. 110 et seq.; E. C. Kemble, *Fundamental Principles of Quantum Mechanics*, McGraw-Hill (1937), pp. 462 et seq.

Thus, if x is a principal axis of the polarizability tensor, the polarizability in this direction is

$$(\alpha_{xx}(\nu_0))_{ll} = \sum_k \frac{2\,|(\mu_x)_{lk}|^2 (E_k - E_l)}{(E_l - E_k)^2 - (h\nu_0)^2} \tag{12.6–16a}$$

And the polarizability averaged over all directions is

$$(\alpha(\nu_0))_{ll} = \tfrac{1}{3}[(\alpha_{xx}(\nu_0))_{ll} + (\alpha_{yy}(\nu_0))_{ll} + (\alpha_{zz}(\nu_0))_{ll}] \tag{12.6–16b}$$

This is the quantum mechanical analog to the classical result due to Drude, given in Eq. 12.5–16.

If all the molecules were in the state l, the index of refraction would be given by the Clausius-Mosotti equation analogously to the classical expression given in Eq. 12.5–20, thus:

$$\left(\frac{\eta^2 - 1}{\eta^2 + 2}\right)_{ll} = \frac{4\pi}{3} n(\alpha(\nu_0))_{ll} \tag{12.6–17}$$

Here n is the number of molecules per cm^3. If the distribution of molecules over the energy levels is characteristic of thermal equilibrium, the probability that the molecule is in the lth level is

$$P_l = g_l e^{-E_l/kT} / \sum_i g_i e^{-E_i/kT} \tag{12.6–18}$$

in which g_i is the statistical weight of the ith state. Accordingly, the index of refraction is given by

$$\left(\frac{\eta^2 - 1}{\eta^2 + 2}\right) = \frac{4\pi n}{3} \left\{ \frac{\sum_l (\alpha(\nu_0))_{ll} g_l e^{-E_l/kT}}{\sum_l g_l e^{-E_l/kT}} \right\} \tag{12.6–19}$$

This formula was first derived by Kramers[7, 8] on the basis of the correspondence principle. The negative terms give rise to "negative dispersion" or negative f-values which would be difficult to understand on a classical basis.

It is interesting to compare these quantum mechanical results with the classical results of Drude, discussed in the previous section. First, it is noticed that the dependence of the polarizability and index of refraction on the frequency of the radiation is the same. The quantum mechanical treatment provides a better interpretation of the constants. The characteristic natural frequencies corresponding to Drude's ν_i are the frequencies of emission or absorption:

$$\nu_{lk} = (E_k - E_l)/h \tag{12.6–20}$$

[7] H. A. Kramers, *Nature*, **113**, 673 (1924); **114**, 310 (1924).

[8] J. H. Van Vleck, *Electric and Magnetic Susceptibilities*, Oxford University Press (1932), p. 361.

where E_l and E_k are the energies of the lth and kth states of the molecule, respectively. The quantum mechanical analog to Eq. 12.5–18 is then

$$(\alpha(\nu_0))_{ll} = \frac{e^2}{4\pi^2 m} \sum_k \frac{f_{lk}}{\nu_{lk}^2 - \nu_0^2} \tag{12.6–21}$$

Here the f_{lk} are the oscillator strengths corresponding to a transition, from a state l to a state k and are defined by

$$f_{lk} = \frac{2}{3} \frac{h\nu_{lk}}{(e^2/a_0)} \frac{|\mu_{lk}|^2}{(e^2 a_0^2)} \tag{12.6–22}$$

where $$|(\mu)_{lk}|^2 = |(\mu_x)_{lk}|^2 + |(\mu_y)_{lk}|^2 + |(\mu_z)_{lk}|^2$$

The oscillator strengths defined by Eq. 12.6–22 refer to individual states of the molecule. If the molecule possesses degenerate states, it is convenient to indicate the degenerate quantum number explicitly. For example, the energy levels of an atom are degenerate in the magnetic quantum number m (unless an external field is present, as in problems involving the Zeeman effect). Then a state is characterized by a double subscript such as lm where l stands for the set of all of the quantum numbers other than m and an oscillator strength, $f_{lm;\,km'}$ is associated with the transition from lm to km'. From Eq. 12.6–21 it is seen that the polarizability of a molecule in the state lm is

$$(\alpha(\nu_0))_{lm,\,lm} = \frac{e^2}{4\pi^2 m} \sum_{km'} \frac{f_{lm,\,km'}}{\nu_{lk}^2 - \nu_0^2} \tag{12.6–23}$$

However, the quantity which is usually of interest is the average polarizability for molecules in the states of the degenerate level. This is

$$(\alpha(\nu_0))_{ll} = \frac{1}{2L_l + 1} \sum_m (\alpha(\nu_0))_{lm,\,lm} = \frac{e^2}{4\pi^2 m} \sum_k \frac{\bar{f}_{lk}}{\nu_{lk}^2 - \nu_0^2} \tag{12.6–24}$$

where the $\bar{f}_{lk}$ are the average oscillator strengths defined by

$$\bar{f}_{lk} = \frac{1}{2L_l + 1} \sum_m \sum_{m'} f_{lm,\,km'} \tag{12.6–25}$$

and $(2L_l + 1)$ is the degeneracy of the lth level. The sum of the $\bar{f}_{lk}$ over all the discrete and continuous energy states k is equal to the total number of electrons in the system. This is called the Reiche-Kuhn-Thomas f-sum rule.[9]

[9] W. Kuhn, *Zeit. Phys.*, **33**, 408 (1925); H. A. Bethe, *Handbuch der Physik* (Second Ed.), Springer (1933), XXIV/I, p. 434; E. U. Condon and G. H. Shortley, *Theory of Atomic Spectra*, Cambridge University Press (1935), p. 108.

One difficulty in applying the dispersion formulae is that transitions to the continuous, as well as to the discrete, energy states must be included in all the summations. The effect of the continua is often important and sometimes difficult to estimate.[10]

The dispersion relations and the oscillator strengths discussed here play a very important role in determining the long range forces between molecules (§ 13.3).

7. Scattering of Electromagnetic Waves[1–5]

The scattering of electromagnetic radiation may occur with or without changes in the frequency. When there is no frequency change, the phenomenon is called *Rayleigh scattering*. When there is a frequency shift, the scattering is referred to as *Raman scattering*. We consider here only the Rayleigh scattering. This is due to scattering from the individual molecules and interference effects arising from the density fluctuations in the scattering medium.[6] The theory presented here applies to both visible light and x-rays. The scattering of visible light gives rise to opalescence such as is observed in the neighborhood of the critical point. The scattering of x-rays provides an experimental means for evaluating the radial distribution function[7] $g(r)$.

Let us consider the scattering of electromagnetic waves in a medium containing N molecules in which the scattering is sufficiently weak that it is necessary to consider only the singly scattered beam. The results may then be expressed in terms of the radial distribution function $g(r)$. The consideration of multiple scattering introduces distribution functions of higher order. Let $\boldsymbol{k}_0$ be the vectorial wave number of the electromagnetic waves before the scattering and $\boldsymbol{k}$ the wave number after the scattering. Inasmuch as this discussion is restricted to elastic scattering, $k_0 = k = 2\pi/\lambda$, where λ is the wavelength of the light. The directions of the vectors $\boldsymbol{k}_0$ and $\boldsymbol{k}$ indicate the directions of the incident and scattered beams.

[10] J. A. Wheeler, *Phys. Rev.*, **43**, 258 (1933).

[1] J. de Boer, *Reports on Progress in Physics*, **12**, 305, The Physical Society, London (1949).

[2] M. Born, *Optik*, Edwards (1943). Also Lord Rayleigh, *Phil. Mag.*, **41**, 447 (1871).

[3] J. Cabannes, *Diffusion moléculaire de la lumière*, Presses Universitaires de France (1929), Ch. 14 by Y. Rocard.

[4] G. Oster, *Chem. Revs.*, **43**, 319 (1948).

[5] S. Chandrasekhar, *Radiative Transfer*, Oxford University Press (1950).

[6] Fluctuations in density are discussed in § 2.6.

[7] The radial distribution function $g(r)$ is discussed in detail in § 4.9 in connection with the equation of state at high densities.

The phase difference between the waves scattered in a particular direction by molecules i and j is illustrated in Fig. 12.7–1. The path of the ray through j is longer than the path through i by the sum of the distances a and b. The angle between $\boldsymbol{k}_0$ and $\boldsymbol{k}$ is θ. The angle η_0 is the angle between the vectors $\boldsymbol{k}_0$ and $(\boldsymbol{r}_j - \boldsymbol{r}_i)$, and the angle η is the angle between the vectors $\boldsymbol{k}$ and $(\boldsymbol{r}_j - \boldsymbol{r}_i)$. The distance a is clearly $r_{ij} \cos \eta_0$,

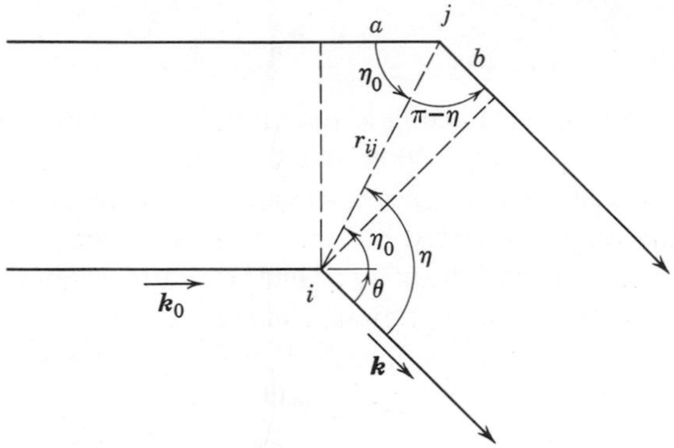

Fig. 12.7–1. The phase difference between waves scattered by molecules i and j.

and the distance b is $r_{ij} \cos (\pi - \eta)$ or $-r_{ij} \cos \eta$. Thus the phase difference between the two waves, which is the sum of the distances multiplied by k, is

$$k_0 r_{ij} \cos \eta_0 - k r_{ij} \cos \eta \quad \text{or} \quad (\boldsymbol{k}_0 - \boldsymbol{k}) \cdot (\boldsymbol{r}_j - \boldsymbol{r}_i) \tag{12.7–1}$$

Let A be the amplitude of the outgoing electromagnetic wave after scattering by a single molecule. Then the magnitude of the electric vector at the point $\boldsymbol{r}$ due to scattering from the molecule j is

$$\frac{A}{|\boldsymbol{r} - \boldsymbol{r}_j|} e^{i\delta_i} e^{i(\boldsymbol{k}_0 - \boldsymbol{k})\cdot(\boldsymbol{r}_j - \boldsymbol{r}_i)} \tag{12.7–2}$$

where δ_i is the phase of the wave incident at molecule i. Now let us consider the radiation at a distance R from the scattering molecules, which is large compared to the dimensions of the volume containing the molecules (that is, $R \gg r_i$ for all i). The electric vector associated with the scattered wave is then

$$\mathscr{E}_s = \frac{A}{R} e^{i\delta_i} e^{-i(\boldsymbol{k}_0 - \boldsymbol{k})\cdot\boldsymbol{r}_i} \sum_{j=1}^{N} e^{i(\boldsymbol{k}_0 - \boldsymbol{k})\cdot\boldsymbol{r}_j} \tag{12.7–3}$$

The energy density in the scattered beam may be obtained immediately from this equation:

$$I = \frac{1}{4\pi} \mid \mathscr{E}_s \mid^2 = \frac{A^2}{4\pi R^2} \sum_{i=1}^{N} \sum_{j=1}^{N} \cos\left[(\boldsymbol{k}_0 - \boldsymbol{k}) \cdot \boldsymbol{r}_{ij}\right] \tag{12.7-4}$$

First, we perform separately the summation for $i = j$ and for $i \neq j$ and obtain

$$I = \frac{A^2}{4\pi R^2}\left[N + \sum_{i=1}^{N} \sum_{\substack{j=1 \\ j \neq i}}^{N} \cos\left[(\boldsymbol{k}_0 - \boldsymbol{k}) \cdot \boldsymbol{r}_{ij}\right]\right] \tag{12.7-5}$$

If the scattering molecules form a macroscopically homogeneous phase having a volume V, the energy density of the scattered light can be expressed in terms of the radial distribution function $g(r)$. In an element of volume $d\boldsymbol{r}_j$ (within V) at a distance r_{ij} from a molecule i, there are $ng(r_{ij})$ molecules. By arguments similar to those used in § 2.6b, the summations in Eq. 12.7-5 can be replaced by integrals over the volume of the matter.

$$I = \frac{A^2}{4\pi R^2}\left[N + n^2 \int_V \int_V g(r_{ij}) \cos\left[(\boldsymbol{k}_0 - \boldsymbol{k}) \cdot \boldsymbol{r}_{ij}\right] d\boldsymbol{r}_i \, d\boldsymbol{r}_j\right] \tag{12.7-6}$$

Furthermore, the volume integral can be split into two terms by adding and subtracting the volume integral which would be obtained if $g(r_{ij})$ were unity. Thus, the energy density of the scattered light can be written in the form

$$I = I_m + I_s + I_i \tag{12.7-7}$$

where

$$I_m = \frac{A^2 N}{4\pi R^2} \tag{12.7-8}$$

$$I_s = \frac{A^2 n^2}{4\pi R^2} \int_V \int_V \cos\left[(\boldsymbol{k}_0 - \boldsymbol{k}) \cdot \boldsymbol{r}_{ij}\right] d\boldsymbol{r}_i \, d\boldsymbol{r}_j \tag{12.7-9}$$

$$I_i = \frac{A^2 n^2}{4\pi R^2} \int_V \int_V (g(r_{ij}) - 1) \cos\left[(\boldsymbol{k}_0 - \boldsymbol{k}) \cdot \boldsymbol{r}_{ij}\right] d\boldsymbol{r}_i \, d\boldsymbol{r}_j \tag{12.7-10}$$

These terms have the significance:

(i) I_m is the light scattered by the individual molecules without interference. In this sense, I_m is the molecular contribution to the scattering.

(ii) I_s is the light scattered with interference as a result of the geometry of the surface of the matter. It is this scattering which is largely responsible for the diffraction pattern resulting from light striking a droplet.[8]

[8] L. Brillouin, *J. Appl. Phys.*, **20**, 1110 (1949).

If the matter were concentrated in a sphere of radius R_0, the integrations can be carried out to give

$$I_s = \frac{4\pi n A^2}{R^2 s^6} [\sin (sR_0) - (sR_0) \cos (sR_0)]^2 \tag{12.7-11}$$

where

$$s = | \boldsymbol{k}_0 - \boldsymbol{k} | = 2k \sin \frac{\theta}{2} = \frac{4\pi}{\lambda} \sin \frac{\theta}{2} \tag{12.7-12}$$

(iii) I_i is the light scattered by virtue of the microscopic inhomogeneity or the turbidity of the medium. Since $[g(r_{ij}) - 1]$ is appreciably different from zero only when r_{ij} is small compared to the macroscopic dimensions of the matter, little error is introduced if the range of integration in Eq. 12.7–10 is increased so as to permit r_{ij} to become infinite. Then I_i becomes

$$\begin{aligned} I_i &= \frac{n^2 A^2}{4\pi R^2} \int_V d\boldsymbol{r}_i \int_0^\infty r_{ij}^2 dr_{ij} \int_0^{2\pi} d\phi_{ij} \int_0^\pi [g(r_{ij}) - 1] \cos (sr_{ij} \cos \theta_{ij}) \sin \theta_{ij} d\theta_{ij} \\ &= \frac{nNA^2}{R^2} \int_0^\infty [g(r) - 1] \frac{\sin (sr)}{sr} r^2 \, dr \end{aligned} \tag{12.7-13}$$

These scattering formulae may be used to describe the scattering of two types of electromagnetic radiation: *visible light*, for which the wavelength λ is large in comparison with the size of the molecular clusters, and *x-rays*, for which the wavelength λ is of the order of magnitude of molecular dimensions. Both types of scattering may be described by Eq. 12.7–7, 8, 9, and 13 by specifying the amplitude A, which is dependent upon the character of the electromagnetic waves. In the remainder of the section we neglect surface scattering so that I is $I_m + I_i$.

a. Scattering of visible light

For light waves in the visible region where the wavelength is long compared with the molecular dimensions, it may be shown that

$$A = k^2 \mu^{(\text{ind})} \sin \gamma \tag{12.7-14}$$

where $\mu^{(\text{ind})}$ is the dipole moment induced in the molecule by the wave and γ is the angle between the induced dipole and the direction of propagation of the scattered wave. For spherically symmetric molecules, the induced dipole is in the direction of the electric vector of the incident beam. Let us consider a polar coordinate system with the direction of the pole in the direction of the incident beam (that is, in the direction of $\boldsymbol{k}_0$). Then the direction of the electric vector of the incident beam is specified by the polar angle $\pi/2$ and the azimuthal angle ϕ_0. Let the direction of the scattered beam (that is, the direction of $\boldsymbol{k}$) be given by θ and ϕ. Then the angle γ is given by

$$\cos \gamma = \sin \theta \cos (\phi - \phi_0) \tag{12.7–15}$$

The electric vector of the scattered wave is perpendicular to the direction of propagation $\boldsymbol{k}$, and in the plane containing $\boldsymbol{k}$ and the induced dipole.

The induced dipole moment $\boldsymbol{\mu}^{(\text{ind})}$ is simply related to the polarizability α of the molecule and the local field $\mathscr{E}^{(\text{loc})}$;

$$\boldsymbol{\mu}^{(\text{ind})} = \alpha \mathscr{E}^{(\text{loc})} \tag{12.7–16}$$

The local field is discussed in § 12.2c. To a good approximation

$$\boldsymbol{\mu} = \tfrac{1}{3}\alpha (\epsilon + 2)\mathscr{E} \tag{12.7–17}$$

in which ϵ is the dielectric constant of the medium and $\mathscr{E}$ is the electric vector of the incident wave. Thus we obtain finally

$$A = \tfrac{1}{3}k^2\alpha(\epsilon + 2)\mathscr{E}[1 - \sin^2 \theta \cos^2 (\phi - \phi_0)]^{1/2} \tag{12.7–18}$$

for the amplitude of the electric vector associated with the scattered light waves.

The energy density of the scattered light of visible wavelength is given by Eq. 12.7—7, in which the expression, given above, for A must be inserted. For light of these wavelengths, the range of correlation between the positions of molecules in the medium is small compared with λ. Hence sr is small for all values of r such that $g(r)$ is appreciably different from unity. Thus $\sin (sr)$ may be expanded, and the expression for the energy density of the scattered light becomes

$$I = \frac{N}{4\pi} \frac{A^2}{R^2} \left[1 + 4\pi n \int_0^\infty [g(r) - 1] r^2 \, dr - \frac{2\pi}{3} n s^2 \int_0^\infty [g(r) - 1] r^4 \, dr + \cdots \right] \tag{12.7–19}$$

A comparison of this expression with Eq. 2.6–31 shows that the first two terms are closely related to the fluctuations in density. In fact, in the limit of long wavelengths ($s \to 0$) the higher terms in the series are zero, and the intensity is exactly related to the fluctuations in the density. This is the approximation considered by Rayleigh, in which the scattering is assumed to take place from clusters of dimensions small compared to the wavelength. The added terms in this series are important either if the wavelength is small (large s) or if the range of correlation is large so that $g(r)$ approaches unity slowly.

Let us now define a parameter ξ by the relation

$$\xi^2 = \frac{2\pi}{3} n \int_0^\infty [g(r) - 1] r^4 \, dr \tag{12.7–20}$$

This parameter measures the range of correlation between pairs of molecules, that is, it measures roughly the size of the clusters present. In terms of this quantity and the result given by Eq. 2.6–32, the expression for the energy density given in Eq. 12.7–19 becomes

$$I = \frac{N}{4\pi} \frac{A^2}{R^2} \left[\frac{kT}{(\partial p/\partial n)_T} - s^2\xi^2 + \ldots \right] \tag{12.7–21}$$

Then, using the expression for the scattering amplitude (Eq. 12.7–18) and the definition of s (Eq. 12.7–12), we may rewrite this expression explicitly in the form:

$$I = \frac{4\pi^3}{9} \frac{N |\mathscr{E}|^2}{R^2} \frac{\alpha^2(\epsilon + 2)^2}{\lambda^4} [1 - \sin^2\theta \cos^2(\phi - \phi_0)] \times \left[\frac{kT}{(\partial p/\partial n)_T} - 16\pi^2 \frac{\xi^2}{\lambda^2} \sin^2 \frac{\theta}{2} \right] \tag{12.7–22}$$

By means of Eq. 12.5–5 this expression may be written in terms of the energy density of the incident beam, $I_0 = \frac{1}{4\pi} |\mathscr{E}|^2$, so that the fraction of the beam scattered is

$$\frac{I}{I_0} = \frac{16\pi^4}{9} \frac{N}{R^2} \frac{\alpha^2(\epsilon + 2)^2}{\lambda^4} [1 - \sin^2\theta \cos^2(\phi - \phi_0)] \times \left[\frac{kT}{(\partial p/\partial n)_T} - 16\pi^2 \frac{\xi^2}{\lambda^2} \sin^2 \frac{\theta}{2} \right] \tag{12.7–23}$$

If the incident beam is *polarized*, the scattering for a particular value of θ is a maximum in the plane $\phi = \phi_0 + (\pi/2)$, normal to the direction of the electric vector of the incident beam. In this plane the intensity is independent of the polar angle θ, except for the small second-order term. In the plane containing the electric vector, $\phi = \phi_0$, the intensities forward ($\theta = 0$) and backward ($\theta = \pi$) are the same, but perpendicular scattering (at $\theta = \pi/2$) is zero.

The intensity of the light scattered from an *unpolarized* beam is obtained by averaging the expression given by Eq. 12.7–23 over all values of ϕ_0. The result is

$$\frac{I}{I_0} = \frac{8\pi^4}{9} \frac{N}{R^2} \frac{\alpha^2(\epsilon + 2)^2}{\lambda^4} [1 + \cos^2\theta] \left[\frac{kT}{(\partial p/\partial n)_T} - \frac{16\pi^2\xi^2}{\lambda^2} \sin^2 \frac{\theta}{2} \right] \tag{12.7–24}$$

This distribution is, of course, cylindrically symmetric. The intensities of the light scattered in the forward direction and in the backward direction are the same. At $\theta = \pi/2$ the intensity is one half of the value of the intensity at $\theta = 0$ or $\theta = \pi$.

The blue of the sky[9] is due to the fluctuations in the density of the air. The λ^4 in the denominator of Eq. 12.7–24 gives rise to a strong wavelength dependence so that the short wavelengths of the sun's spectrum are preferentially scattered. The red sunsets and sunrises are due to the fact that the long wavelength radiation is preferentially unscattered. Another factor in determining the color of the sky is, of course, the scattering due to dust and smoke particles.[10]

The expressions for the scattering of light given in Eqs. 12.7–23 and 24 are not valid in the neighborhood of the critical point. The expressions predict infinite scattering at the critical point; clearly this is not correct, although the scattering does become large. Ornstein and Zernike[3,11] have attempted to modify the derivation of the scattering expressions to obtain an expression valid at the critical point. The modification, which is an approximation, is based on the concept of a correlation between fluctuations in density in neighboring volumes. The intensity of light scattered from an unpolarized beam may be written in terms of a quantity, σ, which is interpreted as an average diameter of clusters of molecules or scattering centers:

$$\frac{I}{I_0} = \frac{\dfrac{8\pi^4}{9}\dfrac{N}{R^2}\alpha^2(\epsilon + 2)^2(1 + \cos^2\theta)kT}{\lambda^4(\partial p/\partial n)_T + 2\pi^2\sigma^2\epsilon\lambda^2 kT\sin^2\dfrac{\theta}{2}} \tag{12.7–25}$$

Under conditions not in the neighborhood of the critical point, this expression reduces to that given above in Eq. 12.7–24. In the neighborhood of the critical point (where $(\partial p/\partial n)_T$ is zero) this theory predicts that the scattering varies[12] as the λ^{-2} instead of the λ^{-4} variation. Equation 12.7–25 has been used[13] to obtain the approximate size of the molecular

[9] S. Chandrasekhar and D. Elbert, *Nature*, **167**, 51 (1951). See also Lord Rayleigh's *Collected Works*.

[10] G. P. Kuiper, *Atmosphere of Planets*, University of Chicago Press (1948), Chapter by Van de Hulst.

[11] L. S. Ornstein and F. Zernike, *Proc. Acad. Sci. Amsterdam*, **17**, 793 (1914); *Physik. Z.*, **27**, 761 (1926). See also L. Rosenfeld, *Theory of Electrons*, North-Holland (1951), p. 80.

[12] D. K. Bhattacharyya ["Experimental Studies of the Critical Opalescence of Carbon Dioxide," *Proc. Indian Assoc. Cultural Sci.* (1923), p. 8] found that the scattering is almost proportional to λ^{-1}. Y. Rocard and M. Ponte (see Ref. 3) did not succeed in verifying the λ^{-2} proportionality.

[13] H. Cataldi and H. G. Drickamer, *J. Chem. Phys.*, **18**, 650 (1950).

clusters in the neighborhood of the critical point from experimental observations of the light scattering. The cluster sizes obtained by this method are in reasonable agreement with those obtained by interpretation of the observed variations of the density with height (see § 5.2d). A difficulty with the theory is that, at the critical point, the integral of the intensity over all solid angles is infinite. A more recent theory of Rocard avoids this difficulty but does not involve explicitly the diameter of a cluster.[14] Apparently much further work is required before a satisfactory theory can be established.

b. Scattering of x-rays

The wavelength of x-rays is of the order of molecular dimensions, and accordingly independent scattering is produced by each electron. It may be shown that the amplitude, A, of the electromagnetic wave scattered by a single electron is

$$A = (e/mc^2)\mathscr{E} \sin \gamma \tag{12.7–26}$$

where, as above, γ is the angle between the electric vector of the incident beam and the direction of propagation of the scattered beam. When an electromagnetic wave is scattered by an atom containing several electrons, the scattering amplitude is complicated because of the interference of the scattered waves from the various electrons. Furthermore, for a fluid made up of polyatomic molecules, the scattering amplitude is also complicated by the interference of the waves from the various atoms constituting one molecule. The scattering amplitude A cannot usually be obtained theoretically, but may be evaluated from experimental measurements of the scattering of x-rays in a dilute gas.

Let us now apply Eq. 12.7–7 to the scattering of x-rays. We use I_m in place of A as the experimentally determined quantity. Then Eq. 12.7–7 for the scattered intensity becomes

$$I = I_m \left[1 + \frac{4\pi n}{s} \int [g(r) - 1] r \sin sr \, dr\right] \tag{12.7–27}$$

Now we consider the scattering of an unpolarized beam of x-rays. The scattered intensity depends only on the polar angle θ, which may be replaced by the parameter s, defined by Eq. 12.7–12 and is given by the average of Eq. 12.7–27 over the azimuthal angle, ϕ. Since ϕ appears only in I_m, the result is given by a similar expression in which $I_m(s)$ depends on the average of $|A|^2$ over the angle ϕ. The value of $I_m(s)$ is a property of the molecules and is independent of the density. According to Eq. 4.9–1, $g(r)$ approaches $\exp(\varphi(r)/kT)$ in the low-density limit. Hence in

[14] Y. Rocard, *Compt. rend.*, **195**, 771 (1932); *J. phys. et radium*, **4**, 165 (1933).

the limit of low densities, $I(s)$ is linear in the density for each value of s. That is, at zero density the scattering $I_m(s)$ is entirely a molecular phenomenon, and the interference between the waves from the various molecules becomes negligible. This fact is the basis of a method of obtaining experimentally the values of $I_m(s)$. The value of $I_m(s)$ is of interest in itself because of its close connection with the molecular structure.

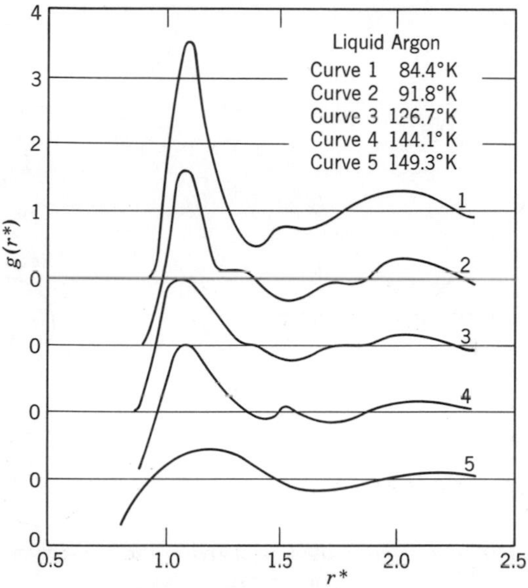

Fig. 12.7–2. Experimental curves of the radial distribution function, $g(r)$. The curves are given as a function of the reduced distance $r^* = r/\sigma$, where $\sigma = 3.42$ Å. [This figure is taken from the review article of J. de Boer, Reports on Progress in Physics, **12**, 305 (1949) and is based on the experimental measurements of A. Eisenstein and N. S. Gingrich, *Phys. Rev.*, **62**, 261 (1942).]

The experimental values of $I_m(s)$, the scattering at zero density, and of $I(s)$, the scattering at finite density, may be used in Eq. 12.7–27 to obtain the radial distribution function. By a Fourier inversion it follows from Eq. 12.7–27 that

$$g(r) = 1 + \frac{1}{2\pi^2 nr} \int_0^\infty \left[\frac{I_m(s)}{I(s)} - 1\right] s \sin sr\, ds \tag{12.7–28}$$

Experimental curves of the radial distribution function for liquid argon, determined in this manner, are shown in Fig. 12.7–2.

APPENDIX A.   THE TWO-CENTER EXPANSION COEFFICIENTS[1]

$$B_{n_a, n_b}^{|m|}(r_i, r_j; r_{ab})$$

Analytical expressions for the expansion coefficients $B_{n_a, n_b}^{|m|}(r_i, r_j; r_{ab})$ have been worked out for four regions of the variables r_i, r_j, and r_{ab}. These four regions are shown in Fig. 12.A–1. For the study of the interaction

$$
\begin{array}{ll}
\text{I} & r_{ab} > r_i + r_j \\
\text{II} & r_{ab} + r_i < r_j \\
\text{III} & r_{ab} + r_j < r_i \\
\text{IV} & |r_i - r_j| \leqslant r_{ab} \leqslant (r_i + r_j)
\end{array}
$$

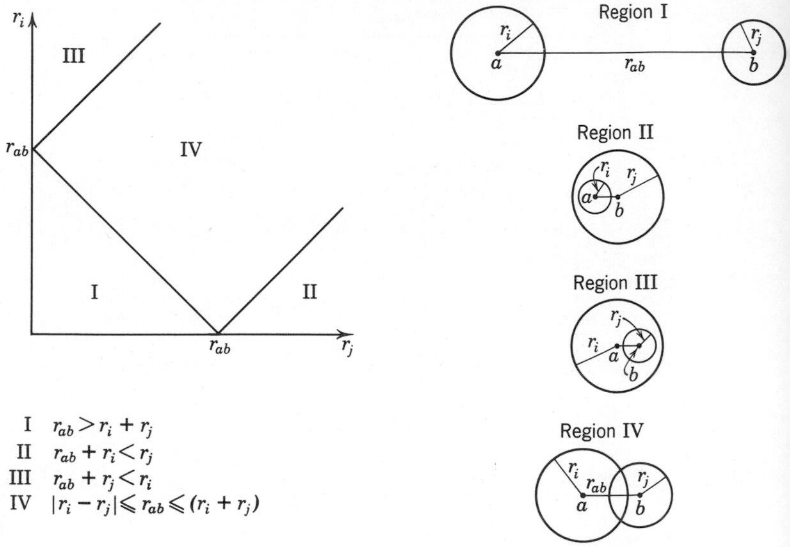

Fig. 12.A–1. The four regions used in deriving the two-center expansion coefficients.

of two widely separated charge distributions, the expansion coefficients for Region I alone need be considered. When two charge distributions overlap, the expansion coefficients for Regions II, III, and IV must be used.

Region I: $[r_{ab} > r_i + r_j]$

$$B_{n_a, n_b}^{|m|}(r_i, r_j; r_{ab}) = \frac{(-1)^{n_b + m}(n_a + n_b)!}{(n_a + |m|)!(n_b + |m|)!} \frac{r_i^{n_a} r_j^{n_b}}{r_{ab}^{n_a + n_b + 1}} \qquad (12.\text{A}-1)$$

Region II: $[r_{ab} + r_i < r_j]$

$$B_{n_a, n_b}^{|m|}(r_i, r_j; r_{ab}) = \begin{cases} \dfrac{(-1)^{n_a + n_b}(n_b - |m|)!}{(n_b - n_a)!(n_a + |m|)!} \dfrac{r_i^{n_a} r_j^{-n_b - 1}}{r_{ab}^{n_a - n_b}} & n_b \geqslant n_a \\[12pt] 0 & n_b < n_a \end{cases}$$

$$(12.\text{A}-2)$$

[1] R. J. Buehler and J. O. Hirschfelder, *Phys. Rev.*, **83**, 628 (1951); **85**, 149 (1952).

Region III: $[r_{ab} + r_j < r_i]$

$$B^{|m|}_{n_a, n_b}(r_i, r_j; r_{ab}) = \begin{cases} \dfrac{1}{(n_a - n_b)!} \dfrac{(n_a - |m|)!}{(n_b + |m|)!} \dfrac{r_i^{-n_a-1} r_j^{n_b}}{r_{ab}^{n_b-n_a}} & n_a \geqslant n_b \\ 0 & n_a < n_b \end{cases} \tag{12.A–3}$$

Region IV: $[|r_i - r_j| \leqslant r_{ab} \leqslant (r_i + r_j)]$

$$B^{|m|}_{n_a, n_b}(r_i, r_j; r_{ab}) = \sum_{k,\, l} \frac{A^m_{n_a, n_b}(k, l)}{D^{|m|}_{n_a, n_b}} \frac{r_i^{k-n_a-1} r_j^{l-n_b-1}}{r_{ab}^{k+l-n_a-n_b-1}} \tag{12.A–4}$$

The coefficients $A^{|m|}_{n_a, n_b}$ and $D^{|m|}_{n_a, n_b}$ for $n_a, n_b = 0, 1, 2, 3$ and the appropriate m values are given in Table 12.A–1. The functions for which $n_a > n_b$ are not given, since they may be determined by permutation of indices according to the rule:

$$B^{|m|}_{n_a, n_b}(r_i, r_j; r_{ab}) = (-1)^{n_a + n_b} B^{|m|}_{n_b, n_a}(r_j, r_i; r_{ab}) \tag{12.A–5}$$

For values of n_a or n_b not given in Table 12.A–1, the following general formula may be used for $B^{|m|}_{n_a, n_b}(r_i, r_j; r_{ab})$ in Region IV:

$$B^{|m|}_{n_a, n_b}(r_i, r_j; r_{ab}) = S^{|m|}_{n_a, n_b} \sum_{u=0}^{2m} \sum_{v=0}^{n_a-|m|} \sum_{w=0}^{n_b-|m|} T_{n_a}(t)\, U^{|m|}(u)\, V^{|m|}_{n_a}(v)\, W^{|m|}_{n_b}(w) \tag{12.A–6}$$

Here $t = u + v + w$ and

$$S^{|m|}_{n_a, n_b} = \frac{(-1)^{n_b-|m|}(2n_b + 1)}{2^{n_a+n_b+1}} \frac{(n_a - |m|)!\,(n_b - |m|)!}{(n_a + |m|)!\,(n_b + |m|)!} \frac{1}{r_{ab}} \tag{12.A–7}$$

$$T_{n_a}(t) = \left[\frac{1}{2t+2}\left[1 - \left(\frac{r_{ab} - r_j}{r_i}\right)^{2t+2}\right] - \frac{1}{2t - 2n_a + 1}\left[1 - \left(\frac{r_{ab} + r_j}{r_i}\right)^{2t-2n_a+1}\right] \right] \left(\frac{r_j}{r_i}\right)^{n_a-1} \left(\frac{r_i^2}{r_{ab}^2 + r_j^2}\right)^t \tag{12.A–8}$$

$$U^{|m|}(u) = \frac{(-1)^u (|m|)!}{u!} \sum_{k=k_1}^{|m|} \frac{(-1)^k (2k)!}{k!\,(2k - u)!\,(m - k)!} \left(\frac{r_{ab}^2 + r_j^2}{2 r_{ab} r_j}\right)^{2k}$$
$$k_1 = \frac{u}{2} \text{ or } \frac{u+1}{2} \tag{12.A–9}$$

TABLE 12.A–1

EXPANSION COEFFICIENTS FOR REGION IV

$$B^m_{n_a n_b}(r_i, r_j; r_{ab}) = \sum_{k,l} \frac{A^m_{n_a n_b}(k,l)}{D^m_{n_a n_b}} \frac{r_i^{k-n_a-1}\, r_j^{l-n_b-1}}{r_{ab}^{k+l-n_a-n_b-1}}$$

Note: With this formula and the table can be computed the expansion coefficients $B^m_{n_a n_b}$ in Region IV, with indices equal to or less than 3. The summation extends over all entries in the table. The largest value of $(k + l)$ is $2(n_a + n_b + 1)$.

n_b		0	1	1	1	2	2	2	3
n_a		0	0	1	1	0	1	1	0
m		0	0	0	1	0	0	1	0
$D^m_{n_a n_b}$		4	16	16	64	32	256	512	256
k	l	$A^m_{n_a n_b}(k, l)$							
0	0	−1	3	2	1	−5	−25	−5	35
	1	2	0	0	0	0	0	0	0
	2	−1	−6	−9	−9	5	60	20	−28
	3	0	0	8	16	0	0	0	0
	4	0	3	0	−9	5	−30	−30	−14
	6	0	0	−1	1	−5	−20	20	−28
	8	0	0	0	0	0	15	−5	35
1	0	2	−8	0	0	16	0	0	−128
	1	2	0	0	0	0	0	0	0
	3	0	−8	0	0	0	0	0	0
	5	0	0	0	0	16	0	0	0
	7	0	0	0	0	0	0	0	−128
2	0	−1	6	−9	−9	−15	180	60	140
	2	0	6	0	18	−10	−60	−60	84
	4	0	0	9	−9	−15	60	−60	84
	6	0	0	0	0	0	−180	60	140
3	0	0	0	8	16	0	−256	−128	0
	3	0	0	−16	16	0	0	0	0
	5	0	0	0	0	0	384	−128	0
4	0	0	−1	0	−9	5	90	90	−70
	2	0	0	9	−9	5	−60	60	−84
	4	0	0	0	0	0	−270	90	−70
6	0	0	0	−1	1	−1	20	−20	28
	2	0	0	0	0	0	60	−20	28
8	0	0	0	0	0	0	−9	3	−5

TABLE 12.A–1 (*continued*)

n_b		2	2	2	3	3	3	3	3
n_a		2	2	2	1	1	2	2	2
m		0	1	2	0	1	0	1	2
$D^m_{n_a n_b}$		256	1536	12288	256	1024	3072	12288	49152
k	l	$A^m_{n_a n_b}(k, l)$							
0	0	−19	−9	−3	21	7	189	49	7
	2	75	50	25	−42	−21	−630	−210	−42
	4	−150	−150	−150	14	14	735	315	105
	5	128	128	256	0	0	0	0	0
	6	−50	0	−150	0	14	−420	−140	−140
	8	25	−25	25	21	−21	315	−105	105
	10	−9	6	−3	−14	7	−294	126	−42
	12	0	0	0	0	0	105	−35	7
2	0	75	50	25	−210	−105	−1050	−350	−70
	2	−100	−100	−100	84	84	1470	630	210
	4	50	0	150	0	42	−420	−140	−140
	6	−100	100	−100	−84	84	−420	140	−140
	8	75	−50	25	210	−105	1470	−630	210
	10	0	0	0	0	0	−1050	350	−70
3	0	0	0	0	384	256	0	0	0
	7	0	0	0	−512	256	0	0	0
4	0	−150	−150	−150	−210	−210	3675	1575	525
	2	50	0	150	0	−126	−1260	−420	−420
	4	150	−150	150	126	−126	−630	210	−210
	6	−450	300	−150	420	−210	−2940	1260	−420
	8	0	0	0	0	0	7875	−2625	525
5	0	128	128	256	0	0	−4608	−2048	−1024
	5	768	−512	256	0	0	0	0	0
	7	0	0	0	0	0	−15360	5120	−1024
6	0	−50	0	−150	0	70	2100	700	700
	2	−100	100	−100	−84	84	1260	−420	420
	4	−450	300	−150	−140	70	2940	−1260	420
	6	0	0	0	0	0	10500	−3500	700
8	0	25	−25	25	21	−21	−525	175	−175
	2	75	−50	25	42	−21	−1470	630	−210
	4	0	0	0	0	0	2625	875	−175
10	0	−9	6	−3	−6	3	294	−126	42
	2	0	0	0	0	0	630	−210	42
12	0	0	0	0	0	0	−75	25	−5

TABLE 12.A–1 (*continued*)

n_b		3	3	3	3
n_a		3	3	3	3
m		0	1	2	3
$D^m_{n_a n_b}$		10240	49152	245760	2949120
k	l	$A^m_{n_a n_b}(k, l)$			
0	0	520	131	20	5
	2	−2450	−735	−147	−49
	4	4900	1715	490	245
	6	−7350	−2695	−1225	−1225
	7	5120	2048	1024	2048
	8	0	−735	0	−1225
	10	−1470	539	−245	245
	12	980	−343	98	−49
	14	−250	75	−15	5
2	0	−2450	−735	−147	−49
	2	5880	2058	588	294
	4	−4410	−1617	−735	−735
	6	0	588	0	980
	8	4410	−1617	735	−735
	10	−5880	2058	−588	294
	12	2450	−735	147	−49
4	0	4900	1715	490	245
	2	−4410	−1617	−735	−735
	4	0	294	0	490
	6	−2940	1078	−490	490
	8	14700	−5145	1470	−735
	10	−12250	3675	−735	245
6	0	−7350	−2695	−1225	−1225
	2	0	588	0	980
	4	−2940	1078	−490	490
	6	−19600	6860	−1960	980
	8	61250	−18375	3675	−1225
7	0	5120	2048	1024	2048
	7	−102400	30720	−6144	2048
8	0	0	−735	0	−1225
	2	4410	−1617	735	−735
	4	14700	−5145	1470	−735
	6	61250	−18375	3675	−1225
10	0	−1470	539	−245	245
	2	−5880	2058	−588	294
	4	−12250	3675	−735	245
12	0	980	−343	98	−49
	2	2450	−735	147	−49
14	0	−250	75	−15	5

$$V_{n_a}^{|m|}(v) = \left(\frac{2r_{ab}}{r_j}\right)^{n_a-|m|} \left(\frac{r_{ab}^2 + r_j^2}{4r_{ab}^2}\right)^v$$

$$\sum_{p=p_1}^{n_a-|m|-v} \frac{(-1)^{n_a-|m|-v-p}(2\,|\,m\,|+2v+2p)!\,[(r_{ab}^2 - r_j^2)/4r_{ab}^2]^p}{p!\,(p+v+m)!\,(p+2v-n_a+|\,m\,|)!\,(-p-v+n_a-|\,m\,|)!}$$

(12.A–10)

$$p_1 = n_a - |\,m\,| - 2v \text{ when } v \leqslant \tfrac{1}{2}(n_a - |\,m\,|) \text{ or } \tfrac{1}{2}(n_a - |\,m\,| - 1);$$

$$\text{otherwise } p_1 = 0$$

$$W_{n_b}^{|m|}(w) = \frac{(-1)^w}{w!} \sum_{q=0}^{q_2} \frac{(-1)^q (2n_b - 2q)!\,[(r_{ab}^2 + r_j^2)/2r_{ab}r_j]^{n_b-|m|-2q}}{(n_b - q)!\,(n_b - |\,m\,| - 2q - w)!\,q!}$$

(12.A–11)

$$q_2 = \tfrac{1}{2}(n_b - |\,m\,| - w) \text{ or } \tfrac{1}{2}(n_b - |\,m\,| - w - 1)$$

The summation indices assume only integral values so that the choices of k_1, p_1, and q_2 are unique. The explicit evaluation of the coefficients $A_{n_a,n_b}^{|m|}(k, l)$ and $D_{n_a,n_b}^{|m|}$ is accomplished by further expansion of T, U, V, and W.

APPENDIX B. THE REPRESENTATION COEFFICIENTS OF THE THREE DIMENSIONAL ROTATION GROUP

In this appendix we consider the explicit form and some of the properties of the representation coefficients of the three-dimensional rotation group. Since the representation coefficients are closely related to the spherical harmonics, it is necessary to preface this discussion with a precise definition of the spherical harmonics used throughout this book.

The ordinary *Legendre polynomials* are defined by the relation,

$$P_l(x) = \frac{(-1)^l}{2^l l!} \frac{d^l}{dx^l} (1 - x^2)^l \qquad (12.\text{B–1})$$

for all integer $l \geqslant 0$, whereas the *associated Legendre functions* are defined by[1]

$$P_l^m(x) = P_l^{-m}(x) = (1 - x^2)^{|m|/2} \frac{d^{|m|}}{dx^{|m|}} P_l(x) \qquad (12.\text{B–2})$$

[1] Several sign and normalization conventions are in current use. The conventions adopted here are those of H. Margenau and G. M. Murphy, *The Mathematics of Physics and Chemistry* [Van Nostrand (1956)] and, for $m \geqslant 0$ (but not for $m < 0$), those of E. Jahnke and F. Emde, *Tables of Functions* [Dover (1945)].

for all integer m. It follows from this definition that the functions are identically zero for all values of m outside the range $-l \leqslant m \leqslant l$. The first few polynomials are

$$P_0^0(x) = P_0(x) = 1$$

$$P_1^0(x) = P_1(x) = x$$

$$P_1^1(x) = (1 - x^2)^{1/2}$$

$$P_2^0(x) = P_2(x) = \tfrac{1}{2}(3x^2 - 1)$$

$$P_2^1(x) = 3(1 - x^2)^{1/2}\, x$$

$$P_2^2(x) = 3(1 - x^2)$$

$$P_3^0(x) = P_3(x) = \tfrac{1}{2}(5x^3 - 3x)$$

$$P_3^1(x) = \tfrac{3}{2}(1 - x^2)^{1/2}\,(5x^2 - 1)$$

$$P_3^2(x) = 15(1 - x^2)x$$

$$P_3^3(x) = 15(1 - x^2)^{3/2}$$

$$P_4^0(x) = P_4(x) = \tfrac{1}{8}(35x^4 - 30x^2 + 3)$$

$$P_4^1(x) = \tfrac{5}{2}(1 - x^2)^{1/2}\,(7x^3 - 3x)$$

$$P_4^2(x) = \tfrac{15}{2}(1 - x^2)\,(7x^2 - 1)$$

$$P_4^3(x) = 105(1 - x^2)^{3/2}\, x$$

$$P_4^4(x) = 105(1 - x^2)^2$$

The *normalized spherical harmonics* are defined in terms of these functions in the following manner:

$$Y_l^m(\theta, \phi) = i^{|m|-m} \sqrt{\frac{(2l+1)}{4\pi}\frac{(l-|m|)!}{(l+|m|)!}}\, P_l^m(\cos\theta) e^{im\phi} \qquad (12.\text{B–}3)$$

These functions are orthonormal in the sense that

$$\int_0^{2\pi}\int_0^{\pi} Y_l^m(\theta, \phi)^* \, Y_{l'}^{m'}(\theta, \phi) \sin\theta \, d\theta \, d\phi = \delta_{ll'}\delta_{mm'} \qquad (12.\text{B–}4)$$

The sign of the normalization factor used here is such that

$$Y_l^m(\theta, \phi) = (-1)^m Y_l^{-m}(\theta, \phi)^* \qquad (12.\text{B–}5)$$

With this particular choice of the sign of the normalization factor, the spherical harmonics are related by the following recursion relations:

$$\sqrt{(l+m+1)(l-m)}\, Y_l^{m+1}(\theta, 0) = \left[m \cot\theta - \frac{d}{d\theta}\right] Y_l^m(\theta, 0) \quad (12.B\text{-}6)$$

$$\sqrt{(l+m)(l-m+1)}\, Y_l^{m-1}(\theta, 0) = \left[m \cot\theta + \frac{d}{d\theta}\right] Y_l^m(\theta, 0) \quad (12.B\text{-}7)$$

$$\sqrt{2l+1}\cos\theta\, Y_l^m(\theta, 0) = \left[\begin{array}{l} \sqrt{\dfrac{(l-m)(l+m)}{2l-1}}\, Y_{l-1}^m(\theta, 0) \\ + \sqrt{\dfrac{(l-m+1)(l+m+1)}{2l+3}}\, Y_{l+1}^m(\theta, 0) \end{array}\right] \quad (12.B\text{-}8)$$

$$\sqrt{2l+1}\sin\theta\, Y_l^m(\theta, 0) = \left[\begin{array}{l} \sqrt{\dfrac{(l+m-1)(l+m)}{2l-1}}\, Y_{l-1}^{m-1}(\theta,0) \\ - \sqrt{\dfrac{(l-m+1)(l-m+2)}{2l+3}}\, Y_{l+1}^{m-1}(\theta,0) \end{array}\right] \quad (12.B\text{-}9)$$

$$\sqrt{2l+1}\sin\theta\, Y_l^m(\theta, 0) = \left[\begin{array}{l} -\sqrt{\dfrac{(l-m)(l-m-1)}{2l-1}}\, Y_{l-1}^{m+1}(\theta,0) \\ + \sqrt{\dfrac{(l+m+1)(l+m+2)}{2l+3}}\, Y_{l+1}^{m+1}(\theta,0) \end{array}\right] \quad (12.B\text{-}10)$$

Let us consider two Cartesian coordinate systems with a common origin but rotated with respect to one another. The relative orientation of the two coordinate systems may be described by use of the Eulerian angles[2] α, β, γ. Let us denote the original coordinate system by unbarred

[2] The angles α, β, and γ are often denoted by ϕ, θ, and χ. See, for example, L. Pauling and E. B. Wilson, Jr., *Introduction to Quantum Mechanics*, McGraw-Hill (1935), p. 276. The angles θ and ϕ are the usual angles used in spherical coordinates to give the orientation of the new z-axis. The angle χ is a measure of the rotation of the coordinate system or object about its new z-axis.

coordinates and the new coordinate system by barred coordinates. The meaning of the Eulerian angles may be described by considering the following set of rotations. The original coordinate system is rotated by an angle, α, about the z-axis in the counterclockwise direction (so that the x-axis moves toward the y-axis). The coordinate system is then tipped

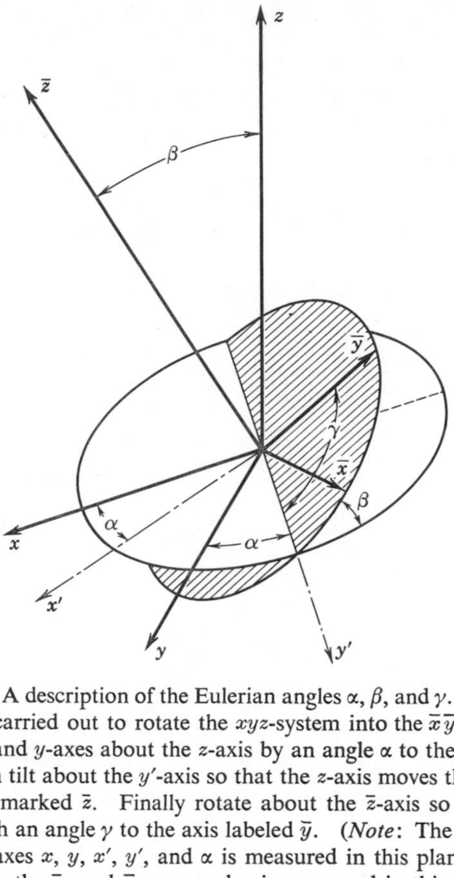

Fig. 12.B–1. A description of the Eulerian angles α, β, and γ. The following procedure is carried out to rotate the xyz-system into the $\bar{x}\bar{y}\bar{z}$ system: First, rotate the x- and y-axes about the z-axis by an angle α to the axes marked x' and y'. Then tilt about the y'-axis so that the z-axis moves through an angle β to the axis marked $\bar{z}$. Finally rotate about the $\bar{z}$-axis so that the y'-axis moves through an angle γ to the axis labeled $\bar{y}$. (*Note*: The unshaded plane contains the axes x, y, x', y', and α is measured in this plane. The shaded plane contains the $\bar{x}$- and $\bar{y}$-axes, and γ is measured in this plane.)

by an angle β about the new y-axis so that the z-axis moves in the new xz-plane in the direction corresponding to the positive x-direction. The coordinate system is now rotated by an angle, γ, about the new z-axis in the counterclockwise direction. The final position of the coordinates is that of the barred coordinates. The orientation of the barred coordinates which have been rotated by a rotation (α, β, γ) from the position of the unbarred coordinates is illustrated in Fig. 12.B–1.

Let θ and ϕ be the polar coordinates of a point on a unit sphere in terms of the old coordinate system and $\bar{\theta}$ and $\bar{\phi}$ be the coordinates in terms of the new coordinate system. Then it may be shown that

$$Y_l^n(\theta, \phi) = \Sigma_m D^l(R)_{mn}\, Y_l^m(\bar{\theta}, \bar{\phi}) \tag{12.B-11}$$

The expansion coefficients $D^l(R)_{mn}$ are functions of the rotation $R = (\alpha, \beta, \gamma)$ which takes the unbarred into the barred coordinate system. The $D^l(R)_{mn}$ with a fixed value of l form a $(2l + 1)$-dimensional matrix. It may be shown that these matrices multiply in the same manner as the rotations themselves. That is,

$$\Sigma_n D^l(R)_{mn} D^l(S)_{nm'} = D^l(RS)_{mm'} \tag{12.B-12}$$

where RS is the net result of the rotation S followed by rotation R. Thus the matrices form a representation of the three-dimensional rotation group.[3] The spherical harmonics form the basis of the representation.

The representation coefficients are of the form

$$D^l(R)_{nm} = e^{in\gamma} d^l(\beta)_{nm} e^{im\alpha} \tag{12.B-13}$$

in which l is a positive integer or zero. The $d^l(\beta)_{nm}$ are, except for a normalization factor, the Jacobi polynomials with arguments $x = \cos\beta$. An explicit expression for the $d^l(\beta)_{nm}$ is

$$d^l(\beta)_{nm} = (-1)^m \sqrt{\frac{(l-n)!\,(l-m)!}{(l+n)!\,(l+m)!}} \qquad n > 0 \;;\; m > 0$$

$$\times \Sigma_s \frac{(-1)^s\, n!\, m!}{(s-m)!\,(s-n)!\,(n+m-s)!} \left(\frac{1+x}{1-x}\right)^{(n+m-s)/2} P_l^s(x) \tag{12.B-14}$$

The expressions for negative values of the indices are given by the relations

$$d^l(\beta)_{n,-m} = (-1)^{l+n} d^l(\pi - \beta)_{n,m} \qquad n > 0; m > 0 \tag{12.B-15}$$

$$d^l(\beta)_{-n,m} = (-1)^{l+m} d^l(\pi - \beta)_{n,m} \qquad n > 0; m > 0 \tag{12.B-16}$$

$$d^l(\beta)_{-n,-m} = (-1)^{n+m} d^l(\beta)_{n,m} \qquad n > 0; m > 0 \tag{12.B-17}$$

[3] E. P. Wigner, *Gruppentheorie und ihre Anwendung auf die Quantenmechanik der Atomspektren*, Edwards Brothers (1944).

The $d^l(\beta)_{nm}$ may also be written[4] in several equivalent forms (all n and m):

$$d^l(\beta)_{nm} = (-1)^m \sqrt{\frac{(l-n)!\,(l-m)!}{(l+n)!\,(l+m)!}}$$

$$\times \sum_s \frac{(-1)^s\,(l+s)!}{(l-s)!\,(s-m)!\,(s-n)!} \sin^{2s-n-m}\frac{\beta}{2} \cos^{n+m}\frac{\beta}{2} \qquad (12.B\text{-}18)^5$$

$$d^l(\beta)_{nm} = (-1)^{n+m} \sum_s \frac{(-1)^s\sqrt{(l+n)!\,(l-n)!\,(l+m)!\,(l-m)!}}{(l-n-s)!\,(l+m-s)!\,(s-m+n)!\,s!}$$

$$\times \cos^{2l-n+m-2s}\frac{\beta}{2} \sin^{n-m+2s}\frac{\beta}{2} \qquad (12.B\text{-}19)$$

The representation coefficients are orthogonal in the sense that

$$\int D^l(R)_{nm}{}^* D^{l'}(R)_{n'm'} \sin\beta \, d\alpha \, d\beta \, d\gamma = \delta_{ll'}\delta_{nn'}\delta_{mm'} \frac{8\pi^2}{2l+1} \qquad (12.B\text{-}20)$$

From the form of the representation coefficients, Eq. 12.B–14, and the definition of the spherical harmonics, Eq. 12.B–3, it follows immediately that

$$D^l(R)_{n0} = (-1)^n\,[4\pi/(2l+1)]^{1/2}\, Y_l^n(\beta, \gamma) \qquad (12.B\text{-}21)$$

$$D^l(R)_{0m} = [4\pi/(2l+1)]^{1/2}\, Y_l^m(\beta, \alpha) \qquad (12.B\text{-}22)$$

The product of two representation coefficients may be written as a sum of representation coefficients in the form

$$D^l(R)_{nm}\, D^{l'}(R)_{n'm'} = \sum_L s^{ll'}_{L,n,n'}\, s^{ll'}_{L,m,m'}\, D^L(R)_{n+n',\, m+m'} \qquad (12.B\text{-}23)$$

An explicit expression for the coefficients, $s^{ll'}_{L,n,n'}$, which are known as

[4] The representation coefficients are defined by the properties of the group only to within a similarity transformation. The coefficients are, however, specified completely by the specification of the bases, that is, by the normalization of the spherical harmonics. The $d^l(\beta)_{nm}$ introduced here, differ from the analogous quantities of Wigner (*loc. cit.*) by a factor of $(-1)^{n+m}$. Our representations are identical with those of Margenau and Murphy (*loc. cit.*).

[5] A detailed derivation of this form of the $d^{(l)}(\beta)_{nm}$ is given by C. F. Curtiss, *The Separation of the Rotational Coordinates from the N-Particle Schroedinger Equation, II*, University of Wisconsin OOR-2, Dec. 4, 1952.

the Wigner or Clebsch-Gordan coefficients, has been given by Wigner[3, 6, 7] and tables of the coefficients in which l' is one or two have been given by Wigner[3] and Condon and Shortley.[6] The $s^{ll'}_{L,n,n'}$ have the following symmetry properties:

$$s^{ll'}_{L,n,n'} = (-1)^{l+l'+L}\, s^{l'l}_{L,n',n} = (-1)^{l+L+n'}\sqrt{\frac{2L+1}{2l+1}}\, s^{Ll'}_{l,n+n',-n'} \qquad (12.B\text{–}24)$$

and satisfy the following orthogonality relations:

$$\sum_n s^{ll'}_{L,n,m-n}\, s^{ll'}_{L',n,m-n} = \delta_{LL'} \qquad (12.B\text{–}25)$$

$$\sum_L s^{ll'}_{L,n,m-n}\, s^{ll'}_{L,n',m-n'} = \delta_{nn'} \qquad (12.B\text{–}26)$$

It may easily be shown from the above expressions that the three dimensional ($l = 1$) representation is

$$D^1(R) = \begin{pmatrix} \frac{1}{2}e^{-i\gamma}(1+\cos\beta)e^{-i\alpha} & \frac{1}{\sqrt{2}}e^{-i\gamma}\sin\beta & \frac{1}{2}e^{-i\gamma}(1-\cos\beta)e^{i\alpha} \\ -\frac{1}{\sqrt{2}}\sin\beta e^{-i\alpha} & \cos\beta & \frac{1}{\sqrt{2}}\sin\beta e^{i\alpha} \\ \frac{1}{2}e^{i\gamma}(1-\cos\beta)e^{-i\alpha} & -\frac{1}{\sqrt{2}}e^{i\gamma}\sin\beta & \frac{1}{2}e^{i\gamma}(1+\cos\beta)e^{i\alpha} \end{pmatrix} \qquad (12.B\text{–}27)$$

The basis of this representation is

$$Y_1^{-1}(\theta,\phi) = -\sqrt{\frac{3}{8\pi}}\sin\theta e^{-i\phi} = -\sqrt{\frac{3}{8\pi}}\left(\frac{x-iy}{r}\right) \qquad (12.B\text{–}28)$$

$$Y_1^{0}(\theta,\phi) = \sqrt{\frac{3}{4\pi}}\cos\theta = \sqrt{\frac{3}{4\pi}}\left(\frac{z}{r}\right) \qquad (12.B\text{–}29)$$

$$Y_1^{1}(\theta,\phi) = \sqrt{\frac{3}{8\pi}}\sin\theta e^{i\phi} = \sqrt{\frac{3}{8\pi}}\left(\frac{x+iy}{r}\right) \qquad (12.B\text{–}30)$$

The representation, Eq. 12.B–27, differs by a similarity transformation from the rotation matrix R, itself, which has as its basis, x/r, y/r, and z/r.

[6] See also E. U. Condon and G. H. Shortley, *Theory of Atomic Spectra*, Cambridge University Press (1935). The coefficients $s^{ll'}_{L,n,n'}$ are denoted by $(l, l', n, n' \mid l, l', L, n+n')$ by Condon and Shortley. The Racah coefficients which are related to the Wigner coefficients are discussed by L. C. Biedenharn, J. M. Blatt, and M. E. Rose, *Revs. Mod. Phys.*, **24**, 249 (1952).

[7] The differences between our representation coefficients and those of Wigner (see footnote 4) do not affect the values of the $s^{ll'}_{L,n,n'}$.

We may use the special case of the relations, Eq. 12.B–23, with $l' = 1$, to obtain the generalization of the recursion relations, Eqs. 12.B–8, 9, and 10, which apply to the representation coefficients:

$$\cos\beta D^l(R)_{nm} = \frac{\sqrt{(l-n)(l+n)(l-m)(l+m)}}{l(2l+1)} D^{l-1}(R)_{nm} + \frac{nm}{l(l+1)} D^l(R)_{nm} + \frac{\sqrt{(l-n+1)(l+n+1)(l-m+1)(l+m+1)}}{(l+1)(2l+1)} D^{l+1}(R)_{nm} \tag{12.B–31}$$

$$\sin\beta e^{-i\alpha} D^l(R)_{nm} = +\frac{\sqrt{(l-n)(l+n)(l+m-1)(l+m)}}{l(2l+1)} D^{l-1}(R)_{n,m-1} - \frac{n\sqrt{(l-m+1)(l+m)}}{l(l+1)} D^l(R)_{n,m-1} - \frac{\sqrt{(l-n+1)(l+n+1)(l-m+1)(l-m+2)}}{(l+1)(2l+1)} D^{l+1}(R)_{n,m-1} \tag{12.B–32}$$

$$\sin\beta e^{i\alpha} D^l(R)_{nm} = -\frac{\sqrt{(l-n)(l+n)(l-m-1)(l-m)}}{l(2l+1)} D^{l-1}(R)_{n,m+1} - \frac{n\sqrt{(l-m)(l+m+1)}}{l(l+1)} D^l(R)_{n,m+1} + \frac{\sqrt{(l-n+1)(l+n+1)(l+m+1)(l+m+2)}}{(l+1)(2l+1)} D^{l+1}(R)_{n,m+1} \tag{12.B–33}$$

APPENDIX 12C. MATRIX COMPONENTS OF THE DIPOLE MOMENT FOR OPTICAL TRANSITIONS

The state of a hydrogen atom is characterized by the four quantum numbers: n, the principal quantum number; l, the azimuthal quantum number; m_l (or simply m without the subscript), the magnetic quantum number or the component of the orbital angular momentum in the z-direction; and m_s, the spin orientation quantum number. States for various values of the azimuthal quantum number have the special designations: $l = 0$, called s-state; $l = 1$, p-state; $l = 2$, d-state; $l = 3$,

f-state; etc. The spatial part of the wave function for the hydrogen atom can be written in the form[1]

$$\psi(n, l, m) = R_{n,l}(r) Y_l^m(\theta, \phi) \tag{12.C-1}$$

Here the $Y_l^m(\theta, \phi)$ are the normalized spherical harmonics defined in Eq. 12.B-3; and the $R_{n,l}(r)$ are the normalized radial distribution functions related to the associated Laguerre functions. Using Eqs. 12.B-8, 12.B-9, and 12.B-10, it may be shown that the squares of the absolute values of the matrix components of the dipole moment (defined by Eq. 12.6-7) for optical transitions of a hydrogen atom are given by

$$|(n, l, m \mid \mu_z \mid n', l-1, m')|^2 = \delta_{mm'} e^2 a_0^2 \left(\frac{l^2 - m^2}{4l^2 - 1}\right) G(n, l; n', l-1) \tag{12.C-2}$$

$$\begin{aligned} |(n, l, m \mid \mu_x \mid n', l-1, m')|^2 &= |(n, l, m \mid \mu_y \mid n', l-1, m')|^2 \\ &= [\delta_{m+1,m'}(l-m-1)(l-m) + \delta_{m-1,m'}(l+m-1)(l+m)] \\ &\quad \times \frac{e^2 a_0^2}{4(4l^2-1)} G(n, l; n', l-1) \end{aligned} \tag{12.C-3}$$

Here the functions $G(n, l; n', l-1)$ are the integrals[2]

$$G(n, l; n', l-1) = \frac{1}{a_0^2}\left[\int_0^\infty r^3 R_{n,l} R_{n',l-1}\, dr\right]^2 \tag{12.C-4}$$

Values of the $G(n, l; n', l-1)$ are given in Table 12.C-1. It is seen that in all cases the largest values occur for $n = n'$, and the values become very small as $|n - n'|$ becomes large.

The values of the matrix components of the dipole moment for a number of different elements are given[3] in Table 12.C-2. The ground levels of all the elements given in this table are S-states. The optical transition for which the dipole moment is given is the transition from the ground state to the first excited P-state. The energy of this transition and the oscillator strength are also shown.

[1] L. Pauling and E. B. Wilson, Jr., *Quantum Mechanics*, McGraw-Hill (1935), p. 132.

[2] H. A. Bethe, *Handbuch der Physik* (2nd Ed.), Springer (1933), XXIV/1, p. 440 gives a complete set of formulae for the $G(n, l; n', l-1)$ and numerical values for the $G(n, l; n', l-1)$ and the oscillator strengths for all transitions including transitions to the continuous energy states. E. U. Condon and G. H. Shortley, *Theory of Atomic Spectra*, Cambridge University Press (1935), p. 133, give the formulae and numerical values of the $G(n, l; n', l-1)$ for a considerable number of transitions. Note that $R(n, l)$ of Bethe and of Condon and Shortley is $rR(n, l)$ in terms of the notation used here and in Pauling and Wilson.

[3] G. W. King and J. H. Van Vleck, *Phys. Rev.*, **55**, 1165 (1939).

TABLE 12.C–1[2]

VALUES OF $G(n, l;\ n', l-1)$ FOR HYDROGEN ATOMS

	2p	3p	4p	5p
1s	1.66479	0.267	0.093	0.044
2s	27.00	9.18	1.64	0.60
3s	0.88	162.	29.9	5.1
4s	0.15	6.0	540.	72.6
5s	0.052	0.9	21.2	1125.
		3d	**4d**	**5d**
2p		22.52	2.92	0.95
3p		101.2	57.2	8.8
4p		1.7	432.	121.9
5p		0.23	9.1	1181.25
			4f	**5f**
3d			104.6	11.0
4d			252.0	197.8
5d			2.75	900

TABLE 12.C–2[3]

TRANSITION DIPOLE MOMENTS AND OSCILLATOR STRENGTHS

Atom	*Energy of Transition* S → P ($e^2/2a_0$)	*Oscillator Strength* f_{SP}	$\lvert(\mu_z)_{SP}\rvert^2$ ($e^2a_0^2$)
H	0.7500	0.416	0.555
Li	0.1358	0.7500	5.52
Na	0.1546	0.9755	6.31
K	0.1184	∼0.98	8.28
Rb	0.1154	∼0.98	8.47
Cs	0.1019	0.98	9.62
Zn	0.4261	∼1.2	2.82
Cd	0.3981	1.20	3.01
Hg	0.4926	1.19	2.42

By $|(\mu_z)_{SP}|^2$ is meant

$$\sum_{m'=-1}^{1} |(n, 0, 0 | \mu_z | n', 1, 0)|^2 \tag{12.C-5}$$

The oscillator strengths are

$$f_{SP} = \frac{(E_P - E_S)}{(e^2/2a_0)} \frac{|(\mu_z)_{SP}|^2}{(e^2a_0^2)} \tag{12.C-6}$$

The dipole moments for the transitions from the ^1S ground state of helium to the ^1P, $(1s)$ (np) configuration is given[4] in Table 12.C-3.

TABLE 12.C-3[4]

TRANSITION DIPOLE MOMENTS FROM THE GROUND STATE OF HELIUM

n	$|(\mu_z)_{SP}|^2$ $(e^2a_0^2)$	n	$|(\mu_z)_{SP}|^2$ $(e^2a_0^2)$
2	0.224	5	0.0100
3	0.0547	6	0.00588
4	0.0204	7	0.00351

The total oscillator strength, f, from the ground state to the continuum[5] is 0.437 for hydrogen, 1.58 for helium, 0.24 for lithium, and 0.0021 for sodium.

PROBLEMS

1. Consider two water molecules with the center of gravities separated by 4 Å and determine the energy and relative orientation of minimum energy. Use Pople's model of a water molecule as described by Fig. 13.8-1 and Table 13.8-1.

2. Show that the interaction between two non-overlapping charge distributions cannot be of the form $\varphi = be^{-ar}$ for any distribution of charges.

3. Calculate the index of refraction as a function of frequency for the hydrogen atom in the ground state and also, the polarizability at zero frequency. The oscillator strengths are given in Table 12.C-1.

[4] J. P. Vinti, *Phys. Rev.*, **42** 632 (1932).
[5] J. A. Wheeler, *Phys. Rev.*, **43** 258 (1933).

· 13 ·

The Theory of Intermolecular Forces

The greater portion of this book is concerned with the calculation of the properties of gases and liquids. It has been shown that statistical mechanics provides us with a means for obtaining theoretical expressions for various equilibrium and non-equilibrium properties of substances in terms of the potential energy of interaction between a pair of molecules. In order to make practical calculations on the basis of the theoretical development, it is further necessary to assume an analytic form for the interaction potential. A summary of the various empirical potential functions which are used in this book is given in § 1.3. It is the purpose of this and the following chapter to discuss the present status of our theoretical knowledge of intermolecular forces,[1] which forms the basis for these idealized models.

Up to this point it has been assumed that it is indeed always possible to express the energy of interaction as a function of the intermolecular separation and the mutual orientations of the interacting pair. In the first section of this chapter we discuss the applicability of the concept of an intermolecular potential by means of a detailed analysis of the molecular collision processes. It is found that the concept of a potential energy function is useful in the limit as two molecules come together slowly. This concept breaks down if, in a distance of one de Broglie wavelength,[2,3] the energy of interaction changes by an amount comparable to the separation between neighboring potential energy surfaces. For example, fast collisions, encountered in either hot atom chemistry or the study of molecular beams, cannot be thought of in terms of a single potential energy function. There are, in addition, a few special cases in which two potential energy surfaces come very close together, so that even thermal collisions do not follow a single potential curve.

It is convenient, although artificial, to divide intermolecular forces

[1] An introduction to the theory of intermolecular forces is given in § 1.3.

[2] H. Pelzer and E. P. Wigner, *Z. physik. Chem.*, **B15**, 445 (1932).

[3] J. O. Hirschfelder and E. P. Wigner, *J. Chem. Phys.*, **7**, 616 (1939).

into two types—*long-range* (*van der Waals*) *forces* and *short-range* (*valence* or *chemical*) *forces*. This chapter is concerned mainly with the general theoretical development of the long-range forces. These forces can be described rigorously in terms of the physical properties of the separated molecules. A rigorous treatment of short-range forces cannot be given in terms of properties of the separated molecules. Instead it is necessary to consider each molecular pair as a special case. The calculation of the intermolecular forces for a considerable number of molecular pairs is discussed in Chapter 14. In both this and the following chapter very little is said about the magnetic interactions between molecules which possess magnetic moments, for example, free radicals and molecules in excited states. In the treatment of such molecules it is necessary to include additional terms in the Hamiltonian describing the molecular interaction. The form of the Hamiltonian which includes these magnetic interactions is discussed in Appendix A at the end of this chapter.

In the discussion of long-range forces it is customary to consider four types of forces: (i) electrostatic forces, (ii) induction forces, (iii) dispersion forces (London forces), and (iv) resonance forces. The forces between two non-polar molecules, which have no resultant angular momentum, are of the dispersion type. When a non-polar molecule interacts with a polar molecule both dispersion and induction forces occur. When two polar molecules collide, electrostatic forces also come into play. Resonance forces occur between two identical molecules, when the quantum numbers of the two molecules are such that the optical selection rules permit the free exchange of a photon from one molecule to the other. The electrostatic forces (§ 12.1) and the induction forces can be understood classically. The London dispersion forces and the resonance forces, on the other hand, are strictly quantum mechanical in origin.

The dispersion forces are given detailed consideration in §§ 13.3 and 4; resonance forces are discussed in § 13.6. From the standpoint of perturbation theory, the chemical (short-range), electrostatic, induction, and resonance forces all appear together as first-order perturbation terms in the energy. Dispersion forces, however, appear as second-order perturbations in the energy. In variational treatments all the effects are merged together, provided that the trial wave function has sufficient flexibility. Thus the distinction between the various types of forces is somewhat fictitious and actually leads to serious difficulties when we try to obtain the total force by combining the short-range and the long-range forces as in Chapter 14.

The long-range forces between asymmetrical non-polar molecules are considered in § 13.4 When the molecules are within two collision diameters of each other, the intermolecular forces become quite different from those of spherical molecules. The energy no longer varies as $1/r_{ab}^6$, and there may be orientations for which the energy is either a maximum or a minimum for no simply ascertainable reason. Considerably more work will have to be done before the nature of these forces becomes clear.

Up to the present time the role of dipoles in intermolecular forces has been pretty well understood. Quadrupoles, however, have received comparatively little attention until recently. The reason for this is that it has been only within the last few years that a good experimental means (microwave spectra) has been available for the measurement of quadrupole moments. Furthermore, the molecular quantum mechanics is just now coming to the point where it is possible to calculate quadrupole moments theoretically (see §§ 13.8 and 14.4b). The interactions between electric multipoles are discussed in §§ 13.5 and 6 and the use of microwave spectra to obtain important information about molecules is described in § 13.7.

The determination of intermolecular forces from the properties of crystals at temperatures close to the absolute zero is discussed in § 13.9. The type of crystal lattice, the separation between the molecules, the heat of sublimation, and the heat capacity or Debye characteristic temperature can be calculated using any assumed form for the potential energy between pairs of molecules. The agreement between the experimental and the calculated values provides a sensitive test of the potential function. Up to the present time, these properties of crystals have been used mainly to determine the forces between noble gas molecules. However, the properties of crystals may prove even more useful in determining the forces between complicated polyatomic molecules.

The results of this chapter provide a theoretical basis for some of the empirical potential energy functions which have been used in connection with the equation of state and transport property calculations. Many of the results given here are far too complicated for use in the previous developments. They will, however, be needed as further progress is made in the science of relating bulk properties of matter to the properties of the constituent molecules. For example, for the transport property calculations of polyatomic molecules (see § 7.6) the quantities which must be evaluated are the differential collision cross-sections I_{ij}^{kl}. These quantities describe the scattering as well as the changes in molecular quantum numbers during a collision. Unfortunately there is not as yet a single case where these important quantities have been determined. The difficulties encountered in their evaluation are described in § 13.6 in connection with the interaction between two symmetrical polar molecules.

1. Intermolecular Potential Energy Functions

We begin this section with a qualitative discussion of the applicability and limitations of the concept of an intermolecular potential energy function. We then proceed to formulate the problem of molecular interactions in quantum mechanical language, and discuss the approximations which are introduced by the separation of electronic and nuclear motions of the pair of colliding molecules. This enables us to understand more clearly the validity of the concept of the intermolecular potential function. Then it is shown that the virial theorem provides important information about the nature of both inter- and intra-molecular forces. We then discuss an important theorem of quantum mechanics, which shows that the force on any nucleus in a system of nuclei and electrons is exactly the classical electrostatic attraction exerted on the nucleus in question by the other nuclei and by the electron charge distribution, the latter being computed from the Schrödinger equation. Finally we indicate how the intermolecular potential energy function may be calculated by means of quantum mechanics.

a. The concept of an intermolecular potential energy function

In § 12.1 the electrostatic forces between sets of charges or charge distributions are discussed in detail. In this section we wish to extend this discussion and to examine further the special case of the interaction between two molecules. For this purpose we consider two molecules a and b, which together contain ν nuclei and n electrons. Each electron carries a charge $-e$, and the αth nucleus carries a charge $Z_\alpha e$. The configurations of the nuclei and the electrons are given symbolically by $\boldsymbol{r}^\nu \equiv \boldsymbol{r}_1, \boldsymbol{r}_2, \cdots, \boldsymbol{r}_\alpha, \cdots, \boldsymbol{r}_\nu$ and $\boldsymbol{r}^n \equiv \boldsymbol{r}_1, \boldsymbol{r}_2, \cdots, \boldsymbol{r}_i, \cdots, \boldsymbol{r}_n$, respectively. Similarly we use the symbols $\boldsymbol{r}^{\nu a}$ and $\boldsymbol{r}^{na}$ for the configurations of the ν_a nuclei and the n_a electrons of molecule a, and similar symbols for molecule b (Greek indices for nuclei and Roman indices for electrons).

In the formulation of the problem of the interaction of two molecules, several different forms of the potential function arise as a result of separating off various modes of motion. First of all, we write down the complete potential energy of the system of nuclei and electrons, such as we would use as the potential in the Hamiltonian describing the complete system. A second form is obtained by separating off the electronic degrees of freedom to obtain the potential energy for the nuclear motions. In most problems the vibrational quantum numbers are not likely to change during the course of a collision,[1–6] and it is convenient to separate off the vibrational modes of motion to give a third form for the potential, which is a function only of the intermolecular separation and the relative orientation of the molecules. A fourth form results from a separation of the rotational as well as the vibrational modes; however, this is not particularly useful inasmuch as the rotational quantum numbers are very likely to change during the course of a collision. The most common forms for the potential energies are then: the second form for the interaction of atoms, and the third form for the interaction of molecules. In order to show the relationship between the various forms and to clarify the notation which is used, we give the following summary:

I: *Electronic and Nuclear Motions Not Separated*

A pair of molecules may be regarded as a system of nuclei and electrons which interact according to the Coulombic force law. According to Eq. 12.1–1a the total potential energy of the system is

$$\Phi_e \equiv \Phi_e(\mathbf{r}^\nu, \mathbf{r}^n) = \tfrac{1}{2} \sum_{i=1}^{n} \sum_{\substack{j=1 \\ j \neq i}}^{n} \frac{e^2}{r_{ij}} - \sum_{i=1}^{n} \sum_{\alpha=1}^{\nu} \frac{Z_\alpha e^2}{r_{i\alpha}} + \tfrac{1}{2} \sum_{\alpha=1}^{\nu} \sum_{\substack{\beta=1 \\ \beta \neq \alpha}}^{\nu} \frac{Z_\alpha Z_\beta e^2}{r_{\alpha\beta}} \tag{13.1–1}$$

(The subscript e is added to indicate that it is this potential which is used to obtain the electronic wave function in § 13.1b.) This potential function is zero when all the nuclei and electrons are separated from one another. As pointed out in Eq. 12.1–3, when a system of two molecules (two discrete sets of charges) is under consideration, it is convenient to divide the total potential energy into three parts: the self-energy of the

[1] The probable number of collisions required to transfer energy from translational motion to vibrational motion and cause a unit increase in the vibrational quantum number may be estimated from measurements on the dispersion and absorption of sound. The dispersion and absorption of sound due to such "relaxation phenomena" are discussed in § 11.4b. The probable number of collisions is the experimentally observed relaxation time divided by the mean time between collisions. Experimentally[2, 3] it is observed that at 20°C the number of collisions required to transfer energy to the vibrational mode is: 34,000 for Cl_2; 7500 for N_2O; and 50,000 for CO_2. In other molecules it has been observed[4] that if the vibrational mode is a "libration" or hindered rotation the number may be as low as 50. The theory of the interchange of vibrational and translational energy has been considered by Zener.[5, 6]

[2] A. Eucken, *Österr. Chem.-Ztg.*, **20**, 1 (1935).

[3] K. F. Herzfeld, Freie Weglänge und Transporterscheinungen in Gasen, *Hand- und Jahrbuch der Chemischen Physik*, **3**, 97 (1939), Akademische Verlagsgesellschaft M.B.H. (Leipzig).

[4] J. D. Lambert and J. S. Rowlinson, *Proc. Roy. Soc.* (*London*), **A204**, 424 (1950).

[5] C. Zener, *Phys. Rev.*, **37**, 556 (1931).

[6] C. Zener, *Proc. Cambridge Phil. Soc.*, **29**, 136 (1933).

molecule a, $\Phi_a(\boldsymbol{r}^{\nu a}, \boldsymbol{r}^{na})$, the self-energy of molecule b, $\Phi_b(\boldsymbol{r}^{\nu b}, \boldsymbol{r}^{nb})$, and the energy of interaction, $\varphi_{ab}(\boldsymbol{r}^{\nu}, \boldsymbol{r}^{n})$. The self-energies are defined by expressions analogous to that given above for Φ_e, and the energy of interaction is defined by:

$$\varphi_e \equiv \varphi_{ab}(\boldsymbol{r}^{\nu}, \boldsymbol{r}^{n}) = \Phi_e(\boldsymbol{r}^{\nu}, \boldsymbol{r}^{n}) - \Phi_a(\boldsymbol{r}^{\nu a}, \boldsymbol{r}^{na}) - \Phi_b(\boldsymbol{r}^{\nu b}, \boldsymbol{r}^{nb}) \quad (13.1\text{–}2)$$

This potential energy function is so defined that it is zero when the two molecules are separated from one another sufficiently far.

II: *Electronic and Nuclear Motions Separated (the Born-Oppenheimer Separation)*

If the electronic and nuclear motions are considered to be separable, then it is possible to obtain a wave equation which describes the electronic motion with respect to the nuclei in a fixed orientation. It then becomes useful to introduce the symbol Φ_n, which stands for the potential energy of the system in a particular nuclear configuration:[7]

$$\Phi_n \equiv \Phi_n(k \mid \boldsymbol{r}^{\nu}) \quad (13.1\text{–}3)$$

This function depends on the electronic quantum numbers of the system, which we here designate symbolically with the letter k. When the system under consideration consists of two molecules, it is convenient to introduce, as before, a potential energy function which goes to zero as the molecules are separated from one another. Accordingly, we define the function $\varphi_{ab}(\boldsymbol{r}^{\nu})$ by

$$\varphi_{ab}(\boldsymbol{r}^{\nu}) \equiv \varphi_{ab}(k_a, k_b \mid \boldsymbol{r}^{\nu}) = \Phi_n(k \mid \boldsymbol{r}^{\nu}) - \Phi_a(k_a \mid \boldsymbol{r}^{\nu a}) - \Phi_b(k_b \mid \boldsymbol{r}^{\nu b}) \quad (13.1\text{–}4)$$

in which k_a and k_b stand for the sets of electronic quantum numbers describing molecules a and b. There is hence a different intermolecular potential function for each electronic state k_a, k_b.

III: *Electronic and Vibrational Motions Separated from the Other Motions*

If it is further possible to consider the vibrational motion as separable from the other nuclear motions, we can speak of the intermolecular potential function between a pair of molecules in certain electronic and vibrational states. We then use the potential energy function:

$$\varphi_{ab}(r, \omega_a, \omega_b) \equiv \varphi_{ab}(k_a, v_a; k_b, v_b \mid r, \omega_a, \omega_b) \quad (13.1\text{–}5)$$

This potential function depends on the intermolecular distance, r, and the orientations of the molecules ω_a, ω_b, and of course on the quantum

[7] In this and the following formulae the vertical bar separates the quantum numbers from the variables.

numbers for the electronic motion (k_a, k_b) and for the vibrational motion (v_a, v_b). It is sometimes convenient to average the potential function defined in Eq. 13.1–5 by averaging over all orientations of the molecules with a Boltzmann factor as a weighting factor:

$$\bar{\varphi}_{ab} \equiv \bar{\varphi}_{ab}(k_a, v_a; k_b, v_b \,|\, r, T) = \frac{\int \varphi_{ab}(r, \omega_a; \omega_b) e^{-\varphi_{ab}(r, \omega_a, \omega_b)/kT}\, d\omega_a\, d\omega_b}{\int e^{-\varphi_{ab}(r, \omega_a, \omega_b)/kT}\, d\omega_a\, d\omega_b} \tag{13.1–6}$$

It should be noted that this average potential is temperature dependent.

IV: *All Types of Motion Separated from One Another*

If it is possible to consider distinct electronic, vibrational, rotational, and translational motions, it is convenient to use the potential function:

$$\varphi_{ab}(r) \equiv \varphi_{ab}(k_a, v_a, j_a, m_a; k_b, v_b, j_b, m_b \,|\, r) \tag{13.1–7}$$

in which the m_a and m_b are the magnetic quantum numbers and the j_a and j_b are the remaining rotational quantum numbers. This potential function depends on the intermolecular distance and parametrically on the electronic, vibrational, and rotational quantum numbers. It is sometimes convenient to work with an average potential function, in which an average over the magnetic quantum numbers has been performed:

$$\langle \varphi_{ab} \rangle \equiv \langle \varphi_{ab}\, (k_a, v_a, j_a; k_b, v_b, j_b \,|\, r) \rangle = \frac{\sum_{m_a} \sum_{m_b} \varphi_{ab}(m_a, m_b \,|\, r)}{\sum_{m_a} \sum_{m_b} 1} \tag{13.1–8}$$

This average potential is not temperature dependent. It is also possible to define a temperature-dependent average quantity by analogy with Eq. 13.1–6, by taking the Boltzmann average of $\langle \varphi_{ab} \rangle$ over other quantum states.

In order to be specific, let us consider the interaction between two atoms having atomic numbers Z_a and Z_b, and having n_a and n_b electrons, respectively. For convenience we designate the electrons in a by the subscript i and those in b by j. The geometry is then that shown in Fig. 12.1–2. Considering only electrostatic interactions among the various electrons and nuclei, we may write the potential energy as

$$\varphi_e = \frac{Z_a Z_b e^2}{r_{ab}} + \sum_{i=1}^{n_a} \sum_{j=1}^{n_b} \frac{e^2}{r_{ij}} - \sum_{i=1}^{n_a} \frac{Z_b e^2}{r_{bi}} - \sum_{j=1}^{n_b} \frac{Z_a e^2}{r_{aj}} \tag{13.1–9}$$

Since the wave functions used in quantum mechanics are usually expressed in terms of a very few spherical harmonics, it is convenient to express the various terms in φ_e in terms of spherical harmonics. The two-center expansion in Eq. 12.1–28 is used to express the second term, and the third and fourth terms are given by the one-center expansion in Eq. 12.1–25. If the internuclear separation r_{ab} is larger than $(r_i + r_j)$ for all the electrons, the expansion may be written in the form

$$\varphi_e = \frac{(Z_a - n_a)(Z_b - n_b)e^2}{r_{ab}} + \sum_{k=1}^{\infty} \frac{b_{k+1}}{r_{ab}^{k+1}} \tag{13.1–10}$$

where

$$\begin{aligned} b_{k+1} = &- e^2\Big[Z_b \sum_{i=1}^{n_a} r_i^k P_k(\cos\theta_i) + (-1)^k Z_a \sum_{j=1}^{n_b} r_j^k P_k(\cos\theta_j)\Big] \\ &+ e^2 \sum_{k_b=0}^{k} \sum_{m=-k_<}^{k_<} \sum_{i=1}^{n_a} \sum_{j=1}^{n_b} \frac{(-1)^{m+k_b} k!\, r_i^{k-k_b} r_j^{k_b}}{(k - k_b + |m|)!\,(k_b + |m|)!} \\ &\times P_{k-k_b}^m(\cos\theta_i) P_{k_b}^m(\cos\theta_j) e^{im(\phi_j - \phi_i)} \end{aligned} \tag{13.1–11}$$

Here $k_<$ is the lesser of k_b and $k - k_b$.

For the interaction of neutral atoms, b_2 is zero and the first few terms of this expansion written in Cartesian coordinates are

$$\frac{b_3}{r_{ab}^3} = -\frac{e^2}{r_{ab}^3} \sum_{i=1}^{n_a} \sum_{j=1}^{n_b} [2z_i z_j - x_i x_j - y_i y_j] \tag{13.1–12a}$$

$$\frac{b_4}{r_{ab}^4} = -\frac{3}{2}\frac{e^2}{r_{ab}^4} \sum_{i=1}^{n_a} \sum_{j=1}^{n_b} [z_i r_j^2 - z_j r_i^2 + (2x_i x_j + 2y_i y_j - 3z_i z_j)(z_j - z_i)] \tag{13.1–12b}$$

$$\frac{b_5}{r_{ab}^5} = -\frac{3}{4}\frac{e^2}{r_{ab}^5} \sum_{i=1}^{n_a} \sum_{j=1}^{n_b} \left[\begin{array}{c} -r_i^2 r_j^2 + 5r_j^2 z_i^2 + 5r_i^2 z_j^2 + 15 z_i^2 z_j^2 \\ - 2(-4z_i z_j + y_i y_j + x_i x_j)^2 \end{array}\right] \tag{13.1–12c}$$

This form of φ_e is used in the calculation of the long-range forces considered in this chapter. In order for Eq. 13.1–10 to be valid, it is necessary that for all electrons the condition $r_{ab} > (r_i + r_j)$ be satisfied. In the regions where this condition does not hold, φ_e can be expressed as a power series in reciprocal powers of r_i and r_j. At very large separations the long-range forces can be expressed rigorously as inverse power series in r_{ab}, but at smaller separations (because of the terms in inverse powers of r_i and r_j) the forces contain exponentials involving the nuclear separation. The forces are therefore very difficult to calculate for intermediate separations. A method for treating this intermediate range is considered in detail in § 14.1, where the interaction of two hydrogen atoms is discussed.

Let us now interpret the interaction between two atoms by means of Eq. 13.1–4. For such a system the nuclear configuration is defined by the separation between the atoms. Hence the potential energy surfaces are one-dimensional as shown schematically in Fig. 13.1–1. These electronic energy functions serve as the intermolecular potential energy functions for the motion of the nuclei. Usually it is convenient to take as the zero of energy for the intermolecular potential energy the electronic energy of the separated atoms. In Fig. 13.1–1 we see a number of different

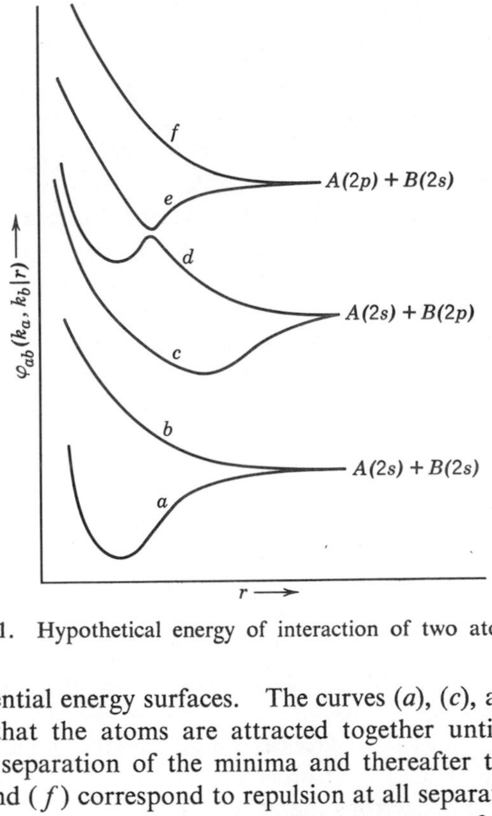

Fig. 13.1–1. Hypothetical energy of interaction of two atoms, A and B.

types of potential energy surfaces. The curves (a), (c), and (e) have deep minima so that the atoms are attracted together until they reach the internuclear separation of the minima and thereafter they are repelled. Curves (b) and (f) correspond to repulsion at all separations.

Whether or not intermolecular potential energy surfaces are useful in the description of collision processes depends upon the validity of the separation of the electronic from the nuclear motions. In slow collisions this is a good assumption; in a fast collision it is not tenable. In a fast collision interactions between the electronic and the nuclear motions lead to transitions from one potential energy surface to another. For example, in Fig. 13.1–1 there is a small probability that a collision which started out along curve (a) might end up along curve (f). However, when two potential energy surfaces such as (*e*) and (*d*) almost cross there is a very high probability that a collision which starts out along curve (*e*) will end up along curve (*d*).

b. Approximations introduced by the separation of electronic and nuclear motions (the Born-Oppenheimer separation)

The validity of the use of intermolecular potential functions in collision processes is based upon the separability of the electronic and nuclear motions. On this account let us examine the errors which are introduced by assuming this separability.[8, 9]

We first set up the Hamiltonian for the combined system of electrons and nuclei. In Appendix 13.A a complete expression for the Hamiltonian, including the effect of external electric and magnetic fields, is given. If the molecules have resultant electronic spin or orbital angular momentum, some of the magnetic interaction terms in this expression may become important from the standpoint of determining intermolecular forces. Otherwise it suffices to consider only the electrostatic interactions between the particles. This is the approximation considered here.

In most collision problems it is convenient to use a center of gravity coordinate system. On this account, we subtract the operator representing the kinetic energy of the center of gravity of the system from the complete Hamiltonian operator. This leads to the following Hamiltonian for the relative motion:[10]

$$\mathscr{H} = \mathscr{H}_e - \sum_\alpha \frac{\hbar^2}{2m_\alpha}\left(\frac{\partial}{\partial \boldsymbol{r}_\alpha}\cdot\frac{\partial}{\partial \boldsymbol{r}_\alpha}\right) + \frac{\hbar^2}{2M}\left[\sum_{\alpha,\beta}\left(\frac{\partial}{\partial \boldsymbol{r}_\alpha}\cdot\frac{\partial}{\partial \boldsymbol{r}_\beta}\right) + 2\sum_{\alpha,i}\left(\frac{\partial}{\partial \boldsymbol{r}_\alpha}\cdot\frac{\partial}{\partial \boldsymbol{r}_i}\right) + \sum_{i,j}\left(\frac{\partial}{\partial \boldsymbol{r}_i}\cdot\frac{\partial}{\partial \boldsymbol{r}_j}\right)\right] \tag{13.1–13}$$

where

$$\mathscr{H}_e = -\sum_i \frac{\hbar^2}{2m}\left(\frac{\partial}{\partial \boldsymbol{r}_i}\cdot\frac{\partial}{\partial \boldsymbol{r}_i}\right) + \Phi_e(\boldsymbol{r}^\nu, \boldsymbol{r}^n) \tag{13.1–14}$$

Here the subscripts α and β refer to the various nuclei and the i and j refer to the various electrons. The m_α are the masses of the nuclei, m

[8] M. Born and J. R. Oppenheimer, *Ann. Phys.*, **84**, 457 (1927); D. R. Bates, A. Fundaminsky, H. S. W. Massey, and J. W. Leech, *Phil. Trans. Royal Soc.* (London), **A** (No. 860), 93 (1950).

[9] H. Pelzer and E. P. Wigner, *Z. Physik. Chem.*, **B15**, 445 (1932).

[10] Equation 13.1–13 maintains symmetry among all the N particles. However, E. C. Kemble [*Fundamental Principles of Quantum Mechanics*, McGraw-Hill (1937), p. 63] expresses $\mathscr{H}$ in terms of $3N$-3 independent coordinates as, for example, the positions relative to some one particle.

is the mass of an electron, and M is the total mass of the molecular system. The potential energy Φ_e is the quantity defined in Eq. 13.1–1. The wave equation for the combined electronic and nuclear motions is then

$$\mathscr{H}\Omega(\boldsymbol{r}^\nu, \boldsymbol{r}^n) = -\frac{\hbar}{i}\frac{\partial \Omega}{\partial t} \tag{13.1–15}$$

where $\Omega(\boldsymbol{r}^\nu, \boldsymbol{r}^n)$ is the complete wave function for the system.

The separation of the nuclear from the electronic coordinates may be treated as a perturbation problem. The unperturbed electronic wave functions are obtained by considering a situation in which all the nuclei are fixed in a particular configuration $\boldsymbol{r}^\nu$. (This seems fairly reasonable inasmuch as classically the electronic motion is usually considerably faster than the nuclear motion.) The electronic wave functions, $\psi_k(\boldsymbol{r}^\nu, \boldsymbol{r}^n)$, for this hypothetical situation satisfy the equation

$$\mathscr{H}_e\psi_k(\boldsymbol{r}^\nu, \boldsymbol{r}^n) = \Phi_n(k \mid \boldsymbol{r}^\nu)\psi_k(\boldsymbol{r}^\nu, \boldsymbol{r}^n) \tag{13.1–16}$$

Here the $\Phi_n(k \mid \boldsymbol{r}^\nu)$ are the energy levels of the system corresponding to the electronic state, with a collection of electronic quantum numbers represented by k. According to Eq. 13.1–4 the $\Phi_n(k \mid \boldsymbol{r}^\nu)$ are closely related to the intermolecular potential energy function φ_{ab}. The $\psi_k(\boldsymbol{r}^\nu, \boldsymbol{r}^n)$ for any fixed nuclear configuration form a complete orthonormal set of functions in the electron space. That is, any function of the electronic coordinates may be expressed as a linear combination of the $\psi_k(\boldsymbol{r}^\nu, \boldsymbol{r}^n)$. Thus without loss of generality the wave function, $\Omega(\boldsymbol{r}^\nu, \boldsymbol{r}^n)$, for the combined electronic and nuclear motions in the original problem can be expressed in the form:

$$\Omega(\boldsymbol{r}^\nu, \boldsymbol{r}^n) = \Sigma_k \chi_k(\boldsymbol{r}^\nu)\psi_k(\boldsymbol{r}^\nu, \boldsymbol{r}^n) \tag{13.1–17}$$

Substitution of this relation into Eq. 13.1–15, multiplication of both sides of the equation by $\psi_l^*(\boldsymbol{r}^\nu, \boldsymbol{r}^n)$, and integration over the electron space leads to the result:

$$-\Sigma_\alpha \frac{\hbar^2}{2m_\alpha}\left(\frac{\partial}{\partial \boldsymbol{r}_\alpha}\cdot\frac{\partial}{\partial \boldsymbol{r}_\alpha}\right)\chi_l + \frac{\hbar^2}{2M}\Sigma_{\alpha,\beta}\left(\frac{\partial}{\partial \boldsymbol{r}_\alpha}\cdot\frac{\partial}{\partial \boldsymbol{r}_\beta}\right)\chi_l + \Phi_n(l \mid \boldsymbol{r}^\nu)\chi_l$$
$$+ \Sigma_k\left(\boldsymbol{A}_{lk}\cdot\Sigma_\alpha\frac{\partial \chi_k}{\partial \boldsymbol{r}_\alpha}\right) + \Sigma_k B_{lk}\chi_k + \Sigma_k\Sigma_\alpha\left(\boldsymbol{C}_{lk\alpha}\cdot\frac{\partial \chi_k}{\partial \boldsymbol{r}_\alpha}\right) = -\frac{\hbar}{i}\frac{\partial \chi_l}{\partial t} \tag{13.1–18}$$

The quantities A_{lk}, B_{lk}, and $C_{lk\alpha}$ are defined as

$$A_{lk} = \frac{\hbar^2}{M} \int \psi_l^* \left(\Sigma_\beta \frac{\partial}{\partial \mathbf{r}_\beta} + \Sigma_i \frac{\partial}{\partial \mathbf{r}_i} \right) \psi_k \, d\mathbf{r}^n \tag{13.1–19}$$

$$B_{lk} = - \Sigma_\alpha \frac{\hbar^2}{2m_\alpha} \int \psi_l^* \left(\frac{\partial}{\partial \mathbf{r}_\alpha} \cdot \frac{\partial}{\partial \mathbf{r}_\alpha} \right) \psi_k \, d\mathbf{r}^n$$

$$+ \frac{\hbar^2}{2M} \int \psi_l^* \left(\Sigma_{\alpha,\beta} \frac{\partial}{\partial \mathbf{r}_\alpha} \cdot \frac{\partial}{\partial \mathbf{r}_\beta} + 2 \Sigma_{\alpha,i} \frac{\partial}{\partial \mathbf{r}_\alpha} \cdot \frac{\partial}{\partial \mathbf{r}_i} + \Sigma_{i,j} \frac{\partial}{\partial \mathbf{r}_i} \cdot \frac{\partial}{\partial \mathbf{r}_j} \right) \psi_k \, d\mathbf{r}^n \tag{13.1–20}$$

$$C_{lk\alpha} = - \frac{\hbar^2}{m_\alpha} \int \psi_l^* \frac{\partial}{\partial \mathbf{r}_\alpha} \psi_k \, d\mathbf{r}^n \tag{13.1–21}$$

Equation 13.1–18 then is the differential equation for the $\chi_k(\mathbf{r}^\nu)$ which can in principle be solved after the $\Phi_n(l \,|\, \mathbf{r}^\nu)$ have been obtained from Eq. 13.1–16. This then gives the description of the motion of the nuclei.

The quantities A_{lk}, B_{lk}, and $C_{lk\alpha}$ may be simplified by the following arguments. Since the potential energy of the system, as well as the kinetic energy relative to the center of gravity, is independent of a translation of the complete system, it follows that the $\psi_k(\mathbf{r}^\nu, \mathbf{r}^n)$ depend only on the relative configuration of the various particles. First consider the effect on the electronic wave function of a translation $\Delta \mathbf{r}$ in each of the nuclear coordinates. Then consider the effect on the electronic wave function of a translation $-\Delta \mathbf{r}$ in each of the electronic coordinates. It is clear that

$$\psi_k(\mathbf{r}^\nu + \Delta \mathbf{r}^\nu, \mathbf{r}^n) = \psi_k(\mathbf{r}^\nu, \mathbf{r}^n - \Delta \mathbf{r}^n) \tag{13.1–22}$$

Then when the two functions are expanded in Taylor series, it follows that

$$\Sigma_\alpha \frac{\partial \psi_k}{\partial \mathbf{r}_\alpha} = - \Sigma_i \frac{\partial \psi_k}{\partial \mathbf{r}_i} \tag{13.1–23}$$

and

$$\Sigma_{\alpha,\beta} \frac{\partial}{\partial \mathbf{r}_\alpha} \frac{\partial}{\partial \mathbf{r}_\beta} \psi_k = \Sigma_{i,j} \frac{\partial}{\partial \mathbf{r}_i} \frac{\partial}{\partial \mathbf{r}_j} \psi_k \tag{13.1–24}$$

If we use these results, it is apparent from Eq. 13.1–19 that the A_{lk} are zero, and it follows that the second integral in Eq. 13.1–20 vanishes, so that

$$B_{lk} = - \Sigma_\alpha \frac{\hbar^2}{2m_\alpha} \int \psi_l^* \left(\frac{\partial}{\partial \mathbf{r}_\alpha} \cdot \frac{\partial}{\partial \mathbf{r}_\alpha} \right) \psi_k \, d\mathbf{r}^n \tag{13.1–25}$$

The integrals $C_{lk\alpha}$ cannot be further simplified.

The terms involving B_{lk} and $C_{lk\alpha}$ are usually small and can be neglected.

From Eqs. 13.1–23 and 24 it follows that derivatives with respect to nuclear coordinates are of roughly the same order of magnitude as derivatives with respect to electron coordinates. Thus it is easy to show that the terms involving B_{lk} are of the order of $(m/M)K_e$, where K_e is the electronic kinetic energy. Similarly, the terms involving $\boldsymbol{C}_{lk\alpha}$ are of the order of magnitude of $\sqrt{(m/M)K_eK_n}$, where K_n is the kinetic energy of the nuclei. Since m/M lies between 0.0005 and 0.000002, the error introduced by neglecting these terms in ordinary molecular problems is very small. For example, the error in the energy of the ground state of the hydrogen molecule amounts to approximately 0.005 kcal per mole. Thus, ordinarily Eq. 13.1–18 may be simplified by neglecting the quantities B_{lk} and $\boldsymbol{C}_{lk\alpha}$, and accordingly the nuclear motion is determined by the solutions to the equations

$$-\sum_\alpha \frac{\hbar^2}{2m_\alpha}\left(\frac{\partial}{\partial \boldsymbol{r}_\alpha}\cdot\frac{\partial}{\partial \boldsymbol{r}_\alpha}\right)\chi_l + \frac{\hbar^2}{2M}\sum_{\alpha,\beta}\left(\frac{\partial}{\partial \boldsymbol{r}_\alpha}\cdot\frac{\partial}{\partial \boldsymbol{r}_\beta}\right)\chi_l + \Phi_n(l\,|\,\boldsymbol{r}^\nu)\chi_l = -\frac{\hbar}{i}\frac{\partial \chi_l}{\partial t} \tag{13.1–26}$$

From this equation it is clear that the $\Phi_n(l\,|\,\boldsymbol{r}^\nu)$ as determined from Eq. 13.1–16 do in fact serve as the potential energy functions for the nuclear motion.

Eyring and Polanyi[11] have pointed out that, by changing the coordinates from the $\boldsymbol{r}_\alpha$ to a linear combination of the $\boldsymbol{r}_\alpha$, it is possible to eliminate the cross-terms $\left(\frac{\partial}{\partial \boldsymbol{r}_\alpha}\cdot\frac{\partial}{\partial \boldsymbol{r}_\beta}\right)\chi_l$ in Eq. 13.1–26 and express the equation for nuclear motion in the form of a Schrödinger equation in $3\nu - 3$ dimensions, where ν is the total number of nuclei. To express the nuclear motion in terms of the $3\nu - 6$ relative coordinates of the nuclei it is further necessary to separate off the rotational motion of the molecular system. It has been done, but results are complicated.[12]

Actually the B_{lk} and $\boldsymbol{C}_{lk\alpha}$ terms provide coupling between the various electronic states, which is usually weak. In a collision in which the molecules start at large separations in electronic states characterized by the set of quantum numbers, l, they can come apart in some other electronic states, k. The transition between the l and the k states usually takes place when the nuclear configuration is such that there is only a very small energy separation between $\Phi_n(l\,|\,\boldsymbol{r}^\nu)$ and $\Phi_n(k\,|\,\boldsymbol{r}^\nu)$. The theory of

[11] H. Eyring and M. Polanyi, *Z. physik. Chem.*, **B12**, 279 (1931); J. O. Hirschfelder, Ph.D. Dissertation, Princeton University (1936).

[12] C. F. Curtiss, J. O. Hirschfelder, and F. T. Adler, *J. Chem. Phys.*, **18**, 1638 (1950); J. O. Hirschfelder and E. P. Wigner, *Proc. Nat. Acad. Sci.*, **21**, 113 (1935); C. F. Curtiss, *J. Chem. Phys.*, **21**, 1199 (1953).

such *non-adiabatic collisions* has been discussed by Kallman and London,[13] Rice,[14] Landau,[15] and Zener.[16] A large percentage of the collisions between molecules in excited states is non-adiabatic in this sense. The quenching of energy of excitation by the transfer of energy in collisions has been the subject of a considerable amount of experimental and theoretical research.[17] Some high energy collisions between molecules in their ground states may also result in electronic transitions.[18]

An approximate expression for the probability of a non-adiabatic collision between two atoms may be described in the following manner.

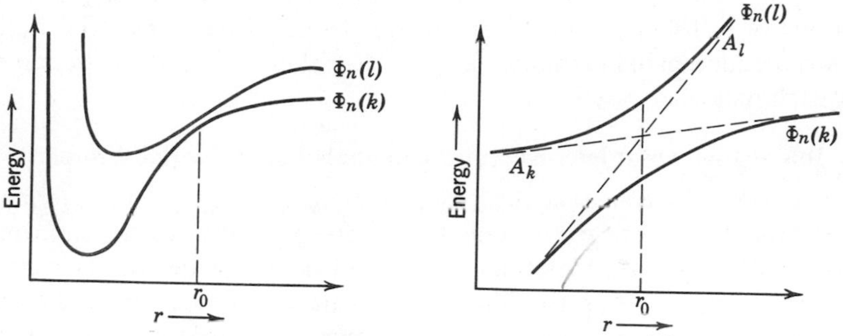

Fig. 13.1–2. (*Left*) Two potential energy functions which almost cross. (*Right*) Enlarged section of the region where $\Phi_n(l)$ and $\Phi_n(k)$ are close together.

If two potential energy functions of the same symmetry, $\Phi_n(l \mid r)$ and $\Phi_n(k \mid r)$, have almost the same value in the vicinity of a point r_0, as shown in Fig. 13.1–2, we can draw straight line asymptotes A_l and A_k which connect $\Phi_n(l)$ and $\Phi_n(k)$ before and after their near miss. Let us now define the following quantities: r_0, the separation for which $\Phi_n(l) - \Phi_n(k)$ has a minimum value $2\epsilon(l, k)$; $s_l = (dA_l/dr)_{r_0}$ and $s_k = (dA_k/dr)_{r_0}$, the slopes of the straight-line asymptotes; and $v(r_0) = (dr/dt)_{r_0}$, the relative velocity of the collision when the molecules are separated by a distance r_0. Then the probability P that the system jumps from the potential

[13] Kallman and London, *Z. physik. Chem.*, **B2**, 207 (1929). Application of variational principles to collision problems represents an important recent development by S. Altshuler, *Phys. Rev.*, **89**, 1278 (1953).

[14] O. K. Rice, *Proc. Natl. Acad. Sci.*, **17**, 34 (1931).

[15] L. Landau, *Physik Z. Sowjetunion*, **2**, 46 (1932).

[16] C. M. Zener, *Proc. Roy. Soc.* (*London*), **A137**, 696 (1933); **A140**, 660 (1933).

[17] N. F. Mott and H. S. W. Massey, *Theory of Atomic Collisions*, Oxford University Press, 2nd Ed. (1950), p. 281. Also A. V. Phelps and J. P. Molnar, *Phys. Rev.*, **89**, 1202 (1953).

[18] H. Eyring, J. Walter, and G. E. Kimball have a nice discussion of non-adiabatic collisions [*Quantum Chemistry*, Wiley (1944), p. 326].

$\Phi_n(l)$ to the potential $\Phi_n(k)$ (or vice versa) during a collision is approximately[18]

$$P = \exp\left[-\frac{4\pi^2(\epsilon(l, k))^2}{hv(r_0)\,|\,s_l - s_k\,|}\right] \tag{13.1–27}$$

in which h is Planck's constant. Thus the closer the potential curves approach each other, the higher the kinetic energy of the collision, and the greater the angle between the two potential curves, the greater is the probability of a transition.

When an appreciable fraction of the collisions are non-adiabatic, the classical notion of intermolecular forces loses its significance, but the results of collision processes can still be described on a statistical basis. Thus the concept of intermolecular potentials should be carefully examined in each particular case.

c. Information about intermolecular potentials from the virial theorem

Slater[19] has shown that the virial theorem can be used to determine the ratio of the average electronic kinetic energy to the average electronic potential energy in a molecular system. This use of the virial theorem has led to a better understanding of the nature of both inter- and intra-molecular forces. It has also led to a number of interesting applications. For example, Cottrell used Slater's results to determine the shifts in the electronic energy levels of molecules from experimental p-V-T data when a gas is subjected to very high pressure (see § 4.3c). Another application of the virial theorem is in the quantum mechanical calculation of approximate binding energies. For such a calculation, a scale factor is introduced in the approximate wave function and adjusted so as to give the lowest energy (see Appendix B at the end of this chapter). The adjustment of the scale constant automatically serves to establish the correct ratio of the average electronic kinetic to potential energy.

Let us consider a molecular system composed of n electrons and ν nuclei which attract and repel each other according to the Coulomb law (we neglect magnetic interactions). When the system is in an equilibrium state, then according to the virial theorem the average potential energy is the negative of twice the kinetic energy. Even when the nuclei are held in fixed non-equilibrium configurations, the virial theorem can be applied. Because of the separability of the electronic and nuclear coordinates, the virial theorem provides quite a bit of information about the non-equilibrium case.

The potential energy of the molecular system under consideration is

[19] J. C. Slater, *J. Chem. Phys.*, **1**, 687 (1933). See also M. Born, W. Heisenberg, and P. Jordan, *Z. Physik*, **35**, 557 (1925–26).

given by Eq. 13.1–1. Inasmuch as this potential energy function is a homogeneous function of the coordinates of degree -1, according to Eq. 1.4–29 we may write

$$\tfrac{1}{2}\sum_{i=1}^{n}\overline{(\boldsymbol{r}_i \cdot \boldsymbol{F}_i)} + \tfrac{1}{2}\sum_{\alpha=1}^{\nu}\overline{(\boldsymbol{r}_\alpha \cdot \boldsymbol{F}_\alpha)} = \tfrac{1}{2}\overline{\Phi}_e \tag{13.1–28}$$

$\boldsymbol{F}_i$ and $\boldsymbol{F}_\alpha$ are the forces acting on the ith electron and the αth nucleus, respectively. But the virial of the forces acting on the electrons is equal to the average value of the kinetic energy of the electrons, $\overline{K}_e$, according to Eq. 1.4–28:

$$-\tfrac{1}{2}\sum_{i=1}^{n}\overline{(\boldsymbol{r}_i \cdot \boldsymbol{F}_i)} = \overline{K}_e \tag{13.1–29}$$

The motion of the electrons is fast compared to the motion of the nuclei. Hence as far as the electrons are concerned, the nuclei are stationary. With this assumption Eqs. 13.1–28 and 29 give

$$\overline{K}_e = -\tfrac{1}{2}\overline{\Phi}_e + \tfrac{1}{2}\sum_{\alpha=1}^{\nu}(\boldsymbol{r}_\alpha \cdot \boldsymbol{F}_\alpha) \tag{13.1–30}$$

But now the force on the αth nucleus is given by

$$\boldsymbol{F}_\alpha = -\frac{\partial}{\partial \boldsymbol{r}_\alpha}\Phi_n \tag{13.1–31}$$

in which Φ_n is the potential energy of the system for a particular nuclear configuration. In the Schrödinger equation for the electronic motion (Eq. 13.1–16), Φ_n plays the role of the total electronic energy, so that for a fixed nuclear configuration:

$$\overline{K}_e + \overline{\Phi}_e = \Phi_n \tag{13.1–32}$$

Substitution of Eq. 13.1–31 into Eq. 13.1–30 gives

$$\overline{K}_e = -\tfrac{1}{2}\overline{\Phi}_e - \tfrac{1}{2}\sum_{\alpha=1}^{\nu}\left(\boldsymbol{r}_\alpha \cdot \frac{\partial}{\partial \boldsymbol{r}_\alpha}\Phi_n\right) \tag{13.1–33}$$

If the potential energy Φ_n is a function only of the distances $r_{\alpha\beta}$ between the nuclei, then

$$\sum_\alpha\left(\boldsymbol{r}_\alpha \cdot \frac{\partial}{\partial \boldsymbol{r}_\alpha}\Phi_n\right) = \tfrac{1}{2}\sum_\alpha\sum_{\substack{\beta \\ (\alpha\neq\beta)}} r_{\alpha\beta}\frac{\partial\Phi_n}{\partial r_{\alpha\beta}} \tag{13.1–34}$$

Hence Eq. 13.1–33 can be rewritten as

$$\overline{K}_e + \tfrac{1}{2}\overline{\Phi}_e = -\tfrac{1}{4}\sum_\alpha\sum_{\substack{\beta \\ (\alpha\neq\beta)}} r_{\alpha\beta}\frac{\partial\Phi_n}{\partial r_{\alpha\beta}} \tag{13.1–35}$$

Now this result can be combined with Eq. 13.1–32 to give the following two relations:

$$\bar{K}_e = -\Phi_n - \tfrac{1}{2} \sum_\alpha \sum_\beta{}_{(\alpha \neq \beta)} r_{\alpha\beta} \frac{\partial \Phi_n}{\partial r_{\alpha\beta}} \tag{13.1–36}$$

$$\bar{\Phi}_e = +2\Phi_n + \tfrac{1}{2} \sum_\alpha \sum_\beta{}_{(\alpha \neq \beta)} r_{\alpha\beta} \frac{\partial \Phi_n}{\partial r_{\alpha\beta}} \tag{13.1–37}$$

We have thus succeeded in obtaining expressions for the average electronic kinetic and potential energy in terms of Φ_n. Equations 13.1–36 and 37 are very useful in understanding the changes which take place in the electronic states of molecules under the influence of very high pressure. (See § 4.3c)

Let us now consider a collision between two closed-shell atoms, such as argon. If it is assumed that argon obeys a Lennard-Jones (6-12) potential:

$$\Phi_n = +4\epsilon \left[\left(\frac{\sigma}{r}\right)^{12} - \left(\frac{\sigma}{r}\right)^{6}\right] + \text{a constant} \tag{13.1–38}$$

Consequently, the average electronic kinetic energy is

$$\bar{K}_e = -\tfrac{1}{2}\bar{\Phi}_e + 12\epsilon \left[2\left(\frac{\sigma}{r}\right)^{12} - \left(\frac{\sigma}{r}\right)^{6}\right] \tag{13.1–39}$$

Thus for such atoms:

$$\begin{aligned} r > 2^{1/6}\sigma \ &, \quad \bar{K}_e < -\tfrac{1}{2}\bar{\Phi}_e \\ r = 2^{1/6}\sigma \ &, \quad \bar{K}_e = -\tfrac{1}{2}\bar{\Phi}_e \\ r < 2^{1/6}\sigma \ &, \quad \bar{K}_e > -\tfrac{1}{2}\bar{\Phi}_e \end{aligned} \tag{13.1–40}$$

where $r = 2^{1/6}\sigma$ is the equilibrium separation of the atoms.

d. Equivalence of classical and quantum mechanical intermolecular forces

It has been proven by Hellmann and Feynman[20] that the forces on the nuclei determined from a quantum mechanical potential energy surface are just exactly what we would expect on the basis of classical electrostatics and a knowledge of the electron probability density. In other words, once the distribution of the electron cloud has been determined from the solution of the Schrödinger equation, the forces on the nuclei may be calculated according to the electrostatic interaction formula given

[20] H. Hellmann, *Quantenchemie*, Leipzig, Deuticke & Co. (1937), p. 285; R. P. Feynman, *Phys. Rev.*, **56**, 340 (1939).

in Eq. 12.1-7.[21] This theorem—referred to as the *Hellman-Feynman theorem*—is very useful in establishing the qualitative connection between the distribution of the electronic charges in the molecules and the intermolecular forces. It also simplifies greatly our notions of the nature of intermolecular forces. We should note that spin and exchange effects play an important role in determining the electron cloud, but, once this electron distribution has been fixed, the forces are principally classical electrostatic forces. Previously there had been a tendency to assume that spin and exchange effects played a direct rather than a secondary role in determining these forces.

Let us now consider a system of ν nuclei and n electrons in which the nuclear and electronic motions are separable. The normalized electronic wave functions $\psi \equiv \psi_k(\mathbf{r}^\nu, \mathbf{r}^n)$ satisfy the Schrödinger equation given in Eq. 13.1-16, and the $\Phi_n \equiv \Phi_n(k \mid \mathbf{r}^\nu)$ are the energy levels of the system. The latter may be expressed in the form:

$$\Phi_n = \int \psi^* \mathscr{H}_e \psi \, d\mathbf{r}^n \tag{13.1-41}$$

Substitution of this into Eq. 13.1-31 gives for the force on the αth nucleus in the x-direction:

$$F_{\alpha x} = -\int \psi^* \frac{\partial \mathscr{H}_e}{\partial x_\alpha} \psi \, d\mathbf{r}^n - \int \frac{\partial \psi^*}{\partial x_\alpha} \mathscr{H}_e \psi \, d\mathbf{r}^n - \int \psi^* \mathscr{H}_e \frac{\partial \psi}{\partial x_\alpha} \, d\mathbf{r}^n \tag{13.1-42}$$

This may be simplified by taking into account the Hermitian nature of the operator $\mathscr{H}_e$ and the properties of the wave functions. The result is[22]

$$F_{\alpha x} = -\int \psi^* \frac{\partial \mathscr{H}_e}{\partial x_\alpha} \psi \, d\mathbf{r}^n = -\int \psi^* \frac{\partial \Phi_e}{\partial x_\alpha} \psi \, d\mathbf{r}^n \tag{13.1-43}$$

[21] The Hellmann-Feynman theorem is derived on the basis of the usual Hamiltonian, considering only electrostatic interactions between the particles. If we took into consideration the small spin and orbital coupling terms in the complete Hamiltonian given in Appendix 13A, small deviations from their result would be found.

[22] Since $\mathscr{H}_e$ is a real Hermitian operator,

$$\int \psi^* \mathscr{H}_e \frac{\partial \psi}{\partial x_\alpha} \, d\mathbf{r}^n = \int \frac{\partial \psi}{\partial x_\alpha} \mathscr{H}_e \psi^* \, d\mathbf{r}^n$$

Furthermore, ψ^* satisfies the Schrödinger equation,

$$\mathscr{H}_e \psi^* = \Phi_n \psi^*$$

Therefore the last two terms of Eq. 13.1-42 can be rewritten as

$$-\Phi_n \left[\int \frac{\partial \psi^*}{\partial x_\alpha} \psi \, d\mathbf{r}^n + \int \psi^* \frac{\partial \psi}{\partial x_\alpha} \, d\mathbf{r}^n \right] = -\Phi_n \frac{\partial}{\partial x_\alpha} \left[\int \psi^* \psi \, d\mathbf{r}^n \right] = 0$$

from which Eq. 13.1-43 is obtained. Since the kinetic energy part of $\mathscr{H}_e$ does not depend on the x_α, $(\partial \mathscr{H}_e / \partial x_\alpha) = (\partial \Phi_e / \partial x_\alpha)$.

Now, according to the definition of Φ_e in Eq. 13.1–1, we may write

$$\frac{\partial \Phi_e}{\partial x_\alpha} = \frac{\partial}{\partial x_\alpha}\left(\sum_{\alpha'>\beta} \frac{Z_{\alpha'} Z_\beta e^2}{r_{\alpha'\beta}}\right) - \textstyle\sum_i Z_\alpha e^2 \frac{\partial}{\partial x_\alpha}\left(\frac{1}{r_{i\alpha}}\right) \tag{13.1–44}$$

The last term is closely related to the electric field in the x-direction produced by the αth nucleus at the position of the ith electron, which is

$$\mathscr{E}_{\alpha x}(\boldsymbol{r}_i) = Z_\alpha e \frac{\partial}{\partial x_\alpha}\left(\frac{1}{r_{i\alpha}}\right) = -\frac{Z_\alpha e(x_\alpha - x_i)}{r_{i\alpha}^{\ 3}} \tag{13.1–45}$$

Hence Eq. 13.1–43 can now be written as

$$F_{\alpha x} = -\frac{\partial}{\partial x}\left(\textstyle\sum_\beta{}' \frac{Z_\alpha Z_\beta e^2}{r_{\alpha\beta}}\right) + \textstyle\sum_i e \displaystyle\int \psi^* \psi \mathscr{E}_{\alpha x}(\boldsymbol{r}_i)\, d\boldsymbol{r}^n \tag{13.1–46}$$

This may be further simplified by noting that the charge density ρ_1 for electron 1 is given by:

$$\rho_1 = e \textstyle\int \psi^* \psi\, d\boldsymbol{r}_2\, d\boldsymbol{r}_3 \cdots d\boldsymbol{r}_n \tag{13.1–47}$$

Furthermore, because of the identity of the electrons in the system, this must be the same for all n electrons. Hence the total electron charge density ρ at a point is just equal to $n\rho_1$. Hence we may finally write the expression for the x-component of the force acting on the αth nucleus as

$$F_{\alpha x} = -\frac{\partial}{\partial x_\alpha}\left(\textstyle\sum_\beta{}' \frac{Z_\alpha Z_\beta e^2}{r_{\alpha\beta}}\right) + \displaystyle\int \rho \mathscr{E}_{\alpha x}\, d\boldsymbol{r} \tag{13.1–48}$$

This completes the proof of the Hellmann-Feynman theorem.

This important result implies that the force on any nucleus (considered fixed) in any system of nuclei and electrons is just the classical electrostatic force exerted on the nucleus in question by the other nuclei and by the electron charge distribution for all the electrons. That is, the force on a nucleus is the charge on that nucleus times the electric field at that point due to the other nuclei and the electric field calculated classically from the electron charge distribution. If a wave function is calculated for a single nuclear configuration, the Hellmann-Feynman theorem permits a direct calculation of all the nuclear forces. This is a considerable saving in work over the usual scheme of calculating the energy of the system at a large number of nuclear configurations, and results in a considerable increase in the accuracy.

From the Hellmann-Feynman results it is clear that in order that the atoms corresponding to two nuclei attract each other, there must be a concentration of electron charge between them which attracts both nuclei. To a considerable extent a nucleus moves because of its attraction to its own electron cloud. In the antisymmetrical $^3\Sigma$ state of H_2, a node in the electron charge density lies midway between the nuclei. Therefore the electron density is decreased between the nuclei, and the atoms repel each other. Similarly the van der Waals forces of attraction may be interpreted as a distortion of the electron distributions in the molecules such that the electron density becomes larger on the side toward the colliding molecule.

A very interesting visual presentation of the meaning of the Hellmann-Feynman theorem has been given by Berlin.[23] Parts of the electron cloud tend to bind the nuclei together, and other parts of the electron cloud tend

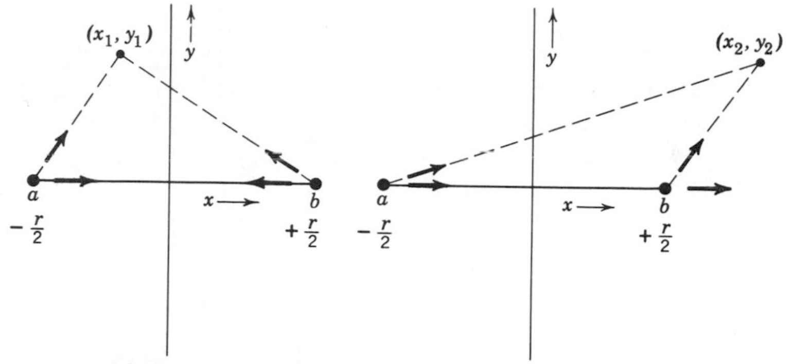

Fig. 13.1–3. Binding and antibinding in a diatomic molecule consisting of nuclei a and b with nuclear charges Z_a and Z_b.

to separate the nuclei. For example, consider the diatomic molecule pictured in Fig. 13.1–3. Let x be the distance along the internuclear axis measured from the midpoint of the two nuclei separated by a distance r and let y be the distance of a point from the x-axis. Figure 13.1–3a shows a point in the electron cloud (x_1, y_1) which would necessarily correspond to binding. That is, an element of negative charge located at the point (x_1, y_1) leads to a coulombic force on nucleus a which has a component in the x-direction that tends to pull a toward b. Similarly the coulombic force exerted by the negative charge on b has a component in the $-x$-direction and also tends to pull b toward a. Thus the negative charge at (x_1, y_1) helps to bind together the molecule ab. Now consider the situation (x_2, y_2) of Fig. 13.1–3b. A negative charge placed at this point leads to coulombic forces pulling both a and b in the x-direction. If the component of force F_{bx} on b in the x-direction is greater than the component of force

[23] T. Berlin, *J. Chem. Phys.*, **19**, 208 (1951).

F_{ax} on a in the x-direction, a differential force $F_{bx} - F_{ax}$ is set up, which tends to separate the two nuclei. That is, a negative charge at (x_2, y_2) under these conditions would be antibinding. The criterion for the boundary surfaces between the binding and antibinding zones is

$$F_{ax} = F_{bx} \tag{13.1–49}$$

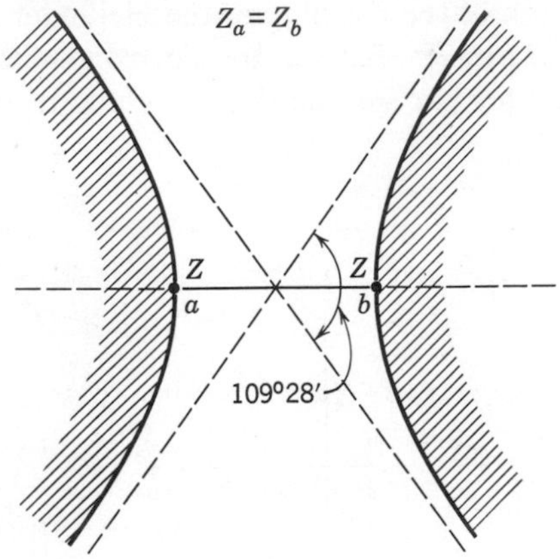

Fig. 13.1–4. Homonuclear molecule, $Z_a = Z_b$.

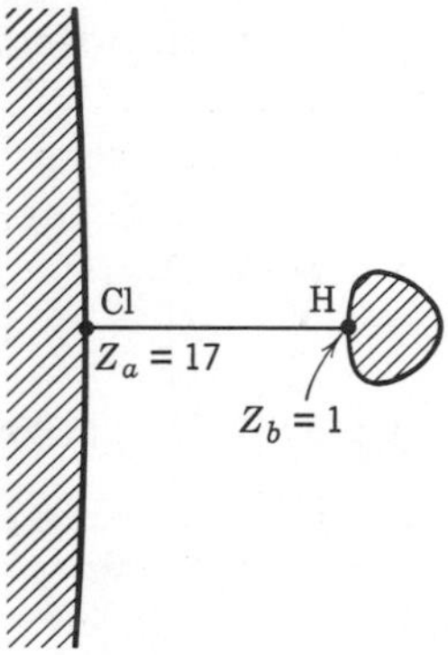

Fig. 13.1–5. Hydrogen chloride molecule, $Z_a/Z_b = 17$.

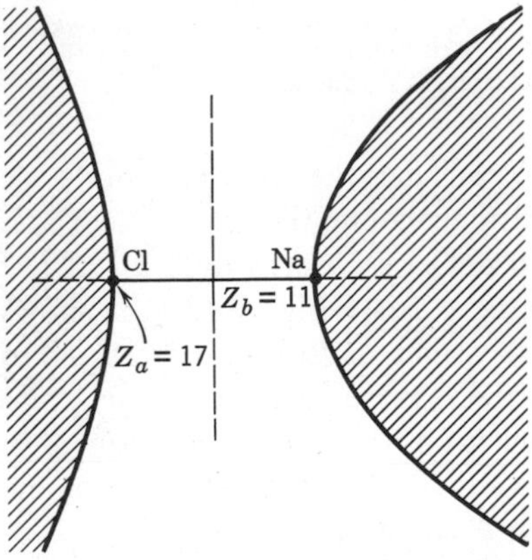

Fig. 13.1–6. Sodium chloride molecule $Z_a/Z_b = 17/11$.

or, if Coulomb's law is used,

$$Z_a \left[x + \frac{r}{2}\right] \left[\left(x + \frac{r}{2}\right)^2 + y^2\right]^{-3/2} = Z_b \left[x - \frac{r}{2}\right] \left[\left(x - \frac{r}{2}\right)^2 + y^2\right]^{-3/2} \tag{13.1–50}$$

For a homonuclear molecule (with $Z_a = Z_b$), the boundary surfaces satisfy the equation

$$y^6 - 3y^2 \left[x^2 - \left(\frac{r}{2}\right)^2\right]^2 - 2\left[x^2 - \left(\frac{r}{2}\right)^2\right]\left[x^4 - \left(\frac{r}{2}\right)^4\right] = 0 \tag{13.1–51}$$

The boundary curves, as shown in Fig. 13.1–4, are similar to hyperbolas and have asymptotes which are straight lines intersecting with the tetrahedral angle, 109° 28′. The antibinding region is cross-hatched in the figures. As the ratio of Z_a/Z_b increases, one of the surfaces flattens out to approach the surface $x = -r/2$, while the other surface curls back onto itself to form a closed region which approaches the single point ($x = r/2$, $y = 0$).

For hydrogen chloride, with $Z_a/Z_b = 17$, as shown in Fig. 13.1–5, the little antibinding region extends from the hydrogen nucleus at $x = r/2$ to about $x = 0.82r$ and between $y = \pm 0.19r$. For sodium chloride, with $Z_a/Z_b = 17/11$, as shown in Fig. 13.1–6, the surfaces look more like the homonuclear case, with the surface passing through the Cl slightly flattened and the surface passing through the Na slightly curled.

An analysis similar to this could be made to determine in which regions of space the electron cloud would help to attract two molecules and in which regions of space the electron cloud would tend to increase the repulsion between the molecules. In any case, that part of the electron cloud which lies directly between the two molecules is always binding.

e. Quantum mechanical calculation of the intermolecular potential energy

The quantum mechanical calculation of the energy of interaction between two molecules is basically the same as the calculation of the binding energy of a single molecule. Many detailed examples are given in Chapter 14. The two principal methods of solution are the variational and the perturbation methods (see § 1.6e).[24] In addition, there is the recently developed generalized self-consistent field method which we discuss presently. The variational method has the advantage that the energy calculated on this basis is always too high, so that the addition of more terms or more adjustable parameters to the approximate wave function is bound to reduce the error. The variational method may be applied to any intermolecular potential calculation, regardless of whether the molecules are close together or far apart. Both the variational and the perturbation methods apply more correctly to the calculation of the energy of interaction between two molecules than to the calculation of the binding energy of a single molecule, since the energy of interaction is truly small compared with the ionization potentials and other measures of molecular energies. The first-order perturbation method applies to calculations of the chemical or repulsive forces which arise when the molecules are close together and their electron clouds overlap. It can also be used to calculate the long-range forces between molecules having permanent dipole or multipole moments (see §§ 13.5 and 6). The second-order perturbation method, however, is needed to

[24] An excellent discussion of these methods is given by P. Gombás, *Theorie und Lösungsmethoden des Mehrteilchenproblems der Wellenmechanik*, Birkhäuser (Basel, 1950); N. F. Mott and I. N. Sneddon, *Wave Mechanics and Its Applications*, Oxford (1948); and H. Eyring, J. Walter, and G. E. Kimball, *Quantum Chemistry*, Wiley (1944).

calculate the long-range forces which arise through the induction of electric moments in one molecule by the electric field of the other molecule (see §§ 13.3 and 13.4).

The calculation of the chemical or repulsive forces by the first-order perturbation method is particularly simple when the bond structures in the two molecules are well determined so that no resonance need be considered. If the electrons in the molecules a and b are located in general one-electron orbitals $a_1(1)$, $a_2(1)$, . . . and $b_1(2)$, $b_2(2)$, . . . , respectively (where the subscript designates the orbital and the number in parentheses designates the electron), the total energy of the combined system of the two interacting molecules is given by[25]

$$E_{\text{approx}} = Q + \Sigma_p L_{ab} - \tfrac{1}{2}\Sigma_u L_{ab} \qquad (13.1\text{–}52)$$

Here $\Sigma_p L_{ab}$ is the sum of the exchange integrals between pairs forming shared electron bonds; $\Sigma_u L_{ab}$ is the sum of the exchange integrals between all unpaired electron orbitals; and Q is the sum of all coulombic interactions plus the sum of the energies due to the long-range energy of

[25] The nomenclature of molecular quantum mechanics is as follows:

(1) *Coulombic Energy Integrals.* The coulombic energy of the system is given for a four-electron system by

$$\int a_1(1)^* a_2(2)^* b_1(3)^* b_2(4)^* \mathscr{H} a_1(1) a_2(2) b_1(3) b_2(4)\, d\boldsymbol{r}^4$$

When the Hamiltonian $\mathscr{H}$ is expressed as a sum of terms, the coulombic energy becomes a sum of integrals, each one of which is called a "coulombic integral."

(2) *Single Exchange Energy Integrals.* The single exchange energy integrals are of the form

$$\int a_1(3)^* a_2(2)^* b_1(1)^* b_2(4)^* \mathscr{H} a_1(1) a_2(2) b_1(3) b_2(4)\, d\boldsymbol{r}^4$$

These may be reduced to the form $\int a_1(3)^* b_1(1)^* \frac{e^2}{r_{13}} a_1(1) b_1(3)\, d\boldsymbol{r}_1\, d\boldsymbol{r}_3$.

(3) *Multiple Exchange Energy Integrals.* The multiple exchange energy integrals differ from the single exchange energy integrals in the sense that more than one pair of electrons is exchanged between the initial and final products of orbitals. An example would be

$$\int a_1(3)^* a_2(4)^* b_1(1)^* b_2(2)^* \frac{e^2}{r_{13}} a_1(1) a_2(2) b_1(3) b_2(4)\, d\boldsymbol{r}^4$$

(4) *Overlap Integrals.* The term overlap integral can be used in either the generic sense, $\int \psi_1^* \psi_2\, d\boldsymbol{r}^N$, to express the lack of orthogonality between two wave functions, or else it may be used to express the lack of orthogonality between two orbitals, a_1 and b_1,

$$\int a_1(1)^* b_1(1)\, d\boldsymbol{r}_1$$

dispersion, induction, and dipole interactions. The part of Q arising from coulombic interactions, Q_c, is given by

$$Q_c = \sum_{\substack{\alpha>\beta \\ \text{all pairs} \\ \text{of nuclei}}} \frac{Z_\alpha Z_\beta e^2}{r_{\alpha\beta}} + \sum_{\substack{\text{all} \\ \text{orbitals}}} J_a + \sum_{\substack{\text{all} \\ \text{pairs}}} K_{ab} \tag{13.1–53}$$

where

$$K_{ab} = \iint a(1)^* b(2)^* \frac{e^2}{r_{12}} a(1) b(2)\, d\boldsymbol{r}_1\, d\boldsymbol{r}_2 \tag{13.1–54}$$

$$J_a = -\int a(1)^* \textstyle\sum_\alpha \dfrac{Z_\alpha e^2}{r_{1\alpha}} a(1)\, d\boldsymbol{r}_1 \tag{13.1–55}$$

The exchange integrals of Eq. 13.1–52 have the form

$$L_{ab} = \iint a(1)^* b(2)^* \frac{e^2}{r_{12}} b(1) a(2)\, d\boldsymbol{r}_1\, d\boldsymbol{r}_2 \tag{13.1–56}$$

In Eq. 13.1–52, the multiple exchange integrals and the overlap integrals have been neglected.

The energy of interaction of a pair of molecules is then calculated in the following manner. The energy, E_{approx}, is calculated first for the system of the two molecules in a state of collision; then for the two molecules separated by a very large distance. The difference of these two energies is the energy of interaction. The energies of interaction calculated in this manner should be quite accurate.

The generalized self-consistent field method, recently developed by Slater,[26] should be very useful in the calculation of intermolecular energies. The process is first applied to each of the separated molecules and then it is applied to the combined system. Let $a_0^{(0)}(\boldsymbol{r}_1)$, $a_1^{(0)}(\boldsymbol{r}_1)$, $a_2^{(0)}(\boldsymbol{r}_1) \ldots$ form a complete set of orthogonal one electron molecular orbitals for electron 1 in molecule a. Then various approximate wave functions for molecule a can be formed by taking different linear combinations of Slater determinants formed from these orbitals. By taking a linear combination of an infinite number of Slater determinants, it is possible to approach the exact wave function. In practice, however, it is found that a very good function is obtained by taking only a few Slater determinants corresponding to the interaction between a few chemically significant configurations.

[26] J. C. Slater, *Phys. Rev.*, **91**, 528 (1953), and **81**, 385 (1951). Also *Electronic Structure of Atoms and Molecules*, Solid State and Molecular Theory Group of Massachusetts Institute of Technology, Technical Report No. 3 (February, 1953). For a complete discussion of the standard Hartree and Hartree-Fock self-consistent field methods see P. Gombás, *Theorie und Lösungsmethoden des Mehrteilchenproblems der Wellenmechanik*, Birkhäuser (Basel, 1950).

Let us assume an approximate wave function, $\psi^{(0)}_{\text{approx}}$, made up of a particular linear combination of Slater determinants expressed in terms of the set of orbitals, $a_0^{(0)}$, $a_1^{(0)}$, $a_2^{(0)}$, ... Then we can uniquely specify an effective potential energy field $\Phi^{(0)}(\boldsymbol{r}_1)$ in which any of the electrons (for example, electron one) moves,

$$\Phi^{(0)}(\boldsymbol{r}_1) = \frac{\int \psi^{(0)*}_{\text{approx}} \Phi_e \psi^{(0)}_{\text{approx}} \, d\boldsymbol{r}_2 \, d\boldsymbol{r}_3 \ldots d\boldsymbol{r}_n}{\int \psi^{(0)*}_{\text{approx}} \psi^{(0)}_{\text{approx}} \, d\boldsymbol{r}_2 \, d\boldsymbol{r}_3 \ldots d\boldsymbol{r}_n} \tag{13.1-57}$$

The function $\Phi^{(0)}(\boldsymbol{r}_1)$ is the potential energy of interaction between electron 1 and all the other electrons, averaged over all their motions and spins and the nuclei, held in fixed positions. This follows from the fact that

$$d\boldsymbol{r}_1 \int \psi^{(0)*}_{\text{approx}} \psi^{(0)}_{\text{approx}} \, d\boldsymbol{r}_2 \, d\boldsymbol{r}_3 \ldots d\boldsymbol{r}_n \tag{13.1-58}$$

is the probability of electron 1 being in $d\boldsymbol{r}_1$ averaged over the motions and spins of each of the other electrons. Alternatively, $\Phi^{(0)}(\boldsymbol{r}_1)$ is the potential energy of interaction of an electron (with a particular spin) at $\boldsymbol{r}_1$ with an electronic charge distribution

$$-(n-1)e \frac{\int \psi^{(0)*}_{\text{approx}} \psi^{(0)}_{\text{approx}} \, d\boldsymbol{r}_3 \ldots d\boldsymbol{r}_n}{\int \psi^{(0)*}_{\text{approx}} \psi^{(0)}_{\text{approx}} \, d\boldsymbol{r}_2 \, d\boldsymbol{r}_3 \ldots d\boldsymbol{r}_n} \tag{13.1-59}$$

and the nuclei held at their fixed positions. Now $\Phi^{(0)}(\boldsymbol{r}_1)$ is used as the potential for a one-electron Schrödinger equation to obtain a new set of molecular orbitals, $a_0^{(1)}(\boldsymbol{r}_1)$, $a_1^{(1)}(\boldsymbol{r}_1)$, . . . ,

$$\left[-\frac{\hbar^2}{2m}\left(\frac{\partial}{\partial \boldsymbol{r}_1} \cdot \frac{\partial}{\partial \boldsymbol{r}_1}\right) + \Phi^{(0)}(\boldsymbol{r}_1)\right] a_k^{(1)}(\boldsymbol{r}_1) = \epsilon_k^{(1)} a_k^{(1)}(\boldsymbol{r}_1) \tag{13.1-60}$$

Here the ϵ_k is the energy of an electron in the kth orbital. The new orbitals $a^{(1)}(\boldsymbol{r}_1)$ now serve to define a new one-electron potential field $\Phi^{(1)}(\boldsymbol{r}_1)$, and this process is repeated until it converges to a self-consistent potential field.

For a combined system of two colliding molecules, we start with an approximate wave function $\psi^{(0)}_{\text{approx}}$ formed by antisymmetrizing the products of approximate wave functions for the separated molecules. In terms of this $\psi^{(0)}_{\text{approx}}$, we form a $\Phi^{(0)}(\boldsymbol{r}_1)$. From the one-electron potential we get a set of molecular orbitals for the combined system.

Then, repeating the process until it converges, we obtain the total energy of the combined system and hence the energy of interaction.

This process seems peculiarly well adapted to high-speed machine calculations. Already, Meckler[27] has shown that the process converges quickly and easily in the case of molecular oxygen. The total energy of the molecule corresponding to the potential $\Phi^{(0)}(\boldsymbol{r}_1)$ gives the first-order perturbation, and the energy corresponding to $\Phi^{(1)}(\boldsymbol{r}_1)$ gives essentially the second-order perturbation. Since the $\Phi^{(0)}(\boldsymbol{r}_1)$, $\Phi^{(1)}(\boldsymbol{r}_1)$, etc., in general have the same symmetry as the molecule, considerable simplifications can be made in the determination of the orbitals by the use of group theory.

2. The Polarizability of Molecules[1]

The polarizability of molecules plays a very important role in several of the theories of long-range intermolecular forces discussed in subsequent sections. Accordingly we devote this section to a discussion of the calculation of polarizabilities. First the general quantum mechanical theory is presented, and this theory is applied to the calculation of the polarizability of molecular hydrogen. Then the principle of additivity of polarizabilities is discussed. And finally the use of screening constants to calculate polarizabilities and other molecular properties is considered.

When a molecule is placed in an electric field a displacement of charges results such that a dipole is induced. The magnitude of this induced dipole is given by

$$\boldsymbol{\mu}^{(\mathrm{ind})} = (\boldsymbol{\alpha} \cdot \mathscr{E}) \tag{13.2–1}$$

in which $\boldsymbol{\alpha}$ is the polarizability tensor of the molecule. If the molecule has a permanent dipole moment $\boldsymbol{\mu}$, the energy of the molecule in an electric field minus that of the molecule outside the field may be obtained from Eqs. 12.1–35 and 12.2–2:

$$E - E_0 = -(\boldsymbol{\mu} \cdot \mathscr{E}) - \tfrac{1}{2}(\mathscr{E} \cdot \boldsymbol{\alpha} \cdot \mathscr{E}) \tag{13.2–2}$$

in which E_0 is the energy of the unperturbed molecule, and E is that for the molecule under the influence of the electric field $\mathscr{E}$.

It should be pointed out that Eq. 13.2–1 is valid only for low field strengths. In molecular collisions the electric field strengths are so large that there is some question[2] as to whether the usual polarizabilities suitable for low field strength still apply. At a distance of 3 Å from an electronic charge, the field strength is 5.3×10^5 esu per cm or 160 million volts per cm. At a distance of 3 Å from a dipole molecule with a dipole

[27] A. Meckler, Solid State and Molecular Theory Group of Massachusetts Institute of Technology, Quarterly Progress Report, July, 1952, p. 62; October, 1952, p. 19.

[1] The polarizability of matter is discussed in § 12.2.

[2] C. A. Coulson, A. Maccoll, and L. Sutton, *Trans. Faraday Soc.*, **48**, 106 (1952).

moment of 3 debyes[3] and with a separation of charge of 2 Å, the electric field is about 75 million volts per cm. Coulson, Maccoll, and Sutton have developed a theory showing that the polarizability of benzene and other conjugated and aromatic molecules (where the shape and electrical properties of the molecules are very different in different directions), increases a great deal at field strengths of the order of 100 million volts per cm.

a. Variational method[4] for the calculation of polarizabilities

The polarizability of molecules can be approximated by a simple variational procedure suggested by Hylleraas[5] and Hasse.[6] Let us consider an unperturbed molecule containing n electrons and ν nuclei for which the quantum mechanical Hamiltonian operator is $\mathscr{H}_0$. The energy of the molecule in its ground state is designated by E_0. Associated with this energy is a wave function Ψ_0, which satisfies the Schrödinger equation and a normalization condition:

$$\mathscr{H}_0\Psi_0 = E_0\Psi_0 \tag{13.2–3}$$

$$\int \Psi_0^*\Psi_0 \, d\boldsymbol{r}^n = 1 \tag{13.2–4}$$

When the molecule is subjected to an external disturbing influence (such as an electric field) there is a contribution to the Hamiltonian, $\mathscr{H}_1$, due to the perturbation effect. The total Hamiltonian for the perturbed molecule is then

$$\mathscr{H} = \mathscr{H}_0 + \mathscr{H}_1 \tag{13.2–5}$$

Corresponding to this Hamiltonian there is a wave function Ψ and an energy E. The perturbed wave function can be written approximately as[7]

$$\Psi = (1 + A\mathscr{H}_1)\Psi_0 \tag{13.2–6}$$

[3] 1 debye $= 10^{-18}$ esu.

[4] The variational method as an approximate means of solving the Schrödinger equation is discussed in § 1.6e–i.

[5] E. Hylleraas, *Z. Physik*, **65**, 209 (1930).

[6] H. R. Hassé, *Proc. Cambridge Phil. Soc.*, **26**, 542 (1930); **27**, 66 (1931).

[7] We assume that the molecule is not moving with respect to the electric field. Then the wave functions for the stationary state can be taken to be real. Hence in the following discussion the Ψ_0 are assumed to be real. Also, the term $\mathscr{H}_1$ is usually a function rather than a general operator. Without these conditions, the following analysis is somewhat more lengthy but the results are very similar.

in which A is a variational parameter. This parameter is evaluated by requiring that the approximate value of the energy

$$E = \frac{\int \Psi' \mathscr{H} \Psi' \, d\boldsymbol{r}^n}{\int \Psi' \Psi' \, d\boldsymbol{r}^n} \tag{13.2–7}$$

be a minimum.

Substitution of the Hamiltonian given in Eq. 13.2–5 and of Ψ' given in Eq. 13.2–6 into this expression for the energy gives

$$E = \frac{\int \Psi_0[(\mathscr{H}_0 + \mathscr{H}_1) + A(\mathscr{H}_1\mathscr{H}_0 + \mathscr{H}_0\mathscr{H}_1 + 2\mathscr{H}_1^2) + A^2(\mathscr{H}_1\mathscr{H}_0\mathscr{H}_1 + \mathscr{H}_1^3)]\Psi_0 \, d\boldsymbol{r}^n}{\int \Psi_0[1 + 2A\mathscr{H}_1 + A^2\mathscr{H}_1^2]\Psi_0 d\boldsymbol{r}^n} \tag{13.2–8}$$

When use is made of the properties of the unperturbed wave functions (see Eqs. 13.2–3 and 4), this expression assumes the form

$$E - E_0 = \frac{W_1 + (Q_1 + 2W_2)A + (Q_2 + W_3)A^2}{1 + 2W_1A + W_2A^2} \tag{13.2–9}$$

in which $W_1 = \int \Psi_0 \mathscr{H}_1 \Psi_0 \, d\boldsymbol{r}^n$

$$W_2 = \int \Psi_0 \mathscr{H}_1^2 \Psi_0 \, d\boldsymbol{r}^n$$

$$W_3 = \int \Psi_0 \mathscr{H}_1^3 \Psi_0 \, d\boldsymbol{r}^n$$

$$Q_1 = \int \Psi_0 (\mathscr{H}_0 - E_0) \mathscr{H}_1 \Psi_0 \, d\boldsymbol{r}^n$$

$$Q_2 = \int \Psi_0 \mathscr{H}_1 (\mathscr{H}_0 - E_0) \mathscr{H}_1 \Psi_0 \, d\boldsymbol{r}^n$$

When the constant A is varied so as to minimize the value of E, Eq. 13.2–9 gives the shift in the energy level due to the perturbing effect. Let us now apply this result to the special case of a molecule in an electric field.

In order to study the polarizability of a neutral molecule, the perturbation is taken to be a uniform electric field of intensity $\mathscr{E}_x$ in the x-direction. The perturbing potential is then

$$\mathscr{H}_1 = -e\mathscr{E}_x \left[-\sum_{i=1}^{n} x_i + \sum_{\alpha=1}^{\nu} Z_\alpha x_\alpha\right] \tag{13.2–10}$$

Here e is the absolute value of the charge on an electron. The x_i and x_α are the x-coordinates of the electrons and nuclei, respectively, and the Z_α are the atomic numbers of the nuclei. Now the x-component of the permanent dipole moment of the undisturbed molecule is given by

$$\mu_x = \int \Psi_0[-e\{\sum_{i=1}^{n} x_i - \sum_{\alpha=1}^{\nu} Z_\alpha x_\alpha\}]\Psi_0 \, d\mathbf{r}^n$$

$$= -e[\sum_{i=1}^{n} \bar{x}_i - \sum_{\alpha=1}^{\nu} Z_\alpha x_\alpha] \qquad (13.2\text{–}11)$$

in which a bar indicates a quantum mechanical averaging with respect to the unperturbed wave function. Since all electrons are equivalent, we can drop the subscript on $\bar{x}_i$ and call it $\bar{x}$, the average x-coordinate of an electron. Thus it may be seen that when the integral W_1, defined above, is evaluated for the perturbation potential in Eq. 13.2–10, the result may be written as

$$W_1 = -\mu_x \mathscr{E}_x \qquad (13.2\text{–}12)$$

The expression given in Eq. 13.2–9 for the energy shift is then

$$E - E_0 = -\mu_x \mathscr{E}_x + \frac{A(Q_1 + 2W_2 - 2\mu_x^2 \mathscr{E}_x^2) + A^2(Q_2 + W_3 + W_2 \mu_x \mathscr{E}_x)}{1 - 2A\mu_x \mathscr{E}_x + A^2 W_2} \qquad (13.2\text{–}13)$$

This expression for the energy shift is of the same form as Eq. 13.2–2. Hence the evaluation of the integrals Q_i and W_i enables us to calculate the coefficient of $\mathscr{E}_x^2$, which is simply related to the polarizability.

First we notice from the definitions of the W_i that both the W_3 and $W_2 \mu_x \mathscr{E}_x$ are proportional to $\mathscr{E}_x^3$. Hence these terms do not contribute to the polarizability and need not be considered further here. The integral Q_1 may be shown to be zero, and the other integrals in Eq. 13.2–13 may be shown to have the following values:[8]

$$W_2 = \mu_x^2 \mathscr{E}_x^2 + e^2 \mathscr{E}_x^2 n \left[\overline{(x_1 - \bar{x})^2} + (n-1)\,\overline{(x_1 - \bar{x})(x_2 - \bar{x})}\right] \qquad (13.2\text{–}14)$$

$$Q_2 = \tfrac{1}{2} a_0 e^4 n \mathscr{E}_x^2 \qquad (13.2\text{–}15)$$

[8] The expression for W_2 is obtained by substituting $\mathscr{H}_1$ (Eq. 13.2–10) into the definition of W_2 (Eq. 13.2–9) and making use of Eq. 13.2–11:

$$W_2 = e^2 \mathscr{E}_x^2 [\Sigma_{i,j} \overline{x_i x_j} - 2(\Sigma_\alpha Z_\alpha x_\alpha)(\Sigma_i \bar{x}_i) + (\Sigma_\alpha Z_\alpha x_\alpha)^2]$$

$$= \mu_x^2 \mathscr{E}_x^2 + e^2 \mathscr{E}_x^2 \, \Sigma_{i,j} \overline{(x_i - \bar{x}_i)(x_j - \bar{x}_j)}$$

Use of the fact that $\bar{x}$ is the same for all n electrons (because $|\Psi_0|^2$ is symmetric with respect to interchange of any pair of electrons) gives the expression in Eq. 13.2–14.

in which n is the number of electrons in the molecule, and $a_0 = (\hbar^2/me^2) = 0.5292$ Å is the Bohr radius. The term $\overline{(x_1 - \bar{x})^2}$ is the mean square deviation of an electron from its average position in the x-direction. The term $\overline{(x_1 - \bar{x})(x_2 - \bar{x})}$ gives the average correlation between the instantaneous x-coordinates of two different electrons. This correlation would be zero for a molecular orbital wave function. However, for polyatomic molecules this correlation is appreciably large if the wave function is either of a chemical bond type using atomic orbitals or else the wave function is of the correlated molecular orbital type.

The variational parameter A may be determined by setting $(\partial E/\partial A)$ equal to zero and solving for A. In the limit of low electric field strength (that is, in the limit $\mathscr{E}_x \to 0$), it may easily be shown that A varies as $\mathscr{E}_x^2$ and has the form,

$$A = \frac{(\mu_x^2 \mathscr{E}_x^2 - W_2)}{Q_2} \tag{13.2–16}$$

To evaluate Q_1 and Q_2 it is necessary to examine $(\mathscr{H}_0 - E_0)\mathscr{H}_1\Psi_0$. The only parts of the operators $\mathscr{H}_0$ and $\mathscr{H}_1$ which do not commute are the kinetic energy term of $\mathscr{H}_0$ and the electronic term of $\mathscr{H}_1$. In particular,

$$\frac{\partial^2}{\partial x_i^2}(x_i \Psi_0) = x_i \frac{\partial^2 \Psi_0}{\partial x_i^2} + 2\frac{\partial \Psi_0}{\partial x_i}$$

and

$$(\mathscr{H}_0 - E_0)\mathscr{H}_1\Psi_0 = -2e\mathscr{E}_x \Sigma_i \frac{\hbar^2}{2m}\frac{\partial \Psi_0}{\partial x_i}$$

Then the integral Q_1 becomes

$$Q_1 = -2e\mathscr{E}_x \left(\frac{\hbar^2}{2m}\right) \Sigma_i \int \Psi_0 \frac{\partial \Psi_0}{\partial x_i} dr^n$$

$$= -2e\mathscr{E}_x \left(\frac{\hbar^2}{2m}\right) n \int \Psi_0 \frac{\partial \Psi_0}{\partial x_1} dr^n$$

where use has been made of the identity of the electrons. Integration and use of the fact that $\Psi_0^2 = 0$ at $x_1 = \pm\infty$ gives $Q_1 = 0$.

The integral for Q_2 is

$$Q_2 = -e^2\mathscr{E}_x^2 \left(\frac{\hbar^2}{m}\right) n\, \Sigma_i \int \Psi_0 x_i \frac{\partial \Psi_0}{\partial x_1} dr^n$$

The terms with $i \neq 1$ cannot contribute; hence

$$Q_2 = -e^2\mathscr{E}_x^2 \left(\frac{\hbar^2}{m}\right) n \int \Psi_0 x_1 \frac{\partial \Psi_0}{\partial x_1} dr^n$$

It is easy to show by integration by parts that

$$\int \Psi_0 x_1 \frac{\partial \Psi_0}{\partial x_1} dr^n = -\tfrac{1}{2}$$

so that

$$Q_2 = \tfrac{1}{2} e^2 \mathscr{E}_x^2 \left(\frac{\hbar^2}{m}\right) n$$

with the result that

$$E - E_0 = -\mu_x \mathscr{E}_x - \frac{(\mu_x{}^2 \mathscr{E}_x{}^2 - W_2)^2}{Q_2} \tag{13.2–17}$$

Comparison of this result with Eq. 13.2–2, and the use of the expressions given in Eqs. 13.2–14, 15 for Q_2 and W_2, yields the following formula for the xx-component of the polarizability:

$$\alpha_{xx} = \frac{4n}{a_0}\left[\overline{(x_1 - \bar{x})^2} + (n-1)\,\overline{(x_1 - \bar{x})\,(x_2 - \bar{x})}\right]^2 \tag{13.2–18a}$$

This result, which is valid for molecules, is a generalization of the expression for the polarizability of atoms which was obtained by Kirkwood.[9]

The polarizability of an atom is isotropic. If the wave function for an atom is approximated by an atomic orbital wave function, the second term in Eq. 13.2–18a vanishes. Furthermore, in an atom, $\bar{x} = 0$ and $\overline{x_1{}^2} = \overline{y_1{}^2} = \overline{z_1{}^2} = \frac{1}{3}\overline{r_1{}^2}$. Thus Eq. 13.2–18a becomes

$$\alpha = \frac{4}{9a_0} \sum_i \left(\overline{r_i^2}\right)^2 \tag{13.2–18b}$$

This expression serves as a simple approximate method for estimating polarizabilities. For the hydrogen atom this equation gives $\alpha = 4a_0{}^3$, which is in fair agreement with the experimental value $\alpha = 4.5a_0{}^3$. For the helium atom Eq. 13.2–18b gives $\alpha = 1.0a_0{}^3$ (for the simplest approximate wave function, the product of two hydrogen orbitals), whereas the experimental value is $1.37a_0{}^3$. A fairly good value is obtained for molecular hydrogen[10] using Eq. 13.2–18a.

b. The polarizability of molecular hydrogen

Very accurate values of the polarizability of molecular hydrogen and its isotopes have been calculated by Ishiguro, Arai, Kotani, and Mizushima.[11] They used the eleven-term James and Coolidge[12] wave function for the normal unperturbed hydrogen molecule. They assumed that, under the influence of the external electric field, the wave function is modified by the addition of ten adjustable constants times James and

[9] J. G. Kirkwood, *Physik. Z.*, **33**, 57 (1932).
[10] J. O. Hirschfelder, *J. Chem. Phys.*, **3**, 555 (1935).
[11] E. Ishiguro, T. Arai, M. Kotani, M. Mizushima, *J. Phys. Soc.* (*England*), **A65**, 178 (1952).
[12] H. M. James and A. S. Coolidge, *J. Chem. Phys.*, **1**, 825 (1933).

Coolidge type terms. The ten constants were then varied so as to give the lowest energy. In this way they obtained the results given in Table 13.2–1. The experimental values for the dielectric constant of molecular hydrogen at 0°C and 1 atm vary from 1.000259 to 1.000273, so that the theoretical value of 1.000267 is quite satisfactory. There is considerable variation in the experimental values for the polarizabilities. The most careful measurements have been made by Volkmann.[13] His experimental measurements are listed in Table 13.2–1.

TABLE 13.2–1

THEORETICAL AND EXPERIMENTAL VALUES OF THE POLARIZABILITIES AND THE DIELECTRIC CONSTANT ϵ' OF MOLECULAR HYDROGEN (FOR ZERO FREQUENCY)

$\alpha_{\|}$ = polarizability (in Å^3) in direction parallel to bond

$\alpha_{\perp}$ = polarizability (in Å^3) perpendicular to bond

α = mean value of polarizability $= \frac{1}{3}(\alpha_{\|} + 2\alpha_{\perp})$

	Experimental[13]	Theoretical[11]		
	H_2	H_2	HD	D_2
$\alpha_{\|}$	0.934	0.9746	0.9651	0.9537
$\alpha_{\perp}$	0.718	0.6968	0.6917	0.6856
α	0.790	0.7894	0.7829	0.7749
ϵ' (0°C, 1 atm)	1.000259 to 1.000273	1.0002666	1.0002643	1.0002616

c. The additivity of bond polarizabilities

A quick estimate of the polarizability of a complex molecule may be obtained by adding the contributions of the various constituent bonds to the polarizability. The validity of this method may be justified by means of the theoretical development given in § 13.2a.

Let it be assumed that the electrons in an n-electron molecule may be divided into a number of groups $A, B, C, \ldots$ containing $n_A, n_B, n_C, \ldots$ electrons, respectively. These groups are supposed to be more or less independent of one another, so that the wave function (before being antisymmetrized) can be factored into a product of a set of functions, each

[13] H. Volkmann, *Ann. der Physik*, **24**, 457 (1935).

representing one of the electron groups. We use the notation x_{Ai} to indicate the coordinate of the ith electron in the group A. The average quantity, $\bar{x}_A$, is the value of x_{Ai} averaged with respect to the unperturbed wave function of group A. Then the summations given in § 13.2a can be written

$$\sum_{i=1}^{n} \bar{x}_i = n_A \bar{x}_A + n_B \bar{x}_B + \cdots$$

$$\sum_{i=1}^{n} \sum_{j=1}^{n} \overline{x_i x_j} = \sum_i \sum_j \overline{x_{Ai} x_{Aj}} + \sum_i \sum_j \overline{x_{Bi} x_{Bj}} + \cdots$$
$$+ \sum_i \sum_j \overline{x_{Ai} x_{Bj}} + \sum_i \sum_j \overline{x_{Bi} x_{Aj}} + \cdots \qquad (13.2\text{–}19)$$

and, therefore:

$$\sum_{i=1}^{n} \sum_{j=1}^{n} \overline{(x_i - \bar{x})(x_j - \bar{x})} = \sum_i \sum_j \overline{(x_{Ai} - \bar{x}_A)(x_{Aj} - \bar{x}_A)}$$
$$+ \sum_i \sum_j \overline{(x_{Bi} - \bar{x}_B)(x_{Bj} - \bar{x}_B)} + \cdots$$
$$+ \sum_i \sum_j \overline{(x_{Ai} - \bar{x}_A)(x_{Bj} - \bar{x}_B)} + \cdots$$

But, if the wave function can really be separated into electron groups, there is no statistical correlation between the motions of electrons in two separate groups, and

$$\overline{(x_{Ai} - \bar{x}_A)(x_{Bj} - \bar{x}_B)} = 0 \qquad (13.2\text{–}20)$$

Thus the polarizability can be expressed as the sum of the polarizabilities of the constituent groups:

$$\alpha = \alpha_A + \alpha_B + \alpha_C + \cdots \qquad (13.2\text{–}21)$$

The additivity of the polarizability is then a measure of the separability of the molecule into electron groups, such as inner shell electrons and electrons in chemical bonds. Table 13.2–2 gives the polarizability of a number of bonds as estimated by Denbigh.[14] Notice that the polarizability of a bond is different in the direction parallel to the bond, $\alpha_{||}$, from the polarizability perpendicular to the bond, $\alpha_{\perp}$. If the electric field makes the angle θ with a chemical bond, the polarizability, α_θ, is given by[15]

$$\alpha_\theta = \alpha_{||} \cos^2 \theta + \alpha_{\perp} \sin^2 \theta \qquad (13.2\text{–}22)$$

Averaging α_θ over all orientations (solid angles) leads to an average value of the bond polarizability:

$$\alpha = \tfrac{1}{3}(\alpha_{\parallel} + 2\alpha_{\perp}) \tag{13.2–23}$$

The average polarizability of a molecule is then the sum of the average polarizabilities of its bonds.

TABLE 13.2–2

BOND POLARIZABILITIES[14]

	$\alpha_{\parallel} \times 10^{25}$ (cm^3)	$\alpha_{\perp} \times 10^{25}$ (cm^3)
C—C (aliphatic)	18.8	0.2
C—C (aromatic)	22.5	4.8
C=C	28.6	10.6
C≡C	35.4	12.7
C—H (aliphatic)	7.9	5.8
C—Cl	36.7	20.8
C—Br	50.4	28.8
C=O (carbonyl)	19.9	7.5
C=O (CO_2)	20.5	9.6
C=S (CS_2)	75.7	27.7
C≡N (HCN)	31	14
N—H (NH_3)	5.8	8.4
S—H (H_2S)	23.0	17.2

These bond polarizabilities are very useful in calculations of the inverse sixth-power energy of attraction (London dispersion forces) between either non-polar or polar polyatomic molecules. This is discussed in § 13.3. However, these simple rules for obtaining the polarizability of molecules do not work well for molecules in which there is resonance between two or more bond structures.

Experimental values of the polarizability are given in Table 13.2–3. The quantities α_1, α_2, and α_3 are the three principal components of the polarizability. The mean polarizability is $\alpha = \tfrac{1}{3}(\alpha_1 + \alpha_2 + \alpha_3)$.

[14] K. G. Denbigh, *Trans. Faraday Soc.*, **36**, 936 (1940)

[15] In a Cartesian coordinate system with the z-axis along the bond, the polarizability tensor for a bond has the form

$$\boldsymbol{\alpha} = \begin{pmatrix} \alpha_{\perp} & 0 & 0 \\ 0 & \alpha_{\perp} & 0 \\ 0 & 0 & \alpha_{\parallel} \end{pmatrix}$$

Equation 13.2–22 gives the zz-component of the polarizability in the new coordinate system resulting from rotation through the angle θ.

TABLE 13.2–3[a]

POLARIZABILITY OF MOLECULES

Molecule	$\alpha \cdot 10^{25}$ (cm^3)	$\alpha_1 \cdot 10^{25}$ (cm^3)	$\alpha_2 \cdot 10^{25}$ (cm^3)	$\alpha_3 \cdot 10^{25}$ (cm^3)	Location of Principal Axes and Direction of Dipole Moment; Structure of Molecule
H_2	7.9	9.3	7.1	7.1	α_1 symm. axis
N_2	17.6	23.8	14.5	14.5	α_1 symm. axis
O_2	16.0	23.5	12.1	12.1	α_1 symm. axis
Cl_2	46.1	66.0	36.2	36.2	α_1 symm. axis
HF	24.6	(9.6)	(7.2)	(7.2)	α_1 symm. axis
HCl	26.3	31.3	23.9	23.9	α_1 symm. axis
HBr	36.1	42.2	33.1	33.1	α_1 symm. axis
HI	54.4	65.8	48.9	48.9	α_1 symm. axis
N_2O	30.0	48.6	20.7	20.7	α_1 symm. axis; molecule linear and unsymm. N≡N=O
CO	19.5	26.0	16.25	16.25	α_1 symm. axis
CO_2	26.5	40.1–41.0	19.7–19.3	19.7–19.3	α_1 symm., linear
SO_2	37.2	54.9	27.2	24.9	$\mu=\mu_3$; $\alpha_{2\perp}$ to OSO-plane
H_2S	37.8	40.4	34.4	40.1	$\mu=\mu_3$; $\alpha_{2\perp}$ to HSH-plane
CS_2	87.4	151.4	55.4	55.4	α_1 = symm. axis; linear molecules
NH_3	22.6	24.2	21.8	21.8	α_1 symm. axis; $\mu = \mu_1$; pyramidal
$(CN)_2$	50.1	77.6	36.4	36.4	α_1 symm. axis, linear
HCN	25.9	39.2	19.2	19.2	α_1 symm. axis, linear
CH_4	26.0	26.0	26.0	26.0	Reg. tetrahedron
C_2H_6	44.7	54.8	39.7	39.7	α_1 symm. axis
$CH_2{=}CH_2$	42.6	(56.1)	(35.9)	(35.9)	α_1 symm. axis
CH≡CH	33.3	51.2	24.3	24.3	α_1 symm. axis, linear
C_3H_8	62.9	50.1	69.3	69.3	$\alpha_{1\perp}$ CCC-plane
C_6H_6	103.2	63.5	123.1	123.1	$\alpha_{1\perp}$ plane of ring
CH_3Cl	45.6	54.2	41.4	41.4	$\mu=\mu_1$; α_1 symm. axis
CH_2Cl_2	64.8	50.2	84.7	59.6	$\mu=\mu_3$; $\alpha_{1\perp}$ ClCCl-plane
$CHCl_3$	82.3	66.8	90.1	90.1	α_1 symm. axis; $\mu=\mu_1$
CCl_4	105.	105.	105.	105.	Reg. tetrahedron
CH_3OH	32.3	40.	25.6	31.4	Calc'd for $\mu \perp$ OC; $\angle(\alpha_1, \mu) = 70°$

[a] The polarizabilities given here are taken from Landolt-Börnstein, *Zahlenwerte und Functionen*, Springer (1951), Vol. I, Part 3, pp. 510 et seq.

Illustrative Example

Problem. Calculate α_{xx}, α_{yy}, α_{zz}, and α for the ethylene molecule.

Solution. We choose the coordinate system in such a way that the axes are along the principal axes of the molecule:

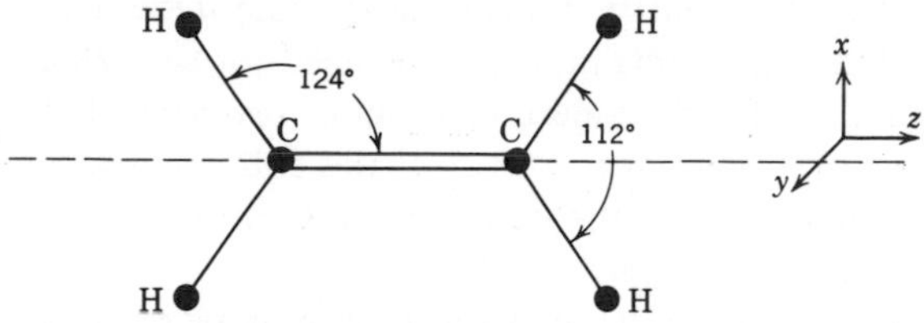

According to Eq. 13.2–22 and Table 13.2–2 we obtain the polarizability along the C=C axis:

$$\begin{aligned}\alpha_{zz} &= (\alpha_{\parallel})_{C=C} + 4(\alpha_{\parallel})_{C-H}\cos^2 56° + 4(\alpha_{\perp})_{C-H}\sin^2 56° \\ &= 28.6 + 4(7.9)\,(0.5592)^2 + 4(5.8)\,(0.8290)^2 \\ &= 28.6 + 9.9 + 15.9 = 54.4 \times 10^{-25}\ \text{cm}^3\end{aligned}$$

The polarizability perpendicular to the C=C axis in the plane of the molecule is

$$\begin{aligned}\alpha_{xx} &= (\alpha_{\perp})_{C=C} + 4(\alpha_{\parallel})_{C-H}\cos^2 34° + 4(\alpha_{\perp})_{C-II}\sin^2 34° \\ &= 10.6 + 4(7.9)\,(0.8290)^2 + 4(5.8)\,(0.5592)^2 \\ &= 10.6 + 21.7 + 7.3 = 39.6 \times 10^{-25}\ \text{cm}^3\end{aligned}$$

The polarizability perpendicular to the plane of the molecule is

$$\begin{aligned}\alpha_{yy} &= (\alpha_{\perp})_{C=C} + 4(\alpha_{\perp})_{C-H} = 10.6 + 4(5.8) \\ &= 10.6 + 23.2 = 33.8 \times 10^{25}\ \text{cm}^3\end{aligned}$$

According to Eq. 13.2–23 and Table 13.2–2 we get for the angle average of the molecular polarizability:

$$(\alpha)_{C_2H_4} = \sum_{\text{all bonds}} \alpha = \sum_{\text{all bonds}} \tfrac{1}{3}(\alpha_{\parallel} + 2\alpha_{\perp})$$

$$\alpha \text{ for C=C bond:} \quad \tfrac{1}{3}(28.6 + (2)\,(10.6)) = 16.6$$

$$\alpha \text{ for C—H bond:} \quad \tfrac{1}{3}(7.9 + (2)\,(5.8)) = 6.5$$

Hence $(\alpha)_{C_2H_4} = (16.6) + 4(6.5) = 42.6 \times 10^{-25}$ cm³. It should be noted that this is the same as $\alpha = \frac{1}{3}(\alpha_{xx} + \alpha_{yy} + \alpha_{zz})$.

d. Estimation of the polarizability and other properties of atoms by the use of screening constants

The polarizability and many of the other physical properties of atoms, such as size, diamagnetic susceptibility, electric susceptibility, and ionization potential, can be estimated easily and quite accurately by means of "screening constants." The basis for this treatment is the fact that an electron in an atom does not "feel" the presence of the nucleus completely, inasmuch as the electron is screened from the nucleus by the other electrons. Hence, although the charge on the nucleus is Ze, an electron in the atom acts as though it is moving in the field of a nucleus of charge $(Z - S)e$. The quantity S is called the *screening constant*. From a knowledge of one property of an atom it is possible to determine a set of screening constants. These constants may then be used for the calculation of some other property. Of the numerous systems proposed for the empirical determination of atomic properties[16, 17] the following scheme devised by Slater[18] and later justified theoretically by Gombás and Gáspár[19] is the most successful.

We assume that each electron in the atom may be represented by a wave function of the form

$$\psi_{n^*,l,m} = R_{n^*}(r)\, Y_l^m(\theta,\phi)$$
$$R_{n^*}(r) = r^{n^*-1} e^{-(Z-S)\frac{r}{n^*}} \tag{13.2–24}$$

Here the $Y_l^m(\theta, \phi)$ are the normalized spherical harmonics defined by Eq. 12.B–3 and r is in units of the Bohr radius, $a_0 = 0.5292$ Å. At large distances this function behaves like a hydrogen-like wave function of principle quantum number n^* in a field of nuclear charge $(Z - S)$. The *effective quantum number* n^* and the *effective nuclear charge* $(Z - S)$ for the various electrons in an atom are given by the following empirical rules:

(i) If the principal quantum number of an electron is n, the value of n^* is obtained from this table:

n	1	2	3	4	5	6
n^*	1	2	3	3.7	4.0	4.2

(ii) For determining $(Z - S)$, the electrons are divided into the following groups, each having a different shielding constant:

$1s$	$2s$	$3s$	$3d$	$4s$	$4d$	$4f$	$5s$	$5d$	. . .
	$2p$	$3p$		$4p$			$5p$		

That is, the s and p for a given n are grouped together, but the d and the f are each considered separately. The groups are considered to be arranged from inside out in the order given above, with the $1s$ as the innermost.

[16] L. Pauling and J. Sherman, *Z. Krist.*, **81**, 1(1932).
[17] L. Pauling, *Proc. Roy. Soc.* (*London*), **A114**, 181 (1927).
[18] J. C. Slater, *Phys. Rev.*, **36**, 57 (1930).
[19] P. Gombás and R. Gáspár, *Acta Phys. Sci. Hung.*, **1**, 317 (1952).

(iii) The screening constant S is formed for any group of electrons from the following contributions:

(a) Nothing from any shell outside the one being considered.

(b) An amount 0.35 from each other electron in the group considered (except in the $1s$ group where 0.30 is used instead).

(c) If the shell considered is an s or p shell, an amount 0.85 is contributed from each electron, with total quantum number less by one; and an amount 1.00 from each electron still further in.

(d) If the shell is a d or f shell, each electron in the groups closer in contributes 1.00 to the screening constant.

Several illustrative examples are now given to show how n^* and S are calculated.

Illustrative Examples

Problem. Find the effective nuclear charges $(Z - S)$ and the effective principal quantum number n^* for (a) normal carbon, $C(1s^2, 2s^2, 2p^2)$, and (b) singly ionized carbon, $C(1s^2, 2s^2\,2p)$. For carbon, $Z = 6$.

Solution.

(a) $(Z - S)_{1s} - 6 - 0.30 - 5.70 \qquad n_1^* = 1$

$(Z - S)_{2s,\,2p} = 6 - (3)(0.35) - (2)(0.85) = 3.25 \qquad n_2^* = 2$

(b) $(Z - S)_{1s} = 6 - 0.30 = 5.70 \qquad n_1^* = 1$

$(Z - S)_{2s,\,2p} = 6 - (2)(0.35) - (2)(0.85) = 3.60 \qquad n_2^* = 2$

Problem. Find the effective nuclear charges $(Z - S)$ and n^* for the 26 electrons in normal iron, $Fe(1s^2, 2s^2, 2p^6, 3s^2, 3p^6, 3d^6, 4s^2)$.

Solution

$$\left.\begin{aligned}(Z - S)_{1s} &= 26 - 0.30 = 25.70 && n_1^* = 1.00\\ (Z - S)_{2s,\,2p} &= 26 - (7)(0.35) - (2)(0.85) = 21.85 && n_2^* = 2.00\\ (Z - S)_{3s,\,3p} &= 26 - (7)(0.35) - (8)(0.85) - (2)(1.00) = 14.75 &&\\ (Z - S)_{3d} &= 26 - (5)(0.35) - (18)(1.00) = 6.25 && n_3^* = 3.00\\ (Z - S)_{4s} &= 26 - (1)(0.35) - (14)(0.85) - (10)(1.00) = 3.75 && n_4^* = 3.70\end{aligned}\right.$$

For the calculation of polarizabilities and diamagnetic susceptibilities of atoms[20] we need to know $\overline{r_i^2}$. For the wave function given in Eq. 13.2–24, the average value of the kth power of the radius for the ith

[20] For atoms the diamagnetic susceptibility per mole is $\tilde{N}\chi^{(m)} = -\dfrac{e^2\tilde{N}}{6mc^2}\sum_i \overline{r_i^2} = -\dfrac{7.92 \times 10^{-7}}{a_0^2}\sum_i \overline{r_i^2}$. See J. H. Van Vleck, *Electric and Magnetic Susceptibilities*, Oxford University Press (1932), p. 91.

electron is given by

$$\overline{r_i^k} = \frac{\int_0^\infty r^{k+2} |R_i|^2 \, dr}{\int_0^\infty r^2 |R_i|^2 \, dr} = \left[\frac{n_i^*}{2(Z-S_i)}\right]^k \left[\prod_{j=1}^{k} (2n_i^* + j)\right] a_0^k \tag{13.2-25}$$

Hence a knowledge of the screening constants and the effective quantum numbers affords a means for computing atomic polarizabilities. In addition these empirically determined constants may be used to calculate ionization energies and atomic radii. The following examples serve to illustrate the usefulness of the method of screening constants.

Illustrative Examples

Problem. Calculate the polarizability and diamagnetic susceptibility of atomic hydrogen in its ground state.

Solution. Here $(Z - S) = 1$ and $n^* = 1$ so that

$$\overline{r^2} = \left[\frac{n^*}{2(Z-S)}\right]^2 (2n^* + 1)(2n^* + 2)a_0^2 = \left(\frac{1}{2}\right)^2 (3)(4)a_0^2 = 3a_0^2$$

According to Eq. 13.2-18b, the polarizability is $\frac{4}{9a_0}(\overline{r^2})^2 = 4a_0^3$. The diamagnetic susceptibility is $\tilde{N}\chi^{(m)} = -7.92 \times 10^{-7}\, \overline{r^2}/a_0^2 = -2.38 \times 10^{-6}$ cc/mole.

Problem. Calculate the polarizability and diamagnetic susceptibility of carbon atoms in their ground states.

Solution.

$$\overline{r^2_{1s}} = \left[\frac{1}{2(5.70)}\right]^2 (3)(4)\, a_0^2 = 0.0923a_0^2$$

$$\overline{r^2_{2s,2p}} = \left[\frac{2}{2(3.25)}\right]^2 (5)(6)\, a_0^2 = 2.84a_0^2$$

The polarizability is $(4/9)\,[2(0.0923)^2 + 4(2.84)^2]a_0^3 = 14.35a_0^3$. The diamagnetic susceptibility is $\tilde{N}\chi^{(m)} = -7.92 \times 10^{-7}[2(0.0923) + 4(2.84)] = -9.14 \times 10^{-6}$ cc/mole.

Problem. The energy required to strip all the electrons from a ν-electron atom in a particular state is

$$E = -13.603 \sum_{i=1}^{\nu} \left(\frac{Z - S_i}{n_i^*}\right)^2 \text{ electron volts} \tag{13.2-26}$$

where 13.603 is the value of $e^2/2a_0$ in electron volts. Calculate the energy of both normal and singly ionized carbon, and finally calculate the ionization energy of carbon.

Solution. For normal carbon $C(1s^2, 2s^2, 2p^2)$:

$$E = -13.603\left[2(5.70)^2 + 4\left(\frac{3.25}{2}\right)^2\right] = -1027.5 \text{ ev}$$

For singly ionized carbon, $C(1s^2, 2s^2, 2p)$:

$$E' = -13.603 \left[2(5.70)^2 + 3\left(\frac{3.60}{2}\right)^2\right] = -1016.1 \text{ ev}$$

The energy of ionization is then

$$E_{\text{ion}} = E' - E = -1016.1 + 1027.5 = 11.4 \text{ ev}$$

Problem. The radius of a particular electron shell is defined as the distance at which the electron charge density $e\,|\,\psi\,|^2$ is a maximum. This distance is

$$[r]_{\max} = \frac{n^{*2}a_0}{Z - S} \tag{13.2–27}$$

(These atomic radii are useful in estimating internuclear distances in valence compounds, the bond distance being the sum of the two atomic radii of the two atoms or ions which are joined.) Calculate the atomic radius for the 4*s* electrons in iron.

Solution.
$$[r]_{\max} = \frac{(3.7)^2}{3.75}(0.5292) = 1.93 \text{ Å}$$

3. The London Dispersion Forces between Symmetrical Molecules[1, 2]

In the quantum mechanical calculation of the energy of interaction between two molecules, the *London dispersion forces* appear in the second-order perturbation terms. They are called dispersion forces because the perturbation terms are expressed in terms of the same oscillator strengths, f_{lk}, as appear in the equations for the dispersion of light (see § 12.6).

The classical explanation of the dispersion forces between two molecules *a* and *b* is as follows. At any instant the electrons in molecule *a* have a definite configuration so that molecule *a* has an instantaneous dipole moment (even if it possesses no permanent electric moment). This instantaneous dipole in molecule *a* induces a dipole in molecule *b*. The interaction between these two dipoles results in a force of attraction between the two molecules. The dispersion force is then this instantaneous force of attraction averaged over all instantaneous configurations of the electrons in molecule *a*. This explanation seems qualitatively correct and quite plausible. This mechanism, however, is not apparent from the quantum mechanical derivations. On this account, it is best that we do not stress the classical significance of these forces.

We begin by discussing a simple treatment of dispersion forces based on a Drude model (see § 12.5) of the molecules as three-dimensional oscillators. Next we discuss the second-order perturbation. The weakening of the dispersion forces at extremely large intermolecular separations due to

[1] H. Margenau, *Revs. Mod. Phys.*, **11**, 1 (1939).

[2] F. London, *Trans Faraday Soc.*, **33**, 8 (1937); *Z. physik. Chem.*, **B11**, 222 (1930).

retardation effects (the finite velocity of propagation of electromagnetic radiation) is discussed at the end of this section.

a. A simplified theory of dispersion forces based upon the Drude model

In § 12.5c, a simple theory of dispersion of light based on a molecular model suggested by Drude is discussed. Here we apply the same model to the treatment of the dispersion forces between molecules, to obtain expressions for the forces in terms of the polarizability of the molecules. The Drude model for molecule *a* consists of a pair of harmonically and isotropically bound particles of equal opposite charges of strength e_a and reduced mass m_a. (In the discussion in § 12.5c the molecular model consists of a set of harmonically bound particles. Here for simplicity we consider only a single pair of particles.) The force constant is denoted by k_a, so that the vibration frequency is $\nu_a = (1/2\pi)\sqrt{k_a/m_a}$. Similar considerations apply to molecule *b*.

We first consider the equations of motion of the pair of molecules separated by a distance r_{ab}. The system of two molecules has six modes of vibration. If the molecules are separated sufficiently far, the vibrations frequencies consist of a triply degenerate value of ν_a (corresponding to the unperturbed vibration of molecule *a*) and a triply degenerate value of ν_b (corresponding to the vibrations of molecule *b*). As the molecules approach one another the vibration frequencies are perturbed. The energy of interaction between the molecules is then obtained by quantum mechanical arguments. If all six of the degrees of vibrational freedom are in their ground states, the energy of interaction is the difference between the zero point energy of the perturbed system and the zero point energy of the two separated molecules. Clearly, the method also gives the energy of interaction between molecules in excited vibrational states but these interactions are difficult to interpret.

Let $\boldsymbol{\delta r}_a$ and $\boldsymbol{\delta r}_b$ represent the displacements of vibrators *a* and *b* from their equilibrium positions. The potential energy of the system consists of the sum of the contributions due to the displacements of the oscillators,

$$\varphi_a = \tfrac{1}{2}k_a(\boldsymbol{\delta r}_a)^2; \quad \varphi_b = \tfrac{1}{2}k_b(\boldsymbol{\delta r}_b)^2, \tag{13.3–1}$$

and a term representing the electrostatic interaction. If the molecules are sufficiently far apart (so that the concept of ideal dipoles applies), this energy of interaction is given by Eq. 12.1–45 or the term $b_3/r_{ab}{}^3$ in Eq. 13.1–10. In Cartesian coordinates this expression is

$$\varphi_{ab} = \frac{e_a e_b}{r_{ab}{}^3}\,[\delta x_a\,\delta x_b + \delta y_a\,\delta y_b - 2\delta z_a\,\delta z_b] \tag{13.3–2}$$

where the *z*-axis is taken to be the direction of the intermolecular axis.

The force on vibrator a is the negative of the gradient of the potential energy of the system with respect to $\boldsymbol{\delta r}_a$. Thus according to Newton's second law the equations of motion of the system take the form of three pairs of coupled equations:

$$
\begin{cases}
m_a \dfrac{d^2(\delta x_a)}{dt^2} = -k_a\,\delta x_a - \dfrac{e_a e_b}{r_{ab}^{\ 3}}\,\delta x_b \\[2ex]
m_b \dfrac{d^2(\delta x_b)}{dt^2} = -k_b\,\delta x_b - \dfrac{e_a e_b}{r_{ab}^{\ 3}}\,\delta x_a
\end{cases}
$$

$$
\begin{cases}
m_a \dfrac{d^2(\delta y_a)}{dt^2} = -k_a\,\delta y_a - \dfrac{e_a e_b}{r_{ab}^{\ 3}}\,\delta y_b \\[2ex]
m_b \dfrac{d^2(\delta y_b)}{dt^2} = -k_b\,\delta y_b - \dfrac{e_a e_b}{r_{ab}^{\ 3}}\,\delta y_a
\end{cases}
\qquad (13.3\text{–}3)
$$

$$
\begin{cases}
m_a \dfrac{d^2(\delta z_a)}{dt^2} = -k_a\,\delta z_a + 2\,\dfrac{e_a e_b}{r_{ab}^{\ 3}}\,\delta z_b \\[2ex]
m_b \dfrac{d^2(\delta z_b)}{dt^2} = -k_b\,\delta z_b + 2\,\dfrac{e_a e_b}{r_{ab}^{\ 3}}\,\delta z_a
\end{cases}
$$

The solutions of the equations of change depend on the initial conditions. However, after a very short time, the transients decay and the solutions are periodic. If solutions of the form $\delta x_a = A_x e^{2\pi i\nu t}$, $\delta y_a = A_y e^{2\pi i\nu t}$, etc., are substituted into the differential equations, we obtain a set of linear homogeneous equations for the amplitudes. These equations possess solutions only if the determinant of the coefficients is zero. This provides a "secular" or determinantal equation for the vibration frequencies. The determinant may be factored, and we obtain two identical equations of the form:

$$(k_a - m_a 4\pi^2\nu^2)\,(k_b - m_b 4\pi^2\nu^2) = \frac{e_a^{\ 2} e_b^{\ 2}}{r_{ab}^{\ 6}} \qquad (13.3\text{–}4)$$

and one equation of the form

$$(k_a - m_a 4\pi^2\nu^2)\,(k_b - m_b 4\pi^2\nu^2) = \frac{4e_a^{\ 2} e_b^{\ 2}}{r_{ab}^{\ 6}} \qquad (13.3\text{–}5)$$

The system under consideration has six vibrational degrees of freedom and six fundamental vibration frequencies. However, because of the cylindrical symmetry (the x and y axes are equivalent) there are two pairs of doubly degenerate values. These values are the roots of Eq. 13.3-4.

The two non-degenerate values are the roots of Eq. 13.3–5. The equations for the vibration frequencies may be rewritten in terms of the vibration frequencies of the isolated molecules and the polarizabilities. According to the discussion of § 12.5c, the polarizability (of the Drude model of a molecule) in a stationary electric field (a field of zero frequency) is given by Eq. 12.5–16 as

$$\alpha_a = \frac{e_a^{\,2}}{4\pi^2 m_a \nu_a^{\,2}} \tag{13.3–6}$$

Thus the equations for the vibration frequencies can be rewritten in the form

$$(\nu_a^{\,2} - \nu^2)(\nu_b^{\,2} - \nu^2) = \nu_a^{\,2}\nu_b^{\,2}\,\frac{\alpha_a\alpha_b}{r_{ab}^{\;6}} \tag{13.3–7}$$

$$(\nu_a^{\,2} - \nu^2)(\nu_b^{\,2} - \nu^2) = 4\nu_a^{\,2}\nu_b^{\,2}\,\frac{\alpha_a\alpha_b}{r_{ab}^{\;6}} \tag{13.3–8}$$

A quantum mechanical treatment of the system under consideration leads to an expression for the energy which is the sum of six terms, one for each normal mode. That is, the energy is

$$\text{Total energy} = \sum_{i=1}^{6} h\nu_i(n_i + \tfrac{1}{2}) \tag{13.3–9}$$

where the ν_i are the classical vibration frequencies, given by the methods just discussed. The n_i are the vibrational quantum numbers associated with each normal mode. The energy of interaction is the difference between the total energy of the system and that of the separated molecules. The energy of interaction between two molecules in their lowest vibrational state is

$$\varphi_{ab}^{(\text{dis})} = \frac{h}{2}\left(\sum_{i=1}^{6} \nu_i - 3\nu_a - 3\nu_b\right) \tag{13.3–10}$$

Clearly the existence of an energy of interaction depends on the existence of the zero-point energy—a purely quantum mechanical concept.

There are two special cases in which Eqs. 13.3–7 and 8 may be solved explicitly for the fundamental frequencies $\nu_x^{(1)}$, $\nu_y^{(1)}$, etc. These are:

1. Systems in which the perturbation is small compared to the difference between the natural frequencies, that is, in which

$$\frac{\sqrt{\alpha_a\alpha_b}}{r_{ab}^{\;3}} \ll \frac{|\nu_a - \nu_b|}{\sqrt{\nu_a\nu_b}}$$

In this case

$$\begin{cases} \nu_x^{(1)} = \nu_y^{(1)} = \nu_a - \dfrac{\nu_a \nu_b^2 \alpha_a \alpha_b}{2(\nu_b^2 - \nu_a^2) r_{ab}^6} \\[2ex] \nu_x^{(2)} = \nu_y^{(2)} = \nu_b + \dfrac{\nu_a^2 \nu_b \alpha_a \alpha_b}{2(\nu_b^2 - \nu_a^2) r_{ab}^6} \\[2ex] \nu_z^{(1)} = \nu_a - \dfrac{2\nu_a \nu_b^2 \alpha_a \alpha_b}{(\nu_b^2 - \nu_a^2) r_{ab}^6} \\[2ex] \nu_z^{(2)} = \nu_b + \dfrac{2\nu_a^2 \nu_b \alpha_a \alpha_b}{(\nu_b^2 - \nu_a^2) r_{ab}^6} \end{cases} \qquad (13.3\text{–}11)$$

2. Systems in which the two molecules are alike and the perturbation is small, that is, in which

$$\begin{cases} \nu_a = \nu_b = \nu_0 \\ \alpha_a = \alpha_b = \alpha \\ \text{and } \dfrac{\alpha}{r_{ab}^3} \ll 1 \end{cases} \qquad (13.3\text{–}12)$$

In this case

$$\begin{cases} \nu_x^{(1)} = \nu_y^{(1)} = \nu_0 \left[1 + \dfrac{\alpha}{2r_{ab}^3} - \dfrac{\alpha^2}{8r_{ab}^6} + \cdots\right] \\[2ex] \nu_x^{(2)} = \nu_y^{(2)} = \nu_0 \left[1 - \dfrac{\alpha}{2r_{ab}^3} - \dfrac{\alpha^2}{8r_{ab}^6} + \cdots\right] \\[2ex] \nu_z^{(1)} = \nu_0 \left[1 + \dfrac{\alpha}{r_{ab}^3} - \dfrac{\alpha^2}{2r_{ab}^6} + \cdots\right] \\[2ex] \nu_z^{(2)} = \nu_0 \left[1 - \dfrac{\alpha}{r_{ab}^3} - \dfrac{\alpha^2}{2r_{ab}^6} + \cdots\right] \end{cases} \qquad (13.3\text{–}13)$$

Let us now consider the total energy of the system of two interacting vibrators in its ground state. That is, we consider a collision between two molecules each in its ground state and assume that there is no jump in the vibrational quantum numbers during the collision. If the perturbation is small compared to the difference between the natural frequencies (Case 1, above), then the energy of interaction (that is, the difference between the total energy of the system and that of the separated atoms) is

$$\varphi_{ab}^{(\text{dis})} = -\frac{3}{2}\left(\frac{h\nu_a \nu_b}{\nu_a + \nu_b}\right)\frac{\alpha_a \alpha_b}{r_{ab}^6} \qquad (13.3\text{–}14)$$

If the molecules are alike and the perturbation is small (Case 2, above), we find that the energy of interaction is

$$\varphi_{ab}^{(\text{dis})} = -\tfrac{3}{4}\,h\nu_0 \frac{\alpha^2}{r_{ab}{}^6} \tag{13.3–15}$$

It is to be noted that this expression is a special case of that given by Eq. 13.3–14.

We have thus obtained expressions for the interactions between non-polar molecules—"dispersion forces." The expressions are based on a highly idealized model, but the results are interesting. The dependence of the potential on the polarizabilities of the individual molecules and the inverse sixth-power dependence on an intermolecular distance are consistent with the results of more exact treatments.

b. Second-order perturbation treatment of dispersion forces

A more exact treatment of the dispersion forces between two real molecules may be based on either a variational or a perturbation solution of the quantum mechanical problem. At very large separations, the exchange integrals decrease exponentially with distance and become negligible with respect to the coulombic integrals. Hence it is not necessary to antisymmetrize the wave functions with respect to the electronic coordinates, and the zero-order wave function of the system is taken to be a simple product of wave functions of the separated molecules. A detailed calculation by the variational method of the energy of interaction of two hydrogen atoms is discussed in § 14.1. Here we consider the application of the results of second-order perturbation theory to the general theory of dispersion forces.

In "spherical" molecules all the nuclei are effectively located at a single center so that, insofar as the long-range interactions are concerned, the molecules behave as single atoms. According to the discussion of § 13.1, the quantum mechanical problem of calculating the intermolecular potential energy is the problem of determining the electronic energy for a particular configuration. The total potential energy of the system is Φ_e, given by Eq. 13.1–1. The portion representing the interaction between the two molecules, φ_e (Eq. 13.1–2), acts as the perturbation potential.

The perturbation potential φ_e is expanded in inverse powers of the separation in Eq. 13.1–10. To obtain the leading term in the expansion of the dispersion energy it is necessary to consider only the first non-vanishing term in the expansion of φ_e, that is, the term $b_3/r_{ab}{}^3$. The first-order perturbation energy, which is the average of φ_e weighted according to the square of the unperturbed wave function, is zero if the atoms (or molecules) have no resultant angular momentum (for example, atoms in S states). Hence it is necessary to consider the second-order perturbation. If the atoms (or molecules) have resultant angular momenta, the results of first-order perturbation are not zero. These first-order perturbation effects are considered in § 13.6 as multipole-multipole electrostatic interactions. They are superimposed on the (second-order perturbation) dispersion forces discussed here.

The perturbation method of solving quantum mechanical problems is discussed in § 1.6. Let us characterize the state of an isolated molecule a by the magnetic quantum number m_a and denote the set of remaining quantum numbers symbolically by k_a, and similarly for molecule b. The energies of the separated molecules, which are clearly degenerate in the magnetic quantum numbers, are denoted by E_{k_a} and E_{k_b}. The zero-order wave function of the combined system (that is, the pair of colliding molecules) is then taken to be the product of the wave functions of the isolated molecules:

$$\psi_{ab}(k_a m_a k_b m_b \mid \boldsymbol{r}^n) = \psi_a(k_a m_a \mid \boldsymbol{r}^{na})\psi_b(k_b m_b \mid \boldsymbol{r}^{nb}) \quad (13.3\text{–}16)$$

The expression for the second-order perturbation energy given by Eq. 1.6–55 is strictly applicable only to non-degenerate systems. However, as is well known, the expression may be applied to degenerate systems if the "proper" degenerate wave functions are used. Hence we find that the second-order perturbation energy of the system, that is, the dispersion energy between the molecules, is

$$\varphi_{ab}^{(\text{dis})}(k_a m_a k_b m_b \mid r_{ab}) = -\sum_{\substack{k_a',\, m_a'\\ k_b',\, m_b'}}{}' \frac{|(k_a m_a k_b m_b \mid \varphi_e \mid k_a' m_a' k_b' m_b')|^2}{E_{k_a'} + E_{k_b'} - E_{k_a} - E_{k_b}} \quad (13.3\text{–}17)$$

The sum is to be taken over all quantum numbers, except that those terms for which $k_a' = k_a$ and $k_b' = k_b$ are to be omitted. The matrix elements in the numerator are defined by

$$(k_a m_a k_b m_b \mid \varphi_e \mid k_a' m_a' k_b' m_b') \quad (13.3\text{–}18)$$

$$= \iint \psi_a^*(k_a m_a | \boldsymbol{r}^{na})\psi_b^*(k_b m_b | \boldsymbol{r}^{nb})\varphi_e \psi_a(k_a' m_a' | \boldsymbol{r}^{na})\psi_b(k_b' m_b' | \boldsymbol{r}^{nb})\, d\boldsymbol{r}^{na} d\boldsymbol{r}^{nb}$$

If we let $\varphi_e = b_3/r_{ab}^3$ and if we use the explicit expression for b_3 as given by Eq. 13.1–12a, the expression for the dispersion energy (Eq. 13.3–17) becomes

$$\varphi_{ab}^{(\text{dis})}(k_a m_a k_b m_b \mid r_{ab}) = \frac{e^4}{r_{ab}^6} \sum_{\substack{k_a',\, m_a'\\ k_b'\, m_b'}}{}' \frac{\begin{bmatrix} (k_a m_a | x_a | k_a' m_a')(k_b m_b | x_b | k_b' m_b') \\ +(k_a m_a | y_a | k_a' m_a')(k_b m_b | y_b | k_b' m_b') \\ -2(k_a m_a | z_a | k_a' m_a')(k_b m_b | z_b | k_b' m_b') \end{bmatrix}^2}{E_{k_a} + E_{k_b} - E_{k_a'} - E_{k_b'}} \quad (13.3\text{–}19)$$

We are usually interested only in the average intermolecular potential for collisions involving molecules in states characterized by all values of the magnetic quantum numbers. If this expression for the dispersion energy is averaged over the magnetic quantum numbers of both molecules, we obtain an expression which may be written simply in terms of the "quantum mechanical oscillator strengths" defined by Eq. 12.6–22:

$$\varphi_{ab}^{(\mathrm{dis})}(k_a k_b \mid r_{ab}) = \frac{3}{2}\left(\frac{eh}{2\pi}\right)^4 \frac{1}{r_{ab}{}^6 m^2} \times \sum_{k_a', k_b'} \frac{f_a(k_a, k_a') f_b(k_b, k_b')}{[E_{k_a} - E_{k_a'}]\,[E_{k_b} - E_{k_b'}]\,[E_{k_a} + E_{k_b} - E_{k_a'} - E_{k_b'}]} \tag{13.3–20}$$

in which m is the mass of the electron.

It should be noted that the perturbation method is useful (that is, a good approximation) only if the perturbation is small compared to the difference between the energy levels or, more precisely, only if

$$\frac{e^2}{r_{ab}{}^3}\left|(k_a m_a \mid x_a \mid k_a' m_a')\,(k_b m_b \mid x_b \mid k_b' m_b')\right| \ll \left| E_{k_a} + E_{k_b} - E_{k_a'} - E_{k_b'} \right| \tag{13.3–21}$$

is satisfied for all values of the quantum numbers and if similar conditions are satisfied for the y and z directions. Systems in which this condition is not satisfied should be solved by a variational method (for example, see § 13.6c).

From the definition of the oscillator strengths (Eq. 12.6–22), it is seen that $f_a(k_a, k_a')$ has the same sign as $(E_{k_a'} - E_{k_a})$. Hence it follows directly from the expression for the dispersion energy that, for molecules in their ground states, $\varphi_{ab}^{(\mathrm{dis})}$ is negative, and the force is one of attraction. Molecules in excited states may either attract or repel one another.

Let us define a constant c such that

$$\varphi_{ab}^{(\mathrm{dis})} = -c/r_{ab}{}^6 \tag{13.3–22}$$

Eisenschitz and London[3] have evaluated the summation. They find that for the interaction between two normal hydrogen atoms

$$c = 6.47 e^2 a_0{}^5 \tag{13.3–23}$$

where a_0 is the radius of the first Bohr orbit, 0.5292 Å. This value is to be compared with a more exact value of

$$c = 6.50 e^2 a_0{}^5 \tag{13.3–24}$$

obtained by a variational method.[4] It is interesting to note that in the

[3] R. Eisenschitz and F. London, *Z. Physik*, **60**, 491 (1930).

[4] L. Pauling and J. Y. Beach, *Phys. Rev.*, **47**, 686 (1935).

perturbation calculation, an appreciable fraction of the dispersion energy comes from the continuous energy states.

The expression for dispersion energy (Eq. 13.3–20) is in terms of the oscillator strengths. An estimate of the latter quantities may be obtained from measurements of the variation of the index of refraction of light with frequency. From Eqs. 12.6–17 and 22 we find that

$$\frac{\eta^2 - 1}{\eta^2 + 2} = \frac{ne^2h^2}{3\pi m} \sum_{k_a, k_a'} \frac{f_a(k_a, k_a')}{(E_{k_a'} - E_{k_a})^2 - h^2\nu^2} \tag{13.3–25}$$

in which m is the mass of an electron. Actually Mulliken[5] has shown that very often there is essentially only one transition from the ground state which has an appreciable dipole moment matrix element. In these cases only one $f_a(k_a, k_a')$ is important, and the variation of the index of refraction with frequency may be approximated by a single term, that is, by the expression

$$\frac{\eta^2 - 1}{\eta^2 + 2} = \frac{4\pi n}{3} \frac{A}{E_I^2 - h^2\nu^2} \tag{13.3–26}$$

where A and E_I are empirical constants. The constant E_I is interpreted as an average or effective energy difference. The constant A is proportional to the value of the oscillator strength and hence proportional to the static polarizability, which is given by Eq. 12.6–21 as

$$\alpha(0) = \frac{e^2h^2}{4\pi^2 m} \sum_{k_a, k_a'} \frac{f(k_a, k_a')}{(E_{k_a'} - E_{k_a})^2} \tag{13.3–27}$$

These concepts lead to an approximate expression for the dispersion energy,

$$\varphi_{ab}^{(\text{dis})} = -\frac{3}{2}\left(\frac{E_{Ia}E_{Ib}}{E_{Ia} + E_{Ib}}\right)\frac{\alpha_a\alpha_b}{r_{ab}^6} \tag{13.3–28}$$

in terms of the static polarizabilities of the individual molecules and the empirical constants, E_{Ia} and E_{Ib}. It is often found that the E_I's are approximately equal to the ionization energies. This approximate form is closely related to the results of § 13.3a, which are based on Drude's idealized model. Since the ionization potentials of most molecules are of the same order of magnitude, it follows from this last result that, to a good approximation, the interaction between a pair of unlike molecules is related to the interactions between like molecules in the following manner:

$$c_{ab} = \sqrt{c_{aa}c_{bb}} \tag{13.3–29}$$

This is the basis of one of the "combining laws" for the force constants discussed in Chapters 3 and 8 (Eqs. 3.6–9 and 8.4–9).

[5] R. S. Mulliken, *J. Chem. Phys.*, **7**, 14, 20, 121, 339, 353, 364, 570 (1939); **8**, 234, 382 (1940).

Two other approximate expressions for the dispersion energy may be mentioned. Lennard-Jones[6] obtained the following expression by approximate quantum mechanical arguments:

$$c_{ab} = 6mc^2\{\alpha_a\chi_a^{(m)} + \alpha_b\chi_b^{(m)}\} \tag{13.3–30}$$

where m is the mass of an electron, c is the velocity of light, and $\chi^{(m)}$ is the magnetic susceptibility. By other arguments, Slater and Kirkwood[7] obtained the approximate relation

$$c_{ab} = \frac{\frac{3}{2}e^2\sqrt{a_0}\,\alpha_a\alpha_b}{\sqrt{\alpha_a/n_a^0} + \sqrt{\alpha_b/n_b^0}} \tag{13.3–31}$$

where n_a^0 and n_b^0 are the number of electrons in the outer shells of the two molecules, and a_0 is the radius of the first Bohr orbit, 0.5292 Å. This relation may be criticized in that it does not take into account the electrons in the inner shells, and there are additional terms which should be added if the molecules are not monatomic.

c. Higher terms in the expression for the dispersion energy

In the discussions of §§ 13.3a and 3b, only the first non-vanishing term in the expansion of φ_e was considered. If the higher terms in the expansion of φ_e (that is, b_4/r_{ab}^4, b_5/r_{ab}^5, . . .) are considered, we obtain terms in the expression for the dispersion energy proportional to the inverse eighth, tenth, . . . powers of the separation distance, thus:

$$\varphi_{ab}^{(\mathrm{dis})} = -\frac{c}{r_{ab}^{\ 6}} - \frac{c'}{r_{ab}^{\ 8}} - \frac{c''}{r_{ab}^{\ 10}} - \cdots \tag{13.3–32}$$

In § 13.3b it is shown how the coefficient c can be calculated for any kind of atom. The calculations of the additional coefficients c' and c'' for real atoms or molecules have been carried out for only two cases, the interaction of two hydrogen atoms (see § 14.1) and the interaction of two helium atoms (see § 14.2). For Drude's model, however, the calculations may be carried out easily.

Let us assume, as in § 13.3a, that a molecule can be idealized as a three-dimensional simple harmonic oscillator[8] with a single classical frequency ν_0. Mulliken's[5] experimental observation that only one transition is

[6] J. E. Lennard-Jones, *Interatomic Forces*, Indian Association for Cultivation of Science, Calcutta (1939). Equation 13.3–30 may be obtained from Eq. 13.3–28 by making use of screening constants and the approximate relations for α, $\chi^{(m)}$, and the ionization relations used in the illustrative examples of § 13.2e.

[7] J. C. Slater and J. G. Kirkwood, *Phys. Rev.*, **37**, 682 (1931); J. G. Kirkwood, *Physik. Z.*, **33**, 57 (1932).

[8] H. Margenau, *J. Chem. Phys.*, **6**, 897 (1938).

effective in transferring charge between atoms is the justification for using a single frequency. In this case the wave function for the isolated molecule is[9]

$$\psi(n_x, n_y, n_z) = H_{n_x}(\sqrt{\beta}x)H_{n_y}(\sqrt{\beta}y)H_{n_z}(\sqrt{\beta}z)e^{-\frac{\beta}{2}r^2} \tag{13.3–33}$$

where n_x, n_y, and n_z are the vibrational quantum numbers in the three directions and H_n are the Hermite polynomials. The quantity β is

$$\beta = \frac{m}{\hbar^2} h\nu_0 = \frac{e^2}{\alpha\hbar\nu_0} \tag{13.3–34}$$

where m is the reduced mass of the oscillator. The second form is based on Eq. 13.3–6, which gives α in terms of m.

Let us assume that the wave functions of the isolated molecules a and b have the form given in Eq. 13.3–33 but with different values of β corresponding to different fundamental frequencies, ν_a and ν_b, and different polarizabilities, α_a and α_b. We keep terms in φ_e through the inverse fifth power in r_{ab}, so that

$$\varphi_e = b_3/r_{ab}{}^3 + b_4/r_{ab}{}^4 + b_5/r_{ab}{}^5 \tag{13.3–35}$$

where b_3, b_4, and b_5 are given by Eq. 13.1–12. This expression can be substituted into Eq. 13.3–17 to obtain the dispersion energy. When both molecules are in their ground states (all the quantum numbers equal zero), it is found that [10]

$$c = \frac{3}{2}\frac{h\nu_a\nu_b\alpha_a\alpha_b}{(\nu_a + \nu_b)} \tag{13.3–36}$$

$$c' = \frac{45}{8}\frac{h^2\nu_a\nu_b\alpha_a\alpha_b}{e^2}\left[\frac{\alpha_a\nu_a}{2\nu_a + \nu_b} + \frac{\alpha_b\nu_b}{\nu_a + 2\nu_b}\right] \tag{13.3–37}$$

$$c'' = \frac{315}{16}\frac{h^3\nu_a{}^2\nu_b{}^2\alpha_a{}^2\alpha_b{}^2}{e^4(\nu_a + \nu_b)} \tag{13.3–38}$$

These expressions reduce to those obtained by Margenau[8] when the two molecules are alike, and provide the best means of estimating the contributions of the higher approximations to the dispersion energy.

We might suppose that the third-order perturbations would introduce a term in $\varphi_{ab}^{(\text{dis})}$ varying as $1/r_{ab}{}^9$. This term, however, is zero because of the symmetry (that is, the selection rules) of the simple harmonic oscillator wave functions (Eq. 13.3–33).

[9] L. Pauling and E. B. Wilson, Jr., *Introduction to Quantum Mechanics*, McGraw-Hill (1935), Section 11.

[10] J. F. Hornig and J. O. Hirschfelder, *J. Chem. Phys.*, **20**, 1812 (1952).

The constants c, c', c'' have been calculated by the above expressions for a number of common substances.[11] The values are given in Table 13.3–1. Also given are the values of $c^0_{\text{visc}} = 4\epsilon\sigma^6$, the coefficient of $1/r^6$ in the Lennard-Jones potential as determined from viscosity. These latter values should not be compared with the c of Eq. 13.3–32, but rather with a quantity c^0_{calc} defined by:

$$c^0_{\text{calc}} = c + \frac{c'}{\sigma^2} + \frac{c''}{\sigma^4} \qquad (13.3\text{–}39)$$

In Table 13.3–1 we also show values of this quantity c^0_{calc} for comparison with $c^0_{\text{visc}} = 4\epsilon\sigma^6$. For H_2 and He there is excellent agreement between c^0_{visc} and c^0_{calc}, but in all other cases c^0_{visc} is between 1.5 and 2.5 times as large as c^0_{calc}. In general, c' and c'' contribute approximately 20 per cent to c^0_{calc}. The significance of this deviation is not understood. It may be that the short-range forces fall off faster than the $1/r^{12}$ term in the Lennard-Jones (6-12) potential would indicate, so that the attractive forces need not be so large in order to give the same total potential.

TABLE 13.3–1

COMPARISON OF THEORETICAL AND EMPIRICAL CALCULATIONS OF THE DISPERSION ENERGY

Gas	Quantum Mechanical Calculations[8]				Empirical Calculation	Comparison
	$c \times 10^{60}$ erg-cm^6	$c' \times 10^{76}$ erg-cm^8	$c'' \times 10^{92}$ erg-cm^{10}	$c^0_{\text{calc}} \times 10^{60}$ erg-cm^6	$c^0_{\text{visc}} \times 10^{60}$ erg-cm^6	$\left(\frac{c^0_{\text{visc}}}{c^0_{\text{calc}}}\right)$
H_2	11.4	31.	45.	15.5	12.57	0.811
He	1.23	1.89	1.65	1.52	1.29	0.849
Ne	4.67	6.9	5.3	5.64	9.50	1.68
A	55.4	120.	136.	66.7	109.2	1.64
Kr	107.	275.	370.	130.	232.	1.79
Xe	233.	710.	1120.	280.	561.2	2.00
N_2	57.2	120.	130.	66.8	125.6	1.88
O_2	39.8	96.	120.	48.8	102.3	2.10
Cl_2	321.	1000.	1630.	386.	957.	2.48
CH_4	112.	310.	440.	135.	257.9	1.91
CO_2	152.	410.	590.	180.	427.1	2.37
HCl	111.	320.	480.	144.	259.1	1.80

[11] For Hg the calculated value for c is 255×10^{-60} erg-cm^6 [F. London, *Z. physik. Chem.*, **B11**, 222 (1930)].

d. The influence of "retardation" on the dispersion forces at large distances

When two neutral, non-polar, non-excited molecules are separated by a very large distance, the dispersion energy is considerably smaller than that predicted by the expressions derived previously in this section. This is due to "retardation"—that is, the effect of the finite velocity of propagation of electromagnetic radiation. The reduction in the force of attraction may be described qualitatively in the following manner. The first molecule has an instantaneous dipole which sets up an electromagnetic field; at a time r_{ab}/c later ($c =$ the velocity of light), this field induces an electric moment in the second molecule; and at a time $2r_{ab}/c$, the electric field from the induced dipole returns to the first molecule. Now, however, the instantaneous dipole in the first molecule has changed both in direction and in magnitude in the intervening time so that the energy of interaction is somewhat reduced. This effect was suggested[12] as an explanation of the stability of lyophobic colloids, in which the long-range forces appear to be somewhat smaller than might be expected.

Casimir and Polder[13] have considered the problem of the retardation effects from the standpoint of quantum electrodynamics. Since their treatment is quite difficult, we shall discuss only the results. They first considered the interaction of a neutral molecule with a conducting wall. At small separations they found the usual London expression for the energy of interaction,

$$\varphi = -\frac{\alpha h\nu_0}{8r^3} \qquad r \ll c/\nu_0 \tag{13.3–40}$$

where c is the velocity of light, and ν_0 is the most important frequency in the expressions for the index of refraction, the polarizability, and the dispersion energy. That is, ν_0 is the frequency associated with the energy E_I of Eq. 13.3–26. As is mentioned in connection with the discussion of this equation, $h\nu_0$ is often approximately equal to the ionization energy.

At separations large compared to the characteristic length,

$$\lambda_0 = c/\nu_0 \tag{13.3–41}$$

Casimir and Polder[13] found that the energy of interaction between a neutral molecule and a wall is

$$\varphi = -\frac{3hc\alpha}{16\pi^2 r^4} \qquad r \gg c/\nu_0 \tag{13.3–42}$$

That is, the energy of interaction is smaller at large separations by a

[12] E. J. W. Verwey, J. T. G. Overbeek, and K. van Ness, *Theory of Stability of Lyophobic Colloids*, Elsevier Publishing Co., Amsterdam (1948).

[13] H. B. G. Casimir and D. Polder, *Phys. Rev.*, **73**, 360 (1948).

factor of $3\lambda_0/2\pi^2 r$ due to retardation effects. Figure 13.3–1 shows how this factor varies with distance.

If $h\nu_0$ is expressed in electron volts, then $\lambda_0 = 12{,}394/h\nu_0$. The ionization potential is of the order of 10 ev. Hence the characteristic length λ_0 is of the order of 1200 Å. Using this result, we see from Fig. 13.3–1 that at about 400 Å the retardation effects reduce the energy by about a factor of one-half.

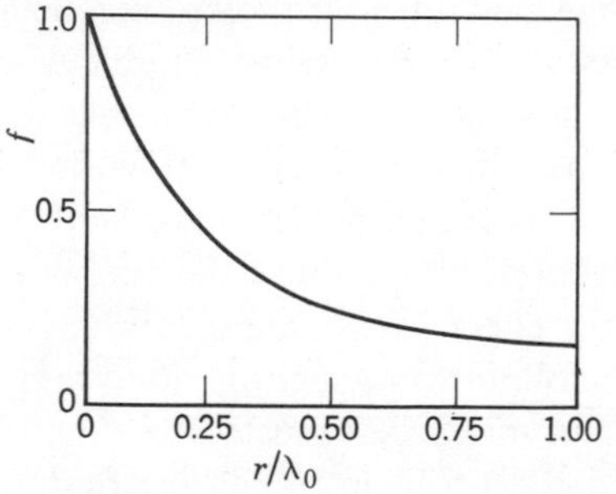

Fig. 13.3–1. Correction factor to the interaction between a neutral atom and a conducting wall due to retardation. The energy of interaction is $\varphi = -f\left(\frac{\alpha h\nu_0}{8r^3}\right)$.

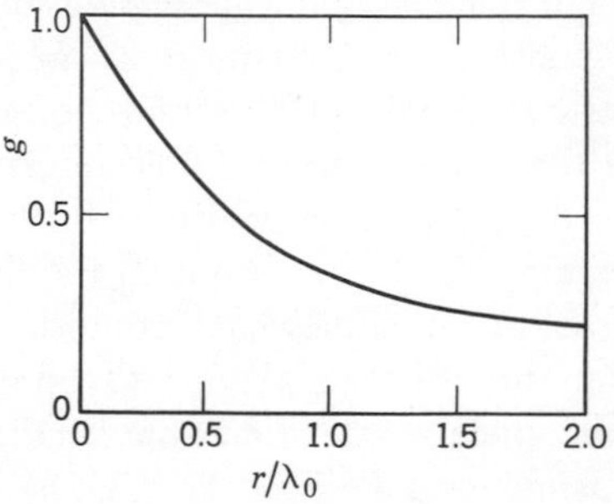

Fig. 13.3–2. Correction factor to the interaction between two neutral non-polar molecules due to retardation effects. This factor is to be used in Eq. 13.3–43.

The energy of interaction between two neutral non-polar molecules separated at a distance r is considerably more difficult to derive than the energy of interaction of a molecule with a conducting wall. The first, second, third, and fourth order perturbations have been considered. The result obtained[13] is that the energy of interaction is

$$\varphi^{(\text{dis})} = -g\left(\frac{3}{4}\frac{\alpha^2 h\nu_0}{r^6}\right) \tag{13.3–43}$$

where g is a factor varying from unity (for $r \ll \lambda_0$) to $23\lambda_0/6\pi^2 r$ (for $r \gg \lambda_0$). For intermediate separations g is shown by Fig. 13.3–2. Since $\lambda_0 \approx 1200$ Å, the effect of retardation becomes important at distances of the order of 200 or 300 Å.

Thus the effect of retardation is negligible for the interaction of small molecules. However, this effect becomes important for high polymers or other large molecules.

4. Dispersion Forces between Asymmetric Molecules

The dispersion forces between asymmetric molecules differ from those between spherically symmetric molecules in two ways: (i) At large separations the energy of dispersion varies as $1/r_{ab}{}^6$, but its magnitude depends upon the relative orientations of the molecules. (ii) At intermediate separations the energy of dispersion deviates from $1/r_{ab}^6$ (becoming considerably smaller than would be expected from extrapolating the energy at large separations) and is extremely sensitive to the relative orientations of the two molecules. In this section we discuss first the dispersion forces at large separations. Then we summarize London's[1] general treatment of the dispersion forces at intermediate separations. Finally we discuss the calculations of Coulson and Davies[2] of the dispersion forces for a particular model, suitable for the representation of conjugate double-bond or aromatic molecules.

In conjugated double-bond systems an electric charge moves easily from one end of the molecule to the other. An induced dipole in such a molecule has a very large separation between its positive and negative charges. For this reason the conjugated double-bond and the aromatic molecules have quite an anomalous energy of dispersion. Moreover, the energy may have a number of maxima and minima, with respect to changes in the separation and the relative orientations—a very surprising quantum mechanical result.

a. Dispersion forces between asymmetric molecules at large separations

The theoretical framework discussed in § 13.3a has been used by London[1] to calculate the dispersion forces between two asymmetric molecules at large separations. Let us consider two molecules a and b which have axial symmetry. Because of this symmetry, each molecule has two principal components of the polarizability (see § 13.2): polarizabilities along the intermolecular axis, $\alpha_{\|}(a)$ and $\alpha_{\|}(b)$, and the polarizabilities normal to the intermolecular axis, $\alpha_{\perp}(a)$ and $\alpha_{\perp}(b)$. The molecules are assumed to be anisotropic three-dimensional oscillators with the fundamental frequencies, $\nu_{\|}(a)$ and $\nu_{\|}(b)$ for vibrations along the axis, and doubly degenerate frequencies, $\nu_{\perp}(a)$ and $\nu_{\perp}(b)$, for vibrations perpendicular to the axis. We indicate the orientation of the two molecules by means of the angles θ_a, ϕ_a; θ_b, ϕ_b (for a definition of these angles see Fig. 12.1–5). For molecules satisfying this description it may be shown[1] that the generalization of Eq. 13.3–14 for asymmetric molecules is

$$\varphi^{(\text{dis})} = -\frac{c(\theta_a, \phi_a; \theta_b, \phi_b)}{r_{ab}^{6}} \tag{13.4–1}$$

in which $c(\theta_a, \phi_a; \theta_b, \phi_b)$ is the angle-dependent coefficient:

$$\begin{aligned} c(\theta_a, \phi_a; \theta_b, \phi_b) &= (A - B - B' + C)[\sin\theta_a \sin\theta_b \cos(\phi_b - \phi_a) - 2\cos\theta_a \cos\theta_b]^2 \\ &\quad + 3(B - C)\cos^2\theta_a + 3(B' - C)\cos^2\theta_b + (B + B' + 4C) \end{aligned} \tag{13.4–2}$$

[1] F. London, *J. Phys. Chem.*, **46**, 305 (1942).
[2] C. A. Coulson and P. L. Davies, *Trans. Faraday Soc.*, **48**, 777 (1952).

The quantities A, B, B', and C are defined as

$$A = \frac{h}{4} \alpha_{||}(a)\alpha_{||}(b) \frac{\nu_{||}(a)\nu_{||}(b)}{\nu_{||}(a) + \nu_{||}(b)} \tag{13.4–3}$$

$$B = \frac{h}{4} \alpha_{||}(a)\alpha_{\perp}(b) \frac{\nu_{||}(a)\nu_{\perp}(b)}{\nu_{||}(a) + \nu_{\perp}(b)} \tag{13.4–4}$$

$$B' = \frac{h}{4} \alpha_{\perp}(a)\alpha_{||}(b) \frac{\nu_{\perp}(a)\nu_{||}(b)}{\nu_{\perp}(a) + \nu_{||}(b)} \tag{13.4–5}$$

$$C = \frac{h}{4} \alpha_{\perp}(a)\alpha_{\perp}(b) \frac{\nu_{\perp}(a)\nu_{\perp}(b)}{\nu_{\perp}(a) + \nu_{\perp}(b)} \tag{13.4–6}$$

In this section the subscript $_{ab}$ is omitted from the $\varphi^{(\mathrm{dis})}$ in order to simplify the notation. The value of the dispersion energy (Eq. 13.4–1), averaged over all orientations of the two oscillators, is

$$\overline{\varphi^{(\mathrm{dis})}} = -\frac{2}{3r_{ab}^{6}} [A + 2(B + B') + 4C] \tag{13.4–7}$$

Equations 13.4–1 and 7 reduce to the results for isotropic molecules when the parallel and perpendicular polarizabilities and frequencies are set equal ($A = B = B' = C$). The parallel and perpendicular polarizabilities can be estimated by the methods and tables given in § 13.2. The frequencies are not difficult to estimate since it is unlikely that $\nu_{||}$ and $\nu_{\perp}$ are very different. Thus little error is introduced by assuming that $\nu_{||} = \nu_{\perp} = \nu$ and setting $h\nu = I$, the ionization potential, as in the case of spherical molecules.[3] This treatment of dispersion forces in asymmetrical molecules is useful in the consideration of the interaction between two hydrogen molecules (§ 14.4).

b. Dispersion forces between asymmetric molecules at intermediate separations

A simple theory for the dispersion forces between asymmetrical molecules in their ground states at intermediate separations has been developed by London.[1] According to Eq. 13.3–17 the dispersion energy for asymmetrical (as well as spherical) molecules in their ground states is given by the second-order perturbation formula:

$$\varphi^{(\mathrm{dis})} = -\sum_{\substack{k_a', m_a' \\ k_b', m_b'}} \frac{|(0,0;0,0|\varphi_e|k_a', m_a'; k_b', m_b')|^2}{(E_{k_a'} - E_{0_a}) + (E_{k_b'} - E_{0_b})} \tag{13.4–8}$$

[3] J. de Boer, *Physica*, **9**, 363 (1942), independently derived Eq. 13.4–1, assuming that $\nu_{||} = \nu_{\perp}$.

The expansion of φ_e in powers of $(1/r_{ab})$ given in Eq. 13.1–10 is not applicable to polyatomic molecules. Hence we must use the original expression for φ_e given in Eq. 13.1–2.

Some of the approximations which were used in the treatment of the symmetrical molecules may also be used in the treatment of asymmetrical molecules. First, it may be noted from Eq. 13.3–20 that the only transitions which contribute to the leading term in $\varphi^{(\mathrm{dis})}$ (that is, the term proportional to $1/r_{ab}{}^6$) are those for which the quantum states of molecules a and b change simultaneously. Second, it should be observed that there is a dipole moment associated with each of the transitions which contribute to the lead term (see Eq. 12.6–7). And, third, there is only *one* particular transition which is important in transferring charge between atoms. Hence it is possible to reduce the summation in Eq. 13.4–8 to a single term. If both $k_a' \neq 0$ and $k_b' \neq 0$, the terms $Z_a Z_b e^2/r_{ab}$, $\sum_{i=1}^{n_a} Z_b e^2/r_{bi}$, and $\sum_{j=1}^{n_b} Z_a e^2/r_{aj}$ in φ_e do not contribute to the matrix components. Accordingly, we can approximate Eq. 13.4–8 by the simple expression

$$\varphi^{(\mathrm{dis})} = -\frac{|(0, 0; 0, 0 \,|\, \varphi_e \,|\, k_a', 0; k_b', 0)|^2}{(E_{k'_a} - E_{0_a}) + (E_{k'_b} - E_{0_b})} \qquad (13.4\text{–}9)$$

in which

$$(0, 0; 0, 0 \,|\, \varphi_e \,|\, k_a', 0; k_b', 0)$$
$$= \sum_{i=1}^{n_a}\sum_{j=1}^{n_b} \iint \psi_a{}^*(0, 0)\psi_b{}^*(0, 0) \frac{e^2}{r_{ij}} \psi_a(k_a', 0)\psi_b(k_b', 0)\, d\boldsymbol{r}^{n_a}\, d\boldsymbol{r}^{n_b} \qquad (13.4\text{–}10)$$

where n_a and n_b are the numbers of electrons in molecules a and b, respectively.

Let us define the electron density ρ_a associated with the transition $(0, 0) \to (k_a', 0)$ in molecule a by

$$\rho_a = \iint \cdots \int \psi_a{}^*(0, 0)\psi_a(k_a', 0)\, d\boldsymbol{r}_2 \cdots d\boldsymbol{r}_{n_a} \qquad (13.4\text{–}11)$$

Let us also define $\boldsymbol{R}_a(-)$ as the "center of gravity" of the region where ρ_a is negative and $\boldsymbol{R}_a(+)$ as the "center of gravity" of the region where ρ_a is positive:

$$\boldsymbol{R}_a(-) = \frac{\int (\rho_a - |\rho_a|)\, \boldsymbol{r}_1\, d\boldsymbol{r}_1}{\int (\rho_a - |\rho_a|)\, d\boldsymbol{r}_1} \qquad (13.4\text{–}12)$$

$$\boldsymbol{R}_b(+) = \frac{\int (\rho_a + |\rho_a|)\, \boldsymbol{r}_1\, d\boldsymbol{r}_1}{\int (\rho_a + |\rho_a|)\, d\boldsymbol{r}_1} \qquad (13.4\text{–}13)$$

But now the electric moment associated with the transition is given by Eq. 12.6–7:

$$\begin{aligned}\boldsymbol{\mu}_a(0, 0 \mid k_a', 0) &= e \int \psi_a^*(0, 0)\psi_a(k_a', 0) \left(\sum_{i=1}^{n_a} \boldsymbol{r}_i\right) d\boldsymbol{r}^{n_a} \\ &= (\boldsymbol{R}_a(+) - \boldsymbol{R}_a(-))\epsilon_a \qquad (13.4\text{–}14)\end{aligned}$$

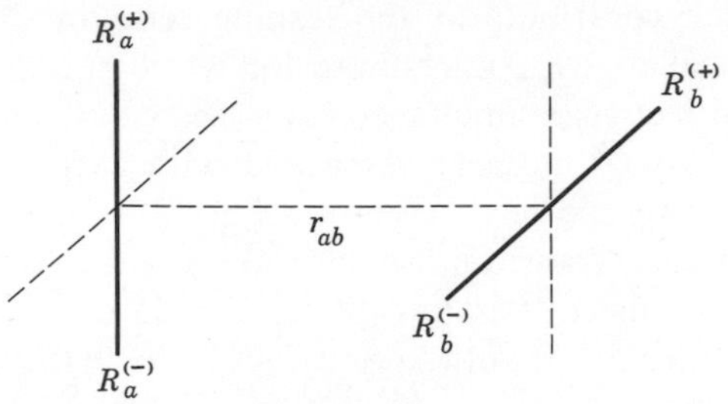

Orientation *A*

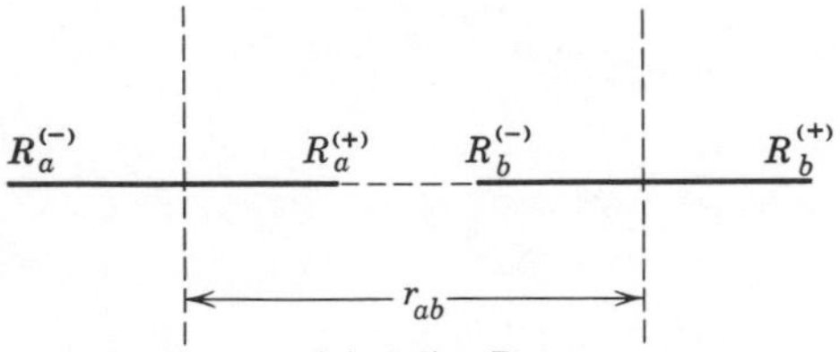

Orientation *B*

Fig. 13.4–1. For orientation *A*, $|R_a(+) - R_b(+)| = |R_a(+) - R_b(-)| = |R_a(-) - R_b(+)| = |R_a(-) - R_b(-)|$ and $\varphi^{(\mathrm{dis})} = 0$. For orientation *B*, the $R_a(+)$ and $R_b(-)$ are so close together that $\varphi^{(\mathrm{dis})}$ is given by Eq. 13.4–17.

The second form of this expression serves as the definition of the charge, ϵ_a, involved in the transition. The quantities ϵ_b, $\boldsymbol{R}_b(+)$, and $\boldsymbol{R}_b(-)$ may be defined analogously. In terms of these quantities, it may be shown[1] that Eq. 13.4–9 becomes

$$\varphi^{(\mathrm{dis})} = -\frac{\epsilon_a^2 \epsilon_b^2}{h(\nu_a + \nu_b)} \left[\frac{1}{|\boldsymbol{R}_a(+) - \boldsymbol{R}_b(+)|} + \frac{1}{|\boldsymbol{R}_a(-) - \boldsymbol{R}_b(-)|} - \frac{1}{|\boldsymbol{R}_a(-) - \boldsymbol{R}_b(+)|} - \frac{1}{|\boldsymbol{R}_a(+) - \boldsymbol{R}_b(-)|} \right]^2 \qquad (13.4\text{–}15)$$

Here $h\nu_a$ and $h\nu_b$ are the values of $(E_{k_a} - E_{0_a})$ and $(E_{k_b} - E_{0_b})$.

To illustrate the orientation dependence of the dispersion energy let us consider two extreme cases, the two orientations A and B shown in Fig. 13.4–1. In orientation A both molecules are perpendicular to the intermolecular axis and perpendicular to each other. In orientation B both molecules lie in the same line, with their dipoles pointing in the same direction. For these special orientations Eq. 13.4–15 gives

$$\text{Orientation } A: \quad \varphi^{(\text{dis})} = 0 \tag{13.4–16}$$

$$\text{Orientation } B: \quad \varphi^{(\text{dis})} = \frac{\epsilon_a{}^2 \epsilon_b{}^2}{h(\nu_a + \nu_b)} \frac{1}{|\boldsymbol{R}_a(+) - \boldsymbol{R}_b(-)|^2} \tag{13.4–17}$$

Perhaps the simplest way of understanding the energy of interaction between two asymmetrical molecules is to think of the molecules as real dipoles with the separation $[\boldsymbol{R}(+) - \boldsymbol{R}(-)]$ between the charges. The geometry of the interacting molecules is described by Fig. 12.1–5. Let us define D as the ratio of real dipole-dipole interaction energy to the ideal dipole-dipole energy.

$$D = \frac{\varphi_{\text{real dipole-dipole}}}{\varphi_{\text{ideal dipole-dipole}}}$$

$$= \frac{r_{ab}{}^3 \left[\dfrac{1}{|\boldsymbol{R}_a(+) - \boldsymbol{R}_b(+)|} + \dfrac{1}{|\boldsymbol{R}_a(-) - \boldsymbol{R}_b(-)|} - \dfrac{1}{|\boldsymbol{R}_a(+) - \boldsymbol{R}_b(-)|} - \dfrac{1}{|\boldsymbol{R}_a(-) - \boldsymbol{R}_b(+)|} \right]}{|\boldsymbol{R}_a(+) - \boldsymbol{R}_a(-)|\,|\boldsymbol{R}_b(+) - \boldsymbol{R}_b(-)|(-2\cos\theta_a\cos\theta_b + \sin\theta_a\sin\theta_b\cos(\phi_b - \phi_a))} \tag{13.4–18}$$

The ratio D is shown in Fig. 12.1–6 for four orientations of dipoles in which $l = |\boldsymbol{R}_a(+) - \boldsymbol{R}_a(-)| = |\boldsymbol{R}_b(+) - \boldsymbol{R}_b(-)|$. In terms of D, Eq. 13.4–15 can be written

$$\varphi^{(\text{dis})} = \frac{-[\mu_a(00; k_a', 0)\mu_b(00; k_b', 0)]^2 D^2[-2\cos\theta_a\cos\theta_b + \sin\theta_a\sin\theta_b\cos(\phi_b - \phi_a]^2}{h(\nu_a + \nu_b) r_{ab}{}^6} \tag{13.4–19}$$

As may be seen from Fig. 12.1–6, for most orientations of the two molecules, D approaches unity when r_{ab} becomes large. Hence $\varphi^{(\text{dis})}$ varies as $1/r_{ab}{}^6$ for large separations, but it continues to show strong dependence on the mutual orientations of the two molecules. It may also be seen that this limiting behavior is practically attained when $r_{ab} \geq 2l$, where l can be taken as the larger of $|\boldsymbol{R}_a(+) - \boldsymbol{R}_a(-)|$ and $|\boldsymbol{R}_b(+) - \boldsymbol{R}_b(-)|$.

c. Energy of dispersion for interaction of long conjugated double-bond or aromatic molecules

Coulson and Davies[2] have derived a set of molecular wave functions representing various electronic quantum states for long conjugated double-bond aromatic molecules. They used these wave functions to make a direct calculation of the dispersion energy for a considerable number of relative orientations and separations of the two molecules. The essential difference between their treatment and that discussed in the previous subsection is that the London treatment assumes that a transition to only one of the excited electronic states makes an appreciable contribution to the dispersion energy. (Furthermore, London has not given any indication as to how we can tell which of the excited states this is.) On the other hand, Coulson and Davies consider all the excited states for a particular molecular model. They find that the most important contribution is given by the transition which corresponds to the jumping of one electron in each molecule from the least bonding (or highest energy) of the bonding molecular orbitals to the lowest energy of the non-bonding molecular orbitals. At large separations (see Table 13.4–2) all the other transitions can be neglected.

As the conjugated double-bond (or aromatic) molecules approach each other, the forces become highly directional, with the molecules preferring to approach each other at an angle such that the two molecules are in different planes. The fact that almost all organic molecular crystals such as naphthalene and anthracene have planes of adjacent molecules non-parallel indicates that these conclusions are correct. (A great deal of additional research is needed to clarify this problem.)

The following explanation of the directional forces has been offered by Coulson.[4] We can imagine, classically, an electric oscillator in which there are a certain number of standing waves in each mode of vibration. The electrical potential of such oscillators or antenna systems has strong directional properties. Now since, in the transition from classical to quantum theory, we replace the standing waves by de Broglie waves, in the normal modes of electronic motions we may expect the same sort of directional properties. This is exactly what Coulson and Davies obtained by detailed calculation. Let us now summarize their method and results.

We consider a linear molecule made up of $2k$ similar atoms, equally spaced, with a separation l between neighbors, as shown in Fig. 13.4–2.

[4] C. A. Coulson, private communication, December 13, 1951.

In order to represent a polyene chain, in all the numerical work l is taken to be 1.4 Å, the normal C — C separation. If we take $l/2$ to be the atomic radius to be added at each end of the molecule, the total length of the molecule is $L = 2kl$. Let us suppose that each atom contributes one electron to the set of metallic or mobile electrons. The extended-oscillator property of the molecules is shown by allotting the electrons to molecular orbitals which extend over the full length of the molecule. For the purposes of the present calculations, it is convenient to associate these electrons with $2p\pi$ atomic orbitals.[5]

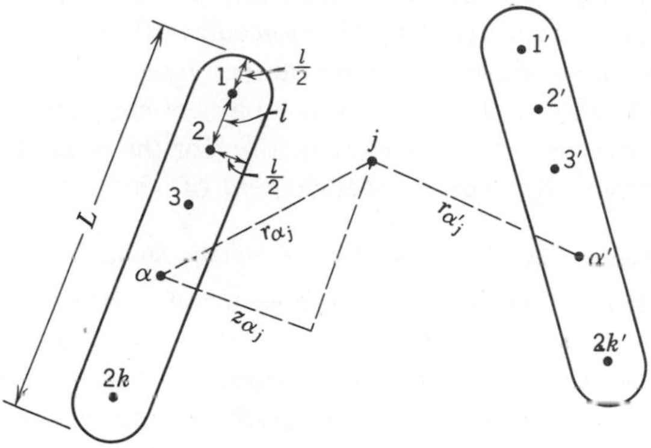

Fig. 13.4–2. Geometry which Coulson and Davies assumed for the interaction of two linear molecules.

Let z be a direction perpendicular to the line of the molecule. Then the explicit expression for the normalized $2p\pi$ orbital associated with the αth nucleus occupied by the jth electron is

$$\phi_\alpha(j) = \sqrt{c^5/\pi}\, z_{\alpha j} e^{-cr_{\alpha j}} \tag{13.4–20}$$

Here c is an adjustable screening constant. In the numerical work c is taken to be $1.625/a_0$, which is appropriate for a $2p\pi$ orbital in carbon. The overlap integrals are neglected, since it is assumed that the $\phi_\alpha(j)$ are mutually orthogonal.

With the set of $2k$ atomic orbitals it is possible to form $2k$ linear combinations known as molecular orbitals,

$$\chi_i(j) = \sum_{\alpha=1}^{2k} \sqrt{\frac{2}{2k+1}} \sin\left(\frac{i\alpha\pi}{2k+1}\right) \phi_\alpha(j) \tag{13.4–21}$$

[5] For a discussion of atomic orbitals, Slater determinants, etc., see, for example, C. A. Coulson, *Valence*, Oxford University Press (1952) or K. S. Pitzer, *Quantum Chemistry*, Prentice-Hall (1953).

If β, which is negative, is the resonance integral[6] between adjacent atoms, the energy of an electron in the jth molecular orbital relative to its energy in an isolated atomic orbital is

$$\epsilon_j = 2\beta \cos\left(\frac{j\pi}{2k+1}\right) \tag{13.4–22}$$

A reasonable value of β, suggested by Mulliken, Rieke, and Brown[7] on the basis of spectroscopic and combustion data, is -40 kcal per mole. Since β is negative, the smaller the value of j, the lower the energy. When $1 \leq j \leq k$, ϵ_j is negative and the molecular orbitals are bonding. When $k + 1 \leq j \leq 2k$, ϵ_j is positive and the molecular orbitals are antibonding.

The ground state of the molecule is obtained by filling each of the lower k molecular orbitals ($i = 1, 2, \cdots k$) with pairs of electrons in accordance with the Pauli principle. The wave function for the ground state is then the Slater determinant,[5] the diagonal element of which is

$$\chi_1(1)\bar{\chi}_1(2)\chi_2(3)\bar{\chi}_2(4) \cdots \chi_k(2k-1)\bar{\chi}_k(2k) \tag{13.4–23}$$

Here the bar denotes one spin, and the absence of a bar denotes the other. Excited states are represented by configurations in which one or more electrons are raised to the antibonding orbitals. The only excited states that need be considered in the present problem, are the singlet states in which only one electron is raised to an antibonding orbital. A state in which an electron in the pth bonding molecular orbital is raised to the qth antibonding orbital is known as the state (pq). The wave function for this state is the sum of two Slater determinants whose diagonal elements are

$$\begin{cases} \chi_1(1)\bar{\chi}_1(2) \cdots \chi_p(2p-1)\bar{\chi}_q(2p) \cdots \chi_k(2k-1)\bar{\chi}_k(2k) \\ \chi_1(1)\bar{\chi}_1(2) \cdots \chi_q(2p-1)\bar{\chi}_p(2p) \cdots \chi_k(2k-1)\bar{\chi}_k(2k) \end{cases} \tag{13.4–24}$$

Now let us consider the interaction of two such molecules. The dispersion energy is given by Eq. 13.4–8. In the summation of Eq. 13.4–8 the most important excited state is characterized by $(k_a, k_a + 1; k_b, k_b + 1)$ and is the one in which one electron in each molecule is raised from the highest bonding state to the lowest excited state.

In evaluating the matrix components, all of the three- and four-center integrals are neglected. Since only comparatively large separations are being considered, only the coulombic integrals contribute. A computational difficulty arises in considering the orientations in which the two molecules are not parallel, so that the direction of the π orbitals in the two molecules are different. The integrals which occur are related to those

[6] See Coulson, Ref. 5, p. 76.

[7] R. Mulliken, C. Rieke, and W. Brown, *J. Am. Chem. Sci.*, **63**, 41 (1941).

which were evaluated by Bartlett.[8] The evaluation of the integrals is greatly simplified by the approximation that the exponential terms can be ignored at the distances considered here. Because of the number of integrals occurring, $2k = 6$ is the practical limit to the evaluation of the matrix elements for all the excited states. However, from the calculation of the matrix component between the ground state and $(k_a, k_a + 1; k_b, k_b + 1)$ and a knowledge of the relative importance of the other states for $2k = 2, 4$, and 6, it is possible to make a good estimate of the energies of interaction of really long molecules.

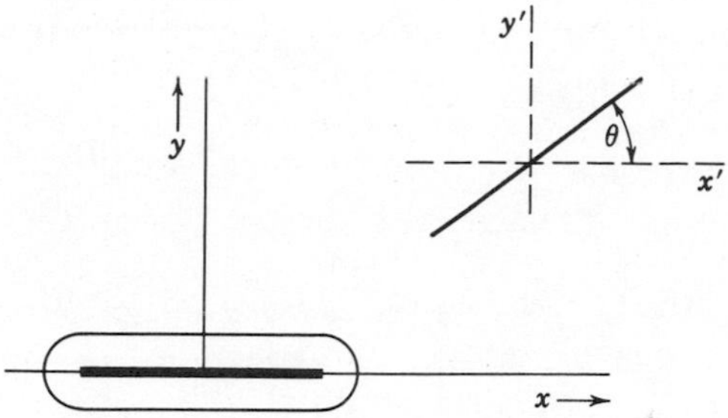

Fig. 13.4–3. The coordinates used to specify the position one molecule with respect to another.

Four coordinates, x, y, θ, and ϕ, are required to specify an arbitrary position of the second molecule with respect to the first. These coordinates are illustrated in Fig. 13.4–3 and may be defined in the following manner. The x-axis is taken as the axis of the first molecule. The y-axis then originates at the center of the first molecule, is perpendicular to the x-axis, and is in a plane containing the center of the second molecule. The relative position of the center of the second molecule is then described by assigning a value of x and y. The axes x' and y' are drawn through the center of the second molecule parallel to the x and y axes. The angle, θ, is the angle between the axis of the second molecule and the x'-axis. The plane formed by the x'-axis and the axis of the second molecule makes an angle ϕ with the xy-plane.

Let us now discuss the results which are obtained for the three different orientations of the two molecules shown in Fig. 13.4–4:

Orientation I. *Molecules Parallel to Each Other and Perpendicular to the Intermolecular Axis* $(x = \theta = \phi = 0)$

The results of calculations for this orientation, illustrated in Fig. 13.4–4a, are given in Table 13.4–1. When y/L is greater than 1.8, the

[8] J. H. Bartlett, *Phys. Rev.*, 37, 507 (1931).

energy varies as the inverse sixth power of y as would be expected from the London theory. At smaller separations the energy of interaction is much less than would be expected from a continuation of the inverse

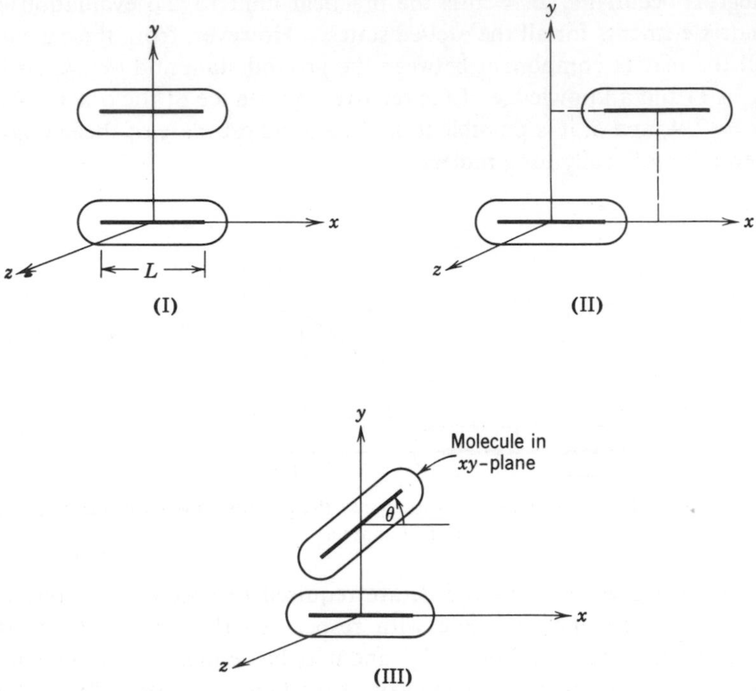

Fig. 13.4–4. The three orientations considered in the interaction between long molecules.

sixth-power law. For small values of y/L the energy is proportional to $2k + 1 \approx L$; for large separations it is proportional to $(2k + 1)^5 \approx L^5$. For values of y/L larger than 1.8, the energy of interaction is approximately

$$\varphi^{(\mathrm{dis})} = -16 \frac{e^4 l^4}{y^6 \pi^9 \beta} (2k + 1)^5 \qquad (13.4\text{–}25)$$

TABLE 13.4–1[2]

VALUES OF INTERACTION ENERGY $-\varphi^{(\mathrm{dis})}$ FOR ORIENTATION I
(calories/mole)

$2k$	$y = 4$ Å	$y = 8$ Å	$y = 15$ Å	$y = 20$ Å	$y = 30$ Å	$y = 50$ Å
2	121.	2.33	0.627	0.0567	0.06507	0.1134
4	935.	34.1	1.06	0.199	0.07343	0.09050
6	2620.	140.	5.58	1.12	0.1084	0.05965
10	7950.	668.	39.6	9.10	0.996	0.0517
20	—	—	382.	116.	16.9	1.16

Since Davies[9] has shown that the polarizability of a long molecule varies as L^3 and its ionization potential varies as L^{-1}, the London theory also leads to the proportionality of $\phi^{(\text{dis})}$ with L^5, but the numerical coefficient seems to be somewhat different. Coulson and Davies[2] have found that for large molecules the contribution of the $2p\sigma$ electrons to the dispersion energy is much less than for $2p\pi$ electrons, so they believe the present model is quite accurate.

The contributions to the dispersion energy corresponding to the various transitions are given in Table 13.4-2 for hexatriene, $CH_2{=}CH{-}CH{=}CH{-}CH{=}CH_2$, for which $2k = 6$. It is apparent that the largest contribution comes from the (33; 44) transition. This transition is the one in which an electron in each molecule jumps from the highest energy (or least bonding) bonding molecular orbital to the lowest energy non-bonding orbital. At 4 Å separation, there is an appreciable contribution from

TABLE 13.4-2[2]

RELATIVE IMPORTANCE OF DIFFERENT TRANSITIONS FOR ORIENTATION I HEXATRIENE ($2k = 6$)

(energy given in calories/mole)

Transition	Degeneracy or Equivalent Number of Terms	Energy Required for Transition	Contributions to $-\varphi^{(\text{dis})}$ from Various Transitions		
			$y = 4$ Å	$y = 8$ Å	$y = 15$ Å
(33; 44)	1	71,000	2205.0	135.5	5.50
(33; 55)	4	135,000	366.0	4.1	0.02
(33; 46)	4	125,000	6.5	0.09	0.03
(32; 45)	2	135,000	3.7	0.04	0.03
(32; 56)	8	190,000	0.04	0.03	0.004
(32; 65)	4	190,000	14.8	0.02	0.0001
(33; 66)	4	180,000	17.1	0.02	0.00009
(22; 55)	1	200,000	3.7	0.005	0.00004
(31; 46)	2	180,000	0.03	0.0008	0.0003
(22; 66)	4	244,000	0.8	0.0004	0.000002
(31; 66)	4	234,000	0.03	0.00009	0.000002
(21; 56)	2	244,000	0.005	0.00001	0.000001
(11; 66)	1	288,000	0.001	0.000005	0.000000003
Dispersion energy = sum of energy contributions			2620.	140	5.58

[9] P. L. Davies, *Trans. Faraday Soc.*, **48**, 789 (1952).

the (33; 55) transition. However, at larger separations the dispersion energy can be calculated with little error by considering the (33; 44) transition and neglecting all others.

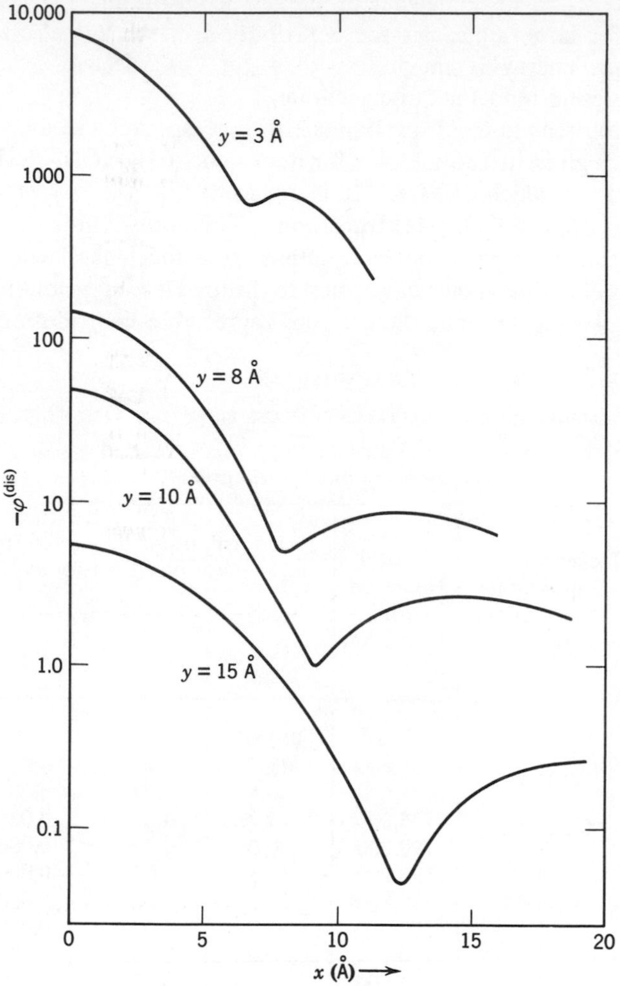

Fig. 13.4–5. The dispersion energy for orientation II. [From C. A. Coulson and P. L. Davies, *Trans. Faraday Soc.*, **48**, 777 (1952).]

Orientation II. *Molecules in the Displaced Parallel Configuration* (*Variation of x and y with $\theta = \phi = 0$*)

The variation of the intermolecular energy with the displacement x for two parallel molecules, as shown in Fig. 13.4–4b, is given in Fig. 13.4–5.

For each separation y, the energy of attraction, $-\varphi^{(\mathrm{dis})}$, is a maximum for no displacement, $x = 0$, then passes through a minimum for some displacement $x_0(y)$. The position of these minima is difficult to explain, since the contribution of each excited state to $-\varphi^{(\mathrm{dis})}$ exhibits the same

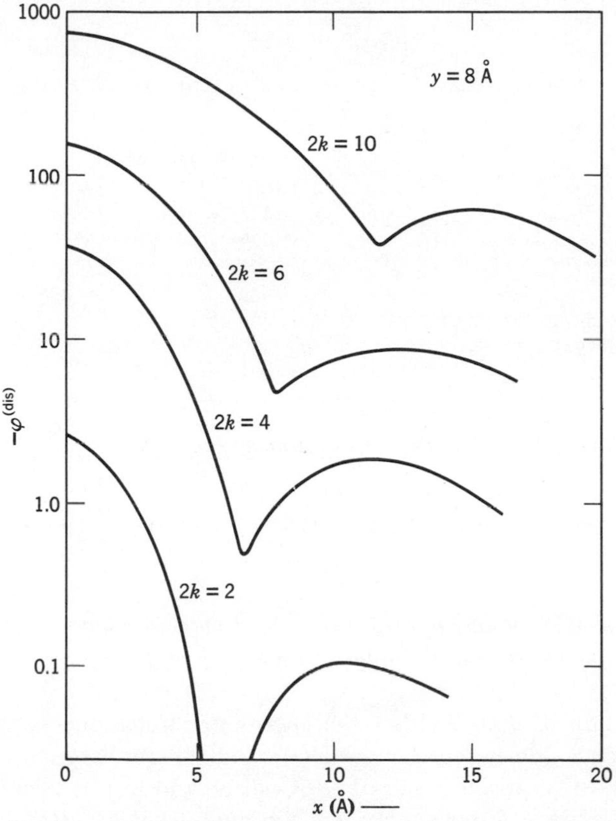

Fig. 13.4-6. The dependence of the dispersion energy on the molecule length for orientation II with $y = 8$ Å. [From C. A. Coulson and P. L. Davies, *Trans. Faraday Soc.*, **48**, 777 (1952).]

sort of phenomena, with the minima occurring at different places. The complicated pattern is similar to the interaction of two radiating antennae. Figure 13.4-6 shows the variations of the energy of interaction with molecule size for $y = 8$ Å for various values of x. From this study it appears that there are strong forces tending to hold the molecules parallel and opposite to one another.

The energy of attraction, $-\varphi^{(\text{dis})}$, is a maximum when the two molecules are parallel to each other and perpendicular to the internuclear axis. There is an angle γ_0 at which the energy of attraction passes through a minimum, and there is an angle γ_2 at which it has a secondary maximum. The values of γ_0 and γ_2 are given in Table 13.4-3.

TABLE 13.4–3[2]

VALUES OF γ_0 AND γ_2 AS FUNCTIONS OF THE SEPARATION y

Molecule	*Separation y* (Å)	γ_0	γ_2
$2k = 6$	3	66°	69°
	8	44°	56°
	10	42°	56°
	15	39°	53°
Long chain ($2k$ large)	$y/L \gg 1$	35°	51°

For long-chain molecules ($2k$ large) at a large separation,

$$\varphi^{(\text{dis})} = -16 \frac{e^4 l^4}{\pi^9 y^6 \beta} (2k + 1)^5 \cos^2 \gamma (3 \sin^2 \gamma - 1)^2 \quad (13.4\text{–}26)$$

Orientation III. *Rotation of Second Molecule in Plane of the Two Molecules* (*Variation of* θ *and* y *with* $x = \phi = 0$)

The variation of θ shows that the energy of attraction, $-\varphi^{(\text{dis})}$, is a maximum for θ somewhere between 60° and 90° for large molecules. This is the most surprising result of the Coulson and Davies calculations. For the case of $2k = 2$, the energy is a minimum when $\theta = 0$ and is zero when $\theta = 90°$. Thus, for $2k = 2$, $\varphi^{(\text{dis})}_{\theta=90°} - \varphi^{(\text{dis})}_{\theta=0°}$ is 5 cal per mole when $y = 7$ Å, and 120 cal per mole when $y = 4$ Å. Figure 13.4–7 shows the variation of $-\varphi^{(\text{dis})}$ for the molecule $2k = 6$ when $y = 7$ Å. This shows that, energetically, an angle of 60° to 90° is preferred, and there is an energy barrier for hindered rotation of the molecule of around 240 cal per mole. In a similar way, butadiene ($2k = 4$) would have an energy barrier of around 860 cal per mole when $y = 4.2$ Å. This type of preferred angle seems to occur for the interactions of naphthalene, anthracene, and other aromatic molecules. It can be seen from Fig. 13.4–7 that the results are very sensitive to the treatment of the higher excited states.

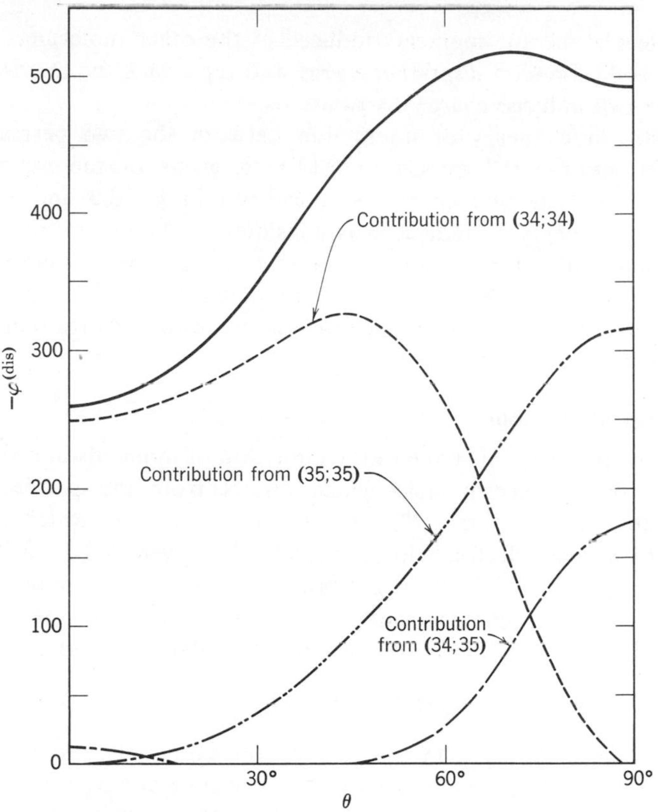

Fig. 13.4–7. The dispersion energy for hexatriene ($2k = 6$) for orientation III, showing the contribution of the various terms with $y = 7$ Å. [From C. A. Coulson and P. L. Davies, *Trans. Faraday Soc.*, **48**, 777 (1952).]

5. Forces between Molecules Having Permanent Electric Moments[1,2]

Let us consider the long-range energy of interaction between two real molecules having permanent electric moments as being made up of the sum of three terms:[3]

$$\varphi = \varphi^{(\text{es})} + \varphi^{(\text{ind})} + \varphi^{(\text{dis})} \tag{13.5–1}$$

The contribution $\varphi^{(\text{es})}$ represents the purely *electrostatic interaction* between the permanent charge distributions of the two molecules. The term $\varphi^{(\text{ind})}$ is the Debye-Falkenhagen *energy of induction* and represents the energy of the interactions between the permanent charge distribution

[1] H. Margenau, *Revs. Mod. Phys.*, **11**, 1 (1939).

[2] F. London, *Trans. Faraday Soc.*, **33**, 8 (1937).

[3] Resonance forces are considered separately in § 13.6.

of one molecule and the moments induced in the other molecule. The term $\varphi^{(\text{dis})}$ is the London *dispersion energy* and represents the interaction between the two induced charge distributions.

The electrostatic energy of interaction between the two permanent charge distributions is discussed in § 12.1 in terms of the multipole moments. The dispersion energy is considered in §§ 13.3 and 4. In this section the energy of induction is considered. For many purposes we use an intermolecular potential averaged over the orientations of the two interacting molecules. This average potential is discussed here and the relative sizes of the various contributions to the average potential are examined.

a. The energy of induction

The energy of induction is due to the induction of moments in a charge distribution by the electric field which results from the presence of another charge distribution. The energy of a molecule, which has a polarizability $\boldsymbol{\alpha}$, in an electric field of intensity $\mathscr{E}$ is given by Eq. 12.2–2 as $-\frac{1}{2}(\mathscr{E} \cdot \boldsymbol{\alpha} \cdot \mathscr{E})$. Thus, if $\mathscr{E}_a(\boldsymbol{r}_b)$ represents the field at molecule b due to molecule a (a similar meaning is assigned to $\mathscr{E}_b(\boldsymbol{r}_a)$), the contribution of the induction effects to the intermolecular potential energy is

$$\varphi^{(\text{ind})} = -\tfrac{1}{2}(\mathscr{E}_a(\boldsymbol{r}_b) \cdot \boldsymbol{\alpha}_b \cdot \mathscr{E}_a(\boldsymbol{r}_b)) - \tfrac{1}{2}(\mathscr{E}_b(\boldsymbol{r}_a) \cdot \boldsymbol{\alpha}_a \cdot \mathscr{E}_b(\boldsymbol{r}_a)) \qquad (13.5\text{–}2)$$

The electric fields, in terms of the electrostatic potentials, are given by Eq. 12.1–10. The electrostatic potentials in turn are given by Eq. 12.1–27 in terms of the multipole moments of the charge distributions.

We consider the special case in which the polarizabilities of the molecules are isotropic, so that the tensors $\boldsymbol{\alpha}_a$ and $\boldsymbol{\alpha}_b$ may be replaced by the scalars α_a and α_b. We further assume that the charge distributions are cylindrically symmetric, so that the quadrupole moments may be characterized by single scalar quantities Q_a and Q_b (see Eq. 12.1–17). In this case the induction energy is

$$\begin{aligned}\varphi^{(\text{ind})} = &- \frac{C_a{}^2\alpha_b + C_b{}^2\alpha_a}{2r^4} - \frac{2C_a\mu_a\alpha_b\cos\theta_a + 2C_b\mu_b\alpha_a\cos\theta_b}{r^5} \\ &- \frac{\mu_a{}^2\alpha_b(3\cos^2\theta_a + 1) + \mu_b{}^2\alpha_a(3\cos^2\theta_b + 1)}{2r^6} \\ &- \frac{3C_aQ_a\alpha_b(3\cos^2\theta_a - 1) + 3C_bQ_b\alpha_a(3\cos^2\theta_b - 1)}{4r^6} \qquad (13.5\text{–}3) \\ &- \frac{3\mu_aQ_a\alpha_b\cos^3\theta_a + 3\mu_bQ_b\alpha_a\cos^3\theta_b}{r^7} \\ &- \cdots\end{aligned}$$

where C_a and C_b are the net charges on the molecules; and θ_a and θ_b are the angles between the axes of symmetry of the molecules and the line joining the centers of the molecules. The terms in $\varphi^{(\text{ind})}$ varying as $1/r^4$ and $1/r^5$ are important in the interaction between an ion and a neutral molecule. The term varying as $1/r^6$ is the lead term in the interaction between neutral molecules with dipole moments. However, in the pressure broadening of the microwave spectra of ammonia by noble gases, the term varying as $1/r^7$ is all important,[4] as we discuss in § 13.7.

b. The potential energy of interaction averaged over orientations

The potential energy of interaction between non-spherical molecules depends on the orientations of the two molecules. However, in many applications we require this potential energy averaged over all orientations of the two molecules. In a dilute gas at equilibrium, the probability of finding two molecules separated by a distance r and oriented in a particular manner is proportional to the Boltzmann factor $\exp\{-\varphi(r_{ab}, \omega_a, \omega_b)/kT\}$. Thus, the average potential energy which we consider is the average over all orientations, with this factor as a weight factor:

$$\bar{\varphi}(r_{ab}, T) = \frac{\iint \varphi(r_{ab}, \omega_a, \omega_b) e^{-\varphi(r_{ab}, \omega_a, \omega_b)/kT}\, d\omega_a\, d\omega_b}{\iint e^{-\varphi(r_{ab}, \omega_a, \omega_b)/kT}\, d\omega_a\, d\omega_b} \tag{13.5–4}$$

It is to be noted that this average potential is temperature dependent.

The expressions for φ are usually quite complex, so that it is difficult to evaluate the integrals of Eq. 13.5–4. However, for all values of r_{ab} such that for all orientations $|\varphi - \bar{\varphi}|$ is small compared to kT, it is convenient to expand the exponential in the following manner:

$$\bar{\varphi} = \frac{\iint \varphi e^{-(\varphi-\bar{\varphi})/kT}\, d\omega_a\, d\omega_b}{\iint e^{-(\varphi-\bar{\varphi})/kT}\, d\omega_a d\omega_b} = \frac{\iint \varphi[1 - (\varphi - \bar{\varphi})/kT + \cdots]\, d\omega_a\, d\omega_b}{\iint [1 - (\varphi - \bar{\varphi})/kT + \cdots]\, d\omega_a\, d\omega_b}$$

Thus we obtain[5]

$$\begin{aligned} \bar{\varphi} = {} & \frac{1}{64\pi^6} \iint \varphi\, d\omega_a\, d\omega_b \\ & - \frac{1}{kT}\left[\frac{1}{64\pi^6}\iint \varphi^2\, d\omega_a\, d\omega_b - \left\{\frac{1}{64\pi^6}\iint \varphi\, d\omega_a\, d\omega_b\right\}^2\right] + \cdots \end{aligned} \tag{13.5–6}$$

as the expansion of the average potential in powers of $1/kT$.

[4] P. W. Anderson, *Phys. Rev.*, **80**, 511 (1950).

[5] In the evaluation of the spatial average, it is convenient to make use of the following:

$\overline{\cos^2\theta} = \frac{1}{3}$; $\overline{\sin^2\theta} = \frac{2}{3}$; $\overline{\cos^2(\phi_a - \phi_b)} = \frac{1}{2}$

$\overline{\cos^4\theta} = \frac{1}{5}$; $\overline{\sin^2\theta\cos^2\theta} = \frac{2}{15}$; $\overline{\sin^4\theta} = \frac{8}{15}$ $\overline{\cos^4(\phi_a - \phi_b)} = \frac{3}{8}$

Equation 13.5–6 gives the average potential, $\bar{\varphi}(r_{ab}, T)$ in terms of integrals of the angle-dependent potential, $\varphi(r_{ab}, \omega_a, \omega_b)$, which in itself is the sum of three terms as shown in Eq. 13.5–1. A detailed consideration of these equations shows that to a good approximation the cross-terms are negligible,[1, 2] and

$$\bar{\varphi} = \bar{\varphi}^{(\mathrm{es})} + \bar{\varphi}^{(\mathrm{ind})} + \bar{\varphi}^{(\mathrm{dis})} \tag{13.5–7}$$

where $\bar{\varphi}^{(\mathrm{es})}$ is given by an expression similar to Eq. 13.5–6 but with $\varphi^{(\mathrm{es})}$ replacing φ, and similar relations hold for the $\bar{\varphi}^{(\mathrm{ind})}$ and $\bar{\varphi}^{(\mathrm{dis})}$. Let us now consider each of these contributions separately and inquire as to their primary dependence on the intermolecular distance.

The *average electrostatic interaction* can be evaluated by considering the molecules to be general multipole charge distributions. Substituting the general expression for $\varphi^{(\mathrm{es})}$, given by Eq. 12.1–33, into Eq. 13.5–6 and making use of the orthogonality of the representation coefficients, Eq. 12.B–20, we find that

$$\begin{aligned}\bar{\varphi}^{(\mathrm{es})} &= \frac{C_a C_b}{r} \\ &- \frac{1}{kT} \sum_{\substack{n_1 n_2 \\ m_1 m_2 \\ m}} \frac{(n_1 - |m_1|)!(n_2 - |m_2|)![(n_1+n_2)!]^2}{(n_1+|m|)!(n_1-|m|)!(n_1+|m_1|)!(n_2+|m|)!(n_2-|m|)!} \\ &\times \frac{|\bar{Q}_{n_1}^{m_1}(a)|^2 \, |\bar{Q}_{n_2}^{m_2}(b)|^2}{(n_2+|m_2|)!(2n_1+1)(2n_2+1)} \frac{1}{r^{2(n_1+n_2+1)}}\end{aligned} \tag{13.5–8}$$

The term in which both n_1 and n_2 are zero is not included in the sum. Then, since

$$\sum_m \frac{1}{(n_1+m)!\,(n_1-m)!\,(n_2+m)!\,(n_2-m)!} = \frac{(2n_1+2n_2)!}{(2n_1)!\,(2n_2)!\,[(n_1+n_2)!]^2} \tag{13.5–9}$$

we obtain

$$\begin{aligned}\bar{\varphi}^{(\mathrm{es})} &= \frac{C_a C_b}{r} \\ &- \frac{1}{kT} \sum_{\substack{n_1 n_2 \\ m_1 m_2}} \frac{(n_1-|m_1|)!\,(n_2-|m_2|)!\,(2n_1+2n_2)!}{(n_1+|m_1|)!\,(n_2+|m_2|)!\,(2n_1)!\,(2n_2)!\,(2n_1+1)(2n_2+1)} \\ &\times \frac{|\bar{Q}_{n_1}^{m_1}(a)|^2 \, |\bar{Q}_{n_2}^{m_2}(b)|^2}{r^{2(n_1+n_2+1)}}\end{aligned} \tag{13.5–10}$$

It is interesting to note that the only contribution to the direct angular average of $\bar{\varphi}^{(es)}$, that is $\iint \varphi^{(es)}\, d\omega_a\, d\omega_b$, is the coulombic interaction between the total charges C_a and C_b on the two molecules. If the molecules act as neutral ideal dipoles the only term in the sum of the last equation which contributes is the term with $n_1 = n_2 = 1$ and $m_1 = m_2 = 0$, and

$$\bar{\varphi}^{(es)} = -\frac{2}{3}\left(\frac{\mu_a{}^2\mu_b{}^2}{kT}\right)\frac{1}{r^6} \tag{13.5–11}$$

The expression for the energy of induction (for the special case of cylindrically symmetric molecules) is given by Eq. 13.5–3. If this expression is used in Eq. 13.5–6, it is found that the *average induction energy* is independent of T up to terms of $1/r_{ab}{}^8$, and is given by

$$\begin{aligned}\bar{\varphi}^{(ind)} = &-\tfrac{1}{2}\alpha_b\left[\frac{C_a{}^2}{r^4} + \frac{2\mu_a{}^2}{r^6} + \frac{3Q_a{}^2}{r^8} + \cdots\right] \\ &-\tfrac{1}{2}\alpha_a\left[\frac{C_b{}^2}{r^4} + \frac{2\mu_b{}^2}{r^6} + \frac{3Q_b{}^2}{r^8} + \cdots\right]\end{aligned} \tag{13.5–12}$$

From this expression we see that the potential energy of interaction between a neutral nonpolar molecule a and a neutral polar molecule b contains the term $-\alpha_a\mu_b{}^2/r^6$. This term is taken into account in the derivation[6] of the combining laws, Eqs. 3.10–15 and 16 and 8.6–3 and 4. The use of the angle average in this derivation is justified, because the induction contribution is small compared with the dispersion contribution.

[6] If we assume that the valence and dispersion contributions to the intermolecular potential $\varphi(r)$ are given by the Lennard-Jones (6-12) potential, then the interaction of a polar and a nonpolar molecule is given by

$$\varphi(r) = 4\epsilon_{ab}\left[\left(\frac{\sigma_{ab}}{r}\right)^{12} - \left(\frac{\sigma_{ab}}{r}\right)^{6}\right] - \frac{\alpha_a\mu_b{}^2}{r^6}$$

This expression is also of the Lennard-Jones (6-12) form with parameters σ_{ab}' and ϵ_{ab}' given by

$$\sigma_{ab}' = \sigma_{ab}\left[1 + \frac{\alpha_a\mu_b{}^2}{4\epsilon_{ab}\sigma_{ab}{}^6}\right]^{-1/6} = \tfrac{1}{2}(\sigma_{aa} + \sigma_{bb})\xi^{-1/6}$$

$$\epsilon_{ab}' = \epsilon_{ab}\left[1 + \frac{\alpha_a\mu_b{}^2}{4\epsilon_{ab}\sigma_{ab}{}^6}\right]^{2} = \sqrt{\epsilon_{aa}\epsilon_{bb}}\,\xi^2$$

where (assuming $\sigma_{ab} \approx \sqrt{\sigma_{aa}\sigma_{bb}}$)

$$\xi = 1 + \frac{\alpha_a}{4\sigma_{aa}{}^3}\,\frac{\mu_b{}^2}{\epsilon_{bb}\sigma_{bb}{}^3}\sqrt{\frac{\epsilon_{bb}}{\epsilon_{aa}}}$$

For symmetrical molecules, the *dispersion energy* is independent of the orientation of the molecules so that, from Eq. 13.3–32,

$$\bar{\varphi}^{(\text{dis})} = \varphi^{(\text{dis})} = -\frac{c}{r^6} - \frac{c'}{r^8} - \frac{c''}{r^{10}} - \cdots \qquad (13.5\text{–}13)$$

The first term is associated with the interaction between two mutually induced dipoles, and the subsequent terms describe the interactions between higher induced moments.

TABLE 13.5–1

SUMMARY OF THE CONTRIBUTIONS TO THE INTERACTION BETWEEN LIKE POLAR MOLECULES[2]

	$\mu \times 10^{18}$ esu	$\alpha \times 10^{24}$ cm^3	$h\nu_0$ volts	Electrostatic $\bar{\varphi}^{(\text{es})}r^6$ ($T = 293°$K) $\left(\frac{2}{3}\right)\frac{\mu^4}{293k} \times 10^{60}$ 10^{-60} erg-cm^6	Dispersion $\bar{\varphi}^{(\text{dis})}r^6$ $\frac{3}{4}\alpha^2 h\nu_0 \times 10^{60}$ 10^{-60} erg-cm^6	Induction $\bar{\varphi}^{(\text{ind})}r^6$ $2\mu^2\alpha \times 10^{60}$ 10^{-60} erg-cm^6
CO	0.12	1.99	14.3	0.0034	67.5	0.057
HI	0.38	5.4	12	0.35	382	1.68
HBr	0.78	3.58	13.3	6.2	176	4.05
HCl	1.03	2.63	13.7	18.6	105	5.4
NH_3	1.5	2.21	16	84	93	10
H_2O	1.84	1.48	18	190	47	10

c. The relative magnitude of the contributions to the intermolecular potential

For the interactions between like symmetrical molecules the lead term in the expressions for each of the three contributions—the electrostatic, the induction, and the dispersion effects—varies as $1/r_{ab}^6$. The factors are $-2\mu^4/3kT$, $-2\mu^2\alpha$, and $-\frac{3}{4}\alpha^2 h\nu_0$, respectively. Hence in order to compare the relative magnitude of the three contributions it is necessary only to compare the three coefficients. Table 13.5–1 gives the values for some typical molecules.[2] It is apparent that the induction effect is never important in the interaction between neutral molecules. The dispersion effect, however, is important even in the interaction between molecules with large dipole moments.

The energy of attraction between a non-polar molecule a and an ion b of charge C_b is

$$\varphi = -\frac{C_b{}^2\alpha_a}{2r^4} - \frac{3\alpha_a\alpha_b h\nu_0}{4r^6} \tag{13.5–14}$$

The first term is the energy of induction between the charge and the induced dipole; the second term is the London dispersion energy between the two mutually induced dipoles. In order to illustrate the relative sizes of the two terms, let us consider the values at a distance equal to the "kinetic theory collision diameter." At this distance the total potential (including the repulsive terms) is approximately zero. The interaction energies at this separation are given[7] in Table 13.5–2. It is evident that the ion-dipole term is the larger, but the dispersion energy is by no means negligible.

TABLE 13.5–2[6]

ENERGY OF INTERACTION AT THE "KINETIC THEORY COLLISION DIAMETER"

	Li^+		Na^+		K^+		Rb^+		Cs^+	
	$\varphi^{(ind)}$	$\varphi^{(dis)}$	$\varphi^{(ind)}$	$\varphi^{(dis)}$	$\varphi^{(ind)}$	$\varphi^{(dis)}$	$\varphi^{(ind)}$	$\varphi^{(dis)}$	$\varphi^{(ind)}$	$\varphi^{(dis)}$
He	−202	−46	−134	−37	−71	−37	−55	−35	−43	−41
Ne	−298	−58	−202	−50	−111	−53	−87	−52	−69	−62
A	−781	−142	−557	−116	−322	−114	−257	−114	−210	−136
Kr	−931	−165	−668	−130	−402	−125	−323	−123	−266	−145
Xe	−1200	−209	−883	−162	−538	−148	−437	−143	−363	−169
H_2	−429	−94	−301	−71	−173	−62	−137	−60	111	−68
N_2	−658	−100	−472	−83	−283	−86	−228	−88	−188	−104
O_2	−728	−133	−520	−104	−303	−97	−242	−95	−196	−110
CO_2	−1000	−179	−730	−144	−441	−137	−359	−138	−293	−163

Note. The first entry is the ion-dipole energy ($\sim 1/r_{ab}{}^4$) and the second is the London dispersion energy ($\sim 1/r_{ab}{}^6$). All energies are given in units of 10^{-15} erg.

d. Hydrogen bonds as electrostatic forces

The term "hydrogen bond" was coined by Latimer and Rodebush[8] to characterize the strong energy of interaction between an OH or an NH group with O, N, F, or Cl atoms. At one time the strength of the hydrogen bonds was thought to be due to some sort of quantum mechanical resonance. However, all the present evidence indicates that hydrogen

[7] H. Margenau, *Philosophy of Science*, **8**, 603 (1941).

[8] W. M. Latimer and W. H. Rodebush, *J. Am. Chem. Soc.*, **42**, 1419 (1920).

bonds are usually electrostatic interactions between the pertinent groups.[9] The exact location of the electrical charges is important since the groups can get sufficiently close together that the concept of ideal dipole forces does not apply. The interactions between water molecules discussed in § 13.8 is a good example. Davies[10] has made a very thorough study of the physical aspects of hydrogen bonds. He lists the following binding energies of hydrogen bond dimers and polymers in the gas phase:[11]

	ΔH
$6HF \rightleftharpoons (HF)_6$	6800 cal/mole
$2HCOOH \rightleftharpoons (HCOOH)_2$	7060
$2CH_3COOH \rightleftharpoons (CH_3COOH)_2$	$9430 - 4.88T$
$2CH_3COOD \rightleftharpoons (CH_3COOD)_2$	7950
$2C_2H_5COOH \rightleftharpoons (C_2H_5COOH)_2$	9200
$3C_2H_5COOH \rightleftharpoons (C_2H_5COOH)_3$	8000
$2(C_2H_5COOD) \rightleftharpoons (C_2H_5COOD)_2$	7040

Because of the large energy of interaction between these molecules, only a small fraction exist in the form of monomers in the gas phase. Consequently their virial coefficients[12] and transport coefficients[13] are correspondingly anomalous.

6. Quantum Mechanical Treatment of Resonance and Electrostatic Forces

Let us now consider the interaction of two molecules from a completely quantum mechanical point of view. Here the orientations as well as the motions in the electronic and vibrational degrees of freedom are specified implicitly by the quantum numbers in a statistical sense. The energy of

[9] The character changes from electrostatic to homopolar when the groups are squeezed together as in the very short hydrogen bonds occurring in crystals of acid salts such as KH_2PO_4. See A. R. Ubbelohde, *J. chim. phys.*, **46**, 429 (1949).

[10] M. Davies, *Annual Reports of the Chemical Societies for 1946*, **43**, 5 (England, 1947).

[11] The slight tendency of acetaldehyde to form dimers [$2CH_3CHO \rightleftharpoons (CH_3CHO)_2$, $\Delta H = 2610$ kcal/mole] has been considered as an example of hydrogen bonding. However, this example is in no way different from acetone and other polar gases which cannot form hydrogen bonds.

[12] A. E. Alexander and J. D. Lambert, *Trans. Faraday Soc.*, **37**, 421 (1941). J. D. Lambert, G. A. H. Roberts, J. S. Rowlinson, and V. J. Wilkinson, *Proc. Roy. Soc.* (*London*), **A196**, 113 (1949). J. D. Lambert and E. D. T. Strong, *Proc. Roy. Soc.* (*London*), **A200**, 566 (1950).

[13] P. M. Craven and J. D. Lambert, *Proc. Roy. Soc.* (*London*), **A205**, 439 (1951) —Viscosity. J. D. Lambert, E. N. Stanies, and S. D. Woods, *ibid.*, **A200**, 262 (1950) —Thermal conductivity.

interaction is then of Type IV, as discussed in § 13.1a. The quantum mechanical treatment of intermolecular forces differs from the classical treatment in two respects. First, there is often the possibility of resonance forces which have no classical analog. Second, the orientations of the molecules are only partially specified by the quantum numbers. The quantum mechanical interaction between two molecules in definite quantum states may be compared with the classical interaction averaged over all orientations with the square of the wave function as the weight factor. Resonance sometimes plays an important role in the interaction between two non-polar molecules (usually between two like molecules). In addition, resonance often complicates the electrostatic interaction between polar molecules. When resonance occurs, the energy of interaction is abnormally large, sometimes in the sense of attraction, sometimes repulsion.

We begin this section by considering the types of resonance forces which may occur between molecules. We then discuss the quantum mechanical interaction between two ideal dipoles imbedded in linear or axially symmetric molecules; this provides an example of pure electrostatic interaction, sometimes complicated by resonance. Next two specific examples of the interaction between an ion and a neutral molecule are discussed: the interaction of a proton with an excited hydrogen atom, and that of a proton with an excited helium atom. The first is an example of sharp resonance, the second illustrates near-resonance. The section is concluded with a discussion of first-order quadrupole-quadrupole interactions of atoms (neither one in an *S*-state). This is somewhat complicated since the treatment used depends upon whether or not the separation between neighboring energy levels is small or large compared with kT. The interactions involving free radicals or molecules in excited states give rise to forces similar to those considered in this section.

a. The nature of resonance forces

The possibility of resonance forces arises whenever the interaction removes a degeneracy in the wave functions. That is, resonance is associated with the possibility of hybridization of the wave functions. In the long-range interactions between molecules such hybridization is effective in producing resonance only when the states making up the hybrid have very nearly the same energy in the limit of large separations. If they have exactly the same energy, the resonance is sharp. If they have nearly the same energy, the resonance does not become effective until somewhat smaller separations.

There are two types of resonance: *resonance between molecules* and *resonance within one molecule*. Resonance between molecules is effective in the collisions between like molecules having quantum numbers such that the molecule in the lower energy state can, by the absorption of a photon, undergo a transition to a state with the quantum numbers of the other molecule without violating the selection rules for electric dipole radiation. If these conditions on the quantum numbers are not satisfied, the effectiveness of the resonance in modifying the interaction potential is greatly reduced. The possibility of resonance within a single molecule is illustrated by the interaction of a proton with an excited hydrogen atom. For this interaction the azimuthal quantum number is no longer a "good" quantum number, and the wave function is a hybridized sum of hydrogen atom orbitals all having the same value of the principal and the magnetic quantum numbers but different values of the azimuthal quantum number.

Resonance introduces a splitting of potential energy surfaces. That is, when the molecules collide they have a certain a priori probability of following any one of several potential energy surfaces. The a priori probability is proportional to the statistical mechanical degeneracy of the particular energy surface. The energy of resonance may be positive or negative, but at large separations the sum of the resonance energies weighted by their a priori probabilities is zero.

Let us now consider the two types of resonance phenomena; first, the resonance between molecules and then the resonance within one molecule.

i. *Resonance between Molecules*

A state of resonance exists between two like molecules a and b when a quantum of energy can be emitted readily by a and absorbed by b.[1] In the combined molecular system it is not possible according to quantum mechanics to specify the state of molecule a and that of molecule b separately. Instead, if $\psi_a(i)$ is the wave function of molecule a in state i, the wave function for the two-molecule system may be either of two functions:

$$\Psi(g) = \psi_a(i)\psi_b(j) + \psi_a(j)\psi_b(i) \qquad (13.6\text{–}1)$$

$$\Psi(u) = \psi_a(i)\psi_b(j) - \psi_a(j)\psi_b(i) \qquad (13.6\text{–}2)$$

A collision between the two molecules can therefore follow potential energy surfaces characterized by the (g) states or surfaces characterized by the (u) states. The first-order perturbation theory gives for the energy of

[1] R. Eisenschitz and F. London, *Z. Physik.*, **60**, 491 (1930), first pointed out the existence of this resonance phenomenon.

interaction in the two states:

$$\varphi^{(\text{res})}(g) = \iint \Psi^*(g)\varphi_e\Psi(g)\, d\mathbf{r}^{n_a}\, d\mathbf{r}^{n_b} \Big/ \iint \Psi^*(g)\Psi(g)\, d\mathbf{r}^{n_a}\, d\mathbf{r}^{n_b} \qquad (13.6\text{–}3)$$

$$\varphi^{(\text{res})}(u) = \iint \Psi^*(u)\varphi_e\Psi(u)\, d\mathbf{r}^{n_a}\, d\mathbf{r}^{n_b} \Big/ \iint \Psi^*(u)\Psi(u)\, d\mathbf{r}^{n_a}\, d\mathbf{r}^{n_b} \qquad (13.6\text{–}4)$$

Inasmuch as we are interested only in the terms varying as $1/r_{ab}{}^3$—the largest resonance interaction—it suffices to replace φ_e by the leading term in the series expansion of φ_e given in Eq. 13.1–10. Then the expressions in Eqs. 13.6–3, 4 lead at once to

$$\varphi^{(\text{res})}(g) = -\varphi^{(\text{res})}(u) = -\frac{1}{r_{ab}{}^3}\,[|(\mu_x)_{ij}|^2 + |(\mu_y)_{ij}|^2 - 2\,|(\mu_z)_{ij}|^2] \quad (13.6\text{–}5)$$

where the $(\mu_x)_{ij}$, $(\mu_y)_{ij}$, $(\mu_z)_{ij}$ are the components of the dipole moment associated with the transition of a single molecule from the state i to the state j (see Eq. 12.6–7) and the coordinate z is along the line of nuclei. The existence of strong resonance interaction therefore depends upon the non-vanishing of the dipole moment associated with the transition.

In order for resonance interaction to occur, it is necessary for at least one of the molecules to be in an excited state. For example, two H-atoms in their ground state do not exhibit resonance forces, whereas such forces do come into play in the interaction between one H-atom in the $1s$ and another H-atom in the $2p$ state.[2] From Appendix 12C we see that the only non-vanishing dipole moment matrix components for the transitions of a hydrogen atom from the $1s$ to the various $2p$ states are

$$|(\mu_z)_{1s,\,2p_z}|^2 = |(\mu_x)_{1s,\,2p_x}|^2 = |(\mu_y)_{1s,\,2p_y}|^2 = 0.555e^2a_0{}^2$$

Thus the resonance energy has four possible values:

$$\varphi^{(\text{res})} = \pm 1.110\,\frac{e^2}{a_0}\,\frac{1}{(r_{ab}/a_0)^3} \quad \text{or} \quad \pm 0.555\,\frac{e^2}{a_0}\,\frac{1}{(r_{ab}/a_0)^3} \qquad (13.6\text{–}6)$$

In one-sixth of the collisions between a $1s$ and a $2p$ hydrogen atom the interaction energy is given by $1.110e^2a_0{}^2/r_{ab}{}^3$; in one-sixth of the collisions the energy is $-1.110e^2a_0{}^2/r_{ab}{}^3$; in one-third of the collisions the energy is $0.555e^2a_0{}^2/r_{ab}{}^3$; and in one-third of the collisions it is $-0.555e^2a_0{}^2/r_{ab}{}^3$.

This result, Eq. 13.6–6, is easily generalized to the resonance forces arising in the collision of any atom in an S-state with a like atom in a P-state.[2] In all such cases, the interacting system can fall into the following classes: Σ_g, Σ_u, Π_u, Π_g, and each class has a separate potential energy function. King and Van Vleck showed that the resonance energy

[2] G. W. King and J. H. Van Vleck, *Phys. Rev.*, **55**, 1165 (1935)

corresponding to each of these classes can be expressed in the form

$$\varphi^{(\mathrm{res})} = \begin{cases} +2\dfrac{|(\mu_z)_{SP}|^2}{r_{ab}^3}, & \Sigma_g \\ -2\dfrac{|(\mu_z)_{SP}|^2}{r_{ab}^3}, & \Sigma_u \\ +\dfrac{|(\mu_z)_{SP}|^2}{r_{ab}^3}, & \Pi_u \\ -\dfrac{|(\mu_z)_{SP}|^2}{r_{ab}^3}, & \Pi_g \end{cases} \qquad (13.6\text{–}7)$$

In Table 12.C–2, the values of $|(\mu_z)_{SP}|^2$ are given for a number of different atoms for transitions from the ground (S) state to the first excited (P) state. Comparing Eq. 13.6–6 with Eq. 13.6–7, we see that in the collision between a 1s and 2p hydrogen atom, the Σ states are the ones for which $\varphi^{(\mathrm{res})} = \pm 1.10 \dfrac{e^2 a_0^2}{r_{ab}^3}$, and the Π states are the ones for which $\varphi^{(\mathrm{res})} = \pm 0.555 \dfrac{e^2 a_0^2}{r_{ab}^3}$. As far as the long range interactions (varying as $1/r_{ab}^3$) are concerned, the singlet and the triplet states have the same energies. Since both singlet and triplet g and u states can be formed without violating the Pauli exclusion principles, the Π states have twice the probability of occurring compared to the Σ states.

For H, Li, Na, K, Rb, Cd, and Hg there is definite experimental evidence that either the Σ_g or the Π_u state corresponds to stable molecules at small separations in spite of the fact that their resonance energy is positive for large separations. Figure 13.6–1 shows the shape of their potential energy curves. For sodium the maximum in the potential energy is about 0.7 kcal per mole; for lithium it may be as much as 2.8 kcal per mole. In all these cases the resonance energy is large and extends to very large separations. The resonance energy has the value of kT for room temperature (0.6 kcal per mole) at a separation of 6 to 20 Å, depending upon the substance.

ii. *Resonance within One Molecule*

Some molecules have degenerate states which are separated by the perturbation produced by the interaction with a second molecule. In such cases there is the possibility of resonance forces. A simple example of this type of phenomenon is the interaction of a proton with an excited hydrogen atom.

At first sight we might suppose that it would be necessary to consider the possibility of the electron oscillating between the centers a and b by writing the wave function in the form $\Psi = \Psi_a(1) + \Psi_b(1)$, where $\Psi_a(1)$ is the wave function of atom a plus proton b and $\Psi_b(1)$ is the wave

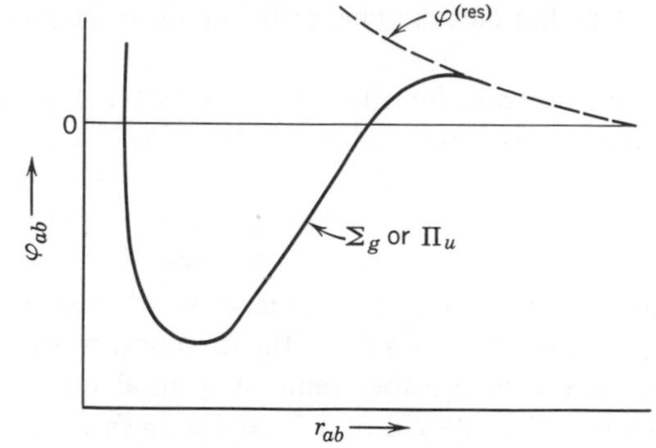

Fig. 13.6–1.

function of proton a plus atom b. However, it is easy to show that exactly the same energy at large separations is obtained by taking $\Psi = \Psi_a(1)$ and omitting $\Psi_b(1)$. The effect of including both $\Psi_a(1)$ and $\Psi_b(1)$ in the wave function is to introduce terms in the energy which fall off exponentially with the separation and are only appreciable when the separation is small. Thus the proton is considered purely as a source of electrostatic potential rather than as a particle. Let us consider the

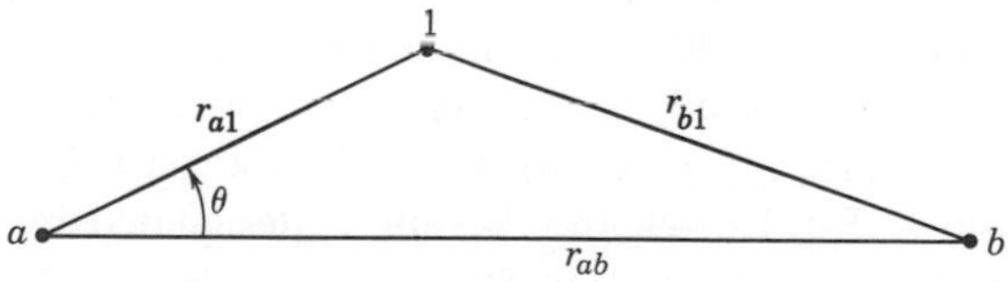

Fig. 13.6–2. Coordinates used in discussing the interaction of a proton and an H-atom.

situation illustrated by Fig. 13.6–2, with the electron a distance r_{a1} from the center of the atom and the angle between the internuclear axis and the radius vector from a to the electron designated as θ_{a1}. The perturbation energy on the atom due to the proton is

$$\varphi_e = \frac{e^2}{r_{ab}} - \frac{e^2}{r_{b1}} = -\frac{e^2}{r_{ab}}\left[\left(\frac{r_{a1}}{r_{ab}}\right) P_1(\cos\theta_{a1}) + \left(\frac{r_{a1}}{r_{ab}}\right)^2 P_2(\cos\theta_{a1}) + \cdots\right] \tag{13.6–8}$$

For present purposes we are interested only in determining the term in the resonance energy, $\varphi^{(\mathrm{res})}$, which varies as $1/r_{ab}^2$. Such terms are surprising since we expect this dependence on separation for electrostatic charge–dipole forces, and yet the hydrogen atom has no dipole. As we show presently, the hybridization of the wave function actually produces a polar distribution of the electric charge in the atom and results in this term.

As an example, let us consider the state in which the proton and the H-atom are far apart, the latter having a principal quantum number, $n = 2$. The energy of the hydrogen atom is the same in the state with the azimuthal quantum number $l = 0$ (a $2s$ state) and the states with $l = 1$ ($2p$ states). Under the influence of the proton's electric field, the azimuthal quantum number is no longer a good quantum number. However, if the z-direction is taken to be the direction of the internuclear axis, the magnetic quantum number remains a good quantum number. Thus the wave function is a hybrid of a $2s$ and a $2p$ function,

$$\Psi \equiv \Psi_a(1) = \alpha\psi_{2s}(1) + \beta\psi_{2p_z}(1) \tag{13.6–9}$$

Since the magnetic quantum number is unaffected by the perturbation, the only orbitals which are not mutually orthogonal are those which have the same value of the magnetic quantum number.[3] In this case the only possibility is for the magnetic quantum number to be zero (the only value in the $2s$ state). Physically speaking, the magnetic quantum number zero represents the fact that there is no component of angular momentum in the direction of the internuclear axis.

The resonance energy is the solution of the first-order perturbation equation given in Eq. 1.6–49. The linear combination of wave functions given in Eq. 13.6–9 is used as the zero-order wave function, and the leading term of φ_e (see Eq. 13.1–10) is used for the perturbation potential. In the notation of Eq. 1.6–49, the $2s$ state is designated by the subscript 1 and the $2p$ state by 2; the parameter λ is $-e/r_{ab}^2$. Accordingly we write

$$\mathscr{H}^{(1)} = -er_{a1}P_1(\cos\theta_{a1}) \tag{13.6–10}$$

$$E - E_1^{(0)} = E - E_2^{(0)} = \varphi^{(\mathrm{res})} \tag{13.6–11}$$

Then the secular equation may be written as

$$\begin{vmatrix} \varphi^{(\mathrm{res})} + \lambda\mathscr{H}_{11}^{(1)} & \lambda\mathscr{H}_{12}^{(1)} \\ \lambda\mathscr{H}_{21}^{(1)} & \varphi^{(\mathrm{res})} + \lambda\mathscr{H}_{22}^{(1)} \end{vmatrix} = 0 \tag{13.6–12}$$

[3] C. A. Coulson, *Valence*, Oxford University Press (1952), p. 71.

The matrix elements of the perturbation are:

$$\mathscr{H}^{(1)}_{11} = -e\int \psi_{2s}^*(1) r_{a1} P_1(\cos\theta_{a1})\psi_{2s}(1)\, d\boldsymbol{r}_1 = -(\mu_z)_{2s,\,2s} = 0 \qquad (13.6\text{–}13)$$

$$\mathscr{H}^{(1)}_{22} = -e\int \psi^*_{2p_z}(1) r_{a1} P_1(\cos\theta_{a1})\psi_{2p_z}(1)\, d\boldsymbol{r}_1 = -(\mu_z)_{2p_z,\,2p_z} = 0 \qquad (13.6\text{–}14)$$

$$\mathscr{H}^{(1)}_{12} = \mathscr{H}^{(1)}_{21} = -e\int \psi_{2s}^*(1) r_{a1} P_1(\cos\theta_{a1})\psi_{2p_z}(1)\, d\boldsymbol{r}_1 = -(\mu_z)_{2s,\,2p_z} \qquad (13.6\text{–}15)$$

The value of the matrix element $(\mu_z)_{2s,\,2p_z}$ is given in Appendix 12C. Thus the resonance energy is

$$\varphi^{(\text{res})} = \mp\lambda(\mu_z)_{2s,\,2p_z} = \pm 3\,\frac{e^2}{a_0}\,\frac{1}{(r_{ab}/a_0)^2} \qquad (13.6\text{–}16)$$

The inverse-square dependence of $\varphi^{(\text{res})}$ on the separation is a much longer range interaction energy than the $1/r_{ab}^4$ dependence which is normally expected between an ion and a nonpolar molecule. In a collision between a proton and a hydrogen atom, with principal quantum number $n = 2$, there is an equal probability that the resonance energy of interaction will be positive or negative. The complete energy of interaction between a proton and a hydrogen atom is the sum of the resonance and the electrostatic interactions (this is discussed in § 13.6d).

b. Quantum mechanical interaction of two ideal dipoles imbedded in linear molecules

The detailed interaction between dipoles is very important from the standpoint of understanding the behavior of the transport coefficients of polar gases and also for the understanding of the pressure broadening of microwaves (see § 13.7). The quantum mechanical calculation of the energy of two interacting linear dipole molecules can be performed by the use of the first- and second-order perturbation theory. The first-order electrostatic interaction (with energy varying as $1/r_{ab}^3$) vanishes except for the cases of resonance. The quantum mechanical specification of the orientation of the dipoles is the reason for this behavior. A linear dipole is specified by the azimuthal quantum number j and the magnetic quantum number m. The combination of j and m fixes the axis of rotation of the molecule to within certain limits. However, the dipole moment of the molecule at any instant is perpendicular to the axis of rotation. As a result, if the rotational axes for the two molecules are fixed, the four configurations shown in Fig. 13.6–3 are equally probable, and it is reasonable that the first-order electrostatic energy averaged over the wave functions for the two molecules vanishes.

The wave functions for an isolated linear molecule are the normalized spherical harmonics $Y_j^m(\theta, \phi)$ given in Eq. 12.B–3. The indices j and m are the azimuthal quantum number and the magnetic quantum number, respectively. The energy of the molecule in the jth state is

$$E_j = \frac{h^2 j(j+1)}{8\pi^2 I} \qquad (13.6\text{–}17)$$

in which I is the moment of inertia of the molecule.

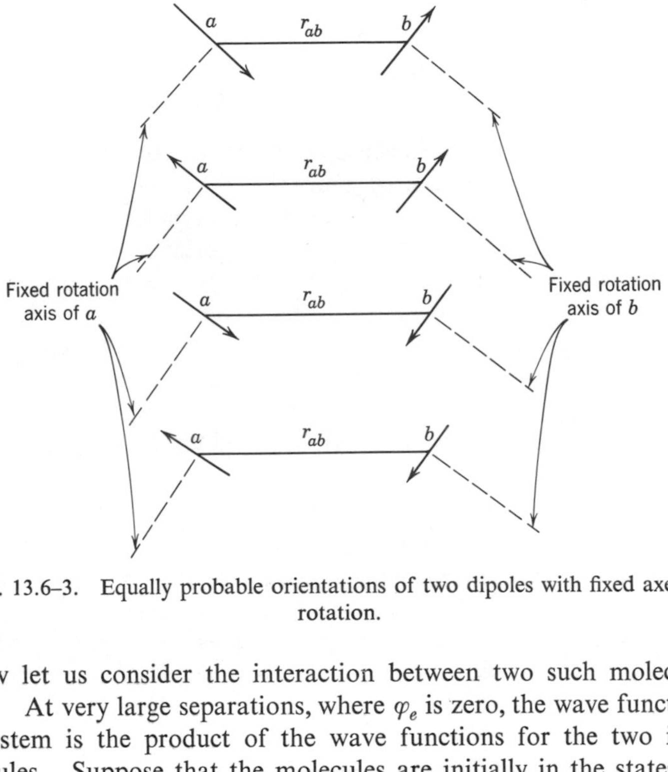

Fig. 13.6–3. Equally probable orientations of two dipoles with fixed axes of rotation.

Now let us consider the interaction between two such molecules, a and b. At very large separations, where φ_e is zero, the wave function for the system is the product of the wave functions for the two isolated molecules. Suppose that the molecules are initially in the states j_a, m_a and j_b, m_b, respectively. Then the unperturbed wave function for the system is

$$\psi^0(j_a, m_a; j_b, m_b) = Y_{j_a}^{m_a}(\theta_a, \phi_a) Y_{j_b}^{m_b}(\theta_b, \phi_b) \qquad (13.6\text{–}18)$$

The product of b_3/r_{ab}^3 times ψ^0 is a linear combination of, at most, twelve of the ψ^0:

$$\frac{b_3}{r_{ab}^3}\psi^0(j_a, m_a; j_b, m_b) = \frac{\mu_a \mu_b}{r_{ab}^3} \Sigma_i v_i \psi_i^0 \qquad (13.6\text{–}19)$$

Here the states designated by the subscript i are

$$\begin{cases} \psi_1{}^0 = \psi^0(j_a + 1, m_a; j_b + 1, m_b) \\ \psi_2{}^0 = \psi^0(j_a + 1, m_a + 1; j_b + 1, m_b - 1) \\ \psi_3{}^0 = \psi^0(j_a + 1, m_a - 1; j_b + 1, m_b + 1) \end{cases}$$
$$\begin{cases} \psi_4{}^0 = \psi^0(j_a - 1, m_a; j_b - 1, m_b) \\ \psi_5{}^0 = \psi^0(j_a - 1, m_a + 1; j_b - 1, m_b - 1) \\ \psi_6{}^0 = \psi^0(j_a - 1, m_a - 1; j_b - 1, m_b + 1) \end{cases}$$
$$\begin{cases} \psi_7{}^0 = \psi^0(j_a + 1, m_a; j_b - 1, m_b) \\ \psi_8{}^0 = \psi^0(j_a + 1, m_a + 1; j_b - 1, m_b - 1) \\ \psi_9{}^0 = \psi^0(j_a + 1, m_a - 1; j_b - 1, m_b + 1) \end{cases} \quad (13.6\text{–}20)$$
$$\begin{cases} \psi_{10}{}^0 = \psi^0(j_a - 1, m_a; j_b + 1, m_b) \\ \psi_{11}{}^0 = \psi^0(j_a - 1, m_a + 1; j_b + 1, m_b - 1) \\ \psi_{12}{}^0 = \psi^0(j_a - 1, m_a - 1; j_b + 1, m_b + 1) \end{cases}$$

The values of the numerical constants, v_i, are readily determined from Eqs. 12.B–8, 9, and 10. Those states have zero values of their v_i (and can be disregarded) which have either negative values of j or values of $|m|$ greater than the corresponding j. We shall designate the original state by the subscript 0.

London[4] used a perturbation method (which he calls *the method of unsharp resonance*) to solve the problem. He formed an approximate wave function made up of a linear combination of $\psi_0{}^0$, together with the functions for the (twelve at most) states with which it interacts according to Eq. 13.6–19. The best value for the energy which can be obtained from such a linear combination is given by the solution to the secular equation. This secular equation has a particularly simple form since those states with i greater than zero do not interact with any other states except 0. Furthermore, the diagonal elements of 1, 2, and 3; 4, 5, and 6; 7, 8, and 9; and 10, 11, and 12 are equal by groups of three. Thus the secular equation has non-zero elements along the zeroth row, down the zeroth column, and along the diagonal. Carrying out the indicated multiplications and rearranging, we obtain (for the general case) the fifth-order equation for $\varphi(j_a, m_a; j_b, m_b \mid r_{ab})$:

$$\frac{r_{ab}{}^6}{\mu_a{}^2\mu_b{}^2}\varphi = \frac{a_1{}^2}{\varphi - \epsilon_1} + \frac{a_2{}^2}{\varphi - \epsilon_2} + \frac{a_3{}^2}{\varphi - \epsilon_3} + \frac{a_4{}^2}{\varphi - \epsilon_4} \quad (13.6\text{–}21)$$

[4] F. London, *Z. Physik*, **63**, 245 (1930); see also H. Margenau, *Revs. Mod. Phys.*, **11**, 1 (1939).

Here the ϵ_i are given by:

$$\begin{aligned}
\epsilon_1 &= \frac{h^2}{4\pi^2}\left[\frac{(j_a+1)}{I_a} + \frac{(j_b+1)}{I_b}\right] \\
\epsilon_2 &= \frac{h^2}{4\pi^2}\left[-\frac{j_a}{I_a} - \frac{j_b}{I_b}\right] \\
\epsilon_3 &= \frac{h^2}{4\pi^2}\left[\frac{(j_a+1)}{I_a} - \frac{j_b}{I_b}\right] \\
\epsilon_4 &= \frac{h^2}{4\pi^2}\left[-\frac{j_a}{I_a} + \frac{j_b+1}{I_b}\right]
\end{aligned} \tag{13.6–22}$$

and the a_i^2 are given by

$$a_1^2 = v_1^2 + v_2^2 + v_3^2$$

$$= \frac{\left[\begin{array}{l} 4[(j_a+1)^2 - m_a^2][(j_b+1)^2 - m_b^2] \\ +\frac{1}{4}(j_a+m_a+1)(j_a+m_a+2)(j_b-m_b+1)(j_b-m_b+2) \\ +\frac{1}{4}(j_a-m_a+1)(j_a-m_a+2)(j_b+m_b+1)(j_b+m_b+2) \end{array}\right]}{[4(j_a+1)^2-1][4(j_b+1)^2-1]}$$

$$a_2^2 = v_4^2 + v_5^2 + v_6^2$$

$$= \frac{\left[\begin{array}{l} 4(j_a^2 - m_a^2)(j_b^2 - m_b^2) \\ +\frac{1}{4}(j_a-m_a-1)(j_a-m_a)(j_b+m_b-1)(j_b+m_b) \\ +\frac{1}{4}(j_a+m_a-1)(j_a+m_a)(j_b-m_b-1)(j_b-m_b) \end{array}\right]}{(4j_a^2-1)(4j_b^2-1)} \tag{13.6–23}$$

$$a_3^2 = v_7^2 + v_8^2 + v_9^2$$

$$= \frac{\left[\begin{array}{l} 4[(j_a+1)^2 - m_a^2][j_b^2 - m_b^2] \\ +\frac{1}{4}(j_a+m_a+1)(j_a+m_a+2)(j_b+m_b-1)(j_b+m_b) \\ +\frac{1}{4}(j_a-m_a+1)(j_a-m_a+2)(j_b-m_b-1)(j_b-m_b) \end{array}\right]}{[4(j_a+1)^2-1][4j_b^2-1]}$$

$$a_4^2 = v_{10}^2 + v_{11}^2 + v_{12}^2$$

$$= \frac{\left[\begin{array}{l} 4[j_a^2 - m_a^2][(j_b+1)^2 - m_b^2] \\ +\frac{1}{4}(j_a+m_a)(j_a+m_a-1)(j_b+m_b+1)(j_b+m_b+2) \\ +\frac{1}{4}(j_a-m_a)(j_a-m_a-1)(j_b-m_b+1)(j_b-m_b+2) \end{array}\right]}{[4j_a^2-1][4(j_b+1)^2-1]}$$

For large separations (except in the cases of resonance which we discuss presently), φ becomes small compared to the ϵ_i, and the terms on the right-hand side of Eq. 13.6–21 can be expanded in a series in powers of φ,

$$\frac{r_{ab}^{\ 6}}{\mu_a^{\ 2}\mu_b^{\ 2}}\varphi = -\Sigma_i \frac{a_i^{\ 2}}{\epsilon_i}\left[1 + \frac{\varphi}{\epsilon_i} + \frac{\varphi^2}{\epsilon_i^{\ 2}} + \ldots\right] \tag{13.6–21a}$$

Considering only the first three terms on the right-hand side of Eq. 13.6–21a leads to a quadratic equation, the only physically significant solution to which is expressible in the form of the series:

$$\varphi = -\frac{\mu_a^{\ 2}\mu_b^{\ 2}}{r_{ab}^{\ 6}} B_1 + \frac{\mu_a^{\ 4}\mu_b^{\ 4}}{r_{ab}^{\ 12}} B_1B_2 - \frac{\mu_a^{\ 6}\mu_b^{\ 6}}{r_{ab}^{\ 18}}(B_1B_2^{\ 2} + B_1^{\ 2}B_3) + \cdots \tag{13.6–24}$$

where the B_i are given by

$$B_i = \sum_{k=1}^{4} \frac{a_k^{\ 2}}{\epsilon_k^{\ i}} \tag{13.6–25}$$

Here $\epsilon_k^{\ i}$ is the ith power of ϵ_k.

Next let us consider the collisions between two like molecules. In this case $\mu_a = \mu_b = \mu$ and the moments of inertia $I_a = I_b = I$. Let us define a parameter z which is proportional to the sixth power of the separation, and define a reduced interaction potential, φ':

$$z = \left(\frac{h^2}{4\pi^2 I\mu^2}\right)^2 r_{ab}^{\ 6}, \qquad \varphi' = \left(\frac{4\pi^2 I}{h^2}\right)\varphi \tag{13.6–26}$$

Then Eq. 13.6–21 can be written in the form

$$z\varphi' = \frac{a_1^{\ 2}}{\varphi' - (j_a + j_b + 2)} + \frac{a_2^{\ 2}}{\varphi' + (j_a + j_b)} + \frac{a_3^{\ 2}}{\varphi' - (j_a - j_b + 1)} + \frac{a_4^{\ 2}}{\varphi' - (j_b - j_a + 1)} \tag{13.6–27}$$

The reduced interaction potential is then, regardless of particular molecular constants, a function only of z and depends parametrically on the rotational quantum numbers of the interacting molecules.

From Eq. 13.6–27, it is clear that in those cases where $|j_a - j_b| = 1$ the denominator of either the third or the fourth term becomes φ'. As we shall show, the energy of interaction at large separations becomes proportional to $r_{ab}^{\ 3}$ instead of $r_{ab}^{\ 6}$, and resonance degeneracy exists between the states with $j_a = j_b + 1$ and $j_b = j_a + 1$. Let us consider $j_a = j_b + 1$; then Eq. 13.6–27 can be written (after multiplying through by φ'):

$$z\varphi'^2 + \left[\frac{a_1^{\ 2}}{-\varphi' + (2j_a + 1)} + \frac{a_2^{\ 2}}{-\varphi' - (2j_a - 1)} + \frac{a_3^{\ 2}}{-\varphi' + 2}\right]\varphi' - a_4^{\ 2} = 0 \tag{13.6–28}$$

For sufficiently large separations φ' becomes small compared to either $(2j_a + 1)$ or 2. Thus, for large separations, Eq. 13.6–28 can be expanded in a series in powers of φ'. Considering the first three terms leads to a quadratic equation for φ',

$$(z + D_1)\varphi'^2 + D_2\varphi' - a_4^2 = 0 \tag{13.6–29}$$

where

$$D_1 = \frac{a_1^2}{(2j_a + 1)^2} - \frac{a_2^2}{(2j_a - 1)^2} + \frac{a_3^2}{4}$$
$$D_2 = \frac{a_1^2}{2j_a + 1} - \frac{a_2^2}{2j_a - 1} + \frac{a_3^2}{2} \tag{13.6–30}$$

The solutions to Eq. 13.6–29 are

$$\varphi' = -\tfrac{1}{2}\left(\frac{D_2}{z + D_1}\right) \pm \frac{1}{2}\sqrt{\left(\frac{D_2}{z + D_1}\right)^2 + \left(\frac{4a_4^2}{z + D_1}\right)} \tag{13.6–31}$$

Expanding these solutions in powers of $1/z^{1/2}$, we get two asymptotic solutions valid for large separations:

$$\varphi_+' = \frac{a_4}{z^{1/2}} - \frac{D_2}{2z} + \frac{a_4}{z^{3/2}}\left(\frac{D_2^2}{8a_4^2} - \frac{D_1}{2}\right) + \cdots \tag{13.6–32}$$

$$\varphi_-' = -\frac{a_4}{z^{1/2}} - \frac{D_2}{2z} - \frac{a_4}{z^{3/2}}\left(\frac{D_2^2}{8a_4^2} - \frac{D_1}{2}\right) + \cdots \tag{13.6–33}$$

When a state of resonance exists, there are, therefore, two interaction potentials, one positive at large separations, the other negative, and the energy at large separations varies as $z^{-1/2}$ or $1/r_{ab}^3$.

The values of B_1, B_2, and B_3 for non-resonating systems and the values of a_4, D_1, and D_2 for resonant systems are given in Table 13.6–1.

For many purposes, it suffices to know $\varphi(j_1, j_2)$, the energy of interaction of the two dipoles averaged (algebraically) over all the magnetic quantum states. This averaging over the magnetic quantum states corresponds to a classical spatial averaging over all orientations of the axes of rotation of the dipoles (keeping the angular momentum about these axes constant). The result, varying as $1/r_{ab}^6$, has no simple classical analogy. London[4] found that at large separations, $\varphi(j_1, j_2)$ can be expressed in the form

$$\varphi(j_1, j_2) = \frac{8\pi^2 I_a \mu_a^4}{3h^2 r^6} G(j_1, j_2) \tag{13.6–34}$$

TABLE 13.6–1
IMPORTANT PARAMETERS FOR THE INTERACTION OF TWO LIKE LINEAR DIPOLE MOLECULES

(a) Non-resonance Cases:

	m_a	m_b	B_1	B_2	B_3
$j_a = 0,\ j_b = 0$	0	0	0.33333333	0.16666667	0.08333333
$j_a = 0,\ j_b = 2$	0	0	−0.28571429	0.42857143	−0.39285714
	0	1	−0.22619048	0.36011905	−0.32663690
	0	2	−0.04761905	0.15476190	−0.12797619
$j_a = 1,\ j_b = 1$	0	0	0.58000000	0.84500000	0.66125000
	0	1	0.41000000	0.35250000	0.33812500
	1	1	0.32000000	0.28000000	0.27000000
	1	−1	0.07000000	0.09250000	0.03562500
$j_a = 1,\ j_b = 3$	0	0	−0.22567901	0.37691358	−0.29983882
	0	1	−0.20074074	0.34703704	−0.27532922
	0	2	−0.12592593	0.25740741	−0.20180041
	0	3	−0.00123457	0.10802469	−0.07925240
	1	−3	−0.01790124	0.04552469	−0.02936814
	1	−2	−0.10370370	0.14907407	−0.13289609
	1	−1	−0.16074074	0.22092593	−0.20407922
	1	0	−0.18901235	0.26108025	−0.24291752
	1	1	−0.18851852	0.26953704	−0.24941101
	1	2	−0.15925926	0.24629630	−0.22355967
	1	3	−0.10123457	0.19135802	−0.16536351
$j_a = 2,\ j_b = 2$	0	0	0.57482993	0.62159864	0.59119898
	0	1	0.50170068	0.53103741	0.50641298
	0	2	0.28231293	0.25935374	0.25205499
	1	2	0.17687075	0.16638322	0.15421863
	1	−1	0.39965986	0.42077664	0.39825444
	1	1	0.48299320	0.49716553	0.47869426
	1	2	0.34353741	0.31916100	0.31509826
	2	−2	0.02721088	0.04024943	0.02158919
	2	−1	0.17687075	0.16638322	0.15421863
	2	2	0.36054422	0.34580499	0.34334845

(b) Resonance Cases

	m_a	m_b	a_4	D_2	D_1
$j_a = 0, j_b = 1$	0	0	0	0.71111111	0.60000000
	0	1	0	0.47777778	0.45000000
$j_a = 1, j_b = 2$	0	0	0.58554005	−0.08571429	−0.23968254
	0	1	0.55205245	−0.03396825	−0.16798942
	0	2	0.43643578	0.12126984	0.04708995
	1	−2	0.09759001	−0.02412698	−0.09470899
	1	−1	0.16903085	0.12095238	0.01031746
	1	0	0.23904572	0.19523810	0.07063492
	1	1	0.30860670	0.19873016	0.08624339
	1	2	0.37796448	0.13142857	0.05714286

Here the $G(j_1, j_2)$ are the numbers given in Table 13.6–2. If $|j_1 - j_2|$ is large,

$$G(j_1, j_2) \rightarrow \frac{1}{2[(j_1 - j_2)^2 - 1]} \tag{13.6–35}$$

For the resonance cases where $j_1 = j$ and $j_2 = j - 1$, or vice versa,

$$G(j, j-1) = G(j-1, j) = -\frac{4j^4 - j^2 + 1}{4(4j^2 - 1)^2} \tag{13.6–36}$$

TABLE 13.6–2

$G(j_1, j_2)$

j_2 \ j_1	0	1	2	3	4
0	−0.5	−0.111	0.25	0.100	0.0555
1	−0.111	−0.5	−0.0678	0.194	0.0786
2	0.25	−0.0678	−0.5	−0.0645	0.181
3	0.100	0.194	−0.0645	−0.5	−0.0336
4	0.0555	0.0786	0.181	−0.0336	−0.5

Such a detailed treatment of the interaction of dipoles is required for a precise interpretation of the transport properties of polar molecules and the pressure broadening of microwaves considered in § 13.7.

c. Quantum mechanical interaction between two ideal dipoles imbedded in symmetrical tops

The quantum mechanical interaction of two dipoles can also be treated if the dipoles are imbedded in spheres (molecules whose three principal moments of inertia are equal) or symmetrical tops (molecules in which two of the principal moments of inertia are equal). This is a realistic model of polar molecules. The treatment is very similar to that of the interaction of linear dipoles.

The wave function of a molecule consisting of an ideal dipole imbedded in a symmetrical top depends on a third quantum number, k, which specifies the component of angular momentum in the direction of the dipole moment. If $k = 0$, the situation is much the same as for the linear dipole. However, if k is not zero, there is a resultant electric moment in the direction of the internuclear axis. This can be seen from Fig. 13.6–4.

If we assume that the axis of rotation is fixed by the quantum numbers j and m (as in the linear dipole example) and the orientation of the dipole with respect to this axis is fixed by the quantum number, k, the dipole is constrained to oscillate between the two positions shown in Fig. 13.6–4. Thus if the quantum numbers k_a and k_b for the two molecules are both different from zero, there is a first-order electrostatic interaction between the two molecules, and an energy varying as $1/r_{ab}^3$.

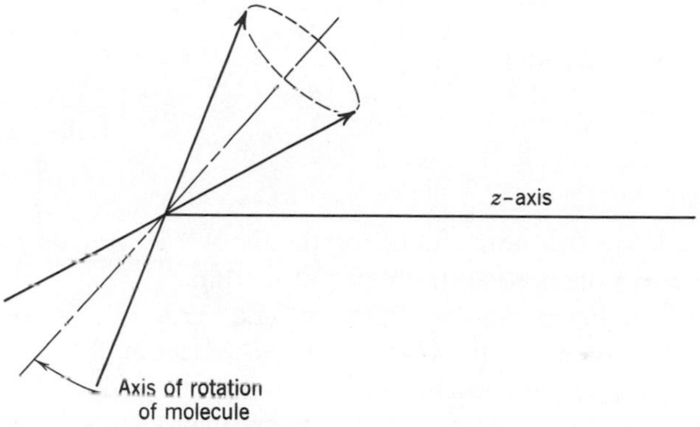

Fig. 13.6–4. Possible positions of a dipole if the axis of rotation of the molecule is not in the direction of the dipole. In addition to the motion shown, the axis of rotation rotates about the z-axis.

The wave functions of a pair of isolated symmetrical tops[5–7] are products of the representation coefficients given in Eq. 12.B–13:

$$\psi^0(j_a, k_a, m_a; j_b, k_b, m_b) = \frac{\sqrt{(2j_a + 1)(2j_b + 1)}}{8\pi^2} D^{j_a}(R_a)_{k_a m_a} D^{j_b}(R_b)_{k_b m_b} \qquad (13.6\text{–}37)$$

The quantum numbers have the significance that $\frac{h^2}{4\pi^2} j(j+1)$ is the square of the total angular momentum, $\frac{h}{2\pi} k$ is the component of angular momentum along the symmetry axis of the molecule, and $\frac{h}{2\pi} m$ is the

[5] L. Pauling and E. B. Wilson, Jr., *Introduction to Quantum Mechanics*, McGraw-Hill (1935), p. 275.
[6] D. M. Dennison, *Revs. Mod. Phys.*, **3**, 280 (1931).
[7] L. Infeld and T. E. Hull, *Revs. Mod. Phys.*, **23**, 32 (1951).

component of angular momentum along some arbitrary direction fixed in space. The quantum numbers can have the values:

$$k = -j, -j+1, \cdots, 0, \cdots, j-1, j$$
$$m = -j, -j+1, \cdots, 0, \cdots, j-1, j$$
$$j = 0, 1, 2, \cdots$$

The energy for the pair of isolated molecules is

$$\mathscr{H}_{00}(j_a, k_a, m_a; j_b, k_b, m_b) = \frac{h^2}{8\pi^2}\left[\begin{array}{l} \dfrac{j_a(j_a+1)}{(I_1)_a} + k_a^2\left(\dfrac{1}{(I_3)_a} - \dfrac{1}{(I_1)_a}\right) \\ + \dfrac{j_b(j_b+1)}{(I_1)_b} + k_b^2\left(\dfrac{1}{(I_3)_b} - \dfrac{1}{(I_1)_b}\right) \end{array}\right] \tag{13.6–38}$$

in which the I_3 are the moments of inertia about the symmetry axis, and the I_1 are the two other equal moments of inertia.

Just as for the linear dipolar molecules (Eq. 13.6–19), the product of the interaction potential times an unperturbed wave function can be expressed as a linear combination of a large number (up to 27) unperturbed wave functions. This follows directly from the relations between the representation coefficients which are given in Eqs. 12B–31, 32, and 33. As a result, if we write the product of the interaction potentials times an unperturbed wave function in the form:

$$\frac{b_3}{r_{ab}^{\ 3}}\psi^0(j_a, k_a, m_a; j_b, k_b, m_b) = \Sigma_i v_i \psi^0(j_a', k_a', m_a'; j_b', k_b', m_b') \tag{13.6–39}$$

the expansion coefficients (or matrix components) v_i can have non-vanishing values only if $k_a' = k_a$, $k_b' = k_b$, $m_a' + m_b' = m_a + m_b$, $j_a' = j_a$ or $(j_a \pm 1)$, $j_b' = j_b$ or $(j_b \pm 1)$, and $m_a' = m_a$ or $(m_a \pm 1)$. For the general case, this represents a set of twenty-seven possible wave functions with which any particular wave function can interact. The problem is much more complicated for the symmetrical top than for the linear dipole problem, since there are interactions which occur in both the first-order and the second-order perturbation theory. The interactions in which the j and k for the two molecules remain unchanged are considered to be first-order interactions, and at large separations they give the most important contributions to the energy of interaction. The first-order terms arise only if both k_a and k_b are different from zero.

Margenau and Warren[8] have considered the first-order interactions. Even these are complicated. For each value of j_a, k_a; j_b, k_b the energy of

[8] H. Margenau and D. T. Warren, *Phys. Rev.*, **51**, 748 (1937).

the system splits into a large number of energy levels. All those states for which $m_a + m_b$ has the same value interact and form their own secular equation. Thus for the case where $j_a = j_b = k_a = k_b = 1$, the following six forms for the energies of interaction satisfy the secular equation:

$$\varphi_{ab} = \begin{cases} -2\dfrac{\mu_a\mu_b}{4r_{ab}^3} \text{ (doubly degenerate)} \\[2ex] -\dfrac{\mu_a\mu_b}{4r_{ab}^3} \text{ (doubly degenerate)} \\[2ex] +(1-\sqrt{3})\dfrac{\mu_a\mu_b}{4r_{ab}^3} \\[2ex] +\dfrac{\mu_a\mu_b}{4r_{ab}^3} \text{ (doubly degenerate)} \\[2ex] +2\dfrac{\mu_a\mu_b}{4r_{ab}^3} \\[2ex] +(1+\sqrt{3})\dfrac{\mu_a\mu_b}{4r_{ab}^3} \end{cases} \qquad (13.6\text{–}40)$$

The symmetrical top dipoles differ from the linear dipoles in that the mean value of φ_{ab} does not vanish for the first-order interactions. This is consistent with the fact that symmetrical dipole molecules have a first-order Stark effect.

Carroll[9] has calculated the second order interactions averaged over all magnetic quantum numbers. Because of the large number of states which would have to be considered simultaneously, it would be difficult (but not impossible) to calculate the energy of interaction through the second-order terms in a manner analogous to London's treatment of the linear dipoles.

d. Long-range interactions between a proton and a hydrogen or helium atom

The interaction of a proton with a hydrogen or helium atom in its ground state is typical of the interaction of an ion with a neutral non-polar molecule. The interaction of a proton with an excited hydrogen atom introduces two additional effects—the excited hydrogen atom has (except for *s*-states) quadrupole moments so that there are electrostatic forces; then, too, the degeneracy of the excited states introduces the sharp resonance forces discussed in § 13.6a. The interaction of a proton with

[9] K. Carroll, *Phys. Rev.*, **53**, 310 (1938).

an excited helium atom has the same sort of electrostatic forces, but the near-degeneracy of the excited states leads to resonance forces which are much less important.

It is easy to show that an atom having an azimuthal quantum number, L, has multipoles of order $n = 0, 2, \cdots, 2L$. Thus an atom in an S-state, with $L = 0$, has no multipole moments; an atom in a P-state, with $L = 1$, has a quadrupole moment; an atom in its D-state, with $L = 2$, has both quadrupole and "sixteenopole" moments; etc. (See § 12.1 for the definitions of the multipoles).

Thus no direct electrostatic interaction (only induced dipole forces) is expected between a proton and an atom in an S-state. However, charge-quadrupole forces do occur between a proton and atoms in all other states. Since the ground states of the hydrogen and the helium atoms are S-states, such forces occur only in excited states. The charge-quadrupole forces vary as $1/r_{ab}^3$ and are therefore of longer range than the charge-induced-dipole forces which vary as $1/r_{ab}^4$. However, for some values of the magnetic quantum number the charge-quadrupole forces are attractive and for others, they are repulsive. The charge-quadrupole energy averaged over the magnetic quantum number (corresponding to a classical spatial average over all orientations of the atom) vanishes.

The energy of interaction between a proton and hydrogen atom or a helium atom in the ground state is the usual charge-induced dipole energy, $\varphi^{(\mathrm{ind})} = -\alpha e^2/2r_{ab}^4$, uncomplicated by either resonance or direct electrostatic interactions. However, the electrostatic interactions between a proton and an excited hydrogen or a helium atom are examples in which resonance within one molecule affects the nature of the long-range intermolecular forces. In a collision between a proton and an excited hydrogen atom, resonance leads to terms in the interaction energy varying as $1/r_{ab}^2$, as explained in § 13.6a. This resonance exists because all the states of a hydrogen atom with the same principal quantum number, n, have exactly the same energy. For a helium atom, states with the same principal quantum numbers for the two electrons have only slightly different energies for different values of the azimuthal quantum numbers. Thus in the interaction between a proton and an excited helium atom, the resonance is not nearly so strong, and it neither produces a term varying as $1/r_{ab}^2$ nor does it affect the normal charge-quadrupole term varying as $1/r_{ab}^3$, but it does add a term varying as $1/r_{ab}^4$ which is added to the charge-induced dipole energy.

i. *Interaction of a Proton with a Hydrogen Atom*

The interaction between a proton and a hydrogen atom is one of the few problems of molecular quantum mechanics which can be solved exactly. At large separations the energy of interaction of a proton and a hydrogen atom can be calculated exactly[10–12] in terms of a power series in inverse powers of the separation,

$$\varphi = +\frac{E_2}{r_{ab}^{\ 2}} + \frac{E_3}{r_{ab}^{\ 3}} + \frac{E_4}{r_{ab}^{\ 4}} + \cdots \tag{13.6–41}$$

Each of the E_i is obtained exactly in terms of the E_i for smaller i. Similarly the wave function can be expanded in a power series in $1/r_{ab}$,

$$\psi = \psi_0 + \frac{1}{r_{ab}}\psi_1 + \frac{1}{r_{ab}^{\ 2}}\psi_2 + \cdots \tag{13.6–42}$$

Let $\mathscr{H}_0$ be the Hamiltonian of an unperturbed hydrogen atom and let E_0 be the energy of the particular state of the unperturbed hydrogen atom under consideration. The perturbation potential, arising from the field of the proton, is given in Eq. 13.6–8. If we substitute the power series expansions of the perturbation potential, interaction energy, and wave functions into the Schrödinger equation, and equate like powers of $1/r_{ab}$, the following set of simultaneous equations is obtained:

$$\begin{aligned} (\mathscr{H}_0 - E_0)\psi_0 &= 0 \\ (\mathscr{H}_0 - E_0)\psi_1 &= 0 \end{aligned} \tag{13.6–43}$$

$$(\mathscr{H}_0 - E_0)\psi_2 - r_{a1}P_1(\cos\theta_{a1})\psi_0 = +E_2\psi_0$$

$$(\mathscr{H}_0 - E_0)\psi_3 - r_{a1}P_1(\cos\theta_{a1})\psi_1 - r_{a1}^{\ 2}P_2(\cos\theta_{a1})\psi_0 = E_2\psi_1 + E_3\psi_0$$

$$\cdots = \cdots$$

The solution of these equations is greatly simplified by using parabolic coordinates ($\zeta = r_a(1 + \cos\theta_a)$, $\eta = r_a(1 - \cos\theta_a)$, ϕ_a) instead of spherical coordinates, since all the equations are separable in the parabolic coordinates.

For the interaction between a proton and an H-atom in the ground state, Coulson[10] obtained the following interaction energy:

$$\varphi_{ab} = -\frac{e^2}{a_0}\left[\begin{aligned} &\frac{9/4}{(r_{ab}/a_0)^4} + \frac{0}{(r_{ab}/a_0)^5} + \frac{15/2}{(r_{ab}/a_0)^6} + \frac{213/4}{(r_{ab}/a_0)^7} \\ &+ \frac{7755/64}{(r_{ab}/a_0)^8} + \frac{1773/2}{(r_{ab}/a_0)^9} + \frac{86049/16}{(r_{ab}/a_0)^{10}} \end{aligned}\right] \tag{13.6–44}$$

[10] C. A. Coulson, *Proc. Roy. Soc., Edinburgh*, **A61**, 20 (1941).
[11] C. A. Coulson and C. M. Gillam, *Proc. Roy. Soc., Edinburgh*, **A62**, 360 (1948).
[12] M. K. Krogdahl, *Astrophys. J.*, **100**, 311 (1944).

For the interaction of a proton with a hydrogen atom in an excited state, Mrs. Krogdahl[12] solved the equations and obtained the results shown in Table 13.6–3. Here n, l, m are the usual principal, azimuthal, and magnetic quantum numbers and E_0 is the energy of the unperturbed hydrogen atom. The energies obtained in this manner include the induction energy and represent the complete interaction. It should be noted that the potential energy functions split. For example, an atom with principal quantum number $n = 3$ and magnetic quantum number $m = 0$ can interact with a proton according to any one of three potential functions:

$$\begin{aligned} \varphi_1 &= \frac{e^2}{a_0}\left[\frac{36}{(r_{ab}/a_0)^3}\right] \\ \varphi_2 &= \frac{e^2}{a_0}\left[+\frac{9}{(r_{ab}/a_0)^2} - \frac{72}{(r_{ab}/a_0)^3}\right] \\ \varphi_3 &= \frac{e^2}{a_0}\left[-\frac{9}{(r_{ab}/a_0)^2} - \frac{72}{(r_{ab}/a_0)^3}\right] \end{aligned} \tag{13.6–45}$$

Coulson and Gillam[11] showed how to generalize Mrs. Krogdahl's results to obtain the interaction energy accurate to any desired power of $1/r_{ab}$.

The energy of interaction at small and intermediate separations of a proton with a hydrogen atom in any of its states is discussed in § 14.5. This system comprises the diatomic hydrogen ion, H_2^+, which has been studied extensively since it is one of the few problems in molecular quantum mechanics which can be solved exactly.

ii. *The Interaction between a Proton and an Excited Helium Atom*

The interaction between a proton and an excited helium atom can be treated in much the same manner as the interaction with a hydrogen atom. The essential difference is that the states with the same principal quantum number but different azimuthal quantum numbers have slightly different energies. As a result the resonance is not "sharp," and the energy of interaction has the form[13]

$$\varphi_{ab} = \frac{e^2}{a_0}\left[\frac{(q/a_0^2)}{2(r_{ab}/a_0)^3} - \frac{(\alpha'/a_0^3)}{2(r_{ab}/a_0)^4} + \cdots\right] \tag{13.6–46}$$

Here the q is the quadrupole moment of the particular state of the isolated

[13] M. K. Krogdahl, *Astrophys. J.*, **100**, 333 (1944).

TABLE 13.6–3

ENERGY OF INTERACTION OF A PROTON WITH A HYDROGEN ATOM[12] IN UNITS OF e^2/a_0

$$\varphi(r_{ab}) = \frac{e^2}{a_0}\left[\frac{E_2}{(r_{ab}/a_0)^2} + \frac{E_3}{(r_{ab}/a_0)^3} + \frac{E_4}{(r_{ab}/a_0)^4} + \cdots\right]$$

n	$\lvert m \rvert$	l	E_0	E_2	E_3	E_4
1	0	0	−1/2	0	0	−9/4
2	1	1	−1/8	0	+6	−78
	0	0, 1	−1/8	±3	−6	
3	2	2	−1/18	0	+36	−1377
	1	1, 2	−1/18	±9/2	+9	
	0	0, 1, 2	−1/18	0	+36	
				±9	−72	
4	3	3	−1/32	0	+120	−3360
	2	2, 3	−1/32	±6	+72	
	1	1, 2, 3	−1/32	0	+120	
				±12	−72	
	0	0, 1, 2, 3	−1/32	±6	+72	
				±18	−312	
5	4	4	−1/50	0	+300	−46875/4
	3	3, 4	−1/50	±15/2	+225	
	2	2, 3, 4	−1/50	0	+300	
				±15	0	
	1	1, 2, 3, 4	−1/50	+15/2	+225	
				±45/2	−375	
	0	0, 1, 2, 3, 4	−1/50	0	+300	
				±15	0	
				±30	−900	

helium atom. The α' differ from the polarizability of the isolated helium atom because of the near resonance. The values of α' were calculated on the assumption that the wave function of the helium atom perturbed by the proton is made up of a linear combination of the near-resonance states. The φ_{ab} were then determined as solutions to the corresponding secular equations. The value of α' is then simply related to the coefficient of the $1/r_{ab}^4$ in the power series expansion of φ_{ab}. The values of q/a_0^2 and α'/a_0^3 are given in Table 13.6–4.[14]

TABLE 13.6–4[14]

QUADRUPOLE MOMENT, q, AND A QUANTITY, α', FOR A HELIUM ATOM IN VARIOUS STATES

In each configuration one of the electrons is in a 1s state and the other electron is in a state designated by the quantum numbers, n, l, m.

n	l	m	q/a_0^2	α'/a_0^3	n	l	m	q/a_0^2
2	0	0	0	+428	5	3	0	−600
2	1	0	−24	−428	5	4	0	−3000/7
2	1	1	12		5	1	1	600
					5	2	1	−2700/7
3	0	0	0	−20,362	5	3	1	−450
3	1	0	−144	+42,429	5	4	1	−2550/7
3	2	0	−72	−22,067	5	2	2	5400/7
3	1	1	72		5	3	2	0
3	2	1	−36		5	4	2	−1200/7
3	2	2	72					
					6	0	0	0
4	0	0	0	+85,964	6	1	0	−2520
4	1	0	−480	+136,366	6	2	0	−11736/7
4	2	0	−288	+3,357,782	6	3	0	−1392
4	3	0	−192	−3,580,110	6	4	0	−7920/7
4	1	1	240		6	5	0	−840
4	2	1	−144		6	1	1	1260
4	3	1	−144		6	2	1	−5868/7
4	2	2	288		6	3	1	−1044
4	3	2	0		6	4	1	−6732/7
					6	5	1	−756
5	0	0	0		6	2	2	11736/7
5	1	0	−1200		6	3	2	0
5	2	0	−5400/7		6	4	2	−3168/7
					6	5	2	−504

[14] The values given are readily obtained from those tabulated in Ref. 13.

e. Quadrupole-quadrupole forces between atoms neither of which is in an S-state

The interaction of two atoms, neither one in an S-state, is discussed as an example of quadrupole-quadrupole interaction. It is interesting to note that there are a number of different interaction potentials that the collision system can follow, each corresponding to a different set of "molecular" quantum numbers for the combined system of two atoms. These energies of interaction (which vary as $1/r_{ab}^5$) are very large compared to the energy of dispersion. For example, two oxygen atoms may have an energy of attraction of 0.6 kcal per mole at a separation of 3.0 Å; two boron atoms may have this energy at 5.1 Å; or a carbon atom may attract an oxygen atom with this energy at a separation of 3.2 Å. Similar forces are expected between free radicals or between other molecules possessing resultant electronic angular momentum, and they help to explain some of the anomalous chemical and physical properties which such molecules display.

Knipp[15] has considered the energy of interaction between two atoms neither of which is in an S-state. Here the first-order quadrupole-quadrupole energy does not vanish. Depending on the values of the magnetic quantum numbers, some atoms are attracted and some are repelled by a particular atom.

A system of two atoms forms a "diatomic molecule." At large separations, where there are no interactions, the wave functions for the states having specified molecular quantum numbers are linear combinations of products of the atomic wave functions.[16] If the spins of the two atoms are S_1 and S_2, the total spin of the "molecule" may have the values:

$$S = S_1 + S_2, S_1 + S_2 - 1, \cdots, |S_1 - S_2| \tag{13.6–47}$$

For present purposes the quantum numbers Λ, Ω, and Γ are important:

$\Lambda = |m_{L_1} + m_{L_2}|$ is the quantum number representing the absolute value of the component of orbital angular momentum along the internuclear axis. Λ can have all integer values from 0 to $L_1 + L_2$, where L_1 and L_2 are the orbital momenta of the atoms. According to convention, states are designated Σ, Π, Δ, Φ, . . . according as $\Lambda = 0, 1, 2, 3, \ldots$. Because Λ is the absolute value of $m_{L_1} + m_{L_2}$, the Π, Δ, Φ, . . . states are doubly degenerate, since the component along the internuclear axis may be either positive or negative, but Σ states are not degenerate.

[15] J. K. Knipp, *Phys. Rev.*, **53**, 734 (1938).

[16] E. Wigner and E. Witmer, *Z. Physik*, **51**, 859 (1928); R. S. Mulliken, *Phys. Rev.*, **36**, 1440 (1930); F. Hund, *Z. Physik*, **63**, 723 (1930); H. Sponer, *Molekulspektren*, Springer (1936), II, pp. 132–7.

$\Omega = | m_{J_1} + m_{J_2} |$ is the quantum number representing the absolute value of the component of total angular momentum along the internuclear axis.

$\Gamma = | m_{J_1} + m_{L_2} |$ is a special quantum number of mixed characteristic.

The calculation of the energy of interaction of atoms at large separations is complicated by the fact that the splitting due to atomic spin-orbit interactions may be of the same order of magnitude. The spin-orbit splitting varies from 0.0018 ev in the case of the ground state of boron to 0.94 ev

TABLE 13.6–5a[15]

ATOMS WITH INCOMPLETE *p* SHELLS

(An asterisk after an element means the spin-orbit splitting of lowest energy term is less than 0.036 ev or 0.6 kcal/mole.)

Element	Ground Level		$B(L)$	$D(J)$	Radius of Maximum Charge Density of Outer Orbital in Units of a_0		$\overline{[r(n, l)^2]}$ in Units of a_0^2	
					Slater Screening Constants	Self-consistent Fields	Slater Screening Constants	Self-consistent Fields
B*	$2p$	$^2P_{1/2}{}^0$	−0.6325	0	1.54	1.80	4.4	9.12
Al*	$3p$	,,	,,	,,	2.57		10	
Ga	$4p$	,,	,,	,,	2.74		11	
In	$5p$	,,	,,	,,	3.20		14	
Tl	$6p$	,,	,,	,,	3.53		17	
C*	$2p^2$	$^3P_0$	0.6325	0	1.23	1.26	2.8	4.882
Si*	$3p^2$	,,	,,	,,	2.17		7.3	
Ge	$4p^2$	,,	,,	,,	2.42		8.5	
Sn	$5p^2$	,,	,,	,,	2.83		11	
Pb	$6p^2$	,,	,,	,,	3.12		14	
O*	$2p^4$	$^3P_2$	−0.6325	−0.3743	0.88	0.85	1.4	2.440
S	$3p^4$	,,	,,	,,	1.65		4.2	
Se	$4p^4$	,,	,,	,,	1.97		5.6	
Te	$5p^4$	,,	,,	,,	2.30		7.5	
F	$2p^5$	$^2P_{3/2}{}^0$	0.6325	0.4472	0.77	0.73	1.1	1.82
Cl	$3p^5$	,,	,,	,,	1.48		3.4	
Br	$4p^5$	,,	,,	,,	1.80		4.7	
I	$5p^5$	,,	,,	,,	2.11		6.2	

for the lowest term of thallium. If the spin-orbit separation is small compared to the energy of interaction, which is of the order of kT, we consider the orbital quantum number, L, of the atom to be significant; if

TABLE 13.6–5b[15]

ATOMS WITH INCOMPLETE d SHELLS

(Numbers in parentheses are positions of maximum radial density of the two electrons in the s shell lying outside the incomplete d shell. These electrons are most effective in determining the radius of the atoms.)

Element	Ground Level		$B(L)$	$D(J)$	Radius of Maximum Charge Density of Outer Orbital, in Units of a_0 — Slater Screening Constants	$\overline{[r(n, l)^2]}$ in Units of a_0^2 — Slater Screening Constants
Sc*	$3d4s^2$	$^2D_{3/2}$	−0.5345	−0.4472	3.00(4.55)	14
Y	$4d5s^2$	”	”	”	4.55(5.33)	30
La	$5d6s^2$	”	”	”	5.33(5.88)	40
Ti	$3d^24s^2$	$^3F_2$	−0.2213	−0.1833	2.47(4.35)	9.5
Zr	$4d^25s^2$	”	”	”	3.75(5.08)	20
Hf	$5d^26s^2$	”	”	”	4.38(5.60)	27
V	$3d^34s^2$	$^4F_{3/2}$	0.2213	0.1533	2.09(4.15)	6.8
W	$5d^45s^2$	$^5D_0$	0.5345	0	3.23(5.11)	15
Fe	$3d^64s^2$	$^5D_4$	−0.5345	−0.4006	1.44(3.65)	3.2
Co	$3d^74s^2$	$^4F_{9/2}$	−0.2213	−0.1935	1.32(3.51)	2.7
Ni	$3d^84s^2$	$^3F_4$	0.2213	0.2003	1.21(3.38)	2.3
Ir	$5d^9$	$^2D_{5/2}$	0.5345	0.4782	2.58	9.4

the spin-orbit splitting is large compared to kT, the total angular momentum, J, of the atom is significant. For these reasons collisions of three types are considered:

A. Both atoms 1 and 2 have spin-orbit splitting small compared to kT.
B. Atom 1 has a spin-orbit splitting large compared to kT while atom 2 has a small splitting.
C. Both atoms 1 and 2 have large spin-orbit splittings.

Knipp[15] expressed the energy of interaction as obtained by first-order perturbation in the three cases in the following manner:

$$\text{A:}\quad \varphi = \frac{e^2}{r^5}\,\overline{[r(n, l)^2]_1}\;\overline{[r(n, l)^2]_2}B_1(L_1)B_2(L_2)\lambda(L_1; L_2; \Lambda)$$

$$\text{B:}\quad \varphi = \frac{e^2}{r^5}\,\overline{[r(n, l)^2]_1}\;\overline{[r(n, l)^2]_2}D_1(J_1)B_2(L_2)\lambda(J_1; L_2; \Gamma) \qquad (13.6\text{–}48)$$

$$\text{C:}\quad \varphi = \frac{e^2}{r^5}\,\overline{[r(n, l)^2]_1}\;\overline{[r(n, l)^2]_2}D_1(J_1)D_2(J_2)\lambda(J_1; J_2; \Omega)$$

TABLE 13.6–6a[15]

VALUES OF $\lambda(h_1, h_2, \delta)$ FOR INTEGER VALUES OF δ

δ	$h_1 = 1$ $h_2 = 1$	2 1	3 1	4 1	1.5 1.5	2 2
0	0 *ea*	−1.014 *a*	−1.225 *a*	−1.305 *a*	2.4 *ea*	2.774 *ea*
					0 *ea*	−1.060 *ea*
	3.6 *fb*	2.324 *b*	2.096 *b*	2.013 *b*	3.2 *fb*	3.261 *fb*
	0 *fb*	−0.295 *b*	−0.382 *b*	−0.418 *b*	−0.8 *fb*	1.508 *fb*
						−0.484 *fb*
1	0 *e*	2.456	2.061	1.972	−1.6 *e*	1.202 *e*
		0.047	−0.170	−0.289		−0.917 *e*
		−1.489	−1.401	−1.392		
	−2.4 *f*				1.2 *f*	1.127 *f*
					−0.8 *f*	−1.413 *f*
2		0.356	2.199	1.367	0.4 *e*	−2.000 *e*
		−2.891	0.230	0.347		
			−1.939	−1.424		
	0.6 *f*				−2.8 *f*	0.857 *f*
						−1.857 *f*
3		1.014	0.646	2.032		0.857 *e*
			−3.096	−0.032		
				−1.710		
					1.2	−2.571 *f*
4			1.225	0.853		
				−3.222		
						1.714 *f*
5				1.354		

The values of $B(L)$, $D(J)$, and $\overline{[r(n, l)^2]}$ are given in Table 13.6–5 for the ground states for many of the elements. Values for $\overline{[r(n, l)^2]}$, the mean-square radius of the electron, obtained from both the Slater screening constants and the self-consistent fields are given in Table 13.6–5. This quantity is very sensitive to the charge distribution. The coefficients λ are given in Table 13.6–6.

TABLE 13.6–6b[15]

VALUES OF $\lambda(h_1, h_2, \delta)$ FOR HALF-INTEGRAL VALUES OF δ

δ	$h_1 = 1.5$ $h_2 = 1$	2 1.5	4.5 1
0.5	2.746 0 −1.049	2.864 1.551 −0.377 −1.168	1.977 −0.399 −1.345
1.5	0.176 −2.722	0.916 −1.195 −1.872	1.916 −0.206 −1.476
2.5	0.848	0.619 −2.770	1.883 0.125 −1.774
3.5		1.434	2.054 0.518 −2.339
4.5			0.934 −3.270
5.5			1.401

In Table 13.6–6 there are several states corresponding to each set of arguments. The spectroscopic notation of the state is designated by the letters following the entry in the following manner. Let us define $c = w_1 w_2 (-1)^{h_1+h_2}$, where w is the parity of the electronic state. The spectroscopic notation of the states corresponding to the various energies is then obtained by the following rules.

If the atoms are different:

a means that state is Σ^+ if $c = -1$
or Σ^- if $c = +1$,
b means that state is Σ^+ if $c = +1$
or Σ^- if $c = -1$

If the atoms are the same:

e means that state is *g* if *S* is odd
u if *S* is even
and Σ states are negative,
f means that state is *g* if *S* is even
or *u* if *S* is odd
and Σ states are positive.

For other cases, the spectroscopic notation of the states is clear, and the symbols *a*, *b*, *e*, *f*, can be ignored, but the energies of interaction are still given by the above expressions. Table 13.6–7 gives the values of λ obtained for a few typical examples.

TABLE 13.6–7[15]

VALUES OF λ FOR A FEW TYPICAL MOLECULES

Molecule	λ	States
F_2 or B_2	+3.6	${}^1\Sigma_g{}^+$, ${}^3\Sigma_u{}^+$
	+0.6	${}^1\Delta_g$, ${}^3\Delta_u$
	0.0	${}^1\Pi_u$, ${}^3\Pi_g$, ${}^1\Sigma_g{}^+$, ${}^1\Sigma_u{}^-$, ${}^3\Sigma_g{}^-$, ${}^3\Sigma_u{}^+$
	−2.4	${}^1\Pi_g$, ${}^3\Pi_u$ (low-lying states)
C_2 or O_2	+3.6	${}^1\Sigma_g{}^+$, ${}^3\Sigma_u{}^+$, ${}^5\Sigma_g{}^+$
	+0.6	${}^1\Delta_g$, ${}^3\Delta_u$, ${}^5\Delta_g$
	0.0	${}^1\Sigma_u{}^-$, ${}^3\Sigma_g{}^-$, ${}^5\Sigma_u{}^-$, ${}^1\Sigma_g{}^+$, ${}^3\Sigma_u{}^+$, ${}^5\Sigma_g{}^+$ ${}^1\Pi_u$, ${}^3\Pi_g$, ${}^5\Pi_u$
	−2.4	${}^1\Pi_g$, ${}^3\Pi_u$, ${}^5\Pi_g$ (low-lying states)
CO	+3.6	${}^1\Sigma^+$, ${}^3\Sigma^+$, ${}^5\Sigma^+$ (low-lying states)
	+0.6	${}^1\Delta$, ${}^3\Delta$, ${}^5\Delta$
	0.0	${}^1\Sigma^-$, ${}^3\Sigma^-$, ${}^5\Sigma^-$ ${}^1\Sigma^+$, ${}^3\Sigma^+$, ${}^5\Sigma^+$, ${}^1\Pi$, ${}^3\Pi$, ${}^5\Pi$
	−2.4	${}^1\Pi$, ${}^3\Pi$, ${}^5\Pi$

The large magnitude of these quadrupole-quadrupole forces can be seen from the examples shown in Table 13.6–8. Here the separation chosen is approximately twice the equilibrium separation for the normal diatomic molecule. For any other separation, the energy varies inversely as the fifth power of the ratio of the separations.

TABLE 13.6–8[15]

ENERGIES OF ATTRACTION AT DISTANCES OF TWICE THE SUM OF THE ATOMIC RADII

Known States of Diatomic Molecules	r_{ab} (Å)	φ_{ab} (ev)	States giving Largest Energy of Attraction at Large Separations
B_2	3.80	−0.112	$^1\Pi_g$, $^3\Pi_u$
BO $^2\Sigma^+$, $^2\Pi$	2.80	−0.139	$^2\Pi$, $^4\Pi$
C_2 $^3\Pi_u$?	2.66	−0.190	$^1\Pi_g$, $^3\Pi_u$, $^5\Pi_g$
CF	2.10	−0.231	$^2\Pi$, $^4\Pi$
O_2 $^3\Sigma_g^-$, $^1\Sigma_g^+$, $^3\Sigma_u^+$	1.80	−0.341	$^1\Pi_g$, $^3\Pi_u$, $^5\Pi_g$
F_2 $^1\Pi$?	1.54	−0.406	$^1\Pi_g$, $^3\Pi_u$,
BC	3.23	−0.202	$^2\Sigma^-$, $^4\Sigma^-$
BF	2.67	−0.195	$^1\Sigma^+$, $^3\Sigma^+$
CO $^1\Sigma^+$, $^3\Pi$, $^1\Pi$	2.23	−0.347	$^1\Sigma^+$, $^3\Sigma^+$, $^5\Sigma^+$
OF	1.67	−0.549	$^2\Sigma^-$, $^4\Sigma^-$

Note. The atomic radius is defined as the position of the last maximum in the electron density function. The spin-orbit coupling has been neglected and the values for $\overline{r^2}$ taken from the last column of Table 13.6–5. The last four molecules have, in addition, attractive Δ states at this distance, with energies one-sixth the energies of the Σ states and the same multiplicities (neglecting other forces). The known states listed are those which have been observed and which on dissociation go into normal states of the atoms.

Figure 13.6–5 shows the interaction energies at large separations which can result from the collision between a carbon and an oxygen atom in their ground states. The four potential energy curves at large separations split up into eighteen separate potential energy curves at small separations. The ground state for the carbon monoxide molecule is designated as $^1\Sigma^+$. Thus the continuation of the potential energy curve for the ground state of the carbon monoxide molecule to large separations, according to Table 13.6–7, must join with the lowest energy curve shown in Fig. 13.6–5 since two potential energy curves of the same symmetry cannot cross.

The quadrupole-quadrupole interactions discussed here probably play a large role in the interaction and recombination of free radicals. These

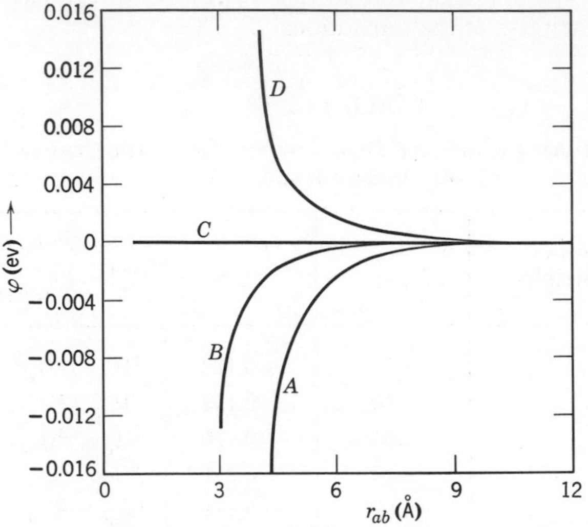

Fig. 13.6–5. The energy of interaction of a carbon atom and an oxygen atom in their ground states: Curve *A* is the energy for the states $^1\Sigma^+$, $^3\Pi$, $^1\Pi$. Curve *B* is for the states $^1\Delta$, $^3\Delta$, $^5\Delta$. Curve *C* is for the states $^1\Sigma^-$, $^3\Sigma^-$, $^5\Sigma^-$, $^1\Sigma^+$, $^3\Sigma^+$, $^5\Sigma^+$, $^1\Pi$, $^3\Pi$, $^5\Pi$. Curve *D* is for the states $^1\Pi$, $^3\Pi$, $^5\Pi$. These curves are reliable only at separations greater than 3 Å.

forces are important in determining the physical properties of substances containing large numbers of excited molecules, such as hot gases or systems in which chemical reactions are taking place rapidly.

7. The Determination of Intermolecular Forces from Pressure Broadening of Microwave Spectra

The pressure broadening of microwave spectra is becoming an important source of information about the multipole moments of molecules and the long-range forces between molecules. At the present time the high resolution of microwave spectrometers virtually eliminates errors due to "slit width," and hence experimental data of high accuracy can be obtained. The theoretical analysis of the data, however, is not very refined, and hence the interpretations of the data are rather crude. In this section we first summarize a few important facts about the broadening of spectral lines and then proceed to show what information can be obtained by the theoretical analysis of pressure-broadening data.

a. The broadening of lines in microwave spectra

Spectral lines have finite width for three reasons: (i) the *natural line width*, $\Delta\nu_N$, due to "radiation damping", (ii) the *Doppler effect broadening*, $\Delta\nu_D$, due to the speed of the molecules; and (iii) the *pressure broadening* $\Delta\nu_{PB}$, due to the forces between the molecules. At microwave frequencies (5×10^4 to 10^{10} sec^{-1}) the width of the lines due to radiation damping and the Doppler effect is very small compared to the width associated with the pressure broadening. At a convenient pressure of about 1 mm Hg, the pressure broadening of the lines is twenty to one hundred times the width due to the Doppler effect, and the latter is far greater than the width due to radiation damping. The explanation of pressure broadening involves the dipole moments, the quadrupole moments, and the polarizabilities of the molecules. Very often line widths provide a means for finding the probability of energy transfer from translation to rotation in collisions. Long-range forces are particularly important in this transfer, so that in some cases the observed cross-section for transferring translational to rotational energy is actually larger than the kinetic theory cross-section.

i. *Natural Line Width Due to Radiation Damping*[1, 2]

Let us consider the transition between energy levels E_1 and E_2. Inasmuch as these levels have finite widths ΔE_1 and ΔE_2, a spectral line associated with a transition between the two levels has a natural half width $\Delta\nu_N$. If molecules spend an average length of time t_1 in the state 1 with energy E_1, then according to the uncertainty principle,

$$t_1\,\Delta E_1 = \hbar \tag{13.7–1}$$

Furthermore $1/t_1$ can be interpreted as the rate of spontaneous transitions from state E_1 to all states k for which $E_k < E_1$. In terms of the "oscillator strengths" defined by Eq. 12.6–22,

$$\frac{1}{t_1} = \frac{8\pi^2 e^2}{mc^3} \sum_k \nu_{1k}^{\,2} f_{1k} \tag{13.7–2}$$

where the ν_{1k} and the f_{1k} are the frequencies and the oscillator strengths associated with the downward transitions from 1 to k. Thus Weisskopf

[1] H. Margenau and W. W. Watson, *Revs. Mod. Phys.*, **8**, 22 (1936).

[2] W. Gordy, W. V. Smith, and R. Trambarulo, *Microwave Spectroscopy*, Wiley (1953), Chapter 4.

and Wigner[3] and Hoyt[3] found that the intensity distribution within the line is given by

$$I(\nu) = \Delta\nu_N/[(\nu_{21} - \nu)^2 + (\Delta\nu_N)^2] \tag{13.7-3}$$

where

$$\Delta\nu_N = \frac{4\pi e^2}{mc^3}\left[\sum_k \nu_{1k}{}^2 f_{1k} + \sum_l \nu_{2l}{}^2 f_{2l}\right] \tag{13.7-4}$$

is the half width. Here, every state k has an energy lower than E_1, and every state l has an energy lower than E_2. The bracket in Eq. 13.7–4 has a maximum possible value of the order of $\nu_{21}{}^2/3$. Thus the maximum value of the natural half width is 10^{-4} Å and is independent of wavelength.

ii. *Doppler Effect Broadening of the Spectral Lines*[1, 2]

A molecule moving with a speed v in the direction of the propagation of light absorbs a frequency

$$\nu = \nu_0(1 - v/c) \tag{13.7-5}$$

where the ν_0 is the frequency at zero velocity. When the thermal distribution of the velocities of the molecules in a gas is taken into account, it may be shown that

$$\Delta\nu_D = \frac{\nu_0}{c}\sqrt{\frac{8RT\ln 2}{M}} \tag{13.7-6}$$

is the half width due to the Doppler effect.

iii. *Pressure Broadening of Microwave Lines*[2]

A very detailed theory of pressure broadening has been developed by P. W. Anderson,[4] and a simplified version has been presented by W. V. Smith and R. Howard.[5] The important terms in the treatment of the microwave pressure broadening are quite different from those which are important in the study of the pressure broadening of optical spectra.[1] Just as in the case of the natural line width, the uncertainty principle can be used to explain the half width of the lines, $\Delta\nu_{PB}$, in terms of a characteristic time, τ:

$$\tau h\,\Delta\nu_{PB} = \hbar \quad \text{or} \quad \Delta\nu_{PB} = 1/2\pi\tau \tag{13.7-7}$$

The time τ is the average interval of time that the radiation processes are

[3] V. Weisskopf and E. Wigner, *Z. Physik*, **63**, 54 (1930); **65**, 18 (1931). Also F. Hoyt, *Phys. Rev.*, **36**, 860 (1931).

[4] P. W. Anderson, *Phys. Rev.*, **76**, 647 (1949); **80**, 511 (1950). See also M. Mizushima, *Phys. Rev.*, **83**, 94 (1951).

[5] W. V. Smith and R. Howard, *Phys. Rev.*, **79**, 132 (1950).

uninterrupted by collisions. For rigid-sphere molecules of diameter σ_{PB} moving with an average speed Ω, the time, τ, is the mean length of time between collisions:[6]

$$\tau = \frac{1}{\sqrt{2}\, n\pi\sigma_{PB}^2\, \Omega} \tag{13.7–8}$$

Here n is the number of molecules per cubic centimeter. These last two relations may be combined to obtain the definition of the microwave pressure-broadening collision diameter, σ_{PB}, in terms of the observed line width:

$$2\Delta\nu_{PB} = \sqrt{2}\, n\Omega\sigma_{PB}^2 \tag{13.7–9}$$

In a gas containing two species of molecules, a and b, the pressure broadening of a line of gas a is given by

$$2\Delta\nu_{PB} = \sqrt{2}\, [n_a\Omega_a(\sigma_{PB})_{aa}^2 + n_b\Omega_{ab}(\sigma_{PB})_{ab}^2] \tag{13.7–10}$$

Here $\Omega_{ab} = \sqrt{(\Omega_a^2 + \Omega_b^2)/2}$ is the average speed and $(\sigma_{PB})_{ab}$ the pressure broadening collision diameter of the mixed collisions.

These relations are always used to define the microwave collision diameter regardless of the law of force between the molecules. The significance of σ_{PB}, however, depends upon the law of force and the nature of the collisions. The time τ is always the time between collisions. A collision is said to have occurred in either of two limiting cases: *adiabatic collisions* in which the phase of the emitted radiation is changed by a considerable amount, and *non-adiabatic* collisions in which there is a quantum jump and an energy exchange between the molecule under consideration and the molecule with which it is colliding. In optical pressure broadening, the adiabatic collisions are all-important, and the non-adiabatic collisions can be ignored. In microwave pressure broadening, on the other hand, the adiabatic collisions can usually be ignored. Let the probability of a transition in molecule a from rotational state j_a to state j_a' be $|a_{j_a j_a'}|^2$. The probability that a jump occurs during the entire course of a collision is then $|a_{j_a j_a'}(t = \infty)|^2$. According to Anderson's rigorous theory, all non-adiabatic collisions for which $|a_{j_a j_a'}(t = \infty)|^2 \geq \frac{1}{4}$ are effective for producing pressure broadening in the sense of determining the effective rigid sphere diameter σ_{PB} and the time τ to be used in Eqs. 13.7–7, 8, 9, and 10. The value of σ_{PB} then gives a direct measure of the probability for energy transfer usually from translation to rotation, as a result of collisions.

[6] Equation 13.7–8 agrees with the mean length of time between collisions τ of Eq. 1.2–1, with $\xi' = \sqrt{2}$

The transition probabilities may be obtained by means of time-dependent perturbation theory.[7] Let $\mathscr{H}_a$ be the quantum mechanical Hamiltonian operator for isolated molecule a. In a collision with another molecule b, there must be added to this Hamiltonian the perturbation due to the potential of interaction between the two molecules. We then indicate the time-dependent perturbation by

$$\varphi(t) = \varphi_{ab}(j_a, m_a; j_b, m_b \mid r_{ab}(t)) \tag{13.7–11}$$

That is, the perturbing potential depends clearly on the quantum states of the two interacting molecules and is an implicit function of time through the inter-molecular separation $r_{ab}(t)$. The dependence of r_{ab} on t is given by the trajectory of the colliding pair. In terms of this perturbing potential, the time-dependent Schrödinger equation can be written

$$[\mathscr{H}_a + \varphi(t)]\Psi(\boldsymbol{r}^{\nu_a}, t) = -\frac{\hbar}{i}\frac{\partial \Psi}{\partial t} \tag{13.7–12}$$

The wave function may be written as a linear combination of the initial state j_a and the final state j_a':

$$\Psi(t) = a_{j_a j_a}(t)\Psi_{j_a} + a_{j_a j_a'}(t)\Psi_{j_a'} \tag{13.7–13}$$

Before a collision takes place ($t = -\infty$), the molecule is in state j_a so that

$$a_{j_a j_a}(-\infty) = 1 \qquad a_{j_a j_a'}(-\infty) = 0 \tag{13.7–14}$$

After a collision ($t = \infty$), the probability that a transition from state j_a to j_a' has occurred is given by the square of the absolute value of the quantity

$$a_{j_a j_a'}(\infty) = -\frac{1}{\hbar}\int \psi_{j_a}{}^* \left[\int_{-\infty}^{\infty} \varphi(t) e^{-(i/\hbar)(E_{j_a'} - E_{j_a})t} dt\right] \psi_{j_a'}\, d\boldsymbol{r}_a \tag{13.7–15}$$

The collision diameter σ_{PB} is the distance of closest approach or the "miss distance" (if the trajectory were a straight line) for a critical collision such that $| a_{j_a j_a'}(t = \infty) |^2 = \frac{1}{4}$. If the value of σ_{PB} is large compared to the kinetic theory collision diameter of the molecules, as is frequently the case, the critical trajectory is almost a straight path and to a good approximation,

$$r_{ab}{}^2(t) = \sigma_{PB}{}^2 + v^2 t^2 \tag{13.7–16}$$

where v is the relative velocity of the two molecules at the start of their collision. Furthermore, Anderson showed that if hv/σ_{PB} is less than $(E_{j_a'} - E_{j_a})$ as is usually the case, only a few per cent error is introduced by neglecting the exponential in Eq. 13.7–15.

[7] H. M. Foley, *Phys. Rev.*, **69**, 616 (1946).

b. Information about long-range forces from pressure broadening

We now illustrate how the above results may be used to obtain specific information about long-range forces between molecules. That is, we consider various forms for the interaction potential $\varphi(t)$ in Eq. 13.7–11.

i. *Dipole-Dipole Interaction*

The energy of interaction of two dipoles is given by Eq. 12.1–47. Let us assume that the critical trajectory is a straight path with a distance of closest approach σ_{PB}. The direction of the radius vector from molecule a to molecule b at the point of closest approach is taken to be the direction of the polar axis for the frames of reference with respect to which the θ_a', θ_b', and θ_{ab}' are measured. The other angles ϕ_a', ϕ_b', and ϕ_{ab}' are measured with respect to the plane of the collision. For a straight-path critical collision, $r_{ab}(t)$ is given by Eq. 13.7–16, $\cos\theta_{ab}'$ is equal to b/r_{ab} (where b is the impact parameter defined in connection with Eq. 1.5–20), $\sin\theta_{ab}'$ is equal to vt/r_{ab}, and ϕ_{ab}' is zero. If we ignore the exponential in Eq. 13.7–15 and perform the integration over time before computing the matrix elements for the rotational transitions, the result is[4]

$$\int_{-\infty}^{\infty} \varphi_{ab}(t)\,dt = \frac{2\mu_a\mu_b}{v\sigma_{PB}^2}\left[-\cos\theta_a'\cos\theta_b' + \sin\theta_a'\sin\theta_b'\sin\phi_a'\sin\phi_b'\right] \tag{13.7–17}$$

The transition probabilities are then obtained by multiplying Eq. 13.7–17 by the wave functions for the initial and final states and integrating over the molecular coordinates. The results are somewhat complicated by resonance interactions, such as those discussed in §§ 13.6b and 13.6c. Anderson[1] and Mizushima[4] have derived expressions for the pressure broadening of symmetrical top and linear polar molecules, as well as for ammonia. The ammonia molecules behave like the symmetrical tops, except that they have an extra degree of freedom corresponding to the possibility of inversion.

Actually the self-broadening of the spectra of ammonia is a particularly simple example because the rotational energies are sufficiently large that only a few transitions or matrix elements need be considered. The agreement between Anderson's theory and the experimental observations is indicated in Table 13.7–1. Since the average collision velocity is proportional to the square root of the temperature, σ_{PB} is proportional to $T^{-1/4}$ This temperature dependence has been confirmed by Howard and Smith.[5]

At the present time, the self-broadening of the spectra of linear polar molecules is somewhat less well understood than that of the symmetric top molecules. It might be thought then that the pressure broadening

TABLE 13.7–1

LINE BREADTH PARAMETER $\Delta\nu$ FOR THE NH_3 INVERSION SPECTRUM AT ROOM TEMPERATURE[a]

		$\Delta\nu$(Mc/mm Hg)		σ_{PB} (cm × 10^{-8})
J	*K*	*Observed*	*Theoretical*	*Observed*
2	1	15.5	15.5	10.4
3	1	14.5	14	10.1
3	2	19	20	11.6
3	3	27	27	13.8
4	4	27	27.5	13.8
5	1	11	11	8.8
5	2	15.5	15	10.4
5	3	20	20	11.9
5	5	28	29	14.1
6	3	18.5	17	11.4
6	4	21.5	21	15.2
6	6	28	29	14.1
7	5	24.5	22	13.1
7	6	23.5	26	12.7
8	7	24.5	26	13.1
10	9	25	27	13.3
11	9	17.5	24.5	11.1

[a] Table given by Anderson[4] and modified by W. V. Smith (private correspondence, October, 1952). See Ref. 2, p. 195.

of gas mixtures would be even harder to interpret. However, this is not the case. The experimental cross-sections of the symmetric top molecules CH_3Cl and $CHCl_3$, relative to the broadening of the ammonia 3, 3 line, may be explained on the same basis as the self-broadening of the ammonia. The experimental results for these molecules are shown in Table 13.7–2.

TABLE 13.7–2[5]

σ_{PB} (FOR COLLISIONS WITH NH_3) AND DIPOLE MOMENTS FROM PRESSURE BROADENING OF THE $j = 3$, $k = 3$ AMMONIA LINE BY OTHER GASES[5]

Colliding Molecule	σ_{PB} (Å)	$\mu \times 10^{18}$(esu)
NH_3	13.8	1.44
COS	7.56	0.720
HCN	10.0	2.96
ClCN	11.9	2.80
CH_3Cl	11.3	1.87
CH_2Cl_2	10.3	1.59
$CHCl_3$	13.7	0.95
SO_2	10.4	1.7

ii. *Dipole-Quadrupole Interaction*[5]

Consider the interaction between a molecule with a dipole moment μ_a and a colliding molecule with a quadrupole moment Q_b. Here the perturbing potential associated with the interaction is given by

$$\varphi(t) = \frac{3}{4}\frac{\mu_a Q_b}{r^4(t)}\begin{bmatrix} \cos\theta_a'(1 - 3\cos^2\theta_b') \\ +2\cos\theta_b'\sin\theta_b'\sin\theta_a'\cos(\phi_a' - \phi_b') \end{bmatrix} \tag{13.7–18}$$

where θ_a', θ_b', ϕ_a', and ϕ_b' are the polar and azimuthal angles of the dipole and the quadrupole with respect to the internuclear axis. Substituting this expression into Eq. 13.7–15, integrating, and averaging the magnitude of the interaction over the angles, we obtain

$$\sigma_{PB}^3 = \frac{0.84\mu_a Q_b}{\hbar v_{ab}} \tag{13.7–19}$$

From the pressure broadening of the $j = 3$, $k = 3$ NH_3 line by other molecules, the quadrupole moments given in Table 13.7–3 were determined. In this table $q = Q/e$ in accordance with Eq. 12.1–17.

iii. *Interaction of a Dipole Molecule with a Non-polar Molecule not considering Quadrupoles*

Initially, P. W. Anderson[8] suggested that the pressure broadening of the spectrum of a polar molecule *a* as the result of collisions with a non-polar molecule *b* which do not have a quadrupole moment is due to dipole-induced dipole forces. In this case, the perturbing potential is given by Eq. 13.5–3:

$$\varphi(t) = -\frac{\mu_a^2\alpha_b}{2r^6(t)}(1 + 3\cos^2\theta) \tag{13.7–20}$$

The $\cos^2\theta$ term does lead to a small transition probability which Anderson evaluated by the group theoretical methods of Racah.[9] However, the calculated line widths were much too small. Therefore, Anderson[8] wondered whether the quadrupole moment Q_b of the polar molecule is instrumental in producing the pressure broadening. The next term in φ for this case is given by Eq. 13.5–3:

$$\varphi(t) = -\frac{3\mu_a Q_a \alpha_b}{r^7(t)}\cos^3\theta \tag{13.7–21}$$

This interaction term leads to a much larger transition coefficient than Eq. 13.7–20.

[8] P. W. Anderson, *Phys. Rev.*, **76**, 647 (1949).
[9] G. Racah, *Phys. Rev.*, **62**, 438 (1942).

TABLE 13.7–3

MOLECULAR QUADRUPOLE MOMENTS OBTAINED FROM MICROWAVE COLLISION DIAMETERS[a]

Molecule	$\sigma \times 10^8$ (cm) Kinetic Theory	$\sigma \times 10^8$ (cm) from NH_3 3, 3 Line Broadening	q_{rot} (cm^2) $\times 10^{16}$ (*b*)
N_2	4.09	5.54	0.31[c]
O_2	4.02	3.86	<0.11[d] / 0.04[e]
NO	3.90	5.64	0.29
CO	3.96	5.97	0.33
CO_2	4.46	7.59	0.64
COS		7.56	0.60
CS_2		7.72	0.64
N_2O	4.35	7.32	0.91[c]
HCN		10.0	1.60
ClCN		11.9	2.39
C_2H_2		8.79	1.10
C_2H_4	4.79	6.67	0.48
C_2H_6	4.86	5.64	<0.27
H_2			$q = 0.261$[f]

[a] W. Gordy, W. V. Smith, and R. Trambarulo, *Microwave Spectroscopy*, Wiley (1953), p. 345.

[b] Values of q_{rot} are for the rotating molecules.

[c] Average of experimental values is used here to calculate q_{rot}.

[d] The value $\sigma = 4.18 \times 10^{-8}$ cm, which is considered to be most reliable, is used to obtain the upper limit for q_{rot}.

[e] R. S. Anderson, W. V. Smith, and W. Gordy, *Phys. Rev.*, **82**, 264 (1951), obtained this value from measurements of the line widths of the fine structure of the microwave spectrum of oxygen. The accuracy of this number is still questionable.

[f] q for H_2 is the value relative to the internuclear axis rather than the value for rotating molecules. The quadrupole moment was measured by J. Harrick and N. F. Ramsey [*Phys. Rev.*, **88**, 228 (1952)] using a molecular beam microwave resonance method [N. F. Ramsey, *Phys. Rev.*, **78**, 221 (1950)] to measure the rotational magnetic moment. Here $q = \overline{r_{ab}^2} - Q_e$ where $\overline{r_{ab}^2} = 0.591$ Å^2 and r_{ab} is the internuclear separation and $Q_e = 0.330$ Å^2 is the quantity which Harrick and Ramsey define as the "quadrupole moment of the electron distribution." This result agrees well with the theoretical value $q = 0.248 \times 10^{-16}$ cm^2 calculated by H. M. James and A. S. Coolidge [*Astrophys. J.*, **87**, 447 (1938)]. The $N(r)$ of James and Coolidge is one half of our q.

For the ammonia $j = 3$, $k = 3$ line,

$$\sigma_{PB} = 1.22 \left(\frac{e\mu_a q_a \alpha_b}{v_{ab}\hbar} \right)^{1/6} \qquad (13.7\text{–}22)$$

The quadrupole moment for ammonia is $q = 0.2759 \times 10^{-16}$ cm^2. The results of this calculation are shown in Table 13.7–4 for the pressure broadening of the $j = 3$, $k = 3$ line of NH_3. The discrepancy in the case of A has not been explained. The quadrupole moment of O_2 is the cause of the difference between its experimental and theoretical values.

TABLE 13.7–4

σ_{PB} FROM PRESSURE-BROADENING OF THE $j = 3$, $k = 3$ LINE OF NH_3

Colliding Molecule	σ_{PB} (Å)	
	Experimental (Eq. 13.7–9)	Theoretical (Eq. 13.7–22)
H_2	2.71	2.57
He	2.00	2.15
A	3.73	3.42
O_2	3.86	3.35

iv. *Quadrupole-Quadrupole Interaction*

Mizushima[4] has studied the quadrupole-quadrupole interactions. He successfully calculated the self-broadening of the O_2 spectrum, including its temperature variation.

8. Determination of the Quadrupole Moment of the Water Molecule

In § 13.4 we show that the intermolecular forces for asymmetrical molecules depend sensitively on the exact positions of the electrical charges within a molecule. For studying the interaction of two water molecules one needs a detailed model, in which the spatial locations of each of six different sets of electrical charges are specified. Such models have been determined independently by theoretical and by empirical means. The models thus obtained are in substantial agreement with one another. In terms of these models it is possible to explain accurately the physical properties of ice, water, and steam.

For some of the physical properties in the gas phase, it is sufficiently accurate to represent the electrical properties of the molecule by ideal dipoles and quadrupoles. The quadrupole moments of water are evaluated in this section. These results supplement the microwave determinations of quadrupole moments given in the preceding section.

a. Theoretical determination[1, 2]

In the earliest theoretical treatments of the H_2O molecule it was supposed that the electrons in the oxygen atom are in the orbitals $(1s)^2\,(2s)^2\,(2p_z)^2\,(2p_x)\,(2p_y)$. According to this picture, the $2p_x$ and $2p_y$ electrons are then available to form bonds with the two H-atoms. Pople[1] has found that it is more accurate to say that the $2s$ and $2p$ orbitals are "hybridized"[3] to give tetrahedral symmetry as in the single valence carbon orbitals. Two of these orbitals are singly occupied, and these are available for bonding with the H-atoms. In order to obtain the correct dipole moment ($\mu = 1.84 \times 10^{-18}$ esu) and the correct H-O-H angle (105°), it was found necessary to assume an angle of 120.2° between the two non-bonding orbitals.

The electrons in the non-bonding orbitals are called "lone pair electrons" because their charge distributions are concentrated on the side of the oxygen atom away from the hydrogen atoms. These lone pairs are responsible for the wurtzite structure of ice. Figure 13.8–1 shows the location of the oxygen nucleus and its two inner electrons; the two protons, H and H′; the centers, c and c', of the charge distributions for the pairs of bonding electrons; and the centers, a and a', of the charge distribution for the lone pairs. The coordinates of these points are given in Table 13.8–1. The dipole moment of water lies along the z-axis. In Table 13.8–2 are given the various contributions to the z component of the dipole moment (relative to the oxygen nucleus as origin). This table also contains the contributions to the quantities Θ_{xx}, Θ_{yy}, and Θ_{zz} (relative to the oxygen nucleus as origin) which are related by Eq. 12.1–15 to the quadrupole moments. Duncan and Pople calculated these quantities by determining both the arithmetic and the root-mean-square averaged values of the coordinates corresponding to the various components of the charge distribution. The fact that these averages are quite different makes it difficult to explain the electrical properties of a molecule accurately in terms of a point charge model. From Table 13.8–2 it is apparent that the lone pair electrons play a major role in determining the electrical moments of the molecule.

[1] J. A. Pople, *Proc. Roy. Soc. (London)*, **A202**, 323 (1950).

[2] A. Duncan and J. Pople, *Trans. Faraday Soc.*, **49**, 217 (1953), have extended the theoretical treatment of H_2O and made similar calculations for NH_3 and HF.

[3] A discussion of "hybridization" may be found, for example, in H. Eyring, J. Walter, and G. E. Kimball, *Quantum Chemistry*, Wiley (1944), or C. A. Coulson, *Valence*, Oxford University Press (1952).

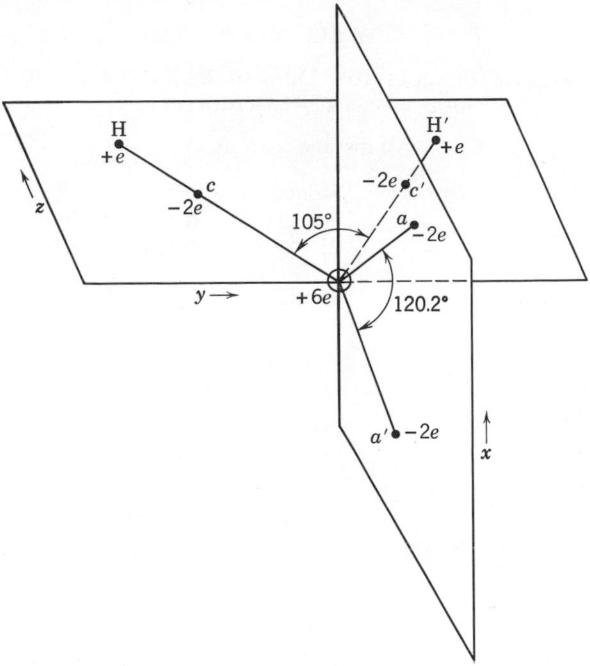

Fig. 13.8–1. Theoretical model of the water molecules as suggested by Duncan and Pople.[2]

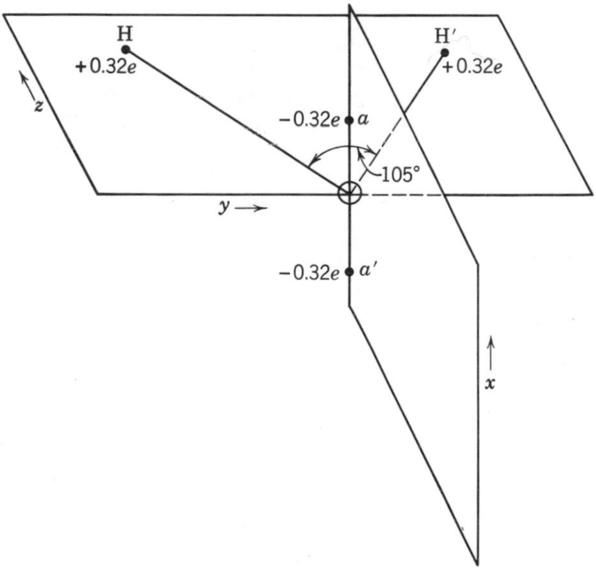

Fig. 13.8–2. Empirical model of the water molecules as suggested by Rowlinson.[4, 5]

TABLE 13.8–1

COORDINATES OF CHARGES FOR DUNCAN AND POPLE'S THEORETICAL MODEL OF THE H_2O MOLECULE[2]

(All distances are in Å)

Particles	*Symbol*[a]	*Charge*	z	y	x
Lone pair electrons	a	$-2e$	−0.158	0.0	0.275
	a'	$-2e$	−0.158	0.0	−0.275
Oxygen nucleus and the two $1s$ electrons	O	$6e$	0.0	0.0	0.0
Binding electrons	c'	$-2e$	0.355	0.463	0.0
	c	$-2e$	0.355	−0.463	0.0
Protons	H′	e	0.586	0.764	0.0
	H	e	0.586	−0.764	0.0

[a] Symbols refer to Fig. 13.8–1.

TABLE 13.8–2[2]

THEORETICAL CONTRIBUTIONS TO THE DIPOLE AND QUADRUPOLE MOMENTS OF THE H_2O MOLECULE

Particles	μ_z (10^{-18} esu)	Θ_{xx} (10^{-26} esu)	Θ_{yy} (10^{-26} esu)	Θ_{zz} (10^{-26} esu)
Lone pairs	+3.03	−3.463	−1.906	−2.422
Binding electrons	−6.82	−3.084	−9.080	−6.697
Protons	+5.63	0.000	+5.506	+3.318
Total moments relative to oxygen as origin	+1.84	−6.547	−5.480	−5.801
Total moments relative to center of mass as origin	+1.84	−6.547	−5.480	−5.951

For most purposes it is desirable to define the quadrupole moments with respect to the center of mass as origin. This does not affect Θ_{xx} or Θ_{yy}, but the value of Θ_{zz} is slightly changed. From Eq. 12.1–16, it follows that the values of the quadrupole moments relative to the center of mass are

$$\begin{aligned} Q_{xx} &= -1.663 \times 10^{-26} \text{ esu} \\ Q_{yy} &= +1.538 \times 10^{-26} \text{ esu} \\ Q_{zz} &= +0.125 \times 10^{-26} \text{ esu} \end{aligned} \tag{13.8-1}$$

By an analysis similar to the treatment of the water molecule, Duncan and Pople[2] have shown that for ammonia the contributions to the moments relative to nitrogen as the origin (letting the z-axis be the direction of the dipole moment) have the values given in Table 13.8–3.

TABLE 13.8–3[2]

THEORETICAL CONTRIBUTIONS TO THE DIPOLE AND QUADRUPOLE MOMENTS OF THE NH_3 MOLECULE

Particles	μ_z (10^{-18} esu)	$\Theta_{xx} = \Theta_{yy}$ (10^{-26} esu)	Θ_{zz} (10^{-26} esu)
Lone pairs	+3.67	−1.335	−2.631
Binding electrons	−7.68	−13.851	−8.411
Protons	+5.48	+6.361	+2.080
Total moments relative to nitrogen as origin	+1.46	−8.825	−8.962

b. Empirical determination[4, 5]

The quadrupole moment of water has been determined empirically by Rowlinson, who compared the experimental values of the second virial coefficient of water vapor with values calculated on the basis of an assumed intermolecular potential of the form

$$\varphi(r,\theta_1,\theta_2,\phi) = 4\epsilon\left[\left(\frac{\sigma}{r}\right)^{12} - \left(\frac{\sigma}{r}\right)^{6} - \frac{t^*}{\sqrt{2}}\left(\frac{\sigma}{r}\right)^{3} g - \frac{u^*}{\sqrt{2}}\left(\frac{\sigma}{r}\right)^{4} h\right] \quad (13.8\text{–}2)$$

in which $g(\theta_1, \theta_2, \phi)$ and $h(\theta_1, \theta_2, \phi)$ are functions of the three angles which describe the mutual orientation of two water molecules given in Eqs. 1.3–32 and 3.10–19, respectively.[6] The parameters t^* and u^* are simply related to the dipole and quadrupole moments of the molecules:

$$t^* = \frac{1}{\sqrt{8}}\frac{\mu^2}{\epsilon\sigma^3} \qquad u^* = \frac{3}{4\sqrt{2}}\frac{\mu Q}{\epsilon\sigma^4} \quad (13.8\text{–}3)$$

[4] J. S. Rowlinson, *Trans. Faraday Soc.*, **47**, 120 (1951). N. Bjerrum [*Kgl. Danske Videnskab. Selskabs* (*Math.-Phys.-Medd.*), **27**, 1 (1951); *Science*, **115**, 385 (1952)] has made a similar determination.

[5] See § 3.10g for a discussion of Rowlinson's calculation of the effect of dipole-quadrupole interaction on the second virial coefficient.

[6] Actually five angles are required to specify the mutual orientation of two water molecules. The potential function above describes the interaction between two cylindrically symmetric charges, such as are shown in Fig. 3.10–6, obtained by averaging the charge distribution of water molecules rotated about their dipole axes.

Rowlinson assumed that the molecules in the water vapor are rotating rapidly about their axis of symmetry (z-axis) so that effectively the molecules have cylindrical symmetry and $Q = Q_{zz}$. When the second virial coefficient was evaluated for this potential and the results compared with the experimental values for water, the following values of the potential parameters were found:[4]

$$\sigma = 2.725 \text{ Å} \qquad \epsilon = 707 \text{ cal/mole} \qquad t^* = 1.2 \qquad u^* = 0.654 \tag{13.8–4}$$

Rowlinson assumed a four-charge model of the H_2O molecule as shown in Fig. 13.8–2. A knowledge of the dipole and the quadrupole moment is then sufficient to determine the coordinates of the charges. This information is listed in Table 13.8–4. From this table the following components of the quadrupole moment tensor (relative to oxygen as the origin) are obtained:

$$\begin{aligned} Q_{xx} &= -3.30 \times 10^{-26} \text{ esu} \\ Q_{yy} &= +2.85 \times 10^{-26} \text{ esu} \\ Q_{zz} &= +0.45 \times 10^{-26} \text{ esu} \end{aligned} \tag{13.8–5}$$

There is a large difference between the quadrupole moment obtained by Rowlinson[4] as compared with the values of Pople.[2] The Rowlinson values are probably unreliable because the point charge model underestimates the contributions of the outer regions of a molecule to its quadrupole moments; also, he has idealized the quadrupole forces in his study of vapor. Nevertheless, good empirical agreement has been obtained.

TABLE 13.8–4

COORDINATES OF CHARGES FOR ROWLINSON'S EMPIRICAL MODEL OF THE H_2O MOLECULE[4,7]

(All distances in Å)

Particles	*Symbol*[a]	*Charge*	z	y	x
Binding electrons	a	$-0.32e$	0.0	0.0	0.51
	a'	$-0.32e$	0.0	0.0	-0.51
Protons	H′	$0.32e$	0.584	0.762	0.0
	H	$0.32e$	0.584	-0.762	0.0

[a] Symbols refer to Fig. 13.8–2.

This charge distribution predicts the heat of sublimation at 0°K to be 11.10 kcal per mole (as compared with the experimental value of 11.32. The predicted value of the distance between nearest neighbors,

[7] J. S. Rowlinson, private communication (1951).

2.73 Å, also agrees well with the experimental value of 2.72 Å. Another interesting feature is that this model leads to an energy preference for the wurtzite over the diamond-type lattice and permits random orientations at room temperature. These results are also in agreement with experiment. However, Campbell[8] has examined various proposed point-charge models of H_2O and showed that in ice the higher-order multipole moments through the fifth are important. Furthermore, the energy of interaction depends upon the assumed relative orientations not only of neighbors but also of more distant molecules.

9. The Determination of Intermolecular Forces from Properties of Crystals at Absolute Zero

There are three properties[1] of a crystal which can be used in the determination of the intermolecular forces: the *enthalpy of sublimation* at 0°K, per molecule $h_0^{(\text{subl})}$, the *distance between nearest neighbors* at 0°K d_0, and the *Debye characteristic temperature* θ_D. In addition the type of crystal lattice sometimes provides a sensitive criterion of the shape of the potential energy function.

The total energy of the crystal lattice at absolute zero U_0 is the sum of the potential energy of the lattice Φ_0 and the zero-point energy K_0 associated with the zero-point vibrations of the molecules in the lattice:

$$U_0 = \Phi_0 + K_0 = Nh_0^{(\text{subl})} \tag{13.9–1}$$

The zero-point energy is given in terms of the Debye characteristic temperature[2] by

$$K_0 = \tfrac{9}{8}Nk\theta_D \tag{13.9–2}$$

In the calculation of the total potential energy of the lattice it is usually assumed that the forces between the molecules are additive.[3] That is, we write

$$\Phi_0 = \tfrac{1}{2}NE(0; d_0) \tag{13.9–3}$$

[8] E. S. Campbell, *J. Chem. Phys.*, **20**, 1411 (1952).

[1] These properties of the crystal, as well as the melting lines of solids, have been studied from the standpoint of the quantum mechanical principle of corresponding states by J. de Boer and his coworkers. See, for example, J. de Boer, *Physica*, **14**, 139 (1948); J. de Boer and B. S. Blaisse, *Physica*, **14**, 149 (1948); R. J. Lunbeck, Doctoral Dissertation, Amsterdam (1951), in Dutch.

[2] See, for example, J. E. Mayer and M. G. Mayer, *Statistical Mechanics*, Wiley (1940), Ch. 11.

[3] There is some evidence that the forces in crystals are not quite additive (see § 3.4a) because of the importance of overlap and exchange integrals. This lack of additivity manifests itself in deviations from the *Cauchy conditions*, relating the coefficients of elasticity of a crystal.

where N is the number of molecules in the lattice and $E(0; d_0)$ is the energy of interaction of one molecule with all its neighbors, evaluated for the lattice in which the distance between nearest neighbors is d_0.

The separation between nearest neighbors in the crystal at absolute zero differs from the separation r_{min} at which the intermolecular potential energy function $\varphi(r)$ has a minimum because of: (1) the zero-point energy, and (2) the attraction of a molecule to molecules beyond its nearest neighbors. The effect of the zero-point energy is to expand the lattice[4] (for argon, the expansion is approximately 0.05 Å in d_0; and for neon, about 0.15 Å.). The attraction to non-nearest neighbors tends to contract the lattice.[5] For face-centered cubic crystals made up of molecules to which the Lennard-Jones (6-12) potential applies, the linear dimensions of the lattice are contracted approximately 3 per cent because of this effect. For Ne, $(d_0 - r_{min}) = 3.20 - 3.16 = +0.04$ Å and for A, $(d_0 - r_{min}) = 3.81 - 3.87 = -0.06$ Å. The most complete and general theoretical treatments have been carried out for the Lennard-Jones potential functions. However, many special calculations have also been made for the Buckingham, the Buckingham-Corner, and other intermolecular potential energy functions (see §§ 3.7 and 9).

a. The potential energy of the crystal lattice at absolute zero

For the purposes of this discussion we write the quantity $E(0; d_0)$ (defined by Eq. 4.4–20) as

$$E(0; d_0) = \Sigma_i n_i \varphi(r_i) \tag{13.9–4}$$

where r_i is the distance from a particular molecule to the ith kind of lattice point, and n_i is the number of molecules which occupy such lattice points. The values of r_i and n_i for five types of crystal lattices and the relations between d_0 (the distance between nearest neighbors) and v_0 (the specific volume of the crystal) are given in Table 13.9–1. With the aid of Table 13.9–1 it is possible to determine $E(0; d_0)$ for any particular intermolecular potential function. For example, if the potential energy function is a repulsion varying as the inverse s power of the separation $(\varphi_s(r) = b/r^s)$, then

$$E(0; d_0) = bC_s/d_0^{\,s} \tag{13.9–5}$$

The constants C_s are given in Table 13.9–2 for four types of crystals.

[4] J. Corner, *Trans. Faraday Soc.*, **44**, 914 (1948); **35**, 711 (1939).
[5] J. E. Lennard-Jones, *Physica*, **4**, 941 (1937).

TABLE 13.9–1

DISTANCE TO NEIGHBORING MOLECULES IN A CRYSTAL[a]

(a) Face-Centered Cubic (Cubic Close Packed) Crystal

$$d_0 = 2^{1/6} v_0^{1/3} = 1.1224 v_0^{1/3}$$

r_i^2/d_0^2	n_i	r_i^2/d_0^2	n_i
1	12	33	96
2	6	34	48
3	24	35	48
4	12	36	36
5	24	37	120
6	8	38	24
7	48	39	48
8	6	40	24
9	36	41	48
10	24	42	48
11	24	43	120
12	24	44	24
13	72	45	120
15	48	47	96
16	12	48	24
17	48	49	108
18	30	50	30
19	72	51	48
20	24	52	72
21	48	53	72
22	24	54	32
23	48	55	144
24	8	57	96
25	84	58	72
26	24	59	72
27	96	60	48
28	48	61	120
29	24	63	144
31	96	64	12
32	6	65	48

TABLE 13.9–1 (*continued*)

(b) Hexagonal Close Packed Crystal[a]

$d_0 = 2^{1/6} v_0^{1/3} = 1.1224 v_0^{1/3}$

r_i^2/d_0^2	n_i	r_i^2/d_0^2	n_i	r_i^2/d_0^2	n_i	r_i^2/d_0^2	n_i
1	12	18	18	35	24	$50\frac{2}{3}$	12
2	6	$18\frac{1}{3}$	12	$35\frac{2}{3}$	12	51	36
$2\frac{2}{3}$	2	$18\frac{2}{3}$	12	36	18	$51\frac{2}{3}$	48
3	18	19	24	$36\frac{1}{3}$	24	52	36
$3\frac{2}{3}$	12	$19\frac{2}{3}$	12	37	72	$52\frac{1}{3}$	12
4	6	$20\frac{1}{3}$	12	$37\frac{2}{3}$	12	53	36
5	12	21	36	38	24	$53\frac{2}{3}$	24
$5\frac{2}{3}$	12	$21\frac{2}{3}$	24	$38\frac{1}{3}$	12	54	18
6	6	22	12	$38\frac{2}{3}$	36	$54\frac{1}{3}$	6
$6\frac{1}{3}$	6	$22\frac{1}{3}$	18	39	36	$54\frac{2}{3}$	36
$6\frac{2}{3}$	12	$22\frac{2}{3}$	12	$39\frac{1}{3}$	6	55	48
7	24	23	24	$39\frac{2}{3}$	24	$55\frac{1}{3}$	18
$7\frac{1}{3}$	6	$23\frac{1}{3}$	12	40	12	$55\frac{2}{3}$	24
$8\frac{1}{3}$	12	$23\frac{2}{3}$	48	$40\frac{1}{3}$	12	$56\frac{1}{3}$	24
9	12	24	2	41	24	57	48
$9\frac{2}{3}$	24	25	36	$41\frac{2}{3}$	48	58	36
10	12	26	24	42	36	$58\frac{1}{3}$	24
$10\frac{1}{3}$	12	$26\frac{1}{3}$	12	$42\frac{1}{3}$	12	$58\frac{2}{3}$	24
$10\frac{2}{3}$	2	$26\frac{2}{3}$	12	$42\frac{2}{3}$	2	59	36
11	12	27	42	43	72	$59\frac{1}{3}$	6
$11\frac{1}{3}$	6	$27\frac{1}{3}$	6	$43\frac{1}{3}$	12	$59\frac{2}{3}$	60
$11\frac{2}{3}$	24	$27\frac{2}{3}$	12	$43\frac{2}{3}$	12	60	12
12	6	28	24	45	60	$60\frac{1}{3}$	24
$12\frac{1}{3}$	12	$28\frac{1}{3}$	12	$45\frac{2}{3}$	36	61	72
13	24	29	12	$46\frac{1}{3}$	6	$61\frac{2}{3}$	24
$13\frac{2}{3}$	12	$29\frac{2}{3}$	36	$46\frac{2}{3}$	24		
$14\frac{1}{3}$	6	$30\frac{1}{3}$	12	47	48		
$14\frac{2}{3}$	24	$30\frac{2}{3}$	24	$47\frac{1}{3}$	12		
15	12	31	72	$47\frac{2}{3}$	24		
$15\frac{1}{3}$	12	$31\frac{1}{3}$	12	48	6		
$15\frac{2}{3}$	24	$31\frac{2}{3}$	24	$48\frac{1}{3}$	12		
16	6	$32\frac{1}{3}$	12	49	60		
$16\frac{1}{3}$	12	33	48	$49\frac{2}{3}$	48		
17	24	$33\frac{2}{3}$	24	50	30		
$17\frac{2}{3}$	24	34	24	$50\frac{1}{3}$	24		

TABLE 13.9–1 (*continued*)

(c) Body-Centered Cubic Lattice[b]

$d_0 = 2^{-2/3}\, 3^{1/2}\, v_0^{1/3} = 1.0911 v_0^{1/3}$

r_i^2/d_0^2	n_i	r_i^2/d_0^2	n_i	r_i^2/d_0^2	n_i	r_i^2/d_0^2	n_i
1	8	4	8	8	24	12	30
$1\frac{1}{3}$	6	$5\frac{1}{3}$	6	9	32		
$2\frac{2}{3}$	12	$6\frac{1}{3}$	24	$10\frac{2}{3}$	12		
$3\frac{2}{3}$	24	$6\frac{2}{3}$	24	$11\frac{2}{3}$	48		

(d) Simple Cubic Lattice[b]

$d_0 = v_0^{1/3}$

1	6	5	24	10	24	14	48
2	12	6	24	11	24		
3	8	8	12	12	8		
4	6	9	30	13	24		

(e) Diamond Structure[b]

$d_0 = 2^{-1/3}\, 3^{1/2}\, v_0^{1/3} = 0.8660 v_0^{1/3}$

1	4	$6\frac{1}{3}$	12	$11\frac{2}{3}$	24	17	24
$2\frac{2}{3}$	12	8	24	$13\frac{1}{3}$	24		
$3\frac{2}{3}$	12	9	16	$14\frac{1}{3}$	12		
$5\frac{1}{3}$	6	$10\frac{2}{3}$	12	16	8		

[a] T. Kihara and S. Koba, *J. Phys. Soc. Japan*, **7**, 348 (1952).

[b] J. Prins and H. Petersen, *Physica*, **3**, 147 (1936).

TABLE 13.9–2

C_s, THE CONSTANTS FOR THE POTENTIAL ENERGY OF A CRYSTAL

s	Face-Centered (Close-Packed) Cubic[a, b]	Hexagonal[a, b] Close-Packed	Body-Centered Cubic[b]	Simple[b] Cubic
4	25.33830		22.63872	16.5323
5	16.9675		14.7585	10.3775
6	14.45392	14.45489	12.2533	8.40192
7	13.35939	13.36035	11.05424	7.4670
8	12.80194	12.80282	10.355	6.94580
9	12.49255	12.49332	9.8945	6.6288
10	12.31125	12.31190	9.564	6.4261
11	12.2009		9.31326	6.29229
12	12.13188	12.13229	9.11418	6.2021
13	12.08772		8.95180	6.140
14	12.05899	12.05923	8.8167	6.09818
15	12.04002		8.70298	6.06876
16	12.02736	12.02748	8.60625	6.04826
17	12.0198		8.52363	6.0339
18	12.01300	12.01306	8.45250	6.02388
19	12.009353		8.39138	6.01682
20	12.006280		8.33860	6.011863
21	12.004496		8.29306	6.008369
22	12.00306		8.253675	6.00590
23	12.00218		8.219626	6.004170
24	12.001511		8.19015	6.002945
25	12.001075		8.16465	6.00208
26	12.000748		8.1425	6.001470
27	12.000531		8.123469	6.001040
28	12.00037		8.106921	6.000734
29	12.000263		8.092593	6.000519
30	12.000185		8.080186	6.000367

[a] T. Kihara and S. Koba, *J. Phys. Soc. Japan*, **7**, 348 (1952).
[b] J. E. Lennard-Jones and A. E. Ingham, *Proc. Roy. Soc.* (*London*), **A107**, 636 (1925).

For the Lennard-Jones (t, s) intermolecular potential function $(\varphi(r) = br^{-s} - cr^{-t})$, the potential energy of the crystal at absolute zero can be expressed in the form

$$E(0; d_0) = \frac{bC_s}{d_0{}^s} - \frac{cC_t}{d_0{}^t} \tag{13.9–6}$$

where the constants C_s and C_t are the same as those found for the inverse power repulsions and given in Table 13.9–2. The rare gas atoms crystallize in a face-centered cubic lattice. Kihara and Koba,[6] however, note that for $t = 6$ and for any value of s, the $E(0)$ of Eq. 13.9–4 has a lower value for the hexagonal close-packed structure than for the face-centered cubic structure. This may be due to a deviation of the actual intermolecular potential from the Lennard-Jones form or it may be due to the effects of zero-point energy.

b. The zero-point energy of the crystal lattice at absolute zero

The Debye characteristic temperature can be calculated in terms of the increase in the potential energy of the crystal when one molecule is displaced from its lattice point by a distance r (see Eq. 4.4–20). However, for the purposes of calculating the Debye temperature it is not necessary to know the increment in the potential energy of the crystal for each orientation of the displacement, but rather the value spatially averaged over all orientations of the displacement,[7,8]

$$E(r; d_0) - E(0; d_0) = \Sigma_i n_i \tfrac{1}{2} \int_0^\pi [\varphi(\sqrt{r_i^2 + r^2 - 2rr_i \cos\theta}) - \varphi(r_i)] \sin\theta \, d\theta \tag{13.9–7}$$

If only the nearest neighbors are considered, Eq. 13.9–7 reduces to Eq. 4.6–2. At very low temperatures, the displacements, r, are small compared to the distance between lattice points so that the intermolecular potential can be expanded in a power series in r about the point r_i. The integrals in Eq. 13.9–7 can then be evaluated explicitly, and the result is

$$E(r; d_0) - E(0; d_0) = \Sigma_i n_i \left[\frac{1}{3}\left(\frac{r}{r_i}\right)^2 \left\{ r_i \varphi'(r_i) + \frac{1}{2} r_i^2 \varphi''(r_i) \right\} + \frac{1}{5}\left(\frac{r}{r_i}\right)^4 \left\{ \frac{1}{6} r_i^3 \varphi'''(r_i) + \frac{1}{24} r_i^4 \varphi''''(r_i) \right\} + \cdots \right] \tag{13.9–8}$$

For small vibrations, the terms in powers of r higher than the second can be neglected, and the square of the fundamental frequency $\nu(d_0)$ for a

[6] T. Kihara and S. Koba, *J. Phys. Soc. Japan*, **7**, 348 (1952).

[7] O. K. Rice, *J. Am. Chem. Soc.*, **63**, 3 (1941); Eqs. 13.9–8 and 9 are generalizations of equations given by Rice.

[8] Equation 13.9–7 reduces to Eq. 4.7–3 for a face-centered cubic lattice considering a Lennard-Jones (6-12) potential, if interactions with nearest neighbors only are considered.

molecule of mass, m_a, moving in such a three dimensional potential well[7] is

$$\nu^2(d_0) = \frac{1}{2\pi^2 m_a}\left[\tfrac{1}{3}\Sigma_i n_i \left(\frac{1}{r_i}\,\varphi'(r_i) + \tfrac{1}{2}\varphi''(r_i)\right)\right] \qquad (13.9\text{–}9)$$

The quantity ν^2 given by Eq. 13.9–9 is approximately the average value of the square of the frequencies in the crystal.[7] If we assume the Debye distribution of frequencies, the maximum or (Debye) frequency is $(5/3)^{1/2}\nu(d_0)$, and the Debye characteristic temperature is

$$\theta_D(d_0) = (5/3)^{1/2}\,\frac{h\nu(d_0)}{k} \qquad (13.9\text{–}10)$$

The zero-point energy K_0 in the crystal at absolute zero is then given by Eq. 13.9–2.

Rice[7] has made a careful study of the temperature variation of the internal energy of noble gas crystals in the neighborhood of the absolute zero. At higher temperatures (around 73°K for argon) there is sufficient disorder in the crystal to introduce important deviations in the frequency distribution. However, at very low temperatures, the assumption of the Debye distribution is satisfactory.

The equilibrium separation at absolute zero may be estimated theoretically by minimizing the sum of the potential and zero-point energies:

$$\frac{d}{d(d_0)}\,U_0 = \frac{d}{d(d_0)}\,[\tfrac{1}{2}NE(0;\,d_0) + \tfrac{9}{8}Nk\theta_0(d_0)] = 0 \qquad (13.9\text{–}11)$$

Thus, for any assumed form of pair potential energy function all the properties of the crystal at absolute zero can be calculated. Or, conversely, the experimental data can be used to determine the pair potential energy function.

c. Determination of the forces between noble gas atoms

By applying the methods discussed above, O. K. Rice[7] found the energy of interaction between two argon atoms given in Eq. 3.9–8. Similarly, Corner[9] fitted the Buckingham-Corner potentials of neon and argon (see Table 3.7–1) and recently Mason and W. E. Rice fitted the modified Buckingham potential of Ne, A, Kr, and Xe (see § 3.7). Previously Kane[10] fitted Buckingham potentials

$$\varphi(r) = b\exp(-ar) - c/r^6 - c'/r^8 \qquad (13.9\text{–}12)$$

[9] J. Corner, *Trans. Faraday Soc.*, **44**, 914 (1948), gives tables useful for fitting the Buckingham-Corner potential in problems involving face-centered cubic lattices. Previously R. Buckingham, *Proc. Roy. Soc.* (*London*), **A168**, 264 (1938), fitted Buckingham potentials to neon and argon but he did not take into account the effect of zero-point energy in expanding the crystal lattice.

to the low-temperature crystal data for argon, neon, krypton, and xenon, and his work illustrates the procedure. He tried two values for a: $a_1 = 4.782$, and $a_2 = 2.899$. The value a_1 was found theoretically by Bleick and Mayer (see § 14.2) to be correct for neon-neon interactions; a_2 was found by Born and Mayer[11] to be suitable for alkali halides. For neon, argon, and xenon, Kane took c' to be zero; for krypton he used the value for c' determined theoretically by Buckingham.[12] The values of b and c were then adjusted to fit the experimental values of both the heat of sublimation and the separation between neighbors at absolute zero. The suitability of either a_1 or a_2 was then determined by comparing the calculated with the observed Debye frequencies. The results of Kane's calculations are shown in Table 13.9–3. Both the calculations of Corner and those of Mason and W. E. Rice are probably somewhat more accurate.

TABLE 13.9–3[10]

DETERMINATION OF THE INTERMOLECULAR POTENTIAL FUNCTION FROM EXPERIMENTAL SOLID-STATE DATA

	Experimental[a] Values			Calculated Quantities				
	d_0 (Å)	$h_0^{(\mathrm{subl})}$ (cal/mole)	θ_D (°K)	a (Å)$^{-1}$	b (10^{-12} erg)	c (10^{-12} erg Å^6)	c' (10^{-12} erg Å^8)	θ_D (°K)
Neon	3.20	448	64	4.782	10,250	8.07	0	60
				2.899	97	14.0	0	53
Argon	3.83	1850	80	4.782	830,000	87.4	0	105
				2.899	1,600	125	0	81
Krypton	3.95	2678	63	4.782	2,180,000	148	0	91
				2.899	3,135	209	0	68
				2.899	3,550	190	587	70
Xenon	4.34	3778	55	4.782	18,400,000	354	0	87
				2.899	11,730	477	0	65

[a] Here $h_0^{(\mathrm{subl})}$ is the experimental value for the heat of sublimation at 0°K not corrected for zero-point energy.

[10] G. Kane, *J. Chem. Phys.*, **7**, 603 (1939).
[11] M. Born and J. Mayer, *Z. Physik*, **75**, 1 (1932).
[12] R. Buckingham, *Proc. Roy. Soc.* (*London*), **A160**, 94 (1937).

At the present time the interpretation of low-temperature crystal data has been used only for determining the potentials for spherically symmetric molecules. It is likely that this method will prove extremely useful for complex unsymmetrical molecules.

APPENDIX A. COMPLETE HAMILTONIAN FOR A SYSTEM IN EXTERNAL ELECTRIC AND MAGNETIC FIELDS[1]

In most treatments of the energy of a molecular system (with nuclei held fixed) the Hamiltonian for the electronic system has been assumed to be $\mathscr{H}_e$. However, in addition to $\mathscr{H}_e$, the complete Hamiltonian should contain additional terms which correct for the magnetic interactions and the relativistic effects. These correction terms may be important in determining (1) the probability of a transition from one quantum state to another in high-velocity collisions such as occur in "hot atom" chemistry or in molecular beam experiments; (2) the potential energy in low-velocity collisions of heavy molecules such as I_2, where the collision may serve to uncouple the spin and orbital moments of the molecule; and (3) the intermolecular forces between free radicals, electronically excited molecules, or very long molecules of biological interest. Let $\mathscr{E}_i$ be the external electric field strength, $\mathscr{H}_i$ be the external magnetic field strength, and $\mathscr{A}_i$ be the (external magnetic) vector potential—all at the position of electron i. Furthermore, let the operator for the spin and linear momenta of the ith electron be, respectively, $\boldsymbol{s}_i$ and $\boldsymbol{p}_i = \frac{\hbar}{i}\frac{\partial}{\partial \boldsymbol{r}} + \frac{e}{c}\mathscr{A}_i$. Then the Hamiltonian, correct to terms varying as $(1/c)^2$, where c is the velocity of light, is given by[1, 2]

$$\mathscr{H} = \mathscr{H}_e + \mathscr{H}_1 + \mathscr{H}_2 + \mathscr{H}_3 + \mathscr{H}_4 + \mathscr{H}_5 + \mathscr{H}_6 \quad (13.A\text{–}1)$$

[1] The authors wish to thank A. Sessler, J. H. Van Vleck, W. Kleiner, H. A. Bethe, J. C. Slater, and W. Pauli for their help in the preparation of this appendix. Sessler is responsible for the introduction of the second term in $\mathscr{H}_2$ and for the discussion of $\mathscr{H}_2$. The approximate Hamiltonian, Eq. 13.A–8, and the discussion of $\mathscr{H}_6$ are due to Van Vleck. Kleiner corrected an error which we had previously made in $\mathscr{H}_1$.

[2] H. A. Bethe, *Handbuch der Physik*, Vol. 24, I (J. Springer, 2nd Ed., 1933), p. 377. Other discussions of the Hamiltonian are given by G. Breit, *Phys. Rev.*, **39**, 616 (1932); H. A. Bethe and E. Fermi, *Z. Physik*, **77**, 296 (1932); E. U. Condon and G. H. Shortley, *The Theory of Atomic Spectra*, Cambridge University Press (1935); L. H. Allen, C. W. Ufford, and J. H. Van Vleck, *Astrophys. J.*, **109**, 42 (1949); G. Breit and R. E. Meyerott, *Phys. Rev.*, **72**, 1023 (1947) and **75**, 1447 (1948); G. Breit, G. E. Brown, and G. Arfken, *Phys. Rev.*, **76**, 1299 (1949).

where $\mathscr{H}_e$ is given by Eq. 13.1–14, and

$$\mathscr{H}_1 = \frac{e^2\hbar}{2m^2c^2}\left\{\sum_{i,\alpha} \frac{Z_\alpha}{r_{\alpha i}^3} [(\boldsymbol{r}_i - \boldsymbol{r}_\alpha) \times \boldsymbol{p}_i] \cdot \boldsymbol{s}_i - \sum_{i,j\neq i} \frac{1}{r_{ij}^3} [(\boldsymbol{r}_i - \boldsymbol{r}_j) \times \boldsymbol{p}_i] \cdot \boldsymbol{s}_i + \sum_{i,j\neq i} \frac{2}{r_{ij}^3} ([(\boldsymbol{r}_i - \boldsymbol{r}_j) \times \boldsymbol{p}_j] \cdot \boldsymbol{s}_i)\right\} \tag{13.A–2}$$

$$\mathscr{H}_2 = \frac{e^2\hbar^2}{m^2c^2} \sum_{i>j} \frac{1}{r_{ij}^5} [r_{ij}^2(\boldsymbol{s}_i \cdot \boldsymbol{s}_j) - 3(\boldsymbol{s}_i \cdot (\boldsymbol{r}_i - \boldsymbol{r}_j))(\boldsymbol{s}_j \cdot (\boldsymbol{r}_i - \boldsymbol{r}_j))] - \frac{8\pi}{3}\frac{e^2\hbar^2}{m^2c^2} \sum_i \sum_{j>i} (\boldsymbol{s}_i \cdot \boldsymbol{s}_j)\delta(\boldsymbol{r}_i - \boldsymbol{r}_j) \tag{13.A–3}$$

$$\mathscr{H}_3 = -\frac{ie^2\hbar}{4m^2c^2} \sum_i \left\{\sum_\alpha \frac{Z_\alpha}{r_{\alpha i}^3} (\boldsymbol{r}_i - \boldsymbol{r}_\alpha) . \boldsymbol{p}_i - \sum_{j\neq i} \frac{(\boldsymbol{r}_i - \boldsymbol{r}_j) \cdot \boldsymbol{p}_i}{r_{ij}^3}\right\} \tag{13.A–4}$$

$$\mathscr{H}_4 = -\frac{e^2}{2m^2c^2} \sum_{i>j} \left\{\frac{1}{r_{ij}} (\boldsymbol{p}_i \cdot \boldsymbol{p}_j) + \frac{1}{r_{ij}^3} ((\boldsymbol{r}_i - \boldsymbol{r}_j) \cdot ((\boldsymbol{r}_i - \boldsymbol{r}_j) \cdot \boldsymbol{p}_j)\boldsymbol{p}_i)\right\} \tag{13.A–5}$$

$$\mathscr{H}_5 = -\frac{1}{8m^3c^2} \sum_i p_i^4 \tag{13.A–6}$$

$$\mathscr{H}_6 = \frac{e\hbar}{2m^2c^2} \sum_i ([\mathscr{E}_i \times \boldsymbol{p}_i] \cdot \boldsymbol{s}_i) - \frac{i\hbar e}{4m^2c^2} \sum_i (\mathscr{E}_i \cdot \boldsymbol{p}_i) + \frac{e\hbar}{mc} \sum_i (\mathscr{H}_i \cdot \boldsymbol{s}_i) \tag{13.A–7}$$

Here the various terms have the following significance:

$\mathscr{H}_1$ has two parts: The first and largest term is the spin-orbit interaction between the spin of an electron and the magnetic moment associated with its motion. The rest of $\mathscr{H}_1$ gives the "spin-other orbit" interaction between the spin of one electron and the magnetic moment associated with the motion of another electron.

$\mathscr{H}_2$ gives the spin-spin magnetic coupling terms which are often quite appreciable.[3] The second term in $\mathscr{H}_2$ with the Dirac delta functions, $\delta(\boldsymbol{r}_i - \boldsymbol{r}_j)$, must be introduced to take into account the fact that the first term in $\mathscr{H}_2$ is not well defined for overlapping charge distributions, since the radial average of $1/r_{ij}^3$ is infinite whereas the multiplying angular integrals give zero. The first term in $\mathscr{H}_2$ is therefore to be calculated with a small sphere cut out about each electron—or equivalently, by

[3] The second term is due to E. Fermi, *Z. Physik*, **60**, 320 (1930).

setting all indeterminate quantities equal to zero. This relation for $\mathscr{H}_2$ reduces to the Fermi formula for the S-state hyperfine structure when applied to an electron and a proton.

$\mathscr{H}_3$ contains correction terms which Dirac introduced because of electron spin. These terms are present even for one electron.

$\mathscr{H}_4$ represents the magnetic orbit-orbit coupling terms of the electrons.

$\mathscr{H}_5$ is the approximate relativistic correction to the kinetic energy for the change of the electron mass with velocity.

$\mathscr{H}_6$ gives the effect of external electric and magnetic fields. The first two terms are relativistic corrections for the electric field effects and are usually negligible. The magnetic term has so far been found important only in connection with the hyperfine structure of S-levels where the electronic wave functions are large at the nucleus. In such a case the electric field at the nucleus plays the role of the "external" field.

At long ranges such that the charge distributions do not overlap, the terms $\mathscr{H}_1$ through $\mathscr{H}_6$ may be replaced by a term representing the usual interaction between two dipoles. That is, if $\boldsymbol{\alpha}_i$ is the orbital angular momentum operator of the ith electron, for large separations

$$\mathscr{H} = \mathscr{H}_e + \frac{e^2\hbar^2}{4m^2c^2} \sum_{i>j} \frac{1}{r_{ij}^5} \Big[r_{ij}^2(\boldsymbol{\alpha}_i + 2\boldsymbol{s}_i) \cdot (\boldsymbol{\alpha}_j + 2\boldsymbol{s}_j) - 3[(\boldsymbol{\alpha}_i + 2\boldsymbol{s}_i) \cdot (\boldsymbol{r}_i - \boldsymbol{r}_j)] \, [(\boldsymbol{\alpha}_j + 2\boldsymbol{s}_j) \cdot (\boldsymbol{r}_i - \boldsymbol{r}_j)] \Big] \tag{13.A-8}$$

APPENDIX B. THE RATIO OF KINETIC TO POTENTIAL ENERGY OF ELECTRONS IN A MOLECULAR SYSTEM

The virial theorem can be used to improve approximate molecular wave functions. Fock[1] showed that the virial theorem is automatically satisfied for any quantum mechanical system whose potential is a homogeneous function of the coordinates, if a scale factor is introduced into the approximate charge distribution and varied so as to give the lowest energy. The form which Fock developed is useful for atomic problems.

This theorem has been extended[2] to molecules or metals where internuclear separations may be regarded as parameters. Let $\boldsymbol{r}^n$ and $\boldsymbol{r}^\nu$ be symbolic for the electronic and the nuclear coordinates, and $\psi_1(\boldsymbol{r}^n, \boldsymbol{r}^\nu)$ be an approximate wave function for either the ground state or the lowest energy state of a particular symmetry type. Then a new approximate wave function $\psi_s(\boldsymbol{r}^n, \boldsymbol{r}^\nu)$ can be formed by introducing a scale factor, s, in

[1] V. Fock, *Z. Physik*, **63**, 855 (1930).

[2] J. O. Hirschfelder and J. F. Kincaid, *Phys. Rev.*, **52**, 658 (1937).

such a way that all electronic distances are multiplied by s whereas the nuclear coordinates remain unchanged. Thus, because of the normalization

$$\psi_s(\boldsymbol{r}^n, \boldsymbol{r}^\nu) = s^{(3n/2)}\, \psi_1(s\boldsymbol{r}^n, \boldsymbol{r}^\nu) \tag{13.B–1}$$

From dimensional considerations, it follows that the electronic kinetic energy $K_e^{(s)}(\boldsymbol{r}^\nu)$ corresponding to the new wave function is simply related to $K_e^{(1)}(r^\nu)$, the kinetic energy corresponding to the old function:

$$K_e^{(s)}(\boldsymbol{r}^\nu) = s^2 K_e^{(1)}(s\boldsymbol{r}^\nu) \tag{13.B–2}$$

Similarly the electronic potential energy associated with the new function is related to that of the old by

$$\Phi_e^{(s)}(\boldsymbol{r}^\nu) = s\Phi_e^{(1)}(s\boldsymbol{r}^\nu) \tag{13.B–3}$$

The total electronic energy of the molecule is the sum of the kinetic and potential energies:

$$\Phi_n^{(s)}(\boldsymbol{r}^\nu) = K_e^{(s)}(\boldsymbol{r}^\nu) + \Phi_e^{(s)}(\boldsymbol{r}^\nu) = s^2 K_e^{(1)}(s\boldsymbol{r}^\nu) + s\Phi_e^{(1)}(s\boldsymbol{r}^\nu) \tag{13.B–4}$$

At the equilibrium separation,

$$\left(\frac{\partial \Phi_n^{(s)}(\boldsymbol{r}^\nu)}{\partial \boldsymbol{r}^\nu}\right)_s = s\left[s^2 \frac{dK_e^{(1)}(s\boldsymbol{r}^\nu)}{d(s\boldsymbol{r}^\nu)} + s\,\frac{d\Phi_e^{(1)}(s\boldsymbol{r}^\nu)}{d(s\boldsymbol{r}^\nu)}\right] = 0 \tag{13.B–5}$$

The lowest value of the energy obtained by varying the scale factor is given by

$$\left(\frac{\partial \Phi_n^{(s)}(\boldsymbol{r}^\nu)}{\partial s}\right)_{\boldsymbol{r}^\nu} = 2sK_e^{(1)}(s\boldsymbol{r}^\nu) + \Phi_e^{(1)}(s\boldsymbol{r}^\nu)$$
$$+\, \boldsymbol{r}^\nu\left[s^2 \frac{dK_e^{(1)}(s\boldsymbol{r}^\nu)}{d(s\boldsymbol{r}^\nu)} + s\,\frac{d\Phi_e^{(1)}(s\boldsymbol{r}^\nu)}{d(s\boldsymbol{r}^\nu)}\right] = 0 \tag{13.B–6}$$

When these last two relations are combined, it follows that the best value of s at the equilibrium separation is

$$s = -\tfrac{1}{2}\Phi_e^{(1)}(s\boldsymbol{r}^\nu)/K_e^{(1)}(s\boldsymbol{r}^\nu) \tag{13.B–7}$$

and the best, or lowest value, of the total energy is

$$\Phi_n^{(s)}(\boldsymbol{r}^\nu) = -\tfrac{1}{4}(\Phi_e^{(1)}(s\boldsymbol{r}^\nu))^2/K_e^{(1)}(s\boldsymbol{r}^\nu) \tag{13.B–8}$$

The virial theorem is automatically satisfied by this approximate wave function since, for this value of s,

$$\Phi_n^{(s)}(\boldsymbol{r}^\nu) = -K_e^{(s)}(\boldsymbol{r}^\nu) = \tfrac{1}{2}\Phi_e^{(s)}(\boldsymbol{r}^\nu) \tag{13.B–9}$$

That is, if the approximate charge distribution is expanded or contracted, the size which corresponds to the lowest energy gives the proper ratio of the potential to the kinetic energy. For a non-equilibrium separation, the proper ratio of the potential to the kinetic energies is given by Eqs. 13.1–36 and 37. In order for this ratio to occur, s would need to have the value

$$s = -\frac{\Phi^{(1)}(s\mathbf{r}^\nu)}{4K^{(1)}(s\mathbf{r}^\nu)}\left[1 + \sqrt{1 - \frac{8K^{(1)}(s\mathbf{r}^\nu)}{(\Phi^{(1)}(s\mathbf{r}^\nu))^2}\, \mathbf{r}^\nu \frac{dE^{(s)}(\mathbf{r}^\nu)}{d\mathbf{r}^\nu}}\right] \tag{13.B–10}$$

corresponding to the energy

$$E^{(s)}(\mathbf{r}^\nu) = -\tfrac{1}{2}\left(\mathbf{r}^\nu \cdot \frac{dE^{(s)}(\mathbf{r}^\nu)}{d\mathbf{r}^\nu}\right) - \frac{(\Phi^{(1)}(s\mathbf{r}^\nu))^2}{K^{(1)}(s\mathbf{r}^\nu)}\left[1 + \sqrt{1 - \left(\frac{8K^{(1)}(s\mathbf{r}^\nu)}{(\Phi^{(1)}(s\mathbf{r}^\nu))^2}\, \mathbf{r}^\nu \cdot \frac{dE^{(s)}(\mathbf{r}^\nu)}{d\mathbf{r}^\nu}\right)}\right] \tag{13.B–11}$$

Usually this is the lowest energy obtainable for the nonequilibrium separation, and therefore the value of s must be adjusted by direct energy calculations for non-equilibrium separations.

PROBLEMS

1. Let us consider the two particles which interact according to two potential curves. The curves for the "ground state" and the "excited state" are

$$\varphi_0 = 100\,[e^{-4(r-1)} - 2e^{-2(r-1)}] \text{ kcal/mole}$$

$$\varphi_1 = 50\,[e^{-8(r-1.5)} - 2e^{-4(r-1.5)}] + 50.5 \text{ kcal/mole}$$

Here r is the separation in angstroms.

Calculate the probability that, when two like molecules collide initially in the ground state with a relative velocity, $v(r)$, there is a transition to the excited state. Plot the transition probability as a function of $v(r)$.

2. Calculate the polarizability in the z and x directions for a hydrogen atom with the electron in the $2p_z$ orbital,

$$\psi = \frac{r\cos\theta \exp\left(-\dfrac{r}{2a_0}\right)}{4a_0{}^2\sqrt{2\pi a_0}}$$

3. Calculate the separation for each of the following molecule pairs for which the energy of attraction is 0.6 kcal/mole (kT at room temperature), assuming the most favorable orientations:

(a) A + A
(b) A + HCl
(c) HCl + HCl
(d) C + O (in their ground states)
(e) H(1s) + proton
(f) H(2p) + proton.

4. Given the cubic equation for the energy of interaction of a proton and a helium atom:

$$\varphi^3 + \varphi^2 \left[+ 0.0155023 + \frac{108}{r^3}\right] + \varphi \left[3.19474 \times 10^{-5} + \frac{1.498057}{r^3} + \frac{81}{r^4}\right]$$
$$+ \frac{1.150106 \times 10^{-3}}{r^3} - \frac{0.3524904}{r^4} = 0$$

and the three roots accurate to terms in $1/r^3$,

$$\varphi_1 = 0.0130552 + \frac{a_1}{r^4} + \cdots$$

$$\varphi_2 = 0.00024471 - \frac{72}{r^3} + \frac{a_2}{r^4} + \cdots$$

$$\varphi_3 = -\frac{36}{r^3} + \frac{a_3}{r^4} + \cdots$$

Find the coefficients a_1, a_2, and a_3 of the terms in $1/r^4$.

5. Calculate the quadrupole-quadrupole energy of interaction between two Cl atoms in their ground states. What potential curves arise and which one is associated with the ground state of the Cl_2 molecule?

· 14 ·

Quantum Mechanical Calculations of Intermolecular Forces Ⓝ

Our knowledge of intermolecular forces results from a combination of experimental observations and general theoretical considerations. The theory furnishes the functional forms, and the experiments serve to evaluate the numerical constants. It is most important that theory predict the qualitative aspects of the intermolecular forces so that experimental data may be properly interpreted and new experiments designed to detect some of the salient features. At the present time only the forces between simple molecules, usually in their ground states, are qualitatively understood. Much work remains to determine the forces between other types of molecules and to show how these forces affect the physical and chemical properties. In a few simple cases, such as the interaction between two hydrogen or between two helium atoms, the forces have been calculated on a strictly quantum mechanical basis. However, up to the present time the strictly quantum mechanical results have not been sufficiently accurate to express the intermolecular energy for all separations: small, intermediate, and large. To be specific, large separations are those for which only the sorts of long-range forces, considered in Chapter 13, need be considered; small separations are those for which only chemical forces are important; and intermediate separations are those for which the short-range and the long-range forces merge into one another.

In Chapter 13 the long-range forces are expressed in terms of physical properties of the isolated molecules. First-order and second-order perturbation theory is sufficient to treat the long-range interactions, since the perturbations are truly small. Moreover, it is not necessary to antisymmetrize the wave functions since all the overlap and exchange integrals are negligible. Unfortunately such simplifications are not possible when the molecules are separated by a small or an intermediate distance.

Up to the present time, most of the calculations of intermolecular energies have been made for the very small separations, which are important both from the standpoint of chemical reaction kinetics and from the standpoint of spectroscopy. Very little attention, however, has been given to the determination of intermolecular interactions at intermediate separations such as occur in the vicinity of the equilibrium separation of neighboring molecules in a crystal. The energy of interaction at these intermediate separations determines the physical properties of the gas, liquid, and solid states. Calculations of the energy for intermediate separations are discussed for the interaction of two hydrogen atoms (§ 14.1). In one way this energy is more difficult, and in another way less difficult, to determine than for the smaller separations. It is more difficult in the sense that we require a more complex functional form for the wave function capable of giving both satisfactory energy of dispersion at large separations and chemical binding energy at small separations. But the calculations at intermediate separations are easier in the sense that the many-center coulomb and exchange integrals become numerically less important and their values can be estimated more readily.

The calculation of intermolecular forces for short or intermediate separations requires the use of the variational principle applied on approximate wave functions with many adjustable parameters.[1] Extraordinary numerical accuracy is required since the total energy of the bimolecular system, which is calculated directly, is usually many times 100 electron volts, and from the total energy is subtracted the energy of the isolated molecules to obtain the energy of interaction, which is of the order of one-tenth to one-hundredth of an electron volt. Then, too, only recently have the high-speed computing machines made it feasible to evaluate the myriads of integrals which are required (see Appendix 14.A).

A number of recent developments in the techniques of molecular quantum mechanics[2–6] (see § 13.1e for Slater's generalized self-consistent

[1] J. H. Van Vleck and A. Sherman, "The Quantum Theory of Valence," *Revs. Mod. Phys.*, **7**, 167 (1935). (Still one of the best references for the basic approach to molecular quantum mechanics.)

[2] J. E. Lennard-Jones and J. A. Pople, "The Interaction of Paired Electrons in Chemical Bonds," *Proc. Roy. Soc.* (*London*), **210A**, 190 (1952). Also J. E. Lennard-Jones, *J. Chem. Phys.*, **20**, 1024 (1952).

[3] C. C. Roothaan, "New Developments in Molecular Orbital Theory," *Revs. Mod. Phys.*, **23**, 69 (1951).

[4] G. L. Montet, S. P. Keller, and J. E. Mayer, "Interactions of Closed Shell Ions," *J. Chem. Phys.*, **20**, 1057 (1952).

[5] Per-Olov Löwdin, "Quantum Mechanical Calculations of the Cohesive Energy of Molecules and Crystals," *J. Chem. Phys.*, **19**, 1570 and 1579 (1951).

[6] One of the most interesting recent developments is the generalization of the statistical atomic model of Thomas and Fermi by Amaldi, Dirac, Jensen, Gombás, Feynman, Teller, and others, to include electron spin, exchange forces, and the correlation between the motions of the different electrons. See P. Gombás, *Theorie und Lösungsmethoden des Mehrteilchenproblems der Wellenmechanik*, Birkhäuser (Basel, 1950), Chapter 9. The application of this method to molecules is discussed by P. Gombás, *Die Statistische Theorie des Atoms*, Springer (1949), Chapter 7.

field method) make it seem altogether likely that, within a few years, potential energy curves can be calculated theoretically, which are comparable in accuracy with the experimental determinations.

It is hoped that eventually the intermolecular forces for short or intermediate separations will be expressed in terms of physical properties of the isolated molecules, just as the long range forces are now expressed in terms of the ionization potentials, polarizabilities, and electrical moments. In order to test the validity of any such expressions it will still be necessary to compare such results with very accurate variational calculations for a few special cases.

In this chapter the present state of the theory of intermolecular forces is considered for a few examples for which the interaction energies have been calculated on a strictly theoretical basis:[7]

(1) $H + H$	(5) $H + H_2$
(2) $He + He$	(6) $H_2 + H_2$
(3) $Ne + Ne$	(7) H or H_2 and the various positive and negative hydrogen ions
(4) $A + A$	(8) $He + H^+$ and $He^+ + He'$

In all these calculations, a functional form for an approximate wave function, Ψ_{approx}, is selected as a compromise between accuracy and availability of integrals. The approximate energy for the combined system of the two molecules is determined by the relation[8]

$$E_{\text{approx}} = \frac{\int\int \Psi^*_{\text{approx}} \mathscr{H} \Psi_{\text{approx}} \, d\mathbf{r}^{n_a} \, d\mathbf{r}^{n_b}}{\int\int \Psi^*_{\text{approx}} \Psi_{\text{approx}} \, d\mathbf{r}^{n_a} \, d\mathbf{r}^{n_b}} \tag{14.0–1}$$

Unfortunately in many cases various approximations are made in the integrations so that the error in E_{approx} is due both to the inaccuracy of the approximate wave function and to the errors in the integrations. The numerical value of E_{approx} is minimized by varying as many of the parameters in Ψ_{approx} as is conveniently possible. If E_a and E_b are the total binding energies of the isolated molecules a and b, respectively (relative to all the electrons and nuclei completely separated), the energy of interaction is given by

$$\varphi_{ab} = E_{\text{approx}} - E_a - E_b \tag{14.0–2}$$

[7] Throughout this chapter, a prime indicates an excited state.

[8] As in Chapter 13, n_a and n_b are the number of electrons in molecules a and b, respectively.

For purposes of calculating the whole potential curve from large to small separations, it is necessary to calculate E_a and E_b, using the same sort of approximate wave functions and the same approximations in the integrations as is used for the combined system of two molecules. Otherwise φ_{ab} would not approach zero as the two molecules separate. Even if there were no errors in the integration, the variational principle would not strictly apply to φ_{ab} since there is no guarantee that the error in calculating the energy of the combined system is greater or less than the errors in calculating the energy of the separated molecules. Perhaps one of the greatest uncertainties in the theoretical calculation of intermolecular forces is the procedure for merging the chemical energy of interaction, calculated for small separations, with the energy of dispersion, calculated at large separations. Usually the chemical energy and the dispersion energy are calculated by entirely different methods. If we simply add the dispersion energy to the chemical energy, we obtain entirely different results, depending upon whether or not the terms varying as the inverse eighth power, the inverse tenth power, etc., of the separation are included. On this account it is difficult to assess the theoretical accuracy of the potential functions so obtained.

Attention should be called to the following quantum mechanical treatments of atom-atom interactions not considered in this chapter:[8]

(1) H + He: G. Gentile, *Z. Physik*, **63**, 795 (1930). (Unfortunately Gentile was not able to evaluate many of the integrals required so that the results are not significant. All the integrals are now available so that this problem should be reconsidered.)

(2) N + N: H. Kopineck, *Z. Naturforschung*, **7a**, 22 and 314 (1952). (This is a thorough treatment of the N_2 molecule in the neighborhood of its equilibrium separation, considering explicitly the interactions of 10 electrons.)

(3) Be + Be′: W. Furry and J. Bartlett, *Phys. Rev.*, **39**, 210 (1932). (This is a thorough Heitler-London type treatment of interaction of a normal $(2s)^2$ Be atom with an excited $2s2p$ Be, considering all the resulting energy states and evaluating all integrals. A good listing is given of all integrals used.)

(4) Li + Li: H. James, *J. Chem. Phys.*, **2**, 794 (1934) and *Phys. Rev.*, **43**, 589 (1933); C. Coulson and W. Duncanson, *Proc. Roy. Soc.* (*London*), **A181**, 378 (1943); J. Bartlett and W. Furry, *Phys. Rev.*, **38**, 1615 (1931). (Bartlett and Furry obtained excellent agreement with experiment for the energy of dissociation of Li_2 by making a number of approximations in the Heitler-London treatment. James showed that this agreement is destroyed and the results are unsatisfactory when these approximations are removed. He believes that the inner shell electrons are responsible for the difficulty. Coulson and Duncanson used a molecular orbital method to calculate the binding energy of the normal molecule; however, they did not attain the accuracy of James' calculation.)

(5) Be + H and Be′ + H: C. Ireland, *Phys. Rev.*, **43**, 329 (1933). (Ireland used the Heitler-London method to calculate the whole set of potential energy curves resulting from the interaction of a hydrogen atom with either a normal $(2s)^2$ or an excited $2s2p$ beryllium atom.)

(6) Li + H and Li^+ + H: J. Knipp, *J. Chem. Phys.*, **4**, 300 (1936); E. Hutchisson and M. Muskat, *Phys. Rev.*, **40**, 340 (1932). (Knipp used an eleven-term James and

Coolidge wave function to show that LiH^+ has a $^2\Sigma$ lowest state which has an energy of repulsion of 0.181 ev at a separation of $3a_0$ with respect to $Li^+ + H$. The painstaking James and Coolidge type of calculation which Knipp used led to a much smaller and less satisfactory energy of dissociation than the Hutchisson and Muskat Heitler-London treatment.)

(7) $Li + Li^+$: H. James, *J. Chem. Phys.*, **3**, 9 (1935). (James used a James and Coolidge type wave function and calculated the binding energy of Li_2^+ to be 1.243 ev at a separation of $2.98a_0$.)

(8) K + H: H. Hellmann, *J. Chem. Phys.*, **3**, 61 (1935), and *Acta Physicochimica USSR*, **1**, 913 (1935). (Hellmann developed his own system of approximation, considering the inner shell electrons as satisfying the Fermi-Thomas conditions; the outer electrons satisfy a modified Schrödinger equation. In the case of K + H, his results are admittedly rough. However, Hellmann's approach might be fruitful for intermolecular forces at large separations.)

(9) Na + Na and K + K: N. Rosen, *Phys. Rev.*, **38**, 255 (1931); N. Rosen and S. Ikehara, *Phys. Rev.*, **43**, 5 (1933). (A modified Heitler-London method was used to calculate the energy of interaction of pairs of atoms having one *s* electron in the outer shell. All integrals for interactions of the outer shell electrons are evaluated, and the experimental agreement of binding energy, equilibrium separation, and fundamental frequency for the normal diatomic molecules is excellent.)

1. The Interaction between Two Hydrogen Atoms

Since the interaction of two hydrogen atoms is the simplest example of a molecular interaction, it has been possible to make more detailed and accurate calculations for this system than for any other.[1] To get the best potential energy curves, it is necessary to mesh together many different types of information. If two hydrogen atoms in 1*s* states collide with a small amount of kinetic energy, there is a chance of one in four that they will follow a $^1\Sigma$ energy curve corresponding to the normal H_2 molecule, and there is a chance of three in four that they will follow the $^3\Sigma$ curve corresponding to the lowest repulsive state[2] of H_2. High-energy collisions,

[1] E. C. Kemble and C. M. Zener, *Phys. Rev.*, **33**, 512 (1929), and C. M. Zener and E. C. Kemble, *Phys. Rev.*, **34**, 999 (1929), have made rough calculations of the energy of interactions which result from the collision of a 1*s* hydrogen atom with a hydrogen atom which is initially in either a 2*s* or one of the 2*p* states. From such collisions 8 Σ states and 4 Π states result. Two of the Π states are stable. One, called the B state, has an observed energy of dissociation of 3.37 ev, whereas Zener and Kemble calculate a value of only 2.64 ev. The best estimate of the potential energy curves for the states resulting from a collision between a 1*s* and a 2*p* hydrogen atom are given by G. W. King and J. H. Van Vleck, *Phys. Rev.*, **55**, 1165 (1939). A. S. Coolidge and H. M. James, *J. Chem. Phys.*, **6**, 730 (1938) have made a very accurate (to within 6 kcal/mole) calculation of the energy of the repulsive state $1s\sigma 2p\sigma\ ^3\Sigma_u$ and the attractive state $1s\sigma 2s\sigma\ ^3\Sigma_g$ of hydrogen for separations from $1.3a_0$ to $1.9a_0$, using a 12-term wave function.

[2] At large separations, the energy of the $^1\Sigma$ and of the $^3\Sigma$ are equal so that the relative probability of the two hydrogen atoms finding themselves in one or the other state is simply the ratio of their respective degeneracies (in this case, spin multiplicities), one to three.

such as are often encountered in "hot atom" chemistry, can of course result in either ionization or excitation to other states. The singlet state has the potential energy curve of the normal hydrogen molecule with a (zero energy) collision diameter $\sigma = 0.5$ Å, and a minimum energy of 103 kcal per mole (7160×10^{-15} erg per molecule) at $r = 0.74$ Å. The triplet state has a collision diameter $\sigma = 4.0$ Å, and a minimum energy of 0.0074 kcal per mole (0.514×10^{-15} erg per molecule) at $r = 4.5$ Å.

The functional form of a wave function suitable for calculating the interaction energy at intermediate to large separations must meet the following requirements: (1) it must give good values of the binding energy at small separations; (2) it must give good values of the dispersion energy at large separations; and (3) it must be sufficiently simple that all the exchange and coulombic integrals can be evaluated at a large number of internuclear separations without great difficulty.

Many of the functional forms for approximate wave functions which give satisfactory values for the chemical binding at small separations do not give any energy of dispersion when the atoms are far apart. For example, the Heitler-London type functions

$$\Psi = \psi_a(1)\psi_b(2) + \psi_a(2)\psi_b(1) \tag{14.1-1}$$

would not suffice, since they give zero dispersion energy regardless of the specific form of the one-electron orbitals $\psi_a(1)$ and $\psi_b(1)$. Here the 1 refers to the electron. None of the other standard forms of wave functions, such as the Rosen[3] or the Weinbaum,[4] would suffice either. The Rosen function takes polarization into account. The Weinbaum function includes ionic as well as homopolar terms. Actually, in order to calculate dispersion energy, there must be statistical correlation between the coordinates of the two electrons, as in the classical theory of dispersion energy—at any instant the electron and proton of atom a induce a dipole moment in atom b by affecting the statistical charge distribution of the electron on b; the interaction between the instantaneous and the induced dipole moments results in the energy of attraction.

The simplest functional form for the wave function for either the $^1\Sigma$ or the $^3\Sigma$ state satisfying the above requirements is[5]

$$\begin{aligned}\Psi = {} & a_0(1)b_0(2)[1 + (\alpha Z^2)(x_{a1}x_{b2} + y_{a1}y_{b2}) + \beta Z^2(z_{a1}z_{b2})] \\ & \pm a_0(2)b_0(1)[1 + (\alpha Z^2)(x_{a2}x_{b1} + y_{a2}y_{b1}) + \beta Z^2(z_{a2}z_{b1})] \\ & + \gamma[a_0(1)a_0(2) + b_0(1)b_0(2)]\end{aligned} \tag{14.1-2}$$

[3] N. Rosen, *Phys. Rev.*, **38**, 2099 (1931).
[4] S. Weinbaum, *J. Chem. Phys.*, **1**, 593 (1933).
[5] J. O. Hirschfelder and J. W. Linnett, *J. Chem. Phys.*, **18**, 130 (1950).

The plus sign is for the $^1\Sigma$ and the minus sign is for the $^3\Sigma$ state. The z-axis is taken along the line of nuclei and the x and y axes are perpendicular to this line. By z_{a1} is meant the difference between the z-coordinate of electron 1 and that of nucleus a. The geometry of the problem is shown in Fig. 14.1-1. In Eq. 14.1-2, $a_0(1)$ and $b_0(1)$ are the $1s$ hydrogen-like atomic orbitals, with centers located respectively on atoms a and b with effective nuclear charge Z:

$$a_0(1) = (Z^3/\pi)^{1/2} \exp(-Zr_{a1})$$
$$b_0(1) = (Z^3/\pi)^{1/2} \exp(-Zr_{b1}) \qquad (14.1\text{–}3)$$

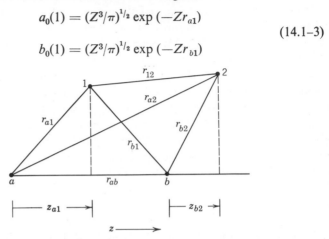

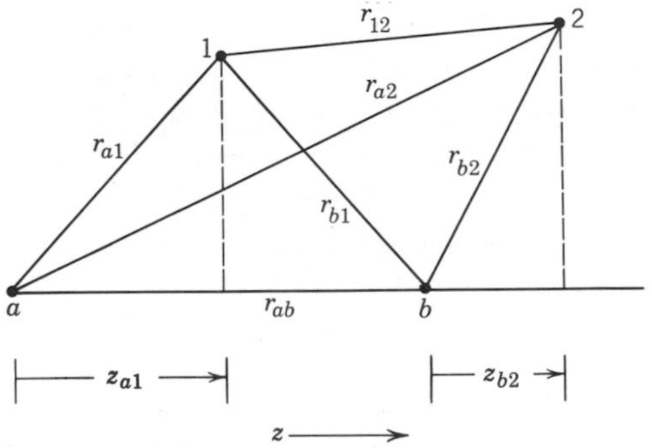

Fig. 14.1-1. Geometry of particles and distances in the hydrogen molecule.

The r_{a1} and r_{b1} in Eq. 14.1-3 are expressed in units of a_0. It is customary in atomic or molecular quantum mechanics to express distances in units of the Bohr radius, $a_0 = 0.5292$ Å, and energy is measured in "atomic units," $e^2/a_0 = 627.46$ (defined) kcal/mole $= 27.206$ electron volts $= 4.3584 \times 10^{-11}$ erg.

The parameters have the following significance:

(i) The parameter Z is called the *effective nuclear charge*, since the atomic orbitals $a_0(1)$ and $b_0(1)$ are solutions to the Schrödinger equation for an electron in the coulombic field of a nucleus of charge Ze. Increasing the value of Z contracts the size of the orbitals. For a fixed internuclear separation, an increase of Z decreases the ratio of the average potential to the average kinetic energy of the electrons. However, at the equilibrium separation, as is shown in Appendix 13.B, varying Z to give the lowest energy automatically establishes the correct ratio of the potential to kinetic energy.

(ii) The parameter γ determines the contribution of the ionic or Weinbaum[4] terms to the approximate wave function. For a molecular orbital wave function, γ would be equal to unity. Because of mutual electron repulsion, the electrons prefer to be near different nuclei at a particular instant. This manifests itself in a value of γ considerably smaller than unity. Because of symmetry considerations, γ is zero for the $^3\Sigma$ state.

(iii) The parameter α establishes the correlation between the instantaneous positions of the two electrons with reference to axes perpendicular to the line of nuclei. The value of α is negative for both the $^1\Sigma$ and the $^3\Sigma$ states at all separations. This means that the charge distribution is greater when the two electrons have opposite signs for their x- or y-coordinates. Thus the negative value of α is simply the result of mutual repulsion of the electrons.

(iv) The parameter β establishes the correlation between the instantaneous positions of the two electrons with respect to distances along the internuclear axis. Positive values of β correspond to the electrons seeking to get as far apart as possible. For both the $^1\Sigma$ and the $^3\Sigma$ states at large internuclear separations, the value of β is positive. The positive value of β at large separations is largely responsible for the energy of dispersion. At small separations, β remains positive for the $^3\Sigma$ state, but becomes negative for the $^1\Sigma$. The negative values of β correspond to a concentration of the negative charge in the region between the nuclei. As is seen in § 13.1, the concentration of negative charge between the nuclei is responsible for the energy of attraction between the atoms. Gurnee and Magee[6] showed that considerable improvement on the Heitler-London or Wang wave function[7] can be obtained by letting the centers of the electron orbitals lie slightly closer together than the positions of the nuclei.

For either the $^1\Sigma$ or the $^3\Sigma$ states at very large separations, γ becomes zero, Z becomes unity, and α becomes

$$\alpha = -\beta/2 = -(a_0/r_{ab})^3 \qquad (14.1\text{–}4)$$

This function is the crudest of the various wave functions which Hassé[8] and Kirkwood[9] used in their calculations of the dispersion energy by a variational calculation. The Hirschfelder-Linnett wave function leads to an energy of interaction at very large separations:

$$\varphi_{ab} = -6\frac{e^2}{a_0}\left(\frac{a_0}{r_{ab}}\right)^6 \qquad (14.1\text{–}5)$$

[6] E. F. Gurnee and J. L. Magee, *J. Chem. Phys.*, **18**, 142 (1950).

[7] See any book on molecular quantum mechanics, for example, L. Pauling and E. B. Wilson, Jr., *Introduction to Quantum Mechanics*, McGraw-Hill (1935).

[8] H. Hassé, *Proc. Cambridge Phil. Soc.*, **26**, 542 (1930); **27**, 66 (1931).

[9] J. G. Kirkwood, *Physik. Z.*, **33**, 57 (1932).

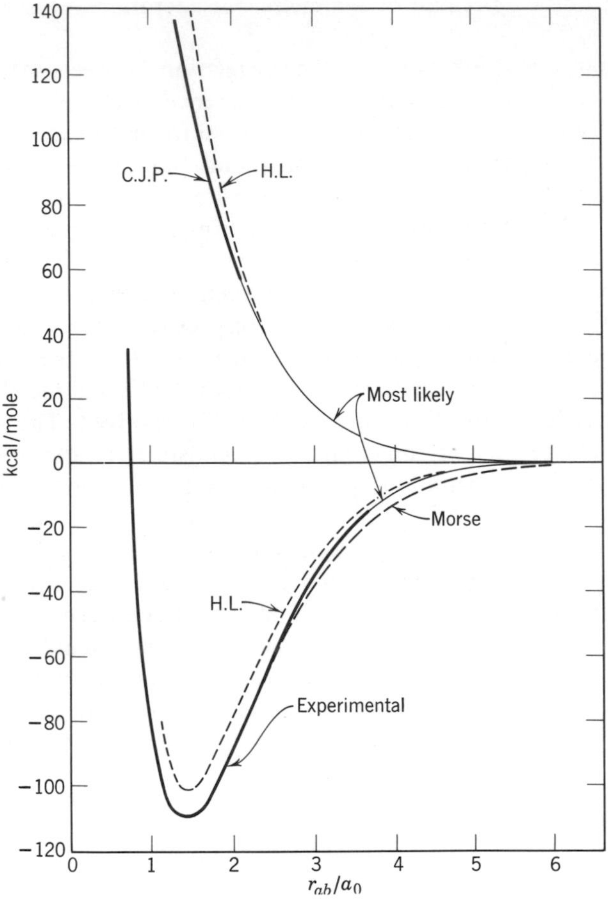

Fig. 14.1–2. Energy of interaction of two 1*s* hydrogen atoms as function of internuclear separation. H.L. = Hirschfelder-Linnett calculations. C.J.P. = Coolidge, James, and Present calculations. M. = Morse curve. Experimental = Rydberg and Beutler determinations from experimental vibrational energies. [From J. O. Hirschfelder and J. W. Linnett, *J. Chem. Phys.*, **18**, 130 (1950).]

This is to be compared with the results of Pauling and Beach,[10, 11]

$$\varphi_{ab} = -\frac{e^2}{a_0}\left[6.49903\left(\frac{a_0}{r_{ab}}\right)^6 + 124.399\left(\frac{a_0}{r_{ab}}\right)^8 + 1135.21\left(\frac{a_0}{r_{ab}}\right)^{10}\right] \tag{14.1–6}$$

Pauling and Beach obtained their precise result, by using a variational procedure and solving a 26th-order secular equation to obtain the numerical coefficient of the inverse sixth-power term, a 17th-order secular equation to obtain the inverse eighth-power term, and a 26th-order secular equation for the inverse tenth-power term. Fortunately, most of the coefficients in the secular equation vanish, but still there are enough non-zero elements to entail an enormous amount of work. Within the past twenty years group theoretical techniques have been developed which would greatly reduce the work involved in these calculations.

a. The $^1\Sigma$ state corresponding to the normal H_2-molecule

The theoretical calculations using the wave function given in Eq. 14.1–2 were carried out from the smallest to the largest separations. In this manner, a single potential energy curve is obtained which merges the energy of dispersion at large separations with the chemical binding energy at small separations. However, at very large separations this wave function does not give the dispersion energy so accurately as it was obtained theoretically by Pauling and Beach,[10] and at small separations the energy is not so accurate as the values that can be obtained from the experimental vibrational energy levels of the hydrogen molecule. The "best" or "most likely" potential energy curve is shown in Fig. 14.1–2, and the results are given in Table 14.1–1. The Hirschfelder-Linnett calculations furnish only the intermediate segment of the "best" or "most likely" potential energy curve.

The most reliable experimental data for normal H_2 up to separations as large as $3.7a_0$ is obtained by Rydberg's[12] and Beutler's[12] analysis (using the Klein method) of the first ten vibrational levels of molecular hydrogen. Their results are given in Table 14.1–2 and are labeled "experimental" in Fig. 14.1–2. The separations are given with an accuracy of 0.005 Å or $0.01a_0$. From Fig. 14.1–2, it appears that the Hirschfelder-Linnett theoretical

[10] L. Pauling and J. Y. Beach, *Phys. Rev.*, **47**, 686 (1935).

[11] J. C. Slater and J. G. Kirkwood, *Phys. Rev.*, **37**, 682 (1931), showed that the numerical coefficient of the inverse sixth-power term must be equal to or greater than 6.4976.

[12] R. Rydberg, *Z. Physik*, **73**, 376 (1931); see also H. Beutler, *Z. physik. Chem.*, **B27**, 287 (1934).

TABLE 14.1–1[5]

MOST LIKELY POTENTIAL ENERGY FOR NORMAL HYDROGEN ($^1\Sigma$)

r_{ab}/a_0	Binding Energy (kcal/mole)	Source of Calculations
0.78	14.38	Rydberg experimental values calculated from observed vibrational energy levels
0.79	20.14	
0.81	26.68	
0.83	33.91	
0.85	41.84	
0.88	50.46	
0.92	59.70	
0.96	69.57	
1.01	80.13	
1.09	91.32	
1.23	103.20	
1.40	109.32[a]	
1.68	103.20	
1.94	91.32	
2.15	80.13	
2.32	69.57	
2.49	59.70	
2.66	50.46	
2.84	41.84	
3.05	33.91	
3.28	26.68	
3.51	20.14	
3.73	14.38	
4.00	10.00	Estimated value required for smooth curve fitting
4.5	3.983	Hirschfelder-Linnett calculations
5.0	1.858	
6.0	0.3995	
7.0	0.0919	
8.0	0.0251	
9.0	0.0097	Pauling and Beach calculations (Eq. 14.1–6).
10.0	0.0044	
11.0	0.0027	
12.0	0.0013	

[a] Maximum binding energy.

curve merges with the Rydberg experimental curve at a separation of around $5a_0$. The theoretical curve is therefore probably quite accurate between $5a_0$ and the point at which dispersion forces become important.

It is interesting to compare the Rydberg experimental values with the usual Morse curve,[13] which is very frequently used because of its simplicity.

$$\varphi_{\text{Morse}} = 109.46[-2 \exp(-x) + \exp(-2x)] \text{ kcal/mole} \quad (14.1\text{–}7)$$

where

$$x = 1.0298((r_{ab}/a_0) - 1.401) \quad (14.1\text{–}8)$$

TABLE 14.1–2[12]

RYDBERG EXPERIMENTAL POTENTIAL ENERGY FOR NORMAL HYDROGEN

Vibrational Level	Binding Energy (kcal/mole)	Minimum Separation		Maximum Separation	
		Angstroms	Atomic Units (a_0)	Angstroms	Atomic Units (a_0)
0	103.20	0.652	1.23	0.887	1.68
1	91.32	0.576	1.09	1.028	1.94
2	80.13	0.536	1.01	1.138	2.15
3	69.57	0.506	0.96	1.228	2.32
4	59.70	0.486	0.92	1.318	2.49
5	50.46	0.466	0.88	1.409	2.66
6	41.84	0.451	0.85	1.504	2.84
7	33.91	0.441	0.83	1.614	3.05
8	26.68	0.431	0.82	1.734	3.28
9	20.14	0.416	0.79	1.855	3.51
10	14.38	0.411	0.78	1.975	3.73
∞	0				

The Morse curve agrees nicely with Rydberg's up to $r_{ab}/a_0 = 2.5$, but for larger separations it gives too much binding energy.

As can be seen from Fig. 14.1–3, the energy of attraction calculated by Hirschfelder and Linnett is greater than that of Pauling and Beach at separations less than $9a_0$. Since Pauling and Beach's calculations did

[13] P. Morse, *Phys. Rev.*, **34**, 57 (1929); see L. Pauling and E. B. Wilson, Jr., *Introduction to Quantum Mechanics*, McGraw-Hill (1935), p. 271.

not take exchange effects into consideration, it appears that this point of crossing of the two calculated curves is the point at which exchange or valence forces become important.

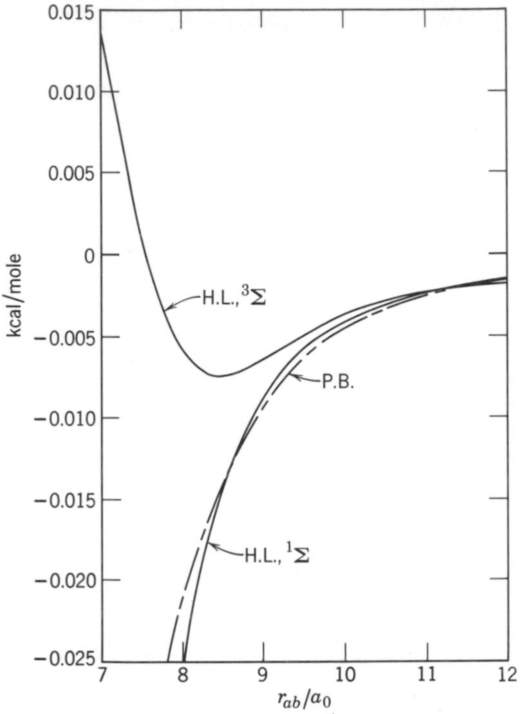

Fig. 14.1–3. Van der Waals energy of interaction of two 1*s* hydrogen atoms. P.B. = Pauling-Beach. H.L. = Hirschfelder-Linnett. [From J. O. Hirschfelder and J. W. Linnett, *J. Chem. Phys.*, **18**, 130 (1950).]

b. The $^3\Sigma$ state corresponding to repulsion of the two 1*s* hydrogen atoms

The "best" or "most likely" potential energy curve for the $^3\Sigma$ state is obtained by using the Pauling and Beach[10] dispersion energy at large separations, the Hirschfelder-Linnett calculations for intermediate separations, and the very accurate theoretical calculations of James, Coolidge, and Present[14] at small separations. The "most likely" energy of interaction is shown in Figs. 14.1–2 and 3, and numerical values are given in Table 14.1–3.

The potential energy curve for the $^3\Sigma$ state has been discussed by James, Coolidge, and Present.[14] Using a highly flexible variational

[14] H. M. James, A. S. Coolidge, and R. D. Present, *J. Chem. Phys.*, **4**, 187 and 193 (1936).

TABLE 14.1–3[5]

Most Likely Potential Energy for Excited Hydrogen

r_{ab}/a_0	Energy of Repulsion (kcal/mole)	Source of Calculations
1.0	245	From James, Coolidge, and Present quantum mechanical calculations. The values are taken from Eq. 14.1–9
1.25	166	
1.5	119	
1.75	88.8	
2.0	68.0	
2.5	30.45	Hirschfelder-Linnett calculations
3.0	16.35	
3.5	8.45	
4.0	4.300	
4.5	2.008	
5.0	0.9074	
6.0	0.1558	
7.0	0.01393	
7.51	0.00000	
8.0	−0.00586	
8.45	−0.0074[a]	
10.0	−0.0038	
12.0	−0.0013	Pauling and Beach calculations. (Eq. 14.1–6). Recommended for $r_{ab}/a_0 \geq 12$

[a] Energy minimum.

function and applying certain corrections, they calculated that for $r_{ab}/a_0 = 1.5$, 1.6, and 1.87 the energies of repulsion are 119.3, 105.6, and 77.9 kcal per mole, respectively. By fitting a formula to their results we obtain

$$\varphi_{\mathrm{JCP}} = 349.7(r_{ab}/a_0)^{-4/3} \exp(-0.357(r_{ab}/a_0)) \text{ kcal/mole} \qquad (14.1\text{–}9)$$

The Hirschfelder-Linnett theoretical curve is 33, 24, and 10 kcal per mole above the James, Coolidge, and Present calculations at their calculated points. This is shown graphically in Fig. 14.1–2. The calculated energy of Hirschfelder-Linnett is 28 per cent above that of James, Coolidge, and Present at $1.5a_0$; 23 per cent above at $1.6a_0$; and 13 per cent above at $1.87a_0$. So both the percentage difference and the absolute difference between the two sets of calculated values are derceasing as r_{ab} increases.

Since the energies calculated by James, Coolidge, and Present are calculated using a much more flexible variation function, there is no doubt that their calculated energies are the more reliable. It seems that the Hirschfelder-Linnett calculations provide a good approximation to the $^3\Sigma$ potential energy curve beyond $2.5a_0$ and that the best overall curve passes through the three points given by James, Coolidge, and Present, and follows the Hirschfelder-Linnett curve for values of r_{ab} greater than $2.5a_0$. Values of this *most likely* potential energy are given in Table 14.1–3[5].

According to Fig. 14.1–3, the $^3\Sigma$ state has a minimum energy of -0.0074 kcal per mole when $r_{ab}/a_0 = 8.45$; the energy of interaction is zero when $r_{ab}/a_0 = 7.51$; and the energy of interaction is positive at smaller separations.

2. The Energy of Interaction between Noble Gas Atoms in Their Ground States

The interaction between noble gas atoms in their ground states provides an excellent opportunity for comparing theory with experiment. The interaction energy is particularly simple because the noble gas atoms have closed outer electron shells. The present theoretical calculations give reasonable potential energy curves, but the "best" interaction energies are obtained from experimental data.

a. Interaction of two helium atoms

The energy of interaction of two helium atoms can be expressed as the sum of four terms:

$$\varphi = \varphi^{(\mathrm{val})} + \varphi^{(\mathrm{ex},\,2)} + \varphi^{(\mathrm{dis},\,6)} + \varphi^{(\mathrm{dis},\,8)} \tag{14.2–1}$$

Here $\varphi^{(\mathrm{val})}$ is the valence or chemical energy of repulsion obtained by a first-order perturbation calculation; $\varphi^{(\mathrm{dis},\,6)}$ and $\varphi^{(\mathrm{d\,s},\,8)}$ are the dispersion energy terms varying as the inverse sixth and inverse eighth powers of the separation, respectively; and $\varphi^{(\mathrm{ex},\,2)}$ is the second-order exchange energy which is discussed presently. The term $\varphi^{(\mathrm{ex},\,2)}$ does not appear with the long-range forces, nor is it important at small separations; but rather it is significant only in the intermediate range where the short- and the long-range forces merge. Let us consider each of these terms separately.

i. *Valence Interaction*

P. Rosen[1] used the first-order perturbation method to calculate the valence energy. This calculation differs from the previous calculations

[1] P. Rosen, *J. Chem. Phys.*, **18**, 1182 (1950).

of Slater,[2] Gentile,[3] and N. Rosen[4] in that P. Rosen evaluated all the integrals, whereas in the previous calculations some of the integrals were neglected and others approximated. He used for the spatially unsymmetrized wave function for the unperturbed helium atom[5]

$$\Psi = \exp\left[-(2.15r_1 + 1.19r_2)/a_0)\right] \tag{14.2–2}$$

and obtained results which can be summarized in the form

$$\varphi_{\mathrm{R}}^{(\mathrm{val})} = 9.25 \times 10^{-10} \exp(-4.40r) \text{ ergs} \tag{14.2–3}$$

where r is expressed in angstroms. This is to be compared with the valence energy which Slater calculated and which has been widely used:

$$\varphi_{\mathrm{S}}^{(\mathrm{val})} = 7.7 \times 10^{-10} \exp(-4.60r) \text{ ergs} \tag{14.2–4}$$

Slater's interaction energy is smaller by a factor of 2.1 at a separation of $r = 5a_0$.

ii. *Second-Order Exchange Energy*

Just as in the first-order perturbation theory where the valence energy is the sum of coulombic and exchange terms, the second-order perturbation leads to both coulombic and exchange terms. The second-order coulombic terms give the usual dispersion energy considered in § 13.3. The second-order exchange terms were not considered in § 13.3 because they fall off with separation exponentially and do not contribute to the long-range forces. They are, however, important for the intermediate separations (particularly for molecules without inner electron shells). The second-order exchange terms are obtained along with the usual dispersion terms, when we compute the second-order perturbation energy using wave functions which are antisymmetrized with respect to the interchange of any two electrons.

Eisenschitz and London[6] studied the second-order exchange terms in the analysis of the interaction of two hydrogen atoms, and Margenau[7] extended their method to the study of the interaction between two helium atoms. There are two ways by which dispersion forces can be calculated, either by a second-order perturbation or by a variational procedure.

[2] J. C. Slater, *Phys. Rev.*, **32**, 349 (1928).

[3] G. Gentile, *Z. Physik*, **63**, 795 (1930).

[4] N. Rosen, *Phys. Rev.*, **38**, 255 (1931).

[5] L. Pauling and E. B. Wilson, Jr., *Quantum Mechanics*, McGraw-Hill (1935), p. 223, give an excellent discussion of the properties of this function. It leads to an energy of the unperturbed atom, which is 0.76 ev higher than the correct value.

[6] R. Eisenschitz and F. London, *Z. Physik*, **60**, 491 (1930).

[7] H. Margenau, *Phys. Rev.*, **56**, 1000 (1939).

The second-order exchange energy appears in either treatment. However, it is somewhat easier to make a rough estimate of $\varphi^{(\mathrm{ex},\,2)}$ by using the simplest sort of variational procedure. Let us consider as the variational function

$$\psi = (1 + \lambda\varphi_e)\psi_0 \tag{14.2–5}$$

where ψ_0 is the antisymmetrized unperturbed wave function; φ_e is the perturbation potential arising from the interaction between the two atoms; and λ is a variational parameter. The calculation of the energy then requires the calculation of integrals of the form

$$\int \psi_0{}^*\varphi_e{}^2\psi_0 \, d\mathbf{r}_1 \, d\mathbf{r}_2 \, d\mathbf{r}_3 \, d\mathbf{r}_4 \tag{14.2–6}$$

For the two helium atoms the unperturbed wave functions have the form

$$\psi_0 = \chi_a(1, 2)\chi_b(3, 4) - \chi_a(3, 2)\chi_b(1, 4) - \chi_a(4,2)\chi_b(3, 1) + \chi_a(3, 4)\chi_b(1, 2) \tag{14.2–7}$$

where $\chi_a(1, 2)$ and $\chi_b(3, 4)$ are wave functions for the ground state of isolated helium atoms. The second-order exchange terms are of the type

$$\iiiint \chi_a(1, 2)\chi_b(3, 4)\varphi_e{}^2\chi_a(3, 2)\chi_b(1, 4) \, d\mathbf{r}_1 \, d\mathbf{r}_2 \, d\mathbf{r}_3 \, d\mathbf{r}_4 \tag{14.2–8}$$

Such integrals vanish at large separations where the charge distributions do not overlap appreciably. Margenau carried through a detailed calculation including all the exchange integrals and determined that, for a system of two helium atoms, the interaction terms (included neither in the first-order perturbation valence, nor in the long-range dispersion forces) are

$$\varphi^{(\mathrm{ex},\,2)} = -5.60 \times 10^{-10} \exp(-5.33r) \text{ ergs} \tag{14.2–9}$$

where r is in angstroms.

iii. *Inverse Sixth-Power Dispersion Energy*

Margenau[7] made an excellent calculation of the inverse sixth-power dispersion energy. He used all the oscillator strengths, f_{0i}, for transitions between the ground level and all excited states of helium, including the continua as calculated by Vinti[8] and Wheeler.[8] He modified the theoretical f_{0i} slightly so as to obtain agreement between the calculated value of the polarizability of helium and the best experimental value.

Substituting these oscillator strengths and the corresponding energies for the various transitions into the equation for the induced-dipole induced-dipole dispersion (Eq. 13.3–20), Margenau obtained the result

$$\varphi_{\mathrm{M}}^{(\mathrm{dis},\,6)} = -\frac{1.39 \times 10^{-12}}{r^6}\ \text{ergs} \tag{14.2–10}$$

where r is in angstroms. The best previous calculation had been made by Slater and Kirkwood,[9]

$$\varphi_{\mathrm{SK}}^{(\mathrm{dis},\,6)} = -\frac{1.49 \times 10^{-12}}{r^6}\ \text{ergs} \tag{14.2–11}$$

The Slater-Kirkwood energy was calculated by a variational procedure which is known to give too large numerical values when applied to a number of other molecule pairs.[7]

iv. *Inverse Eighth-Power Dispersion Energy*

Page[10] used a variational procedure to calculate the inverse eighth-power dispersion energy. He obtained the expression

$$\varphi_{\mathrm{P}}^{(\mathrm{dis},\,8)} = -3.0 \times 10^{-12}/r^8\ \text{ergs} \tag{14.2–12}$$

where r is in angstroms. The value of the constant agrees well with the value calculated by Buckingham[11] (numerical constant, 3.53) and with previous calculations of Margenau.[12]

v. *Total Energy of Interaction and Comparison with Experiment*

Margenau[7] made a careful examination of the errors involved in adding together the valence, second-order exchange, and the dispersion energies to obtain the total energy. He concluded that for the helium-helium interaction little error results in the range of separations of interest for low-energy collisions. Thus we obtain as the "best" theoretical potential energy (Rosen-Margenau-Page)

$$\begin{aligned}\varphi_{\mathrm{RMP}}^{(\mathrm{theory})} &= \varphi_{\mathrm{R}}^{(\mathrm{val})} + \varphi_{\mathrm{M}}^{(\mathrm{ex},\,2)} + \varphi_{\mathrm{M}}^{(\mathrm{dis},\,6)} + \varphi_{\mathrm{P}}^{(\mathrm{dis},\,8)} \\ &= \left[925e^{-4.40r} - 560e^{-5.33r} - \frac{1.39}{r^6} - \frac{3.0}{r^8}\right] \times 10^{-12}\ \text{erg}\end{aligned} \tag{14.2–13}$$

[8] J. A. Wheeler, *Phys. Rev.*, **43**, 258 (1933); and J. P. Vinti, *Phys. Rev.*, **42**, 632 (1932). See also Appendix 12.C.

[9] J. C. Slater and J. G. Kirkwood, *Phys. Rev.*, **37**, 682 (1931).

[10] C. H. Page, *Phys. Rev.*, **53**, 426 (1938).

[11] R. A. Buckingham, *Proc. Roy. Soc.* (*London*), **A160**, 94 (1937).

[12] H. Margenau, *Revs. Mod. Phys.*, **11**, 1 (1939).

where r is in angstroms. This is to be compared with the older Slater-Kirkwood potential

$$\varphi_{SK} = \varphi_{S}^{(val)} + \varphi_{SK}^{(dis,\,6)} = \left[770e^{-4.60r} - \frac{1.49}{r^6}\right] \times 10^{-12} \text{ erg} \qquad (14.2\text{–}14)$$

which has been widely used.

The intermolecular potential energy function for helium has been determined by three empirical methods which are in reasonably good agreement with one another. (i) The second virial coefficient data between about 30°K and 400°K have been analyzed in terms of the Lennard-Jones (6-12) potential by de Boer, Michels, and Lunbeck according to the methods described in § 6.5c, where it is shown how quantum deviations may be taken into account.[13] The potential function so obtained has been found to fit the experimental viscosity data for helium[14] within a few per cent. (ii) The high-temperature second virial coefficient data between 0°C and 1200°C and the viscosity from 200°K to 1100°K have been fitted with a modified Buckingham (6-exp) potential (see § 3.9) by Mason and W. E. Rice.[15] The temperatures were sufficiently high that quantum effects could be completely neglected. (iii) The second virial and viscosity coefficients at very low temperatures have been used by Buckingham, Hamilton, and Massey[16] to determine the intermolecular potential function for helium (see § 3.9). These three experimental potential curves are shown in Fig. 14.2–1 along with the Slater-Kirkwood and the Rosen-Margenau-Page theoretical potential curves.

A discrete vibrational quantum state may exist (see Table 6.4–2) for a pair of He^4 atoms. For the Mason-Rice modified Buckingham (6-exp) potential, Kilpatrick[17] very recently showed that this discrete energy level comes at $E = -4.677 \times 10^{-18}$ erg or $E/\epsilon = -0.003699$. Unfortunately the experimental data are not sufficiently accurate to specify the potential uniquely.

[13] J. de Boer and A. Michels, *Physica*, **5**, 945 (1938). J. de Boer and R. J. Lunbeck, *Physica*, **14**, 510 (1948). R. J. Lunbeck, Doctoral Dissertation, Amsterdam (1951).

[14] J. de Boer and J. van Kranendonk, *Physica*, **14**, 442 (1948).

[15] E. A. Mason and W. E. Rice, *J. Chem. Phys.*, **22**, January (1954).

[16] R. A. Buckingham, J. Hamilton, and H. S. W. Massey, *Proc. Roy. Soc.* (*London*), **A179**, 103 (1941).

[17] J. E. Kilpatrick (private communication, September 15, 1953). Kilpatrick used the Los Alamos MANIAC computer to perform the calculations. He also computed the phase shifts for different values of the angular quantum number and over a considerable range of kinetic energy. His results for the modified Buckingham potential are in considerable disagreement with those which he calculated using the de Boer-Michels-Lunbeck potential.

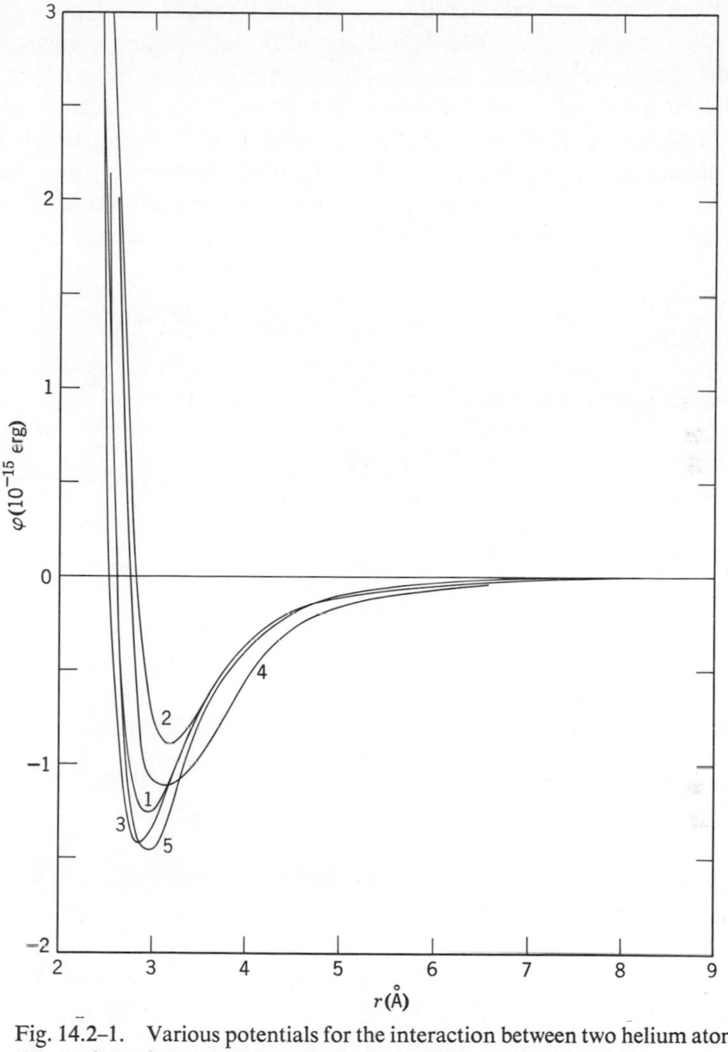

Fig. 14.2–1. Various potentials for the interaction between two helium atoms. *Curves from theory*: (1) Slater-Kirkwood. (2) Rosen-Margenau-Page. *Curves from experimental data:* (3) Lennard-Jones (6-12) potential from low temperature second virial coefficient (de Boer, Michels, and Lunbeck). (4) Modified Buckingham (6-exp) potential from high temperature second virial and viscosity coefficient measurements (Mason and W. E. Rice). (5) Buckingham-Corner potential fitted from low temperature second virial and viscosity coefficient data (Buckingham, Hamilton, and Massey).

b. Interaction of two neon atoms

Bleick and Mayer[18] calculated the energy of repulsion of a pair of closed shell atoms, using the Heitler-London first-order perturbation method. They used one-electron orbitals calculated by Brown,[19] who used the Hartree method of self-consistent fields. Let ψ_{ai} designate an orbital centered on atom a, with the subscript i referring to one of the five orbitals; $1s$, $2s$, $2p_-$, $2p_0$, and $2p_+$. The wave function ψ_{bj} is defined similarly. The interaction energy may be expressed in terms of the quantities L_{ij}, s_{ij}, S, and U_{ij}. The exchange integrals L_{ij} are

$$L_{ij} = e^2 \int \psi_{ai}^*(\mathbf{r}_1)\psi_{bj}^*(\mathbf{r}_2) \frac{1}{r_{12}} \psi_{bj}(\mathbf{r}_1)\psi_{ai}(\mathbf{r}_2)\, d\mathbf{r}_1\, d\mathbf{r}_2 \qquad (14.2\text{–}15)$$

The overlap integrals s_{ij} are

$$s_{ij} = \int \psi_{ai}^* \psi_{bj}\, d\mathbf{r} \qquad (14.2\text{–}16)$$

and the overall overlap S is

$$S = 2\Sigma_{i,\,j} \left| s_{ij} \right|^2 \qquad (14.2\text{–}17)$$

Let $\varphi^{(\mathrm{es})}$ be the classical electrostatic energy of interaction between the two unperturbed charge distributions as given by Eq. 12.1–6b in terms of the charge densities ρ_a and ρ_b about atoms a and b, and let the electrostatic potentials due to atoms a and b be $\mathscr{V}_a$ and $\mathscr{V}_b$. Then,

$$\varphi^{(\mathrm{es})} = \int \mathscr{V}_a \rho_b\, d\mathbf{r} = \int \mathscr{V}_b \rho_a\, d\mathbf{r} \qquad (14.2\text{–}18)$$

In a similar manner, we define

$$U_{ij} = -e^2 \int (\mathscr{V}_{ai} + \mathscr{V}_{bj}) \psi_{ai}^* \psi_{bj}\, d\mathbf{r} \qquad (14.2\text{–}19)$$

where $\mathscr{V}_{ai}$ is the potential due to atom a when an electron in the ith orbital is missing, and $\mathscr{V}_{bj}$ is defined in a similar manner. In terms of these quantities the energy of interaction between two neon atoms is

$$\varphi = \varphi^{(\mathrm{es})} - \frac{2}{1 - S} \Sigma_{i,\,j} (s_{ij} U_{ij} + L_{ij}) \qquad (14.2\text{–}20)$$

[18] W. E. Bleick and J. E. Mayer, *J. Chem. Phys.*, **2**, 252 (1934).
[19] F. W. Brown, *Phys. Rev.*, **44**, 214 (1933).

The potential energy calculated for three values of the separation distance is given in Table 14.2–1.

TABLE 14.2–1

THE ENERGY OF INTERACTION OF TWO NEON ATOMS[18]

r (Å)	S	$\left(\frac{2}{1-S}\right)\Sigma_{i,j}\, S_{ij}U_{ij}$ (10^{-14} erg)	$\left(\frac{2}{1-S}\right)\Sigma_{i,j}\, L_{ij}$ (10^{-14} erg)	$\varphi^{(es)}$ (10^{-14} erg)	φ (10^{-14} erg)
1.8	0.0756	−729	283	−102	344
2.3	0.0115	−79.7	35.3	−9.45	34.9
3.2	0.000271	−1.19	0.663	−0.101	0.426

The energy can be curve fitted by

$$\varphi = \frac{2.97 \times 10^{-8}}{r^{11.63}} \text{ ergs} \tag{14.2–21}$$

where r is the separation in angstroms. This expression agrees with the calculations at $r = 1.8$ and 3.2 Å, but gives 19.8×10^{-14} (instead of 34.9×10^{-14} erg) at $r = 2.3$ Å. A considerably better fit can be obtained with an exponential form,

$$\varphi = 1.9 \times 10^{-8} \exp(-4.782r) \text{ erg} \tag{14.2–22}$$

where r is the separation in angstroms. This equation agrees with the calculations at $r = 1.8$ and 3.2 Å and gives 31.5×10^{-14} erg at $r = 2.3$. This is within 10 per cent of the calculated value. Thus the exponential gives the more accurate representation.

Margenau[7] examined the second-order exchange energy for two interacting neon atoms and found that it is negligibly small. Thus the total energy of interaction is just the sum of the short-range valence energy and the long-range dispersion energy. The experimental determination of the intermolecular potential of neon from equation of state data is discussed in § 3.9. For lack of better information it is assumed that the first-order perturbation gives the repulsive part of the potential and the second-order perturbation gives the attractive part. The complete potential curve is then the sum of these terms. The "best" estimate of the potential function is obtained by adding the attractive part of the Lennard-Jones (6-12) potential to the curve fit of the Bleick and Mayer theoretical results (Eq. 14.2–22), thus:

$$\varphi(\text{theory}) = 1.9 \times 10^{-8} \exp(-4.782r) - \frac{9.95 \times 10^{-12}}{r^6} \text{ erg} \tag{14.2–23}$$

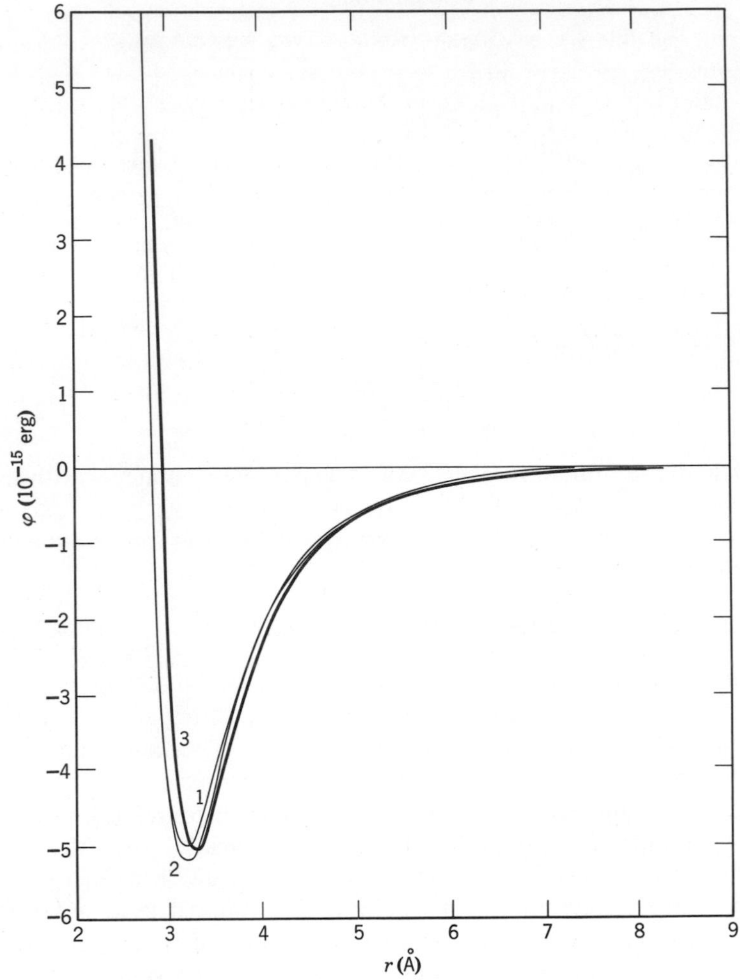

Fig. 14.2–2. Three potential curves for the interaction between two neon atoms. (1) An experimental curve of the Lennard-Jones (6-12) form from viscosity. (2) An experimental curve of the modified Buckingham (6-exp) form fitted to data on the second virial coefficient, viscosity, and properties of the crystal (Mason and W. E. Rice). (3) The theoretical results of Bleick and Mayer, modified to include the dispersion energy.

A comparison of this potential with two experimental functions is illustrated in Fig. 14.2–2. (i) The constants in the Lennard-Jones (6-12) potential are those determined from the coefficient of viscosity[20] as given by Table 8.4–1. These constants are very nearly the same as those obtained by curve-fitting second virial coefficient data. (ii) The parameters in the modified Buckingham (6-exp) potential are those determined by Mason and W. E. Rice[21] from data on the second virial coefficient, viscosity, and the properties of the crystal, as given in Table 3.7–2. We see that there is excellent agreement between the theoretical and the experimental functions.

c. Interaction of two argon atoms

Kunimune[22] used the method developed by Bleick and Mayer for neon to calculate the valence interaction of two argon atoms. The results of Kunimune's calculations are summarized in Table 14.2–2, in which the notation is the same as that used in Table 14.2–1.

TABLE 14.2–2[22]

ENERGY OF INTERACTION OF TWO ARGON ATOMS

r (Å)	S	$\left(\frac{2}{1-S}\right) \Sigma_{i,j} S_{ij} U_{ij}$ (10^{-14} erg)	$\left(\frac{2}{1-S}\right) \Sigma_{i,j} L_{ij}$ (10^{-14} erg)	$\varphi^{(es)}$ (10^{-14} erg)	$\varphi^{(val)}$ (10^{-14} erg)
2.12	0.300	−2750	271	−410	2090
2.64	0.0656	−400	28.2	−44.0	328
3.70	0.00232	−7.63	0.447	−0.98	6.20

The theoretical values given in this table can be curve-fitted with either the inverse power potential

$$\varphi^{(val)} = 6.60 \times 10^{-8}/r^{10.5} \quad \text{erg} \tag{14.2–24}$$

or the exponential form

$$\varphi^{(val)} = 5.15 \times 10^{-8} \exp(-3.68r) \quad \text{erg} \tag{14.2–25}$$

where r is the separation in angstroms. The inverse 10.5 power gives better agreement than any other power. However, for mathematical

[20] J. O. Hirschfelder, R. B. Bird, and E. L. Spotz, *J. Chem. Phys.*, **16**, 968 (1948).

[21] E. A. Mason and W. E. Rice, *J. Chem. Phys.*, **22**, January (1954). These potentials for Ne and A agree well with the Buckingham-Corner potential determined by J. Corner, *Trans. Faraday Soc.*, **44**, 914 (1948) (see Table 3.7–1).

[22] M. Kunimune, *Progress of Theoretical Physics* (*Japan*), **5**, 412 (1950).

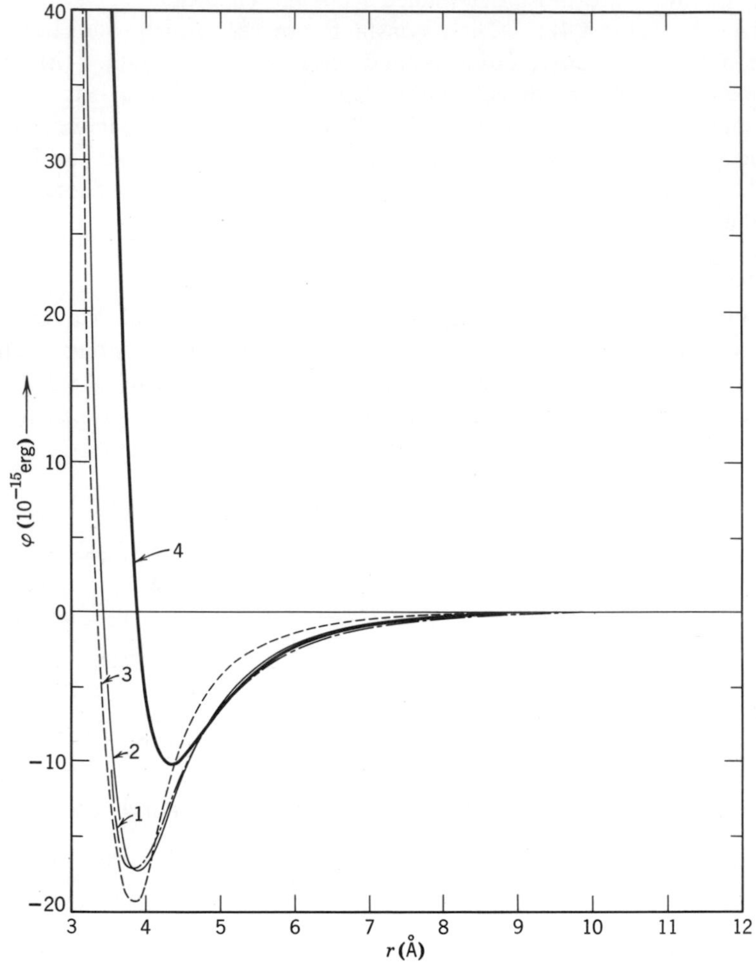

Fig. 14.2–3. Four potential curves for the interaction between two argon atoms. (1) An experimental curve of the Lennard-Jones (6-12) form from viscosity. (2) An experimental curve of the modified Buckingham (6-exp) form fitted to the data on the second virial coefficient and properties of the crystal (Mason and W. E. Rice). (3) An experimental curve due to O. K. Rice. (4) The theoretical results of Kunimune, modified to include the dispersion energy.

convenience, the inverse twelfth power is often more desirable. The best fit of the theoretical data with an inverse twelfth-power law is

$$\varphi^{(\text{val})} = 2.97 \times 10^{-7}/r^{12} \quad \text{erg} \tag{14.2–26}$$

Margenau[7] examined the second-order exchange energy for the interaction of two argon atoms and found that it is negligibly small. Thus the total interaction energy is just the sum of the short-range valence energy and the long-range dispersion energy. Adding the attractive part of the experimental Lennard-Jones (6-12) potential to the theoretical valence energy gives the "best" estimate of a theoretical potential:

$$\varphi(\text{theory}) = 5.15 \times 10^{-8} \exp(-3.68r) - \frac{1.092 \times 10^{-10}}{r^6} \text{ erg} \tag{14.2–27}$$

in which r is in angstroms. Figure 14.2–3 shows a comparison of this potential with three empirically determined potentials. (i) The constants in the Lennard-Jones (6-12) potential are those determined from viscosity[20] as given in Table 8.4–1. The potential parameters from viscosity are in very close agreement with those obtained from second virial coefficient data. (ii) The constants in the modified Buckingham (6-exp) potential are those determined by Mason and W. E. Rice[21] and given in Table 3.7–2. (iii) The potential of O. K. Rice, which is given by Eq. 3.9–8, was obtained from considerations based both on the properties of the crystal and the second virial coefficient. The theoretical and the experimental curves are in good agreement with one another.

3. Interaction of a Hydrogen Atom with a Hydrogen Molecule

The energy of interaction between a hydrogen atom and a hydrogen molecule has received considerable attention. When a hydrogen atom and a hydrogen molecule undergo a collision with a relative kinetic energy of over 7 kcal per mole, there is a chance that the simplest of all chemical reactions will take place:

$$H + H_2 \rightarrow H_2 + H \tag{14.3–1}$$

Ortho-para hydrogen conversions and the reactions between light and heavy hydrogen[1] are often of this type. Low-energy collisions are of interest in flames where the diffusion of hydrogen atoms (or other free radicals) through a valence-saturated gas such as H_2 is important. The cross-sections for very high energy molecular beams of hydrogen atoms colliding with hydrogen molecules have been measured by Amdur.[2]

[1] A. Farkas and L. Farkas, *Orthohydrogen, Parahydrogen, and Heavy Hydrogen*, Cambridge University Press (1935).

[2] I. Amdur, *J. Chem. Phys.*, **11**, 157 (1934).

From the theoretical standpoint the calculation of the energy of the system of three hydrogen atoms by the variational method is the most difficult molecular problem which has been investigated without neglecting some of the important integrals.

a. Eyring semi-empirical method

The qualitative features of the encounter are most easily understood by using the Eyring "semi-empirical" method to calculate the potential energy surface[3–5] for the system of three hydrogen atoms a, b, c. The semi-empirical scheme is a further approximation to the first-order perturbation approximation, considered in § 13.1e, where the energy of a system composed of many atoms is expressed in terms of the binding energies of each pair of the atoms considered as a separate diatomic molecule. From Eq. 13.1–53 it follows that the *coulombic energy* of the system, Q_c, can be expressed as the sum of terms C_{ab} (called the *coulombic energy of the diatomic molecule a–b*) and the terms E_a (called the *energy of the separated atom a*):

$$Q_c = \sum_{\substack{\text{all}\\ \text{pairs}\\ \text{of atoms}}} C_{ab} + \sum_{\substack{\text{all}\\ \text{atoms}}} E_a \tag{14.3–2}$$

Here C_{ab} is

$$\begin{aligned} C_{ab} = \frac{Z_a Z_b e^2}{r_{ab}} &- \sum_{\substack{j\\ \text{orbitals}\\ \text{in atom } b}}^{n_b} \int b_j(1)^* \frac{Z_a e^2}{r_{aj}} b_j(1)\, d\mathbf{r}_1 \\ &- \sum_{\substack{i\\ \text{orbitals}\\ \text{in atom } a}}^{n_a} \int a_i(1)^* \frac{Z_b e^2}{r_{bi}} a_i(1)\, d\mathbf{r}_1 \\ &+ \sum_{\substack{j\\ \text{orbitals}\\ \text{in } a}}^{n_a} \sum_{\substack{i\\ \text{orbitals}\\ \text{in } b}}^{n_b} \iint a_i(1)^* b_j(2)^* \frac{e^2}{r_{12}} a_i(1) b_j(2)\, d\mathbf{r}_1\, d\mathbf{r}_2 \end{aligned} \tag{14.3–3}$$

and E_a is the sum of all the terms in Q_c which do not involve any orbitals or nuclei except those of atom a. The decomposition of Q_c into C_{ab} and E_a terms requires no approximation. However, the identification of C_{ab} as the coulombic energy of a diatomic molecule assumes that the orbitals in the diatomic molecule are unaffected by the presence of other atoms; the identification of E_a as the total energy of atom a assumes that the orbitals in the isolated atoms are the same as those in the diatomic molecules and are unaffected by the presence of other atoms. Thus it is

[3] H. Eyring and M. Polanyi, *Z. Phys. Chem.*, **B12**, 279 (1931).
[4] J. O. Hirschfelder, H. Eyring, and B. Topley, *J. Chem. Phys.*, **4**, 170 (1936).
[5] J. O. Hirschfelder, *J. Chem. Phys.*, **9**, 645 (1941).

clear that the semi-empirical scheme cannot be expected to be quantitatively accurate, although it is very useful from a qualitative standpoint.

In a system of three hydrogen atoms there is only one electron in each atom. Hence there is only one exchange integral, L_{ab}, connected with each pair of atoms (that is, with each diatomic molecule), and this is defined by Eq. 13.1–56. According to the first-order perturbation theory (Eq. 13.1–52), it follows that the binding energy $\varphi_{ab}(r_{ab})$ of a hydrogen molecule a–b having an internuclear separation r_{ab} is given by

$$\varphi_{ab}(r_{ab}) = C_{ab}(r_{ab}) + L_{ab}(r_{ab}) \tag{14.3–4}$$

For convenience, or for lack of better information, the function $\varphi_{ab}(r_{ab})$ is usually taken to be the Morse curve energy[6] for the diatomic molecule a–b. For the hydrogen molecule the Morse curve energy φ_{H_2} is given by Eq. 14.1–7.

The semi-empirical scheme makes the additional assumption that C_{ab} and L_{ab} are proportional to φ_{ab},

$$\begin{aligned} C_{ab}(r_{ab}) &= n\varphi_{ab}(r_{ab}) \\ L_{ab}(r_{ab}) &= (1 - n)\varphi_{ab}(r_{ab}) \end{aligned} \tag{14.3–5}$$

Here n is called "the fraction of the energy which is coulombic" and it is usually taken to be a constant independent of r_{ab}. For H_2, Sugiura[7] made a direct calculation of the integrals and found that n varies a great deal with internuclear separation as shown[5] in Fig. 14.3–1. For a considerable range of separations of particular interest in most collision problems n is approximately 0.14. All too generally, it has been assumed by chemists that for all molecules n is equal to 0.14. Actually $n = 0.20$ is required[5] to obtain agreement between the calculated and the observed activation energy for the reaction $H + H_2 \rightarrow H_2 + H$ when the corrections for the zero point energy of the system are made properly. The notion of a constant value of n leads to spurious minima[8] in the potential energy surfaces for three atoms, and surely this assumption is not tenable for internuclear separations as small as the equilibrium separations of the diatomic molecules. The fallacy of assuming that n is 0.14 is borne out by the work of Rosen and Ikehara,[9] who made calculations for the alkalies, similar to those of Heitler-London and Suguira for hydrogen. They found that for Li_2, $n = 0.23$; for Na_2, $n = 0.32$; and for

[6] P. M. Morse, *Phys. Rev.*, **34**, 57 (1929); see L. Pauling and E. B. Wilson, Jr., *Quantum Mechanics*, McGraw-Hill (1935), p. 271.

[7] Y. Sugiura, *Z. Physik*, **45**, 484 (1927).

[8] L. S. Kassel, *Kinetics of Homogeneous Gas Reactions*, Chemical Catalog Co. (1932), p. 57.

[9] N. Rosen and S. Ikehara, *Phys. Rev.*, **43**, 5 (1933).

K_2, $n = 0.38$. Similarly Voge[10] showed that for the carbon-hydrogen bond, $n = 0.63$.

The first-order perturbation treatment of a three-atom system with one electron in each atom recognizes the possibility that the chemical bond may be either between a and b or between b and c (the bond wave function for a bond between a and c is a linear combination of the wave functions for the two other bonding situations and therefore does not represent anything new). When the interaction between the two bonding situations is taken into account, the first-order perturbation treatment gives for the total energy of the system

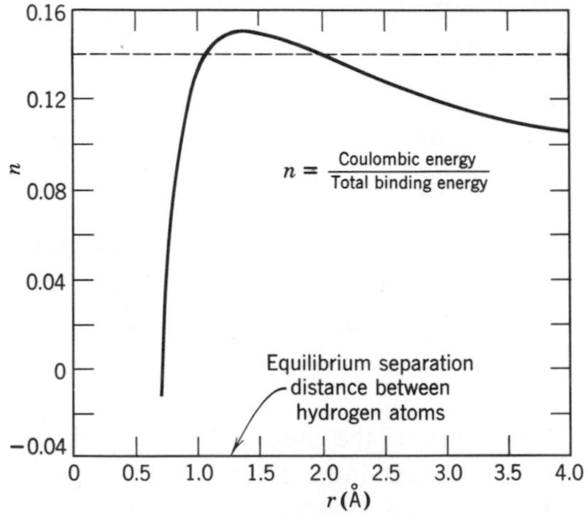

Fig. 14.3–1. Fractions of coulombic energy according to the Heitler-London-Sugiura approximation. [From J. O. Hirschfelder, *J. Chem. Phys.*, **9**, 645 (1941).]

$$E_{\text{approx}} = Q_c \mp \sqrt{L_{ab}^2 + L_{bc}^2 + L_{ac}^2 - L_{ab}L_{bc} - L_{ab}L_{ac} - L_{bc}L_{ac}} \tag{14.3–6}$$

Now when the semi-empirical expressions for the coulombic and exchange energies are substituted into this expression, it follows that the energy of interaction $\varphi_{a,bc}$ of a hydrogen atom a with a hydrogen molecule bc (relative to the molecule separated from the atom), is given by

$$\begin{aligned}\varphi_{a,bc} = D_{H_2} + n\,[\varphi_{H_2}(r_{ab}) + \varphi_{H_2}(r_{bc}) + \varphi_{H_2}(r_{ac})] \\ \mp (1-n)\sqrt{\begin{aligned}&\varphi_{H_2}(r_{ab})^2 + \varphi_{H_2}(r_{bc})^2 + \varphi_{H_2}(r_{ac})^2 - \varphi_{H_2}(r_{ab})\varphi_{H_2}(r_{bc}) \\ &- \varphi_{H_2}(r_{ab})\varphi_{H_2}(r_{ac}) - \varphi_{H_2}(r_{bc})\varphi_{H_2}(r_{ac})\end{aligned}}\end{aligned} \tag{14.3–7}$$

[10] H. Voge, *J. Chem. Phys.*, **4**, 581 (1936).

Here D_{H_2} is the energy of dissociation of the hydrogen molecule minus the zero point energy. Thus $D_{H_2} = 108.8$ kcal per mole. Figure 14.3–2 shows the potential of interaction of a hydrogen molecule colliding with a hydrogen atom. The two atoms of the hydrogen molecule are held at the equilibrium internuclear distance. The contours are lines of constant potential energy for various positions of the atom. At large distances

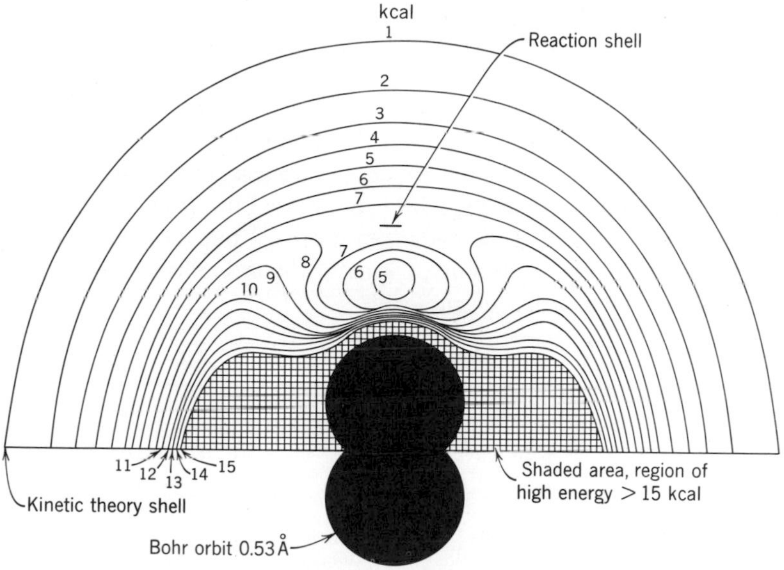

Fig. 14.3–2. Potential for an H-atom approaching an H_2 molecule. [From J. O. Hirschfelder, H. Eyring, and D. Topley, *J. Chem. Phys.*, **4**, 170 (1936).]

the atom is attracted by weak dispersion forces. At small distances the attraction changes to repulsion. An atom of only average room temperature thermal velocity is repelled before it reaches the first contour line. At large distances the contours are nearly spherical. However, a high-energy atom can penetrate farther into the interior of the molecule if it collides parallel to the line of nuclei than if its path is perpendicular to this axis! If the atom has sufficient energy and if it approaches parallel to the line of nuclei, it will cross over the energy pass marked "reaction shell." From this point on it is attracted. If the diatomic molecule is not constrained, it expands slightly as the atom approaches, and after the atom has reached the reaction shell, all three atoms vibrate violently. Eventually one of the outer atoms departs. If the departing atom belonged to the original molecule, a chemical reaction has taken place. Otherwise the collision results only in the transfer of kinetic to internal energy.

One of the principal difficulties in the use of the semi-empirical scheme is that we do not know the energy of binding of a normal diatomic molecule for large internuclear separations. The Morse curves are exceedingly poor approximations at large separations,[11,12] and this makes the semi-empirical schemes useless for quantitative calculations.

b. Direct first-order perturbation and dispersion energy calculation of the energy of interaction

A direct calculation of the first-order perturbation energy for the interaction of a hydrogen atom with a hydrogen molecule is much more satisfying than the semi-empirical calculations. With new integration techniques it would not be difficult to evaluate all the required three-center integrals,[13] and the problem appears quite tractable. Such calculations have already been performed for symmetrical-linear and equilateral-triangle configurations of three hydrogen atoms,[14] but these results have little interest from the standpoint of kinetic theory collisions between a hydrogen atom and a hydrogen molecule.

TABLE 14.3–1[15]

Separation	First-Order Perturbation or Repulsive Energy		Dispersion Energy or Attractive Energy
r (Å)	Configuration A (10^{-15} erg)	Configuration B (10^{-15} erg)	10^{-15} erg
2.205	173.6	231.2	141.0
2.646	39.8	55.96	39.94
3.087	8.87	12.45	14.10
3.528	1.69	2.59	5.82
3.969	0.333	0.495	2.701
4.410	0.066	0.096	1.370

[11] H. M. Hulburt and J. O. Hirschfelder, *J. Chem. Phys.*, **9**, 61 (1941).

[12] J. O. Hirschfelder and J. W. Linnett, *J. Chem. Phys.*, **18**, 130 (1950); see also § 14.1.

[13] R. Taylor, *Proc. Phys. Soc.* (*England*), **A64**, 249 (1951); see also Appendix 14.A.

[14] J. O. Hirschfelder, H. Eyring, and N. Rosen, *J. Chem. Phys.*, **4**, 121 (1936); **4**, 130 (1936). J. O. Hirschfelder, H. Eyring, and B. Topley, *J. Chem. Phys.*, **4**, 170 (1936). J. O. Hirschfelder, D. P. Stevenson, and H. Eyring, *J. Chem. Phys.*, **5**, 896 (1937). D. P. Stevenson and J. O. Hirschfelder, *J. Chem. Phys.*, **5**, 933 (1937). J. O. Hirschfelder, *J. Chem. Phys.*, **6**, 795 (1938). J. O. Hirschfelder and C. N. Weygandt, *J. Chem. Phys.*, **6**, 806 (1938).

Margenau[15] made a rough approximation of three-center exchange integrals. This enabled him to calculate the repulsive part of the potential by the first-order perturbation method, using a Heitler-London or Wang type wave function with an effective nuclear charge, $Z = 1.20$ (two other values of Z were considered, one smaller and one larger, but they did not lead to as reasonable results). Margenau considered the two configurations:

(*A*) *The atom approaching the molecule perpendicular to the line of the nuclei:*

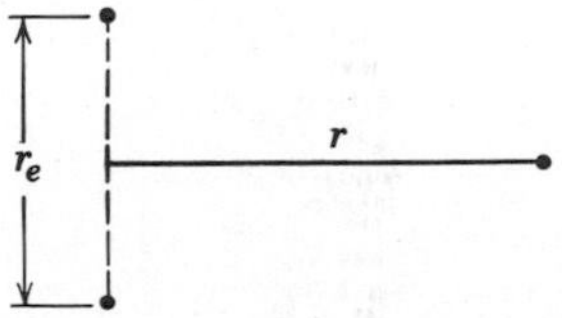

Here $r_e = 0.73$ Å is the equilibrium separation of the atoms in H_2.

(*B*) *The atom approaching the molecule along the line of nuclei:*

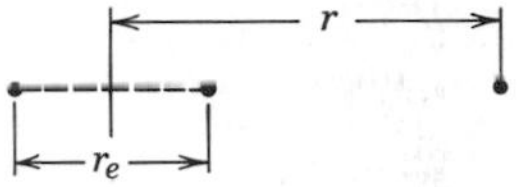

Margenau's results are given in Table 14.3–1.

The attractive part of the potential energy (dispersion energy) was calculated separately by the procedures given in § 13.3. For the hydrogen atom, Margenau used the oscillator strength $f = 1$ and the corresponding resonance energy $0.487e^2/a_0$ (which gives the correct coefficient of r^{-6} for the interaction of two hydrogen atoms). For the hydrogen molecule, he used the two dispersion terms (which Wolf and Herzfeld[16] found to give remarkably accurate results for the variation of the index of refraction with frequency). Their oscillator strengths and resonance energies are

$$\begin{aligned} f_1 &= 0.69 \qquad E_1 = 0.630e^2/a_0 \\ f_2 &= 0.84 \qquad E_2 = 0.492e^2/a_0 \end{aligned} \tag{14.3–8}$$

The dispersion energy then becomes

$$\varphi^{(\mathrm{dis})}_{\mathrm{H,\,H_2}} = \left[-\frac{8040}{r^6_{\mathrm{H,\,H_2}}} - \frac{39700}{r^8_{\mathrm{H,\,H_2}}}\right] \times 10^{-15}\ \mathrm{erg} \qquad (r \text{ in Å}) \tag{14.3–9}$$

[15] H. Margenau, *Phys. Rev.*, **66**, 303 (1944); **64**, 131 (1943).

[16] K. L. Wolf and K. F. Herzfeld, *Handbuch der Physik*, Vol. 20 (1928).

In this calculation the asymmetry of the H_2 molecule has been neglected. However, the variation in the dispersion energy with orientation can be estimated by the methods of § 13.4 by taking into account the difference in the parallel and perpendicular polarizabilities.

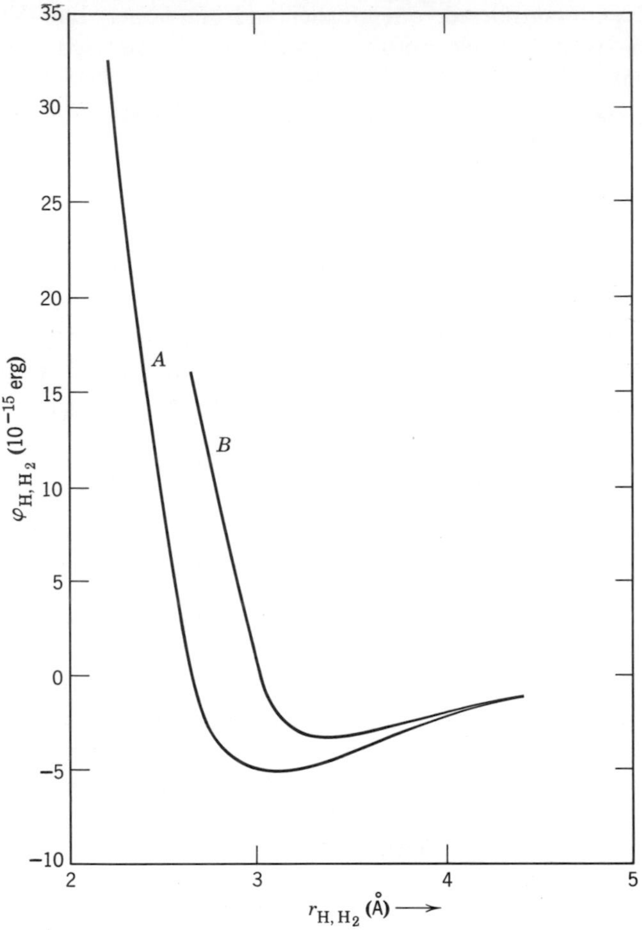

Fig. 14.3–3. Potential of interaction between a hydrogen atom and a hydrogen molecule for configurations A and B.

Figure 14.3–3 shows the total potentials obtained by combining the attractive and repulsive parts of the potential:

$$\varphi_{H,H_2} = \varphi_{H,H_2}^{(\text{First-order perturbation})} + \varphi_{H,H_2}^{(\text{dis})} \qquad (14.3\text{–}10)$$

The collision diameter for the configuration A is $\sigma = 2.85$ Å and the depth of the potential is $\epsilon = 5 \times 10^{-15}$ erg; for B, $\sigma = 3.03$ Å and $\epsilon = 3.5 \times 10^{-15}$ erg. Taking the asymmetry of the polarizabilities into consideration would have the effect of increasing ϵ slightly for B and decreasing it for A.

4. Interaction between Two Hydrogen Molecules

The interaction of two hydrogen molecules is one of the most complicated examples for which detailed quantum mechanical calculations have been made. Considering the crude approximations which have been made, the theoretical potential agrees very well with the energy of interaction deduced from experiments. The energy of interaction φ_{H_2, H_2} is the sum of four terms:

$$\varphi_{H_2, H_2} = \varphi^{(val)} + \varphi^{(Q,Q)} + \varphi^{(dis, 6)} + \varphi^{(dis, 3)} \qquad (14.4\text{–}1)$$

Here $\varphi^{(val)}$ is the chemical or valence energy arising from the overlapping of the wave functions; $\varphi^{(Q, Q)}$ is the electrostatic quadrupole-quadrupole interaction energy; $\varphi^{(dis, 6)}$ is the term in the energy of dispersion which varies as the inverse sixth power of the separation; and $\varphi^{(dis, 8)}$ is the term in the energy of dispersion which varies as the inverse eighth power of the separation. An accurate first-order perturbation calculation of the energy of interaction would give the quadrupole-quadrupole along with the valence energy. However, because of the approximations inherent in the present treatment, the quadrupole-quadrupole interaction requires separate consideration. Let us examine the calculations which have been made of the various types of interaction energy.

a. The chemical or valence energy

The calculation of the chemical or valence energy of interaction is the most difficult part of determining the energy of interaction between two hydrogen molecules. In either a first-order perturbation or a variational treatment, a considerable number of three and four center multiple exchange integrals arise. Formulae are now available for evaluating all these integrals.[1] For the single example of four hydrogen atoms in a line, each separated by $1.4a_0$ from its neighbor, Taylor has evaluated all these integrals and calculated the energy of interaction.[2] Undoubtedly, similar calculations will be made shortly for various configurations of two hydrogen molecules. However, until recently, these integrals appeared very formidable. They are numerically large so that any attempt to approximate them must be done quite accurately. However, if *all* the multiple exchange (both energy and overlap) integrals are set equal to zero, in many problems, the values of the interaction energy calculated by

[1] M. P. Barnett and C. A. Coulson, *Phil. Trans. Roy. Soc. (London)*, **A243**, 221 (1951); see also Appendix 14.A, references 11 and 12.

[2] R. Taylor, *Proc. Phys. Soc.*, **A64**, 249 (1951).

the first-order perturbation method have been found to be more accurate than those in which the calculated values of the multiple exchange energies have been included.[3–5] The reason for this seems obscure, but it must involve a cancellation of errors in the following manner: The energy of interaction calculated by the first-order perturbation method can be expressed as the ratio of a sum of energy integrals to a sum of overlap integrals. For each energy integral in the numerator there is a corresponding overlap integral in the denominator. If the approximate wave function were accurate, the ratio of any pair of these integrals would be the same for any pair and equal to exactly the energy of interaction of the system so that no error would result from neglecting a pair of the multiple exchange integrals, one from the numerator and the corresponding one from the denominator.

De Boer[6] used the first-order perturbation, or Heitler-London, method to calculate the energy of interaction between two hydrogen molecules. He used hydrogen-like atomic orbitals with a screening constant nearly unity. In making the calculations, he set all the multiple exchange integrals equal to zero and neglected all the integrals which represent the influence of electron exchange within the molecules on the coulombic interaction between the molecules. Evett and Margenau[7] recently performed a similar calculation including estimated values for all the integrals which de Boer omitted. It is difficult to know which set of calculations is the more reliable. However, the de Boer results are more convenient because they are expressed in closed form with explicit dependence on orientation. For this reason, only the de Boer treatment is considered in the remainder of this section.

Over the whole range of separation from $4a_0$ to $10a_0$ of the two hydrogen

[3] C. A. Coulson, *Valence*, Oxford University Press (1952).

[4] R. Buckingham and A. Dalgarno, *Proc. Roy. Soc.* (*London*), **A213**, 327 (1952).

[5] J. O. Hirschfelder, *J. Chem. Phys.*, **9**, 645 (1941).

[6] J. de Boer, *Physica*, **9**, 363 (1942).

[7] A. A. Evett and H. Margenau, *Phys. Rev.*, **90**, 1021 (1953), and *J. Chem. Phys.*, **21**, 958 (1953), used in their wave functions an effective nuclear charge, $Z = 1.166$, the value which gives the best energy for a hydrogen molecule in its ground state having equilibrium separation between the atoms. For the four positions discussed in this section, the Evett and Margenau results (designated by the subscript, EM) differ from those of de Boer by the following numerical factors:

Position	*a*	*b*	*c*	*d*
$\varphi_{\mathrm{EM}}^{(\mathrm{val})}/\varphi_{\mathrm{I}}^{(\mathrm{val})}$	0.3	1.0	1.8	1.8

Both sets of valence energies have the same dependence on the intermolecular separation. The Evett and Margenau papers supersede those of H. Margenau, *Phys. Rev.*, **63**, 131 and 385 (1943), which contained numerical errors which led to spurious results.

molecules a–b and c–d, de Boer found that the valence energy can be expressed in the form

$$\varphi_{\mathrm{I}}^{(\mathrm{val})} = 2.78 \frac{e^2}{a_0} \begin{bmatrix} e^{-1.87 r_{ac}/a_0} + e^{-1.87 r_{bc}/a_0} \\ + e^{-1.87 r_{ad}/a_0} + e^{-1.87 r_{bd}/a_0} \end{bmatrix} \tag{14.4–2}$$

However, this equation is sometimes inconvenient to use because the dependence of $\varphi^{(\mathrm{val})}$ on the angles is given implicitly through the four internuclear distances. On this account, de Boer made an approximation to Eq. 14.4–2 which he recommends when the two molecules are separated by distances ranging from $6a_0$ to $8a_0$. This particular range is most significant for the low energy collisions, which are important in determining both the transport properties and the virial coefficients. De Boer's approximation of Eq. 14.4–2 has the form

$$\varphi_{\mathrm{II}}^{(\mathrm{val})} = \frac{e^2}{a_0} \left[\begin{aligned} & 4800 \left(\frac{a_0}{r}\right)^{11} + 129360 \left(\frac{a_0}{r}\right)^{13} [13 \cos^2 \theta_{ab} + 13 \cos^2 \theta_{cd} - 2] \\ & + 412010 \left(\frac{a_0}{r}\right)^{15} \begin{bmatrix} 1 - 15 \cos^2 \theta_{ab} - 15 \cos^2 \theta_{cd} - 195 \cos^2 \theta_{ab} \cos^2 \theta_{cd} \\ + 2 [\sin \theta_{ab} \sin \theta_{cd} \cos (\phi_{ab} - \phi_{cd}) - 14 \cos \theta_{ab} \cos \theta_{cd}]^2 \end{bmatrix} \\ & + 68640 \left(\frac{a_0}{r}\right)^{15} \begin{bmatrix} 6 - 90 \cos^2 \theta_{ab} - 90 \cos^2 \theta_{cd} \\ + 255 \cos^4 \theta_{ab} + 255 \cos^4 \theta_{cd} \end{bmatrix} \end{aligned} \right] \tag{14.4–3}$$

Here the angles θ_{ab} and θ_{cd} correspond to θ_a and θ_b, respectively, in Fig. 12.1–5 and r is the separation between the centers of the two molecules. Unfortunately the angular dependence of Eq. 14.4–3 is quite complicated.

In order to get a rough idea of how the energy of interaction varies with the orientation of the molecules, let us consider four basic orientations of the molecules. Table 14.4–1 gives the values of $\varphi_{\mathrm{I}}^{(\mathrm{val})}$ and $\varphi_{\mathrm{II}}^{(\mathrm{val})}$ for these four configurations.

Taking the spatial average of $\varphi^{(\mathrm{val})}$ over all orientations of the two molecules (see § 13.5), we obtain the relation

$$\bar{\varphi}_{\mathrm{II}}^{(\mathrm{val})} = \frac{e^2}{a_0} \left[48{,}000 \left(\frac{a_0}{r}\right)^{11} + 862{,}400 \left(\frac{a_0}{r}\right)^{13} + 8{,}788{,}200 \left(\frac{a_0}{r}\right)^{15} \right] + \frac{1}{kT} (\cdots) + \cdots \tag{14.4–4}$$

The term in $1/kT$ can be neglected since direct calculations have shown that its value is always less than 2 per cent of the first term.

b. The long-range energy of interaction

The long-range energy of interaction of two hydrogen molecules is the sum of three terms $\varphi^{(Q,Q)}$, $\varphi^{(\text{dis},6)}$, and $\varphi^{(\text{dis},8)}$.

i. *The Quadrupole-Quadrupole Interaction*

The energy of quadrupole-quadrupole interaction is given by Eq. 1.3–10 in terms of the quadrupole moment of the normal hydrogen molecule

$$q_{H_2} = r_{HH}^2 - 4\overline{z_1^2} + 4\overline{x_1^2} \tag{14.4–5}$$

Here $\overline{z_1^2}$ is the mean square value of the z-coordinate (measured from the center of the molecule along the internuclear axis) of one of the electrons in the molecule averaged over the electronic charge distribution. Similarly $\overline{x_1^2}$ is the mean square value of the coordinate of one of the electrons in a direction perpendicular to the internuclear axis. The separation between the two hydrogen atoms is designated r_{HH}. A very accurate calculation of q_{H_2} was made by James and Coolidge,[8] who used their complete thirteen-term wave function. They obtained the result

$$q_{H_2} = \left[0.248 + 0.172\left(\frac{r_{HH}}{a_0} - 1.4\right) - 0.115\left(\frac{r_{HH}}{a_0} - 1.4\right)^2\right] \times 10^{-16}\ \text{cm}^2 \tag{14.4–6}$$

Since the equilibrium H–H separation in the hydrogen molecule is $1.4a_0$, the theoretical quadrupole moment for hydrogen is $q_{H_2} = 0.248 \times 10^{-16}$ cm^2. This value is to be compared with the experimental value of Harrick and Ramsey (see footnote to Table 13.7–3), $q_{H_2} = 0.220 \times 10^{-16}$ cm^2.

Other calculations of q_{H_2} have been made by Coulson,[9] using a self-consistent field for H_2 and by Massey and Buckingham,[10] using a Wang type eigenfunction. They obtained the values 0.325×10^{-16} cm^2 and 0.141×10^{-16} cm^2, respectively. The large difference between the various calculated values of the quadrupole moment shows that it is very sensitive to the exact electronic charge distribution.

Values of $\varphi^{(Q,Q)}$ using the James and Coolidge quadrupole moment are given in Table 14.4–1 for the four basic orientations of the molecules. When $\varphi^{(Q,Q)}$ is averaged spatially over all orientations of the molecules the value is zero (as is explained in § 13.5).

[8] H. M. James and A. S. Coolidge, *Astrophys. J.*, **87**, 438 (1938).
[9] C. A. Coulson, *Proc. Cambridge Phil. Soc.*, **34**, 204 (1938).
[10] H. Massey and R. Buckingham, *Proc. Roy. Irish Acad.*, **A45**, 31 (1938).

TABLE 14.4–1

THEORETICAL ENERGY OF INTERACTION OF TWO HYDROGEN MOLECULES

Position a 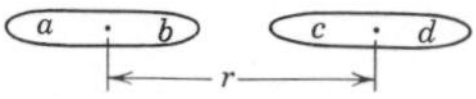 $\theta_{ab} = \theta_{cd} = 0$

(Energies in units of 10^{-15} erg)

r (a_0)	r (Å)	$\varphi_{I}^{(val)}$	$\varphi_{II}^{(val)}$	$\varphi^{(Q,Q)}$	$\varphi^{(dis,6)}$	$\varphi^{(dis,8)}$	φ_{I}	φ_{II}
5.0	2.65	289.0	285.5	16.3	−38.8	−12.9	253.6	250.1
5.5	2.91	113.5	78.7	10.2	−21.9	−6.0	95.8	61.0
6.0	3.18	44.55	24.68	6.57	−12.99	−3.01	35.12	15.25
6.5	3.44	17.49	8.63	4.40	8.04	1.59	12.26	3.40
7.0	3.70	6.87	3.30	3.04	−5.15	−0.877	3.88	0.31
7.5	3.97	2.70	1.37	2.15	−3.41	−0.505	0.94	−0.40
8.0	4.23	1.058	0.604	1.559	−2.312	−0.301	0.004	−0.450
8.5	4.50	0.415	0.283	1.151	−1.607	−0.186	−0.227	−0.359
9.0	4.76	0.163	0.139	0.865	−1.140	−0.117	−0.229	−0.253
9.5	5.03	0.064	0.072	0.660	−0.824	−0.076	−0.176	−0.168
10.0	5.29	0.025	0.038	0.511	−0.606	−0.051	−0.121	−0.108

Position b 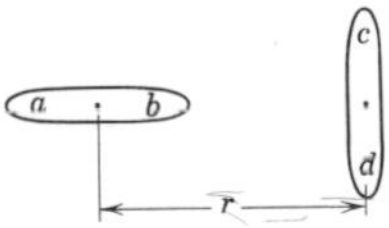 $\theta_{ab} = 0, \quad \theta_{cd} = \frac{\pi}{2}, \quad \phi_{ab} - \phi_{cd} = 0$

r (a_0)	r (Å)	$\varphi_{I}^{(val)}$	$\varphi_{II}^{(val)}$	$\varphi^{(Q,Q)}$	$\varphi^{(dis,6)}$	$\varphi^{(dis,8)}$	φ_{I}	φ_{II}
5.0	2.65	75.3	102.2	−8.2	−31.6	−12.9	22.6	49.5
5.5	2.91	29.9	31.8	−5.1	−17.8	−6.0	1.0	2.9
6.0	3.18	11.83	11.07	−3.29	−10.57	−3.01	−5.04	−5.8
6.5	3.44	4.68	4.23	−2.20	−6.54	−1.59	−5.65	−6.10
7.0	3.70	1.85	1.75	−1.52	−4.19	−0.877	−4.74	−4.84
7.5	3.97	0.729	0.775	−1.076	−2.770	−0.505	−3.622	−3.576
8.0	4.23	0.288	0.364	−0.780	−1.880	−0.301	−2.673	−2.597
8.5	4.50	0.113	0.179	−0.576	−1.307	−0.186	−1.956	−1.890
9.0	4.76	0.045	0.092	−0.433	−0.928	−0.117	−1.433	−1.386
9.5	5.03	0.018	0.049	−0.330	−0.671	−0.076	−1.059	−1.028
10.0	5.29	0.007	0.027	−0.255	−0.493	−0.051	−0.792	−0.772

TABLE 14.4–1 (*continued*)

Position *c* 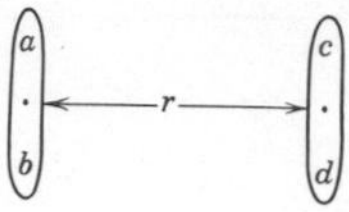 $\theta_{ab} = \theta_{cd} = \frac{\pi}{2}, \quad \phi_{ab} - \phi_{cd} = 0$

r (a_0)	r (Å)	$\varphi_{\text{I}}^{(\text{val})}$	$\varphi_{\text{II}}^{(\text{val})}$	$\varphi^{(Q,\,Q)}$	$\varphi^{(\text{dis},\,6)}$	$\varphi^{(\text{dis},\,8)}$	φ_{I}	φ_{II}
5.0	2.65	35.8	36.0	6.1	−27.5	−12.9	1.5	1.7
5.5	2.91	14.2	12.9	3.8	−15.5	−6.0	−3.5	−4.8
6.0	3.18	5.65	5.06	2.46	−9.20	−3.01	−4.10	−4.69
6.5	3.44	2.24	2.13	1.65	−5.69	−1.59	−3.39	−3.50
7.0	3.70	0.887	0.956	1.140	−3.647	−0.877	−2.497	−2.428
7.5	3.97	0.351	0.453	0.807	−2.411	−0.505	−1.758	−1.656
8.0	4.23	0.139	0.225	0.584	−1.637	−0.301	−1.215	−1.129
8.5	4.50	0.054	0.117	0.432	−1.138	−0.186	−0.838	−0.775
9.0	4.76	0.022	0.063	0.324	−0.807	−0.117	−0.578	−0.537
9.5	5.03	0.009	0.035	0.248	−0.584	−0.076	−0.403	−0.377
10.0	5.29	0.003	0.020	0.192	−0.429	−0.051	−0.285	−0.268

Position *d* 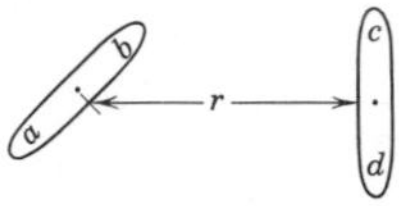 $\theta_{ab} = \theta_{cd} = \frac{\pi}{2}, \quad \phi_{ab} - \phi_{cd} = \frac{\pi}{2}$

r (a_0)	r (Å)	$\varphi_{\text{I}}^{(\text{val})}$	$\varphi_{\text{II}}^{(\text{val})}$	$\varphi^{(Q,\,Q)}$	$\varphi^{(\text{dis},\,6)}$	$\varphi^{(\text{dis},\,8)}$	φ_{I}	φ_{II}
5.0	2.65	35.2	34.8	2.0	−26.8	−12.9	−2.5	−2.9
5.5	2.91	14.0	12.6	1.3	−15.1	−6.0	−5.8	−7.2
6.0	3.18	5.58	4.98	0.82	−8.99	−3.01	−5.60	−6.20
6.5	3.44	2.22	2.11	0.55	−5.56	−1.59	−4.38	−4.49
7.0	3.70	0.879	0.949	0.380	−3.564	−0.877	−3.182	−3.112
7.5	3.97	0.348	0.451	0.269	−2.356	−0.505	−2.244	−2.141
8.0	4.23	0.138	0.224	0.195	−1.599	−0.301	−1.567	−1.481
8.5	4.50	0.055	0.116	0.144	−1.112	−0.186	−1.099	−1.038
9.0	4.76	0.021	0.062	0.108	−0.789	−0.117	−0.777	−0.736
9.5	5.03	0.008	0.035	0.083	−0.570	−0.076	−0.555	−0.528
10.0	5.29	0.003	0.020	0.064	−0.419	−0.051	−0.403	−0.386

ii. *The Inverse Sixth-Power Dispersion Energy*

The fact that hydrogen molecules are slightly non-spherical complicates the problem of determining the inverse sixth-power energy of dispersion. In order to treat this problem, de Boer[6] used Eq. 13.4–2 with the assumption that the fundamental vibration frequencies parallel and perpendicular to the molecular axis are equal.[11] This equation then expresses the $\varphi^{(\text{dis},\,6)}$ in terms of the spatially averaged energy $\bar{\varphi}^{(\text{dis},\,6)}$, and the anisotropy of the polarizability,

$$\kappa = \frac{\alpha_{\parallel} - \alpha_{\perp}}{\alpha_{\parallel} + 2\alpha_{\perp}} \tag{14.4–7}$$

The value which we used in computing Table 14.4–1 is $\kappa = 0.1173$, which comes from the theoretical results of Ishiguro, Arai, Kotani, and Mizushima (see § 13.2b). The best experimental value is $\kappa = 0.091$. De Boer assumed that $\kappa = 0.137$. The spatially averaged dispersion energy is treated on the same basis as though the molecules were spherical.

The most reliable calculation of the spatially averaged energy of dispersion is that of Margenau.[7] He idealized the problem by assuming that only two transitions are effective in producing dispersion. This is a good approximation since Wolf and Herzfeld[12] were able to fit the experimental index of refraction of hydrogen as a function of frequency remarkably accurately with a two-term dispersion formula. Margenau used the oscillator strengths and the energies associated with the oscillator strengths (Eq. 14.3–8) as determined empirically by Wolf and Herzfeld. Substituting these oscillator strengths and energies into Eq. 13.3–20, Margenau obtained

$$\bar{\varphi}^{(\text{dis},\,6)} = -10.9\,\frac{e^2}{a_0}\left(\frac{a_0}{r}\right)^6 \tag{14.4–8}$$

The numerical constant 10.9 is to be compared with the value 14.2 determined by de Boer on the basis of the one-term approximation (Eq. 13.3–28). Values of $\varphi^{(\text{dis},\,6)}$ are given in Table 14.4–1 for the four basic orientations of the two molecules and in Table 14.4–2 for the spatial average.

[11] Massey and Buckingham (Ref. 10) used a variational method with Wang-type hydrogen molecule wave functions to calculate the dispersion energy. Their calculated values range from 1.4 to 1.7 times larger than the ones which we suggest. Margenau (Ref. 7) comments that the Hassé type of variational method used by Massey and Buckingham usually gives too large an energy of interaction. The angular dependence of the Massey and Buckingham potential is quite different from that of Eq. 13.4–2. Buckingham (private communication, November 1950) reports a slight error in the numerical coefficients in the dispersion energy expressions for the Massey and Buckingham calculations using the Wang (but not the Coulson) functions.

[12] K. L. Wolf and K. F. Herzfeld, *Handbuch der Physik*, J. Springer, Vol. 20 (1928).

TABLE 14.4–2

COMPARISON OF EXPERIMENTAL AND THEORETICAL ENERGY OF INTERACTION OF TWO HYDROGEN MOLECULES

(Energies in units of 10^{-15} erg)

r (a_0)	r (Å)	$\bar{\varphi}_{\text{II}}^{(\text{val})}$	$\bar{\varphi}^{(\text{dis, 6})}$	$\bar{\varphi}^{(\text{dis, 8})}$	$\bar{\varphi}_{\text{II}}^{(\text{total})}$	$\bar{\varphi}_{\text{experiment}}^{(\text{total})}$
5.0	2.65	86.2	−30.4	−12.9	42.9	31.4
5.5	2.91	26.9	−17.2	−6.0	3.7	0.8
6.0	3.18	9.46	−10.18	−3.01	−3.73	−4.84
6.5	3.44	3.65	−6.30	−1.59	−4.24	−4.81
7.0	3.70	1.53	−4.04	−0.877	−3.39	−3.77
7.5	3.97	0.682	−2.669	−0.505	−2.492	−2.762
8.0	4.23	0.323	−1.812	−0.301	−1.790	−1.991
8.5	4.50	0.160	−1.259	−0.186	−1.285	−1.436
9.0	4.76	0.083	−0.894	−0.117	−0.928	−1.043
9.5	5.03	0.045	−0.646	−0.076	−0.677	−0.766
10.0	5.29	0.025	−0.475	−0.051	−0.501	−0.569

iii. *The Inverse Eighth-Power Dispersion Energy*

The contribution of the inverse eighth-power dispersion energy to the total interaction energy of two hydrogen molecules is so small that it is not necessary to estimate its variation with the orientations of the molecules. Margenau[7] used the Wolf and Herzfeld[12] oscillator strengths and energies to calculate the inverse eighth-power dispersion energy. However, rather than develop special two-term formulae, he took the average values of f_1 and f_2 and of E_1 and E_2 and used the single oscillator approximation, Eq. 13.3–37, to obtain

$$\varphi^{(\text{dis, 8})} = -116 \frac{e^2}{a_0} \left(\frac{a_0}{r}\right)^8 \tag{14.4–9}$$

c. The total interaction energy and comparison with experiment

The total energy of interaction for the four basic orientations of the molecules is given in Table 14.4–1. According to the two theoretical forms of the valence energy (Eqs. 14.4–2 and 3), there are two sets of values of the total energy. Since Eq. 14.4–3 was obtained by de Boer by curve fitting $\varphi_{\text{I}}^{(\text{val})}$ for separations from $r = 6a_0$ to $8a_0$, the total energy φ_{I} should be more reliable than φ_{II}. These potentials are compared in Fig. 14.4–1. The agreement between the two total energies is very good for orientations *b*, *c*, and *d*, but not for orientation *a*. The principal advantage of φ_{II} is that the energy is given as a sum of powers of the sines

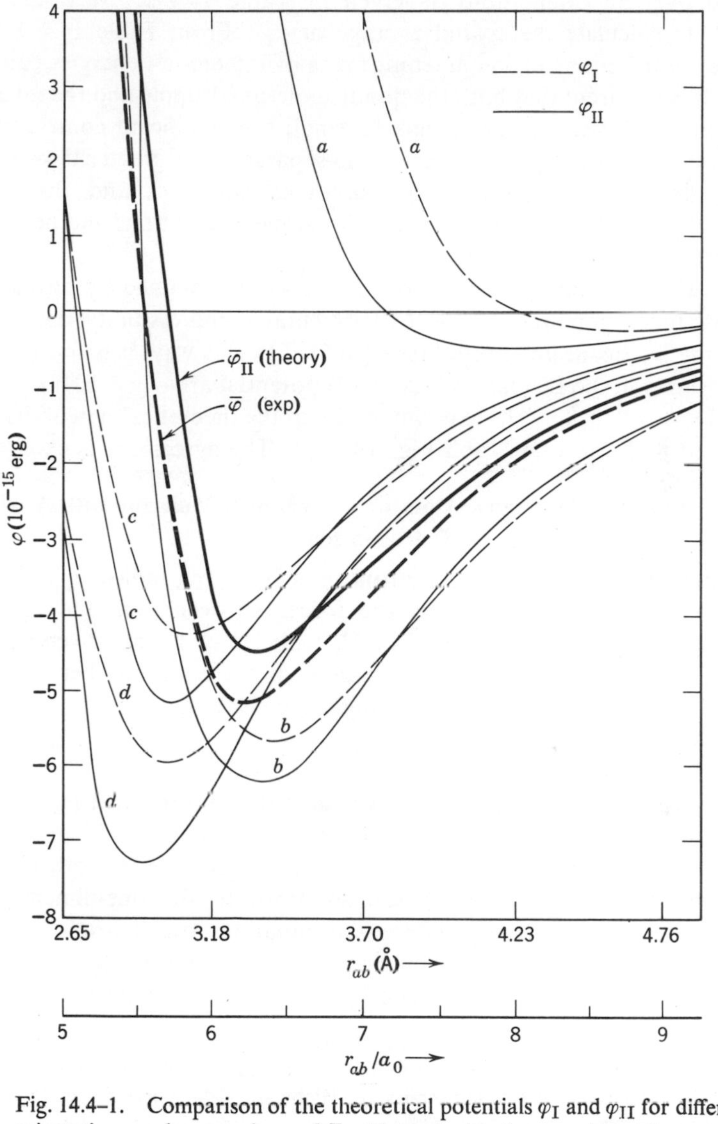

Fig. 14.4–1. Comparison of the theoretical potentials $\varphi_{\rm I}$ and $\varphi_{\rm II}$ for different orientations and comparison of $\bar{\varphi}_{\rm II}$ (theory) with the experimental energy of interaction of two hydrogen molecules.

and cosines of the angles.[13] In this form, we may calculate the spatial average over all orientations as given in Table 14.4–2. It would be difficult to calculate the spatial average of φ_{I}. From Table 14.4–1 the relative contributions of the different types of interaction energies can be seen. It is apparent that both the quadrupole-quadrupole and the inverse eighth-power dispersion forces make a small but significant contribution to the interaction energy. At very large separations, r greater than $11a_0$, the quadrupole-quadrupole energy becomes dominant and the total energy of interaction becomes positive for some orientations and negative for others.

A reliable experimental energy of interaction is obtained by fitting the Lennard-Jones potential to the experimental compressibility data and correcting for quantum effects[14] (see § 6.5). In this way, it is found that the constants in the Lennard-Jones (6-12) potential are $\epsilon = 5.107 \times 10^{-15}$ erg and $\sigma = 2.928$ Å. The experimental and the theoretical potentials are compared in Table 14.4–2 and Fig. 14.4–1. The agreement is excellent.

5. Interaction of a Hydrogen Atom or a Hydrogen Molecule with Various Hydrogen Ions

The interaction of a hydrogen atom or a hydrogen molecule with the various hydrogen ions illustrates the forces between ions and neutral molecules. The interactions of H or H_2 with H^+ or H^- are given in this section. In addition there is a discussion of the collisions between H_2 and H_2^+ and the probability of forming ionic clusters.

a. The interaction H + H^+

The interaction of a proton with a hydrogen atom to form H_2^+ is one of the few problems of molecular quantum mechanics which can be solved exactly. The Schrödinger equation is separable in both elliptic and parabolic coordinates, and the solutions to the one-dimensional second-order linear ordinary differential equations which result may be obtained by successive approximations as accurately as desired. The most accurate calculations for the ground state have been made by

[13] For some theoretical purposes, it is desirable to express the energy of interaction as a simpler function of the orientations of the molecules. On this account Wang Chang (Doctoral Dissertation, University of Michigan, 1944) curve fitted de Boer's potential by the form:

$$\varphi^{(\text{total})} = [\alpha + \beta(\cos^2\theta_{ab} + \cos^2\theta_{cd})]r^{-12} - cr^{-6}$$

She obtained the constants $\alpha = 4.438 \times 10^{-9}$ erg Å^{12}, $\beta = 4.784 \times 10^{-9}$ erg Å^{12}, $c = 1.25 \times 10^{-11}$ erg Å^{6}.

[14] J. de Boer, *Physica*, **14**, 139 (1948). R. J. Lunbeck, Doctoral Dissertation, University of Amsterdam (1951).

Hylleraas,[1] Sandeman,[2] Hellmig,[3] and Johnson.[4] The energies of many of the excited states have been calculated by Teller.[5] Figure 14.5–1 shows the energy of the ground ($1s\sigma$) state, as calculated by Hylleraas, and the excited states, as calculated by Teller. The spectrum of H_2^+ has not been

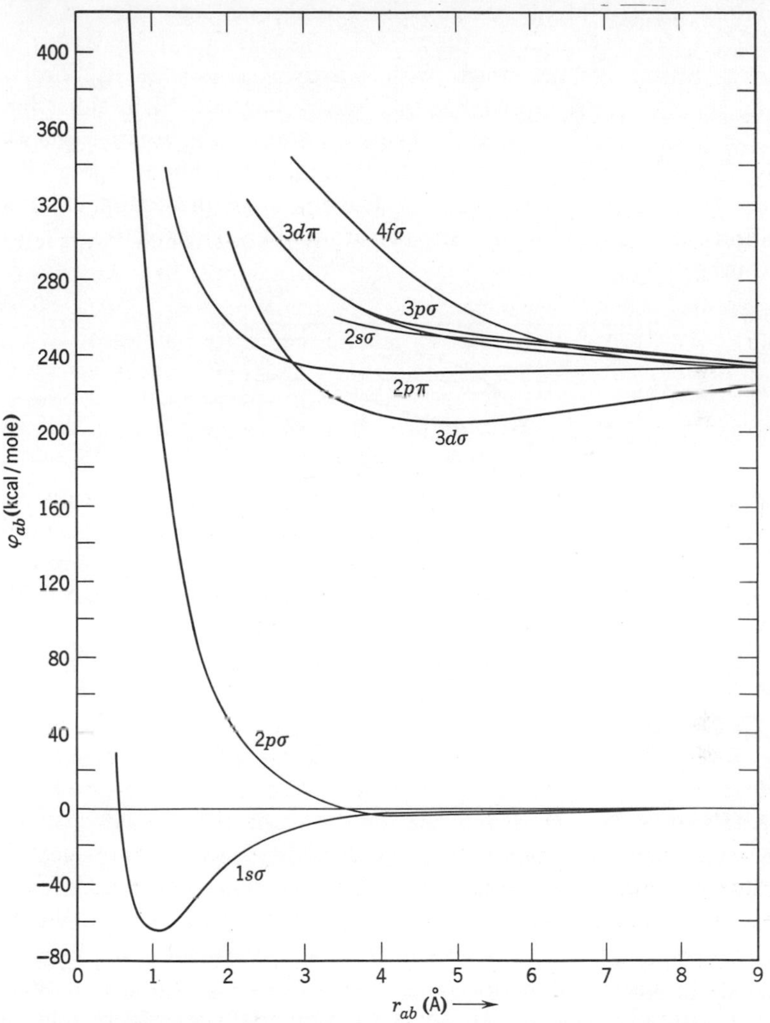

Fig. 14.5–1. The energy of the ground state ($1s\sigma$) of H_2^+ as calculated by Hylleraas[1] and the excited states as calculated by Teller.[5]

[1] E. A. Hylleraas, *Z. Physik*, **71**, 739 (1931).
[2] J. Sandeman, *Proc. Roy. Soc. Edinburgh*, **55**, 72 (1935).
[3] E. Hellmig, *Z. Physik*, **104**, 694 (1937).
[4] V. A. Johnson, *Phys. Rev.*, **60**, 373 (1941).
[5] E. Teller, *Z. Phys.*, **61**, 458 (1930).

observed, but Beutler and Jünger[6] have determined the energy of dissociation of the ground state of H_2^+ from the binding energy and ionization potential of the hydrogen molecule. Their experimental value, 61.07 kcal per mole, agrees almost perfectly with the theoretical energy of dissociation, 61.01 kcal per mole. The equilibrium separation of H_2^+ is 1.06 Å.

When a proton collides slowly with a hydrogen atom in its normal $1s$ state, there is equal probability that the system will be in either the $1s\sigma(^2\Sigma_g^+)$ or the $2p\sigma(^2\Sigma_u^+)$ state. The $2p\sigma$ state has a negative energy (corresponding to attraction) at very large separations, but at separations less than 5.9 Å the energy is positive. The energy of interaction, at large separations, of a proton with hydrogen atoms in various states is considered in § 13.6d.

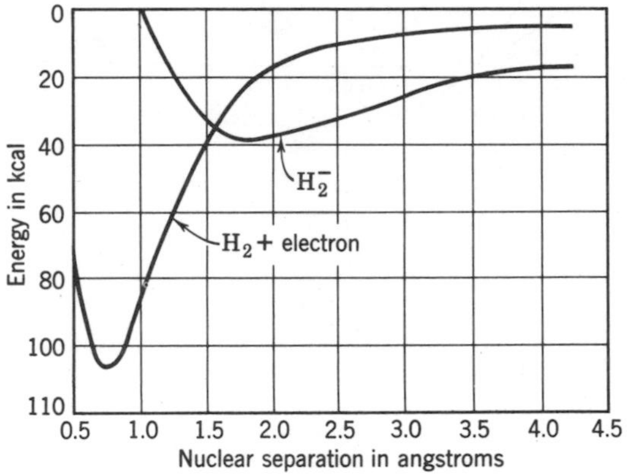

Fig. 14.5–2. Potential energy[7] curves of H_2 and H_2^-.

b. The interaction H + H⁻

The interaction of a hydrogen atom with H^- might be expected to result in the formation of an H_2^- ion. However, the H_2^- has never been observed, and for the following reasons it seems improbable that it ever will be observed. The calculations of Eyring, Hirschfelder, and Taylor[7] show that H_2^- has a minimum energy of —37.4 kcal per mole at an internuclear separation of 1.8 Å. However, the potential curve for H_2 plus an electron cuts the H_2^- curve close to this point, as is shown in Fig. 14.5–2. Thus a collision between an H^- and a H atom leads to an H_2 molecule and a free electron.

[6] H. Beutler and H. O. Jünger, *Z. Physik*, **100**, 80 (1936).
[7] H. Eyring, J. O. Hirschfelder, and H. S. Taylor, *J. Chem. Phys.*, **4**, 479 (1936).

c. The interactions $H + H_2^+$, $H_2 + H^+$, and $H_2 + H_2^+$

The interactions $H + H_2^+$, $H_2 + H^+$, and $H_2 + H_2^+$ all lead to the formation of the H_3^+ ion. This triatomic hydrogen ion is observed in a mass spectrograph when hydrogen gas is ionized at pressures high enough to permit collisions between H_2^+ and hydrogen molecules.[8] Actually, it appears that on nearly every collision the following reaction takes place:

$$H_2^+ + H_2 \rightarrow H_3^+ + H \tag{14.5–1}$$

The H_3^+ might also be formed by collisions between H^+ and H_2 or between H_2^+ and H. The spectrum of H_3^+ has been looked for but never found. The quantum mechanical calculations of the energy of the H_3^+ have been made[9–12] by using $1s$ hydrogen-like orbitals in many combinations and varying the parameters. The H_3^+ is very stable (if isolated) and has an energy lower by more than 184 kcal per mole than the energy of two separated hydrogen atoms and a proton. Thus the chemical reaction of Eq. 14.5–1 is certainly exothermic by more than 11 kcal per mole and probably by 38 kcal per mole.[13] The triatomic hydrogen ion has a stable configuration in which the separation between the nuclei is about 1.79 Å and the nuclei form an approximately equilateral triangle. Two of the vibration frequencies should be infrared active in the wave number region of 1100 cm^{-1} and capable of experimental observation.

The energy of attraction of a proton to a hydrogen molecule is shown in Fig. 14.5–3. The contours give the energy of the system when the hydrogen molecule is held fixed (with the atoms held fixed in their normal equilibrium separation) and the proton is brought up to the position. The black circles, of roughly one Bohr radius in size, outline the location of the hydrogen molecule. The cross-hatched region corresponds to

[8] H. D. Smyth, *Revs. Mod. Phys.*, **3**, 347 (1931); W. Bleakney, *Phys. Rev.*, **40**, 496 (1932); **35**, 1180 (1930); T. R. Hogness and E. G. Lunn, *Phys. Rev.*, **26**, 44 (1925); C. J. Brasefield, *Phys. Rev.*, **31**, 52 (1928); K. E. Dorsch and H. Kallmann, *Z. Physik*, **53**, 80 (1929).

[9] J. O. Hirschfelder, H. Eyring, and N. Rosen, *J. Chem. Phys.*, **4**, 121 (1936); **4**, 130 (1936).

[10] J. O. Hirschfelder, H. Diamond, and H. Eyring, *J. Chem. Phys.*, **5**, 695 (1937).

[11] D. P. Stevenson and J. O. Hirschfelder, *J. Chem. Phys.*, **5**, 933 (1937).

[12] J. O. Hirschfelder, *J. Chem. Phys.*, **6**, 795 (1938); J. O. Hirschfelder and C. N. Weygandt, *J. Chem. Phys.*, **6**, 806 (1938).

[13] The 11 kcal/mole corresponds to a comparison of the calculated energy of H_3^+ with the exact energy of H_2 and of H. Because the H_3^+ calculation was made by a variational treatment, this 11 kcal/mole must be a lower limit. The 38 kcal/mole is made by comparing the calculated energy of H_3^+ with values of the energy of H_2 and H calculated with the same type of approximate wave functions as for the H_3^+. Since there is no way of telling whether the error in the H_2 energy is larger or smaller than that of H_3^+, the 38 kcal/mole may be either too small or too large.

configurations which would be energetically difficult to attain. At large distances, the energy of attraction of a proton to a hydrogen molecule is given by the dispersion energy,

$$E = -\frac{e^2\alpha_{H_2}}{2r^4_{H^+,H_2}} \tag{14.5–2}$$

Here the α_{H_2} is the polarizability of H_2 and, according to Table 13.2–1, the value to be used varies between 0.6968×10^{-24} cm³ (when the proton approaches perpendicular to the molecular axis) to 0.9746×10^{-24} cm³

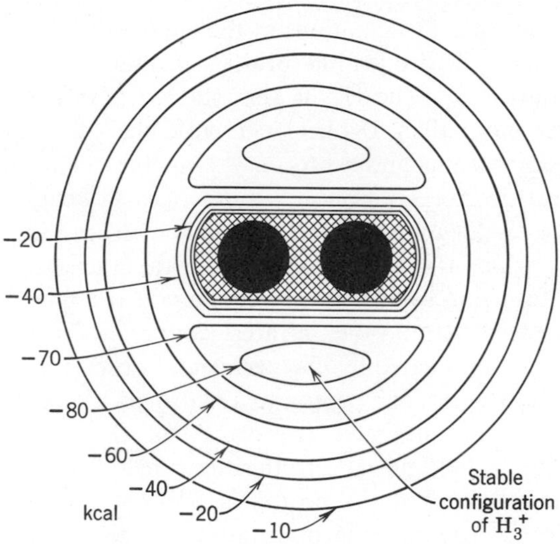

Fig. 14.5–3. Energy of interaction of a proton approaching a hydrogen molecule. [From J. O. Hirschfelder, *J. Chem. Phys.*, **6**, 795 (1938).]

(when the proton approaches parallel to the molecular axis). The r_{H^+,H_2} is the separation between the proton and the center of the hydrogen molecule. The values of the pure electrostatic interaction, as given by Eq. 14.5–2, correspond to the contours for —10, —20, and —40 kcal per mole. At closer distances, however, the chemical forces become important.

d. The interaction $H_2 + H^-$

The interaction of a hydrogen molecule with an H^- ion might be expected to result in the formation of an H_3^- ion. However, the H_3^- ion has never been observed. A quantum mechanical variational calculation[11] shows that at very large separations an H^- ion is attracted to H_2, but at smaller separations there is repulsion since H_3^- dissociates into

$H_2 + H^-$, with the liberation of 65.0 kcal per mole energy. Thus H_3^- is very similar in its behavior to H_2^-. Entropy considerations also favor the decomposition of H_3^-. Thus (assuming that the frequency of vibration of the H_2 with respect to the H^-, in wave numbers, is 100 cm^{-1} and in the equilibrium configuration the H^- is separated from the H_2 by 2.8 Å), it can be shown[11] that the equilibrium concentration of H_3^- is given by

$$\frac{[H_3^-]}{[H^-]} = 0.2 p_{H_2} \tag{14.5–3}$$

The brackets indicate concentrations, and p_{H_2} is the pressure of hydrogen in atmospheres.

e. Clusters of ions[7]

The general problem of clustering of ions may be formulated in terms of the equilibrium

$$A + B^+ \rightleftharpoons AB^+ \tag{14.5–4}$$

for which we can write the equilibrium constant K in terms of the partition functions, z, for the several species as follows:

$$\frac{[AB^+]}{[A]\,[B^+]} = K = \frac{z_{AB^+}}{z_A z_{B^+}} \exp\left(-u_0/kT\right) \tag{14.5–5}$$

If r represents the distance between ion B^+ and the clustering molecule,

$$u_0 = -\frac{a}{2}\frac{e^2}{r^4}$$

where

$$a = [\alpha + \mu^2/3kT] \tag{14.5–6}$$

α is the polarizability, and μ is the dipole moment of molecule A (see § 13.5). The calculation of partition functions is discussed in § 2.5. The partition function for the cluster is

$$z_{AB^+} = z_{\mathrm{A}}^{(\mathrm{rot})} z_{\mathrm{B}}^{(\mathrm{rot})} z_{\mathrm{A}}^{(\mathrm{vib})} z_{\mathrm{B}}^{(\mathrm{vib})} \frac{8\pi^2 C_{AB^+} kT}{h^2} \times \left(2 \sinh \frac{h\nu_{AB^+}}{2kT}\right)^{-1} \left[\frac{2\pi(m_A + m_B)kT}{h^2}\right]^{3/2} \tag{14.5–7}$$

Here $C_{AB^+} = r^2 m_A m_B/(m_A + m_B)$, and ν_{AB^+} is the fundamental vibration frequency of the molecule AB^+ (considered as a diatomic molecule). From Eq. 14.5–5, Eq. 14.5–7, and the equations for the partition functions of A and B^+, it can be shown that

$$K = 3.822 \left[\frac{M_A + M_B}{M_A M_B}\right]^{1/2} \frac{r^2 e^{(277a/r^4)}}{\sinh (h\nu_{AB^+}/2kT)} \text{ moles/cm}^3 \quad (14.5\text{–}8)$$

Here M_A and M_B are the molecular weights; a is expressed in units of Å^3, and r is the separation in angstroms. For the frequency ν_{AB^+} it is reasonable to assume a value of 100 cm^{-1} so that, at 300°K, $\sinh\left(\frac{h\nu_{AB^+}}{2kT}\right) = 0.2403$. If the partial pressure of A is p_A atmospheres, the concentration of A is $4.0600 \times 10^{-5} p_A$ moles per cm^3 at 300°K. Therefore, assuming $\nu_{AB^+} = 100$ cm^{-1} and the temperature to be 300°K, Eq. 14.5–8 leads to the result:

$$\frac{[AB^+]}{[B^+]} = 0.000646 \left(\frac{M_A + M_B}{M_A M_B}\right)^{1/2} r^2 p_A \exp\left(\frac{277a}{r^4}\right) \quad (14.5\text{–}9)$$

For ion clusters in hydrogen, if we assume that $r = 2.8$ Å and $a = 0.8$, Eq. 14.5–9 shows that

$$\frac{[H_2 \cdot H_2^+]}{[H_2^+]} = 0.186 p_{H_2} \text{ (atmospheres)} \quad (14.5\text{–}10)$$

$$\frac{[H_2 \cdot H_3^+]}{[H_3^+]} = 0.173 p_{H_2} \text{ (atmospheres)} \quad (14.5\text{–}11)$$

Additional calculations show that at atmospheric pressure, the probability of clusters of two molecules about a hydrogen ion is approximately the square of the probability for clusters of one molecule attached to the ion.

6. Interaction of a Helium Atom with an Excited Helium Atom or a Proton

The interactions of a normal helium atom with an excited helium atom or a proton leads to the formation of diatomic molecules. It is shown in this section how the "inert gases" may enter into chemical combination. The diatomic molecules and ions discussed here have long lifetimes and must be considered in any treatment of electrical discharges or other violent forms of excitation.

a. Interaction of a normal and a metastable helium atom

The interaction of a normal helium atom with a helium atom excited to the first triplet or singlet metastable state leads to a tightly bound diatomic molecule. This type of binding is often referred to as "van der Waals" or "polarization" binding[1] although this is a misnomer, as we shall see

[1] G. Herzberg, *Spectra of Diatomic Molecules*, Van Nostrand, 2nd Ed. (1950), p. 377.

presently. The energy of interaction is the sum of the short-range "valence energy," $\varphi^{(\mathrm{val})}$, and the dispersion energy, $\varphi^{(\mathrm{dis})}$.

Buckingham and Dalgarno[2] used the Heitler-London first-order perturbation method to calculate the valence energy of interaction at separations ranging from a_0 to $12a_0$. They used the Morse-Young-Haurwitz[3] type of analytical wave functions for the isolated helium atoms. Thus the spatial part of the wave function for the normal helium atom was taken to be

$$a_{1s,\,1s}(1, 2) = N_{11} \exp\left(-\frac{1.69}{a_0}(r_{a1} + r_{a2})\right) \tag{14.6-1}$$

and the spatial part of the wave function for either the triplet or singlet states of the excited atom was taken to be

$$a_{1s,\,2s}(1, 2) = N_{12}\left(\frac{r_{a2}}{a_0} - 2.93415\right)\exp\left(-1.22\frac{r_{a1}}{a_0} - 0.61\frac{r_{a2}}{a_0}\right) \tag{14.6-2}$$

Here the N_{11} and N_{12} are the normalization constants. The excited states of the helium atom corresponding to $1s2p$ configurations were ignored, since these energy states lie more than one electron volt higher than the $1s2s$ states. Buckingham and Dalgarno succeeded in evaluating all the integrals which occur in the first-order perturbation calculation, and they obtained the results given in Table 14.6-1.

The energy of dispersion was calculated using Buckingham's formula[4]

$$\varphi^{(\mathrm{dis})} = -\frac{4}{9}\frac{e^2}{a_0^{\,3}}\sum_{i=1}^{n_a}\sum_{j=1}^{n_b}\frac{(\overline{r_i^{\,2}})^2(\overline{r_j^{\,2}})^2}{(\overline{r_i^{\,2}}) + (\overline{r_j^{\,2}})} \tag{14.6-3}$$

Here the $\overline{r_i^{\,2}}$ is the mean square radius of electron i in atom a, and the $\overline{r_j^{\,2}}$ is the mean square radius of electron j in atom b, averaged over their respective charge distributions. Using the Morse-Young-Haurwitz wave functions for the helium atoms, Buckingham and Dalgarno found the energy of dispersion to be

$$\varphi^{(\mathrm{dis})} = -19\left(\frac{a_0}{r_{ab}}\right)^6\frac{e^2}{a_0} \tag{14.6-4}$$

They also calculated the dispersion energy, using the self-consistent field charge distributions in the normal and excited helium atoms as given by Wilson and Lindsay.[5] The self-consistent field calculations led to an energy of dispersion 1.5 times as large as that given by the analytical

[2] R. Buckingham and A. Dalgarno, *Proc. Roy. Soc.* (*London*), **A213**, 327 (1952).
[3] P. M. Morse, L. A. Young, and E. S. Haurwitz, *Phys. Rev.*, **48**, 948 (1935).
[4] R. A. Buckingham, *Proc. Roy. Soc.* (*London*), **160A**, 94 (1937).
[5] E. B. Wilson and R. B. Lindsay, *Phys. Rev.*, **47**, 681 (1935).

TABLE 14.6–1

ENERGY OF INTERACTION BETWEEN A NORMAL (1s1s) HELIUM ATOM AND A METASTABLE (1s2s) EXCITED SINGLET OR TRIPLET HELIUM ATOM

r_{ab}/a_0	$\varphi^{(\text{val})}$ (10^{-15} erg)				$\varphi^{(\text{dis})}$ (10^{-15} erg)
	$^3\Sigma_u$	$^3\Sigma_g$	$^1\Sigma_u$	$^1\Sigma_g$	
1.0	+29800.0	+67600.0	+26800.0	+51100.0	
2.0	− 1120.0	+10070.0	− 1918.0	+ 9819.0	
2.5	− 847.3	+ 4385.0	− 1440.0	+ 4472.0	
3.0	− 61.0	+ 2310.0	− 308.6	+ 2521.0	
4.0	+ 451.1	+ 920.9	+ 400.1	+ 977.6	−202.1
5.0	+ 266.3	+ 351.3	+ 259.8	+ 359.1	− 53.0
6.0	+ 130.8	+ 144.7	+ 130.8	+ 145.1	− 17.7
7.0	+ 58.0	+ 60.6	+ 58.4	+ 60.1	− 7.0
8.0	+ 24.8	+ 25.3	+ 24.8	+ 25.3	− 3.14
9.0	+ 10.0	+ 10.0	+ 10.0	+ 10.4	− 1.57
10.0	+ 3.5	+ 3.5	+ 3.5	+ 3.5	− 0.83
11.0	+ 1.3	+ 1.3	+ 1.3	+ 1.3	− 0.48
12.0	+ 0.4	+ 0.4	+ 0.4	+ 0.4	− 0.27

wave functions in Eq. 14.2–7. However, Buckingham and Dalgarno discarded the self-consistent field result, since they felt that the self-consistent field greatly exaggerated the spread of the 2s orbital.

At separations less than $4a_0$ the dispersion energy is a small fraction of the total energy, and Buckingham and Dalgarno arbitrarily set the dispersion energy equal to zero. At separations greater than $4a_0$ they add the valence and the dispersion energies to obtain the total energy of interaction:

$$\varphi = \varphi^{(\text{val})} + \varphi^{(\text{dis})} \tag{14.6–5}$$

The results are shown in Fig. 14.6–1. The $^3\Sigma_u$ and $^1\Sigma_u$ states have minimum energies at about $2.1a_0$ and positive maxima of 6.7 and 6.0 kcal per mole, respectively, at a separation of about $4a_0$. The energy of dissociation calculated for the $^3\Sigma_u$ state is approximately 23 to 28 kcal per mole. This energy is to be compared with the value of 51.5 kcal per mole at a separation of $2.0a_0$ determined from experimental data by Mulliken.[6] The calculated energy of dissociation of the $^1\Sigma_u$ state is 37 to 39 kcal per mole, but there do not seem to be any experimental

[6] R. S. Mulliken, *Revs. Mod. Phys.*, **4**, 1 (1932).

data with which to compare this value. The energies of the $^3\Sigma_g$ and $^1\Sigma_g$ states are positive at all separations less than $12a_0$. At sufficiently large separations these g states have very shallow minima in their interaction energies, but these are beyond the range of the present calculations.

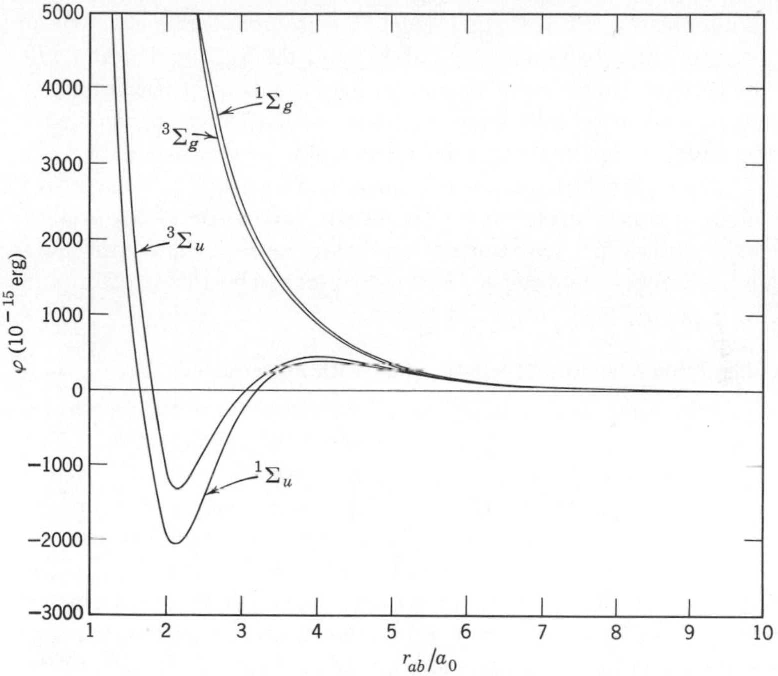

Fig. 14.6–1. The $^1\Sigma_u$ and $^1\Sigma_g$ states result from a collision between a normal (1s1s) helium atom and a metastable (1s2s) excited singlet helium atom. The $^3\Sigma_u$ and $^3\Sigma_g$ states result from the collision of a normal helium atom with a metastable (1s2s) excited triplet helium atom. [From R. Buckingham and A. Dalgarno, *Proc. Roy. Soc.* (*London*), **A213**, 327 (1952).]

The existence of the hump in the $^3\Sigma_u$ and $^1\Sigma_u$ potential curves is reminiscent of the potential energy curves arising from resonance interactions considered in § 13.6a. However, there is no resonance involved in the interaction between the normal helium and the (1s2s) excited helium atoms. Instead, the hump must be attributed to the positive valence energy at intermediate separations.

Using the potential energy curves shown in Fig. 14.6–1 and the method of Massey and Smith,[7] Buckingham and Dalgarno[8] calculated the phase

[7] H. S. W. Massey and R. A. Smith, *Proc. Roy. Soc.* (*London*), **A142**, 142 (1933).
[8] R. A. Buckingham and A. Dalgarno, *Proc. Roy. Soc.* (*London*), **A213**, 506 (1952).

shifts, total elastic cross-section, and diffusion cross-section for collisions of a triplet (1s2s) metastable with a normal helium atom. These calculations led to a theoretical estimate of the coefficient of diffusion of the triplet metastable atom passing through normal helium at a total pressure of one mm Hg: $\mathscr{D} = 370$ cm²/sec at 300°K and $\mathscr{D} = 130$ cm²/sec at 77°K. Subsequently, Phelps and Molnar[9] measured the coefficient of diffusion under these two conditions and found them to be 410 and 130 cm²/sec respectively, in excellent agreement with the theory. Buckingham and Dalgarno estimate that the coefficient of diffusion for a singlet (1s2s) metastable atom passing through normal helium would be very nearly the same as for the triplet, when the temperature is less than 650°K; but for higher temperatures, the singlet should have a somewhat smaller coefficient of diffusion. This calculation illustrates how the complicated potential energy functions discussed in this chapter can be used to determine the macroscopic physical properties of gases.

b. The interaction of a normal helium atom with a proton

In § 13.6, the long-range interaction of a helium atom with a proton is considered. Let us now examine the short-range interaction. The energy of interaction has a deep minimum characteristic of a stable diatomic ion. The HeH^+ system is isoelectronic with the hydrogen molecule, but it has the complication of having different electrical charges on the two nuclei. Coulson and Duncanson[10] studied the energy of the ground state of the diatomic ion very extensively. They calculated the binding energy with a five-term James and Coolidge wave function. However, they obtained the lowest energy with a Wang ionic-polar type wave function. If we let a represent the helium atom and b represent the proton, then the orbitals for electron 1 in the helium atom are

$$a_0(1) = \left(\frac{Z_{\rm He}'^3}{\pi}\right)^{1/2} e^{-Z_{\rm He}' r_{a1}} \tag{14.6–6}$$

$$a_c(1) = \left(\frac{Z_{\rm He}''^5}{\pi}\right)^{1/2} r_{a1} \cos\theta_{a1} e^{-Z_{\rm He}'' r_{a1}} \tag{14.6–7}$$

and the orbital for an electron in the vicinity of the proton is

$$b_0(1) = \left(\frac{Z_{\rm H}'^3}{\pi}\right)^{1/2} e^{-Z_{\rm H}' r_{b1}} \tag{14.6–8}$$

Here the $Z_{\rm He}'$, $Z_{\rm He}''$, and $Z_{\rm H}'$ are three different effective nuclear charges.

[9] A. V. Phelps and J. P. Molnar, *Phys. Rev.*, **89**, 1202 (1953).
[10] C. A. Coulson and W. E. Duncanson, *Proc. Roy. Soc.* (*London*), **A165**, 90 (1938).

The spatial part of the Wang ionic-polar wave function is then

$$\Psi = \lambda[a_0(1)b_0(2) + a_0(2)b_0(1)] + \mu a_0(1)a_0(2) + \nu[a_0(1)a_c(2) + a_0(2)a_c(1)] \qquad (14.6\text{–}9)$$

The first term in Eq. 14.6–9 is due to the homopolar binding between one electron in the helium atom and one in the hydrogen; the second term is the purely ionic contribution of both electrons in their lowest state on the helium atom; the third term has both electrons on the helium atom but one of them is polarized to an excited state. The fact that the effective nuclear charges are not the actual nuclear charges makes this a Wang-type function. The special feature of the Coulson-Duncanson treatment is that they succeeded in evaluating all the integrals which arise in this problem.[11] They calculated the following interaction energy of a proton and a normal helium atom:

Separation (a_0)	*Interaction Energy* (*kcal/mole*)
1.25	−47.9
1.50	−53.3
2.00	−37.5
1.446 (equilibrium)	−53.6

At the equilibrium separation, the constants in the wave function are:

$$\lambda = 0.71730 \qquad Z_{\text{He}}' = 1.8900$$

$$\mu = 0.24843 \qquad Z_{\text{He}}'' = 1.5586$$

$$\nu = 0.02979 \qquad Z_{\text{H}}' = 1.5226$$

The zero-point energy for the vibration of HeH^+ about the equilibrium separation is 4.8 kcal per mole. For the interaction of the proton and helium atom, "two-thirds of the stability of the diatomic ion is due to the formation of a covalent bond and one-third is due to the polarization of the He atom."[10, 11]

Coulson and Duncanson have also made an exact calculation for the energy of interaction of a He^+ with a proton. The interaction energy in this case is always positive, and the problem has few physical applications.

[11] J. Y. Beach, *J. Chem. Phys.*, **4**, 353 (1936), calculated the energy of interaction of a helium atom with a proton, but he did not achieve the accuracy in his calculations attained by Coulson and Duncanson because he could not evaluate the exchange and coulombic integrals with unlike effective nuclear charges.

APPENDIX A. INTEGRALS USEFUL IN THE CALCULATION OF INTERMOLECULAR ENERGIES.

There are many standard sources where various integrals, useful in calculating intermolecular energies, are either presented as functions of the internuclear separations or given in tabular form for specified values of the separations and other parameters. The following is a list of a few of these sources.

ONE-CENTER AND TWO-CENTER INTEGRALS

1. C. C. Roothaan, "Study of Two-Center Integrals Useful in Calculations on Molecular Structure, I," *J. Chem. Phys.*, **19**, 1445 (1951) (formulae).
2. K. Rudenberg, "A Study of Two-Center Integrals Useful in Calculations on Molecular Structure, II. The Two-Center Exchange Integrals," *J. Chem. Phys.*, **19**, 1459 (1951) (formulae).
3. C. A. Coulson, "Two-Center Integrals Occurring in the Theory of Molecular Structure," *Proc. Cambridge Phil. Soc.*, **38 (Pt. II)**, 210 (1941) (formulae).
4. R. G. Parr and B. L. Crawford, "On Certain Integrals Useful in Molecular Orbital Calculations," *J. Chem. Phys.*, **16**, 1049 (1948) (formulae).
5. G. Hellmann, *Einführung in die Quantenchemie*, Franz Deuticke (1937) (formulae).
6. C. A. Coulson, "Evaluation of Certain Integrals Occurring in Studies of Molecular Structure," *Proc. Cambridge Phil. Soc.*, **33 (Pt. I)**, 104 (1937) (theory).
7. C. A. Coulson and W. E. Duncanson, "Wave Functions for HeH^{++} and HeH^{+}," *Proc. Roy. Soc. (London)*, **A165**, 90 (1938) (formulae for evaluating exchange integrals for unlike charge centers).

THREE-CENTER AND FOUR-CENTER INTEGRALS

8. M. P. Barnett and C. A. Coulson, "The Evaluation of Integrals Occurring in the Theory of Molecular Structure. Parts I and II," *Phil. Trans. Roy. Soc. London*, **A243**, 221 (1951). (Applies to one and two centers as well as three and four centers. Both theory and formulae given.)
9. J. O. Hirschfelder and C. N. Weygandt, "Integrals Required for Computing the Energy of H_3 and H_3^{+}," *J. Chem. Phys.*, **6**, 795 (1938) (tables).
10. J. O. Hirschfelder, H. Eyring, and N. Rosen, "I. Calculation of Energy of H_3 Molecule," *J. Chem. Phys.*, **4**, 121 (1936) (formulae).
11. S. O. Lundquist and P. O. Löwdin, "On the Calculation of Certain Integrals Occurring in the Theory of Molecules Especially Three-Center and Four-Center Integrals," *Arkiv för Fysik (Stockholm)*, **3**, 147 (1951) (theory and formulae).
12. K. Rüdenberg, "On the Three- and Four-Center Integrals in Molecular Quantum Mechanics," *J. Chem. Phys.*, **19**, 1433 (1951) (theory).
13. J. O. Hirschfelder, Doctoral Dissertation, Princeton University (1936). (Three-center integrals are tabulated for three hydrogen atoms equally spaced in a line.)
14. J. O. Hirschfelder, H. Diamond, and H. Eyring, "Calculation of the Energy of H_3 and H_3^{+}. III," *J. Chem. Phys.*, **5**, 695 (1937). (Three-center integrals are tabulated for three hydrogen atoms in unsymmetrical positions along a line.)

Some of the one- and two-center integrals most frequently used in the calculations of intermolecular energies are given in Table 14.A–1.[1]

[1] These values are taken from J. O. Hirschfelder and J. W. Linnett, *J. Chem. Phys.*, **18**, 130 (1950).

The integrals are defined in terms of:

$$a_o(1) = \left(\frac{Z^3}{\pi}\right)^{1/2} e^{-Zr_{a1}} \tag{14.A-1}$$

$$a_c(1) = \left(\frac{Z^5}{\pi}\right)^{1/2} r_{a1} \cos \theta_{a1} e^{-Zr_{a1}} \tag{14.A-2}$$

$$a_s(1)b_s(2) = \left(\frac{Z^5}{\pi}\right) r_{a1}r_{b2} \sin \theta_{a1} \sin \theta_{b2} \cos (\phi_2 - \phi_1) e^{-Zr_{a1}-Zr_{b2}} \tag{14.A-3}$$

where the $a_o(1)$, $a_c(1)$, $a_s(1)$ are electron orbitals centered on atom a; the 1 designates the electron. Similar orbitals occur for atom b or for electron 2. Letting i or j designate the o, c, or s, we write the integrals as follows:

$$I_{ii} = \int a_i(1)b_i(1)\, d\mathbf{r}_1 \tag{14.A-4}$$

$$G_{ii} = \int a_i(1)^2/r_{b1}\, d\mathbf{r}_1 \tag{14.A-5}$$

$$J_{ii} = \int a_i(1)b_i(1)/r_{a1}\, d\mathbf{r}_1 \tag{14.A-6}$$

$$K_{ij,\,kl} = \iint a_i(1)a_j(1)b_k(2)b_l(2) \frac{1}{r_{12}}\, d\mathbf{r}_1\, d\mathbf{r}_2 \tag{14.A-7}$$

$$L_{ij,\,kl} = \iint a_i(1)b_j(1)a_k(2)b_l(2) \frac{1}{r_{12}}\, d\mathbf{r}_1\, d\mathbf{r}_2 \tag{14.A-8}$$

$$L(a_i, a_j, a_k, b_l) = \iint a_i(1)a_j(1)a_k(2)b_l(2) \frac{1}{r_{12}}\, d\mathbf{r}_1\, d\mathbf{r}_2 \tag{14.A-9}$$

$$I_{ss}' = \iint a_s(1)b_s(1)a_s(2)b_s(2)\, d\mathbf{r}_1\, d\mathbf{r}_2 \tag{14.A-10}$$

$$G_{ss}' = \iint (a_s(1)b_s(2))^2 \frac{1}{r_{b1}}\, d\mathbf{r}_1\, d\mathbf{r}_2 \tag{14.A-11}$$

$$J_{ss}' = \iint a_s(1)b_s(1)a_s(2)b_s(2) \frac{1}{r_{b1}}\, d\mathbf{r}_1\, d\mathbf{r}_2 \tag{14.A-12}$$

$$G_{co} = -G_{oc} = \int a_o(1)a_c(1)/r_{b1}\, d\mathbf{r}_1 \tag{14.A-13}$$

TABLE 14.A–1

$q = Zr_{ab}$	I_{oo}	I_{cc}	I_{ss}'	$Z^{-1}G_{oo}$	$Z^{-1}G_{cc}$
0.0	1.000000	1.000000	2.000000	1.000000	0.500000
1.0	0.858385	0.735759	1.646880	0.729329	0.548950
1.5	0.725173	0.482519	1.308467	0.583688	0.536304
1.75	0.6552725786	0.3514849529	1.133534347	0.5239755402	0.5172387306
2.0	0.586453	0.225559	0.965275	0.472527	0.492661
2.5	0.458308	0.005130	0.668203	0.390567	0.435666
3.0	0.348509	−0.159319	0.438045	0.330028	0.378482
3.5	0.259194	−0.264856	0.274051	0.284542	0.327590
4.0	0.189262	−0.318692	0.164675	0.249581	0.284908
4.5	0.136085	−0.332576	0.095545	0.222071	0.250068
5.0	0.096577238	−0.3189295	0.05376360	0.19994552	0.22185876
6.0	0.047096292	−0.2503540	0.01574933	0.16665949	0.180181700
7.0	0.02218913	−0.1714338	0.004235616	0.142856193	0.151539775
8.0	0.01017569971	−0.107191492	0.0010632933	0.124999873	0.1308487433
10.0	0.002012730219	−0.034912546	0.0000570751761	0.0999999977	0.1029997191
12.0	0.0003747969535	−0.009652558	0.0000026064767	0.083333333	0.0850694374

$q = Zr_{ab}$	$Z^{-1}G_{ss}'$	$Z^{-1}J_{oo}$	$Z^{-1}J_{cc}$	$Z^{-1}J_{ss}'$	$Z^{-1}K_{oo,\,oo}$
0.0	1.000000	1.000000	0.500000	1.000000	0.625000
1.0	0.894694	0.735759	0.306566	0.778930	0.554521
1.5	0.804017	0.557826	0.153402	0.586554	0.490338
1.75	0.7583760654	0.4778783446	0.08371921757	0.4933150199	0.4576042080
2.0	0.714289	0.406006	0.022556	0.407421	0.425974
2.5	0.633281	0.287298	−0.0701144	0.264909	0.368388
3.0	0.563267	0.199148	−0.124468	0.163102	0.319804
3.5	0.503922	0.135888	−0.147841	0.095946	0.279944
4.0	0.453937	0.091578	−0.149578	0.054308	0.247554
4.5	0.411796	0.061100	−0.138168	0.029744	0.221192
5.0	0.3760937	0.04042768	−0.1201601	0.01583449	0.19956908
6.0	0.3194558	0.01735126	−0.08055943	0.004179292	0.16659267
7.0	0.2769694	0.007295056	−0.04848173	0.001021136	0.142844724
8.0	0.244140805	0.003019163651	−0.027116562	0.000234625836	0.124997956
10.0	0.197000003	0.0004993992274	−0.007316955	0.0000107521224	0.099999472
12.0	0.164930556	0.00007987476059	−0.001729596	0.000000427866198	0.083333332

$q = Zr_{ab}$	$Z^{-1}K_{cc,\,cc}$	$Z^{-1}K_{ss,\,ss}$	$Z^{-1}K_{os,\,os}$	$Z^{-1}K_{cs,\,cs}$	$Z^{-1}K_{oc,\,oc}$	$Z^{-1}L_{oo,\,oo}$
0.0	0.391406	0.825000	0.145833	0.042188	0.072916	0.625000
1.0	0.37433	0.773402	0.123914	0.01898	0.042717	0.436651
1.5	0.360048	0.719081	0.103043	0.008325	0.018936	0.296835
1.75	0.352943470	0.688560847	0.0922190597	0.003171535	0.0086000949	0.23611543
2.0	0.345879	0.657139	0.081725	−0.001432	−0.000030	0.184156
2.5	0.331183	0.594686	0.062773	−0.008268	−0.011818	0.106622
3.0	0.314537	0.536225	0.047309	−0.011760	−0.017301	0.058508
3.5	0.295358	0.483922	0.035359	−0.012569	−0.018497	0.030766
4.0	0.274176	0.438333	0.026430	−0.011690	−0.017316	0.015627
4.5	0.252151	0.399107	0.019880	−0.010003	−0.015112	0.007714
5.0	0.2305073	0.365497910	0.01511295	−0.008107280	−0.01268642	0.00371704
6.0	0.1917270	0.311778878	0.009097311	−0.004846741	−0.008510270	0.000814027
7.0	0.1610067	0.271296778	0.005801824	−0.002741192	−0.005669731	0.000167600
8.0	0.137725185	0.239903208	0.0039011236	−0.001544918	−0.003873036	0.0000328960
10.0	0.106504961	0.194539121	0.0019998488	−0.000535527	−0.001998731	0.00000113835
12.0	0.087020932	0.163411431	0.0011574032	−0.000216840	−0.001157364	0.0000000354839

TABLE 14.A–1 (*continued*)

$q = Zr_{ab}$	$Z^{-1}L_{cc,\,cc}$	$Z^{-1}L_{ss,\,ss}$	$Z^{-1}L_{os,\,os}$	$Z^{-1}L_{cs,\,cs}$	$Z^{-1}L_{oc,\,oc}$
0.0	0.391406	0.825000	0.145833	0.042188	0.072916
1.0	0.2035	0.66567	0.11119	0.00845	0.04625
1.5	0.093613	0.51691	0.08153	−0.01550	−0.114956
1.75	0.0675754	0.441865	0.0674753	−0.0246928	−0.1348339
2.0	0.04395	0.37095	0.054758	−0.03114	−0.144307
2.5	0.043284	0.24907	0.034269	−0.03629	−0.138115
3.0	0.061445	0.15813	0.020260	−0.03367	−0.112495
3.5	0.075931	0.095715	0.011433	−0.02715	−0.082014
4.0	0.078505	0.055647	0.006206	−0.01987	−0.055077
4.5	0.070531	0.031249	0.003261	−0.01350	−0.034701
5.0	0.0569410	0.017028	0.00166632	−0.008656	−0.0208652
6.0	0.0294102	0.004688	0.00040649	−0.003105	−0.0066051
7.0	0.0121820	0.001188	0.000092185	−0.0009711	−0.0018605
8.0	0.0043184	0.000283	0.00001973	−0.000275	−0.00047860
10.0	0.000392491	0.0000137	0.0000007952	−0.0000175	−0.000025982
12.0	0.0000265330	0.000000568	0.00000002822	−0.00000089	−0.00000116873

$q = Zr_{ab}$	$Z^{-1}L(a_o, a_o;\ a_o, b_o)$	$Z^{-1}G_{co}$	$Z^{-1}L(a_o, a_c;\ a_o, b_c)$	$Z^{-1}L(a_o, a_s;\ a_o, b_s)$
0.0	0.625	0.0	0.07291666667	0.145833
1.0	0.50704485	0.187988301	0.04063749	0.122314
1.5	0.40536896	0.1816793613	0.01559917	0.10013
1.75	0.3552642088	0.1689187589	0.004775861	0.0887086
2.0	0.30803646	0.1538428958	−0.004239108	0.077650
2.5	0.22559548	0.1232108094	−0.016473472	0.057715
3.0	0.16074246	0.0967894319	−0.021943231	0.041534
3.5	0.1121558092	0.07602178750	−0.022678274	0.029146
4.0	0.07698167	0.06029852650	−0.020684210	0.020042
4.5	0.05215030051	0.04851960921	−0.0174718272	0.010373
5.0	0.034953043	0.03966222452	−0.0140023272	0.009057
6.0	0.015311456	0.02772640534	−0.0080856288	0.003921
7.0	0.006537867888	0.02040042496	−0.00424690746	0.001653
8.0	0.0027387379	0.01562384476	−0.00209458666	0.000673
10.0	0.0004610930366	0.009999974833	−0.000450608960	0.000108
12.0	0.000074658581	0.006944443909	−0.0000872422396	0.000018

PROBLEMS

1. Calculate the energy of interaction of a hydrogen atom and a proton separated by 5 Bohr radii, using the best wave function for which all the energy integrals are given in Table 14.A–1.

2. Use the integrals of Table 14.A–1 to calculate the energy of interaction of a hydrogen atom and a helium atom as a function of separation. Use hydrogen-like atomic orbitals with the same effective charge on the two centers.

Appendix

I. Lennard-Jones (6-12) Potential

A. Force Constants
B. The Second Virial Coefficient and the Zero-Pressure Joule-Thomson Coefficient
C. The Third Virial Coefficient and Its Derivatives
D. The Function $A(T^*)$ for Estimating Third Virial Coefficients for Mixtures
E. Expansion Coefficients for the Classical and Quantum Virial Coefficients
F. Phase Shifts $\eta_l(\kappa\sigma)$ for He^4
G. Phase Shifts $\eta_l(\kappa\sigma)$ for He^3
H. The Compressibility Factor for the Lennard-Jones-Devonshire (3-Shell) Model
J. The Internal Energy for the Lennard-Jones-Devonshire (3-Shell) Model
K. The Heat Capacity for the Lennard-Jones-Devonshire (3-Shell) Model
L. The Entropy for the Lennard-Jones-Devonshire (3-Shell) Model
M. The Integrals $\Omega^{(l,s)\star}$ for the Transport Coefficients
N. The Quantities A$\star$, B$\star$, and C$\star$ for the Transport Coefficients of Mixtures
P. Functions for the Higher Approximations to the Transport Coefficients
Q. The Function $k_T{}^\star$ for Isotopic Thermal Diffusion
R. The Distance of Closest Approach and the Angle of Deflection

II. Stockmayer Potential

A. The Second Virial Coefficient for Polar Gases
B. The Joule-Thomson Coefficient for Polar Gases
C. The Functions $(T^*/t^*)B^\star$ Used to Determine the Intermolecular Parameters
D. The Third Virial Coefficient for Polar Gases

III. Inverse Twelfth-Power Repulsive Potential

The Distance of Closest Approach and the Angle of Deflection

IV. Square-Well Potential

The Integrals $\Omega^{(l,s)\star}$ for the Transport Coefficients

V. Sutherland Potential (with an Inverse Sixth-Power Attraction)

The Integrals $\Omega^{(l,s)\star}$ for the Transport Coefficients

VI. Buckingham-Corner Potential

A. The Second Virial Coefficient
B. The Zero-Pressure Joule-Thomson Coefficient
C. First Quantum Correction to the Second Virial Coefficient
D. First Quantum Correction to the Zero-Pressure Joule-Thomson Coefficient

VII. Modified Buckingham (6-Exp) Potential

A. The Second Virial Coefficient
B. Collision Integral Functions for the Transport Coefficients
C. Functions for the Higher Approximations to the Transport Coefficients
D. The Function β for Isotopic Thermal Diffusion
E. The Quantities A$\star$, B$\star$, and C$\star$ for the Transport Coefficients of Mixtures

VIII. Kihara's Generalized Spherocylindrical and Ellipsoidal Molecules

Functions Determining the Second Virial Coefficient

IX. Polar Molecules

The Reduced Averaged Collision Cross-section $\Omega^{(2,2)\star}$

TABLE I–A

Force Constants for the Lennard-Jones (6-12) Potential

(1) Whenever possible the parameters obtained from viscosity data should be used for making transport property calculations, and parameters from experimental second virial coefficients should be used for calculations of equation of state and thermodynamic properties.

(2) For the lighter gases two sets of force constants are given: those labeled Cl, which were determined using classical formulae (which are not strictly applicable), and those labeled Qu, which were obtained from quantum mechanical formulae. The latter are the true force constants, whereas the former are only "effective" force constants. For accurate calculations and for extrapolations to high temperature the Qu parameters must be used—in conjunction with the quantum mechanical formulae and tabulated functions. The Cl parameters are useful for rough calculations—in conjunction with the classical formulae and tabulated functions.

(3) Force constants are given here for a number of substances which are polar and/or non-spherical and hence are not described by the Lennard-Jones potential. These constants along with the tabulated functions based on the Lennard-Jones potential may, however, be useful for purposes of calculations until the theory needed for describing complex molecules has been developed.

(4) Where two sets of force constants obtained from viscosity data are shown the temperature range of the data from references *a*, *c* is from 80°K to 300°K, and for the data in reference *d* is generally in the range from 300° to 1000°K.

Gas	Force Constants from Viscosity			Force Constants from Second Virial Coefficients			
	ϵ/k (°K)	σ (Å)	Refs. for Data	ϵ/k (°K)	σ (Å)	$b_0 = \frac{2}{3}\pi\tilde{N}\sigma^3$ (cc/mole)	Refs. for Data
Light Gases							
He(Qu)	...	...	...	10.22	2.556	21.07	*A*
He(Cl)	10.22	2.576	*a, b*	6.03	2.63	22.84	*A*
H_2(Qu)	...	...	...	37.00	2.928	31.67	*B*
H_2(Cl)	33.3	2.968	*c, b*	29.2	2.87	29.76	*B*
	38.0	2.915	*d, e, f, g, h*				
D_2(Qu)	...	...	...	37.00	2.928	31.67	*C*
D_2(Cl)	39.3	2.948	*i*	31.1	2.87	29.77	*C*
Noble Gases							
Ne	35.7	2.789	*a*	35.60	2.749	26.21	*D*
	27.5	2.858	*d, e, f*	34.9	2.78	27.10	*E*
A	124.	3.418	*a*	119.8	3.405	49.80	*F*
	116.	3.465	*d, e*	122.	3.40	49.58	*E*
Kr	190.	3.61	*b*	171.	3.60	58.86	*G*
				158.	3.597	58.7	*H*
Xe	229.	4.055	*j*	221.	4.100	86.94	*J*
				217.	3.963	78.5	*H*

TABLE I–A (*continued*)

Gas	Force Constants from Viscosity			Force Constants from Second Virial Coefficients			
	ϵ/k (°K)	σ (Å)	Refs. for Data	ϵ/k (°K)	σ (Å)	$b_0 = \frac{2}{3}\pi\tilde{N}\sigma^3$ (cc/mole)	Refs. for Data
Simple Polyatomic Gases							
Air	97.0	3.617	*c*	99.2	3.522	55.11	*K*
	84.0	3.689	*d, e, k*	102.	3.62	60.34	*L*
N_2	91.5	3.681	*c*	95.05	3.698	63.78	*M*
	79.8	3.749	*d, g*	95.9	3.71	64.42	*E*
O_2	113.	3.433	*c*	117.5	3.58	57.75	*H*
	88.0	3.541	*d*	118.	3.46	52.26	*L*
CO	110.	3.590	*c*	100.2	3.763	67.22	*N*
	88.0	3.706	*d, g*				
CO_2	190.	3.996	*c*	189.	4.486	113.9	*P*
	213.	3.897	*d, h*	205.	4.07	85.05	*Q*
NO	119.	3.470	*c*	131.	3.17	40.	*R*
	91.0	3.599	*j*				
N_2O	220.	3.879	*c*	189.	4.59	122.	*R*
	237.	3.816	*h*				
CH_4	137.	3.822	*c*	148.2	3.817	70.16	*S*
	144.	3.796	*d, l*				
CF_4	...	...	...	152.5	4.70	131.0	*T*
CCl_4	327.	5.881	*b*	...	...	...	...
SO_2	252.	4.290	*d*	...	...	...	...
SF_6	...	...	...	200.9	5.51	211.1	*T*
F_2	112.	3.653	*m*	...	...	...	...
Cl_2	357.	4.115	*n*	...	...	...	...
	257.	4.400	*j*	...	...	...	...
Br_2	520.	4.268	*p, q*	...	...	...	...
I_2	550.	4.982	*n*	...	...	...	...

TABLE I–A (*continued*)

Gas	Force Constants from Viscosity			Force Constants for Second Virial Coefficients			
	ϵ/k (°K)	σ (Å)	Refs. for Data	ϵ/k (°K)	σ (Å)	$b_0 = \frac{2}{3}\pi\tilde{N}\sigma^3$ (cc/mole)	Refs. for Data
Other Inorganic Vapors							
HCl	360.	3.305	*r*	...	...	...	...
HI	324.	4.123	*j*	...	...	...	...
AsH_3	281.	4.06	*b*	...	...	...	...
HgI_2	698.	5.625	*n*	...	...	...	...
$HgBr_2$	530.	5.414	*n*	...	...	...	...
$SnBr_4$	465.	6.666	*n*	...	...	...	...
$SnCl_4$	1550.	4.540	*n*	...	...	...	...
Hg	851.	2.898	*s*	...	...	...	...
Hydro-carbons							
$CH \equiv CH$	185.	4.221	*t*	...	...	...	...
$CH_2{=}CH_2$	205.	4.232	*b*	199.2	4.523	116.7	*U*
C_2H_6	230.	4.418	*b*	243.	3.954	78.	*H*
C_3H_8	254.	5.061	*b*	242.	5.637	226.	*H*
n-C_4H_{10}	410.	4.997	*t*	297.	4.971	155.	*H*
i-C_4H_{10}	313.	5.341	*t*	...	...	...	...
n-C_5H_{12}	345.	5.769	*u*	...	...	...	...
n-C_6H_{14}	413.	5.909	*u*	...	...	...	...
n-C_7H_{16}	...	...	...	282.	8.88	884.	*H*
n-C_8H_{18}	320.	7.451	*b*				
n-C_9H_{20}	240.	8.448	*b*				
Cyclo-hexane	324.	6.093	*u*				
C_6H_6	440.	5.270	*b*				
Other Organic Vapors							
CH_3OH	507.	3.585	*u*				
C_2H_5OH	391.	4.455	*u*				
CH_3Cl	855.	3.375	*n*				
CH_2Cl_2	406.	4.759	*n*				
$CHCl_3$	327.	5.430	*b*				
C_2N_2	339.	4.38	*b*				
COS	335.	4.13	*b*				
CS_2	488.	4.438	*u*				

TABLE I–A (*continued*)

[a] H. L. Johnston and E. R. Grilly, *J. Phys. Chem.*, **46**, 948 (1942).
[b] Landolt-Börnstein, *Physikalisch-Chemische Tabellen*, Springer.
[c] H. L. Johnston and K. E. McCloskey, *J. Phys. Chem.*, **44**, 1038 (1940).
[d] M. Trautz, A. Melster, and R. Zink, *Ann. Physik* (5), **7**, 409–452 (1930) (H_2, Ne, A, Air, N_2, O_2, CO, CO_2, CH_4, SO_2).
[e] M. Trautz and H. E. Binkele, *Ann. Physik* (5), **5**, 561 (1930) (H_2, Ne, A, Air).
[f] M. Trautz and H. Zimmerman, *Ann. Physik* (5), **22**, 189 (1935) (H_2, Ne).
[g] M. Trautz and P. B. Baumann, *Ann. Physik* (5), **2**, 733 (1929) (H_2, Air, N_2, CO).
[h] M. Trautz and F. Kurz, *Ann. Physik* (5), **9**, 981 (1931) (H_2, CO_2, N_2O).
[i] A. van Itterbeek and A. Claes, *Physica*, **5**, 938 (1938).
[j] M. Trautz, R. Heberling, I. Husseini, F. Ruf, and A. Freytag, *Ann. Physik* (5), **20**, 118–144 (1934) (four consecutive papers on Xe, NO, Cl_2, HI).
[k] M. Trautz and W. Weisel, *Ann. Physik* (4), **78**, 305 (1925) (Air).
[l] M. Trautz and K. G. Sorg, *Ann. Physik* (5), **10**, 81 (1931) (CH_4).
[m] F. Kanda, *Bull. Chem. Soc. Japan*, **12**, 465 (1937).
[n] H. Braune, R. Linke, *Z. physik. Chem.*, **A148**, 195 (1930).
[p] A. O. Rankine, *Proc. Roy. Soc.* (*London*), **88**, 582 (1913).
[q] H. Braune, R. Basch, and W. Wentzel, *Z. physik. Chem.*, **A137**, 176, 447 (1928).
[r] M. Trautz and A. Narath, *Ann. Physik*, (5), **7**, 427 (1930) (HCl).
[s] L. F. Epstein and M. D. Powers, *J. Phys. Chem.* (to be published).
[t] T. Titani, *Bull. Chem. Soc. Japan*, **5**, 98 (1930).
[u] T. Titani, *Bull. Chem. Soc. Japan*, **8**, 255 (1933).

A A. Michels and H. Wouters, *Physica*, **8**, 923 (1941).
B A. Michels and M. Goudeket, *Physica*, **8**, 347 (1941).
C A. Michels and M. Goudeket, *Physica*, **8**, 353 (1941).
D R. A. Buckingham, *Proc. Roy. Soc.* (*London*), **A168**, 264 (1938).
E L. Holborn and J. Otto, *Z. Physik*, **33**, 1 (1925).
F A. Michels, Hub. Wijker, and Hk. Wijker, *Physica*, **15**, 627 (1949).
G J. A. Beattie, R. J. Barriault, and J. S. Brierley, *J. Chem. Phys.*, **20**, 1613 (1952).
H D. M. Newitt, *Design of High Pressure Plant and the Properties of Fluids at High Pressures*, Oxford University Press (1940).
J J. A. Beattie, R. J. Barriault, and J. S. Brierley, *J. Chem. Phys.*, **19**, 1222 (1951).
K L. Holborn and H. Schultze, *Ann. Physik*, **47**, 1089 (1915).
L L. Holborn and J. Otto, *Z. Physik*, **10**, 367 (1922).
M A. Michels, H. Wouters, and J. de Boer, *Physica*, **1**, 587 (1934).
N J. Corner, *Proc. Roy. Soc.* (*London*), **58**, 737 (1946).
P A. Michels and C. Michels, *Proc. Roy. Soc.* (*London*), **A153**, 201 (1936).
Q K. E. MacCormack and W. G. Schneider, *J. Chem. Phys.*, **18**, 1269, (1950).
R J. O. Hirschfelder, F. T. McClure, C. F. Curtiss, and D. W. Osborne, *NDRC Report*, **A116** (November, 1946).
S A. Michels and G. W. Nederbragt, *Physica*, **2**, 1000 (1935).
T K. E. MacCormack and W. G. Schneider, *J. Chem. Phys.*, **19**, 849 (1951).
U A. Michels and M. Geldermans, *Physica*, **9**, 967 (1942).

TABLE I–B

THE SECOND VIRIAL COEFFICIENT AND THE ZERO-PRESSURE JOULE-THOMSON COEFFICIENT FOR THE LENNARD-JONES (6-12) POTENTIAL[a]

$$B(T) = b_0 B^\star(T^*) \qquad \mu^0 C_p{}^0 = b_0(B_1{}^\star - B^\star)$$
$$T^* = kT/\epsilon \qquad B_1{}^\star = T^*(dB^\star/dT^*)$$
$$b_0 = \tfrac{2}{3}\pi \tilde{N}\sigma^3 \qquad B_2{}^\star = T^{*2}(d^2B^\star/dT^{*2})$$

T^*	$B^\star$	$B_1{}^\star$	$B_2{}^\star$	$B_1{}^\star - B^\star$
0.30	−27.880581	76.607256	−356.87679	104.488
0.35	−18.754895	45.247713	−189.46536	64.003
0.40	−13.798835	30.267080	−116.36604	44.066
0.45	−10.754975	21.989482	−78.87795	32.744
0.50	−8.720205	16.923690	−57.33952	25.644
0.55	−7.2740858	13.582156	−43.88245	20.8563
0.60	−6.1979708	11.248849	−34.91869	17.4468
0.65	−5.3681918	9.5455096	−28.64050	14.9137
0.70	−4.7100370	8.2571145	−24.06266	12.9672
0.75	−4.1759283	7.2540135	−20.61311	11.4299
0.80	−3.7342254	6.4541400	−17.94190	10.1884
0.85	−3.3631193	5.8034061	−15.82546	9.1665
0.90	−3.0471143	5.2649184	−14.11557	8.3120
0.95	−2.7749102	4.8127607	−12.71081	7.5877
1.00	−2.5380814	4.4282616	−11.53985	6.9663
1.05	−2.3302208	4.0976659	−10.55133	6.4279
1.10	−2.1463742	3.8106421	−9.70744	5.9570
1.15	−1.9826492	3.5592925	−8.97985	5.5419
1.20	−1.8359492	3.3374893	−8.34700	5.1734
1.25	−1.7037784	3.1404074	−7.79217	4.8442
1.30	−1.5841047	2.9642040	−7.30227	4.5483
1.35	−1.4752571	2.8057826	−6.86692	4.2810
1.40	−1.3758479	2.6626207	−6.47777	4.0385
1.45	−1.2847160	2.5326459	−6.12805	3.8174
1.50	−1.2008832	2.4141403	−5.81225	3.6150
1.55	−1.1235183	2.3056683	−5.52578	3.4292
1.60	−1.0519115	2.2060215	−5.26485	3.2579
1.65	−0.98545337	2.1141772	−5.02628	3.0996
1.70	−0.92361639	2.0292621	−4.80738	2.9529
1.75	−0.86594279	1.9505276	−4.60587	2.8165
1.80	−0.81203328	1.8773287	−4.41980	2.6894
1.85	−0.76153734	1.8091057	−4.24750	2.5706
1.90	−0.71414733	1.7453722	−4.08753	2.4595
1.95	−0.66959030	1.6857016	−3.93863	2.3553
2.00	−0.62762535	1.6297207	−3.79972	2.2573
2.10	−0.55063308	1.5275444	−3.54814	2.0782
2.20	−0.48170997	1.4366294	−3.32647	1.9183
2.30	−0.41967761	1.3552188	−3.12974	1.7749
2.40	−0.36357566	1.2819016	−2.95401	1.6455

[a] R. B. Bird and E. L. Spotz, University of Wisconsin, CM-599 (1950).

TABLE I–B (*continued*)

T^*	$B^\star$	$B_1^\star$	$B_2^\star$	$B_1^\star - B^\star$
2.50	−0.31261340	1.2155320	−2.79614	1.5281
2.60	−0.26613345	1.1551691	−2.65355	1.4213
2.70	−0.22358626	1.1000353	−2.52416	1.3236
2.80	−0.18450728	1.0494802	−2.40623	1.2340
2.90	−0.14850215	1.0029572	−2.29831	1.1515
3.00	−0.11523390	0.9600031	−2.19920	1.0752
3.10	−0.08441245	0.9202229	−2.10785	1.0046
3.20	−0.05578696	0.8832774	−2.02340	0.93906
3.30	−0.02913997	0.8488746	−1.94511	0.87802
3.40	−0.00428086	0.8167606	−1.87231	0.82104
3.50	0.01895684	0.7867145	−1.80447	0.76776
3.60	0.04072012	0.7585430	−1.74108	0.71782
3.70	0.06113882	0.7320758	−1.68174	0.67094
3.80	0.08032793	0.7071630	−1.62605	0.62684
3.90	0.09839014	0.6836715	−1.57371	0.58528
4.00	0.11541691	0.6614830	−1.52441	0.54607
4.10	0.13149021	0.6404922	−1.47789	0.50900
4.20	0.14668372	0.6206045	−1.43394	0.47392
4.30	0.16106381	0.6017352	−1.39234	0.44067
4.40	0.17469039	0.5838082	−1.35291	0.40912
4.50	0.18761774	0.5667545	−1.31548	0.37914
4.60	0.19989511	0.5505118	−1.27991	0.35062
4.70	0.21156728	0.5350237	−1.24606	0.32346
4.80	0.22267507	0.5202387	−1.21381	0.29756
4.90	0.23325577	0.5061101	−1.18305	0.27285
5.0	0.24334351	0.4925951	−1.15367	0.24925
6.0	0.32290437	0.3839722	−0.919393	0.06107
7.0	0.37608846	0.3082566	−0.757930	−0.06783
8.0	0.41343396	0.2524801	−0.639879	−0.16095
9.0	0.44059784	0.2097011	−0.549792	−0.23090
10.0	0.46087529	0.1758670	−0.478779	−0.28501
20.0	0.52537420	0.0286638	−0.170403	−0.49671
30.0	0.52692546	−0.0174929	−0.072012	−0.54442
40.0	0.51857502	−0.0393115	−0.024109	−0.55789
50.0	0.50836143	−0.0516478	0.003927	−0.56001
60.0	0.49821261	−0.0593621	0.022147	−0.55758
70.0	0.48865069	−0.0645039	0.034817	−0.55316
80.0	0.47979009	−0.0680819	0.044056	−0.54787
90.0	0.47161504	−0.0706470	0.051031	−0.54226
100.0	0.46406948	−0.0725244	0.056441	−0.53659
200.0	0.41143168	−0.0775400	0.077296	−0.48897
300.0	0.38012787	−0.0765245	0.081397	−0.45665
400.0	0.35835117	−0.0747534	0.082055	−0.43310

TABLE I–C

THE THIRD VIRIAL COEFFICIENT AND ITS DERIVATIVES FOR THE LENNARD-JONES (6-12) POTENTIAL[a]

$T^* = kT/\epsilon$ $\qquad C^\star = C/b_0^2$

$b_0 = \frac{2}{3}\pi\tilde{N}\sigma^3$ $\qquad C_1^\star = T^*(dC^\star/dT^*)$

$C_2^\star = T^{*2}(d^2C^\star/dT^{*2})$

T^*	$C^\star$	$C_1^\star$	$C_2^\star$
0.70	−3.37664	28.68	−220.
0.75	−1.79197	18.05	−140.
0.80	−0.84953	11.60	−92.1
0.85	−0.27657	7.561	−62.1
0.90	+0.07650	4.953	−42.7
0.95	0.29509	3.234	−29.8
1.00	0.42966	2.078	−21.0
1.05	0.51080	1.292	−14.9
1.10	0.55762	0.7507	−10.6
1.15	0.58223	0.3760	−7.52
1.20	0.59240	+0.1159	−5.29
1.25	0.59326	−0.0646	−3.66
1.30	0.58815	−0.1889	−2.46
1.35	0.57933	−0.2731	−1.57
1.40	0.56831	−0.3288	−0.910
1.45	0.55611	−0.3641	−0.420
1.50	0.54339	−0.3845	−0.050
1.55	0.53059	−0.3943	+0.224
1.60	0.51803	−0.3963	0.427
1.65	0.50587	−0.3929	0.572
1.70	0.49425	−0.3858	0.680
1.75	0.48320	−0.3759	0.755
1.80	0.47277	−0.3643	0.806
1.85	0.46296	−0.3516	0.837
1.90	0.45376	−0.3382	0.854
1.95	0.44515	−0.3245	0.859
2.00	0.43710	−0.3109	0.856
2.10	0.42260	−0.2840	0.830
2.20	0.40999	−0.2588	0.794
2.30	0.39900	−0.2355	0.749
2.40	0.38943	−0.2142	0.700
2.50	0.38108	−0.1950	0.651
2.60	0.37378	−0.1777	0.602
2.70	0.36737	−0.1621	0.557
2.80	0.36173	−0.1482	0.514
2.90	0.35675	−0.1358	0.473

[a] R. B. Bird, E. L. Spotz, and J. O. Hirschfelder, *J. Chem. Phys.*, **18**, 1395 (1950).

TABLE I–C (*continued*)

T^*	$C^\star$	$C_1^\star$	$C_2^\star$
3.00	0.35234	−0.1247	0.439
3.10	0.34842	−0.1148	0.400
3.20	0.34491	−0.1060	0.369
3.30	0.34177	−0.09826	0.340
3.40	0.33894	−0.09133	0.313
3.50	0.33638	−0.08510	0.288
3.60	0.33407	−0.07963	0.266
3.70	0.33196	−0.07462	0.246
3.80	0.33002	−0.07024	0.227
3.90	0.32825	−0.06634	0.210
4.00	0.32662	−0.06286	0.194
4.10	0.32510	−0.05989	0.183
4.20	0.32369	−0.05709	0.169
4.30	0.32238	−0.05458	0.156
4.40	0.32115	−0.05237	0.145
4.50	0.32000	−0.05040	0.134
4.60	0.31891	−0.04865	0.125
4.70	0.31788	−0.04712	0.116
4.80	0.31690	−0.04579	0.108
4.90	0.31596	−0.04461	0.100
5.0	0.31508	−0.04359	0.0934
6.0	0.30771	−0.03893	0.0449
7.0	0.30166	−0.03989	0.0258
8.0	0.29618	−0.04231	0.0192
9.0	0.29103	−0.04529	0.0183
10.0	0.28610	−0.04825	0.0199
20.0	0.24643	−0.06437	0.0502
30.0	0.21954	−0.06753	0.0654
40.0	0.20012	−0.06714	0.0717
50.0	0.18529	−0.06566	0.0742
60.0	0.17347	−0.06388	0.0750
70.0	0.16376	−0.06203	0.0748
80.0	0.15560	−0.06025	0.0741
90.0	0.14860	−0.05857	0.0732
100.0	0.14251	−0.05700	0.0722
200.0	0.10679	−0.04599	0.0619
300.0	0.08943	−0.03970	0.0547
400.0	0.07862	−0.03551	0.0496

TABLE I–D

THE FUNCTION $A(T^*)$ FOR ESTIMATING THIRD VIRIAL COEFFICIENTS FOR GASEOUS MIXTURES[a]

$$(C_{ijk})_{\text{L.J.}} = (C_{ijk})_{\text{S.W.}}\, A(T_{ij}^*)A(T_{jk}^*)A(T_{ik}^*)$$

T^*	$A(T^*)$	T^*	$A(T^*)$
1.00	0.71099	3.50	0.86275
1.05	0.74603	3.60	0.86259
1.10	0.76746	3.70	0.86233
1.15	0.78196	3.80	0.86198
1.20	0.79246	3.90	0.86157
1.25	0.80047	4.00	0.86109
1.30	0.80684	4.10	0.86055
1.35	0.81206	4.20	0.85996
1.40	0.81649	4.30	0.85931
1.45	0.82032	4.40	0.85863
1.50	0.82369	4.50	0.85792
1.55	0.82671	4.60	0.85717
1.60	0.82947	4.70	0.85640
1.65	0.83199	4.80	0.85560
1.70	0.83432	4.90	0.85478
1.75	0.83648	5.00	0.85394
1.80	0.83851	6.00	0.84502
1.85	0.84041	7.00	0.83580
1.90	0.84219	8.00	0.82692
1.95	0.84388	9.00	0.81857
2.00	0.84545	10.0	0.81075
2.10	0.84834	20.0	0.75449
2.20	0.85091	30.0	0.71957
2.30	0.85315	40.0	0.69443
2.40	0.85510	50.0	0.67488
2.50	0.85678	60.0	0.65893
2.60	0.85823	70.0	0.64549
2.70	0.85944	80.0	0.63391
2.80	0.86043	90.0	0.62374
2.90	0.86123	100.0	0.61468
3.00	0.86185	200.0	0.55663
3.10	0.86231	300.0	0.52415
3.20	0.86261	400.0	0.50186
3.30	0.86278		
3.40	0.86283		

[a] R. B. Bird, E. L. Spotz, and J. O. Hirschfelder, *J. Chem. Phys.*, **18**, 1395 (1950).

TABLE I–E

Expansion Coefficients for the Second and Third Virial Coefficients (and the Quantum Deviations of the Second Virial Coefficient) for the Lennard-Jones (6-12) Potential[a]

The second virial coefficient (including quantum corrections):

$$B^\star = B_{cl}^\star + \Lambda^{*2} B_{I}^\star + \Lambda^{*4} B_{II}^\star + \cdots$$

$$B_{cl}^\star = \sum_{j=0}^{\infty} b^{(j)} T^{*-(3+6j)/12}$$

$$B_{I}^\star = \sum_{j=0}^{\infty} b_{I}^{(j)} T^{*-(13+6j)/12}$$

$$B_{II}^\star = \sum_{j=0}^{\infty} b_{II}^{(j)} T^{*-(23+6j)/12}$$

The (classical) third virial coefficient:

$$C_{cl}^\star = \sum_{j=0}^{\infty} c^{(j)} T^{*-(j+1)/2}$$

j	$b^{(j)}$	$b_{I}^{(j)}$	$b_{II}^{(j)}$	$c^{(j)}$	j	$b^{(j)}$
0	+1.7330010	8.297 (−2)	−2.630 (−3)	+1.729	21	−9.2768372 (−9)
1	−2.5636934	6.11 (−2)	−9.037 (−3)	−3.203	22	−2.6673193 (−9)
2	−8.6650050 (−1)	7.65 (−2)	−2.549 (−2)	+1.519	23	−7.5168046 (−10)
3	−4.2728224 (−1)	6.79 (−2)	−1.494 (−2)	+0.958	24	−2.0778030 (−10)
4	−2.1662512 (−1)	5.903 (−2)	−1.40 (−2)	+0.429	25	−5.6376036 (−11)
5	−1.0682056 (−1)	3.362 (−2)	−1.12 (−2)	+0.059	26	−1.5024114 (−11)
6	−5.0545862 (−2)	2.01 (−2)	−6.26 (−3)	−0.140	27	−3.9350796 (−12)
7	−2.2890120 (−2)	1.10 (−2)	−5.02 (−3)	−0.210	28	−1.0135315 (−12)
8	−9.9286513 (−3)	5.66 (−3)	−2.941 (−3)	−0.205	29	−2.5684633 (−13)
9	−4.1329383 (−3)	2.692 (−3)	−1.584 (−3)	−0.168	30	−6.4073832 (−14)
10	−1.6547753 (−3)	1.237 (−3)	−8.03 (−4)	−0.123	31	−1.5742194 (−14)
11	−6.3872683 (−4)	5.39 (−3)	−3.839 (−4)	−0.084	32	−3.8108431 (−15)
12	−2.3818733 (−4)	2.234 (−3)	−1.74 (−4)	−0.059	33	−9.0935023 (−16)
13	−8.5982461 (−5)	8.90 (−4)	−7.53 (−5)	−0.035	34	−2.1397782 (−16)
14	−3.0100597 (−5)			−0.020	35	−4.9670392 (−17)
15	−1.0236007 (−5)			−0.011	36	−1.1378186 (−17)
16	−3.3872440 (−6)			−0.006	37	−2.5730157 (−18)
17	−1.0913390 (−6)			−0.004	38	−5.7457408 (−19)
18	−3.4305829 (−7)				39	−1.2674099 (−19)
19	−1.0530464 (−7)				40	−2.7623753 (−20)
20	−3.1597475 (−8)					

[a] The quantities tabulated here come from the following sources:

$b^{(j)}$: R. B. Bird and E. L. Spotz, University of Wisconsin CM-599 (1950).

$b_{I}^{(j)}$, $b_{II}^{(j)}$: J. de Boer, Doctoral Dissertation, Amsterdam (1940), p. 36.

$c^{(j)}$: T. Kihara, *J. Phys. Soc. Japan*, **6**, 184 (1951).

Note: Numbers in parentheses indicate the power of 10 by which the corresponding entry is to be multiplied.

TABLE I–F

PHASE SHIFTS $\eta_l(\kappa\sigma)$ FOR He^4 AS CALCULATED FROM THE LENNARD-JONES (6-12) POTENTIAL[a]

$\kappa\sigma$	$l = 0$	$l = 2$	$l = 4$	$l = 6$
0.25	1.180			
0.50	0.850	0.010		
0.75	0.510	0.050		
1.00	0.205	0.137		
1.50	−0.355	0.415	0.013	
2.00	−0.890	0.510	0.078	
2.50	−1.410	0.390	0.205	0.012
3.00	−1.913	0.105	0.325	0.055
3.50	−2.375	−0.220	0.385	0.113
4.00	−2.800	−0.550	0.375	0.182

[a] Taken from J. de Boer and A. Michels, *Physica*, **6**, 409 (1939).

TABLE I–G

PHASE SHIFTS $\eta_l(\kappa\sigma)$ FOR He^3, MULTIPLIED BY $(2l + 1)$, AS CALCULATED FROM THE LENNARD-JONES (6-12) POTENTIAL[a]

$\kappa\sigma$	$l = 1$	$l = 3$	$l = 5$	$l = 7$	$l = 9$	$l = 11$	$l = 13$	$l = 15$	$l = 17$	$l = 19$
0.0	0.00									
0.2	0.03									
0.4	0.20									
0.6	0.54	0.01								
0.8	0.88	0.04	0.01							
1.0	1.08	0.11	0.01							
1.2	1.08	0.22	0.03	0.01						
1.4	0.92	0.39	0.05	0.01						
1.6	0.65	0.65	0.10	0.02	0.01					
1.8	0.30	0.98	0.17	0.04	0.01					
2.0	−0.09	1.32	0.26	0.05	0.02	0.01				
2.2	−0.51	1.66	0.40	0.08	0.03	0.01	0.01			
2.4	−0.95	1.97	0.55	0.11	0.04	0.02	0.01	0.01		
2.6	−1.40	2.18	0.73	0.15	0.06	0.03	0.01	0.01	0.01	
2.8	−1.87	2.29	0.94	0.21	0.08	0.04	0.02	0.01	0.01	
3.0	−2.34	2.23	1.18	0.27	0.10	0.05	0.02	0.01	0.01	0.01
3.2	−2.82	2.06	1.48	0.35	0.13	0.06	0.03	0.02	0.01	0.01
3.4	−3.29	1.82	1.86	0.44	0.17	0.08	0.04	0.02	0.01	0.01
3.6	−3.77	1.53	2.25	0.55	0.21	0.10	0.05	0.03	0.02	0.01
3.8	−4.24	1.21	2.64	0.68	0.26	0.12	0.06	0.03	0.02	0.01
4.0	−4.72	0.82	3.00	0.82	0.32	0.15	0.08	0.04	0.03	0.02

$\kappa\sigma$	$l = 0$	$l = 2$	$l = 4$	$l = 6$	$l = 8$	$l = 10$	$l = 12$	$l = 14$	$l = 16$	$l = 18$
0.0	0.00									
0.2	0.34									
0.4	0.39									
0.6	0.27	0.02								
0.8	0.11	0.10	0.02							
1.0	−0.07	0.29	0.04	0.01						
1.2	−0.26	0.58	0.09	0.02						
1.4	−0.46	0.93	0.18	0.03	0.01					
1.6	−0.66	1.27	0.29	0.05	0.02	0.01				
1.8	−0.86	1.56	0.44	0.08	0.02	0.01	0.01			
2.0	−1.05	1.66	0.62	0.12	0.03	0.02	0.01			
2.2	−1.25	1.55	0.86	0.18	0.04	0.02	0.02			
2.4	−1.44	1.29	1.13	0.25	0.06	0.03	0.02	0.01		
2.6	−1.63	0.92	1.44	0.33	0.09	0.04	0.02	0.01		
2.8	−1.81	0.49	1.77	0.43	0.12	0.05	0.03	0.02		
3.0	−1.99	0.02	2.11	0.55	0.16	0.06	0.03	0.02	0.01	
3.2	−2.17	−0.46	2.45	0.70	0.21	0.08	0.04	0.03	0.01	
3.4	−2.34	−0.96	2.78	0.87	0.27	0.11	0.05	0.03	0.02	
3.6	−2.51	−1.48	3.02	1.07	0.34	0.14	0.07	0.04	0.02	0.01
3.8	−2.67	−2.00	3.13	1.30	0.41	0.18	0.09	0.04	0.03	0.02
4.0	−2.83	−2.53	3.09	1.54	0.49	0.21	0.11	0.05	0.03	0.02

[a] Taken from J. de Boer, J. van Kranendonk, and K. Compaan, *Physica*, **16**, 545 (1950).

TABLE I–H

The Compressibility Factor pV/NkT Based on the Lennard-Jones–Devonshire (3-shell) Model[a]

$$T^* = kT/\epsilon \qquad v^* = v/\sigma^3 = (a/\sigma)^3/\sqrt{2} = a^{*3}/\sqrt{2}$$

T^* \ a^{*3}	0.8	0.9	1.0	1.2	1.4	1.5	1.6	1.8	2.0	2.2
0.70	215.9	117.27	64.01	17.650	2.358	−0.8136	−2.642	−3.738	−3.566	−3.066
0.75	202.2	109.97	60.26	17.142	2.695	−0.3818	−1.999	−3.059	−2.948	−2.528
0.80	190.2	103.57	56.97	16.528	2.987	+0.0812	−1.442	−2.472	−2.413	−2.062
0.85	179.6	97.92	54.07	15.984	3.240	0.4862	−0.955	−1.960	−1.947	−1.654
0.90	170.13	92.92	51.49	15.500	3.462	0.8429	−0.5276	−1.511	−1.537	−1.296
0.95	161.66	88.40	49.18	15.065	3.657	1.1593	−0.1491	−1.113	−1.1743	−0.9789
1.00	154,02	84.35	47.10	14.672	3.830	1.4411	+0.1881	−0.759	−0.8515	−0.6961
1.05	147.10	80.68	45.21	14.316	3.886	1.6935	0.4897	−0.443	−0.5627	−0.4427
1.1	140.80	77.355	43.50	13.991	4.018	1.9205	0.7608	−0.1585	−0.3030	−0.191
1.2	129.74	71.525	40.50	13.419	4.245	2.311	1.2272	+0.3309	+0.1444	+0.203
1.3	120.38	66.593	37.953	12.932	4.432	2.634	1.6128	0.7357	0.5151	0.528
1.4	111.33	62.365	35.768	12.510	4.587	2.904	1.9355	1.0750	0.8262	0.803
1.6	99.23	55.492	32.205	11.816	4.826	3.326	2.4417	1.6086	1.3168	1.234
1.8	89.03	50.142	28.521	11.266	4.998	3.636	2.8163	2.0054	1.7135	1.557
2.0	80.866	45.856	27.258	10.817	5.123	3.870	3.1010	2.3090	1.9919	1.807
2.5	66.149	38.120	22.172	9.885	5.310	4.248	3.570	2.816	2.460	2.230
3.0	56.330	33.020	20.435	9.284	5.395	4.458	3.841	3.149	2.741	2.486
3.5	49.300	29.262	18.468	8.838	5.427	4.579	4.006	3.336	2.922	2.653
4	44.015	26.438	16.982	8.488	5.430	4.648	4.110	3.457	3.043	2.766
5	36.676	22.471	14.809	7.963	5.393	4.705	4.253	3.595	3.185	2.901
7	28.074	17.897	12.312	7.281	5.259	4.720	4.283	3.684	3.290	3.009
10	21.584	14.307	10.373	6.659	5.087	4.591	4.212	3.673	3.305	3.035
20	13.735	9.998	7.866	5.688	4.576	4.211	3.920	3.486	3.175	2.942
50	8.717	6.969	5.910	4.624	3.905	3.652	3.444	3.122	2.885	2.702
100	6.733	5.630	4.902	4.000	3.462	3.267	3.104	2.849	2.657	2.499
400	4.476	3.962	3.592	3.096	2.777	2.655	2.543	2.319	2.082	1.856

T^* \ a^{*3}	2.4	2.5	2.6	2.8	3.0	3.5	4.0	5.0	6.0
0.70	−2.535	−2.310	−2.107	−1.760	−1.486	−1.0215	−0.7382	−0.399	−0.1841
0.75	−2.070	−1.877	−1.701	−1.402	−1.165	−0.7626	−0.5168	−0.221	−0.0329
0.80	−1.667	−1.501	−1.349	−1.091	−0.885	−0.5366	−0.3234	−0.0661	+0.0990
0.85	−1.315	−1.172	−1.0407	−0.817	−0.6395	−0.3376	−0.1531	+0.0708	0.2149
0.90	−1.004	−0.8808	−0.7681	−0.575	−0.4219	−0.1613	−0.0021	0.1924	0.3173
0.95	−0.729	−0.6232	−0.5265	−0.360	−0.2282	−0.0040	+0.1329	0.3009	0.4084
1.00	−0.483	−0.3932	−0.3105	−0.168	−0.0547	+0.1371	0.2541	0.3985	0.4897
1.05	−0.2624	−0.1865	−0.1162	+0.005	+0.1015	0.2645	0.3634	0.4865	0.5676
1.1	−0.0634	+0.0002	+0.0590	0.161	0.2427	0.3798	0.4626	0.5664	0.6282
1.2	+0.2803	0.3222	0.3623	0.432	0.4880	0.5804	0.6353	0.7057	0.7411
1.3	0.5663	0.5908	0.6151	0.659	0.6933	0.7489	0.7806	0.8230	0.8340
1.4	0.8067	0.8173	0.8287	0.850	0.8673	0.8922	0.9044	0.9230	0.9113
1.6	1.1887	1.177	1.1684	1.156	1.1453	1.122	1.1035	1.084	1.030
1.8	1.476	1.448	1.425	1.387	1.357	1.297	1.256	1.207	1.115
2.0	1.698	1.658	1.624	1.568	1.522	1.435	1.376	1.304	1.161
2.5	2.077	2.017	1.965	1.878	1.806	1.675	1.586	1.471	1.266
3.0	2.310	2.238	2.176	2.070	1.985	1.826	1.719	1.571	1.305
3.5	2.461	2.383	2.314	2.198	2.104	1.928	1.810	1.633	1.321
4	2.565	2.483	2.410	2.287	2.187	2.001	1.874	1.670	1.323
5	2.691	2.605	2.529	2.398	2.291	2.093	1.957	1.700	1.311
7	2.797	2.708	2.630	2.495	2.385	2.178	2.031	1.682	1.271
10	2.829	2.743	2.666	2.534	2.424	2.217	2.048	1.606	1.219
20	2.760	2.683	2.614	2.494	2.394	2.166	1.901	1.402	1.128
50	2.556	2.492	2.431	2.308	2.178	1.829	1.531	1.191	1.056
100	2.348	2.270	2.188	2.020	1.856	1.520	1.305	1.101	1.029
400	1.661	1.579	1.506	1.387	1.296	1.156	1.085	1.026	1.007

[a] R. H. Wentorf, R. J. Buehler, J. O. Hirschfelder, and C. F. Curtiss, *J. Chem. Phys.*, **18**, 1484 (1950).

TABLE I–J

THE REDUCED INTERNAL ENERGY OF GAS IMPERFECTION, $\tilde{U}'/\tilde{N}\epsilon$, BASED ON THE LENNARD-JONES–DEVONSHIRE (3-SHELL) MODEL[a]

T^* \ a^{*3}	0.8	0.9	1.0	1.2	1.4	1.5	1.6	1.8	2.0	2.2
0.70	14.94	2.375	−3.590	−7.374	−7.505	−7.177	−6.785	−5.947	−5.220	−4.638
0.75	15.05	2.451	−3.517	−7.284	−7.446	−7.137	−6.735	−5.906	−5.189	−4.612
0.80	15.16	2.525	−3.444	−7.220	−7.387	−7.084	−6.686	−5.866	−5.157	−4.587
0.85	15.26	2.598	−3.372	−7.156	−7.329	−7.032	−6.637	−5.827	−5.126	−4.562
0.90	15.36	2.675	−3.300	−7.093	−7.271	−6.979	−6.509	−5.788	−5.095	−4.537
0.95	15.45	2.742	−3.228	−7.030	−7.214	−6.927	−6.541	−5.749	−5.064	−4.512
1.00	15.54	2.814	−3.157	−6.967	−7.157	−6.876	−6.494	−5.710	−5.033	−4.487
1.05	15.63	2.885	−3.086	−6.904	−7.120	−6.825	−6.447	−5.672	−5.002	−4.462
1.1	15.71	2.957	−3.015	−6.841	−7.066	−6.774	−6.400	−5.634	−4.972	−4.435
1.2	15.88	3.100	−2.874	−6.717	−6.958	−6.673	−6.308	−5.559	−4.912	−4.385
1.3	16.04	3.244	−2.734	−6.593	−6.851	−6.573	−6.217	−5.485	−4.852	−4.336
1.4	16.19	3.387	−2.596	−6.470	−6.745	−6.475	−6.127	−5.412	−4.792	−4.286
1.6	16.49	3.674	−2.323	−6.226	−6.536	−6.282	−5.951	−5.269	−4.675	−4.188
1.8	16.79	3.958	−2.015	−5.986	−6.331	−6.093	−5.779	−5.129	−4.553	−4.090
2.0	17.08	4.240	−1.758	−5.749	−6.129	−5.908	−5.611	−4.991	−4.438	−3.994
2.5	17.80	4.934	−1.120	−5.217	−5.638	−5.459	−5.204	−4.656	−4.158	−3.755
3.0	18.52	5.666	−0.4897	−4.668	−5.165	−5.028	−4.813	−4.317	−3.886	−3.520
3.5	19.23	6.310	+0.1330	−4.130	−4.707	−4.612	−4.434	−4.002	−3.618	−3.289
4	19.92	6.949	0.7476	−3.602	−4.262	−4.207	−4.066	−3.964	−3.356	−3.061
5	21.38	8.214	1.876	−2.576	−3.405	−3.428	−3.324	−3.097	−2.845	−2.613
7	23.95	10.687	4.124	−0.6285	−1.792	−1.912	−1.982	−1.961	−1.861	−1.745
10	27.73	14.05	7.372	+2.095	+0.5218	+0.1349	−0.1051	−0.3553	−0.4584	−0.4962
20	39.08	24.79	17.21	10.28	7.150	6.213	+5.503	+4.504	+3.841	+3.375
50	69.86	52.31	42.11	30.14	23.75	21.55	19.78	17.08	15.13	13.66
100	114.29	91.08	76.05	57.82	47.18	43.36	40.21	35.30	31.65	28.64
400	311.2	264.5	231.2	186.7	158.3	147.4	137.45	117.14	95.25	74.18

T^* \ a^{*3}	2.4	2.5	2.6	2.8	3.0	3.5	4.0	5.0	6.0
0.70	−4.177	−3.984	−3.810	−3.5129	−3.2666	−2.7997	−2.4644	−2.0005	−1.6861
0.75	−4.156	−3.964	−3.792	−3.4968	−3.2517	−2.7862	−2.4514	−1.9878	−1.6738
0.80	−4.135	−3.945	−3.774	−3.4807	−3.2368	−2.7729	−2.4386	−1.9756	−1.6620
0.85	−4.114	−3.926	−3.756	−3.4656	−3.2219	−2.7596	−2.4260	−1.9636	−1.6506
0.90	−4.093	−3.966	−3.738	−3.4484	−3.2070	−2.7464	−2.4136	−1.9519	−1.6396
0.95	−4.072	−3.887	−3.720	−3.4321	−3.1920	−2.7332	−2.4013	−1.9404	−1.6290
1.00	−4.051	−3.868	−3.702	−3.4158	−3.1770	−2.7201	−2.3891	−1.9292	−1.6188
1.05	−4.030	−3.848	−3.684	−3.3994	−3.162	−2.7070	−2.3770	−1.9181	−1.6088
1.1	−4.009	−3.828	−3.665	−3.3830	−3.1469	−2.6940	−2.3649	−1.9071	−1.5992
1.2	−3.967	−3.789	−3.629	−3.3501	−3.1168	−2.6679	−2.3410	−1.8856	−1.5807
1.3	−3.925	−3.750	−3.592	−3.3171	−3.0864	−2.6418	−2.3173	−1.8645	−1.5632
1.4	−3.883	−3.711	−3.555	−3.2840	−3.0561	−2.6158	−2.2937	−1.8436	−1.5466
1.6	−3.799	−3.632	−3.481	−3.2174	−2.9951	−2.5636	−2.2467	−1.8027	−1.5159
1.8	−3.715	−3.553	−3.407	−3.1505	−2.9338	−2.5113	−2.1998	−1.7623	−1.4882
2.0	−3.631	−3.475	−3.333	−3.0835	−2.8722	−2.4589	−2.1530	−1.7226	−1.4631
2.5	−3.423	−3.279	−3.147	−2.9155	−2.7177	−2.3270	−2.0359	−1.6255	−1.4099
3	−3.216	−3.084	−2.903	−2.7475	−2.5628	−2.1953	−1.9186	−1.5325	−1.3674
3.5	−3.012	−2.891	−2.779	−2.5799	−2.4078	−2.0630	−1.8010	−1.4446	−1.3330
4	−2.810	−2.699	−2.596	−2.4128	−2.2532	−1.9306	−1.6834	−1.3623	−1.3045
5	−2.411	−2.320	−2.235	−2.0808	−1.9451	−1.6660	−1.4485	−1.2153	−1.2606
7	−1.631	−1.577	−1.524	−1.4261	−1.3358	−1.1399	−0.9874	−0.9839	−1.2036
10	−0.5013	−0.4968	−0.489	−0.4670	−0.4396	−0.3641	−0.3456	−0.7479	−1.1556
20	+3.033	+2.895	+2.774	+2.5735	+2.4091	+1.9559	+1.1918	−0.3793	−1.0931
50	12.51	12.00	11.50	10.457	9.263	5.879	2.9761	−0.0967	−1.0520
100	25.66	24.06	22.36	18.81	15.321	8.208	3.804	+0.00948	−1.0376
400	56.17	48.57	41.88	30.99	22.834	10.470	4.5205	0.09335	−1.0266

[a] R. H. Wentorf, R. J. Buehler, J. O. Hirschfelder, and C. F. Curtiss, *J. Chem. Phys.*, 18, 1484 (1950).

TABLE I–K

THE REDUCED HEAT CAPACITY OF GAS IMPERFECTION, $\tilde{C}_v'/\tilde{N}k$, BASED ON THE LENNARD-JONES–DEVONSHIRE (3-SHELL) MODEL[a]

T^* \ a^{*3}	0.8	0.9	1.0	1.2	1.4	1.5	1.6	1.8	2.0	2.2
0.75	2.17	1.494	1.452	1.545	1.177	0.934	0.989	0.804	0.632	0.504
0.80	2.07	1.466	1.447	1.272	1.168	1.054	0.980	0.795	0.628	0.503
0.85	1.99	1.450	1.442	1.268	1.159	1.047	0.971	0.787	0.624	0.502
0.90	1.92	1.443	1.438	1.265	1.150	1.041	0.961	0.780	0.621	0.501
0.95	1.85	1.440	1.432	1.261	1.142	1.034	0.953	0.773	0.617	0.500
1.00	1.79	1.435	1.425	1.258	1.120	1.028	0.946	0.767	0.614	0.500
1.05	1.74	1.435	1.421	1.254	1.100	1.022	0.937	0.760	0.610	0.500
1.1	1.69	1.435	1.416	1.250	1.080	1.015	0.930	0.755	0.607	0.500
1.2	1.617	1.435	1.402	1.242	1.073	1.002	0.916	0.744	0.602	0.497
1.3	1.567	1.435	1.390	1.234	1.065	0.990	0.903	0.734	0.596	0.495
1.4	1.529	1.430	1.380	1.226	1.060	0.977	0.891	0.726	0.591	0.493
1.6	1.493	1.427	1.345	1.210	1.037	0.956	0.869	0.710	0.590	0.489
1.8	1.470	1.417	1.310	1.194	1.019	0.935	0.850	0.696	0.580	0.485
2.0	1.460	1.404	1.283	1.150	1.000	0.918	0.833	0.684	0.568	0.482
2.5	1.440	1.391	1.268	1.096	0.964	0.879	0.798	0.674	0.553	0.473
3.0	1.422	1.376	1.253	1.087	0.931	0.848	0.770	0.654	0.540	0.466
3.5	1.415	1.283	1.237	1.067	0.903	0.821	0.746	0.623	0.529	0.460
4	1.410	1.274	1.196	1.046	0.879	0.799	0.738	0.610	0.520	0.454
5	1.400	1.256	1.127	1.008	0.840	0.772	0.719	0.587	0.505	0.443
7	1.275	1.190	1.108	0.947	0.792	0.728	0.653	0.555	0.482	0.427
10	1.231	1.110	1.060	0.887	0.746	0.665	0.611	0.524	0.459	0.410
20	1.108	1.035	0.946	0.779	0.635	0.584	0.540	0.469	0.417	0.376
50	0.974	0.864	0.773	0.621	0.521	0.483	0.451	0.399	0.359	0.327
100	0.855	0.747	0.656	0.536	0.455	0.423	0.397	0.351	0.313	0.278

T^* \ a^{*3}	2.4	2.5	2.6	2.8	3.0	3.5	4.0	5.0	6.0
0.75	0.417	0.385	0.359	0.321	0.297	0.268	0.258	0.249	0.241
0.80	0.418	0.386	0.360	0.323	0.298	0.266	0.254	0.242	0.232
0.85	0.419	0.387	0.362	0.324	0.298	0.265	0.250	0.237	0.223
0.90	0.419	0.388	0.363	0.325	0.299	0.264	0.247	0.232	0.216
0.95	0.420	0.389	0.364	0.326	0.300	0.262	0.245	0.227	0.209
1.00	0.420	0.390	0.365	0.327	0.300	0.262	0.243	0.224	0.202
1.05	0.421	0.391	0.366	0.328	0.301	0.262	0.241	0.220	0.196
1.1	0.421	0.391	0.366	0.328	0.302	0.261	0.240	0.218	0.190
1.2	0.421	0.392	0.368	0.330	0.303	0.261	0.238	0.213	0.180
1.3	0.421	0.393	0.369	0.331	0.304	0.261	0.237	0.210	0.170
1.4	0.421	0.393	0.369	0.332	0.304	0.261	0.236	0.207	0.162
1.6	0.420	0.393	0.370	0.333	0.306	0.261	0.235	0.203	0.146
1.8	0.419	0.393	0.371	0.335	0.307	0.262	0.234	0.200	0.132
2.0	0.418	0.393	0.371	0.335	0.308	0.262	0.234	0.198	0.120
2.5	0.415	0.391	0.370	0.336	0.309	0.263	0.234	0.190	0.0957
3.0	0.410	0.388	0.368	0.336	0.310	0.264	0.235	0.181	0.0770
3.5	0.406	0.385	0.366	0.335	0.310	0.265	0.235	0.170	0.0629
4	0.403	0.382	0.364	0.333	0.309	0.265	0.235	0.159	0.0525
5	0.396	0.377	0.360	0.330	0.307	0.264	0.233	0.137	0.0388
7	0.384	0.367	0.351	0.324	0.302	0.261	0.224	0.101	0.0235
10	0.371	0.355	0.341	0.316	0.296	0.252	0.200	0.069	0.0138
20	0.344	0.330	0.317	0.294	0.271	0.207	0.130	0.030	0.0050
50	0.296	0.280	0.263	0.227	0.188	0.099	0.0434	0.0067	0.00097
100	0.240	0.218	0.195	0.149	0.107	0.041	0.0145	0.0019	0.00025

[a] R. H. Wentorf, R. J. Buehler, J. O. Hirschfelder, and C. F. Curtiss, *J. Chem. Phys.*, **18**, 1484 (1950).

TABLE I–L

THE REDUCED ENTROPY OF GAS IMPERFECTION, $\tilde{S}'/\tilde{N}k$, BASED ON THE LENNARD-JONES–DEVONSHIRE (3-SHELL) MODEL[a]

T^* \ a^{*3}	0.8	0.9	1.0	1.2	1.4	1.5	1.6	1.8	2.0	2.2
0.70	−8.816	−7.7406	−7.0399	−5.8313	−4.8227	−4.3804	−3.9672	−3.2834	−2.7417	−2.3220
0.75	−8.643	−7.6333	−6.9413	−5.7235	−4.7413	−4.2865	−3.8988	−3.2277	−2.6979	−2.2872
0.80	−8.491	−7.5360	−6.8490	−5.6415	−4.6657	−4.2185	−3.8354	−3.1761	−2.6572	−2.2547
0.85	−8.359	−7.4465	−6.7627	−5.5647	−4.5952	−4.1549	−3.7764	−3.1281	−2.6193	−2.2242
0.90	−8.239	−7.3612	−6.6814	−5.4925	−4.5293	−4.0953	−3.7212	−3.0834	−2.5807	−2.1955
0.95	−8.132	−7.2852	−6.6047	−5.4244	−4.4674	−4.0393	−3.6695	−3.0414	−2.5502	−2.1684
1.00	−8.036	−7.2116	−6.5322	−5.3600	−4.4091	−3.9865	−3.6209	−3.0020	−2.5187	−2.1428
1.05	−7.948	−7.1417	−6.4634	−5.2989	−4.3340	−3.9366	−3.5750	−2.9647	−2.4888	−2.1184
1.1	−7.866	−7.0752	−6.3979	−5.2408	−4.2838	−3.8893	−3.5316	−2.9295	−2.4605	−2.0977
1.2	−7.723	−6.9488	−6.2763	−5.1327	−4.1904	−3.8018	−3.4514	−2.8643	−2.4079	−2.0545
1.3	−7.5965	−6.8372	−6.1652	−5.0338	−4.1050	−3.7221	−3.3786	−2.8051	−2.3600	−2.0148
1.4	−7.4834	−6.7317	−6.0632	−4.9428	−4.0266	−3.6493	−3.3122	−2.7511	−2.3160	−1.9781
1.6	−7.2854	−6.5422	−5.8813	−4.7804	−3.8873	−3.5205	−3.1948	−2.6553	−2.2376	−1.9126
1.8	−7.1145	−6.3759	−5.7108	−4.6390	−3.7664	−3.4092	−3.0936	−2.5727	−2.1717	−1.8551
2.0	−6.9628	−6.2284	−5.5756	−4.5140	−3.6602	−3.3117	−3.0050	−2.5000	−2.1116	−1.8042
2.5	−6.6442	−5.9209	−5.2917	−4.2383	−3.4413	−3.1116	−2.8233	−2.3504	−1.9865	−1.6977
3.0	−6.3855	−5.6645	−5.0623	−4.0386	−3.2688	−2.9544	−2.6805	−2.2339	−1.8869	−1.6120
3.5	−6.1697	−5.4465	−4.8707	−3.8729	−3.1277	−2.8259	−2.5638	−2.1369	−1.8046	−1.5408
4	−5.9854	−5.2962	−4.7068	−3.7320	−3.0088	−2.7179	−2.4655	−2.0545	−1.7345	−1.4798
5	−5.6719	−5.0146	−4.4138	−3.5032	−2.8175	−2.5439	−2.3083	−1.9215	−1.6203	−1.3798
7	−5.2402	−4.5988	−4.0361	−3.1757	−2.5456	−2.2976	−2.0823	−1.7299	−1.4546	−1.2336
10	−4.7916	−4.1602	−3.6502	−2.8508	−2.2792	−2.0538	−1.8587	−1.5388	−1.2876	−1.0849
20	−3.9568	−3.4121	−2.9641	−2.2900	−1.8159	−1.6290	−1.4670	−1.1996	−0.9877	−0.8152
50	−3.0070	−2.5594	−2.2027	−1.6735	−1.3014	−1.1538	−1.0250	−0.8107	−0.6389	−0.4976
100	−2.3994	−2.0251	−1.7277	−1.2864	−0.9738	−0.8490	−0.7395	−0.5502	−0.4084	−0.2881
400	−1.4539	−1.1926	−0.9841	−0.6703	−0.4437	−0.3526	−0.2744	−0.1562	−0.0841	−0.0445

T^* \ a^{*3}	2.4	2.5	2.6	2.8	3.0	3.5	4.0	5.0	6.0
0.70	−1.9982	−1.8619	−1.7402	−1.5323	−1.3611	−1.0393	−0.8104	−0.4954	−0.2812
0.75	−1.9695	−1.8354	−1.7155	−1.5101	−1.3406	−1.0207	−0.7924	−0.4780	−0.2642
0.80	−1.9426	−1.8105	−1.6923	−1.4894	−1.3214	−1.0035	−0.7759	−0.4621	−0.2489
0.85	−1.9172	−1.7871	−1.6704	−1.4698	−1.3033	−0.9874	−0.7606	−0.4476	−0.2352
0.90	−1.8933	−1.7650	−1.6497	−1.4512	−1.2862	−0.9723	−0.7464	−0.4342	−0.2226
0.95	−1.8705	−1.7439	−1.6301	−1.4336	−1.2701	−0.9581	−0.7331	−0.4218	−0.2112
1.00	−1.8490	−1.7239	−1.6113	−1.4169	−1.2547	−0.9446	−0.7206	−0.4103	−0.2006
1.05	−1.8285	−1.7049	−1.5936	−1.4010	−1.2400	−0.9319	−0.7088	−0.3995	−0.1909
1.1	−1.8089	−1.6867	−1.5765	−1.3857	−1.2260	−0.9197	−0.6976	−0.3893	−0.1820
1.2	−1.7723	−1.6526	−1.5446	−1.3571	−1.1998	−0.8970	−0.6768	−0.3705	−0.1658
1.3	−1.7386	−1.6212	−1.5151	−1.3306	−1.1754	−0.8761	−0.6578	−0.3536	−0.1518
1.4	−1.7074	−1.5921	−1.4877	−1.3061	−1.1530	−0.8568	−0.6403	−0.3382	−0.1395
1.6	−1.6512	−1.5396	−1.4383	−1.2616	−1.1123	−0.8220	−0.6089	−0.3108	−0.1190
1.8	−1.6017	−1.4932	−1.3947	−1.2222	−1.0762	−0.7912	−0.5813	−0.2871	−0.1027
2.0	−1.5576	−1.4518	−1.3556	−1.1870	−1.0437	−0.7636	−0.5567	−0.2661	−0.0894
2.5	−1.4647	−1.3644	−1.2729	−1.1120	−0.9748	−0.7049	−0.5044	−0.2228	−0.0656
3.0	−1.3897	−1.2934	−1.2056	−1.0507	−0.9183	−0.6568	−0.4616	−0.1888	−0.0501
3.5	−1.3265	−1.2338	−1.1489	−0.9990	−0.8705	−0.6160	−0.4254	−0.1617	−0.0394
4	−1.2724	−1.1825	−1.1002	−0.9544	−0.8293	−0.5806	−0.3940	−0.1397	−0.0318
5	−1.1833	−1.0978	−1.0194	−0.8803	−0.7605	−0.5216	−0.3415	−0.1068	−0.0220
7	−1.0520	−0.9728	−0.8999	−0.7701	−0.6579	−0.4330	−0.2639	−0.0676	−0.0122
10	−0.9176	−0.8422	−0.7766	−0.6560	−0.5513	−0.3407	−0.1873	−0.0391	−0.0064
20	−0.6714	−0.6080	−0.5494	−0.4444	−0.3530	−0.1779	−0.0772	−0.0119	−0.0018
50	−0.3790	−0.3270	−0.2796	−0.1989	−0.1369	−0.0493	−0.0171	−0.0021	−0.0003
100	−0.1939	−0.1565	−0.1253	−0.0788	−0.0490	−0.0149	−0.0048	−0.0006	−0.00013
400	−0.0236	−0.0174	−0.0128	−0.0071	−0.0040	−0.0011	−0.0004	−0.00008	+0.00002

[a] R. H. Wentorf, R. J. Buehler, J. O. Hirschfelder, and C. F. Curtiss, *J. Chem. Phys.*, **18**, 1484 (1950).

TABLE I–M

The Integrals $\Omega^{(l,s)\star}$ for Calculating the Transport Coefficients for the Lennard-Jones (6-12) Potential

T^*	$\Omega^{(1,1)\star}$	$\Omega^{(1,2)\star}$	$\Omega^{(1,3)\star}$	$\Omega^{(2,2)\star}$	$\Omega^{(2,3)\star}$	$\Omega^{(2,4)\star}$	$\Omega^{(2,5)\star}$	$\Omega^{(2,6)\star}$	$\Omega^{(4,4)\star}$
0.30	2.662	2.256	1.962	2.785	2.535	2.333	2.152	1.990	2.557
0.35	2.476	2.078	1.795	2.628	2.375	2.163	1.978	1.819	2.378
0.40	2.318	1.931	1.663	2.492	2.232	2.016	1.833	1.682	2.223
0.45	2.184	1.808	1.556	2.368	2.105	1.889	1.713	1.574	2.090
0.50	2.066	1.705	1.468	2.257	1.992	1.781	1.614	1.486	1.975
0.55	1.966	1.618	1.396	2.156	1.893	1.689	1.532	1.415	1.875
0.60	1.877	1.543	1.336	2.065	1.806	1.610	1.463	1.356	1.788
0.65	1.798	1.479	1.285	1.982	1.729	1.542	1.406	1.307	1.712
0.70	1.729	1.423	1.242	1.908	1.661	1.484	1.357	1.267	1.645
0.75	1.667	1.375	1.205	1.841	1.602	1.434	1.315	1.231	1.587
0.80	1.612	1.332	1.172	1.780	1.549	1.389	1.278	1.201	1.535
0.85	1.562	1.295	1.144	1.725	1.502	1.350	1.247	1.175	1.488
0.90	1.517	1.261	1.119	1.675	1.460	1.316	1.219	1.152	1.447
0.95	1.476	1.231	1.096	1.629	1.422	1.286	1.194	1.131	1.410
1.00	1.439	1.204	1.076	1.587	1.388	1.258	1.172	1.113	1.377
1.05	1.406	1.179	1.058	1.549	1.357	1.234	1.152	1.097	1.347
1.10	1.375	1.157	1.041	1.514	1.329	1.212	1.135	1.082	1.319
1.15	1.346	1.137	1.027	1.482	1.304	1.192	1.119	1.068	1.294
1.20	1.320	1.119	1.013	1.452	1.280	1.174	1.104	1.056	1.272
1.25	1.296	1.102	1.000	1.424	1.259	1.157	1.091	1.045	1.251
1.30	1.273	1.086	0.9887	1.399	1.239	1.142	1.078	1.035	1.232
1.35	1.253	1.072	0.9780	1.375	1.221	1.128	1.067	1.025	1.215
1.40	1.233	1.059	0.9680	1.353	1.205	1.115	1.057	1.016	1.198
1.45	1.215	1.046	0.9588	1.333	1.189	1.103	1.047	1.008	1.183
1.50	1.198	1.034	0.9502	1.314	1.175	1.092	1.037	1.000	1.169
1.55	1.182	1.023	0.9420	1.296	1.162	1.081	1.029	0.9929	1.156
1.60	1.167	1.013	0.9345	1.279	1.149	1.072	1.022	0.9860	1.144
1.65	1.153	1.004	0.9272	1.264	1.137	1.063	1.014	0.9795	1.133
1.70	1.140	0.9947	0.9205	1.248	1.126	1.054	1.007	0.9735	1.122
1.75	1.128	0.9860	0.9142	1.234	1.116	1.046	1.000	0.9677	1.112
1.80	1.116	0.9780	0.9082	1.221	1.106	1.038	0.9942	0.9623	1.103
1.85	1.105	0.9707	0.9023	1.209	1.097	1.031	0.9875	0.9569	1.094
1.90	1.094	0.9633	0.8968	1.197	1.088	1.024	0.9825	0.9520	1.085
1.95	1.084	0.9567	0.8917	1.186	1.080	1.018	0.9767	0.9473	1.078
2.00	1.075	0.9500	0.8867	1.175	1.073	1.012	0.9717	0.9427	1.070
2.10	1.057	0.9380	0.8775	1.156	1.055	1.000	0.9617	0.9343	1.056
2.20	1.041	0.9267	0.8688	1.138	1.045	0.9895	0.9525	0.9261	1.043
2.30	1.026	0.9167	0.8612	1.122	1.033	0.9800	0.9450	0.9190	1.032
2.40	1.012	0.9073	0.8538	1.107	1.022	0.9710	0.9375	0.9120	1.021
2.50	0.9996	0.8987	0.8470	1.093	1.012	0.9630	0.9300	0.9058	1.012
2.60	0.9878	0.8907	0.8407	1.081	1.002	0.9555	0.9233	0.8996	1.003

TABLE I–M (*continued*)

T^*	$\Omega^{(1,1)\star}$	$\Omega^{(1,2)\star}$	$\Omega^{(1,3)\star}$	$\Omega^{(2,2)\star}$	$\Omega^{(2,3)\star}$	$\Omega^{(2,4)\star}$	$\Omega^{(2,5)\star}$	$\Omega^{(2,6)\star}$	$\Omega^{(4,4)\star}$
2.7	0.9770	0.8833	0.8347	1.069	0.9935	0.9485	0.9175	0.8940	0.9942
2.8	0.9672	0.8767	0.8290	1.058	0.9855	0.9415	0.9117	0.8887	0.9863
2.9	0.9576	0.8700	0.8237	1.048	0.9780	0.9355	0.9058	0.8836	0.9792
3.0	0.9490	0.8640	0.8187	1.039	0.9708	0.9295	0.9008	0.8788	0.9721
3.1	0.9406	0.8580	0.8138	1.030	0.9643	0.9240	0.8958	0.8742	0.9658
3.2	0.9328	0.8520	0.8093	1.022	0.9578	0.9185	0.8908	0.8698	0.9596
3.3	0.9256	0.8473	0.8048	1.014	0.9518	0.9135	0.8867	0.8656	0.9538
3.4	0.9186	0.8420	0.8007	1.007	0.9463	0.9085	0.8825	0.8617	0.9483
3.5	0.9120	0.8373	0.7967	0.9999	0.9408	0.9040	0.8783	0.8577	0.9433
3.6	0.9058	0.8327	0.7928	0.9932	0.9358	0.8995	0.8742	0.8539	0.9383
3.7	0.8998	0.8287	0.7892	0.9870	0.9308	0.8955	0.8700	0.8504	0.9333
3.8	0.8942	0.8240	0.7857	0.9811	0.9263	0.8915	0.8667	0.8469	0.9288
3.9	0.8888	0.8200	0.7822	0.9755	0.9218	0.8875	0.8633	0.8436	0.9246
4.0	0.8836	0.8167	0.7790	0.9700	0.9175	0.8840	0.8592	0.8404	0.9204
4.1	0.8788	0.8127	0.7758	0.9649	0.9133	0.8805	0.8558	0.8371	0.9167
4.2	0.8740	0.8093	0.7727	0.9600	0.9093	0.8770	0.8533	0.8342	0.9125
4.3	0.8694	0.8060	0.7697	0.9553	0.9055	0.8735	0.8500	0.8312	0.9088
4.4	0.8652	0.8027	0.7668	0.9507	0.9018	0.8705	0.8467	0.8283	0.9054
4.5	0.8610	0.7993	0.7640	0.9464	0.8985	0.8670	0.8442	0.8256	0.9021
4.6	0.8568	0.7960	0.7613	0.9422	0.8950	0.8640	0.8408	0.8229	0.8988
4.7	0.8530	0.7933	0.7585	0.9382	0.8918	0.8610	0.8383	0.8202	0.8954
4.8	0.8492	0.7907	0.7560	0.9343	0.8885	0.8585	0.8358	0.8176	0.8925
4.9	0.8456	0.7873	0.7535	0.9305	0.8855	0.8555	0.8332	0.8152	0.8892
5	0.8422	0.7847	0.7510	0.9269	0.8823	0.8530	0.8307	0.8127	0.8863
6	0.8124	0.7607	0.7295	0.8963	0.8565	0.8295	0.8083	0.7912	0.8613
7	0.7896	0.7420	0.7120	0.8727	0.8360	0.8105	0.7902	0.7736	0.8413
8	0.7712	0.7260	0.6973	0.8538	0.8193	0.7945	0.7749	0.7587	0.8246
9	0.7556	0.7127	0.6847	0.8379	0.8048	0.7810	0.7617	0.7458	0.8108
10	0.7424	0.7013	0.6735	0.8242	0.7923	0.7690	0.7501	0.7345	0.7988
20	0.6640	0.6293	0.6048	0.7432	0.7160	0.6950	0.6783	0.6643	0.7242
30	0.6232	0.5909	0.5680	0.7005	0.6750	0.6555	0.6396	0.6264	0.6842
40	0.5960	0.5651	0.5432	0.6718	0.6475	0.6285	0.6135	0.6007	0.6571
50	0.5756	0.5459	0.5248	0.6504	0.6268	0.6085	0.5940	0.5817	0.6367
60	0.5596	0.5307	0.5100	0.6335	0.6105	0.5930	0.5784	0.5664	0.6208
70	0.5464	0.5181	0.4980	0.6194	0.5970	0.5795	0.5657	0.5539	0.6075
80	0.5352	0.5075	0.4878	0.6076	0.5855	0.5685	0.5548	0.5433	0.5963
90	0.5256	0.4984	0.4790	0.5973	0.5755	0.5590	0.5454	0.5342	0.5867
100	0.5170	0.4903	0.4713	0.5882	0.5670	0.5505	0.5371	0.5261	0.5779
200	0.4644	0.4403	0.4233	0.5320	0.5128	0.4978	0.4857	0.4757	0.5246
300	0.4360	0.4135	0.3975	0.5016	0.4835	0.4694	0.4580	0.4486	0.4954
400	0.4170	0.3955	0.3802	0.4811	0.4638	0.4502	0.4393	0.4302	0.4758

TABLE I–N

THE QUANTITIES A★, B★, AND C★ FOR CALCULATING THE TRANSPORT COEFFICIENTS OF MIXTURES FOR THE LENNARD-JONES (6-12) POTENTIAL

T^*	A★	B★	C★
0.30	1.046	1.289	0.8475
0.35	1.062	1.296	0.8392
0.40	1.075	1.296	0.8329
0.45	1.084	1.289	0.8278
0.50	1.093	1.284	0.8251
0.55	1.097	1.275	0.8231
0.60	1.101	1.263	0.8224
0.65	1.102	1.254	0.8223
0.70	1.104	1.242	0.8233
0.75	1.105	1.233	0.8247
0.80	1.105	1.223	0.8265
0.85	1.105	1.216	0.8289
0.90	1.104	1.206	0.8315
0.95	1.103	1.200	0.8342
1.00	1.103	1.192	0.8367
1.05	1.102	1.183	0.8392
1.10	1.102	1.179	0.8417
1.15	1.101	1.172	0.8450
1.20	1.100	1.169	0.8475
1.25	1.099	1.165	0.8508
1.30	1.099	1.159	0.8525
1.35	1.098	1.156	0.8558
1.40	1.097	1.154	0.8583
1.45	1.097	1.148	0.8608
1.50	1.097	1.143	0.8633
1.55	1.096	1.140	0.8658
1.60	1.096	1.137	0.8683
1.65	1.096	1.137	0.8708
1.70	1.095	1.133	0.8725
1.75	1.094	1.129	0.8742
1.80	1.094	1.127	0.8767
1.85	1.094	1.126	0.8783
1.90	1.094	1.124	0.8800
1.95	1.094	1.122	0.8825
2.00	1.094	1.119	0.8842
2.10	1.094	1.116	0.8875
2.20	1.094	1.113	0.8908
2.30	1.094	1.110	0.8933
2.40	1.094	1.108	0.8967
2.50	1.094	1.106	0.8992
2.60	1.094	1.104	0.9017
2.70	1.094	1.103	0.9042
2.80	1.094	1.104	0.9067
2.90	1.095	1.102	0.9083

TABLE I–N (*continued*)

T^*	A*	B*	C*
3.00	1.095	1.101	0.9108
3.10	1.095	1.100	0.9125
3.20	1.096	1.096	0.9133
3.30	1.096	1.099	0.9158
3.40	1.096	1.096	0.9167
3.50	1.097	1.096	0.9183
3.60	1.097	1.095	0.9192
3.70	1.097	1.097	0.9208
3.80	1.097	1.093	0.9217
3.90	1.097	1.093	0.9225
4.00	1.098	1.095	0.9242
4.10	1.098	1.093	0.9250
4.20	1.098	1.093	0.9258
4.30	1.099	1.094	0.9267
4.40	1.099	1.094	0.9275
4.50	1.099	1.092	0.9283
4.60	1.100	1.091	0.9292
4.70	1.100	1.093	0.9300
4.80	1.100	1.095	0.9308
4.90	1.101	1.091	0.9308
5.00	1.101	1.092	0.9317
6.00	1.103	1.090	0.9375
7.00	1.105	1.092	0.9400
8.00	1.107	1.090	0.9425
9.00	1.109	1.091	0.9433
10.00	1.110	1.094	0.9450
20.00	1.119	1.095	0.9475
30.00	1.124	1.095	0.9483
40.00	1.127	1.095	0.9483
50.00	1.130	1.095	0.9483
60.00	1.132	1.096	0.9483
70.00	1.134	1.095	0.9483
80.00	1.135	1.095	0.9483
90.00	1.137	1.096	0.9483
100.00	1.138	1.095	0.9483
200.00	1.146	1.095	0.9483
300.00	1.151	1.095	0.9483
400.00	1.154	1.095	0.9483

TABLE I–P

FUNCTIONS FOR CALCULATING THE HIGHER APPROXIMATIONS TO THE TRANSPORT COEFFICIENTS OF PURE SUBSTANCES FOR THE LENNARD-JONES (6-12) POTENTIAL

$[\eta]_3 = [\eta]_1 f_\eta^{(3)}$ $[\lambda]_3 = [\lambda]_1 f_\lambda^{(3)}$ $[\mathscr{D}]_2 = [\mathscr{D}]_1 f_\mathscr{D}^{(2)}$

T^*	$f_\eta^{(3)}$	$f_\lambda^{(3)}$	$f_\mathscr{D}^{(2)}$
0.30	1.0014	1.0022	1.0001
0.50	1.0002	1.0003	1.0000
0.75	1.0000	1.0000	1.0000
1.00	1.0000	1.0001	1.0000
1.25	1.0001	1.0002	1.0002
1.5	1.0004	1.0006	1.0006
2.0	1.0014	1.0021	1.0016
2.5	1.0025	1.0038	1.0026
3.0	1.0034	1.0052	1.0037
4.0	1.0049	1.0076	1.0050
5.0	1.0058	1.0090	1.0059
10.0	1.0075	1.0116	1.0076
50.0	1.0079	1.0124	1.0080
100.0	1.0080	1.0125	1.0080
400.0	1.0080	1.0125	1.0080

TABLE I–Q

THE FUNCTION $[k_T]_1^\star$ FOR CALCULATING ISOTOPIC THERMAL DIFFUSION FOR THE LENNARD-JONES (6-12) POTENTIAL

$$[k_T]_1^\star = \frac{[k_T]_{\text{L-J(6-12)}}}{[k_T]_{\text{Rig Sph}}}$$

$$T^* = kT/\epsilon$$

T^*	$[k_T]_1^\star$	T^*	$[k_T]_1^\star$	T^*	$[k_T]_1^\star$
0.30	0.086	1.65	0.211	4.0	0.507
0.35	0.035	1.70	0.221	4.1	0.511
0.40	−0.002	1.75	0.230	4.2	0.516
0.45	−0.032	1.80	0.244	4.3	0.520
0.50	−0.048	1.85	0.253	4.4	0.525
0.55	−0.059	1.90	0.263	4.5	0.529
0.60	−0.063	1.95	0.277	4.6	0.533
0.65	−0.063	2.0	0.286	4.7	0.538
0.70	−0.057	2.1	0.305	4.8	0.543
0.75	−0.049	2.2	0.323	4.9	0.542
0.80	−0.039	2.3	0.337	5.	0.547
0.85	−0.025	2.4	0.356	6.	0.578
0.90	−0.010	2.5	0.370	7.	0.591
0.95	+0.005	2.6	0.383	8.	0.604
1.00	0.019	2.7	0.397	9.	0.607
1.05	0.033	2.8	0.411	10.	0.616
1.10	0.047	2.9	0.420	20.	0.625
1.15	0.066	3.0	0.434	30.	0.627
1.20	0.080	3.1	0.443	40.	0.625
1.25	0.099	3.2	0.447	50.	0.623
1.30	0.108	3.3	0.461	60.	0.622
1.35	0.127	3.4	0.466	70.	0.621
1.40	0.141	3.5	0.475	80.	0.621
1.45	0.155	3.6	0.479	90.	0.620
1.50	0.169	3.7	0.489	100.	0.619
1.55	0.183	3.8	0.493	200.	0.615
1.60	0.197	3.9	0.497	300.	0.612
				400.	0.611

TABLE I–R

The Distance of Closest Approach and the Angle of Deflection[a]
[Calculated for the Lennard-Jones (6-12) Potential]

$\chi = \chi(b^*, g^*)$ = angle of deflection

$b^* = b/\sigma$ = reduced impact parameter

$g^{*2} = \frac{1}{2}\mu g^2/\epsilon$ = reduced relative initial kinetic energy

$r_m^*(b^*, g^*) = r_m/\sigma$ = reduced closest distance of approach

$$z = \frac{2/r_m^{*6}}{1 + \sqrt{1 + g^{*2}}}$$

$g^{*2} = 0.1$

z	b^*	r_m^*	χ
0.0025	2.838	2.704	−0.323
0.0040	2.696	2.500	−0.543
0.0050	2.643	2.409	−0.706
0.0063	2.598	2.318	−0.945
0.0075	2.572	2.251	−1.205
0.0100	2.544	2.146	−1.998
0.0110	2.539	2.112	−2.576
0.0120	2.538	2.082	−3.937
0.0126	2.537	2.065	$-\infty$
0.833	2.516	1.027	−5.117
0.835	2.503	1.026	−4.339
0.840	2.470	1.025	−3.416
0.842	2.456	1.025	−3.177
0.850	2.400	1.023	−2.509
0.860	2.328	1.021	−1.943
0.880	2.171	1.017	−1.124
0.900	1.996	1.014	−0.491
0.912	1.881	1.011	−0.150
0.925	1.744	1.009	0.201
0.938	1.593	1.007	0.542
0.950	1.436	1.005	0.862
0.970	1.1195	1.001	1.437
1.000	0	0.9960	π

[a] The parameter z was used in the original numerical evaluation of $\chi(b, g)$. [See J. O. Hirschfelder, R. B. Bird, E. L. Spotz, University of Wisconsin, CF 857, April 8, 1948; *J. Chem. Phys.*, **16**, 968 (1948).] The values of the parameter z are given here to facilitate making interpolations in the table.

TABLE I–R (*continued*)

$g^{*2} = 0.2$

z	b^*	r_m^*	χ
0.0050	2.522	2.400	−0.329
0.0075	2.411	2.243	−0.514
0.0100	2.350	2.138	−0.718
0.0150	2.287	1.998	−1.219
0.0170	2.274	1.957	−1.477
0.0180	2.269	1.938	−1.628
0.0200	2.262	1.905	−1.997
0.0220	2.257	1.875	−2.538
0.0240	2.256	1.848	−3.660
0.0250	2.255	1.835	−5.552
0.0254	2.255	1.830	−9.248
0.0255	2.255	1.829	−13.592
0.0256	2.255	1.828	$-\infty$
0.730	2.242	1.046	−4.140
0.735	2.226	1.045	−4.032
0.740	2.209	1.043	−3.753
0.745	2.192	1.042	−3.472
0.750	2.175	1.041	−3.209
0.755	2.158	1.040	−2.969
0.760	2.140	1.039	−2.751
0.780	2.065	1.034	−2.022
0.800	1.984	1.030	−1.452
0.820	1.897	1.026	−0.982
0.850	1.751	1.020	−0.381
0.860	1.697	1.018	−0.198
0.880	1.583	1.014	0.151
0.900	1.455	1.010	0.493
0.930	1.230	1.004	1.008
0.950	1.046	1.001	1.377
1.000	0	0.9923	π

TABLE I–R (*continued*)

$g^{*2} = 0.4$			
z	b^*	$r_m{}^*$	χ
0.008	2.297	2.204	−0.269
0.010	2.235	2.123	−0.341
0.015	2.138	1.984	−0.530
0.020	2.083	1.892	−0.737
0.025	2.050	1.823	−0.969
0.030	2.029	1.768	−1.235
0.035	2.015	1.723	−1.553
0.040	2.006	1.685	−1.959
0.048	2.002	1.635	−3.127
0.049	2.000	1.629	−3.259
0.050	1.999	1.624	−3.777
0.05366	1.999	1.605	$-\infty$
0.565	1.988	1.084	−5.121
0.570	1.981	1.082	−4.394
0.575	1.974	1.081	−3.954
0.583	1.963	1.078	−3.514
0.590	1.952	1.076	−3.229
0.600	1.938	1.073	−2.920
0.610	1.922	1.070	−2.656
0.650	1.852	1.059	−1.896
0.700	1.750	1.046	−1.180
0.750	1.629	1.034	−0.586
0.800	1.485	1.023	−0.045
0.840	1.347	1.015	0.384
0.850	1.308	1.013	0.492
0.875	1.204	1.008	0.768
0.900	1.086	1.003	1.055
0.913	1.017	1.001	1.213
0.925	0.948	0.9984	1.365
0.938	0.866	0.9961	1.539
0.950	0.780	0.9940	1.713
0.960	0.699	0.9922	1.872
0.970	0.608	0.9905	2.048
0.980	0.498	0.9888	2.253
0.990	0.353	0.9857	2.517
1.000	0	0.9855	π

TABLE I–R (*continued*)

$g^{*2} = 0.6$

z	b^*	r_m^*	χ
0.010	2.188	2.110	−0.230
0.015	2.081	1.972	−0.360
0.020	2.014	1.880	−0.478
0.030	1.940	1.757	−0.752
0.040	1.901	1.675	−1.062
0.050	1.879	1.614	−1.428
0.060	1.867	1.565	−1.887
0.065	1.863	1.545	−2.153
0.070	1.860	1.526	−2.531
0.080	1.857	1.492	−3.746
0.088304	1.857	1.468	$-\infty$
0.407	1.855	1.138	−3.235
0.410	1.853	1.136	−3.561
0.420	1.847	1.132	−3.719
0.440	1.834	1.123	−3.353
0.450	1.827	1.119	−3.164
0.475	1.808	1.109	−2.732
0.500	1.785	1.099	−2.381
0.550	1.733	1.082	−1.789
0.600	1.670	1.067	−1.290
0.650	1.594	1.052	−0.832
0.700	1.505	1.039	−0.362
0.725	1.454	1.033	−0.193
0.750	1.399	1.028	0.007
0.775	1.339	1.022	0.208
0.800	1.273	1.017	0.413
0.825	1.201	1.011	0.622
0.850	1.121	1.006	0.838
0.875	1.031	1.002	1.064
0.900	0.930	0.9968	1.305
0.925	0.811	0.9923	1.569
0.950	0.667	0.9879	1.871
0.975	0.475	0.9836	2.253
1.00	0	0.9795	π

TABLE I–R (*continued*)

$g^{*2} = 0.8$

z	b^*	r_m^*	χ
0.015	2.044	1.961	−0.267
0.020	1.974	1.870	−0.360
0.025	1.925	1.801	−0.456
0.050	1.812	1.605	−0.984
0.075	1.775	1.500	−1.639
0.100	1.761	1.430	−2.535
0.150	1.755	1.336	−7.817
0.1708	1.754	1.308	$-\infty$
0.250	1.751	1.227	−6.091
0.275	1.747	1.208	−4.736
0.290	1.744	1.197	−4.188
0.300	1.741	1.191	−3.891
0.335	1.730	1.169	−3.111
0.350	1.725	1.160	−2.863
0.380	1.711	1.145	−2.518
0.400	1.700	1.135	−2.340
0.450	1.667	1.113	−1.800
0.500	1.627	1.093	−1.430
0.550	1.577	1.076	−1.072
0.600	1.517	1.061	−0.715
0.650	1.446	1.047	−0.375
0.700	1.363	1.034	−0.040
0.750	1.266	1.022	0.299
0.800	1.151	1.011	0.650
0.850	1.012	1.001	1.025
0.870	0.949	0.9969	1.186
0.900	0.840	0.9913	1.446
0.920	0.755	0.9877	1.635
0.950	0.602	0.9824	1.963
0.970	0.469	0.9790	2.235
1.000	0	0.9741	π

TABLE I–R (*continued*)

$g^{*2} = 0.9$

z	b^*	r_m^*	χ
0.015	2.031	1.956	−0.240
0.025	1.908	1.797	−0.408
0.050	1.789	1.601	−0.861
0.075	1.745	1.496	−1.385
0.100	1.726	1.426	−2.005
0.110	1.722	1.404	−2.284
0.120	1.719	1.383	−2.580
0.130	1.716	1.365	−2.889
0.150	1.713	1.333	−3.496
0.160	1.711	1.319	−3.757
0.170	1.710	1.305	−3.964
0.180	1.709	1.293	−4.108
0.190	1.708	1.281	−4.195
0.200	1.707	1.270	−4.235
0.220	1.705	1.250	−4.231
0.230	1.703	1.241	−4.197
0.250	1.700	1.224	−4.074
0.270	1.696	1.208	−3.877
0.300	1.688	1.187	−3.484
0.350	1.669	1.157	−2.787
0.400	1.643	1.132	−2.197
0.450	1.611	1.110	−1.715
0.500	1.569	1.091	−1.304
0.550	1.520	1.073	−0.936
0.600	1.462	1.058	−0.593
0.650	1.392	1.044	−0.262
0.675	1.354	1.037	−0.099
0.700	1.312	1.031	0.064
0.725	1.267	1.025	0.228
0.750	1.218	1.019	0.393
0.800	1.107	1.008	0.733
0.850	0.974	0.9982	1.095
0.900	0.807	0.9988	1.500
0.925	0.704	0.9842	1.732
0.950	0.579	0.9799	2.000
0.975	0.412	0.9756	2.341
1.000	0	0.9715	π

TABLE I–R (*continued*)

$g^{*2} = 0.95$

z	b^*	r_m^*	χ
0.015	2.025	1.954	−0.229
0.025	1.901	1.794	−0.387
0.050	1.778	1.599	−0.812
0.075	1.732	1.494	−1.289
0.100	1.711	1.424	−1.830
0.150	1.695	1.331	−3.000
0.200	1.687	1.269	−3.608
0.210	1.685	1.259	−3.631
0.220	1.683	1.249	−3.631
0.230	1.682	1.240	−3.612
0.240	1.680	1.231	−3.576
0.250	1.678	1.223	−3.524
0.300	1.664	1.186	−3.084
0.350	1.645	1.156	−2.529
0.400	1.619	1.130	−2.021
0.450	1.586	1.108	−1.584
0.500	1.545	1.089	−1.201
0.550	1.495	1.072	−0.852
0.600	1.437	1.057	−0.522
0.650	1.369	1.043	−0.202
0.700	1.290	1.030	0.115
0.750	1.198	1.018	0.436
0.800	1.088	1.007	0.768
0.850	0.957	0.9970	1.123
0.900	0.7925	0.9875	1.521
0.925	0.6912	0.9830	1.750
0.950	0.5682	0.9786	2.014
0.975	0.4045	0.9744	2.351
1.000	0	0.9703	π

TABLE I–R (*continued*)

$g^{*2} = 1$

z	b^*	r_m^*	χ
0.025	1.894	1.792	−0.369
0.050	1.768	1.597	−0.768
0.075	1.721	1.492	−1.207
0.10	1.698	1.422	−1.689
0.15	1.678	1.330	−2.664
0.20	1.668	1.267	−3.178
0.25	1.658	1.221	−3.135
0.30	1.643	1.184	−2.784
0.35	1.623	1.154	−2.320
0.40	1.596	1.129	−1.871
0.45	1.563	1.107	−1.470
0.50	1.522	1.088	−1.109
0.55	1.473	1.071	−0.775
0.60	1.415	1.055	−0.458
0.65	1.348	1.041	−0.148
0.70	1.270	1.028	0.161
0.75	1.178	1.017	0.474
0.80	1.070	1.006	0.800
0.85	0.9410	0.9957	1.149
0.90	0.7795	0.9863	1.541
0.95	0.5588	0.9774	2.027
1.00	0	0.9691	π

$g^{*2} = 1.2$

z	b^*	r_m^*	χ
0.025	1.871	1.784	[illegible]
0.050	1.737	1.589	−0.635
0.075	1.681	1.485	[illegible]
0.10	1.653	1.416	−1.313
0.15	1.624	1.323	−1.922
0.20	1.607	1.261	−2.253
0.25	1.591	1.215	−2.261
0.30	1.572	1.179	−2.053
0.35	1.550	1.149	−1.743
0.40	1.522	1.124	−1.411
0.45	1.487	1.102	−1.091
0.50	1.446	1.083	−0.792
0.55	1.398	1.066	−0.507
0.60	1.342	1.050	−0.232
0.65	1.277	1.036	0.042
0.70	1.202	1.024	0.319
0.75	1.115	1.012	0.604
0.80	1.012	1.001	0.905
0.85	0.8893	0.9910	1.232
0.90	0.7362	0.9817	1.604
0.95	0.5276	0.9728	2.069
1.00	0	0.9646	π

TABLE I–R (*continued*)

z	b^*	r_m^*	χ
	$g^{*2} = 1.4$		
0.025	1.853	1.776	
0.050	1.712	1.582	−0.546
0.075	1.651	1.479	
0.10	1.618	1.410	−1.089
0.15	1.582	1.318	−1.540
0.20	1.560	1.256	−1.779
0.25	1.540	1.210	−1.791
0.30	1.519	1.174	−1.642
0.35	1.494	1.144	−1.407
0.40	1.465	1.119	−1.140
0.45	1.430	1.097	−0.870
0.50	1.389	1.078	−0.605
0.55	1.342	1.061	−0.346
0.60	1.287	1.046	−0.091
0.65	1.223	1.032	0.165
0.70	1.151	1.019	0.426
0.75	1.066	1.008	0.697
0.80	0.9678	0.9968	0.984
0.85	0.8499	0.9867	1.297
0.90	0.7033	0.9774	1.654
0.95	0.5038	0.9686	2.102
1.00	0	0.9604	π
	$g^{*2} = 1.6$		
0.025	1.837	1.769	
0.050	1.692	1.576	−0.481
0.075	1.627	1.473	
0.10	1.591	1.404	−0.938
0.15	1.549	1.312	−1.297
0.20	1.523	1.251	−1.485
0.25	1.500	1.205	−1.494
0.30	1.477	1.169	−1.373
0.35	1.450	1.139	−1.177
0.40	1.420	1.114	−0.947
0.45	1.385	1.093	−0.706
0.50	1.344	1.074	−0.465
0.55	1.297	1.057	−0.224
0.60	1.243	1.041	0.016
0.65	1.181	1.028	0.259
0.70	1.110	1.015	0.508
0.75	1.028	1.003	0.768
0.80	0.9326	0.9927	1.045
0.85	0.8186	0.9827	1.347
0.90	0.6771	0.9734	1.693
0.95	0.4849	0.9647	2.129
1.00	0	0.9565	π

TABLE I–R (*continued*)

$g^{*2} = 1.8$

z	b^*	r_m^*	χ
0.025	1.824	1.762	
0.050	1.675	1.570	−0.432
0.075	1.607	1.467	
0.10	1.568	1.399	−0.827
0.15	1.522	1.307	−1.128
0.20	1.493	1.246	−1.281
0.25	1.468	1.200	−1.285
0.30	1.442	1.165	−1.180
0.35	1.415	1.135	−1.007
0.40	1.383	1.110	−0.801
0.45	1.347	1.088	−0.580
0.50	1.307	1.069	−0.355
0.55	1.260	1.053	−0.128
0.60	1.207	1.037	0.101
0.65	1.146	1.024	0.334
0.70	1.077	1.011	0.575
0.75	0.9968	0.9996	0.826
0.80	0.9038	0.9889	1.094
0.85	0.7930	0.9789	1.388
0.90	0.6558	0.9697	1.726
0.95	0.4694	0.9610	2.151
1.00	0	0.9528	π

$g^{*2} = 2.0$

z	b^*	r_m^*	χ
0.05	1.661	1.564	−0.393
0.10	1.549	1.393	−0.743
0.15	1.500	1.302	−1.001
0.20	1.467	1.241	−1.130
0.25	1.440	1.196	−1.126
0.30	1.413	1.160	−1.033
0.35	1.385	1.131	−0.876
0.40	1.353	1.106	−0.686
0.45	1.317	1.084	−0.480
0.50	1.276	1.066	−0.267
0.55	1.229	1.049	−0.050
0.60	1.177	1.034	0.170
0.65	1.117	1.020	0.396
0.70	1.049	1.007	0.629
0.75	0.9706	0.9960	0.874
0.80	0.8797	0.9853	1.135
0.85	0.7716	0.9754	1.422
0.90	0.6379	0.9662	1.752
0.95	0.4565	0.9575	2.169
1.00	0	0.9493	π

TABLE I–R (*continued*)

z	b^*	$r_m{}^*$	χ
$g^{*2} = 2.5$			
0.05	1.632	1.551	−0.323
0.10	1.512	1.382	−0.597
0.15	1.456	1.292	−0.789
0.20	1.419	1.231	−0.877
0.25	1.388	1.186	−0.868
0.30	1.358	1.151	−0.783
0.35	1.327	1.122	−0.647
0.40	1.294	1.097	−0.481
0.45	1.257	1.076	−0.298
0.50	1.216	1.057	−0.105
0.55	1.170	1.040	0.094
0.60	1.119	1.025	0.299
0.65	1.061	1.012	0.511
0.70	0.9953	0.9992	0.731
0.75	0.9204	0.9878	0.963
0.80	0.8335	0.9772	1.212
0.85	0.7306	0.9674	1.486
0.90	0.6035	0.9582	1.803
0.95	0.4316	0.9496	2.203
1.00	0	0.9415	π
$g^{*2} = 3.0$			
0.05	1.610	1.540	−0.277
0.10	1.484	1.372	−0.504
0.15	1.424	1.282	−0.656
0.20	1.383	1.222	−0.720
0.25	1.349	1.178	−0.703
0.30	1.317	1.142	−0.622
0.35	1.285	1.113	−0.497
0.40	1.251	1.089	−0.345
0.45	1.214	1.068	−0.175
0.50	1.173	1.049	0.006
0.55	1.128	1.033	0.194
0.60	1.077	1.018	0.389
0.65	1.020	1.004	0.591
0.70	0.9566	0.9919	0.802
0.75	0.8839	0.9806	1.026
0.80	0.7999	0.9701	1.266
0.85	0.7008	0.9603	1.532
0.90	0.5786	0.9512	1.839
0.95	0.4136	0.9427	2.228
1.00	0	0.9347	π

TABLE I–R (*continued*)

$g^{*2} = 4.0$

z	b^*	r_m^*	χ
0.05	1.576	1.521	−0.219
0.10	1.444	1.355	−0.390
0.15	1.378	1.266	−0.496
0.20	1.332	1.207	−0.531
0.25	1.295	1.163	−0.503
0.30	1.261	1.128	−0.425
0.35	1.227	1.099	−0.311
0.40	1.192	1.075	−0.172
0.45	1.154	1.054	−0.017
0.50	1.113	1.036	0.149
0.55	1.068	1.020	0.324
0.60	1.020	1.005	0.507
0.65	0.9643	0.9916	0.697
0.70	0.9029	0.9794	0.898
0.75	0.8334	0.9683	1.110
0.80	0.7536	0.9579	1.339
0.85	0.6596	0.9483	1.593
0.90	0.5442	0.9393	1.887
0.95	0.3887	0.9308	2.262
1.00	0	0.9229	π

$g^{*2} = 5.0$

z	b^*	r_m^*	χ
0.05	1.551	1.504	−0.184
0.10	1.413	1.340	−0.321
0.15	1.345	1.253	−0.401
0.20	1.298	1.194	−0.420
0.25	1.258	1.151	−0.385
0.30	1.222	1.116	−0.307
0.35	1.187	1.088	−0.198
0.40	1.151	1.064	−0.066
0.45	1.113	1.043	0.082
0.50	1.073	1.025	0.240
0.55	1.028	1.009	0.407
0.60	0.9799	0.9943	0.582
0.65	0.9263	0.9811	0.766
0.70	0.8666	0.9691	0.959
0.75	0.7994	0.9580	1.164
0.80	0.7223	0.9478	1.387
0.85	0.6318	0.9382	1.633
0.90	0.5209	0.9293	1.919
0.95	0.3719	0.9210	2.284
1.00	0	0.9132	π

TABLE I–R (*continued*)

z	b^*	r_m^*	χ
	$g^{*2} = 10$		
0.05	1.477	1.449	−0.110
0.10	1.334	1.291	−0.179
0.15	1.259	1.207	−0.206
0.20	1.205	1.150	−0.192
0.25	1.162	1.108	−0.141
0.30	1.123	1.075	−0.060
0.35	1.086	1.048	0.043
0.40	1.049	1.025	0.163
0.45	1.011	1.005	0.297
0.50	0.9704	0.9874	0.440
0.55	0.9277	0.9718	0.592
0.60	0.8816	0.9578	0.752
0.65	0.8315	0.9451	0.920
0.70	0.7762	0.9335	1.099
0.75	0.7145	0.9229	1.289
0.80	0.6444	0.9130	1.496
0.85	0.5627	0.9038	1.726
0.90	0.4632	0.8953	1.993
0.95	0.3302	0.8872	2.335
1.00	0	0.8797	π
	$g^{*2} = 15$		
0.05	1.435	1.414	−0.082
0.10	1.291	1.260	−0.127
0.15	1.214	1.178	−0.136
0.20	1.159	1.122	−0.109
0.25	1.115	1.081	−0.051
0.30	1.075	1.049	0.031
0.35	1.037	1.023	0.133
0.40	1.000	1.000	0.250
0.45	0.9620	0.9806	0.379
0.50	0.9225	0.9635	0.518
0.55	0.8807	0.9483	0.664
0.60	0.8360	0.9347	0.819
0.65	0.7875	0.9223	0.982
0.70	0.7344	0.9110	1.155
0.75	0.6754	0.9005	1.339
0.80	0.6086	0.8909	1.540
0.85	0.5310	0.8819	1.763
0.90	0.4368	0.8736	2.023
0.95	0.3111	0.8657	2.356
1.00	0	0.8584	π

TABLE I–R (*continued*)

z	b^*	r_m^*	χ
$g^{*2} = 20$			
0.05	1.405	1.388	−0.066
0.10	1.262	1.237	−0.099
0.15	1.184	1.156	−0.098
0.20	1.129	1.102	−0.064
0.25	1.084	1.062	−0.003
0.30	1.044	1.030	0.081
0.35	1.006	1.004	0.183
0.40	0.9690	0.9818	0.299
0.45	0.9312	0.9627	0.425
0.50	0.8922	0.9460	0.561
0.55	0.8511	0.9311	0.705
0.60	0.8073	0.9176	0.857
0.65	0.7600	0.9055	1.017
0.70	0.7083	0.8944	1.186
0.75	0.6510	0.8841	1.368
0.80	0.5863	0.8747	1.565
0.85	0.5113	0.8659	1.785
0.90	0.4204	0.8577	2.040
0.95	0.2993	0.8500	2.368
1.00	0	0.8428	π
$g^{*2} = 50$			
0.05	1.312	1.304	−0.034
0.10	1.173	1.162	−0.040
0.15	1.096	1.086	−0.017
0.20	1.041	1.035	0.030
0.25	0.9964	0.9971	0.100
0.30	0.9567	0.9672	0.187
0.35	0.9196	0.9427	0.289
0.40	0.8834	0.9220	0.402
0.45	0.8472	0.9040	0.525
0.50	0.8100	0.8883	0.656
0.55	0.7712	0.8743	0.794
0.60	0.7303	0.8617	0.940
0.65	0.6864	0.8503	1.093
0.70	0.6387	0.8399	1.256
0.75	0.5862	0.8303	1.431
0.80	0.5273	0.8214	1.621
0.85	0.4593	0.8131	1.832
0.90	0.3772	0.8054	2.079
0.95	0.2683	0.7982	2.395
1.00	0	0.7914	π

TABLE I–R (*continued*)

$g^{*2} = 100$			
z	b^*	$r_m{}^*$	χ
0.05	1.244	1.239	−0.020
0.10	1.109	1.104	−0.013
0.15	1.035	1.032	0.018
0.20	0.9812	0.9835	0.072
0.25	0.9376	0.9476	0.145
0.30	0.8990	0.9192	0.234
0.35	0.8630	0.8959	0.336
0.40	0.8280	0.8762	0.449
0.45	0.7931	0.8592	0.570
0.50	0.7576	0.8442	0.699
0.55	0.7206	0.8309	0.835
0.60	0.6818	0.8190	0.978
0.65	0.6403	0.8081	1.129
0.70	0.5954	0.7982	1.289
0.75	0.5461	0.7891	1.460
0.80	0.4908	0.7806	1.646
0.85	0.4272	0.7728	1.854
0.90	0.3507	0.7654	2.097
0.95	0.2493	0.7586	2.407
1.00	0	0.7521	π

TABLE II–A

The Second Virial Coefficient for Polar Gases (the Stockmayer Potential Function)[a]

$$B(T) = b_0 B^\star(T^*;\, t^*) \qquad T^* = kT/\epsilon$$

$$= b_0 \tfrac{2}{3}\pi \tilde{N}\sigma^3 \qquad t^* = 8^{-1/2}\mu^{*2} = 8^{-1/2}\mu^2/\epsilon\sigma^3$$

$$B^\star(T^*;\, t^*)$$

T^* \ t^*	0.1	0.2	0.3	0.4	0.5	0.6	0.7
0.30	−31.129	−42.968	−72.01				
0.35	−20.355	−25.879	−38.07	−64.11			
0.40	−14.717	−17.777	−24.090	−36.28	−60.4		
0.45	−11.339	−13.241	−16.985	−23.733	−35.92	−58.8	
0.50	−9.1199	−10.401	−12.841	−17.026	−24.11	−36.36	−59.
0.55	−7.5631	−8.4786	−10.181	−12.996	−17.53	−24.91	−37.3
0.60	−6.4159	−7.1001	−8.3495	−10.360	−13.477	−18.33	−26.0
0.65	−5.5381	−6.0677	−7.0213	−8.5234	−10.789	−14.185	−19.34
0.70	−4.8460	−5.2675	−6.0183	−7.1813	−8.8965	−11.394	−15.05
0.75	−4.2871	−4.6304	−5.2364	−6.1627	−7.5043	−9.413	−12.13
0.80	−3.8268	−4.1116	−4.6110	−5.3659	−6.4433	−7.9476	−10.040
0.85	−3.4414	−3.6815	−4.1000	−4.7271	−5.6113	−6.8267	−8.486
0.90	−3.1142	−3.3193	−3.6758	−4.2045	−4.9432	−5.9457	−7.292
0.95	−2.8330	−3.0103	−3.3166	−3.7695	−4.3961	−5.2373	−6.3523
1.00	−2.5889	−2.7437	−3.0102	−3.4021	−3.9406	−4.6567	−5.5953
1.05	−2.3750	−2.5114	−2.7455	−3.0881	−3.5559	−4.1732	−4.9744
1.10	−2.1862	−2.3072	−2.5145	−2.8167	−3.2271	−3.7649	−4.4572
1.15	−2.0183	−2.1265	−2.3113	−2.5799	−2.9430	−3.4160	−4.0203
1.20	−1.8680	−1.9653	−2.1312	−2.3716	−2.6952	−3.1146	−3.6471
1.25	−1.7328	−1.8208	−1.9706	−2.1870	−2.4773	−2.8519	−3.3249
1.30	−1.6105	−1.6905	−1.8264	−2.0223	−2.2844	−2.6211	−3.0442
1.35	−1.4994	−1.5724	−1.6963	−1.8746	−2.1124	−2.4168	−2.7976
1.40	−1.3980	−1.4649	−1.5784	−1.7413	−1.9581	−2.2348	−2.5795
1.45	−1.3051	−1.3667	−1.4710	−1.6205	−1.8190	−2.0717	−2.3854
1.50	−1.2197	−1.2766	−1.3728	−1.5106	−1.6931	−1.9247	−2.2115
1.55	−1.1410	−1.1937	−1.2827	−1.4101	−1.5785	−1.7917	−2.0549
1.60	−1.0681	−1.1171	−1.1998	−1.3179	−1.4738	−1.6708	−1.9133
1.65	−1.0006	−1.0462	−1.1232	−1.2330	−1.3778	−1.5604	−1.7846
1.70	−0.93775	−0.98038	−1.0523	−1.1547	−1.2896	−1.4594	−1.6674
1.75	−0.87917	−0.91908	−0.98633	−1.0821	−1.2079	−1.3662	−1.5597
1.80	−0.82445	−0.86190	−0.92498	−1.0147	−1.1325	−1.2804	−1.4610
1.85	−0.77322	−0.80844	−0.86772	−0.95197	−1.0625	−1.2011	−1.3699
1.90	−0.72516	−0.75834	−0.81417	−0.89345	−0.99736	−1.1275	−1.2858
1.95	−0.67998	−0.71130	−0.76398	−0.83873	−0.93662	−1.0590	−1.2078
2.00	−0.63745	−0.66707	−0.71686	−0.78747	−0.87985	−0.99526	−1.1353
2.1	−0.55947	−0.58607	−0.63076	−0.69408	−0.77679	−0.87993	−1.0048
2.2	−0.48969	−0.51373	−0.55409	−0.61121	−0.68573	−0.77850	−0.89060
2.3	−0.42693	−0.44877	−0.48540	−0.53721	−0.60472	−0.68865	−0.78989
2.4	−0.37020	−0.39012	−0.42354	−0.47076	−0.53224	−0.60856	−0.70049
2.5	−0.31868	−0.33695	−0.36576	−0.41079	−0.46702	−0.53676	−0.62063
2.6	−0.27172	−0.28852	−0.31668	−0.35642	−0.40807	−0.47205	−0.54292
2.7	−0.22875	−0.24426	−0.27025	−0.30692	−0.35453	−0.41347	−0.48420
2.8	−0.18929	−0.20366	−0.22774	−0.26167	−0.30572	−0.36020	−0.42552
2.9	−0.15295	−0.16630	−0.18867	−0.22018	−0.26106	−0.31159	−0.37210
3.0	−0.11937	−0.13182	−0.15266	−0.18200	−0.22005	−0.26705	−0.32330
3.1	−0.08828	−0.09991	−0.11937	−0.14677	−0.18229	−0.22612	−0.27854
3.2	−0.05941	−0.07030	−0.08852	−0.11417	−0.14740	−0.18839	−0.23738
3.3	−0.03254	−0.04277	−0.05986	−0.08393	−0.11509	−0.15351	−0.19940

[a] This table was prepared by J. S. Rowlinson (see footnote 6 in § 3.10b).

TABLE II–A (*continued*)

T^* \ t^*	0.1	0.2	0.3	0.4	0.5	0.6	0.7
3.4	−0.00748	−0.01710	−0.03318	−0.05580	−0.08509	−0.12118	−0.16427
3.5	+0.01594	+0.00688	−0.00828	−0.02959	−0.05717	−0.09115	−0.13169
3.6	0.03787	0.02931	+0.01501	−0.00511	−0.03113	−0.06318	−0.10140
3.7	0.05844	0.05035	0.03682	+0.01780	−0.00680	−0.03708	−0.07318
3.8	0.07778	0.07011	0.05729	0.30928	+0.01598	−0.01268	−0.04684
3.9	0.09597	0.08869	0.07653	0.05944	0.03736	+0.01018	−0.02219
4.0	0.11312	0.10620	0.09465	0.07841	0.05744	0.03163	+0.00091
4.1	0.12930	0.12272	0.11173	0.09628	0.07633	0.05180	0.02259
4.2	0.14460	0.13833	0.12786	0.11314	0.09414	0.07078	0.04298
4.3	0.15907	0.15309	0.14310	0.12907	0.11095	0.08868	0.06218
4.4	0.17279	0.16708	0.15754	0.14414	0.12684	0.10558	0.08029
4.5	0.18580	0.18034	0.17122	0.15841	0.14187	0.12155	0.09740
4.6	0.19815	0.19293	0.18420	0.17194	0.15611	0.13668	0.11357
4.7	0.20990	0.20489	0.19652	0.18478	0.16962	0.15101	0.12888
4.8	0.22107	0.21627	0.20825	0.19699	0.18245	0.16461	0.14340
4.9	0.23172	0.22711	0.21941	0.20860	0.19465	0.17752	0.15718
5.0	0.24187	0.23744	0.23004	0.21965	0.20625	0.18980	0.17026
6	0.32187	0.31877	0.31360	0.30634	0.29699	0.28552	0.27191
7	0.37532	0.37302	0.36918	0.36380	0.35687	0.34838	0.33832
8	0.41284	0.41106	0.40809	0.40393	0.39857	0.39201	0.38424
9	0.44012	0.43870	0.43633	0.43301	0.42873	0.42349	0.41729
10	0.46049	0.45932	0.45738	0.45466	0.45116	0.44687	0.44179
20	0.52527	0.52495	0.52441	0.52367	0.52271	0.52153	0.52014
30	0.52687	0.52672	0.52647	0.52611	0.52566	0.52510	0.52444
40	0.51854	0.51845	0.51830	0.51809	0.51782	0.51749	0.51710
50	0.50834	0.50828	0.50818	0.50804	0.50876	0.50764	0.50738
60	0.49820	0.49815	0.49808	0.49798	0.49785	0.49769	0.49750
70	0.48864	0.48861	0.48855	0.48847	0.48838	0.48826	0.48811
80	0.47978	0.47976	0.47971	0.47965	0.47957	0.47948	0.47937
90	0.47161	0.47159	0.47155	0.47150	0.47144	0.47136	0.47127
100	0.46406	0.46405	0.46402	0.46398	0.46392	0.46386	0.46379
200	0.41143	0.41142	0.41142	0.41140	0.41139	0.41137	0.41135
300	0.38013	0.38012	0.38012	0.38011	0.38011	0.38010	0.38009
400	0.35835	0.35835	0.35835	0.35834	0.35834	0.35833	0.35833

T^* \ t^*	0.8	0.9	1.0	1.1	1.2	1.3	1.4	1.5
0.55	−58.8							
0.60	−38.5	−59.7						
0.65	−27.3	−40.0						
0.70	−20.50	−28.8	−41.8					
0.75	−16.05	−21.78	−30.4	−43.5				
0.80	−12.973	−17.14	−23.2	−32.0	−45.8			
0.85	−10.759	−13.90	−18.4	−24.7	−34.4	−47.0		
0.90	−9.103	−11.612	−14.92	−19.61	−26.3	−35.7	−50.3	
0.95	−7.828	−9.790	−12.42	−16.00	−21.0	−27.9	−37.8	−52.0
1.00	−6.820	−8.440	−10.54	−13.36	−17.2	−22.3	−29.8	−40.0
1.05	−6.008	−7.342	−9.08	−11.35	−14.3	−18.4	−24.3	−31.0
1.10	−5.3413	−6.4696	−7.915	−9.780	−12.21	−15.42	−19.6	−25.4
1.15	−4.7855	−5.7520	−6.976	−8.534	−10.53	−13.13	−16.5	−21.1
1.20	−4.3161	−5.1537	−6.203	−7.524	−9.20	−11.34	−14.1	−17.7
1.25	−3.9152	−4.6483	−5.559	−6.693	−8.11	−9.90	−12.2	−15.1
1.30	−3.5690	−4.2164	−5.014	−5.998	−7.21	−8.74	−10.7	−13.1
1.35	−3.2676	−3.8438	−4.5484	−5.4111	−6.471	−7.780	−9.41	−11.46
1.40	−3.0030	−3.5193	−4.1466	−4.9092	−5.839	−6.976	−8.38	−10.12
1.45	−2.7691	−3.2345	−3.7970	−4.4762	−5.298	−6.296	−7.51	−9.00

TABLE II–A (*continued*)

T^* \ t^*	0.8	0.9	1.0	1.1	1.2	1.3	1.4	1.5
1.50	−2.5609	−2.9829	−3.4903	−4.0994	−4.831	−5.714	−6.78	−8.08
1.55	−2.3745	−2.7591	−3.2192	−3.7688	−4.426	−5.212	−6.15	−7.29
1.60	−2.2069	−2.5589	−2.9783	−3.4768	−4.069	−4.774	−5.612	−6.62
1.65	−2.0554	−2.3788	−2.7629	−3.2173	−3.7548	−4.3909	−5.145	−6.045
1.70	−1.9180	−2.2165	−2.5697	−2.9860	−3.4760	−4.0532	−4.735	−5.541
1.75	−1.7923	−2.0685	−2.3943	−2.7770	−3.2256	−3.7517	−4.370	−5.097
1.80	−1.6775	−1.9340	−2.2357	−2.5889	−3.0014	−3.4831	−4.046	−4.706
1.85	−1.5720	−1.8110	−2.0912	−2.4183	−2.7990	−3.2419	−3.758	−4.359
1.90	−1.4749	−1.6981	−1.9591	−2.2630	−2.6156	−3.0244	−3.498	−4.049
1.95	−1.3852	−1.5941	−1.8380	−2.1211	−2.4487	−2.8273	−3.265	−3.771
2.00	−1.3021	−1.4982	−1.7265	−1.9910	−2.2963	−2.6479	−3.053	−3.520
2.1	−1.1531	−1.3268	−1.5285	−1.7610	−2.0282	−2.3342	−2.6846	−3.0857
2.2	−1.0234	−1.1785	−1.3580	−1.5643	−1.8002	−2.0693	−2.3758	−2.7248
2.3	−0.90957	−1.0490	−1.2100	−1.3943	−1.6044	−1.8431	−2.1138	−2.4204
2.4	−0.80895	−0.93509	−1.0803	−1.2461	−1.4345	−1.6479	−1.8889	−2.1606
2.5	−0.71944	−0.83413	−0.96584	−1.1159	−1.2860	−1.4780	−1.6940	−1.9368
2.6	−0.63934	−0.74412	−0.86421	−1.0008	−1.1551	−1.3289	−1.5239	−1.7423
2.7	−0.56729	−0.66342	−0.77343	−0.89828	−1.0391	−1.1972	−1.3742	−1.5719
2.8	−0.50216	−0.59072	−0.69191	−0.80654	−0.93559	−1.0802	−1.2416	−1.4215
2.9	−0.44304	0.52492	0.61833	−0.72400	−0.84273	−0.97334	−1.1235	−1.2879
3.0	−0.38917	−0.46511	−0.55165	−0.64940	−0.75908	−0.88152	−1.0177	−1.1687
3.1	−0.33989	−0.41054	−0.49096	−0.58168	−0.68333	−0.79663	−0.92240	−1.0616
3.2	−0.29466	−0.36057	−0.43552	−0.51998	−0.61449	−0.71967	−0.83625	−0.96505
3.3	−0.25302	−0.31468	−0.38472	−0.46355	−0.55167	−0.64962	−0.75801	−0.87758
3.4	−0.21459	−0.27239	−0.33800	−0.41179	−0.49417	−0.58562	−0.68671	−0.79805
3.5	−0.17900	−0.23332	−0.29493	−0.36415	−0.44135	−0.52697	−0.62149	−0.72546
3.6	−0.14598	−0.19713	−0.25510	0.32018	0.39270	−0.47305	−0.56164	−0.65899
3.7	−0.11527	−0.16352	−0.21818	−0.27949	−0.34776	−0.42333	−0.50657	−0.59792
3.8	−0.08664	−0.13225	−0.18388	−0.24176	−0.30615	−0.37736	−0.45574	−0.54166
3.9	−0.05989	−0.10308	−0.15193	−0.20667	−0.26752	−0.33476	−0.40870	−0.48968
4.0	−0.03486	−0.07582	−0.12213	−0.17397	−0.23158	−0.29519	−0.36507	−0.44155
4.1	−0.01140	−0.05030	−0.09426	−0.14345	−0.19807	−0.25834	−0.32451	−0.39687
4.2	+0.01064	−0.02636	−0.06815	−0.11490	−0.16677	−0.22397	−0.28673	−0.35530
4.3	0.03137	−0.00387	−0.04366	−0.08814	−0.13747	−0.19184	−0.25145	−0.31654
4.4	0.05089	+0.01729	−0.02064	−0.06302	−0.11000	−0.16175	−0.21846	−0.28033
4.5	0.06932	0.03723	+0.00103	−0.03941	−0.08421	−0.13353	−0.18755	−0.24645
4.6	0.08672	0.05605	0.02145	−0.01717	−0.05995	−0.10702	−0.15854	−0.21469
4.7	0.10318	0.07383	0.04073	+0.00380	−0.03709	−0.08207	−0.13127	−0.18486
4.8	0.11877	0.09065	0.05896	0.02360	−0.01554	−0.05856	−0.10560	−0.15681
4.9	0.13355	0.10659	0.07620	0.04232	+0.00483	−0.03637	−0.08140	−0.13039
5.0	0.14758	0.12170	0.09255	0.06004	0.02409	−0.01540	−0.05855	−0.10548
6	0.25614	0.23818	0.21799	0.19554	0.17077	+0.14364	+0.11409	+0.08206
7	0.32667	0.31341	0.29853	0.28199	0.26379	0.24389	0.22225	0.19885
8	0.37524	0.36502	0.35355	0.34082	0.32682	0.31154	0.29494	0.27702
9	0.41012	0.40197	0.39283	0.38270	0.37157	0.35942	0.34625	0.33203
10	0.43593	0.42927	0.42180	0.41353	0.40444	0.39453	0.38379	0.37221
20	0.51854	0.51672	0.51468	0.51243	0.50996	0.50728	0.50438	0.50125
30	0.52367	0.52281	0.52184	0.52077	0.51960	0.51833	0.51695	0.51547
40	0.51665	0.51613	0.51556	0.51493	0.51423	0.51348	0.51266	0.51179
50	0.50707	0.50673	0.50635	0.50593	0.50546	0.50496	0.50441	0.50383
60	0.49729	0.49704	0.49676	0.49646	0.49613	0.49576	0.49537	0.49495
70	0.48795	0.48776	0.48755	0.48732	0.48707	0.48679	0.48650	0.48618
80	0.47924	0.47909	0.47893	0.47874	0.47854	0.47833	0.47810	0.47784
90	0.47117	0.47105	0.47091	0.47077	0.47061	0.47043	0.47024	0.47004
100	0.46370	0.46360	0.46349	0.46337	0.46323	0.46309	0.46293	0.46276
200	0.41132	0.41129	0.41126	0.41123	0.41119	0.41115	0.41110	0.41105
300	0.38008	0.38006	0.38005	0.38003	0.38001	0.37999	0.37997	0.37994
400	0.35832	0.35831	0.35830	0.35829	0.35828	0.35827	0.35825	0.35824

TABLE II–B

THE JOULE-THOMSON COEFFICIENT FOR POLAR GASES (STOCKMAYER POTENTIAL)[a]

$$\mu^0 C_p^{\,0} = b_0[B_1^\star - B^\star] \qquad T^* = kT/\epsilon$$

$$b_0 = \tfrac{2}{3}\pi\tilde{N}\sigma^3 \qquad t^* = 8^{-1/2}\,\mu^{*2} = 8^{-1/2}\,\mu^2/\epsilon\sigma^3$$

$$B_1^\star(T^*;\, t^*) - B^\star(T^*;\, t^*)$$

T^* \ t^*	0.1	0.2	0.3	0.4	0.5	0.6	0.7
0.30	123.498	197.638	402.4				
0.35	72.564	103.764	179.79	364.1			
0.40	48.640	64.580	100.272	177.22	349.5		
0.45	35.492	44.773	64.351	103.156	181.58	347.1	
0.50	27.438	33.366	45.340	67.640	109.34	189.8	352.0
0.55	22.1035	26.1573	34.084	48.166	72.96	117.58	200.6
0.60	18.3565	21.2763	26.8448	36.383	52.405	79.68	127.3
0.65	15.6028	17.7928	21.8888	28.7059	39.738	57.691	87.51
0.70	13.5052	15.2019	18.3263	23.4079	31.3874	43.904	63.83
0.75	11.8606	13.2102	15.6644	19.5818	25.5836	34.718	48.76
0.80	10.5403	11.6374	13.6121	16.7158	21.3750	28.2907	38.611
0.85	9.4591	10.3674	11.9883	14.5035	18.2157	23.6106	31.464
0.90	8.5590	9.3226	10.6764	12.7530	15.7751	20.0896	26.238
0.95	7.7987	8.4494	9.5953	11.3386	13.8439	17.3667	22.2972
1.00	7.1487	7.7095	8.6921	10.1751	12.2845	15.2118	19.2456
1.05	6.5870	7.0753	7.9269	9.2036	11.0032	13.4727	16.8297
1.10	6.0970	6.5258	7.2710	8.3816	9.9346	12.0450	14.8801
1.15	5.6661	6.0457	6.7030	7.6778	9.0318	10.8556	13.2805
1.20	5.2843	5.6227	6.2609	7.0694	8.2601	9.8520	11.9493
1.25	4.9437	5.2473	5.7700	6.5385	7.5939	8.9955	10.8272
1.30	4.6382	4.9121	5.3824	6.0716	7.0137	8.2573	9.8708
1.35	4.3627	4.6109	5.0365	5.6582	6.5043	7.6153	9.0475
1.40	4.1129	4.3390	4.7260	5.2896	6.0538	7.0525	8.3325
1.45	3.8855	4.0924	4.4457	4.9591	5.6528	6.5557	7.7068
1.50	3.6776	3.8676	4.1916	4.6613	5.2940	6.1141	7.1550
1.55	3.4870	3.6620	3.9602	4.3916	4.9712	5.7196	6.6655
1.60	3.3113	3.4732	3.7486	4.1463	4.6791	5.3651	6.2285
1.65	3.1492	3.2993	3.5545	3.9222	4.4138	5.0449	5.8365
1.70	2.9990	3.13866	3.3757	3.7168	4.1720	4.7547	5.4832
1.75	2.85950	2.98972	3.21054	3.5279	3.9503	4.4900	5.1627
1.80	2.72960	2.85133	3.05758	3.3536	3.7469	4.2482	4.8715
1.85	2.60837	2.72242	2.91549	3.19224	3.5595	4.0265	4.6055
1.90	2.49495	2.60204	2.78319	3.04254	3.38617	3.8224	4.3620
1.95	2.38863	2.48938	2.65970	2.90328	3.22556	3.6339	4.1380
2.0	2.28878	2.38375	2.54419	2.77342	3.07632	3.45947	3.9314
2.1	2.10628	2.19109	2.33421	2.53836	2.80747	3.14689	3.5635
2.2	1.94360	2.01983	2.14835	2.33137	2.57215	2.87504	3.24571
2.3	1.79774	1.86666	1.98271	2.14779	2.36456	2.63666	2.96873
2.4	1.66625	1.72885	1.83421	1.98389	2.18016	2.42601	2.72533
2.5	1.54710	1.60426	1.70036	1.83675	2.01533	2.23865	2.50995
2.6	1.43869	1.49107	1.57911	1.70393	1.86717	2.07097	2.31811
2.7	1.33963	1.38782	1.46879	1.58350	1.73333	1.92014	2.14628
2.8	1.24877	1.29327	1.36801	1.47379	1.61183	1.78373	1.99151
2.9	1.16516	1.20638	1.27558	1.37347	1.50109	1.65983	1.85143
3.0	1.08796	1.12627	1.19055	1.28140	1.39976	1.54684	1.72415
3.1	1.01650	1.05219	1.11205	1.19663	1.30675	1.44343	1.60802
3.2	0.95015	0.98349	1.03939	1.11834	1.22105	1.34843	1.50166
3.3	0.88839	0.91962	0.97194	1.04582	1.14185	1.26088	1.40391
3.4	0.83078	0.86009	0.90919	0.97846	1.06843	1.17996	1.31382
3.5	0.77692	0.80448	0.85065	0.91575	1.00031	1.10496	1.23052
3.6	0.72646	0.75243	0.79592	0.85724	0.93682	1.03527	1.15329
3.7	0.67910	0.70361	0.74465	0.80251	0.87758	0.97037	1.08154
3.8	0.63454	0.65773	0.69654	0.75122	0.82214	0.90976	1.01468
3.9	0.59258	0.61455	0.65130	0.70308	0.77018	0.85308	0.95227
4.0	0.55299	0.57383	0.60869	0.65779	0.72140	0.79994	0.89387
4.1	0.51559	0.53538	0.56849	0.61512	0.67551	0.75004	0.83913
4.2	0.48018	0.49901	0.53051	0.57486	0.63227	0.70310	0.78772
4.3	0.44664	0.46458	0.49458	0.53680	0.59147	0.65887	0.73938
4.4	0.41481	0.43192	0.46053	0.50079	0.55289	0.61712	0.69380
4.5	0.38457	0.40091	0.42823	0.46666	0.51639	0.57767	0.65078
4.6	0.35582	0.37143	0.39754	0.43427	0.48180	0.54032	0.61014
4.7	0.32843	0.34338	0.36837	0.40351	0.44896	0.50492	0.57167
4.8	0.30234	0.31665	0.34058	0.37424	0.41776	0.47134	0.53522
4.9	0.27742	0.29115	0.31410	0.34637	0.38809	0.43943	0.50062
5.0	0.25364	0.26682	0.28884	0.31981	0.35983	0.40909	0.46776
6.0	0.06411	0.07325	0.08850	0.10993	0.13758	0.17155	0.21194
7.0	−0.06559	−0.05885	−0.04761	−0.03184	−0.01150	0.01345	0.04307
8.0	−0.15923	−0.15404	−0.14539	−0.13326	−0.11762	−0.09846	−0.07572
9.0	−0.22952	−0.22540	−0.21852	−0.20887	−0.19644	−0.18121	−0.16317
10.0	−0.28389	−0.28052	−0.27491	−0.26704	−0.25690	−0.24448	−0.22977
20	−0.49641	−0.49550	−0.49398	−0.49186	−0.48913	−0.48579	−0.48183
30	−0.54427	−0.54384	−0.54313	−0.54212	−0.54084	−0.53926	−0.53740
40	−0.55780	−0.55754	−0.55712	−0.55653	−0.55577	−0.55484	−0.55374
50	−0.55995	−0.55978	−0.55950	−0.55911	−0.55860	−0.55798	−0.55725
60	−0.55754	−0.55741	−0.55721	−0.55693	−0.55656	−0.55611	−0.55558
70	−0.55312	−0.55304	−0.55288	−0.55266	−0.55239	−0.55205	−0.55165
80	−0.54785	−0.54778	−0.54765	−0.54748	−0.54726	−0.54700	−0.54669
90	−0.54224	−0.54219	−0.54208	−0.54195	−0.54177	−0.54156	−0.54130
100	−0.53657	−0.53653	−0.53645	−0.53634	−0.53619	−0.53601	−0.53581
200	−0.48897	−0.48895	−0.48893	−0.48889	−0.48886	−0.48880	−0.48874
300	−0.45665	−0.45664	−0.45663	−0.45661	−0.45660	−0.45657	−0.45654
400	−0.43310	−0.43310	−0.43310	−0.43308	−0.43307	−0.43305	−0.43304

TABLE II–B (*continued*)

T^* \ t^*	0.8	0.9	1.0	1.1	1.2	1.3	1.4	1.5
0.55	360.0							
0.60	213.0	372.0						
0.65	138.2	227.0						
0.70	96.3	150.3	242.0					
0.75	70.72	105.82	163.2	258.4				
0.80	54.24	78.31	116.3	176.8	276.0			
0.85	43.02	60.29	86.6	127.3	192.0	293.0		
0.90	35.071	47.981	66.93	95.50	139.2	206.6	313.0	
0.95	29.234	39.097	53.31	74.12	105.1	151.6	223.0	332.0
1.00	24.818	32.600	43.54	59.20	81.9	115.2	165.0	239.0
1.05	21.395	27.645	36.29	48.40	65.5	90.2	126.0	178.0
1.10	18.6830	23.808	30.776	40.350	53.67	72.42	99.0	137.5
1.15	16.4942	20.766	26.485	34.213	44.77	59.37	79.8	108.7
1.20	14.6991	18.3101	23.078	29.427	37.97	49.57	65.5	87.6
1.25	13.2061	16.2961	20.327	25.623	32.64	42.03	54.7	72.0
1.30	11.9486	14.6216	18.071	22.548	28.39	36.13	46.5	60.4
1.35	10.8780	13.2126	18.1956	20.026	24.980	31.436	39.93	51.21
1.40	9.9574	12.0135	14.6177	17.930	22.167	27.626	34.72	44.02
1.45	9.1590	10.9836	13.2764	16.1663	19.828	24.498	30.49	38.26
1.50	8.4609	10.0913	12.1252	14.6681	17.861	21.895	27.02	33.59
1.55	7.8463	9.3120	11.1284	13.3829	16.192	19.708	24.14	29.76
1.60	7.3015	8.6265	10.2587	12.2709	14.759	17.849	21.71	26.56
1.65	6.8161	8.0198	9.4946	11.3016	13.521	16.257	19.65	23.88
1.70	6.3813	7.4800	8.8194	10.4514	12.4433	14.8825	17.884	21.595
1.75	5.9891	6.9960	8.2178	9.6990	11.4964	13.6838	16.358	19.640
1.80	5.6346	6.5610	7.6804	9.0309	10.6612	12.6337	15.029	17.951
1.85	5.3125	6.1679	7.1974	8.4339	9.9194	11.7072	13.866	16.482
1.90	5.0189	5.8113	6.7614	7.8981	9.2575	10.8855	12.840	15.196
1.95	4.7502	5.4863	6.3661	7.4147	8.6636	10.1524	11.932	14.064
2.0	4.5034	5.1893	6.0064	6.9770	8.1284	9.4952	11.121	13.060
2.1	4.0662	4.6661	5.3769	6.2158	7.2043	8.3684	9.7415	11.3642
2.2	3.6913	4.2207	4.8450	5.5779	6.4361	7.4402	8.6158	9.9944
2.3	3.3666	3.8376	4.3908	5.0369	5.7895	6.6650	7.6835	8.8694
2.4	3.08298	3.5050	3.9987	4.5729	5.2387	6.0093	6.9006	7.9319
2.5	2.83332	3.2138	3.6573	4.1714	4.7650	5.4488	6.2357	7.1414
2.6	2.61200	2.9569	3.3578	3.8210	4.3537	4.7650	5.6653	6.4675
2.7	2.41467	2.72887	3.0932	3.5128	3.9939	4.5439	5.1715	5.8873
2.8	2.23766	2.52523	2.8579	3.2400	3.6769	4.1746	4.7406	5.3836
2.9	2.07805	2.34233	2.6474	2.9970	3.3955	3.8483	4.3616	4.9425
3.0	1.93355	2.17733	2.45819	2.7794	3.1447	3.5585	4.0263	4.5540
3.1	1.80216	2.02781	2.28733	2.5835	2.9197	3.2996	3.7278	4.2096
3.2	1.68218	1.89171	2.13231	2.4064	2.7169	3.0669	3.4606	3.9024
3.3	1.57224	1.76737	1.99111	2.24557	2.5332	2.8571	3.2204	3.6271
3.4	1.47118	1.65338	1.86202	2.09897	2.3664	2.6669	3.0033	3.3790
3.5	1.37798	1.54855	1.74362	1.96485	2.2142	2.4938	2.8063	3.1547
3.6	1.29180	1.45184	1.63466	1.84174	2.0748	2.3357	2.6269	2.9508
3.7	1.21190	1.36238	1.53412	1.72840	1.94677	2.1909	2.4629	2.7651
3.8	1.13761	1.27940	1.44106	1.62375	1.82882	2.0578	2.3126	2.5951
3.9	1.06840	1.20226	1.35472	1.52686	1.71987	1.9352	2.1743	2.4392
4.0	1.00378	1.13036	1.27443	1.43692	1.61984	1.8217	2.0468	2.2955
4.1	0.94332	1.06322	1.19959	1.35326	1.52523	1.71661	1.9287	2.1630
4.2	0.88663	1.00039	1.12967	1.27526	1.43802	1.61898	1.8193	2.0403
4.3	0.83341	0.94150	1.06426	1.20239	1.35669	1.52808	1.7176	1.9265
4.4	0.78333	0.88617	1.00290	1.13415	1.28066	1.44325	1.6229	1.82063
4.5	0.73613	0.83412	0.94527	1.07017	1.20948	1.36395	1.53448	1.72201
4.6	0.69160	0.78508	0.89106	1.01006	1.14272	1.28970	1.45180	1.62993
4.7	0.64951	0.73879	0.83996	0.95349	1.07996	1.22001	1.37433	1.54375
4.8	0.60967	0.69505	0.79173	0.90019	1.02092	1.15452	1.30163	1.46300
4.9	0.57193	0.65365	0.74617	0.84987	0.96526	1.09287	1.23329	1.38720
5.0	0.53611	0.61442	0.70302	0.80230	0.91272	1.03473	1.16892	1.31590
6	0.25886	0.31246	0.37291	0.44039	0.51512	0.59734	0.68732	0.78535
7	0.07743	0.11662	0.16072	0.20985	0.26411	0.32363	0.38858	0.45910
8	−0.04937	−0.01936	0.01437	0.05187	0.09323	0.13851	0.18782	0.24124
9	−0.14227	−0.11848	−0.09177	−0.06211	−0.02944	0.00629	0.04512	0.08714
10	−0.21275	−0.19339	−0.17167	−0.14756	−0.12103	−0.09205	−0.06058	−0.02657
20	−0.47728	−0.47210	−0.46630	−0.45989	−0.45285	−0.44520	−0.43692	−0.42799
30	−0.53524	−0.53280	−0.53006	−0.52704	−0.52373	−0.52013	−0.51624	−0.51205
40	−0.55247	−0.55102	−0.54941	−0.54763	−0.54567	−0.54356	−0.54126	−0.53880
50	−0.55639	−0.55544	−0.55437	−0.55318	−0.55188	−0.55047	−0.54893	−0.54730
60	−0.55498	−0.55429	−0.55351	−0.55267	−0.55174	−0.55071	−0.54962	−0.54844
70	−0.55119	−0.55067	−0.55008	−0.54944	−0.54873	−0.54796	−0.54714	−0.54624
80	−0.54633	−0.54592	−0.54546	−0.54495	−0.54439	−0.54379	−0.54314	−0.54243
90	−0.54102	−0.54068	−0.54030	−0.53990	−0.53945	−0.53896	−0.53843	−0.53787
100	−0.53556	−0.53529	−0.53498	−0.53464	−0.53426	−0.53386	−0.53342	−0.53295
200	−0.48867	−0.48859	−0.48850	−0.48841	−0.48830	−0.48818	−0.48805	−0.48792
300	−0.45651	−0.45647	−0.45643	−0.45638	−0.45632	−0.45627	−0.45621	−0.45614
400	−0.43302	−0.43299	−0.43297	−0.43294	−0.43291	−0.43288	−0.43283	−0.43280

[a] This table was prepared by J. S. Rowlinson (see footnote 6 in § 3.10b).

TABLE II–C

THE FUNCTION $(T^*/t^*)B^*$ USED TO DETERMINE THE PARAMETERS IN THE STOCKMAYER POTENTIAL FROM EXPERIMENTAL SECOND VIRIAL COEFFICIENTS[a]

T^* \ t^*	0.1	0.2	0.3	0.4	0.5	0.6	0.7
0.30	−93.387	−64.452	−72.01				
0.35	−71.243	−45.288	−44.42	−56.10			
0.40	−58.868	−35.554	−32.120	−36.28	−48.3		
0.45	−51.026	−29.792	−25.478	−26.700	−32.33	−44.1	
0.50	−45.600	−26.003	−21.402	−21.283	−24.11	−30.30	−42.0
0.55	−41.597	−23.316	−18.665	−17.870	−19.28	−22.83	−29.3
0.60	−38.495	−21.300	−16.699	−15.540	−16.172	−18.33	−22.3
0.65	−35.998	−19.720	−15.213	−13.851	−14.026	−15.367	−17.96
0.70	−33.922	−18.436	−14.043	−12.567	−12.455	−13.293	−15.05
0.75	−32.153	−17.364	−13.091	−11.555	−11.256	−11.77	−13.00
0.80	−30.614	−16.446	−12.296	−10.732	−10.309	−10.597	−11.474
0.85	−29.252	−15.646	−11.617	−10.045	−9.539	−9.6712	−10.30
0.90	−28.028	−14.937	−11.027	−9.4601	−8.8978	−8.9186	−9.375
0.95	−26.914	−14.299	−10.503	−8.9526	−8.3526	−8.2924	−8.6210
1.00	−25.889	−13.718	−10.034	−8.5053	−7.8812	−7.7612	−7.9933
1.05	−24.938	−13.185	−9.6093	−8.1603	−7.4674	−7.3031	−7.4616
1.10	−24.048	−12.690	−9.2198	−7.7459	−7.0996	−6.9023	−7.0042
1.15	−23.210	−12.227	−8.8600	−7.4172	−6.7689	−6.5473	−6.6048
1.20	−22.416	−11.792	−8.5248	−7.1148	−6.4685	−6.2292	−6.2522
1.25	−21.660	−11.380	−8.2108	−6.8344	−6.1933	−5.9415	−5.9373
1.30	−20.937	−10.988	−7.9144	−6.5725	−5.9394	−5.6791	−5.6535
1.35	−20.242	−10.614	−7.6334	−6.3268	−5.7035	−5.4378	−5.3954
1.40	−19.572	−10.254	−7.3659	−6.0946	−5.4827	−5.2145	−5.1590
1.45	−18.924	−9.9086	−7.1098	−5.8743	−5.2751	−5.0066	−4.9412
1.50	−18.296	−9.5745	−6.8640	−5.6648	−5.0793	−4.8118	−4.7389
1.55	−17.686	−9.2512	−6.6273	−5.4641	−4.8934	−4.6286	−4.5501
1.60	−17.090	−8.9368	−6.3989	−5.2716	−4.7162	−4.4555	−4.3733
1.65	−16.510	−8.6312	−6.1776	−5.0861	−4.5467	−4.2911	−4.2066
1.70	−15.942	−8.8333	−5.9630	−4.9075	−4.3846	−4.1350	−4.0494
1.75	−15.385	−8.0420	−5.7536	−4.7342	−4.2277	−3.9848	−3.8993
1.80	−14.840	−7.7571	−5.5499	−4.5662	−4.0770	−3.8412	−3.7569
1.85	−14.305	−7.4781	−5.3509	−4.4029	−3.9313	−3.7034	−3.6205
1.90	−13.778	−7.2042	−5.1564	−4.2439	−3.7900	−3.5704	−3.4900
1.95	−13.260	−6.9352	−4.9659	−4.0888	−3.6528	−3.4418	−3.3646
2.0	−12.749	−6.6707	−4.7791	−3.9374	−3.5194	−3.3175	−3.2437
2.1	−11.749	−6.1537	−4.4153	−3.6439	−3.2625	−3.0798	−3.0144
2.2	−10.773	−5.6510	−4.0633	−3.3617	−3.0172	−2.8545	−2.7990
2.3	−9.8194	−5.1609	−3.7214	−3.0890	−2.7817	−2.6398	−2.5954
2.4	−8.8848	−4.6814	−3.3883	−2.8246	−2.5548	−2.4342	−2.4017
2.5	−7.9670	−4.2119	−3.0630	−2.5674	−2.3351	−2.2365	−2.2165
2.6	−7.0647	−3.7508	−2.7446	−2.3167	−2.1220	−2.0456	−2.0388
2.7	−6.1763	−3.2975	−2.4323	−2.0717	−1.9145	−1.8606	−1.8676
2.8	−5.3001	−2.8512	−2.1256	−1.8317	−1.7120	−1.6809	−1.7021
2.9	−4.4356	−2.4114	−1.8238	−1.5963	−1.5141	−1.5060	−1.5416
3.0	−3.5811	−1.9773	−1.5266	−1.3650	−1.3203	−1.3353	−1.3856

[a] This table was prepared by J. S. Rowlinson (see footnote 6 in § 3.10b).

TABLE II–C (*continued*)

T^* \ t^*	0.8	0.9	1.0	1.1	1.2	1.3	1.4	1.5
0.30								
0.35								
0.40								
0.45								
0.50								
0.55	−40.4							
0.60	−28.9	−39.8						
0.65	−22.2	−28.9						
0.70	−17.94	−22.4	−29.3					
0.75	−15.05	−18.15	−22.8	−29.7				
0.80	−12.973	−15.24	−18.6	−23.3	−30.5			
0.85	−11.431	−13.13	−15.6	−19.1	−24.4	−31.0		
0.90	10.24	11.612	−13.43	−16.04	−19.7	−24.7	−32.3	
0.95	−9.296	−10.33	−11.80	−13.82	−16.6	−20.4	−25.7	−33.0
1.00	−8.525	−9.378	−10.54	−12.15	−14.3	−17.2	−21.3	−27.0
1.05	−7.886	−8.566	−9.53	−10.83	−12.5	−14.9	−18.2	−22.0
1.10	−7.3443	−7.9073	−8.707	−9.780	−11.19	−13.05	−15.4	−18.6
1.15	−6.8792	−7.3498	−8.022	−8.922	−10.09	−11.62	−13.6	−16.2
1.20	−6.4742	−6.8716	−7.444	−8.208	−9.20	−10.47	−12.1	−14.2
1.25	−6.1175	−6.4560	−6.949	−7.606	−8.45	−9.52	−10.9	−12.6
1.30	−5.7996	−6.0904	−6.518	−7.089	−7.81	−8.74	−9.94	−11.4
1.35	−5.5141	−5.7657	−6.1403	−6.6409	−7.280	−8.079	−9.07	−10.31
1.40	−5.2553	−5.4745	−5.8052	−6.2481	−6.812	−7.513	−8.38	−9.445
1.45	−5.0190	−5.2111	−5.5057	−5.9004	−6.402	−7.022	−7.78	−8.70
1.50	−4.8017	−4.9715	−5.2355	−5.5901	−6.039	−6.593	−7.26	−8.08
1.55	−4.6006	−4.7518	−4.9898	−5.3106	−5.717	−6.214	−6.81	−7.53
1.60	−4.4138	−4.5492	−4.7653	−5.0572	−5.425	−5.876	6.414	7.06
1.65	−4.2393	−4.3611	−4.5588	−4.8260	−5.1629	−5.5731	−6.064	−6.650
1.70	−4.0758	−4.1867	−4.3685	−4.6147	−4.9243	−5.3003	−5.750	−6.280
1.75	−3.9207	−4.0221	−4.1900	−4.4180	−4.7040	−5.0504	−5.463	−5.947
1.80	−3.7744	−3.8680	−4.0243	−4.2364	−4.5021	−4.8228	−5.202	−5.647
1.85	−3.6353	−3.7226	−3.8687	−4.0671	−4.3151	−4.6135	−4.966	−5.376
1.90	−3.5029	−3.5849	−3.7223	−3.9088	−4.1414	−4.4203	−4.747	−5.129
1.95	−3.3764	−3.4539	−3.5841	−3.7601	−3.9791	−4.2410	−4.548	−4.902
2.0	−3.2553	−3.3293	−3.4530	−3.6200	−3.8272	−4.0737	−4.361	−4.693
2.1	−3.0269	−3.0959	−3.2099	−3.3619	−3.5494	−3.7706	−4.0269	4.3200
2.2	−2.8144	−2.8808	−2.9876	−3.1286	−3.3004	−3.5019	−3.7334	−3.9964
2.3	−2.6150	−2.6808	−2.7830	−2.9154	−3.0751	−3.2609	−3.4727	−3.7113
2.4	−2.4269	−2.4936	−2.5927	−2.7188	−2.8690	−3.0423	−3.2381	−3.4570
2.5	−2.2483	−2.3170	−2.4146	−2.5361	−2.6792	−2.8423	−3.0250	−3.2280
2.6	−2.0779	−2.1497	−2.2469	−2.3655	−2.5027	−2.6578	−2.8301	−3.0200
2.7	−1.9146	−1.9903	−2.0883	−2.2049	−2.3380	−2.4865	−2.6502	−2.8294
2.8	−1.7576	−1.8378	−1.9373	−2.0530	−2.1830	−2.3266	−2.4832	−2.6535
2.9	−1.6060	−1.6914	−1.7932	−1.9087	−2.0366	−2.1762	−2.3273	−2.4899
3.0	−1.4594	−1.5504	−1.6550	−1.7711	−1.8977	−2.0343	−2.1808	−2.3374

TABLE II–D. The Third Virial Coefficient for Polar Gases (the Stockmayer Potential Function)[a]

$C(T) = b_0^2 C^\star(T^*; t^*)$ $T^* = kT/\epsilon$ $b_0 = \frac{2}{3}\pi \tilde{N}\sigma^3$ $t^* = 8^{-1/2}\,\mu^{*2} = 8^{-1/2}\,\mu^2/\epsilon\sigma^3$

	$C^\star(T^*; t^*)$										
T^* \ t^*	0.0	0.1	0.2	0.3	0.4	0.5	0.6	0.7	0.8	1.0	1.2
1.0	0.4297	0.4440	0.5304	0.740							
1.2	0.5924	0.6177	0.7162	0.9216	1.268	1.78	2.5	3.4	4.6	7.	
1.4	0.5683	0.5900	0.6679	0.8221	1.075	1.451	2.0	2.7	3.7	6.3	9.
1.6	0.5180	0.5351	0.5940	0.7075	0.8899	1.158	1.53	2.03	2.69	4.72	7.0
1.8	0.4728	0.4861	0.5311	0.6161	0.7507	0.9455	1.214	1.572	2.03	3.36	5.2
2.0	0.4371	0.4476	0.4826	0.5478	0.6496	0.7957	0.995	1.257	1.595	2.46	4.0
2.5	0.3811	0.3873	0.4076	0.4445	0.5195	0.5807	0.6871	0.825	0.999	1.482	2.19
3.0	0.3523	0.3563	0.3692	0.3924	0.4275	0.4761	0.5403	0.6223	0.7248	1.002	1.401
4.0	0.3266	0.3286	0.3350	0.3463	0.3630	0.3859	0.4156	0.4529	0.4986	0.6194	0.7857
6.0	0.3077	0.3085	0.3109	0.3151	0.3213	0.3296	0.3401	0.3532	0.3690	0.4095	0.4640
8.0	0.2962	0.2966	0.2978	0.3000	0.3031	0.3072	0.3124	0.3188	0.3265	0.3459	0.3715
10.0	0.2861	0.2863	0.2871	0.2884	0.2902	0.2926	0.2957	0.2995	0.3039	0.3151	0.3297

[a] J. S. Rowlinson, *J. Chem. Phys.*, **19**, 827 (1951).

TABLE III

THE DISTANCE OF CLOSEST APPROACH AND THE ANGLE OF DEFLECTION FOR THE INVERSE TWELFTH-POWER REPULSIVE POTENTIAL

$$\varphi(r) = 4\epsilon \left(\frac{\sigma}{r}\right)^{12}$$

$$y = \frac{b}{r}, \quad y_m = \frac{b}{r_m}, \quad y_0 = b\left[\frac{\frac{1}{2}\mu g^2}{48\epsilon\sigma^{12}}\right]^{1/12}$$

($\chi' = d\chi/dy_0$ and ψ are quantities needed in the calculation of the quantum deviations of the transport coefficients)

y_0	y_m	χ	χ'	ψ
0.00	0.00000	3.1416	−2.731	3.1416
0.05	0.06148	3.0049	−2.736	2.553
0.10	0.12285	2.8679	−2.744	1.958
0.15	0.18398	2.7303	−2.761	1.356
0.20	0.24475	2.5917	−2.783	0.743
0.25	0.30503	2.4519	−2.811	0.116
0.30	0.36466	2.3105	−2.844	−0.529
0.35	0.42349	2.1673	−2.886	−1.195
0.40	0.48134	2.0217	−2.936	−1.887
0.45	0.53799	1.8736	−2.991	−2.611
0.50	0.59321	1.7225	−3.051	−3.388
0.55	0.64668	1.5684	−3.116	−4.127
0.60	0.69808	1.4109	−3.182	−4.993
0.65	0.74697	1.2504	−3.243	−5.847
0.70	0.79284	1.0871	−3.286	−6.668
0.75	0.83509	0.9228	−3.292	−7.341
0.80	0.87305	0.7596	−3.234	−7.847
0.85	0.90599	0.6020	−3.070	−8.056
0.90	0.93332	0.4559	−2.770	−7.840
0.95	0.95474	0.3282	−2.328	−7.048
1.00	0.97048	0.2249	−1.804	−5.799
1.05	0.98132	0.1477	−1.287	−4.335
1.10	0.98839	0.0943	−0.859	−3.085
1.15	0.99283	0.0592	−0.546	−2.087
1.20	0.99555	0.0371	−0.340	−1.358
1.25	0.99723	0.0232	−0.210	−0.874
1.30	0.99825	0.0148	−0.131	−0.565
1.35	0.99888	0.0093	−0.083	−0.362
1.40	0.99927	0.0061	−0.048	−0.243
1.45	0.99952	0.0041	−0.031	−0.157
1.50	0.99968	0.0026	−0.025	−0.104

TABLE IV

THE INTEGRALS $\Omega^{(l,s)\star}$ FOR CALCULATING THE TRANSPORT COEFFICIENTS FOR THE SQUARE-WELL POTENTIAL[a]

$T^* = kT/\epsilon$		∞	5.00	2.500	1.667	1.250	1.0	0.833	0.500
$1/T^*$		0	0.2	0.4	0.6	0.8	1.0	1.2	2.0
$1/R$	l, s								
0.4	1,1	1.0000	1.1513	1.3388	1.5263	1.7038	1.8713	2.0300	2.5638
	1,2	1.0000	1.0925	1.2113	1.3421	1.4725	1.5996	1.7233	2.1804
	1,3	1.0000	1.0654	1.1483	1.2431	1.3429	1.4418	1.5396	1.9183
	2,2	1.0000	1.1833	1.4333	1.7100	1.9817	2.2417	2.4908	3.3688
0.6	1,1	1.0000	1.0911	1.1894	1.2794	1.3578	1.4267	1.4872	1.6578
	1,2	1.0000	1.0581	1.1257	1.1944	1.2593	1.3191	1.3746	1.5535
	1,3	1.0000	1.0418	1.0916	1.1440	1.1966	1.2467	1.2944	1.4629
	2,2	1.0000	1.0996	1.2335	1.3687	1.4933	1.6052	1.7057	2.0037
0.8	1,1	1.0000	1.0491	1.0947	1.1281	1.1519	1.1700	1.1844	1.2234
	1,2	1.0000	1.0315	1.0688	1.1001	1.1244	1.1432	1.1583	1.1977
	1,3	1.0000	1.0217	1.0515	1.0792	1.1029	1.1222	1.1379	1.1796
	2,2	1.0000	1.0573	1.1259	1.1823	1.2231	1.2520	1.2723	1.3093

[a] E. M. Holleran and H. M. Hulburt, *J. Chem. Phys.*, **19**, 232 (1951).

TABLE V

THE INTEGRALS $\Omega^{(l,s)\star}$ FOR CALCULATING THE TRANSPORT COEFFICIENTS FOR THE SUTHERLAND POTENTIAL WITH AN INVERSE SIXTH-POWER ATTRACTION[a]

ζ	T^*	$\Omega^{(1,1)\star}$	$\Omega^{(1,2)\star}$	$\Omega^{(1,3)\star}$	$\Omega^{(2,2)\star}$	$\Omega^{(2,3)\star}$	$\Omega^{(2,4)\star}$
0.00	∞	1.0000	1.0000	1.0000	1.0000	1.0000	1.0000
0.01	50	1.0034	1.0023	1.0017	1.0036	1.0027	1.0021
0.02	25	1.0072	1.0045	1.0034	1.0074	1.0055	1.0043
0.03	16.67	1.0112	1.0068	1.0052	1.0116	1.0084	1.0066
0.04	12.50	1.0154	1.0091	1.0070	1.0159	1.0114	1.0092
0.05	10.00	1.0198	1.0115	1.0088	1.0205	1.0146	1.0114
0.075	6.67	1.0318	1.0179	1.0137	1.0330	1.0232	1.0177
0.100	5.00	1.0450	1.0246	1.0188	1.0468	1.0325	1.0248
0.125	4.00	1.0592	1.0319	1.0243	1.0617	1.0425	1.0322
0.150	3.33	1.0738	1.0397	1.0302	1.0774	1.0532	1.0400
0.175	2.86	1.0888	1.0479	1.0366	1.0939	1.0645	1.0483
0.200	2.50	1.1042	1.0566	1.0432	1.1115	1.0763	1.0570
0.225	2.22				1.1285		
0.250	2.00	1.1348	1.0751	1.0576	1.1464	1.1014	1.0752
0.375	1.33	1.2096	1.1248	1.0972	1.2376	1.1694	1.1272
0.500	1.00	1.2802	1.1765	1.1379	1.3264	1.2404	1.1837
0.625	0.800	1.3466	1.2284	1.1776	1.4090	1.3101	1.2419
0.750	0.667	1.4090	1.2793	1.2163	1.4846	1.3763	1.2993
0.875	0.571	1.4676	1.3286	1.2542	1.5537	1.4383	1.3547
1.000	0.500	1.5228	1.3757	1.2915	1.6167	1.4957	1.4071
1.125	0.444	1.5748	1.4205	1.3280	1.6753	1.5491	1.4565
1.250	0.400	1.6238	1.4630	1.3635	1.7294	1.5988	1.4980
1.375	0.364	1.6702	1.5034	1.3980	1.7800	1.6452	1.5463
1.500	0.333	1.7142	1.5417	1.4313	1.8275	1.6889	1.5872
1.625	0.308	1.7560	1.5782	1.4634	1.8725	1.7301	1.6258
1.750	0.286	1.7962	1.6131	1.4944	1.9153	1.7693	1.6631
1.875	0.267	1.8344	1.6465	1.5242	1.9560	1.8066	1.6973
2.00	0.250	1.8714	1.6789	1.5529	1.9950	1.8422	1.7305

[a] M. Kotani, *Proc. Phys.-Math. Soc. Japan* (3), **24**, 76 (1942). Kotani tabulated a function $F_s^l(\zeta)$ which bears the following relationship to the $\Omega^{(l,s)\star}$:

$$\Omega^{(l,s)\star} = \frac{F_s^l(\zeta)}{\dfrac{(s+1)!}{4}\left[1 - \frac{1}{2}\,\dfrac{1+(-1)^l}{1+l}\right]}$$

where $\zeta = \epsilon/2kT = 1/2T^*$

TABLE VI–A

THE SECOND VIRIAL COEFFICIENT FOR THE BUCKINGHAM-CORNER POTENTIAL[a]

$$B(T) = 2\pi\tilde{N}r_m{}^3\, F_0(\alpha,\, \beta;\, T^*) \qquad T^* = kT/\epsilon$$

$F_0(\alpha, \beta; T^*)$ for $\beta = 0$

$1/T^*$	T^*	$\alpha = 12.5$	13	13.5	14	14.5
0.01	100.	0.0885	0.0922	0.0958	0.0993	0.1028
0.02	50.	0.1012	0.1050	0.1087	0.1123	0.1158
0.03	33.33	0.1062	0.1102	0.1140	0.1177	0.1212
0.04	25.00	0.1080	0.1121	0.1160	0.1197	0.1233
0.05	20.00	0.1079	0.1121	0.1161	0.1199	0.1236
0.06	16.67	0.1066	0.1109	0.1150	0.1189	0.1226
0.07	14.29	0.1044	0.1088	0.1130	0.1170	0.1207
0.08	12.50	0.1016	0.1061	0.1104	0.1144	0.1183
0.09	11.11	0.0982	0.1029	0.1073	0.1114	0.1153
0.10	10.00	0.0945	0.0993	0.1038	0.1080	0.1120
0.15	6.667	0.0716	0.0771	0.0821	0.0868	0.0913
0.20	5.000	0.0444	0.0506	0.0562	0.0615	0.0664
0.25	4.000	0.0144	0.0213	0.0276	0.0335	0.0389
0.30	3.333	−0.0176	−0.0100	−0.0030	0.0035	0.0094
0.35	2.857	−0.0514	−0.0429	−0.0352	−0.0282	−0.0216
0.40	2.500	−0.0866	−0.0774	−0.0689	−0.0612	−0.0541
0.45	2.222	−0.1233	−0.1132	−0.1040	−0.0956	−0.0879
0.50	2.000	−0.1614	−0.1504	−0.1404	−0.1313	−0.1229
0.55	1.818	−0.2008	−0.1889	−0.1781	−0.1682	−0.1592
0.60	1.667	−0.2413	−0.2287	−0.2170	−0.2064	−0.1967
0.65	1.539	−0.2836	−0.2697	−0.2572	−0.2458	−0.2354
0.70	1.429	−0.3270	−0.3121	−0.2987	−0.2865	−0.2753
0.75	1.333	−0.3718	−0.3559	−0.3416	−0.3285	−0.3165
0.80	1.250	−0.4180	−0.4010	−0.3857	−0.3718	−0.3590

$F_0(\alpha, \beta; T^*)$ for $\beta = 0.2$

$1/T^*$	T^*	$\alpha = 12.5$	13	13.5	14	14.5
0.01	100.	0.0905	0.0942	0.0979	0.1015	0.1050
0.02	50.	0.1034	0.1072	0.1110	0.1146	0.1182
0.03	33.33	0.1086	0.1126	0.1165	0.1202	0.1238
0.04	25.00	0.1105	0.1147	0.1186	0.1224	0.1261
0.05	20.00	0.1106	0.1149	0.1189	0.1228	0.1265
0.06	16.67	0.1094	0.1138	0.1180	0.1220	0.1257
0.07	14.29	0.1074	0.1120	0.1163	0.1203	0.1242
0.08	12.50	0.1047	0.1094	0.1138	0.1180	0.1219
0.09	11.11	0.1016	0.1064	0.1109	0.1152	0.1192
0.10	10.00	0.0981	0.1030	0.1076	0.1120	0.1160
0.15	6.667	0.0762	0.0819	0.0871	0.0919	0.0964
0.20	5.000	0.0501	0.0565	0.0623	0.0677	0.0727
0.25	4.000	0.0212	0.0284	0.0349	0.0409	0.0464
0.30	3.333	−0.0097	−0.0017	0.0055	0.0121	0.0182
0.35	2.857	−0.0424	−0.0336	−0.0256	−0.0183	−0.0116
0.40	2.500	−0.0764	−0.0668	−0.0580	−0.0501	−0.0427
0.45	2.222	−0.1119	−0.1014	−0.0919	−0.0832	−0.0753
0.50	2.000	−0.1488	−0.1373	−0.1269	−0.1175	−0.1089
0.55	1.818	−0.1869	−0.1745	−0.1633	−0.1531	−0.1439
0.60	1.667	−0.2264	−0.2130	−0.2009	−0.1899	−0.1799
0.65	1.539	−0.2672	−0.2527	−0.2397	−0.2280	−0.2172
0.70	1.429	−0.3093	−0.2938	−0.2798	−0.2672	−0.2557
0.75	1.333	−0.3527	−0.3361	−0.3212	−0.3078	−0.2955
0.80	1.250	−0.3975	−0.3798	−0.3639	−0.3496	−0.3365

[a] R. A. Buckingham and J. Corner, *Proc. Roy. Soc.* (*London*), **A189**, 118 (1947); and R. A. Buckingham, private correspondence, Oct. 18, 1952.

TABLE VI–B

THE ZERO-PRESSURE JOULE-THOMSON COEFFICIENT FOR THE BUCKINGHAM-CORNER POTENTIAL[a]

$$\mu^0 \tilde{C}_p{}^0 = 2\pi \tilde{N} r_m{}^3\, G_0(\alpha, \beta; T^*) \qquad T^* = kT/\epsilon$$

$G_0(\alpha, \beta; T^*)$ for $\beta = 0$

$1/T^*$	T^*	$\alpha = 12.5$	13	13.5	14	14.5
0.01	100.	−0.1090	−0.1128	−0.1165	−0.1201	−0.1237
0.02	50.	−0.1166	−0.1206	−0.1245	−0.1283	−0.1318
0.03	33.33	−0.1156	−0.1199	−0.1239	−0.1278	−0.1315
0.04	25.00	−0.1110	−0.1155	−0.1198	−0.1238	−0.1275
0.05	20.00	−0.1040	−0.1087	−0.1132	−0.1173	−0.1213
0.06	16.67	−0.0958	−0.1008	−0.1054	−0.1098	−0.1139
0.07	14.29	−0.0866	−0.0919	−0.0967	−0.1013	−0.1055
0.08	12.50	−0.0767	−0.0822	−0.0873	−0.0920	−0.0965
0.09	11.11	−0.0662	−0.0720	−0.0773	−0.0822	−0.0869
0.10	10.00	−0.0552	−0.0613	−0.0669	−0.0720	−0.0768
0.15	6.667	+0.0047	−0.0028	−0.0096	−0.0159	−0.0217
0.20	5.000	0.0706	+0.0616	+0.0534	+0.0459	+0.0390
0.25	4.000	0.1409	0.1303	0.1207	0.1119	0.1038
0.30	3.333	0.2152	0.2029	0.1917	0.1816	0.1723
0.35	2.857	0.2931	0.2790	0.2663	0.2547	0.2441
0.40	2.500	0.3747	0.3587	0.3442	0.3311	0.3192
0.45	2.222	0.4598	0.4419	0.4257	0.4110	0.3976
0.50	2.000	0.5487	0.5287	0.5107	0.4944	0.4794
0.55	1 818	0.6415	0.6193	0.5994	0.5813	0.5648
0.60	1.667	0.7382	0.7138	0.6919	0.6720	0.6538
0.65	1.539	0.8391	0.8124	0.7883	0.7665	0.7466
0.70	1.429	0.9443	0.9152	0.8889	0.8651	0.8434
0.75	1.333	1.0541	1.0224	0.9938	0.9679	0.9443
0.80	1.250	1.1686	1.1342	1.1031	1.0752	1.0496

$G_0(\alpha, \beta; T^*)$ for $\beta = 0.2$

$1/T^*$	T^*	$\alpha = 12.5$	13	13.5	14	14.5
0.01	100.	−0.1109	−0.1149	−0.1187	−0.1224	−0.1260
0.02	50.	−0.1190	−0.1232	−0.1272	−0.1310	−0.1346
0.03	33.33	−0.1182	−0.1227	−0.1269	−0.1308	−0.1345
0.04	25.00	−0.1139	−0.1186	−0.1230	−0.1271	−0.1309
0.05	20.00	−0.1075	−0.1124	−0.1170	−0.1213	−0.1253
0.06	16.67	−0.0997	−0.1049	−0.1097	−0.1142	−0.1183
0.07	14.29	−0.0909	−0.0964	−0.1014	−0.1061	−0.1105
0.08	12.50	−0.0814	−0.0872	−0.0924	−0.0973	−0.1018
0.09	11.11	−0.0714	−0.0774	−0.0829	−0.0880	−0.0927
0.10	10.00	−0.0608	−0.0671	−0.0729	−0.0782	−0.0831
0.15	6.667	−0.0031	−0.0109	−0.0180	−0.0244	−0.0304
0.20	5.000	+0.0606	+0.0512	+0.0427	+0.0350	+0.0279
0.25	4.000	0.1287	0.1176	0.1076	0.0985	0.0903
0.30	3.333	0.2005	0.1876	0.1761	0.1656	0.1560
0.35	2.857	0.2760	0.2613	0.2480	0.2361	0.2252
0.40	2.500	0.3550	0.3383	0.3233	0.3098	0.2975
0.45	2.222	0.4376	0.4188	0.4020	0.3869	0.3731
0.50	2.000	0.5238	0.5029	0.4842	0.4674	0.4520
0.55	1.818	0.6138	0.5907	0.5700	0.5513	0.5344
0.60	1.667	0.7077	0.6823	0.6595	0.6389	0.6203
0.65	1.539	0.8057	0.7778	0.7529	0.7304	0.7099
0.70	1.429	0.9080	0.8775	0.8503	0.8257	0.8034
0.75	1.333	1.0146	0.9815	0.9520	0.9252	0.9009
0.80	1.250	1.1260	1.0901	1.0580	1.0290	1.0027

[a] R. A. Buckingham and J. Corner, *Proc. Roy. Soc.* (*London*), **A189**, 118 (1947); and R. A. Buckingham, private correspondence, Oct. 18, 1952.

TABLE VI-C

First Quantum Correction to the Second Virial Coefficient for the Buckingham-Corner Potential[a]

$$B_{\mathrm{I}} = (\tilde{N}r_m/kT)\,F_1(\alpha, \beta; T^*) \qquad T^* = kT/\epsilon$$

$F_1(\alpha, \beta; T^*)$ for $\beta = 0$

$1/T^*$	T^*	$\alpha = 12.5$	13	13.5	14	14.5
0.01	100.	0.065	0.069	0.074	0.078	0.083
0 02	50.	0.081	0.085	0.090	0.094	0.099
0.03	33.33	0.091	0.096	0.100	0.105	0.110
0.04	25.00	0.100	0.104	0.109	0.114	0.119
0.05	20.00	0.107	0.111	0.116	0.121	0.127
0.06	16.67	0.113	0.118	0.123	0.128	0.134
0.07	14.29	0.119	0.124	0.129	0.134	0.140
0.08	12.50	0.124	0.129	0.135	0.140	0.146
0.09	11.11	0.129	0.135	0.140	0.146	0.152
0.10	10.00	0.134	0.140	0.145	0.151	0.157
0.15	6.667	0.157	0.164	0.170	0.176	0.183
0.20	5.000	0.179	0.186	0.193	0.200	0.208
0.25	4.000	0.201	0.209	0.217	0.225	0.233
0.30	3.333	0.224	0.232	0.241	0.250	0.258
0.35	2.857	0.247	0.257	0.266	0.276	0.285
0.40	2.500	0.272	0.282	0.293	0.303	0.314
0.45	2.222	0.299	0.310	0.321	0.332	0.344
0.50	2.000	0.326	0.339	0.351	0.363	0.376
0.55	1.818	0.356	0.370	0.383	0.396	0.410
0.60	1.667	0.388	0.402	0.417	0.432	0.447
0.65	1.538	0.422	0.438	0.453	0.470	0.486
0.70	1.429	0.458	0.475	0.493	0.510	0.528
0.75	1.333	0.497	0.515	0.534	0.554	0.573
0.80	1.250	0.539	0.559	0.579	0.600	0.621

$F_1(\alpha, \beta; T^*)$ for $\beta = 0.2$

$1/T^*$	T^*	$\alpha = 12.5$	13	13.5	14	14.5
0.01	100.	0.068	0.072	0.076	0.081	0.085
0.02	50.	0.084	0.088	0.093	0.097	0.102
0.03	33.33	0.094	0.099	0.103	0.108	0.113
0.04	25.00	0.103	0.107	0.112	0.117	0.122
0.05	20.00	0.110	0.114	0.119	0.124	0.129
0.06	16.67	0.116	0.121	0.126	0.131	0.136
0.07	14.29	0.122	0.127	0.132	0.137	0.143
0.08	12.50	0.127	0.132	0.138	0.143	0.149
0.09	11.11	0.132	0.137	0.143	0.149	0.155
0.10	10.00	0.137	0.142	0.148	0.154	0.160
0.15	6.667	0.160	0.166	0.172	0.179	0.186
0.20	5.000	0.182	0.189	0.196	0.203	0.210
0.25	4.000	0.203	0.211	0.219	0.227	0.234
0.30	3.333	0.225	0.234	0.242	0.251	0.259
0.35	2.857	0.248	0.257	0.266	0.275	0.285
0.40	2.500	0.272	0.282	0.292	0.302	0.312
0.45	2.222	0.296	0.307	0.318	0.329	0.340
0.50	2.000	0.323	0.335	0.346	0.358	0.370
0.55	1.818	0.351	0.363	0.376	0.388	0.401
0.60	1.667	0.380	0.394	0.407	0.421	0.434
0.65	1.538	0.411	0.426	0.441	0.455	0.469
0.70	1.429	0.445	0.460	0.476	0.491	0.506
0.75	1.333	0.481	0.496	0.513	0.529	0.545
0.80	1.250	0.518	0.536	0.553	0.571	0.588

[a] Taken from R. A. Buckingham and J. Corner, *Proc. Roy. Soc.* (*London*), **A189**, 118 (1947); and R. A. Buckingham, private correspondence, Oct. 18, 1952.

TABLE VI–D

FIRST QUANTUM CORRECTION TO THE ZERO-PRESSURE JOULE-THOMSON COEFFICIENT FOR THE BUCKINGHAM-CORNER POTENTIAL[a]

$$\mu_I{}^0\tilde{C}_p{}^0 = (\tilde{N}r_m/kT)\, G_1(\alpha, \beta; T^*) \qquad T^* = kT/\epsilon$$

$-G_1(\alpha, \beta; T^*)$ for $\beta = 0$

$1/T^*$	T^*	$\alpha = 12.5$	13	13.5	14	14.5
0.01	100.	0.151	0.160	0.169	0.178	0.188
0.02	50.	0.186	0.195	0.204	0.214	0.224
0.03	33.33	0.210	0.219	0.229	0.239	0.250
0.04	25.00	0.230	0.239	0.249	0.260	0.271
0.05	20.00	0.247	0.257	0.267	0.278	0.290
0.06	16.67	0.262	0.273	0.284	0.295	0.307
0.07	14.29	0.277	0.288	0.299	0.311	0.323
0.08	12.50	0.291	0.302	0.314	0.326	0.339
0.09	11.11	0.304	0.316	0.328	0.341	0.354
0.10	10.00	0.317	0.330	0.342	0.355	0.369
0.15	6.667	0.381	0.396	0.411	0.426	0.441
0.20	5.000	0.446	0.463	0.480	0.497	0.514
0.25	4.000	0.514	0.533	0.553	0.572	0.592
0.30	3.333	0.586	0.608	0.630	0.652	0.674
0.35	2.857	0.664	0.689	0.714	0.739	0.764
0.40	2.500	0.749	0.776	0.805	0.833	0.861
0.45	2.222	0.841	0.872	0.903	0.935	0.967
0.50	2.000	0.941	0.976	1.011	1.047	1.083
0.55	1.818	1.050	1.089	1.129	1.169	1.210
0.60	1.667	1.169	1.213	1.257	1.303	1.349
0.65	1.538	1.298	1.348	1.398	1.449	1.500
0.70	1.429	1.440	1.495	1.551	1.609	1.665
0.75	1.333	1.595	1.656	1.718	1.782	1.845
0.80	1.250	1.762	1.830	1.900	1.971	2.040

$-G_1(\alpha, \beta; T^*)$ for $\beta = 0.2$

$1/T^*$	T^*	$\alpha = 12.5$	13	13.5	14	14.5
0.01	100.	0.157	0.166	0.174	0.183	0.193
0.02	50.	0.193	0.201	0.210	0.219	0.229
0.03	33.33	0.216	0.225	0.235	0.245	0.255
0.04	25.00	0.235	0.245	0.255	0.265	0.276
0.05	20.00	0.252	0.262	0.273	0.284	0.295
0.06	16.67	0.268	0.278	0.289	0.301	0.312
0.07	14.29	0.282	0.293	0.305	0.316	0.329
0.08	12.50	0.296	0.307	0.319	0.332	0.344
0.09	11.11	0.309	0.321	0.334	0.346	0.359
0.10	10.00	0.322	0.335	0.348	0.361	0.374
0.15	6.667	0.385	0.400	0.415	0.430	0.445
0.20	5.000	0.449	0.466	0.483	0.500	0.517
0.25	4.000	0.515	0.534	0.553	0.572	0.591
0.30	3.333	0.584	0.606	0.627	0.648	0.669
0.35	2.857	0.659	0.682	0.706	0.729	0.752
0.40	2.500	0.738	0.764	0.791	0.817	0.842
0.45	2.222	0.824	0.853	0.882	0.911	0.940
0.50	2.000	0.916	0.949	0.981	1.013	1.045
0.55	1.818	1.016	1.052	1.088	1.123	1.157
0.60	1.667	1.125	1.164	1.203	1.241	1.277
0.65	1.538	1.242	1.285	1.327	1.368	1.408
0.70	1.429	1.370	1.416	1.461	1.506	1.549
0.75	1.333	1.507	1.557	1.606	1.654	1.702
0.80	1.250	1.654	1.709	1.762	1.815	1.867

[a] Taken from R. A. Buckingham and J. Corner, *Proc. Roy. Soc.* (*London*), **A189**, 118 (1947); and R. A. Buckingham, private correspondence, Oct. 18, 1952.

TABLE VII–A

THE SECOND VIRIAL COEFFICIENT FOR THE MODIFIED BUCKINGHAM (6-EXP) POTENTIAL[a]

$$B(T) = b_m B^*(\alpha, T^*)$$
$$T^* = kT/\epsilon$$
$$b_m = \tfrac{2}{3}\pi \tilde{N} r_m^{\ 3}$$

T^* \ α	12.0	12.5	13.0	13.5	14.0	14.5	15.0
0.40	−10.347	−10.052	−9.787	−9.548	−9.332	−9.134	−8.953
0.45	−8.060	−7.826	−7.616	−7.427	−7.256	−7.099	−6.956
0.50	−6.536	−6.342	−6.168	−6.012	−5.871	−5.741	−5.623
0.55	−5.455	−5.290	−5.141	−5.008	−4.887	−4.777	−4.676
0.60	−4.653	−4.508	−4.378	−4.262	−4 157	−4.061	−3.973
0.65	−4.035	−3.906	−3.791	−3.688	−3.595	−3.509	−3.431
0.70	−3.546	−3.430	−3.326	−3.233	−3.149	−3.072	−3.002
0.75	−3.149	−3.043	−2.949	−2.864	−2.788	−2.718	−2.654
0.80	−2.822	−2.725	−2.638	−2.560	−2.490	−2.425	−2.366
0.85	−2.547	−2.457	−2.377	−2.304	−2.239	−2.179	−2.125
0.90	−2.313	−2.229	−2.154	−2.087	−2.026	−1.970	−1.919
0.95	−2.111	−2.033	−1.963	−1.899	−1.842	−1.790	−1.742
1.00	−1.9362	−1.8623	−1.7960	−1.7363	−1.6823	−1.6330	−1.5877
1.05	−1.7827	−1.7127	−1.6499	−1.5934	−1.5422	−1.4955	−1.4526
1.10	−1.6470	−1.5805	−1.5208	−1.4671	−1.4184	−1.3740	−1.3332
1.15	−1.5263	−1.4628	−1.4059	−1.3546	−1.3082	−1.2658	−1.2269
1.20	−1.4181	−1.3574	−1.3029	−1.2539	−1.2095	−1.1689	−1.1316
1.25	−1.3208	−1.2625	−1.2103	−1.1632	−1.1206	−1.0816	−1.0459
1.30	−1.2327	−1.1767	−1.1264	−1.0812	−1.0401	−1.0027	−0.9682
1.35	−1.1526	−1.0986	−1.0502	−1.0066	−0.9670	−0.9309	−0.8976
1.40	−1.0795	−1.0274	−0.9806	−0.9385	−0.9002	−0.8653	−0.8332
1.45	−1.0125	−0.9621	−0.9168	−0.8761	−0.8391	−0.8052	−0.7742
1.50	−0.9509	−0.9020	−0.8582	−0.8187	−0.7828	−0.7500	−0.7199
1.55	−0.8941	−0.8467	−0.8041	−0.7657	−0.7309	−0.6990	−0.6698
1.60	−0.8416	−0.7954	−0.7541	−0.7168	−0.6829	−0.6519	−0.6234
1.65	−0.7928	−0.7479	−0.7076	−0.6713	−0.6383	−0.6082	−0.5804
1.70	−0.7475	−0.7037	−0.6645	−0.6291	−0.5969	−0.5675	−0.5404
1.75	−0.7052	−0.6625	−0.6242	−0.5897	−0.5583	−0.5296	−0.5031
1.80	−0.6657	−0.6240	−0.5866	−0.5529	−0.5222	−0.4941	−0.4683
1.85	−0.6287	−0.5880	−0.5514	−0.5184	−0.4884	−0.4609	−0.4357
1.90	−0.5940	−0.5542	−0.5184	−0.4861	−0.4567	−0.4298	−0.4050
1.95	−0.5614	−0.5224	−0.4873	−0.4557	−0.4269	−0.4005	−0.3763
2.0	−0.5307	−0.4924	−0.4581	−0.4271	−0.3988	−0.3730	−0.3492
2.1	−0.4744	−0.4376	−0.4045	−0.3746	−0.3474	−0.3224	−0.2995
2.2	−0.4241	−0.3885	−0.3565	−0.3276	−0.3013	−0.2772	−0.2550

T^* \ α	12.0	12.5	13.0	13.5	14.0	14.5	15.0
2.3	−0.3788	−0.3443	−0.3134	−0.2854	−0.2660	−0.2366	−0.2151
2.4	−0.3379	−0.3045	−0.2744	−0.2473	−0.2225	−0.1999	−0.1789
2.5	−0.3007	−0.2683	−0.2391	−0.2127	−0.1886	−0.1665	−0.1461
2.6	−0.2669	−0.2353	−0.2068	−0.1811	−0.1577	−0.1361	−0.1163
2.7	−0.2359	−0.2051	−0.1774	−0.1523	−0.1294	−0.1083	−0.0889
2.8	−0.2075	−0.1774	−0.1503	−0.1258	−0.1034	−0.0828	−0.0638
2.9	−0.1813	−0.1519	−0.1254	−0.1014	−0.0795	−0.0593	−0.0407
3.0	−0.1572	−0.1283	−0.1024	−0.0789	−0.0574	−0.0377	−0.0194
3.1	−0.1348	−0.1066	−0.0811	−0.0580	−0.0370	−0.0176	0.0003
3.2	−0.1141	−0.0863	−0.0614	−0.0387	−0.0180	0.0010	0.0186
3.3	−0.0948	−0.0675	−0.0430	−0.0207	−0.0004	0.0184	0.0357
3.4	−0.0768	−0.0500	−0.0258	−0.0039	0.0161	0.0345	0.0516
3.5	−0.0600	−0.0336	−0.0098	0.0117	0.0314	0.0496	0.0664
3.6	−0.0442	−0.0183	0.0051	0.0264	0.0458	0.0637	0.0803
3.7	−0.0295	−0.0039	0.0192	0.0401	0.0593	0.0770	0.0933
3.8	−0.0156	0.0096	0.0324	0.0530	0.0719	0.0894	0.1055
3.9	−0.0026	0.0223	0.0448	0.0652	0.0838	0.1011	0.1170
4.0	0.0097	0.0343	0.0564	0.0766	0.0951	0.1121	0.1279
4.1	0.0212	0.0455	0.0674	0.0874	0.1056	0.1225	0.1381
4.2	0.0322	0.0562	0.0779	0.0976	0.1156	0.1323	0.1477
4.3	0.0425	0.0663	0.0877	0.1072	0.1250	0.1415	0.1568
4.4	0.0523	0.0758	0.0970	0.1163	0.1340	0.1503	0.1655
4.5	0.0616	0.0848	0.1058	0.1249	0.1425	0.1586	0.1736
4.6	0.0704	0.0934	0.1142	0.1331	0.1505	0.1665	0.1814
4.7	0.0787	0.1016	0.1222	0.1409	0.1581	0.1740	0.1888
4.8	0.0867	0.1093	0.1297	0.1483	0.1654	0.1811	0.1958
4.9	0.0943	0.1167	0.1369	0.1554	0.1723	0.1879	0.2025
5.	0.1015	0.1237	0.1438	0.1621	0.1789	0.1944	0.2088
6.	0.1581	0.1788	0.1976	0.2147	0.2305	0.2451	0.2586
7.	0.1955	0.2152	0.2331	0.2495	0.2645	0.2785	0.2916
8.	0.2215	0.2406	0.2578	0.2736	0.2882	0.3017	0.3144
9.	0.2403	0.2587	0.2755	0.2909	0.3051	0.3183	0.3307
10.	0.2540	0.2721	0.2885	0.3036	0.3175	0.3305	0.3427
20.	0.2937	0.3102	0.3252	0.3392	0.3522	0.3643	0.3758
30.	0.2903	0.3065	0.3213	0.3349	0.3477	0.3598	0.3712
40.	0.2811	0.2971	0.3118	0.3254	0.3381	0.3502	0.3616
50.	0.2712	0.2872	0.3018	0.3154	0.3281	0.3402	0.3516
60.	0.2619	0.2778	0.2924	0.3059	0.3187	0.3308	0.3423
70.	0.2533	0.2692	0.2837	0.2973	0.3101	0.3222	0.3337
80.	0.2455	0.2613	0.2759	0.2895	0.3022	0.3143	0.3259
90.	0.2384	0.2542	0.2687	0.2823	0.2951	0.3072	0.3188
100.	0.2319	0.2477	0.2622	0.2758	0.2885	0.3007	0.3123
200.	0.1876	0.2033	0.2177	0.2311	0.2438	0.2559	0.2675
300.	0.1624	0.1780	0.1921	0.2053	0.2178	0.2298	0.2413
400.	0.1444	0.1599	0.1739	0.1870	0.1994	0.2112	0.2227

[a] W. E. Rice and J. O. Hirschfelder, *J. Chem. Phys.*, **22** (1954).

TABLE VII–B

Collision Integral Functions[a] for Calculating the Transport Coefficients for the Modified Buckingham (6-Exp) Potential

$$Z^{(l,s)}(T^*) = [T^*(1 - 6/\alpha)]^{1/3} (\sigma/r_m)^2 \, \Omega^{(l,s)\star}(T^*) \qquad T^* = kT/\epsilon$$

$$\alpha = 12$$

T^*	$Z^{(1,1)}$	$Z^{(1,2)}$	$Z^{(1,3)}$	$Z^{(1,4)}$	$Z^{(1,5)}$	$Z^{(3,3)}$
0.	1.1870	1.0551	0.9672	0.9027	0.8572	1.1178
0.1	1.1911	1.0523	0.9584	0.8883	0.8320	1.1079
0.2	1.1662	1.0142	0.0925	0.8113	0.7338	1.0704
0.3	1.1243	0.9515	0.8232	0.7239	0.6475	1.0161
0.4	1.0750	0.8900	0.7597	0.6667	0.6005	0.9641
0.5	1.0282	0.8402	0.7160	0.6328	0.5764	0.9194
0.6	0.9873	0.8025	0.6870	0.6131	0.5643	0.8828
0.7	0.9530	0.7745	0.6679	0.6019	0.5589	0.8536
0.8	0.9248	0.7538	0.6555	0.5959	0.5572	0.8305
0.9	0.9016	0.7387	0.6475	0.5930	0.5576	0.8125
1.0	0.8825	0.7272	0.6425	0.5923	0.5593	0.7985
1.2	0.8541	0.7130	0.6385	0.5942	0.5646	0.7793
1.4	0.8350	0.7058	0.6388	0.5985	0.5711	0.7684
1.6	0.8221	0.7028	0.6414	0.6039	0.5779	0.7625
1.8	0.8135	0.7025	0.6451	0.6096	0.5845	0.7601
2.0	0.8080	0.7037	0.6496	0.6155	0.5910	0.7600
2.5	0.8023	0.7104	0.6616	0.6296	0.6059	0.7654
3.0	0.8031	0.7195	0.6735	0.6425	0.6180	0.7746
3.5	0.8070	0.7288	0.6847	0.6541	0.6305	0.7853
4	0.8126	0.7382	0.6950	0.6644	0.6404	0.7963
5	0.8253	0.7556	0.7129	0.6819	0.6572	0.8174
6	0.8384	0.7709	0.7280	0.6962	0.6705	0.8364
7	0.8509	0.7842	0.7409	0.7081	0.6817	0.8533
8	0.8623	0.7961	0.7520	0.7185	0.6912	0.8680
9	0.8730	0.8067	0.7618	0.7272	0.6993	0.8813
10	0.8829	0.8160	0.7702	0.7351	0.7066	0.8929
12	0.9002	0.8322	0.7848	0.7485	0.7189	0.9133
14	0.9150	0.8457	0.7969	0.7594	0.7292	0.9301
16	0.9280	0.8572	0.8074	0.7690	0.7380	0.9444
18	0.9394	0.8674	0.8164	0.7773	0.7459	0.9568
20	0.9497	0.8762	0.8245	0.7846	0.7530	0.9680
25	0.9710	0.8951	0.8415	0.8007	0.7682	0.9910
30	0.9885	0.9103	0.8555	0.8138	0.7808	1.0094
35	1.0032	0.9232	0.8674	0.8253	0.7921	1.0250
40	1.0157	0.9346	0.8781	0.8355	0.8021	1.0385
45	1.0270	0.9446	0.8876	0.8450	0.8114	1.0508
50	1.0371	0.9538	0.8965	0.8535	0.8199	1.0614
60	1.0549	0.9701	0.9123	0.8691	0.8355	1.0807
70	1.0700	0.9846	0.9264	0.8827	0.8495	1.0978
80	1.0834	0.9973	0.9388	0.8957	0.8622	1.1129
90	1.0959	1.0091	0.9504	0.9074	0.8743	1.1265
100	1.1071	1.0201	0.9615	0.9184	0.8853	1.1391
200	1.1906	1.1038	1.0462	1.0049	0.9729	1.2356

[a] E. A. Mason, *J. Chem. Phys.*, **22**, 169 (1954).

TABLE VII–B (*continued*)

$\alpha = 12$

T^*	$Z^{(2,2)}$	$Z^{(2,3)}$	$Z^{(2,4)}$	$Z^{(2,5)}$	$Z^{(2,6)}$	$Z^{(4,4)}$
0	1.1947	1.0951	1.0221	0.9706	0.9193	1.0927
0.1	1.1983	1.1002	1.0291	0.9750	0.9323	1.1062
0.2	1.2098	1.1094	1.0401	0.9770	0.9188	1.1119
0.3	1.2065	1.0936	0.9978	0.9129	0.8381	1.0843
0.4	1.1799	1.0471	0.9367	0.8453	0.7711	1.0360
0.5	1.1421	0.9974	0.8835	0.7953	0.7280	0.9870
0.6	1.1028	0.9538	0.8428	0.7614	0.7017	0.9450
0.7	1.0667	0.9185	0.8133	0.7391	0.6862	0.9111
0.8	1.0352	0.8907	0.7923	0.7249	0.6775	0.8847
0.9	1.0084	0.8692	0.7775	0.7160	0.6731	0.8642
1.0	0.9859	0.8528	0.7673	0.7108	0.6716	0.8488
1.2	0.9520	0.8309	0.7561	0.7075	0.6736	0.8282
1.4	0.9290	0.8189	0.7525	0.7093	0.6790	0.8170
1.6	0.9137	0.8130	0.7531	0.7139	0.6860	0.8120
1.8	0.9039	0.8111	0.7560	0.7198	0.6936	0.8107
2.0	0.8978	0.8116	0.7604	0.7263	0.7014	0.8119
2.5	0.8930	0.8189	0.7742	0.7435	0.7202	0.8207
3.0	0.8963	0.8300	0.7891	0.7600	0.7374	0.8331
3.5	0.9033	0.8423	0.8035	0.7752	0.7529	0.8466
4	0.9122	0.8546	0.8171	0.7892	0.7668	0.8599
5	0.9313	0.8778	0.8415	0.8135	0.7906	0.8849
6	0.9503	0.8987	0.8623	0.8339	0.8105	0.9072
7	0.9681	0.9172	0.8806	0.8516	0.8275	0.9269
8	0.9845	0.9339	0.8967	0.8670	0.8424	0.9445
9	0.9995	0.9488	0.9110	0.8808	0.8559	0.9602
10	1.0133	0.9624	0.9241	0.8935	0.8678	0.9745
12	1.0381	0.9862	0.9469	0.9153	0.8891	0.9998
14	1.0598	1.0068	0.9664	0.9341	0.9073	1.0213
16	1.0788	1.0248	0.9838	0.9508	0.9236	1.0404
18	1.0958	1.0409	0.9993	0.9658	0.9383	1.0575
20	1.1113	1.0557	1.0134	0.9796	0.9516	1.0731
25	1.1448	1.0875	1.0441	1.0095	0.9812	1.1070
30	1.1729	1.1145	1.0703	1.0353	1.0067	1.1357
35	1.1976	1.1382	1.0935	1.0582	1.0294	1.1608
40	1.2193	1.1593	1.1143	1.0787	1.0499	1.1832
45	1.2393	1.1786	1.1332	1.0976	1.0688	1.2041
50	1.2573	1.1962	1.1509	1.1152	1.0863	1.2228
60	1.2901	1.2283	1.1826	1.1469	1.1180	1.2572
70	1.3189	1.2571	1.2113	1.1756	1.1468	1.2878
80	1.3451	1.2828	1.2370	1.2014	1.1730	1.3157
90	1.3690	1.3068	1.2609	1.2257	1.1973	1.3413
100	1.3915	1.3292	1.2835	1.2481	1.2198	1.3649
200	1.5600	1.4988	1.4547	1.4208	1.3939	1.5470

TABLE VII–B (*continued*)

$\alpha = 13$						
T^*	$Z^{(1,1)}$	$Z^{(1,2)}$	$Z^{(1,3)}$	$Z^{(1,4)}$	$Z^{(1,5)}$	$Z^{(3,3)}$
0	1.1870	1.0551	0.9672	0.9027	0.8572	1.1178
0.1	1.1813	1.0447	0.9528	0.8846	0.8305	1.1020
0.2	1.1618	1.0150	0.9084	0.8217	0.7479	1.0718
0.3	1.1275	0.9619	0.8389	0.7429	0.6681	1.0250
0.4	1.0851	0.9071	0.7807	0.6983	0.6236	0.9787
0.5	1.0436	0.8617	0.7400	0.6575	0.6011	0.9383
0.6	1.0068	0.8268	0.7129	0.6393	0.5904	0.9048
0.7	0.9756	0.8009	0.6953	0.6294	0.5862	0.8780
0.8	0.9498	0.7818	0.6841	0.6244	0.5855	0.8569
0.9	0.9285	0.7678	0.6772	0.6226	0.5871	0.8405
1.0	0.9112	0.7577	0.6732	0.6229	0.5897	0.8279
1.2	0.8854	0.7454	0.6710	0.6266	0.5970	0.8111
1.4	0.8684	0.7400	0.6729	0.6326	0.6052	0.8022
1.6	0.8573	0.7386	0.6770	0.6395	0.6136	0.7981
1.8	0.8503	0.7396	0.6823	6.6468	0.6219	0.7974
2.0	0.8461	0.7421	0.6881	0.6542	0.6299	0.7987
2.5	0.8436	0.7519	0.7032	0.6715	0.6483	0.8073
3.0	0.8472	0.7637	0.7181	0.6875	0.6643	0.8193
3.5	0.8535	0.7757	0.7320	0.7017	0.6785	0.8323
4	0.8614	0.7874	0.7446	0.7145	0.6910	0.8454
5	0.8782	0.8091	0.7671	0.7365	0.7121	0.8700
6	0.8950	0.8282	0.7862	0.7547	0.7296	0.8922
7	0.9107	0.8451	0.8024	0.7702	0.7441	0.9118
8	0.9253	0.8601	0.8166	0.7836	0.7568	0.9294
9	0.9389	0.8734	0.8292	0.7954	0.7678	0.9453
10	0.9514	0.8855	0.8404	0.8059	0.7777	0.9596
12	0.9736	0.9065	0.8599	0.8240	0.7948	0.9847
14	0.9927	0.9245	0.8765	0.8394	0.8094	1.0063
16	1.0096	0.9399	0.8907	0.8528	0.8223	1.0250
18	1.0247	0.9537	0.9034	0.8648	0.8337	1.0417
20	1.0384	0.9659	0.9147	0.8754	0.8440	1.0569
25	1.0674	0.9922	0.9392	0.8987	0.8664	1.0895
30	1.0913	1.0139	0.9596	0.9184	0.8855	1.1166
35	1.1118	1.0328	0.9775	0.9357	0.9027	1.1403
40	1.1296	1.0492	0.9933	0.9510	0.9179	1.1616
45	1.1456	1.0643	1.0076	0.9651	0.9318	1.1806
50	1.1602	1.0778	1.0208	0.9783	0.9447	1.1983
60	1.1861	1.1023	1.0447	1.0017	0.9682	1.2297
70	1.2087	1.1239	1.0659	1.0230	0.9894	1.2577
80	1.2287	1.1431	1.0849	1.0422	1.0089	1.2830
90	1.2469	1.1608	1.1025	1.0598	1.0267	1.3063
100	1.2639	1.1774	1.1193	1.0762	1.0434	1.3277
200	1.3892	1.3027	1.2456	1.2042	1.1723	1.4915

TABLE VII–B (*continued*)

$\alpha = 13$

T^*	$Z^{(2,2)}$	$Z^{(2,3)}$	$Z^{(2,4)}$	$Z^{(2,5)}$	$Z^{(2,6)}$	$Z^{(4,4)}$
0	1.1947	1.0951	1.0221	0.9706	0.9193	1.0927
0.1	1.1985	1.0994	1.0269	0.9709	0.9265	1.0986
0.2	1.2052	1.1090	1.0376	0.9783	0.9247	1.1116
0.3	1.2056	1.0977	1.0077	0.9278	0.8562	1.0944
0.4	1.1862	1.0602	0.9549	0.8664	0.7934	1.0526
0.5	1.1549	1.0164	0.9059	0.8190	0.7519	1.0076
0.6	1.1207	0.9766	0.8676	0.7866	0.7267	0.9681
0.7	1.0882	0.9436	0.8395	0.7653	0.7120	0.9360
0.8	1.0594	0.9175	0.8196	0.7519	0.7043	0.9110
0.9	1.0346	0.8972	0.8057	0.7439	0.7009	0.8917
1.0	1.0138	0.8820	0.7965	0.7398	0.7005	0.8775
1.2	0.9824	0.8618	0.7870	0.7382	0.7044	0.8590
1.4	0.9613	0.8514	0.7850	0.7418	0.7118	0.8499
1.6	0.9475	0.8471	0.7871	0.7481	0.7206	0.8466
1.8	0.9391	0.8465	0.7916	0.7557	0.7299	0.8469
2.0	0.9344	0.8484	0.7976	0.7638	0.7392	0.8496
2.5	0.9327	0.8590	0.8148	0.7844	0.7615	0.8617
3.0	0.9388	0.8731	0.8326	0.8040	0.7817	0.8771
3.5	0.9485	0.8880	0.8497	0.8219	0.7998	0.8931
4	0.9597	0.9027	0.8658	0.8381	0.8161	0.9087
5	0.9831	0.9303	0.8944	0.8668	0.8443	0.9378
6	1.0058	0.9548	0.9191	0.8911	0.8679	0.9637
7	1.0270	0.9769	0.9408	0.9121	0.8885	0.9867
8	1.0464	0.9964	0.9600	0.9309	0.9066	1.0072
9	1.0643	1.0143	0.9773	0.9477	0.9230	1.0257
10	1.0809	1.0306	0.9929	0.9628	0.9377	1.0425
12	1.1105	1.0592	1.0207	0.9898	0.9641	1.0725
14	1.1363	1.0843	1.0449	1.0133	0.9871	1.0984
16	1.1595	1.1064	1.0662	1.0342	1.0076	1.1216
18	1.1801	1.1264	1.0857	1.0530	1.0262	1.1422
20	1.1991	1.1448	1.1033	1.0704	1.0432	1.1611
25	1.2406	1.1847	1.1423	1.1085	1.0812	1.2027
30	1.2758	1.2187	1.1757	1.1416	1.1138	1.2382
35	1.3066	1.2486	1.2052	1.1709	1.1430	1.2694
40	1.3344	1.2757	1.2320	1.1975	1.1694	1.2974
45	1.3595	1.3004	1.2565	1.2217	1.1937	1.3230
50	1.3826	1.3232	1.2792	1.2444	1.2165	1.3466
60	1.4243	1.3644	1.3202	1.2854	1.2577	1.3896
70	1.4615	1.4015	1.3569	1.3224	1.2945	1.4280
80	1.4951	1.4348	1.3906	1.3559	1.3282	1.4628
90	1.5262	1.4656	1.4215	1.3869	1.3595	1.4948
100	1.5546	1.4942	1.4500	1.4161	1.3885	1.5248
200	1.7718	1.7128	1.6699	1.6376	1.6114	1.7518

TABLE VII–B (*continued*)

$\alpha = 14$						
T^*	$Z^{(1,1)}$	$Z^{(1,2)}$	$Z^{(1,3)}$	$Z^{(1,4)}$	$Z^{(1,5)}$	$Z^{(3,3)}$
0	1.1870	1.0551	0.9672	0.9027	0.8572	1.1178
0.1	1.1727	1.0382	0.9481	0.8814	0.8287	1.0987
0.2	1.1575	1.0146	0.9115	0.8281	0.7571	1.0729
0.3	1.1286	0.9684	0.8497	0.7566	0.6836	1.0308
0.4	1.0914	0.9191	0.7963	0.7069	0.6420	0.9891
0.5	1.0542	0.8776	0.7585	0.6773	0.6214	0.9524
0.6	1.0208	0.8455	0.7336	0.6608	0.6121	0.9218
0.7	0.9924	0.8217	0.7176	0.6521	0.6091	0.8974
0.8	0.9688	0.8042	0.7076	0.6483	0.6096	0.8781
0.9	0.9495	0.7917	0.7018	0.6476	0.6121	0.8633
1.0	0.9337	0.7827	0.6989	0.6488	0.6157	0.8519
1.2	0.9106	0.7724	0.6984	0.6542	0.6246	0.8373
1.4	0.8956	0.7686	0.7019	0.6617	0.6342	0.8300
1.6	0.8863	0.7687	0.7074	0.6700	0.6440	0.8273
1.8	0.8808	0.7710	0.7139	0.6784	0.6534	0.8277
2.0	0.8780	0.7747	0.7208	0.6868	0.6625	0.8300
2.5	0.8784	0.7871	0.7853	0.7068	0.6836	0.8406
3.0	0.8843	0.8011	0.7557	0.7252	0.7022	0.8545
3.5	0.8928	0.8152	0.7716	0.7416	0.7188	0.8692
4	0.9025	0.8288	0.7863	0.7565	0.7335	0.8840
5	0.9228	0.8539	0.8125	0.7824	0.7587	0.9121
6	0.9426	0.8764	0.8349	0.8042	0.7796	0.9376
7	0.9612	0.8962	0.8543	0.8229	0.7974	0.9605
8	0.9784	0.9140	0.8715	0.8391	0.8129	0.9812
9	0.9944	0.9300	0.8867	0.8536	0.8266	0.9999
10	1.0092	0.9445	0.9005	0.8666	0.8390	1.0169
12	1.0358	0.9701	0.9245	0.8893	0.8606	1.0468
14	1.0588	0.9918	0.9450	0.9086	0.8792	1.0726
16	1.0794	1.0110	0.9629	0.9255	0.8956	1.0953
18	1.0978	1.0280	0.9789	0.9408	0.9101	1.1157
20	1.1143	1.0436	0.9931	0.9546	0.9235	1.1339
25	1.1501	1.0766	1.0244	0.9844	0.9526	1.1737
30	1.1802	1.1044	1.0507	1.0097	0.9772	1.2070
35	1.2060	1.1281	1.0736	1.0320	0.9992	1.2359
40	1.2286	1.1494	1.0940	1.0520	1.0191	1.2615
45	1.2491	1.1685	1.1125	1.0703	1.0372	1.2848
50	1.2678	1.1862	1.1296	1.0871	1.0538	1.3063
60	1.3008	1.2176	1.1604	1.1179	1.0844	1.3446
70	1.3297	1.2455	1.1877	1.1450	1.1115	1.3789
80	1.3555	1.2708	1.2125	1.1699	1.1363	1.4095
90	1.3789	1.2938	1.2354	1.1926	1.1595	1.4377
100	1.4009	1.3150	1.2568	1.2141	1.1809	1.4637
200	1.5626	1.4758	1.4185	1.3768	1.3452	1.6611

TABLE VII–B (*continued*)

$\alpha = 14$

T^*	$Z^{(2,2)}$	$Z^{(2,3)}$	$Z^{(2,4)}$	$Z^{(2,5)}$	$Z^{(2,6)}$	$Z^{(4,4)}$
0	1.1947	1.0951	1.0221	0.9706	0.9193	1.0927
0.1	1.2017	1.1027	1.0301	0.9742	0.9296	1.0990
0.2	1.2090	1.1128	1.0416	0.9831	0.9309	1.1098
0.3	1.2109	1.1046	1.0168	0.9391	0.8695	1.0965
0.4	1.1947	1.0716	0.9690	0.8825	0.8109	1.0607
0.5	1.1670	1.0317	0.9235	0.8382	0.7718	1.0206
0.6	1.1359	0.9948	0.8878	0.8076	0.7481	0.9846
0.7	1.1060	0.9641	0.8615	0.7877	0.7346	0.9549
0.8	1.0794	0.9397	0.8428	0.7754	0.7277	0.9315
0.9	1.0564	0.9209	0.8300	0.7682	0.7249	0.9135
1.0	1.0370	0.9066	0.8215	0.7647	0.7250	0.9001
1.2	1.0078	0.8882	0.8132	0.7641	0.7299	0.8829
1.4	0.9885	0.8790	0.8122	0.7686	0.7380	0.8746
1.6	0.9761	0.8756	0.8151	0.7756	0.7476	0.8720
1.8	0.9688	0.8759	0.8205	0.7840	0.7580	0.8731
2.0	0.9649	0.8785	0.8271	0.7930	0.7683	0.8764
2.5	0.9651	0.8910	0.8464	0.8162	0.7937	0.8905
3.0	0.9729	0.9069	0.8666	0.8385	0.8172	0.9081
3.5	0.9844	0.9239	0.8862	0.8594	0.8384	0.9267
4	0.9973	0.9409	0.9048	0.8785	0.8575	0.9449
5	1.0244	0.9729	0.9384	0.9121	0.8908	0.9790
6	1.0507	1.0015	0.9675	0.9408	0.9188	1.0092
7	1.0755	1.0274	0.9882	0.9656	0.9428	1.0361
8	1.0982	1.0504	1.0154	0.9875	0.9639	1.0600
9	1.1192	1.0712	1.0357	1.0068	0.9827	1.0816
10	1.1385	1.0902	1.0539	1.0244	0.9996	1.1013
12	1.1731	1.1237	1.0859	1.0554	1.0293	1.1359
14	1.2034	1.1526	1.1136	1.0818	1.0550	1.1656
16	1.2302	1.1781	1.1379	1.1051	1.0777	1.1917
18	1.2540	1.2007	1.1596	1.1261	1.0980	1.2153
20	1.2758	1.2213	1.1792	1.1452	1.1168	1.2364
25	1.3229	1.2659	1.2222	1.1868	1.1576	1.2826
30	1.3622	1.3034	1.2583	1.2222	1.1925	1.3217
35	1.3963	1.3363	1.2902	1.2535	1.2231	1.3559
40	1.4266	1.3653	1.3185	1.2816	1.2510	1.3863
45	1.4543	1.3917	1.3445	1.3070	1.2766	1.4141
50	1.4793	1.4161	1.3684	1.3308	1.2999	1.4396
60	1.5239	1.4596	1.4115	1.3735	1.3427	1.4856
70	1.5636	1.4983	1.4497	1.4118	1.3806	1.5263
80	1.5990	1.5332	1.4846	1.4463	1.4156	1.5633
90	1.6314	1.5656	1.5165	1.4782	1.4474	1.5972
100	1.6612	1.5950	1.5461	1.5079	1.4771	1.6289
200	1.8858	1.8198	1.7713	1.7344	1.7043	1.8674

TABLE VII–B (*continued*)

$\alpha = 15$

T^*	$Z^{(1,1)}$	$Z^{(1,2)}$	$Z^{(1,3)}$	$Z^{(1,4)}$	$Z^{(1,5)}$	$Z^{(3,3)}$
0	1.1870	1.0551	0.9672	0.9027	0.8572	1.1178
0.1	1.1722	1.0378	0.9477	0.8810	0.8285	1.1007
0.2	1.1577	1.0163	0.9153	0.8343	0.7655	1.0765
0.3	1.1320	0.9750	0.8594	0.7687	0.6970	1.0392
0.4	1.0984	0.9300	0.8099	0.7221	0.6579	1.0012
0.5	1.0645	0.8916	0.7747	0.6944	0.6388	0.9672
0.6	1.0337	0.8618	0.7514	0.6792	0.6306	0.9387
0.7	1.0075	0.8397	0.7367	0.6715	0.6285	0.9158
0.8	0.9857	0.8235	0.7278	0.6687	0.6299	0.8978
0.9	0.9678	0.8121	0.7230	0.6687	0.6333	0.8840
1.0	0.9533	0.8040	0.7208	0.6707	0.6378	0.8735
1.2	0.9323	0.7954	0.7218	0.6777	0.6484	0.8605
1.4	0.9191	0.7931	0.7266	0.6867	0.6596	0.8548
1.6	0.9112	0.7944	0.7335	0.6964	0.6708	0.8535
1.8	0.9070	0.7979	0.7412	0.7063	0.6817	0.8554
2.0	0.9054	0.8028	0.7494	0.7159	0.6921	0.8593
2.5	0.9083	0.8179	0.7699	0.7389	0.7160	0.8734
3.0	0.9167	0.8344	0.7896	0.7597	0.7372	0.8903
3.5	0.9273	0.8507	0.8078	0.7783	0.7558	0.9077
4	0.9389	0.8662	0.8245	0.7953	0.7725	0.9245
5	0.9627	0.8951	0.8541	0.8245	0.8012	0.9558
6	0.9856	0.9203	0.8796	0.8494	0.8250	0.9836
7	1.0069	0.9430	0.9017	0.8708	0.8458	1.0086
8	1.0268	0.9632	0.9214	0.8895	0.8638	1.0308
9	1.0449	0.9816	0.9390	0.9063	0.8800	1.0514
10	1.0619	0.9981	0.9549	0.9216	0.8946	1.0699
12	1.0922	1.0277	0.9829	0.9483	0.9205	1.1032
14	1.1188	1.0530	1.0070	0.9715	0.9428	1.1132
16	1.1426	1.0756	1.0284	0.9921	0.9628	1.1579
18	1.1640	1.0957	1.0475	1.0104	0.9805	1.1812
20	1.1834	1.1140	1.0648	1.0273	0.9970	1.2026
25	1.2257	1.1537	1.1029	1.0642	1.0333	1.2494
30	1.2614	1.1872	1.1353	1.0957	1.0642	1.2897
35	1.2923	1.2167	1.1637	1.1234	1.0920	1.3254
40	1.3199	1.2429	1.1890	1.1486	1.1169	1.3574
45	1.3446	1.2666	1.2123	1.1718	1.1397	1.3869
50	1.3675	1.2886	1.2339	1.1929	1.1609	1.4141
60	1.4083	1.3280	1.2726	1.2316	1.1996	1.4631
70	1.4443	1.3630	1.3073	1.2660	1.2340	1.5072
80	1.4766	1.3945	1.3389	1.2974	1.2654	1.5471
90	1.5059	1.4235	1.3675	1.3267	1.2946	1.5837
100	1.5331	1.4505	1.3945	1.3534	1.3217	1.6180
200	1.7372	1.6538	1.5991	1.5596	1.5291	1.8773

TABLE VII–B (*continued*)

$\alpha = 15$

T^*	$Z^{(2,2)}$	$Z^{(2,3)}$	$Z^{(2,4)}$	$Z^{(2,5)}$	$Z^{(2,6)}$	$Z^{(4,4)}$
0	1.1947	1.0951	1.0221	0.9706	0.9193	1.0927
0.1	1.2016	1.1025	1.0306	0.9736	0.9290	1.1061
0.2	1.2081	1.1114	1.0403	0.9828	0.9325	1.1150
0.3	1.2107	1.1061	1.0211	0.9465	0.8796	1.1029
0.4	1.1978	1.0783	0.9791	0.8952	0.8252	1.0705
0.5	1.1739	1.0426	0.9374	0.8536	0.7879	1.0333
0.6	1.1462	1.0088	0.9039	0.8247	0.7654	0.9996
0.7	1.1191	0.9803	0.8791	0.8060	0.7529	0.9718
0.8	1.0945	0.9575	0.8617	0.7946	0.7470	0.9499
0.9	1.0734	0.9400	0.8498	0.7883	0.7454	0.9331
1.0	1.0555	0.9268	0.8423	0.7858	0.7466	0.9209
1.2	1.0285	0.9102	0.8359	0.7872	0.7535	0.9057
1.4	1.0110	0.9027	0.8365	0.7936	0.7637	0.8992
1.6	1.0003	0.9009	0.8412	0.8024	0.7751	0.8982
1.8	0.9944	0.9027	0.8481	0.8124	0.7868	0.9007
2.0	0.9920	0.9067	0.8562	0.8227	0.7986	0.9054
2.5	0.9953	0.9223	0.8786	0.8488	0.8266	0.9222
3.0	1.0059	0.9409	0.9013	0.8734	0.8521	0.9419
3.5	1.0196	0.9602	0.9229	0.8960	0.8750	0.9622
4	1.0345	0.9790	0.9431	0.9169	0.8958	0.9819
5	1.0651	1.0139	0.9796	0.9533	0.9318	1.0187
6	1.0943	1.0452	1.0111	0.9844	0.9623	1.0514
7	1.1213	1.0733	1.0389	1.0115	0.9887	1.0805
8	1.1462	1.0985	1.0634	1.0356	1.0121	1.1064
9	1.1691	1.1212	1.0856	1.0570	1.0332	1.1300
10	1.1904	1.1421	1.1059	1.0766	1.0523	1.1515
12	1.2283	1.1791	1.1416	1.1115	1.0860	1.1895
14	1.2616	1.2111	1.1727	1.1416	1.1154	1.2225
16	1.2911	1.2397	1.2002	1.1683	1.1417	1.2518
18	1.3179	1.2655	1.2250	1.1925	1.1656	1.2781
20	1.3423	1.2887	1.2477	1.2148	1.1873	1.3020
25	1.3954	1.3399	1.2975	1.2634	1.2353	1.3544
30	1.4406	1.3835	1.3400	1.3054	1.2768	1.3992
35	1.4802	1.4219	1.3775	1.3425	1.3138	1.4382
40	1.5152	1.4561	1.4114	1.3759	1.3471	1.4737
45	1.5474	1.4874	1.4424	1.4067	1.3776	1.5057
50	1.5769	1.5163	1.4710	1.4352	1.4060	1.5353
60	1.6298	1.5684	1.5225	1.4865	1.4757	1.5889
70	1.6768	1.6150	1.5687	1.5326	1.5034	1.6365
80	1.7190	1.6569	1.6107	1.5747	1.5453	1.6797
90	1.7580	1.6952	1.6491	1.6132	1.5841	1.7194
100	1.7938	1.7312	1.6850	1.6489	1.6200	1.7562
200	2.0647	2.0026	1.9572	1.9227	1.8945	2.0351

TABLE VII–C

FUNCTIONS FOR CALCULATING THE HIGHER APPROXIMATIONS TO THE TRANSPORT COEFFICIENTS[a] FOR THE MODIFIED BUCKINGHAM (6-EXP) POTENTIAL

The function $f_{\mathscr{D}}^{(3)}$

T^*	$\alpha = 12$	$\alpha = 13$	$\alpha = 14$	$\alpha = 15$
0	1.0020	1.0020	1.0020	1.0020
0.1	1.0017	1.0017	1.0018	1.0018
0.2	1.0010	1.0012	1.0013	1.0014
0.3	1.0002	1.0004	1.0005	1.0006
0.4	1.0001	1.0001	1.0001	1.0002
0.5	1.0002	1.0001	1.0000	1.0000
0.6	1.0003	1.0001	1.0000	1.0000
0.7	1.0003	1.0001	1.0000	1.0000
0.8	1.0002	1.0001	1.0000	1.0000
0.9	1.0002	1.0001	1.0000	1.0000
1.0	1.0001	1.0000	1.0000	1.0001
1.2	1.0001	1.0001	1.0002	1.0003
1.4	1.0001	1.0003	1.0004	1.0006
1.6	1.0003	1.0005	1.0007	1.0009
1.8	1.0006	1.0008	1.0011	1.0013
2.0	1.0009	1.0012	1.0015	1.0017
2.5	1.0017	1.0020	1.0024	1.0028
3.0	1.0024	1.0028	1.0032	1.0037
3.5	1.0030	1.0035	1.0039	1.0044
4	1.0035	1.0041	1.0045	1.0050
5	1.0042	1.0049	1.0053	1.0059
6	1.0047	1.0053	1.0059	1.0064
7	1.0049	1.0057	1.0062	1.0068
8	1.0051	1.0059	1.0065	1.0070
9	1.0052	1.0060	1.0066	1.0072
10	1.0053	1.0061	1.0067	1.0073
12	1.0053	1.0061	1.0068	1.0074
14	1.0053	1.0062	1.0069	1.0075
16	1.0052	1.0061	1.0068	1.0075
18	1.0052	1.0061	1.0068	1.0075
20	1.0051	1.0060	1.0068	1.0075
25	1.0050	1.0059	1.0068	1.0075
30	1.0049	1.0058	1.0067	1.0075
35	1.0048	1.0058	1.0066	1.0075
40	1.0048	1.0058	1.0067	1.0075
45	1.0047	1.0058	1.0066	1.0075
50	1.0047	1.0058	1.0067	1.0076
60	1.0047	1.0058	1.0067	1.0077
70	1.0047	1.0058	1.0068	1.0077
80	1.0047	1.0059	1.0069	1.0078
90	1.0047	1.0059	1.0070	1.0079
100	1.0048	1.0060	1.0070	1.0081
200	1.0053	1.0067	1.0077	1.0088

[a] E. A. Mason, *J. Chem. Phys.*, **22**, 169 (1954).

TABLE VII–C (*continued*)

The function $f_\eta^{(3)}$

T^*	$\alpha = 12$	$\alpha = 13$	$\alpha = 14$	$\alpha = 15$
0	1.0017	1.0017	1.0017	1.0017
0.1	1.0019	1.0018	1.0018	1.0018
0.2	1.0017	1.0021	1.0021	1.0020
0.3	1.0012	1.0014	1.0015	1.0016
0.4	1.0003	1.0005	1.0006	1.0008
0.5	1.0001	1.0001	1.0002	1.0003
0.6	1.0001	1.0000	1.0000	1.0001
0.7	1.0002	1.0001	1.0000	1.0000
0.8	1.0002	1.0001	1.0000	1.0000
0.9	1.0002	1.0001	1.0000	1.0000
1.0	1.0001	1.0001	1.0000	1.0000
1.2	1.0001	1.0001	1.0001	1.0001
1.4	1.0001	1.0002	1.0002	1.0003
1.6	1.0003	1.0004	1.0005	1.0007
1.8	1.0005	1.0007	1.0008	1.0010
2.0	1.0008	1.0011	1.0012	1.0015
2.5	1.0017	1.0020	1.0022	1.0026
3.0	1.0025	1.0029	1.0031	1.0035
3.5	1.0032	1.0036	1.0039	1.0043
4	1.0037	1.0042	1.0046	1.0050
5	1.0045	1.0050	1.0055	1.0058
6	1.0050	1.0055	1.0061	1.0064
7	1.0052	1.0058	1.0066	1.0067
8	1.0054	1.0060	1.0067	1.0070
9	1.0055	1.0061	1.0068	1.0071
10	1.0056	1.0062	1.0069	1.0072
12	1.0057	1.0062	1.0069	1.0073
14	1.0057	1.0063	1.0069	1.0073
16	1.0057	1.0063	1.0069	1.0073
18	1.0057	1.0064	1.0069	1.0073
20	1.0057	1.0064	1.0068	1.0073
25	1.0057	1.0064	1.0068	1.0073
30	1.0057	1.0065	1.0068	1.0074
35	1.0057	1.0065	1.0068	1.0074
40	1.0058	1.0066	1.0068	1.0075
45	1.0058	1.0067	1.0068	1.0075
50	1.0059	1.0068	1.0068	1.0075
60	1.0060	1.0069	1.0069	1.0077
70	1.0061	1.0071	1.0070	1.0078
80	1.0062	1.0072	1.0071	1.0079
90	1.0063	1.0073	1.0072	1.0080
100	1.0064	1.0074	1.0073	1.0082
200	1.0074	1.0084	1.0081	1.0091

TABLE VII-C (*continued*)

The function $f_\lambda^{(3)}$

T^*	$\alpha = 12$	$\alpha = 13$	$\alpha = 14$	$\alpha = 15$
0	1.0027	1.0027	1.0027	1.0027
0.1	1.0029	1.0028	1.0029	1.0028
0.2	1.0027	1.0032	1.0033	1.0032
0.3	1.0020	1.0023	1.0025	1.0026
0.4	1.0006	1.0009	1.0011	1.0013
0.5	1.0002	1.0002	1.0003	1.0005
0.6	1.0002	1.0001	1.0001	1.0001
0.7	1.0003	1.0001	1.0000	1.0000
0.8	1.0003	1.0001	1.0000	1.0000
0.9	1.0003	1.0001	1.0000	1.0000
1.0	1.0002	1.0001	1.0000	1.0000
1.2	1.0002	1.0001	1.0001	1.0002
1.4	1.0002	1.0003	1.0004	1.0005
1.6	1.0004	1.0006	1.0008	1.0010
1.8	1.0008	1.0011	1.0013	1.0016
2.0	1.0013	1.0016	1.0019	1.0022
2.5	1.0026	1.0031	1.0034	1.0039
3.0	1.0038	1.0045	1.0048	1.0054
3.5	1.0049	1.0056	1.0060	1.0067
4	1.0058	1.0065	1.0071	1.0077
5	1.0070	1.0078	1.0085	1.0091
6	1.0077	1.0085	1.0094	1.0099
7	1.0081	1.0090	1.0105	1.0105
8	1.0085	1.0093	1.0104	1.0109
9	1.0087	1.0095	1.0106	1.0111
10	1.0088	1.0097	1.0107	1.0112
12	1.0089	1.0098	1.0109	1.0114
14	1.0089	1.0099	1.0108	1.0114
16	1.0089	1.0099	1.0108	1.0115
18	1.0088	1.0100	1.0108	1.0115
20	1.0089	1.0100	1.0107	1.0114
25	1.0089	1.0101	1.0106	1.0115
30	1.0089	1.0101	1.0106	1.0115
35	1.0090	1.0102	1.0106	1.0116
40	1.0090	1.0103	1.0106	1.0116
45	1.0091	1.0104	1.0106	1.0117
50	1.0092	1.0105	1.0107	1.0118
60	1.0093	1.0108	1.0108	1.0120
70	1.0096	1.0111	1.0109	1.0122
80	1.0097	1.0112	1.0110	1.0124
90	1.0099	1.0114	1.0113	1.0125
100	1.0101	1.0116	1.0114	1.0127
200	1.0115	1.0132	1.0127	1.0141

TABLE VII–D

The Function β for Calculating Isotopic Thermal Diffusion[a] for the Modified Buckingham (6-Exp) Potential

$$[k_T]_2 = \beta \frac{M_1 - M_2}{M_1 + M_2} x_1 x_2$$

T^*	$\alpha = 12$	$\alpha = 13$	$\alpha = 14$	$\alpha = 15$
0	0.3133	0.3133	0.3133	0.3133
0.1	0.2844	0.2865	0.2887	0.2887
0.2	0.2047	0.2264	0.2401	0.2468
0.3	0.0738	0.1110	0.1369	0.1545
0.4	−0.0271	0.0157	0.0484	0.0727
0.5	−0.0829	−0.0389	−0.0037	0.0229
0.6	−0.1038	−0.0616	−0.0256	0.0020
0.7	−0.1031	−0.0623	−0.0270	0.0005
0.8	−0.0902	−0.0509	−0.0162	0.0105
0.9	−0.0690	−0.0317	0.0023	0.0287
1.0	−0.0456	−0.0088	0.0244	0.0498
1.2	0.0071	0.0419	0.0734	0.0981
1.4	0.0580	0.0923	0.1226	0.1466
1.6	0.1050	0.1386	0.1680	0.1911
1.8	0.1476	0.1797	0.2083	0.2310
2.0	0.1841	0.2161	0.2438	0.2665
2.5	0.2570	0.2883	0.3145	0.3380
3.0	0.3103	0.3404	0.3658	0.3890
3.5	0.3469	0.3786	0.4035	0.4270
4	0.3744	0.4060	0.4313	0.4544
5	0.4111	0.4437	0.4679	0.4931
6	0.4312	0.4643	0.4911	0.5134
7	0.4414	0.4778	0.5044	0.5283
8	0.4494	0.4858	0.5131	0.5358
9	0.4531	0.4889	0.5181	0.5427
10	0.4536	0.4911	0.5208	0.5446
12	0.4536	0.4917	0.5233	0.5494
14	0.4512	0.4919	0.5225	0.5495
16	0.4469	0.4887	0.5209	0.5496
18	0.4441	0.4866	0.5187	0.5485
20	0.4387	0.4826	0.5190	0.5479
25	0.4321	0.4764	0.5140	0.5452
30	0.4245	0.4713	0.5106	0.5427
35	0.4188	0.4681	0.5066	0.5429
40	0.4161	0.4648	0.5058	0.5426
45	0.4118	0.4641	0.5038	0.5426
50	0.4093	0.4616	0.5035	0.5429
60	0.4051	0.4598	0.5032	0.5443
70	0.4048	0.4590	0.5044	0.5460
80	p.4034	0.4583	0.5071	0.5474
90	0.4022	0.4584	0.5093	0.5505
100	0.4024	0.4586	0.5095	0.5534
200	0.4110	0.4703	0.5277	0.5727

[a] E. A. Mason, *J. Chem. Phys.*, **22**, 169 (1954).

TABLE VII–E

THE QUANTITIES A*, B*, AND C* FOR CALCULATING THE TRANSPORT PROPERTIES OF MIXTURES[a] FOR THE MODIFIED BUCKINGHAM (6-EXP) POTENTIAL

The function A*

T^*	$\alpha = 12$	$\alpha = 13$	$\alpha = 14$	$\alpha = 15$
0	1.0065	1.0065	1.0065	1.0065
0.1	1.0060	1.0146	1.0247	1.0251
0.2	1.0374	1.0374	1.0445	1.0435
0.3	1.0731	1.0693	1.0729	1.0695
0.4	1.0976	1.0932	1.0946	1.0905
0.5	1.1108	1.1067	1.1070	1.1028
0.6	1.1170	1.1131	1.1128	1.1088
0.7	1.1193	1.1154	1.1145	1.1108
0.8	1.1194	1.1154	1.1142	1.1104
0.9	1.1185	1.1143	1.1126	1.1091
1.0	1.1173	1.1126	1.1106	1.1071
1.2	1.1146	1.1096	1.1067	1.1032
1.4	1.1126	1.1070	1.1037	1.1000
1.6	1.1114	1.1052	1.1013	1.0978
1.8	1.1111	1.1044	1.0999	1.0964
2.0	1.1111	1.1044	1.0990	1.0956
2.5	1.1130	1.1056	1.0987	1.0958
3.0	1.1161	1.1081	1.1002	1.0973
3.5	1.1193	1.1113	1.1026	1.0995
4	1.1226	1.1141	1.1050	1.1018
5	1.1284	1.1194	1.1101	1.1064
6	1.1335	1.1238	1.1147	1.1103
7	1.1377	1.1277	1.1189	1.1136
8	1.1417	1.1309	1.1224	1.1163
9	1.1449	1.1336	1.1255	1.1189
10	1.1477	1.1361	1.1281	1.1210
12	1.1532	1.1406	1.1326	1.1246
14	1.1583	1.1447	1.1366	1.1276
16	1.1625	1.1485	1.1397	1.1300
18	1.1665	1.1517	1.1423	1.1322
20	1.1702	1.1548	1.1449	1.1343
25	1.1790	1.1623	1.1502	1.1385
30	1.1865	1.1691	1.1542	1.1421
35	1.1938	1.1752	1.1578	1.1454
40	1.2005	1.1813	1.1612	1.1480
45	1.2067	1.1867	1.1643	1.1508
50	1.2123	1.1917	1.1668	1.1531
60	1.2230	1.2008	1.1715	1.1573
70	1.2326	1.2092	1.1759	1.1610
80	1.2416	1.2168	1.1796	1.1642
90	1.2492	1.2240	1.1831	1.1674
100	1.2569	1.2300	1.1858	1.1700
200	1.3103	1.2754	1.2068	1.1885

[a] E. A. Mason, *J. Chem. Phys.*, **22**, 169 (1954).

TABLE VII–E (*continued*)

The function B*

T^*	$\alpha = 12$	$\alpha = 13$	$\alpha = 14$	$\alpha = 15$
0	1.1851	1.1851	1.1851	1.1851
0.1	1.1988	1.1955	1.1926	1.1928
0.2	1.2528	1.2407	1.2328	1.2268
0.3	1.3028	1.2895	1.2788	1.2698
0.4	1.3127	1.3019	1.2922	1.2840
0.5	1.3003	1.2922	1.2844	1.2768
0.6	1.2808	1.2737	1.2668	1.2609
0.7	1.2601	1.2539	1.2476	1.2424
0.8	1.2403	1.2346	1.2289	1.2238
0.9	1.2239	1.2172	1.2125	1.2074
1.0	1.2079	1.2025	1.1973	1.1930
1.2	1.1837	1.1780	1.1733	1.1689
1.4	1.1662	1.1612	1.1561	1.1523
1.6	1.1536	1.1490	1.1440	1.1392
1.8	1.1458	1.1394	1.1347	1.1298
2.0	1.1387	1.1324	1.1279	1.1226
2.5	1.1288	1.1222	1.1174	1.1119
3.0	1.1250	1.1167	1.1113	1.1057
3.5	1.1217	1.1136	1.1084	1.1024
4	1.1211	1.1128	1.1067	1.1002
5	1.1225	1.1126	1.1048	1.1001
6	1.1242	1.1131	1.1059	1.0989
7	1.1252	1.1155	1.1067	1.1006
8	1.1278	1.1176	1.1079	1.1009
9	1.1298	1.1185	1.1094	1.1025
10	1.1317	1.1203	1.1103	1.1026
12	1.1351	1.1225	1.1127	1.1050
14	1.1376	1.1247	1.1135	1.1056
16	1.1384	1.1259	1.1149	1.1066
18	1.1405	1.1271	1.1153	1.1070
20	1.1404	1.1274	1.1178	1.1077
25	1.1426	1.1282	1.1176	1.1070
30	1.1426	1.1281	1.1178	1.1058
35	1.1427	1.1279	1.1162	1.1055
40	1.1427	1.1268	1.1159	1.1050
45	1.1418	1.1270	1.1148	1.1035
50	1.1407	1.1255	1.1142	1.1023
60	1.1388	1.1236	1.1119	1.1003
70	1.1378	1.1218	1.1106	1.0980
80	1.1365	1.1198	1.1096	1.0950
90	1.1350	1.1180	1.1077	1.0940
100	1.1331	1.1154	1.1049	1.0922
200	1.1206	1.1021	1.0911	1.0779

TABLE VII–E (*continued*)

The function c*

T^*	$\alpha = 12$	$\alpha = 13$	$\alpha = 14$	$\alpha = 15$
0	0.8889	0.8889	0.8889	0.8889
0.1	0.8835	0.8844	0.8853	0.8853
0.2	0.8697	0.8736	0.8765	0.8779
0.3	0.8463	0.8531	0.8581	0.8613
0.4	0.8279	0.8360	0.8421	0.8467
0.5	0.8172	0.8257	0.8325	0.8376
0.6	0.8128	0.8212	0.8283	0.8337
0.7	0.8127	0.8209	0.8280	0.8334
0.8	0.8151	0.8231	0.8301	0.8354
0.9	0.8193	0.8269	0.8338	0.8391
1.0	0.8240	0.8315	0.8383	0.8434
1.2	0.8348	0.8419	0.8482	0.8532
1.4	0.8453	0.8521	0.8582	0.8629
1.6	0.8549	0.8615	0.8673	0.8718
1.8	0.8636	0.8698	0.8753	0.8797
2.0	0.8709	0.8771	0.8823	0.8867
2.5	0.8855	0.8913	0.8961	0.9005
3.0	0.8959	0.9014	0.9059	0.9102
3.5	0.9031	0.9088	0.9131	0.9174
4	0.9084	0.9141	0.9183	0.9226
5	0.9155	0.9213	0.9253	0.9298
6	0.9195	0.9254	0.9298	0.9337
7	0.9216	0.9280	0.9324	0.9365
8	0.9232	0.9295	0.9342	0.9381
9	0.9241	0.9302	0.9352	0.9394
10	0.9242	0.9307	0.9359	0.9399
12	0.9245	0.9311	0.9366	0.9409
14	0.9243	0.9313	0.9367	0.9412
16	0.9237	0.9310	0.9366	0.9414
18	0.9234	0.9307	0.9364	0.9413
20	0.9226	0.9302	0.9366	0.9414
25	0.9218	0.9295	0.9361	0.9413
30	0.9209	0.9291	0.9358	0.9412
35	0.9203	0.9289	0.9354	0.9415
40	0.9202	0.9288	0.9355	0.9417
45	0.9198	0.9290	0.9355	0.9420
50	0.9197	0.9290	0.9356	0.9423
60	0.9196	0.9293	0.9360	0.9430
70	0.9202	0.9298	0.9367	0.9437
80	0.9205	0.9303	0.9375	0.9444
90	0.9208	0.9309	0.9383	0.9453
100	0.9214	0.9316	0.9387	0.9461
200	0.9271	0.9377	0.9445	0.9520

TABLE VIII

FUNCTIONS NEEDED FOR THE CALCULATION OF THE SECOND VIRIAL COEFFICIENT FOR KIHARA'S GENERALIZED SPHEROCYLINDRICAL AND ELLIPSOIDAL MOLECULES[a]

$X = \epsilon/kT$

$-\log_{10} X$	$F_3(X)$	$F_2(X)$	$F_1(X)$	$F_{-1}(X)$	$F_{-3}(X)$	$F_{-5}(X)$	$F_{-7}(X)$
−0.4	−9.859	−5.211	−1.784				
−0.3	−6.138	−3.008	−0.7761				
−0.2	−4.003	−1.776	−0.2221				
−0.1	−2.673	−1.027	0.1091				
0.0	−1.795	−0.5424	0.3198	1.591	2.683	3.82	5.12
0.1	−1.189	−0.2151	0.4600	1.478	2.392	3.38	4.55
0.2	−0.7587	0.0132	0.5562	1.403	2.204	3.11	4.24
0.3	−0.4465	0.1758	0.6234	1.351	2.084	2.96	4.07
0.4	−0.2170	0.2930	0.6710	1.319	2.009	2.87	4.02
0.5	−0.0469	0.3779	0.7045	1.297	1.968	2.85	4.06
0.6	0.0794	0.4392	0.7279	1.284	1.953	2.87	4.17
0.7	0.1729	0.4829	0.7436	1.276	1.957	2.92	4.35
0.8	0.2415	0.5134	0.7536	1.274	1.977	3.01	4.60
0.9	0.2911	0.5336	0.7591	1.277	2.012	3.14	4.91
1.0	0.3259	0.5459	0.7611	1.282	2.058	3.29	5.29
1.1	0.3493	0.5521	0.7603	1.291	2.116	3.47	5.74
1.2	0.3638	0.5534	0.7575	1.302	2.184	3.68	6.27
1.3	0.3715	0.5510	0.7528	1.315	2.262	3.92	6.91
1.4	0.3737	0.5457	0.7468	1.330	2.349	4.20	7.63
1.5	0.3718	0.5381	0.7396	1.346	2.446	4.51	8.46
1.6	0.3668	0.5287	0.7320	1.364	2.553	4.86	9.42
1.7	0.3594	0.5179	0.7228	1.383	2.669	5.25	10.53
1.8	0.3501	0.5062	0.7135	1.403	2.794	5.68	11.79
1.9	0.3396	0.4937	0.7038	1.424	2.930	6.16	13.24
2.0	0.3281	0.4806	0.6937	1.446	3.075	6.69	14.90

[a] T. Kihara, *J. Phys. Soc. Japan*, **6**, 289 (1951).

TABLE IX

THE REDUCED AVERAGED COLLISION CROSS-SECTION $\Omega^{(2,2)\star}$ FOR POLAR MOLECULES[a, b]

kT/ϵ	δ^*								
	0.00	0.25	0.50	0.75	1.00	1.25	1.50	1.75	2.00
1.0	1.5938	1.7578	1.9312	2.0806	2.1963	2.3025	2.4920	2.5916	2.6199
1.2	1.4568	1.5872	1.7302	1.8661	1.9881	2.1035	2.2749	2.3782	2.4257
1.4	1.3557	1.4622	1.5812	1.7026	1.8224	1.9395	2.0945	2.2051	2.2713
1.6	1.2800	1.3688	1.4689	1.5756	1.6878	1.8019	1.9430	2.0599	2.1413
1.8	1.2216	1.2965	1.3813	1.4739	1.5759	1.6843	1.8128	1.9339	2.0263
2.0	1.1751	1.2390	1.3112	1.3907	1.4817	1.5832	1.6999	1.8224	1.9217
2.2	1.1377	1.1923	1.2539	1.3220	1.4026	1.4957	1.6015	1.7232	1.8258
2.4	1.1066	1.1537	1.2063	1.2643	1.3349	1.4198	1.5155	1.6343	1.7373
2.6	1.0803	1.1212	1.1662	1.2155	1.2769	1.3537	1.4401	1.5544	1.6559
2.8	1.0579	1.0935	1.1321	1.1737	1.2270	1.2961	1.3738	1.4827	1.5812
3.0	1.0385	1.0696	1.1026	1.1377	1.1837	1.2456	1.3153	1.4182	1.5126
3.2	1.0214	1.0488	1.0769	1.1065	1.1460	1.2012	1.2636	1.3601	1.4499
3.4	1.0063	1.0304	1.0544	1.0792	1.1129	1.1621	1.2178	1.3078	1.3926
3.6	0.9928	1.0141	1.0345	1.0552	1.0838	1.1274	1.1770	1.2606	1.3401
3.8	0.9807	0.9996	1.0168	1.0339	1.0581	1.0965	1.1406	1.2179	1.2922
4.0	0.9696	0.9864	1.0009	1.0149	1.0351	1.0690	1.1081	1.1794	1.2485
5	0.9265	0.9359	0.9411	0.9446	0.9510	0.9674	0.9874	1.0334	1.0797
6	0.8960	0.9010	0.9014	0.8994	0.8980	0.9037	0.9118	0.9401	0.9694
7	0.8725	0.8750	0.8727	0.8677	0.8618	0.8609	0.8614	0.8777	0.8946
8	0.8536	0.8545	0.8507	0.8440	0.8356	0.8304	0.8260	0.8342	0.8422
9	0.8378	0.8376	0.8330	0.8254	0.8154	0.8077	0.8000	0.8028	0.8043
10	0.8242	0.8232	0.8183	0.8102	0.7994	0.7901	0.7802	0.7793	0.7760
11	0.8123	0.8108	0.8058	0.7975	0.7863	0.7760	0.7648	0.7613	0.7544
12	0.8017	0.7999	0.7948	0.7865	0.7752	0.7644	0.7523	0.7471	0.7376
13	0.7922	0.7902	0.7851	0.7769	0.7656	0.7546	0.7421	0.7356	0.7243
14	0.7836	0.7814	0.7765	0.7684	0.7572	0.7462	0.7334	0.7262	0.7134
15	0.7756	0.7734	0.7686	0.7606	0.7497	0.7388	0.7260	0.7182	0.7045
16	0.7883	0.7660	0.7613	0.7536	0.7429	0.7322	0.7195	0.7114	0.6971
32	0.6939	0.6924	0.6897	0.6846	0.6782	0.6717	0.6637	0.6569	0.6462
64	0.6262	0.6259	0.6251	0.6213	0.6181	0.6151	0.6114	0.6078	0.6033
128	0.5634	0.5638	0.5640	0.5612	0.5593	0.5579	0.5563	0.5547	0.5528
256	0.5056	0.5061	0.5065	0.5047	0.5035	0.5028	0.5021	0.5014	0.5006
512	0.4528	0.4533	0.4539	0.4527	0.4518	0.4515	0.4512	0.4508	0.4505

[a] The parameters for twelve polar gases to be used with this table are given in Table 8.6–1.

[b] This table is taken from F. J. Krieger, "The Viscosity of Polar Gases," Project Rand Report RM-646, July 1, 1951.

Symbols and Notation

General

h = Planck's constant

$\hbar = h/2\pi$

k = the Boltzmann constant

$\tilde{N}$ = Avogadro's number

R = the gas constant $= \tilde{N}k$

$i = \sqrt{-1}$

c = velocity of light

e = charge on the electron

σ, ϵ = parameters in intermolecular potential functions

$\lambda^2 = h^2/2\pi mkT$

$\Lambda^{*2} = h^2/\sigma^2 m\epsilon$

$b_0 = \frac{2}{3}\pi\tilde{N}\sigma^3$ = second virial coefficient of rigid spheres of diameter σ

t^* = measure of polarity of a molecule (Eq. 3.10–3)

$J_n(x)$ = Bessel functions

$P_l^m(x)$ = associated Legendre polynomials

$Y_l^m(\theta, \phi)$ = spherical harmonics (Appendix 12.B)

$S_n^{(m)}(x)$ = Sonine polynomials (Eq. 7.3–57)

$\Gamma(x)$ = the gamma function

$\mathrm{Ei}(x)$ = the exponential integral function (Eq. 11.7–50)

Classical Mechanics

$\boldsymbol{r}_i, \boldsymbol{p}_i$ = position and momentum of ith particle in Cartesian coordinates

$\boldsymbol{q}_i, \boldsymbol{p}_i$ = generalized coordinates and momenta

$\boldsymbol{v}_i$ = velocity of the ith particle

m_i = mass of ith particle

M_i = molecular weight of the ith species

μ_{ij} = reduced mass of molecules i and j

$\boldsymbol{F}_i$ = force acting on ith particle

$K(\boldsymbol{p}^N) = \sum_{i=1}^{N} (p_i^2/2m_i)$ = kinetic energy of system of N particles

$\Phi(\boldsymbol{r}^N)$ = potential energy of system of N particles

$H(\boldsymbol{r}^N, \boldsymbol{p}^N)$ = Hamiltonian of system of N particles

S = Hamilton-Jacobi function

Ξ = the "virial" (§ 1.4)

$b, g, \chi(b, g)$ = the "impact parameter," the initial relative velocity, and the angle of deflection in a binary collision (§ 1.5)

$\varphi(r)$ = spherically symmetric intermolecular potential function

$\varphi(r, \theta_1, \theta_2, \phi)$ = angular dependent intermolecular potential function

I = moment of inertia

Quantum Mechanics

$\mathscr{p}_i = \dfrac{\hbar}{i}\dfrac{\partial}{\partial \boldsymbol{r}_i}$ = momentum operator for the ith particle

$\mathscr{K} = \sum_i \dfrac{\hbar^2}{2m_i}\left(\dfrac{\partial}{\partial \boldsymbol{r}_i}\cdot\dfrac{\partial}{\partial \boldsymbol{r}_i}\right)$ = kinetic energy operator

$\mathscr{H} = \mathscr{K} + \Phi$ = Hamiltonian operatoı

$\mathscr{M}$ = angular momentum operator

$l, \kappa, \eta_l(\kappa)$ = angular momentum quantum numbers, energy quantum numbers, and phase-shift in a binary collision (§ 1.7)

$\alpha(g, \chi)$ = angular distribution of scattered particles (§ 1.7)

Electrodynamics

$\mathscr{V}$ = electrostatic potential

$\mathscr{A}$ = vector potential

$\mathscr{E}$ = electric field strength

$\mathscr{D}$ = electric displacement

$\mathscr{H}$ = magnetic field strength

$\mathscr{B}$ = magnetic induction

$\mathscr{P}$ = polarization

$\mathscr{M}$ = magnetization

$C = Ze$ = total charge

$\boldsymbol{\mu}$ = dipole moment vector

$\boldsymbol{\Theta}$ = quadrupole moment tensor (Eq. 12.1–15)

$\mathbf{Q}$ = traceless quadrupole moment tensor (Eq. 12.1–16)

$Q = qe$ = scalar value of quadrupole moment of cylindrical charge distributions (Eq. 12.1–17)

$Q_n{}^m$ = expansion coefficients related to multipole moments (Eq. 12.1–18)

$B^{|m|}_{n_a, n_b}$ = two-center expansion coefficients (Eq. 12.1–28)

$\chi^{(e)}$ = electric susceptibility

$\chi^{(m)}$ = magnetic susceptibility

ϵ' = dielectric constant

μ' = magnetic permeability

$\boldsymbol{m}$ = magnetic dipole moment

ρ = charge density

i = strength of electric current

$\boldsymbol{j}$ = current density

I = energy density

ν = frequency

η = index of refraction

f_i = oscillator strengths

α = polarizability

Thermodynamics

p = pressure

T = temperature

x_i = mole fraction of the ith component

V; v = volume; volume per molecule

U; u = internal energy; internal energy per molecule

H; h = enthalpy; enthalpy per molecule

C_p, C_v = specific heat at constant pressure, at constant volume

S = entropy

$G \equiv H - TS$ = Gibbs free energy

$A \equiv U - TS$ = Helmholtz free energy (the "work function")

n = number density (i.e., number of particles per unit volume)

n_i = number density of ith component

ρ = density (i.e., mass per unit volume)

z = effective number density (Eq. 3.2–22)

μ = Joule-Thomson coefficient

μ_i = chemical potential of ith component

f_i = fugacity of ith component

a_i = activity of ith component

$c = \sqrt{(\partial p/\partial \rho)_S}$ = velocity of sound

$\gamma = c_p/c_v$

Statistical Mechanics and Equation of State

$P^{(N)}(\boldsymbol{r}^N, \boldsymbol{p}^N)$, $P^{(N)}(\boldsymbol{r}^N)$, $f^{(N)}(\boldsymbol{r}^N, \boldsymbol{p}^N)$, $n^{(N)}(\boldsymbol{r}^N)$ = distribution functions[1] (classical statistical mechanics)

$\mathscr{P}^{(N)}(\boldsymbol{r}^N; \boldsymbol{r}'^N)$, $\mathscr{P}^{(N)}_{\rho\rho'}$, $\mathscr{N}^{(N)}(\boldsymbol{r}^N)$ = probability density matrices[2] (quantum statistical mechanics)

$g(r)$ = the radial distribution function

$W_N(\boldsymbol{r}^N)$ = the "Boltzmann factor" (Eq. 3.1–6)

$\mathscr{W}_N(\boldsymbol{r}^N)$ = the "Slater sum" (Eq. 6.1–13)

Z_N, Z_{Nq} = classical and quantum mechanical partition functions

z = partition function of a single molecule

$B(T), C(T), D(T) \cdots$ = second, third, fourth $\cdots$ virial coefficients

b_l = cluster integrals

β_k = irreducible integrals (Eq. 3.2–24, 25)

v_f = free volume

a = distance between nearest neighbors in lattice theories of liquid state

γ = surface tension

Kinetic Theory and Transport Properties[3]

ψ_j = summational invariants

$\boldsymbol{\Psi}_j$ = general flux vector

$\boldsymbol{j}$ = mass flux vector

[1] Distribution functions are discussed in § 2.1.

[2] Probability density matrices are discussed in § 2.2.

[3] For definitions of the various kinds of velocities see § 7.2a.

P = momentum flux tensor (pressure tensor)

$\boldsymbol{q}$ = heat flux vector

$\boldsymbol{\epsilon}$ = thermal energy flux vector

$\boldsymbol{\sigma}$ = entropy flux vector

η = coefficient of shear viscosity

κ = coefficient of bulk viscosity

λ = coefficient of thermal conductivity

D_{ij} = multicomponent diffusion coefficients

D_i^T = multicomponent thermal diffusion coefficients

$\mathscr{D}_{ij}$ = binary diffusion coefficients

k_T = thermal diffusion ratio

$\boldsymbol{v}$ = molecular velocity (Chs. 7–10)

$\boldsymbol{v}_0$ = mass average (or "stream") velocity (Chs. 7–10)

$\boldsymbol{v}$ = mass average velocity (Ch. 11)

$\boldsymbol{\omega}$ = number average velocity

$\boldsymbol{V}$ = peculiar velocity

$\bar{\boldsymbol{V}}$ = diffusion velocity

$\boldsymbol{W} = \sqrt{\mu/2kT}\,\boldsymbol{V}$ = reduced velocity

g = initial relative speed in binary encounter

$\gamma = \sqrt{\mu/2kT}\,g$ = reduced initial relative speed

$Q^{(l)}(g)$ = transport cross-sections (Eq. 8.2–2)

$\Omega^{(l,s)}(T)$ = integrals in terms of which the transport coefficients are expressed (Eq. 8.2–3)

$\text{A}^\star, \text{B}^\star, \text{C}^\star$ = quantities which appear in the expressions for the transport coefficients of mixtures (Eq. 8.2–15, 16, 17)

$[\eta_{12}]_1$ = quantity defined in Eq. 8.2–20

$[\lambda_{12}]_1$ = quantity defined in Eq. 8.2–34

$\boldsymbol{d}_i$ = quantity defined in Eqs. 7.3–27 and 11.2–28

b = quantity defined in Eq. 7.3–28

$f_i(\boldsymbol{r}, \boldsymbol{v}_i, t)$ = velocity distribution function (§ 7.1–d)

$f_i^{[r]}(\boldsymbol{r}, \boldsymbol{v}_i, t)$ = terms in Enskog series (Eq. 7.3–11)

$\phi_i(\boldsymbol{r}, \boldsymbol{v}_i, t)$ = perturbation function (Eq. 7.3–21)

Notes Added in Second Printing Ⓝ
(March 1964)

Page 17

L. Monchick has discussed the equivalence of the mean free path and Chapman-Enskog kinetic theory treatments in *Phys. Fluids*, **5**, 1393 (1962).

Page 35

An approximate treatment of transport properties using the Stockmayer potential (Eq. 1.3–33) has been given by L. Monchick and E. A. Mason [*J. Chem. Phys.*, **35**, 1676 (1961)]. See further Notes to pp. 597 and 600.

Page 41

The virial theorem given in § 1.4c can be generalized to the hypervirial theorem by making use of Eq. 1.4–19 [J. O. Hirschfelder, *J. Chem. Phys.*, **33**, 1462 (1960); *Z. physik. Chem.*, *Neue Folge*, **37**, 167 (1963)]. If W is a function of the coordinates and momenta (but not time, explicitly) bounded for the trajectory under consideration, then $\overline{[W,H]} = 0$. The usual virial theorem results from setting $W = \sum_j (\boldsymbol{r}_j \cdot \boldsymbol{p}_j)$. Other choices of W lead to dynamical relations which are called hypervirials. Both the virial and hypervirial theorems apply equally well in quantum and in relativistic mechanics. Since they do not require the forces to be conservative, they can be used in problems involving magnetic fields, wall forces, friction, etc.

Page 65

In reference to footnote 29, it is to be noted that the boundary condition on the solution of the radial wave equation is at the origin, in contrast to the boundary condition on the true one-dimensional wave equation, as discussed in this section. R. E. Langer [*Phys. Rev.*, **51**, 669 (1937)] has shown that, in the lowest WKB approximation this difference leads simply to the replacement of $l(l+1)$ by $(l+\frac{1}{2})^2$ throughout the solution. The effect on the next approximation has been discussed by S. Choi and J. Ross [*Proc. Nat. Acad. Sci.*, **48**, 803 (1962)].

Page 68

The quantum mechanical virial theorem of § 1.6f can be generalized to the hypervirial theorem (see note p. 41) by making use of Eq. 1.6–25 [J. O. Hirschfelder, *J. Chem. Phys.*, **33**, 1462 (1960); S. T. Epstein and J. O. Hirschfelder, *Phys. Rev.*, **123**, 1495 (1961); and J. O. Hirschfelder and C. A. Coulson, *J. Chem.*

Phys., **36**, 941 (1962)]. If $\mathscr{W}$ is any operator involving the coordinates and momenta but not containing time explicitly,

$$\int \psi^*[\mathscr{W}, \mathscr{H}]\psi \, d\mathbf{r}^N = 0$$

The virial theorem results from using the $\mathscr{W}$ corresponding to the classical function $W = \sum_j (\mathbf{r}_j \cdot \mathbf{p}_j)$. Any other choice of $\mathscr{W}$ leads to a new integral relation. The hypervirial relations are useful for improving wave functions, for determining electron correlations, and for determining average properties of charge distributions.

Page 156

See Note p. 544.

Page 157

An analytical expression has been obtained for the fourth virial coefficient for rigid spheres:

$$D = \frac{1}{4480\pi}[2707\pi + 438\sqrt{2} - 4131 \arccos \tfrac{1}{3}]b_0^3$$

See B. R. A. Nijboer and L. van Hove [*Phys. Rev.*, **85**, 777 (1952)]; see also B. R. A. Nijboer and R. Fieschi [*Physica*, **19**, 545 (1953)].

F. H. Ree and W. G. Hoover [*University of California Lawrence Radiation Laboratory*, UCRL-7372, June 5, 1963] have evaluated the fifth and sixth virial coefficients for rigid spheres:

$$E = (0.1103 \pm 0.0003)b_0^4$$

$$F = (0.0386 \pm 0.0004)b_0^5$$

They have also estimated the seventh virial coefficient as:

$$G \doteq (0.0127)b_0^6$$

Page 158

$D(T)$ for the square well has recently been computed by J. A. Barker and J. J. Monaghan [*J. Chem. Phys.*, **36**, 2558 (1962)].

Page 173

$D(T)$ for the Lennard-Jones (6–12) potential has recently been computed by J. A. Barker and J. J. Monaghan [*J. Chem. Phys.*, **36**, 2564 (1962)].

Page 181

The potential parameters for He in Table 3.7–2 should be $r_m = 3.1894$, $\epsilon/k = 7.5628$ and $\alpha = 12.4$. These new values were obtained by J. E. Kilpatrick, W. E. Keller, and E. F. Hammel [*Phys. Rev.*, **97**, 9 (1955)] with the help of E. A. Mason. This potential, which they call MR5, gives excellent agreement with both high and low temperature second virial and viscosity measurements for both He^4 and He^3. The calculations of the quantum mechanical phase shifts and low temperature second virial coefficients were made by J. E. Kilpatrick, W. E. Keller, E. F. Hammel, and N. Metropolis [*Phys. Rev.*, **94**, 1103 (1954)]. The quantum mechanical calculations of the transport cross-sections and collision integrals were made by W. E. Keller [*Phys. Rev.*, **105**, 41 (1957)]. A detailed listing of all of these quantum mechanical properties is given in Document No. 5064 of the ADI Auxiliary Publications, available by remitting $38.75 for photoprints or $10.50 for 35 mm microfilm, to Chief, Photoduplicating Service, Library of Congress, Washington 25, D.C. On the other hand, J. de Boer [*Physica*, **24**, S90, 1958] has compared the values of the second virial coefficient, the viscosity, and the thermal conductivity based on various suggested potentials for helium with experimental values. He found that the MR5 potential gives values of the viscosity and thermal conductivity at low temperatures which are low by about 5 to 10 per cent.

Page 209

In addition to the polar molecule models mentioned in § 3.10 the second virial coefficients have been calculated for the following models:

a. Polarizable rigid spheres with imbedded point dipoles [H. Falkenhagen, *Phys. Zeits.*, **23**, 87 (1922)]
b. Nonpolarizable rigid spheres with imbedded point linear quadrupoles [W. H. Keesom, *Koninkl. Akad. Wetenschap. Amsterdam*, **14**, 614 (1915); W. H. Keesom and C. van Leeuwen, *ibid.*, **14**, 1699 (1916)]
c. Polarizable rigid spheres with imbedded point linear quadrupoles [W. H. Keesom, *Phys. Zeits.*, **22**, 129 (1921)]
d. Nonpolarizable rigid ellipsoids with imbedded point dipoles [C. Muckenfuss, C. F. Curtiss and R. B. Bird, *J. Chem. Phys.*, **23**, 1542 (1955)]
e. Lennard-Jones (6–12) molecules modified to include (i) imbedded point dipoles and polarizability; (ii) imbedded point dipoles and quadrupoles; and (iii) imbedded point dipoles and non-spherical repulsive forces [A. D. Buckingham and J. A. Pople, *Trans. Faraday Soc.*, **51**, 1029 (1955)]

Page 214

Stockmayer potential parameters have been determined from the second virial coefficients of a number of substances in addition to those listed in Table 3.10–1. E. A. Mason has compiled the following table:

Gas	μ (debyes)	t^*	ϵ/k(°K)	σ(Å)	$b_0\left(\frac{\text{cm}^3}{\text{mole}}\right)$	*Ref.*
methyl cyanide	3.98	2.2	219	4.38	106	*a*
n-propanol	1.7	0.5	866	2.61	22.4	*b*
i-propanol	1.7	0.7	715	2.48	19.2	*b*
n-butanol, *i*-butanol	1.7	0.6	876	2.44	18.3	*b*
sec-butanol	1.7	0.6	861	2.46	18.8	*b*
tert-butanol	1.7	0.7	735	2.46	18.8	*b*
i-propylchloride	2.15	0.3	569	4.12	88.2	*b*
methyl ethyl ketone	3.18	0.9	429	4.06	84.60	*c*
methyl n-propyl ketone	2.46	0.8	428	3.61	59.53	*c*
pyridine	2.23	0.4	803	3.41	50.2	*d*
α-picoline	1.92	0.2	1098	3.50	54.3	*d*
perfluorocyclobutane	3.97	1.0	177	6.11	287.1	*e*
fluorobenzene	4.09	0.9	302	5.41	199.5	*f*

[a] J. A. Barker and F. Smith, *Australian J. Chem.*, **13**, 171 (1960).
[b] J. D. Cox, *Trans. Faraday Soc.*, **57**, 1674 (1961).
[c] J. K. Nickerson, K. A. Kobe, and J. J. McKetta, *J. Phys. Chem.*, **65**, 1037 (1961).
[d] J. D. Cox and R. J. L. Andon, *Trans. Faraday Soc.*, **54**, 1622 (1958).
[e] D. R. Douslin, R. T. Moore, and G. Waddington, *J. Phys. Chem.*, **63**, 1959 (1959).
[f] D. R. Douslin, R. T. Moore, J. P. Dawson, and G. Waddington, *J. Am. Chem. Soc.*, **80**, 2031 (1958).

See also Note to p. 597 for Stockmayer potential parameters determined from viscosity.

Page 235

The principle of corresponding states has also been discussed by: I. Prigogine, *The Molecular Theory of Solutions* (North-Holland Publishing Co., Amsterdam, 1957); J. S. Rowlinson, *Liquids and Liquid Mixtures* (Butterworths Scientific Publications, London, 1959); and E. A. Guggenheim, *Mixtures* (Oxford University Press, London, 1952).

Page 239

The Hougen-Watson generalized charts given in § 4.1b have been superseded by several sets of tables in which the compressibility factor z is given as a function of p_r, T_r and an additional parameter which in a sense accounts for the *principle of mechanical equivalence* discussed on p. 236:

1. Tables due to A. L. Lydersen, R. A. Greenkorn, and O. A. Hougen, as given in O. A. Hougen, K. M. Watson and R. A. Ragatz, *Chemical Process Principles*, Wiley, New York, Second Edition (1959)—Chapter 14.

2. Tables due to K. S. Pitzer, D. Z. Lippmann, R. F. Curl, Jr., C. M. Huggins and D. E. Petersen, as summarized in G. N. Lewis, M. Randall, K. S. Pitzer and L. Brewer, *Thermodynamics*, McGraw-Hill, New York (1961)—Appendix 1.

3. Tables prepared by L. Riedel, *Chemie-Ingenieur Technik*, **26**, 83, 257, 679 (1954).

4. Equations developed by J. O. Hirschfelder, R. J. Buehler, H. A. McGee, Jr., and J. R. Sutton, *Ind. Eng. Chem.*, **50**, 375, 386 (1958); errata: *I. and E. C. Fundamentals*, **1**, 224 (1962).

Page 245

In addition to Eqs. 4.1–17 and 4.1–18, L. I. Stiel and G. Thodos [*J. Chem. Eng. Data*, **7**, 234 (1962)] have suggested:

$$\epsilon/k = 65.3T_c(p_c\tilde{V}_c/RT_c)^{18/5}$$

$$\sigma = 0.1866\tilde{V}_c^{1/3}(p_c\tilde{V}_c/RT_c)^{-6/5}$$

in which $\tilde{V}_c$ is expressed in cm³/mole and σ is in Ångströms.

Page 263

An equation of state for hot dense gases has been developed by T. Kihara and T. Hikita [*Fourth International Symposium on Combustion*, Williams and Wilkins, Baltimore (1953), p. 458] in connection with their molecular theory of detonation.

Page 286

The equation of state for rigid non-attracting spheres has been calculated by placing a finite number of molecules in a cell with periodic boundary conditions and using Monte Carlo techniques [W. W. Wood and J. D. Jacobson, *J. Chem. Phys.*, **27**, 1207 (1957) and Proc. Western Joint Computer Conf. (San Francisco, 1959); W. W. Wood, F. R. Parker, and J. D. Jacobson, *Nuovo Cimento* Supplement to **9** (Series X), 133 (1958)]. Z. W. Salsburg and W. W. Wood [*J. Chem. Phys.*, **37**, 798 (1962)] have shown that at the limit of high density, the classical equation of state of rigid spheres agrees with the free-volume theory. Similar calculations using molecular dynamics have been made by B. J. Alder and T. E. Wainwright [*J. Chem. Phys.*, **27**, 1208 (1957), **31**, 459 (1959), and **33**, 1439 (1960)]. It would appear that a first-order phase transition occurs at high density. However, the existence of such a phase transition cannot be concluded until larger systems of molecules are considered.

H. Reiss, H. L. Frisch, and J. L. Lebowitz [*J. Chem. Phys.*, **31**, 369 (1959)] have developed an integral equation solution for the equation of state of rigid spheres. M. S. Wertheim [*Phys. Rev. Letters*, **10**, 321 (1963)] has obtained an exact solution of the Percus-Yevick equation (see Note to p. 321) for rigid spheres. The resulting equation of state is $pV/NkT = (1 + \eta + \eta^2)/(1 - \eta)^3$, where $\eta = b_0/4\tilde{V}$.

B. J. Alder [*J. Chem. Phys.*, **31**, 1666 (1959)] has derived and tabulated the equation of state and thermodynamic properties of a substance composed of square well molecules.

Page 293

Preferable to the Lennard-Jones and Devonshire free volume is the "optimum free volume" which J. G. Kirkwood [*J. Chem. Phys.*, **18**, 380 (1950)] derived as the solution to a non-linear integral equation. J. S. Dahler and J. O. Hirschfelder [*J. Chem. Phys.*, **32**, 330 (1960)] and H. S. Clung and J. S. Dahler [*J. Chem. Phys.*, **37**, 1620 (1962)] calculated tables of solutions to the Kirkwood equations with the approximation that the cell distribution function is spherically symmetrical. This "optimum free-volume" equation of state gives isotherms in the liquid range which correspond to a super-heated crystal. The thermodynamic properties, particularly the entropy, do not agree with experiment in the liquid range. The fact that the Lennard-Jones and Devonshire treatment gives better agreement is regarded as fortuitious.

Page 321

J. K. Percus and G. J. Yevick [*Phys. Rev.*, **110**, 1 (1957)], J. K. Percus [*Phys. Rev. Letters*, **8**, 462 (1962)], J. S. Dahler [*J. Chem. Phys.*, **29**, 1082 (1958)], and J. M. J. van Leeuwen, J. Groeneveld and J. de Boer [*Physica*, **25**, 792 (1959)] have developed important new methods for calculating the radial distribution function. An equation of state at high temperature and density based on the Percus-Yevick equation has been developed by J. S. Rowlinson [*University of Wisconsin Theoretical Chemistry Institute*, WIS-TCI-32 (Aug. 1963)].

Page 421

Further quantum corrections have been calculated by T. Kihara, Y. Midzuno and T. Shizume [*J. Phys. Soc.* (*Japan*), **10**, 249 (1955)]:

$B(T)$ through third quantum correction, for Lennard-Jones (6–12) and (6–9) potentials

$C(T)$ through first quantum correction, for Lennard-Jones (6–9) potential

See also review articles by T. Kihara [*Revs. Mod. Phys.*, **25**, 831 (1953); **27**, 412 (1955); *Adv. Chem. Phys.*, **1**, 267 (1958)]; and A. Pais and G. E. Uhlenbeck [*Phys. Rev.*, **116**, 250 (1959)].

Page 430

The predicted surface tension for He^3 given in Fig. 6.6–4 is in agreement with the subsequent measurements of D. R. Lovejoy [*Canad. J. of Physics*, **33**, 49 (1955)].

Page 434

In connection with Table 6.6–4 it should be pointed out that the vapor pressures of H_2, D_2 and T_2 have been measured by E. R. Grilly [*J. Am. Chem. Soc.*, **73**, 843 (1951)].

Page 441

Several extensive treatments of kinetic theory have appeared: L. Waldmann, *Handbuch der Physik*, Vol. XII (1958), pp. 295–514; H. Grad, *op. cit.*, pp. 205–294; I. Prigogine, *Non-Equilibrium Statistical Mechanics*, Interscience, New

York (1962); and N. N. Bogoliubov, in *Studies in Statistical Mechanics* (ed. J. de Boer and G. E. Uhlenbeck), North-Holland Publishing Company, Amsterdam (1962). The latter is an English translation of the 1946 book of Bogoliubov entitled *Problems of a Dynamical Theory in Statistical Physics.*

Page 479

In connection with the expression for the diffusion velocity in Eq. 7.4–3 it should be noted that various restrictions on the $C_i^{(j)}$ and the A_i imply that for a ν-component mixture there are several relations among the D_{ij} and the D_i^T:

From Eq. 7.3–31:

$$D_{ii} = 0$$

From Eq. 7.3–38:

$$\sum_{i=1}^{\nu} (M_i M_h D_{ih} - M_i M_k D_{ik}) = 0$$

From Eq. 7.3–39:

$$\sum_{i=1}^{\nu} D_i^T = 0$$

Note further that $D_{ij} \neq D_{ji}$.

Page 482

Various reasons may be given for adding and subtracting the term $\frac{5}{2}kT \sum_j n_j \overline{V}_j$ in Eq. 7.4–23. Analytically this operation is convenient in that it leads to a single Sonine polynomial as a factor in the integrand of the second term on the right side. A physical explanation of the appearance of the term quoted above has been offered by Enskog and is quoted by S. Chapman and T. G. Cowling [*The Mathematical Theory of Non-Uniform Gases*, Cambridge University Press (1939)—p. 145]. An alternate explanation is as follows: From Eq. 7.2–26 it follows directly that

$$\begin{aligned} q &= \sum_j \frac{1}{2} n_j m_j \overline{(V_j - \overline{V}_j + \overline{V}_j)^2 (V_j - \overline{V}_j + \overline{V}_j)} \\ &= \sum_j \frac{1}{2} n_j m_j \overline{V}_j^2 \overline{V}_j \\ &\quad + \sum_j \frac{1}{2} n_j m_j \overline{(V_j - \overline{V}_j)^2 (V_j - \overline{V}_j)} \\ &\quad + \sum_j \frac{1}{2} n_j m_j \overline{(V_j - \overline{V}_j)^2} \overline{V}_j \\ &\quad + \sum_j n_j m_j \overline{\overline{V}_j \cdot (V_j - \overline{V}_j)(V_j - \overline{V}_j)} \end{aligned}$$

Since the diffusion velocity $\overline{V}_j$ is small, the first term is negligible. If we now use the approximation that the distribution function f_j is isotropic about $\overline{V}_j$, then the second term vanishes identically, and the fourth term becomes exactly two-thirds of the third term according to the fifth equation from the bottom on p. xxvi. To this approximation

$$q = \frac{5}{3} \sum_j \frac{1}{2} n_j m_j \overline{(V_j - \overline{V}_j)^2} \overline{V}_j$$

If the further approximation is made that the distribution function f_j is Maxwellian about $\overline{\boldsymbol{V}}_j$ then

$$\boldsymbol{q} = \frac{5}{3} \cdot \frac{3}{2} \sum_j n_j kT \overline{\boldsymbol{V}}_j$$

$$= \frac{5}{2} kT \sum_j n_j \overline{\boldsymbol{V}}_j$$

For a still different discussion, see E. A. Guggenheim, *Elements of the Kinetic Theory of Gases*, Pergamon Press (1960), p. 48.

Page 490

Although the expression for $\boldsymbol{q}$ in Eq. 7.4–30 is exact, that in Eq. 7.4–64 contains an approximation introduced by the use of Eq. 7.4–48 to eliminate the $\boldsymbol{d}_i$. The latter equation is based upon Eq. 7.4–35 in which only one term is retained in the Sonine-polynomial expansion of the $C_j^{(h)}$ of Eq. 7.3–35. A similar approximation is inherent in Eq. 7.4–65. On the other hand, the expression for $\lambda'(2)$ in Eq. 7.4–66 is based upon the retention of two terms in the Sonine-polynomial expansion of the A_i of Eq. 7.3–36. The consequences of taking two terms in both of the foregoing expansions have been explored by C. Muckenfuss and C. F. Curtiss [*J. Chem. Phys.*, **29**, 1273 (1958)]. Their primary conclusions are: (1) the expression for λ, which replaces Eqs. 7.4–65 and 66, is considerably simpler (see Note to p. 537), and (2) the last term on the right side of Eq. 7.4–64 becomes considerably more complicated, except for binary mixtures, where $\mathfrak{D}_{ij}(1)$ is simply replaced by $\mathfrak{D}_{ij}(2)$.

Page 498

In connection with § 7.6b and particularly Eq. 7.6–11, A. R. Ubbelohde [*J. Chem. Phys.*, **3**, 219 (1935)] should be credited with the idea that the flow of internal energy is energy transport due to the diffusion of molecules in excited states, each excited state considered as a separate molecular species.

Page 501

E. A. Mason and L. Monchick [*J. Chem. Phys.*, **36**, 1622 (1962)] have extended the work of Wang Chang and Uhlenbeck, Ref. 8, and N. Taxman [*Phys. Rev.*, **110**, 1235 (1958)] to obtain the transport properties of polyatomic and polar gases in terms of collisional relaxation times. For nonpolar gases, Mason and Monchick find that the coefficient of thermal conductivity as given by Eq. 7.6–23 should be decreased by the term

$$(2\eta/\pi)\left(\frac{5}{2} - \frac{\rho\mathfrak{D}}{\eta}\right)^2 \sum_k (\hat{C}_v)_k/Z_k$$

Here $(\hat{C}_v)_k$ is the specific heat of the k-th internal mode and Z_k is the number of collisions required to exchange a quantum of energy of this mode with the translational degrees of freedom. Thus, deviations from the modified Eucken thermal conductivity result from internal degrees of freedom with low collision numbers. In small polyatomic molecules the value of Z for rotations (with the exception of H_2) is generally less than 20, whereas the values of Z for vibrations or electronic modes are usually large, of the order of 10^3 to 10^7. For polar molecules the resonant exchange of rotational energy is sometimes important.

Page 506

The kinetic theory of rigid ovaloids and the equation of conservation of angular momentum discussed in § 7.6d(i) have been considered further by C. F. Curtiss [*J. Chem. Phys.*, **24**, 225 (1956)], by C. F. Curtiss and C. Muckenfuss [*J. Chem. Phys.*, **26**, 1619 (1957); **29**, 1257 (1958)], and P. M. Livingston and C. F. Curtiss [*J. Chem. Phys.*, **31**, 1643 (1959)]. A phenomenological approach to the equation of change of angular momentum has been discussed by H. Grad [*Comm. Pure and Appl. Math.*, **5**, 455 (1952)].

Page 516

In connection with Eq. 8.1–1 there are several relations among the D_{ij} and D_i^T given in the Note to p. 479.

Page 532

The expansion which leads to Eq. 8.2–28 may be developed in the following manner: From Eq. 8.2–25, it may be shown that

$$[\eta_{\text{mix}}]_1 = \sum_{i=1}^{\nu} h_i$$

where the h_i are determined by the set of linear equations

$$\sum_{j=1}^{\nu} H_{ij} h_j / x_j = x_i$$

(This set of equations is closely related to the set, Eqs. 7.4–57. It is, of course, the reverse of this manipulation which leads to Eq. 8.2–25). From this result, it follows simply that

$$h_i = \frac{x_i^2}{H_{ii}} - \frac{x_i}{H_{ii}} \sum_{\substack{j=1 \\ j \neq i}}^{\nu} \frac{H_{ij} h_j}{x_j}$$

Now if it is assumed that the off-diagonal elements $H_{ij} (i \neq j)$ are small, an approximation to the h_i may be obtained by a recursive sequence

$$h_i^{(1)} = x_i^2 / H_{ii}$$

$$h_i^{(s)} = \frac{x_i^2}{H_{ii}} - \frac{x_i}{H_{ii}} \sum_{\substack{j=1 \\ j \neq i}}^{\nu} \frac{H_{ij} h_j^{(s-1)}}{x_j}$$

The result is a series expansion for the h_i, which when used in the first equation above leads to Eq. 8.2–28.

Page 533

An approximation even simpler than Eq. 8.2–30 has been obtained by C. R. Wilke [*J. Chem. Phys.*, **18**, 517 (1950)], who eliminated the binary diffusion coefficients in favor of the viscosities of the pure components. Because of compensating errors, the accuracy of the simpler formula is about as good as that of Eq. 8.2–30. Various modifications of formulas of this type have also been considered by R. S. Brokaw [*J. Chem. Phys.*, **29**, 391 (1958)] and W. E. Francis [*Trans. Faraday Soc.*, **54**, 1492 (1958)].

An entirely analogous procedure can be carried out for the thermal conductivity of mixtures, based on the new equation in the Note to p. 537 for the "monatomic" part of λ_{mix}, and on the equation for λ_{int} in the Note to p. 536. This has been done by E. A. Mason and S. C. Saxena [*Phys. Fluids*, **1**, 361 (1958); see also E. A. Mason and H. von Ubisch, *Phys. Fluids*, **3**, 355 (1960)], R. S. Brokaw [*J. Chem. Phys.*, **29**, 391 (1958); NASA TR R-81 (1961); *Physical Chemistry in Aerodynamics and Space Flight* (Pergamon Press, New York, 1961), p. 238]; and C. O. Neal, Jr. [*Ninth International Symposium on Combustion*, Academic Press, New York (1963), p. 725]. Even earlier, a similar equation had been proposed by A. L. Lindsay and L. A. Bromley [*Ind. Engr. Chem.*, **42**, 1508 (1950)], based on the mean-free-path formula for λ_{mix} derived by A. Wassiljewa [*Physik. Z.*, **5**, 737 (1904)]. Modifications of this to obtain improved accuracy have been proposed by H. Cheung, L. A. Bromley, and C. R. Wilke [*Am. Inst. Chem. Engrs. J.*, **8**, 221 (1962)].

An excellent review of these various formulas of the Sutherland-Wassiljewa type has been given by P. G. Wright and P. Gray [*Trans. Faraday Soc.*, **58**, 1 (1962)], who also give a very illuminating physical interpretation in terms of collisional interference with transport of momentum or energy.

Page 534

Equation 7.6–23 giving the modified Eucken expression for the thermal conductivity of polyatomic molecules is somewhat preferable to the Eucken relation, Eq. 7.6–24 or 8.2–33. For most non-polar gases, $\rho\mathfrak{D}/\eta$ is approximately 1.3 instead of the value 1.0 which is implicit in the Eucken formulation. See the Note to p. 501 for corrections to the coefficient of thermal conductivity due to collisional relaxation times for the various internal degrees of freedom.

Page 536

Equation 8.2–40 is no longer recommended. The coefficient of thermal conductivity for a mixture of polyatomic gases may be written as the sum of three terms

$$\lambda_{mix} = [\lambda_{mix}]_1 + \lambda_{int} + \lambda_{react}$$

Here $[\lambda_{mix}]_1$ is defined by Eq. 8.2–42 (as modified by the Note to p. 537) and represents the coefficient of thermal conductivity of the mixture if each of the components were monatomic; λ_{int} is the contribution due to the internal degrees of freedom of the molecules; and λ_{react} is the contribution resulting from the chemical reactions, if any, which take place between the components. According to J. O. Hirschfelder [*Sixth Symposium (International) on Combustion* (Reinhold Publishing Corp., New York, 1957), p. 351, and *Proceedings of the Joint Conference on Thermodynamics and Transport Properties of Fluids* (Institution of Mechanical Engineers, London, 1958), p. 133],

$$\lambda_{int} = \sum_{i=1}^{\nu} \left[\frac{x_i(\lambda_i - [\lambda_i]_1)}{\sum_{j=1}^{\nu} x_j \mathfrak{D}_{ii}/\mathfrak{D}_{ij}} \right]$$

Here λ_i is the true thermal conductivity of the i-th chemical species and $[\lambda_i]_1$ is defined by Eq. 8.2–31.

The behavior of λ_{react} depends upon the rates of the chemical reactions [J. O. Hirschfelder, *J. Chem. Phys.*, **26**, 274 (1957)]. If the reaction rates in either the forward or reverse directions are sufficiently fast, the steady state chemical composition at all points in the gas (away from the walls) is very nearly in equilibrium with the local temperature. Under these conditions, R. S. Brokaw [*J. Chem. Phys.*, **32**, 1005, 1960; also, J. N. Butler and R. S. Brokaw, *J. Chem. Phys.*, **26**, 1636 (1957)] has shown that for a set of ν chemical species $[k]$ engaged in s chemical reactions which can be written stoichiometrically

$$\sum_{k=1}^{\nu} a_{ik}[k] = 0 \qquad i = 1, 2, \ldots, s$$

it follows that

$$\lambda_{\text{react}} = -(RT^2)^{-1} \begin{vmatrix} A_{11} & \cdots & A_{1s} & \Delta\tilde{H}_1 \\ \vdots & & \vdots & \vdots \\ A_{s1} & \cdots & A_{ss} & \Delta\tilde{H}_s \\ \Delta\tilde{H}_1 & \cdots & \Delta\tilde{H}_s & 0 \end{vmatrix} \begin{vmatrix} A_{11} & \cdots & A_{1s} \\ \vdots & & \vdots \\ A_{s1} & \cdots & A_{ss} \end{vmatrix}^{-1}$$

Here $\Delta\tilde{H}_i = \sum_{k=1}^{\nu} a_{ik}\tilde{H}_k$ is the enthalpy change of the i-th reaction, and the $\tilde{H}_k$ are the enthalpies referred to a common base. Furthermore,

$$A_{ij} = \sum_{k=1}^{s-1} \sum_{l=k+1}^{s} (RT/\mathfrak{D}_{kl}p)x_k x_l[(a_{ik}/x_k) - (a_{il}/x_l)][(a_{jk}/x_k) - (a_{jl}/x_l)]$$

The mole fractions are determined from the chemical equilibrium at the temperature of the point in question. If the chemical reactions are slow, the thermal conductivity depends upon the boundary conditions and is much more difficult to determine [D. H. Secrest and J. O. Hirschfelder, *Phys. Fluids*, **4**, 61 (1961); R. S. Brokaw, *J. Chem. Phys.*, **35**, 1569 (1961)].

Page 537

As a consequence of the Note to p. 490, Eqs. 8.2–42 and 43 are to be replaced by the much simpler relation:

$$[\lambda_{\text{mix}}]_1 = 4 \frac{\begin{vmatrix} L_{11}^{11} & \cdots & L_{1\nu}^{11} & x_1 \\ \vdots & & \vdots & \vdots \\ L_{\nu 1}^{11} & \cdots & L_{\nu\nu}^{11} & x_\nu \\ x_1 & \cdots & x_\nu & 0 \end{vmatrix}}{\begin{vmatrix} L_{11}^{11} & \cdots & L_{1\nu}^{11} \\ \vdots & & \vdots \\ L_{\nu 1}^{11} & \cdots & L_{\nu\nu}^{11} \end{vmatrix}}$$

where the L_{ij}^{11} are given by the last two pairs of equations on p. 538. This formula may also be derived by Kihara's method [E. A. Mason, *J. Chem. Phys.*,

28, 1000 (1958); E. A. Mason and S. C. Saxena, *J. Chem. Phys.*, **31**, 511 (1959)]. (See also, Note to p. 533.)

Page 539

The expressions for the transport coefficients developed in Chap. 7 and discussed in Chap. 8 are valid only in the low density limit. In the actual applications of Eq. 8.2–46, the use of the real pressure rather than that computed from the density and the ideal gas expression, $p = nkT$, may lead to a difference in the computed diffusion coefficient. This difference is simply an indication of the order of magnitude of the error in this theoretical expression due to the finite density of the gas. The theory of density effects on the transport coefficients is still in an elementary stage. The theory of a moderately dense gas of rigid spheres is discussed in Chap. 9. This treatment has been generalized to a gas made up of molecules which interact according to a soft potential by Snider and Curtiss [*Phys. Fluids*, **1**, 122 (1958) and **3**, 903 (1960)], but numerical results have not yet been obtained. It is seen from Eq. 9.3–38 that in the special case of rigid spheres the factor of n in the denominator of the expression for the diffusion coefficient should be replaced by nY_{12}, where, in the case of self-diffusion Y_{12} is $1 + (\frac{5}{8})(b_o/\tilde{V})$ (b_o is the second virial coefficient). On the other hand, if the expression on the right of Eq. 8.2–46 were rewritten in terms of the pressure and the value taken to be that given by the equation of state, a factor of $1 + (b_o/\tilde{V})$ would be introduced. Thus the correct result appears to be a compromise between these two extremes. It should also be pointed out, however, that the "driving force" for diffusion, $\boldsymbol{d}_i$, also contains density dependent terms involving the second virial coefficient [see page 714].

Page 544

J. O. Hirschfelder and M. A. Eliason [*Ann. New York Acad. Sci.*, **67**, 451 (1957)] showed that at high temperatures the effective rigid sphere collision diameter of real molecules required to obtain the transport coefficients or second virial coefficient is the internuclear distance for which the potential energy of interaction is equal to θkT. The appropriate value of θ is found to be:

	thermal conductivity or viscosity	*diffusion*	*second virial*
Steep repulsive potential (varying as r^{-12})	0.83	1.85	0.44
Intermediate range repulsive pot. ($\sim r^{-6}$)	0.91	1.70	0.32
Long range repulsive potential ($\sim r^{-4}$)	0.96	1.59	0.18
Deep minimum attractive potential	−0.58	−0.60	—

Thus one can easily estimate the high temperature properties of gases. For example, the coefficient of viscosity of a gas whose molecules interact according to a steep repulsive potential, $\varphi(r)$, is given by Eq. 8.2–18, with $\Omega^{(2,2)\star} = 1$ and σ taken to be the intermolecular separation at which $\varphi(r) = 0.83\ kT$.

Page 548

In connection with Table 8.3–3, collision integrals $A^{(l)}(\delta)$ for both repulsive and attractive point centers of repulsion are given by T. Kihara, M. H. Taylor, and J. O. Hirschfelder [*Phys. Fluids*, **3**, 715 (1960)]. See also, M. A. Eliason, D. E. Stogryn and J. O. Hirschfelder [*Proc. Nat. Acad. Sci.*, **42**, 546 (1956)].

Page 549

In the Debye-Hückel theory of electrolytic solutions, it has been shown [see J. G. Kirkwood, *J. Chem. Phys.*, **2**, 767 (1934)] that at low concentrations the potential of average force between ions i and j is $(e_ie_j/r) \exp(-r/h)$, where $h = \left[(4\pi/kT) \sum_i n_ie_i^2\right]^{-1/2}$ is the "Debye length." It has been suggested [see R. S. Cohen, L. Spitzer, and P. McR. Routly, *Phys. Rev.*, **80**, 230 (1950)] that this "shielded Coulomb potential" may be used to calculate the angles of deflection and the cross-sections for collisions between charged particles in a low density gas. Liboff [*Phys. of Fluids*, **2**, 40 (1959)] and T. Kihara [*J. Phys. Soc., Japan*, **14**, 402 (1959)] have independently evaluated the $\Omega^{(l,s)}$ integrals using the shielded Coulomb potential.

Page 551

Additional calculations of square-well potential collision integrals have been carried out by S. G. Brush [*University of California Lawrence Radiation Laboratory*, UCRL 7376 (June 1963)].

Page 556

K. W. Ford, D. L. Hill, M. Wakano, and J. A. Wheeler [*Ann. of Phys.*, **7**, 239 (1959)] have calculated the quantum mechanical phase shifts for collisions which classically would have almost orbiting trajectories.

Page 560

In connection with the determination of force constants from viscosity data, it should be pointed out that certain errors in recorded viscosity data may limit the accuracy of the derived potential parameters. With very few exceptions, only the most recent experimental measurements such as those of J. Kestin at Brown University are accurate within 0.5%. For example, the values of H. L. Johnson and co-workers were not corrected for edge effects on his oscillating disc viscometer. Also, most of the measurements of M. Trautz were made relative to the viscosity of a reference gas (air) at a time when the values of the viscosity of air were not known to better than 1.5%.

Page 582

In the second printing of this book we have adopted the convention of K. E. Grew and T. L. Ibbs [*Thermal Diffusion in Gases*, Cambridge University Press

(1952)] that in a two-component system the heavier species is labelled as component "1." With this convention k_T is a positive quantity for most gas pairs at room temperature.

Page 597

Section 8.6a should be deleted, inasmuch as the reduced collision cross-sections in Table IX have been found to be in error. This section should be replaced by the recent work of L. Monchick and E. A. Mason [*J. Chem. Phys.*, **35**, 1676 (1961)]. In their work the Stockmayer potential (Eq. 1.3–33) is used to calculate the reduced collision cross-section integrals, and then the latter are averaged over all orientations, assumed equally probable. From the resulting tables and experimental viscosity data the following Stockmayer potential parameters were obtained: (* indicates "scanty or uncertain data.")

Gas	μ (debyes)	$\sqrt{2}\, t^*$	σ (Å)	ϵ/k(°K)
H_2O	1.85	1.0	2.52	775
NH_3	1.47	0.7	3.15	358
HCl	1.08	0.34	3.36	328
HBr *	0.80	0.14	3.41	417
HI	0.42	0.029	4.13	313
SO_2	1.63	0.42	4.04	347
H_2S *	0.92	0.21	3.49	343
NOCl *	1.83	0.4	3.53	690
$CHCl_3$	1.013	0.07	5.31	355
CH_2Cl_2	1.57	0.2	4.52	483
CH_3Cl	1.87	0.5	3.94	414
CH_3Br *	1.80	0.4	4.25	382
C_2H_5Cl *	2.03	0.4	4.45	423
CH_3OH	1.70	0.5	3.69	417
C_2H_5OH	1.69	0.3	4.31	431
n-C_3H_7OH	1.69	0.2	4.71	495
i-C_3H_7OH	1.69	0.2	4.64	518
$(CH_3)_2O$	1.30	0.19	4.21	432
$(C_2H_5)_2O$	1.15	0.08	5.49	362
$(CH_3)_2CO$	2.88	0.06	4.50	549
CH_3COOCH_3	1.72	0.2	5.04	418
$CH_3COOC_2H_5$	1.78	0.16	5.24	499

Where these values overlap the parameters listed in Table 3.10–1, the values determined from viscosity generally seem more reliable.

The Monchick and Mason tables can be used to calculate diffusion and thermal diffusion as well as viscosity. E. A. Mason and L. Monchick [*J. Chem. Phys.*, **36**, 1622 (1962)] show how to calculate the coefficient of thermal conductivity for polar gases taking into account the rotational relaxation times (see Note, p. 501).

Page 600

The transport properties of polar gas mixtures have been considered by E. A. Mason and L. Monchick [*J. Chem. Phys.*, **36**, 2746 (1962)].

Pages 603 and 604

The entries in the 3, 3 row of Table 8.6–3 referring to the collisions between polar molecules should be modified according to the treatment referred to in the Note to page 600. The values given in Table 8.6–4 should be modified in a similar manner.

Page 620

A reduced thermal conductivity chart for monatomic substances, analogous to Fig. 9.1–4, has been prepared by E. J. Owens and G. Thodos [*A. I. Ch. E. Journal*, **3**, 454 (1957)]; large scale versions of Fig. 9.1–4 and the Owens-Thodos graph are available [O. A. Hougen, K. M. Watson, and R. A. Ragatz, *Chemical Process Principles Charts*, Wiley, New York, Second Edition (1960)]. A reduced thermal conductivity chart for monatomic substances, analogous to Fig. 9.1–5, has been prepared by J. M. Lenoir, W. A. Junk, and E. W. Comings [*Chem. Engr. Prog.*, **49**, 539 (1953)]. A reduced self-diffusion coefficient chart, analogous to Fig. 9.1–5, has been prepared by J. C. Slattery [M.S. Thesis, Chem. Engr. Dept., U. of Wisconsin (1955); see also R. B. Bird, W. E. Stewart, and E. N. Lightfoot, *Transport Phenomena*, Wiley, New York, Second Printing with Corrections (1962), p. 506]. For further information on corresponding states charts see R. C. Reid and T. K. Sherwood, *The Properties of Gases and Liquids*, McGraw-Hill, New York (1958).

Page 624

Figure 9.1–6 should be disregarded in view of the newly determined Stockmayer potential parameters obtained by L. Monchick and E. A. Mason [*J. Chem. Phys.*, **35**, 1676 (1961)].

Page 625

A number of useful empirical relations for estimating the transport properties of liquids have been summarized by R. C. Reid and T. K. Sherwood [*The Properties of Gases and Liquids*, McGraw-Hill, New York (1958): viscosity, pp. 203–219; thermal conductivity, pp. 244–261; diffusivity, pp. 283–299]. Extensive comparisons with experimental data are given. Generally the empirical relations summarized by Reid and Sherwood are to be preferred over the relations given in Section 9.2.

Page 627

In connection with Fn. 3, the three-volume reference work *Rheology* (ed., F. Eirich) Academic Press, New York, 1956 should be mentioned. Chapter 16 of Vol. I by J. G. Oldroyd provides a particularly nice introduction to non-Newtonian flow.

Page 630

It is known that Eq. 9.2–10 is inadequate, since it does not predict the maxima which occur in the viscosity-composition curves for some binary systems. Other empirical relations have been summarized by J. R. Partington, *An Advanced Treatise on Physical Chemistry*, Vol. II, Longmans, Green and Co., London (1951), p. 115 and by Reid and Sherwood (see Note to p. 624).

Page 631

Equation 9.2–13 differs from the older Stokes-Einstein equation by a factor of 2π. Apparently the Stokes-Einstein equation is in better agreement with experimental data. For further information, see J. C. M. Li and P. Chang [*J. Chem. Phys.*, **23**, 518 (1955)] and R. B. Bird, W. E. Stewart and E. N. Lightfoot, *Transport Phenomena*, Wiley, New York, Second Printing with Corrections (1962), p. 513.

Pages 631–632

The diffusion coefficient $\mathfrak{D}_{12}$ used in Eq. 9.2–14 is that used by most experimentalists and is defined in terms of the flux relation:

$$\boldsymbol{j}_1 = -\frac{n^2}{\rho} m_1 m_2 \mathfrak{D}_{12} \frac{\partial}{\partial \boldsymbol{r}} x_1$$

However, Eq. 11.2–50 simplifies as follows for an arbitrary two-component fluid mixture with no thermal diffusion, pressure diffusion, or forced diffusion:

$$\boldsymbol{j}_1 = -\frac{n^2}{\rho} m_1 m_2 \left(D_{12} \frac{\partial \ln a_2}{\partial \ln x_2} \right) \frac{\partial}{\partial \boldsymbol{r}} x_1$$

Figure 9.2–4 then shows that ηD_{12} is linear in concentration for the two systems represented there. Recent studies on acetone-water and acetone-carbon-tetrachloride systems have shown that ηD_{12} is far from linear in the mole fraction [D. K. Anderson, J. R. Hall, and A. L. Babb, *J. Phys. Chem.*, **62**, 404 (1958)]. (*Note that in a binary system D_{12} is the special case of the multicomponent diffusion coefficient in Chapter 11 associated with the chemical potential driving force; the script $\mathfrak{D}_{12}$ is a binary diffusion coefficient associated with a concentration driving force.* This notation is consistent with that used in Chapters 7 and 8 where gaseous systems are discussed, for which $a_i = x_i$. Note further that the nomenclature on diffusion coefficients used in this book is entirely consistent with that used by R. B. Bird, W. E. Stewart, and E. N. Lightfoot, *Transport Phenomena*, Wiley, New York, Second Printing with Corrections (1962).)

Page 646

The diffusion coefficient D_{12} in Eq. 9.3–38 is to be used in Eq. 11.2–33 with the driving force $\boldsymbol{d}_i$ in Eq. 11.2–29 of the present printing. For further comments see Note to p. 714.

Page 687

The expressions for the phase shifts in Eqs. 10.3–8 and 10 were developed by B. Kahn (Ref. 1 on p. 685) using the WKB approximation to the solution of the radial wave equation. R. E. Langer [*Phys. Rev.*, **51**, 669 (1937)] has questioned this application of the WKB method to a radial equation, because the radial coordinate r ranges from 0 to ∞. He made a change of independent variable such that the new independent variable ranges from $-\infty$ to $+\infty$. Langer's expression for $\eta_l^{[1]}(\kappa)$ is similar to Eq. 10.3–8, except that $l(l+1)$ is replaced throughout by $(l+\frac{1}{2})^2$. S. Choi and J. Ross [*Proc. Nat. Acad. Sci.*, **48**, 803 (1962)], following methods similar to those used by Langer, have obtained an expression for $\eta_l^{[2]}(\kappa)$. Specifically these results are:

$$\eta_l^{[1]}(\kappa) = (\pi/2)(l+\tfrac{1}{2}) - \kappa r_m + \int_{r_m}^{\infty} \{[\kappa^2 - \bar{f}_l(r)]^{1/2} - \kappa\}\, dr$$

$$\eta_l^{[2]}(\kappa) = -\frac{1}{24}\int_{r_m}^{\infty} \frac{(\bar{f}_l'''/\bar{f}_l') - (\bar{f}_l''/\bar{f}_l')^2 - (3/r^2)}{(\kappa^2 - \bar{f}_l)^{1/2}}\, dr$$

in which now

$$\bar{f}_l(r) = [2\mu\varphi(r)/\hbar^2] + [(l+\tfrac{1}{2})^2/r^2]$$

De Boer has pointed out to us that, using

$$(l+\tfrac{1}{2}) = [l(l+1)]^{1/2} + 1/(8l) + \mathcal{O}(1/l^2)$$

$$(l+\tfrac{1}{2})^2 = l(l+1) + (\tfrac{1}{4})$$

one may show that the sum $\eta_l^{[1]} + \eta_l^{[2]}$ given above is equal to the sum given by Eqs. 10.3–8 and 10 of the text, except for terms of order

$$\mathcal{O}(1/l^2) \quad \text{and} \quad \mathcal{O}\left(\int \frac{dr}{r^4(\kappa^2 - \bar{f}_l)^{3/2}}\right)$$

Thus, both sets of expressions lead to identical results for the classical cross sections $Q_{\text{cl}}^{(n)}$ and their first quantum corrections $Q_{\text{I}}^{(n)}$.

Page 689

In the first printing of this book $+\frac{1}{6}$ in Eq. 10.3–22 was incorrectly given as $-\frac{1}{6}$; associated with this error, the number $+0.0653$ was incorrectly given as -0.2680. These errors originated in Ref. 6 on p. 687. In going from Eq. 10.2–2 to Eq. 10.3–22, it is necessary to convert from sums on l to integrals over b. To do this, the Euler-Maclaurin expansion is used; this enables one to rewrite the sums in Eq. 10.2–2 as integrals *plus* "extra terms." In the original publication and in the first printing of this book, these "extra terms" were presumed to be of higher order in $\hbar$, and the error in $Q_{\text{I}}^{(1)}$ resulted. This error did not, however, affect $Q_{\text{I}}^{(2)}$.

Page 694

Further details on the applications of the equations of change may be found in *Fluid Dynamics* by L. D. Landau and E. M. Lifshitz, Academic Press (1959). In this book a number of topics are included, such as sound, shock waves, combustion, relativistic fluid dynamics, superfluids, boundary layers, and surface phenomena.

Page 698

In connection with applications of the equations of change given in Eqs. 11.1–1 to 4, it is often necessary to have the equations in terms of curvilinear coordinates or in terms of different dependent variables. For this purpose the tabulations given by R. B. Bird, W. E. Stewart, and E. N. Lightfoot, *Transport Phenomena*, Wiley, New York, Second Printing with Corrections (1962) may be useful: pp. 83–91, 317–324, 559–572, 715–742. For the most part the notation is the same; the salient differences are:

MTGL	*TrPh*
$\partial/\partial \mathbf{r}$	$\boldsymbol{\nabla}$
P	$\boldsymbol{\pi}$
U	$\boldsymbol{\delta}$
$\mathbf{X}_i/m_i$	$\mathbf{g}_i$
$\mathbf{j}_i = n_i m_i \overline{\mathbf{V}}_i$	$\mathbf{j}_i$
$n_i/\tilde{N}$	c_i
n/N	c

Page 699

Several multicomponent generalizations of Eq. 11.1–6 are given on p. 562 of R. B. Bird, W. E. Stewart, and E. N. Lightfoot [*Transport Phenomena*, Wiley, New York, Second Printing with Corrections (1962)]. In obtaining the equation of energy in terms of the temperature it was necessary to use the Gibbs relation, Eq. 11.1–14. In doing this the "kinetic energy of diffusion" was not used (see Note to p. 701).

Page 701

S. R. de Groot and P. Mazur [*Non-Equilibrium Thermodynamics* (North-Holland Publishing, Amsterdam, 1961)], include in their Eq. (39), page 29 an inertial term corresponding to the kinetic energy of diffusion which is missing from our Eq. 11.1–14. This inertial term is negligible if the concentration and velocity gradients are small. This is discussed by C. Truesdell and R. Toupin [*Handbuch der Physik*, III/1, Springer, Berlin (1960), p. 608].

Page 714

In the first printing of this book and in a review article by the authors R. B. Bird, C. F. Curtiss, and J. O. Hirschfelder [*Chem. Engr. Progress Symposium Series, No. 16*, **51**, 69–85 (1955)] the definition of $\boldsymbol{d}_i$ in Eq. 11.2–28 *was* given as

$$\boldsymbol{d}_i = \frac{n_i m_i}{p}\boldsymbol{\Lambda}_i - \frac{n_i m_i}{\rho p}\frac{\partial p}{\partial \mathbf{r}} + \frac{n_i m_i}{\rho p}\sum_{j=1}^{\nu} n_j \mathbf{X}_j$$

That is, this expression must be multiplied by a factor p/nkT to obtain that currently used in this book. The present definition is to be preferred, inasmuch as it is consistent with standard usage in the literature. Also the present definition makes Eq. 11.2–33 entirely consistent with Eqs. 18.4–7 to 18.4–11 of R. B. Bird, W. E. Stewart, and E. N. Lightfoot, *Transport Phenomena*, Wiley, New York, Second Printing with Corrections (1962), p. 567. Furthermore the present definition is identical (for rigid spheres) with that for $\boldsymbol{d}_{12}$ of Chapman and Cowling, *Mathematical Theory of Non-Uniform Gases*, Cambridge University Press (1939), p. 293, Eq. 16.9, 5, at least to terms in the second virial coefficient.

Page 715

The complete definition of the D_{ij} and D_i^T includes the auxiliary relations given in the Note to p. 479.

Page 717

All of the fluxes discussed in § 11.2e are defined with respect to the mass average velocity of the fluid. For flux expressions with other choices of reference frames and concentration units see R. B. Bird, W. E. Stewart, and E. N. Lightfoot, *Transport Phenomena*, Wiley, New York, Second Printing with Corrections (1962)—pp. 496–502 and pp. 560–572, or S. R. de Groot and P. Mazur, *Non-Equilibrium Thermodynamics*, North-Holland, Amsterdam (1962), Chapter XI.

Page 718

For a general fluid the complete definitions of D_{ij} and D_i^T in Eq. 11.2–50 include several auxiliary relations. Because $\sum_i \boldsymbol{d}_i = 0$ we adopt the convention that for a mixture containing ν chemical species:

$$D_{ii} = 0$$

Because $\sum_i \boldsymbol{j}_i = 0$, it follows that

$$\sum_{i=1}^{\nu} (M_iM_hD_{ih} - M_iM_kD_{ik}) = 0$$

and

$$\sum_{i=1}^{\nu} D_i^T = 0$$

Note also that $D_{ij} \neq D_{ji}$. (See Note to p. 479 where the same conventions are discussed relative to the kinetic theory of dilute monatomic gases.)

Page 718

With regard to the application of Eq. 11.2–54 to liquids, some comparisons with experimental data have been made using an equation of this form by E. N. Lightfoot, E. L. Cussler, and R. L. Rettig [*A. I. Ch. E. Journal*, **8**, 708 (1962)].

Page 756

There have been many advances in the theory of flame propagation as given in § 11.7. These have been summarized by J. O. Hirschfelder and C. F. Curtiss [*Advances in Chemical Physics*, *III* (Edited by I. Prigogine, Interscience Publishers, New York, 1961), p. 59]. One of the new results is a proof that there is a maximum amount of heat transfer to the flame-holder such that a steady state flame can propagate. For lesser heat transfer, the flame equations have two solutions, one corresponding to stable flames and the other (with a smaller flame velocity) corresponding to an unstable mode. Thus there is a minimum velocity for stable flame propagation corresponding to the maximum heat transfer.

Page 797

Most of the advances in the theory of detonations, § 11.9, are summarized in the reference given in the Note to p. 756. However, more recently, D. R. White [*Phys. Fluids*, **4**, 465 (1961)] and others have shown experimentally that at least some gaseous detonations have turbulent reaction zones. This makes the whole problem of detonation theory much more difficult.

Page 815

The integrated forms of the equations of change in Section 11.10 are special cases of the "macroscopic balances" used in engineering. These balances include integrated forms of the equations of continuity, motion, and energy, as well as the integrated forms of the equations of change for kinetic energy and angular momentum (see R. B. Bird [*Chem. Engr. Sci.*, **6**, 123 (1957)] and J. C. Slattery and R. A. Gaggioli [*Chem. Engr. Sci.*, **17**, 893 (1962)]).

Page 836

In addition to the multipole expansion formalism given in § 12.1, the following treatments are useful: L. Jansen, *Phys. Rev.*, **110**, 661 (1958) and M. E. Rose, *J. Math. and Phys.*, **37**, 215 (1958).

Page 840

One of the best surveys of molecular quadrupole moments is given by A. D. Buckingham, *Quarterly Review, Chem. Soc.* (*London*), **13**, 183 (1959).

Page 843

The one and two-center expansions of r_{ij}^{-n} (with n a positive integer) is given in terms of Gegenbauer polynomials by I. Prigogine, *Molecular Theory of Solutions* (North-Holland, 1957), p. 265; see also, R. Balescu [*Physica*, **22**, 224 (1956)]. R. S. Sack [*J. Math. Phys.*, **5**, 000 (1964)] has shown that the two-center expansion of r_{ij}^{-1+2m} (where m is a positive integer) can be expressed in terms of the Appell F_4 functions.

Page 888

The best present quantum mechanical method of calculating the refractive indices and the Verdet constant is given by A. Dalgarno and A. E. Kingston [*Proc. Roy. Soc.* (*London*), ***A*259**, 424 (1960)]. They also give values for hydrogen and the inert gases.

Page 925

For further developments in the separation of electronic and nuclear coordinates, § 13.1b, see D. W. Jepsen and J. O. Hirschfelder [*J. Chem. Phys.*, **32**, 1323 (1960)]; A. Fröman [*J. Chem. Phys.*, **36**, 1490 (1962)]; and W. R. Thorson

[*J. Chem. Phys.*, **37**, 433 (1962)]. A clear formulation of the problem is given by M. Born and K. Huang, *Dynamics of Crystal Lattices* (Oxford, 1956).

Page 930

A more detailed derivation of the formulae given in § 13.1c is given by J. O. Hirschfelder, *Second Symposium on Thermophysical Properties*, Princeton, published in the *Progress in International Research on Thermodynamic and Transport Properties* (American Soc. Mechanical Engineers, 1962).

Page 932

A. A. Frost and P. G. Lykos [*J. Chem. Phys.*, **25**, 1299 (1956)] showed that an exact stationary state wave function satisfies the generalized Hellmann-Feynman theorem $\partial E/\partial R = \int \psi^*(\partial \mathscr{H}/\partial R)\psi \, d\mathbf{r}^N / \int \psi^* \psi \, d\mathbf{r}^N$ where R is an arbitrary parameter. G. G. Hall [*Phil. Mag. (London)*, **6**, 249 (1961)] found that an approximate wave function φ satisfies the generalized Hellmann-Feynman theorem provided that φ involves R only through a set of imbedded parameters $a_1(R)$, $a_2(R)$, ... and provided that each of these imbedded parameters is energy optimized for the value of R under consideration. Such wave functions lead to more accurate values of $\partial E/\partial R$ than can be obtained from "unstable" wave functions which do not satisfy the generalized Hellmann-Feynman theorem. The limitations of the generalized Hellmann-Feynman theorem as used with approximate wave functions have been discussed by L. Salem and E. B. Wilson [*J. Chem. Phys.*, **36**, 3421 (1962)].

Page 953

J. O. Hirschfelder and M. A. Eliason [*Ann. New York Acad. Sci.*, **67**, 451 (1957)] have shown that the kinetic theory rigid sphere collision diameter for the collision between two atoms is approximately $\overline{r_a} + \overline{r_b} + 1.8$ Å and that the rigid sphere collision diameter for the collision of two diatomic molecules is approximately $(\frac{4}{3})(\overline{r_a} + \overline{r_b}) + 1.8$ Å, where $\overline{r_a}$ and $\overline{r_b}$ are the mean radii of the outer atomic orbitals of atoms a and b respectively, using Slater orbitals and screening constants. Furthermore, the bond length in a diatomic molecule is approximately $\overline{r_a} + \overline{r_b}$.

Page 954

Equation 13.2–25 is valid only for $k \geq 1$. For $k = -1, -2$:

$$\overline{(r_i)^{-1}} = [(Z - S_i)/n_i^{*2}]a_0^{-1}$$

$$\overline{(r_i)^{-2}} = [2(Z - S_i)^2/n^{*3}(2n^* - 1)]a_0^{-2}$$

Page 960

A. Dalgarno and A. E. Kingston [*Proc. Phys. Soc. (London)*, **73**, 455 (1959) and **78**, 607 (1961)] and A. Dalgarno [*Revs. Mod. Phys.*, **35**, 522 (1963)] have developed a method of calculating the van der Waals constant c (as defined in Eq. 13.3–22) for atom-atom interactions to a precision of better than 10%. They obtained the following results:

c in units of $e^2a_0^5$

	H	He	Ne	Ar	H_2
H	6.5	2.8	5.7	20.2	9.2
He	2.8	1.5	3.1	9.9	4.2
Ne	5.7	3.1	6.6	20.6	8.6
Ar	20.2	9.9	20.6	68.1	29.6
H_2	9.2	4.2	8.6	29.6	13.3
Li	67	22	48	200	88
Na	74	25	52	210	96
K	99	33	68	280	128
Rb	100	34	69	280	132
Cs	120	38	77	320	148

	H	He	He^+	$^1He^*$	$^3He^*$
$^1He^*$	130	42	8.6	11000	5700
$^3He^*$	87	29	6.1	5700	3300

	H^-	He^+	Li^+
H	89	0.66	0.52
He	30	0.38	0.32

Here $^1He^*$ and $^3He^*$ are the first singlet and triplet metastable helium atoms. Dalgarno and Kingston also give the atomic polarizabilities and the oscillator strengths for the above cited atomic species. The H_2 values are averages over all orientations.

Page 961

Equations 13.3–17 et seq: A much more detailed and usable treatment of the dispersion forces between molecules in degenerate states is given by J. S. Dahler and J. O. Hirschfelder [*J. Chem. Phys.*, **25**, 986 (1956)].

Page 964

Y. Midzuno and T. Kihara [*J. Phys. Soc. Japan*, **11**, 1045 (1956)] have pointed out that preferable to Eq. 13.3–30 is the Hassé formula [*Proc. Camb. Phil. Soc.*, **26**, 542 (1930); see also Margenau, Ref. 1 on p. 955]

$$c_{ab} = 6\,mc^2\alpha_a\alpha_b[(\alpha_a/\chi_a{}^{(m)}) + (\alpha_b/\chi_b{}^{(m)})]^{-1}$$

For the interaction of two like molecules, the Hassé value of c_{ab} is one-fourth of the value given by Eq. 13.3–30.

Page 966

See Note to p. 960 for better values of c than are given in Table 13.3–1.

Page 974

S. Aono [*Prog. Theor. Phys.* (*Japan*), **20**, 133 (1958)] found that charge-transfer forces between long, conjugated, double-bond or aromatic molecules are considerably larger than the dispersion forces considered in § 13.4c. Aono also considered the charge-transfer forces in the iodine-benzene complex [*Prog. Theor. Phys.* (*Japan*), **21**, 217 (1959) and **22**, 313 (1959)].

Page 1027

See Note p. 840 regarding molecular quadrupoles.

Page 1042

J. M. Levelt [*Physica*, **26**, 361 (1960)] gives the reduced equation of state of argon and xenon as determined from experimental data. She presents evidence that three-body forces are important in liquid xenon. However, F. Danon and K. S. Pitzer [*J. Phys. Chem.*, **66**, 583 (1962)] present experimental evidence for supposing that both argon and xenon conform to corresponding states even in the solid state. Theoretical calculations showing the relative importance of three-body forces have been made by T. Kihara, *Advances in Chemical Physics* (Edited by I. Prigogine, Interscience, New York, 1958), Vol. I, p. 267; L. Jansen and R. T. McGinnies [*Phys. Rev.*, **104**, 961 (1956); L. Jansen [*Phys. Rev.*, **125**, 1798 (1962)]; and H. W. Graben and R. D. Present [*Phys. Rev. Letters*, **9**, 247 (1962)].

Page 1050

Surveys of recent advances in the quantum mechanical calculations of intermolecular forces are given in Papers from the Conference on Molecular Quantum Mechanics, *Revs. Mod. Phys.*, **32**, April (1960); P. E. Cade, *University of Wisconsin Theoretical Chemistry Report* WIS-AEC-30 (June, 1961); and K. Ruedenberg, *Revs. Mod. Phys.*, **34**, 326 (1962). The best treatments of intermolecular forces are based upon some new techniques in perturbation theory summarized by A. Dalgarno, *Quantum Theory* edited by D. R. Bates (Academic Press, New York, 1961), Volume I, Chapter 5 and by C. Schwartz [*Annals of Phys.*, **2**, 156, 170, and 176 (1959)]. Detailed considerations of long-range interactions are given by A. Dalgarno and N. Lynn [*Proc. Phys. Soc.*, **A69**, 821 (1956) and **A70**, 223 (1957)]; A. Dalgarno and J. T. Lewis [*Proc. Roy. Soc.* (*London*), **A233**, 70 (1955) and *Proc. Phys. Soc.*, **A69**, 57 (1956)]; A. Dalgarno and A. L. Stewart [*Proc. Roy. Soc.* (*London*), **A238**, 269 (1956)]; and L. Salem [*Mol. Phys.*, **3**, 441 (1960) and *J. Chem. Phys.*, **37**, 2100 (1962)].

Of interest in connection with the properties of hot air, are the semi-empirical calculations of the energy of interaction of the following species: N—N, N—N_2, and N_2—N_2, J. T. Vanderslice, E. A. Mason, and E. R. Lippincott [*J. Chem. Phys.*, **30**, 129 (1959)]; O—N, O—N_2, O_2—N_2, O—O and O_2—O_2, J. T. Vanderslice, E. A. Mason, and W. G. Maisch [*J. Chem. Phys.*, **31**, 738 (1959), and **32**, 515 (1960)].

Page 1054

W. Kolos and C. C. Roothaan [*Revs. Mod. Phys.*, **32**, 205 (1960)] have used James and Coolidge type wave functions with up to 50 terms to compute the potential energy curves for the $^1\Sigma_g^+$ ground state and the $^3\Sigma_u^+$, $^1\Sigma_u^+$, $^1\Sigma_g^+$ excited states of the H_2 molecule in the range of internuclear separations between 0.4 a_0 and 4.2 a_0. At separations larger than 4 a_0, the best calculations for the $^1\Sigma_g^+$ ground state and the $^3\Sigma_u^+$ excited state are given by A. Dalgarno and N. Lynn [*Proc. Phys. Soc.*, **A69**, 821 (1956)] who used a special perturbation method. E. R. Davidson [*J. Chem. Phys.*, **35**, 1189 (1961)] has found that the potential energy curve of the first excited $^1\Sigma_g^+$ state of the hydrogen molecule has two minima. An accurate convenient wave function for the ground state of the hydrogen molecule (and the corresponding energies) for internuclear separations covering the range between 1 a_0 and 18 a_0 is given by S. Fraga and B. J. Ransil [*J. Chem. Phys.*, **35**, 1967 (1961)] who used a 12 MO configuration LCAO MO SCF treatment.

Page 1059

In place of Eq. 14.1–6, J. O. Hirschfelder and P. O. Löwdin [*Molec. Phys.*, **2**, 229 (1959)] found by rigorous calculations

$$\varphi_{ab} = -(e^2/a_0)[6.499026(a_0/r_{ab})^6 + 144.8497(a_0/r_{ab})^8 + \cdots]$$

Apparently there is an error in the Pauling and Beach inverse eighth power term.

Page 1060

Currently, the "most likely" potential energy for normal ground state H_2 is given by J. T. Vanderslice, E. A. Mason, and W. G. Maisch [*Molec. Spect.*, **3**, 17 (1959) and **5**, 83 (1960)] who used the Rydberg-Klein-Rees method [see also J. T. Vanderslice, E. A. Mason, and E. R. Lippincott, *J. Chem. Phys.*, **30**, 129 (1959), and J. T. Vanderslice, E. A. Mason, and W. J. Maisch, *J. Chem. Phys.*, **31**, 738 (1959)] to determine the potential energy curve from experimental vibrational energy levels. They obtained:

$-\varphi_{ab}$ (kcal/mol)	r_{ab}/a_0	r_{ab}/a_0
14.212	0.805	3.781
20.007	0.816	3.515
26.561	0.830	3.275
33.836	0.848	3.057
41.788	0.869	2.859
50.407	0.894	2.670
59.668	0.924	2.485
69.587	0.962	2.302
80.144	1.009	2.116
91.363	1.079	1.914
103.255	1.198	1.669

At large separations, the "most likely" potential energy is given by A. Dalgarno and N. Lynn [*Proc. Phys. Soc.*, **A69**, 821 (1956)] who used a special perturbation method to calculate the values:

r_{ab}/a_0	4	5	6	7	8	10	12
$-\varphi_{ab}$(kcal/mol)	10.368	2.479	0.567	0.137	0.0386	0.00580	0.00166

Page 1064

A great deal of research has been conducted on the interaction of two helium atoms, § 14.2a. The limit of small separations as the two helium atoms merge into a beryllium atom has been treated by R. A. Buckingham [*Trans. Faraday Soc.*, **54**, 453 (1958)]; R. A. Buckingham and D. M. Duparc [*Am. Soc. Mech. Eng. Symposium on Thermodynamics and Transport Properties* (Princeton, Jan. 1962), p. 378]; W. A. Bingel [*J. Chem. Phys.*, **30**, 1250 (1959) and **38**, 274

(1963)]. In the range of interatomic separations between 0.5 and 1.0 Å, P. E. Phillipson [*Phys. Rev.*, **125**, 1981 (1962)], has calculated the interaction energy using a 64 configuration wave function. B. J. Ransil [*J. Chem. Phys.*, **34**, 2109 (1961)] used a single configuration LCAO MO SCF approximation to calculate the energy of interaction of two helium atoms for the full range of separations between 0.4 Å and 12 Å. However, these theoretical calculations do not agree with the experimental scattering results of I. Amdur and R. R. Bertrand [*J. Chem. Phys.*, **36**, 1078 (1962)]. The reason for this discrepancy is not now known.

Some similar work on the interaction between a hydrogen and a helium atom has also been carried out. The quantum-mechanical calculations were made by E. A. Mason, J. Ross, and P. N. Schatz [*J. Chem. Phys.*, **25**, 626 (1956)], and compared with the experimental scattering results of I. Amdur and E. A. Mason [*J. Chem. Phys.*, **25**, 630 (1956)]. The agreement was good, but the experiment did not extend into the region of very small separations for which the discrepancy for He-He exists.

Page 1075

The best calculations of the short range energy of interaction between a hydrogen atom and hydrogen molecule are those of S. F. Boys and I. Shavitt [*University of Wisconsin Theoretical Chemistry Institute Report*, WIS-AF-13 (March, 1959)].

J. T. Vanderslice and E. A. Mason [*J. Chem. Phys.*, **33**, 492 (1960)] use a semi-empirical procedure to obtain the energy of repulsion at large separations of H and H_2, as well as H_2 and H_2. For the interaction between H and H_2, they obtain (in good agreement with Margenau): $\varphi = 61.5 \exp(-2.952R)$ e.v. for $0.86\ \text{Å} < R < 2.12\ \text{Å}$. For H_2 and H_2, they obtained (in good agreement with Evett and Margenau): $\varphi = 116.5 \exp(-2.859R)$ e.v. for $0.91\ \text{Å} < R < 2.14\ \text{Å}$. Here the energies are averaged over all orientations.

Page 1083

See Note to p. 1075.

Page 1092

The most extensive treatment of H_2^+ (both ground and excited states) is given by D. R. Bates, K. Ledsham, and A. L. Stewart [*Phil. Trans. Roy. Soc.* (*London*), **A246** (No. 911), 215 (1953)].

Page 1094

The best calculations of the energy of H_2^- are given by I. Fischer-Hjalmars [*Arkiv. Fys.* (*Swedish*), **13**, 481 (1958); **16**, 33 (1959); **20**, 461 (1961); and *J. Chem. Phys.*, **36**, 1081 (1962)]. See also, E. R. Davidson [*J. Chem. Phys.*, **36**, 1080 (1962)].

Page 1098

The best calculation of the interaction of a triplet and a normal helium atom is given by G. H. Brigman, S. J. Brient, and F. A. Matsen [*J. Chem. Phys.*, **34**, 958 (1961)].

Page 1110

The following table contains some additional values of the force constants for the Lennard-Jones (6-12) potential, assembled largely by E. A. Mason:

Gas	ϵ/k (°K)	σ (Å)	Property Used to Determine Constants	Ref.
Light Gases				
He	10.8	2.57	B	*a, b*
H_2	36.7	2.959	$B(-175°$ to $150°C)$	*c*
D_2	35.2	2.952	$B(-175°$ to $150°C)$	*c*
Noble Gases				
Ne	35.8	2.75	B	*a, b*
	33.7	2.756	$B(-150°$ to $700°C)$	*e*
Ar	119	3.41	B	*a, b*
	119.7	3.406	B	*a, f*
	122	3.402	Solid	*a, g*
	124.9	3.423	k_T	*a, h*
	119.5	3.409	$B(-100°$ to $600°C)$	*i*
	125.2	3.405	$B(-190°$ to $-150°C)$	*j*
	122	3.4	$B(-160°$ to $20°C)$	*k*
Kr	173	3.59	B	*a, b*
	165.4	3.604	Solid	*a, l*
	166.7	3.679	$B(0°$ to $600°C)$	*i*
	182.9	3.591	$B(-165°$ to $-135°C)$	*j*
	168.6	3.67	$B(-150°$ to $20°C)$	*k*
	172.7	3.591	B	*m*
Xe	163	4.31	λ, $\mathfrak{D}$	*a, n*
	225.3	4.070	$B(0°$ to $700°C)$	*i*
	163	4.31	$\mathfrak{D}$	*o*
Simple Polyatomic Gases				
N_2	47.6	3.85	$\mathfrak{D}$	*p*
CO	32.8	3.92	$\mathfrak{D}$	*q*
CO_2	186	4.55	$B(0°$ to $150°C)$	*r*
	150	4.07	$\mathfrak{D}$	*s*
	190	4.00	η	*s*
	187.5	4.47	$B(0°$ to $200°C)$	*s*
	203.3	3.91	$B(300°$ to $600°C)$	*s*
	221	4.11	C	*s*
N_2O	193	4.54	$B(0°$ to $150°C)$	*r*
CH_4	148.1	3.809	B, solid, η	*a, t*
	148.2	3.818	B, C	*a, u*
	156.7	3.697	k_T	*a, h*
	148.1	3.809	$B(0°$ to $150°C)$	*v*
	140	3.808	η	*w*

Gas	ϵ/k (°K)	σ (Å)	Property Used to Determine Constants	Ref.
Simple Polyatomic Gases (cont.)				
CF_4	152.1	4.70	B	*x*
CF_3Cl	222	4.92	B	*y*
CF_2Cl_2	286	5.16	B	*y*
$CFCl_3$	346	5.45	B	*y*
CH_2Cl_2	398	4.748	η	*z*
CH_3Cl	355	4.151	η	*z*
SO_2	363	4.026	η	*z*
BF_3	178	4.38	B(20° to 70°C)	*A*
	178	4.22	η	*B*, *C*
SiF_4	148.7	5.59	B(20° to 80°C)	*D*
	147	4.96	η	*B*
	148	4.95	η	*C*
SF_6	259	5.01	η	*B*
	155	5.46	η	*C*
	188.7	5.91	B(20° to 175°C)	*D*
F_2	121	3.61	B	*E*
H_2S	309	3.591	η	*z*
NOCl	668	3.57	η	*z*
Hydrocarbons				
C_2H_6	236	4.384	η	*w*
C_3H_8	206	5.240	η	*w*
n-C_4H_{10}	208	5.869	η	*w*
n-C_5H_{12}	269	6.099	η	*w*
n-C_6H_{14}	423	5.916	η	*w*
n-C_8H_{18}	333	7.407	η	*w*
	260	10.21	B	*F*
n-C_9H_{20}	266	8.302	η	*w*
C_6H_6 (Benzene)	308	6.92	B	*F*
	335	5.628	η	*w*
	195	9.75	B	*G*
$C_6H_5CH_3$ (Toluene)	185	12.0	B	*G*
	377	5.932	η	*w*
$CH_2{=}CH_2$	230	4.066	η	*w*
$CH_3CH{=}CH_2$	303	4.670	η	*w*
Butene-1	319	5.198	η	*w*
Butene-2	259	5.508	η	*w*
i-Butene	425	4.776	η	*w*
3-Methyl-1-Butene	283	5.829	η	*w*
Pentene-2	204	6.476	η	*w*
$CH_2{=}C{=}CH_2$	194.9	6.43	B(20° to 80°C)	*D*
$HC{\equiv}CH$	212	4.114	η	*w*

Gas	ϵ/k (°K)	σ (Å)	Property Used to Determine Constants	Ref.
Hydrocarbons (cont.)				
$CH_3C{\equiv}CH$	261	4.742	η	*w*
Cyclohexane	313	6.143	η	*w*
1,3,5-Trimethylbenzene	234	7.706	η	*w*
2,2,3-Trimethylbutane	178	7.621	η	*w*
i-Butane	217	5.819	η	*w*
Other Organic Vapors				
CH_3OH	452	3.666	η	*z*
C_2H_5OH	415	4.370	η	*z*
$(CH_3)_2O$	412	4.264	η	*z*
$(C_2H_5)_2O$	351	5.539	η	*z*
$(CH_3)_2CO$	519	4.669	η	*z*
CH_3COOCH_3	417	5.054	η	*z*
$CH_3COOC_2H_5$	531	5.163	η	*z*
C_2N_2	175.7	6.81	B(35° to 150°C)	*D*
C_4F_8	222.6	7.03	B(100° to 350°C)	*x*

[a] J. S. Rowlinson, *Ann. Reports of the Chem. Soc., London*, **56**, 22 (1959).

[b] T. Kihara, *Adv. Chem. Phys.*, **1**, 267 (1958).

[c] A. Michels, W. de Graaff, and C. A. ten Seldam, *Physica*, **26**, 393 (1960). The difference between the force constants for H_2 and D_2 is probably real [H. F. P. Knaap and J. J. M. Beenakker, *Physica*, **27**, 523 (1961)].

[d] A. O. Rietveld and A. van Itterbeek, *Physica*, **22**, 785 (1956).

[e] G. A. Nicholson and W. G. Schneider, *Can. J. Chem.*, **33**, 589 (1955).

[f] A. Michels, J. M. Levelt, and W. de Graaff, *Physica*, **24**, 659 (1958).

[g] E. R. Dobbs, B. F. Figgins, G. O. Jones, D. C. Piercey, and D. P. Riley, *Nature*, **178**, 483 (1956); C. Domb and I. J. Zucker, *ibid.*, **178**, 484 (1956); E. R. Dobbs and G. O. Jones, *Reports Progr. Phys.*, **20**, 516 (1957); E. R. Dobbs, B. F. Figgins, and G. O. Jones, *Nuovo Cim.*, Ser. 10, Suppl. 9, 32 (1958).

[h] M. P. Madan, *J. Chem. Phys.*, **23**, 763 (1955).

[i] E. Whalley and W. G. Schneider, *J. Chem. Phys.*, **23**, 1644 (1955).

[j] B. E. F. Fender and G. D. Halsey, Jr., *J. Chem. Phys.*, **36**, 1881 (1962).

[k] G. Thomaes, R. van Steenwinkel, and W. Stone, *Mol. Phys.*, **5**, 301 (1962).

[l] I. J. Zucker, *J. Chem. Phys.*, **25**, 915 (1956).

[m] J. A. Beattie, J. S. Brierley, and R. J. Barriault, *J. Chem. Phys.*, **20**, 1615 (1952).

[n] I. Amdur and T. F. Schatzki, *J. Chem. Phys.*, **27**, 1049 (1957); **29**, 1425 (1959).

[o] I. Amdur and T. F. Schatzki, *J. Chem. Phys.*, **27**, 1049 (1957).

[p] E. B. Winn, *Phys. Rev.*, **74**, 698 (1948); **80**, 1024 (1950) (from measurements between 195° and 353°K).

[q] I. Amdur and L. M. Shuler, *J. Chem. Phys.*, **38**, 188 (1963).

[r] H. W. Schamp, Jr., E. A. Mason, and K. Su, *Phys. Fluids*, **5**, 769 (1962).

[s] I. Amdur, J. Ross, and E. A. Mason, *J. Chem. Phys.*, **20**, 1620 (1952).

[t] H. W. Schamp, E. A. Mason, A. C. B. Richardson, and A. Altman, *Phys. Fluids*, **1**, 329 (1958).

[u] R. Bergeon, *J. Rech. C.N.R.S.*, No. **44**, 171 (1958) (α = 12, 13.5, 15.0).
[v] H. W. Schamp, Jr., E. A. Mason, A. C. B. Richardson, and A. Altman, *Phys. Fluids*, **1**, 329 (1958).
[w] L. W. Flynn and G. Thodos, *A. I. Ch. E. Journal*, **8**, 362 (1962).
[x] D. R. Douslin, R. H. Harrison, R. T. Moore, and J. P. McCullough, *J. Chem. Phys.*, **35**, 1357 (1961).
[y] W. Auer, private communication.
[z] E. A. Mason and L. Monchick, *J. Chem. Phys.*, **35**, 1676 (1961).
[A] C. J. G. Raw, *J. Chem. Phys.*, **34**, 1452 (1961).
[B] C. P. Ellis and C. J. G. Raw, *J. Chem. Phys.*, **30**, 574 (1959).
[C] J. C. McCoubrey and N. M. Singh, *Trans. Faraday Soc.*, **53**, 877 (1957).
[D] S. D. Hamann, W. J. McManamey, and J. F. Pearse, *Trans. Faraday Soc.*, **49**, 351 (1953).
[E] D. White, J-H. Hu, and H. L. Johnston, *J. Chem. Phys.*, **21**, 1149 (1953).
[F] J. F. Connolly and G. A. Kandalic, *Phys. Fluids*, **3**, 463 (1960).
[G] J. D. Cox and R. J. L. Andon, *Trans. Faraday Soc.*, **54**, 1622 (1958).

Page 1126

A tabulation of collision integrals for the Lennard-Jones (6-12) potential, in which previous tabulations are compared and interpolation methods discussed, has been given by P. E. Liley [*Thermophysical Properties Research Center, Report 15*, Purdue University (February 1963)].

Page 1147

The evaluation of the second virial coefficient for the Stockmayer potential has been extended to higher values of t^* by J. A. Barker and F. Smith [*Australian J. Chem.*, **13**, 171 (1960)].

CHEMICAL INDEX

AUTHOR INDEX

SUBJECT INDEX